United States Patriotic Envelopes of World War II

UNITED STATES
PATRIOTIC ENVELOPES
OF
WORLD WAR II

LAWRENCE SHERMAN

James E. Lee Publishing
P.O. Box 36
Cary, IL 60013-0036

Please note:

Cachet numbers appearing in the text and captions are taken from the Cachet Catalogue in Chapter 7, where all recorded cachets are listed alphabetically and numbered 1-11060.

The title page illustration is the central design of cachets 384, 1341, 1342, and 4016, published in 1945 by W.B. Heckman, Evanston, IL.

This book is printed on Utopia II Gloss,
an archival quality, buffered, acid-free paper

ISBN Number: 0–9712608-8-5

Printed in the United States of America

First printing May 2006

James E. Lee Publishing
P.O. Box 36
Cary, IL 60013-0036
847-462-9130
philately2@earthlink.net

For Mimi
and for our grandchildren
Ariel, Nicholas, Andrew, Ella

CONTENTS

vi

Introduction

This book is the successor to *United States Patriotic Covers of World War II*, published in 1999. New information and new ideas mandated a new volume. Advances in printing, allowing an all-color format for the approximately 600 illustrations in the current volume, added to the publishing imperative. In the title, *Patriotic Envelopes* distinguishes this volume from the earlier *Patriotic Covers* and more clearly states the subject of the work.

New information came from people informing me about patriotic envelopes with designs (cachets) not previously catalogued. The result was a significant increase in the number of cachets listed in the current volume (more than 11,060 cachets vs. 9660 listed earlier); this required re-numbering cachets to avoid adding "A" and "B" suffixes to 1,400 previously listed numbers. (Only a few dozen "late-entry" cachets now carry letter suffixes.)

New information from periodicals provided fresh insight into the relationships (Chapter 2) and lives (Chapter 3) of some cachet makers.

Illustrated envelopes designed with charcoal and colored pencil, ink, oil pastels, or watercolor (hand painted patriotic envelopes) are growing in popularity and value. So Chapter 4 includes new information about techniques used by eight outstanding designers of hand painted envelopes, presents checklists of their wartime designs, and illustrates a sampling of their work. A checklist at the end of the chapter, arranged by artist, records the remaining hand painted cachets known to me. In all, 1315 hand painted envelopes are recorded alphabetically by artist and text in Chapter 4, and all are priced there. These hand painted cachets also take their place among the 11060+ designs recorded in the Cachet Catalogue in Chapter 7.

Patriotic envelopes were built on a scaffolding of wartime events. This is discussed and amply illustrated in Chapter 1. They also made important contributions to wartime postal history that are only now beginning to be recognized (Chapters 5 and 6).

———

I am indebted to many people for their contributions to the making of this book:

Publisher James Lee encouraged the scope of this undertaking, and I hope the quality of the work matches the quality of his vision; Ted Bahry, Louis Fiset, Howard Lee, Buddy Rabiner, Jerry Santangelo, and Bill Sherman improved the manuscript by their questions, corrections, and comments; and Eustaquio M. Kirby shared his knowledge of illustrated envelopes and analyzed techniques used to produce hand painted covers.

Jackie Murphy's computer skills got me out of tight spots, especially when graphics boxes did inexplicable things to nearby text; and Ellen Peachey of the American Philatelic Research Library (APRL) found missing dates, volume numbers, or inclusive pages in references. A wonderful resource, the APRL is an at-your-fingertips research library, as near as your computer (at www.stamps.org) and telephone.

Michael Schreiber, Editor of *Linn's Stamp News*, supplied the photograph of George W. Linn that appears in Chapter 3; Mark Sutton allowed me to review and catalogue hundreds of previously unrecorded cachets; and my wife Mimi Sherman resolved compositional and artistic dilemmas and encouraged me through the "Is there no end to the making of this book" phase.

1

Through American Eyes

ENVELOPE ART has flourished in the service of love, money, or war since the mid-nineteenth century.

It all began when postage stamps began, in Great Britain in 1840. The postal reform of that year included prepayment of postage by adhesive stamps, and stamps needed envelopes. William Mulready, a member of the Royal Academy, was commissioned to design an illustrated envelope for the new system of prepaid postage. His illustration featured a printed figure of Britannia and the Imperial Lion at the top center of the envelope face, with four angels flying off to the corners of the world [Figure 1]. This burst of Brittanic pride was the world's first patriotic envelope (or patriotic "cover"), defined here as an envelope that bears an illustration or inscription (a "cachet") with a motif that informs, inspires, or incites in the name of Country. A modern writer noted that Mulready's work "was truly a masterpiece of allegoric art; its symbolism covered the entire face of the envelope except a small portion in which the address might be inscribed."[1]

Alas, though the postage stamp idea soared, Mulready's masterpiece flopped. Neither an expression of romantic love nor of wartime fervor, his illustrated envelope merely celebrated postal communication throughout the Empire. Its high-flown symbolic design was lambasted and caricatured. Laughed to scorn, the envelopes "were almost immediately removed from sale at the post offices. So many of them were left unsold that special furnaces had to be built to burn them after it was decided to authorize their

destruction."[2] Postally used Mulready envelopes are today considered classics of philately.

Twenty years after the failure of the first patriotic envelope, a war—the American Civil War—unleashed the power of the patriotic cover. "The sound of the bugle and the rattling of arms stir deep emotions. . . . As early as 1860, in the Presidential campaign, when patriotic feeling between the North and South was aroused by inevitable war, patriotic envelopes made their appearance. The use of these covers became a passion in both the North and the South, and post offices were made gay with these envelopes, some noble in sentiment and others hysterical."[3]

The attack on April 12, 1861, on Fort Sumter in Charleston harbor made real "the sound of the bugle and the rattling of arms." Soon the May 1861 issue of *United States Mail and Post-Office Assistant*, a four-page

Figure 1. A benign Britannia rules the mails on the world's first patriotic cover, the Mulready envelope of 1840.

Figure 2. Postally used Civil War patriotic cover. The star-spangled figure of Columbia gestures upward toward the rocket's red glare, which reveals "God Save the Union."

monthly newspaper devoted to Post Office Department affairs, was reporting that many letters mailed in the first weeks after Sumter traveled in envelopes bearing printed flag designs. And in June the newspaper noted that "the post office, too, is made the means of dissemination of sentiment, and envelopes with patriotic motto or device are much used in correspondence. . . . They are of every degree of workmanship as far as engraving is concerned—from the finest steel engraving to the coarsest wood—plain and colored, gay and grave, some all love and fervor and others threatening war and devastations."[4]

A modern collector of Civil War patriotic covers observed that their designs reflected "patriotism, the sentimentalities and realities of a soldier's life in war, documentation of great battles, tributes to heroes, [and] biting satire on opposite views." More than a century later, he wrote, these covers still communicated a sense of the depth of feeling engendered by the conflict. At the same time he commented on the vendors of civil war patriotic covers who "quickly saw a lucrative collectors' market early in the war, and enthusiastically promoted the collection of the covers."[5]

A year after the war began, as the enormous cost of the fratricide began to become clear, the *United States Mail and Post-Office Assistant* issue for April 1862 noted: "The rage for envelopes decorated with patriotic or other embellishments seems to be subsiding. . . . The eruption of red, white and blue—of eagles and flag-bearing females—of youths martially arrayed and allegorical figures of various

kinds—is rapidly fading away."[6] A Civil War "flag-bearing female" patriotic cover is shown in Figure 2.

All of these Civil War developments—except for the fading of the rage for patriotic envelope art later in the war—would return in the next century during World War II.

Though patriotic covers were employed in war and peace after the Civil War, the zenith of their use came during World War II, when a flood of illustrated envelopes gushed forth: more than 650 artists and printers produced some 12,000 patriotic designs on envelopes that were sent around the world.

American illustrated envelopes mailed during the 1939-1945 war allowed mailers to add a public message outside to the private message inside, uniting sender and receiver in wartime. They were used by civilians, members of the armed forces, businesses, and government bureaus. Wherever American mail went—and it went nearly everywhere in the world—United States illustrated envelopes in the form of patriotic covers carried images faithfully reflecting the hopes and fears of wartime America. These patriotic covers powerfully evoke the war as seen through American eyes. Their images show us directly how Americans experienced the war, reacted to it, and imagined it from the war's beginning in September 1939 to its end in September 1945.

American envelope art commented on the war even before the United States was thrust into it by the attack on Pearl Harbor on December 7, 1941. But with that event, as everyone and everything in the country became part of the war effort, patriotic covers were created in every area of the United States and were mailed throughout the country from civilian to soldier and back again; from servicemen and women at military bases around the world to friends at home; from collector to avid collector. And unlike the Civil War experience, the number of patriotic covers *increased* with each passing year after Pearl Harbor. The flood crested with VE (Victory in Europe) and VJ (Victory over Japan) Days and then abruptly ended.

Illustrations and inscriptions on United States patriotic envelopes significantly changed as the war swept on in its six year course. Recognizing the evolving themes of wartime patriotic envelopes can

Figure 3. September 1939 cover (cachet 2222) opposing changes in the Neutrality Acts.

Congress into special session to repeal sections of the laws. After much debate Congress repealed its embargo on the sale of munitions. Belligerents—which in fact meant Britain and France—could obtain arms on a cash and carry basis. A Neutrality Patrol consisting of Navy and Coast Guard ships and aircraft was created to observe and report movement of warships of belligerent nations in areas of the western Atlantic. From these beginnings American involvement in the war grew as Hitler's forces conquered western Europe and Britain faced likely invasion.

Few patriotic covers were made in the first months of the war. Shown in Figure 3 (cachet 2222) is an early neutrality cover published by Albert C. Butzen of Detroit, postmarked on September 20, 1939 (even earlier dates in September are known). The cachet's sentiment is a typical response to the outbreak of war in Europe: "Keep U.S.A. out of War." Boxed near the left lower edge is a more controversial view: "Write your Congressman TODAY to keep the Neutrality Act just as it stands."

Overseas events continued to force responses from a reluctant American government and an even more reluctant American public. A national debate between "isolationists" and "interventionists" sprang up as Germany solidified its European conquests and turned its efforts toward destroying Britain's resistance by air attacks and U-boat raids on its Atlantic lifeline.

enhance an appreciation of them and help shape a coherent collection of them. Looking back, we can discern perhaps five stages in the war as Americans experienced it. Each stage determined the images we encounter in the envelope art of World War II.

1939-1941: ISOLATION, INTERVENTION, INFAMY

The enslavement of most of Europe, the deaths of tens of millions of people in Europe and Asia, the eventual destruction of the Third Reich, the apocalyptic end of the Japanese empire—all were set in motion the morning of September 1, 1939, when German forces invaded Poland. Two days later Britain and France responded to the invasion with declarations of war against Germany. The United States remained neutral, but not entirely. From September 1939 there was roiling debate over American strategic interests—in a phrase, isolation vs. intervention. This national debate, strongly echoed in American patriotic covers for two years, ended with the infamy of the Pearl Harbor attack.

The Neutrality Acts of 1935 and 1937, devised to avoid American entanglement in a future European war, prohibited sale of munitions to any "belligerent" nation. Within days of the German invasion of Poland, President Franklin D. Roosevelt called

Figure 4. Pre-Pearl Harbor cover (cachet 2002) from an American in the Eagle Squadron of the Royal Air Force.

Figure 5. Anti-British revision of a patriotic cover (cachet 7908) mailed five weeks before Pearl Harbor.

America was neutral but many Americans wanted passionately to join the fight against Hitler. The patriotic envelope shown in Figure 4 (cachet 2002) tells some of that story. Complete with British military postal mark, it was mailed by an American serving in the Royal Air Force—a "Yank in the RAF." Its cachet contains an American Eagle reminiscent of the Great Seal of the United States (background), a combative eagle (foreground), and initials. "E.S." stood for Eagle Squadron, one of three squadrons manned by American volunteer pilots.

Hundreds of young American men volunteered for service in Britain's Royal Air Force, violating the Neutrality Acts and braving the danger of prosecution. "Many are the stories of how the Eagles came to Britain," wrote an English woman in 1942. "Some stowed away, some walked half way across America, some were imprisoned at the border and sent home, but finally, permission was given to these fine men to come over, and today the Eagles have no less than three squadrons, all day and night operational, and a record for bravery which has won them an honoured place in the records of the Royal Air Force of Britain."[7]

In 1940 and 1941 these voluntary units of American pilots, the Eagle Squadrons, flew combat missions primarily over Britain and German-occupied France. Flying British Hurricane fighters and Spitfires, they were active in interception, bomber escort, and ground attack missions. The first Eagle Squadron, No. 71, operational since January 1941, accounted for more German aircraft "kills" than any

other Allied unit, and numerous decorations were earned by the members of the three squadrons. In September 1942 jurisdiction over the Eagle Squadrons was transferred to the newly formed U.S. Eighth Air Force stationed in Great Britain.

By the summer of 1941 Germany moved east, invading the Soviet Union, while Japanese forces occupied Indochina and were aiming their next thrust (it was thought) at Thailand, or perhaps the East Indies. Gallup polls in late 1941 showed that 85 percent of the American people believed they would be drawn into the European war, and two-thirds forecast war with Japan.

Yet many Americans distrusted Britain and feared entanglement in European conflicts. From September 1940 until the attack on Pearl Harbor, the 60,000 member America First Committee spearheaded a popular movement devoted to keeping the United States out of the war in Europe. The America First Committee was fervently anti-British and anti-Roosevelt. A number of its labels were used on envelopes as cachets, proclaiming "Defend America first," and "We are being pushed into war against the people's wishes." In Figure 5 is an illustrated envelope mailed in November 1941—a little over a month before the Japanese attack on Pearl Harbor—that reflects the passion in the argument even at that late date. On the envelope a label purposely obscures the British flag. The label's printed message to President Roosevelt: "Get U.S. Out of War and KEEP U.S. OUT OF WAR!!" Not content with that, the unknown mailer used a red crayon to cross out "England" and substitute "America" in its place, changing the sentiment of the previously published cachet [cachet 7908] to "There'll always be an America."

—☆—

The Battle of the Atlantic was a relentless, protracted series of naval campaigns that began in earnest after the fall of France in June 1940. With advance bases on the Atlantic, Germany undertook the severing of Britain's maritime connection. If Britain could be starved of food, fuel, and munitions, its will to fight would be destroyed. How serious was this menace? Even Winston Churchill, the indomitable British Prime Minister, feared the power of German submarines. He recalled in 1949: "The only thing that ever really frightened me during the war was the U-boat peril.... Now our life-line, even across the broad oceans, and especially in the entrances to the island, was endangered. I was even more anxious about this battle than I had been about the glorious air fight called the Battle of Britain."[8]

In the agreement known as the "Bases-for-Destroyers" deal, Great Britain ceded to the United States "sovereign rights" for 99 years over sites for bases in the West Indies in exchange for 50 submarine-fighting four-stack destroyers built during or soon after World War I. To complete the defensive arc protecting the western hemisphere, bases on Newfoundland and Bermuda were granted as gifts to the U.S.

Figure 6. World War II postal firsts for overseas American armed forces. A, First overseas branch post office, St. John's, Newfoundland, January 15, 1941. B, First overseas Army Post Office postmark, St. John's, Newfoundland, April 16, 1941. C, First day postal service, APO 809, Narsarssuak, Greenland, June 19, 1941. D, First day postal service, U.S. Naval Air Base, Bermuda, July 14, 1941. E, First day postal service, Marine Detachment, Portland Bight, Jamaica (British West Indies), July 18, 1941. F, First day postal service, APO 806, Antigua (British West Indies), September 15, 1941.

The Post Office Department announced establishment of the first branch post office established for one of these bases, to be located at St. John's, Newfoundland, effective January 1941. Letters postmarked January 15 were carried with the troops to Newfoundland, and returned from there to addressees in the United States. The postmark for the post office read: "American Forces in Newfoundland" [Figure 6A, cachet 883]. On April 16, 1941, this was changed to "American Base Forces A.P.O. 801"— the first Army Post Office (APO) postmark for overseas United States forces in World War II [Figure 6B, cachet 502A]. Four more bases were established in Newfoundland in 1941. The crown colony (not yet confederated with Canada) may have been a cold, damp, and foggy place, but it was of great strategic importance. With ice-free harbors that allowed year-round navigation by destroyers, submarines, and patrol planes, Newfoundland provided essential air and naval cover for convoys steaming to Iceland and Great Britain.

In 1940 little note was taken by American patriotic cover creators while the German blitzkrieg overran most of Europe, the Battle of Britain was at its height, and the Western Desert campaigns were raging in Libya and Egypt. The "Bases-for-Destroyers"

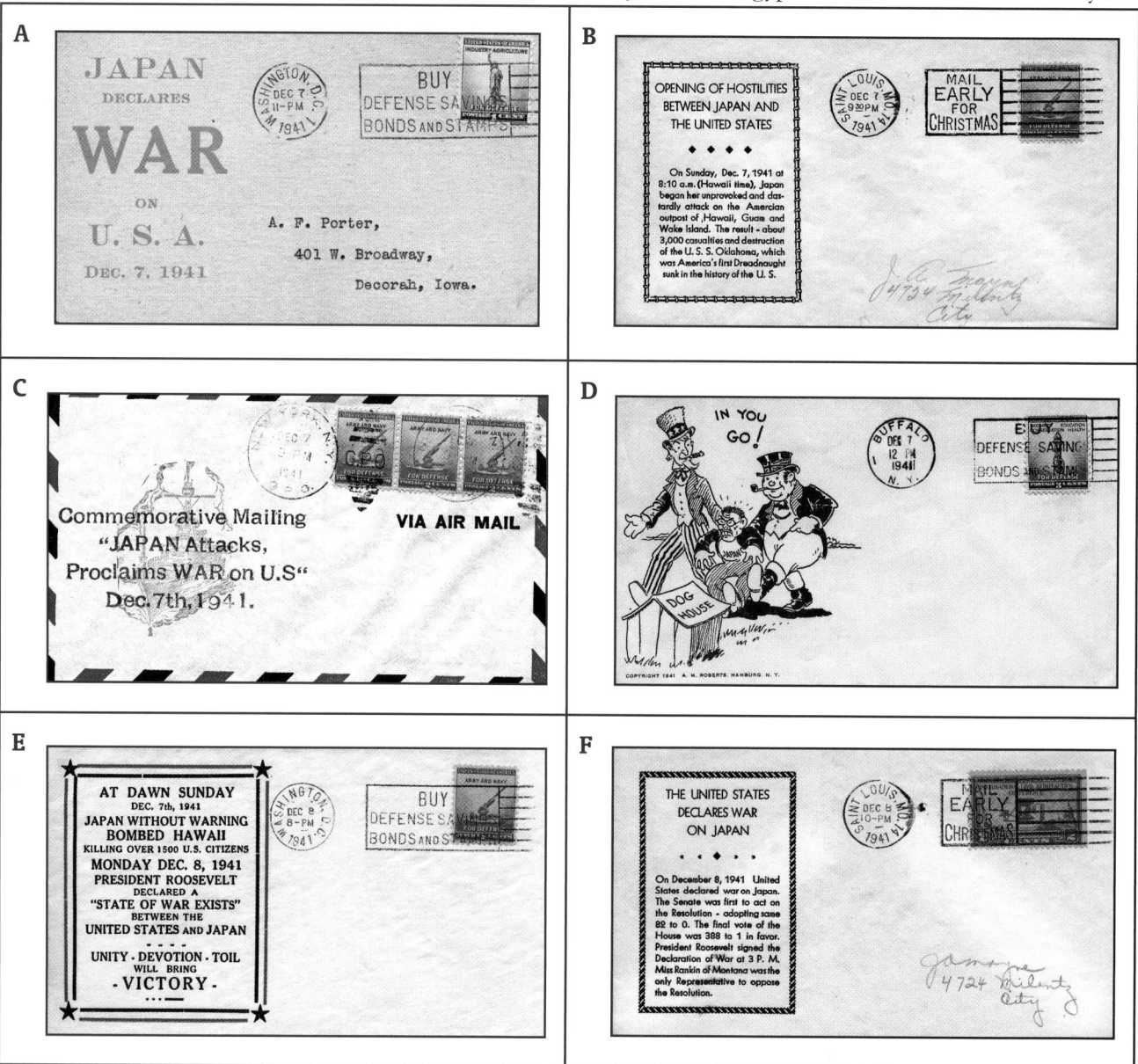

Figure 7. Patriotic covers mailed on the day of the Pearl Harbor attack (A-D) and the next day, when the United States declared war on Japan (E-F). A, Cachet 4022. B, Cachet 5895. C, Cachet 1641. D, Cachet 3782. E, Cachet 717. F, Cachet 7802.

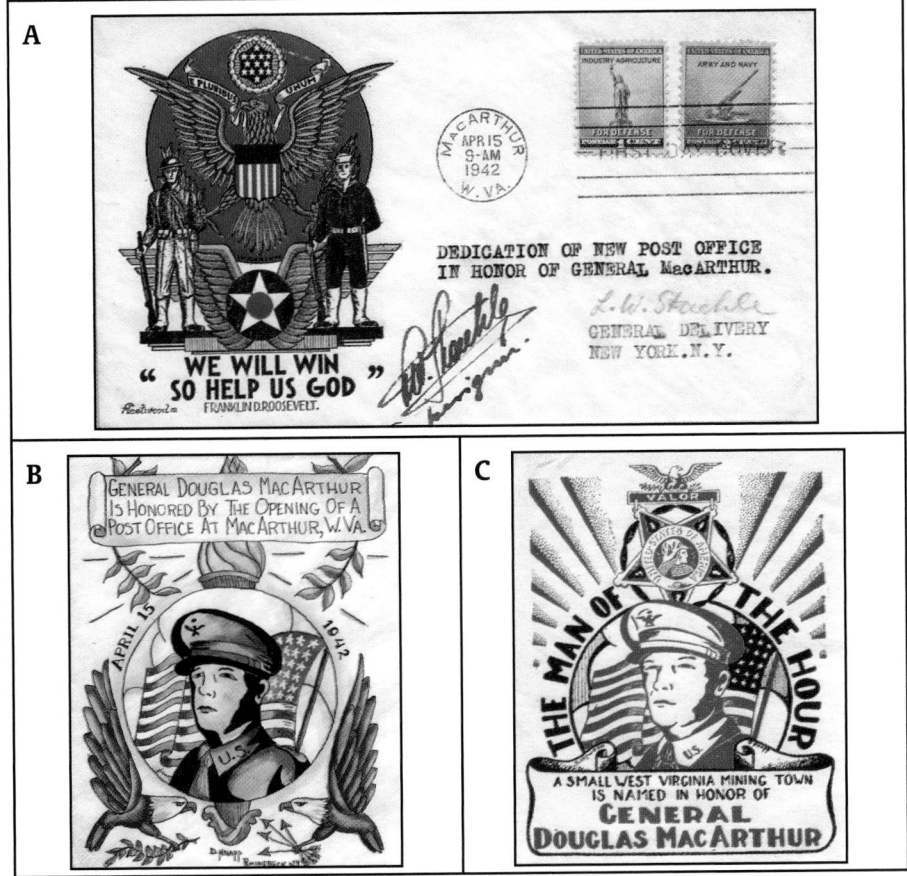

Figure 8. Opening of the MacArthur, West Virginia, post office, April 15, 1942.

—☆—

Admiral Isoroku Yamamoto, commander-in-chief of the Japanese Combined Fleet, warned prime minister Prince Konoye in September 1940, "If I am told to fight regardless of the consequences, I shall run wild for the first six months or a year, but I have utterly no confidence for the second or third year. . . . I hope you will endeavor to avoid a Japanese-American war."[9] In the end Yamamoto lost his argument before the High Command and it was he—known to be bold and inventive in battle—who was chosen to plan and direct the strike in December 1941 against the U.S. Pacific Fleet at Pearl Harbor. It was executed brilliantly. The attack on December 7, 1941 killed more than 2,400 men, crippled the American Pacific fleet, and opened the way for Japanese conquests ranging to the borders of India, the Aleutian Islands, and the threshold of Australia.

Few patriotic envelopes were canceled on December 7, 1941. It was a Sunday, post offices were closed to patrons, and there was little opportunity to have envelopes properly postmarked. A few covers noting the attack did appear immediately after its announcement. On that same afternoon Fidelity Stamp Company printed a cachet on the only stock it had on hand—grey cardboard—and had the cards postmarked at the Washington, DC post office [Figure 7A, cachet 4022]. John A. Mayne of St. Louis managed to have stamped envelopes machine-canceled and mailed to himself on December 7, then created a thermographed cachet recapitulating the "opening of hostilities" between Japan and the United States [Figure 7B, cachet 5895].[10] Other covers postmarked on the date of the Pearl Harbor attack

agreement changed that. In January 1941, as the United States became increasingly involved with guarding Britain's Atlantic lifeline by placing its own men in harm's way, cachet makers began to commemorate wartime events.

In the summer and fall of 1941 collectors sent patriotic covers to the bases to obtain postal markings from them, as well as markings from American military forces newly arrived in Greenland and Iceland (Figures 6C-6F, cachets 8693, 8903, 8695, 5356). The north Atlantic had become a highway—a most dangerous one—connecting the arsenal of democracy to a beleaguered ally. When the U.S. destroyer *Reuben James* was sunk by a German U-boat on October 31, 1941, Congress permitted the arming of merchant ships for self-defense and allowed the ships to enter European waters. The United States was now embarked on helping Britain "by all means short of war." Yet the oceans were broad and the war seemed far away.

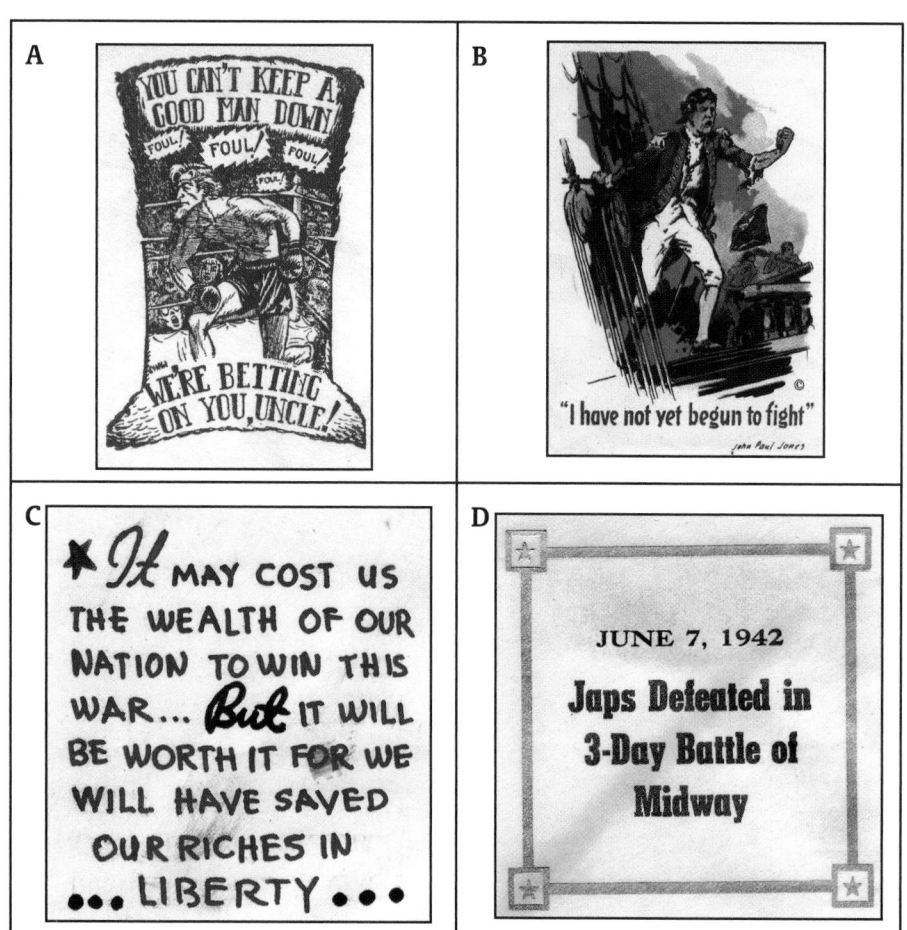

Figure 9. Cachet reactions to events of the first half of 1942.

These were desperate hours for the Allies. The Philippines, the East Indies, Malaya, Singapore, and most of Oceania were controlled by the Japanese. Australia was threatened with invasion. In August came the first American offensive of the war, an invasion of Guadalcanal, Gavutu, and Tulagi in the Solomon Islands. In December, after four months of fighting, the outcome on Guadalcanal was still in doubt.

German U-boats tore at the Atlantic lifeline to Great Britain. Leningrad was besieged. Most of Stalingrad, in ruins, was occupied by German forces. (A Soviet counteroffensive in November eventually trapped the German Sixth Army.) On December 31, Hitler received from Heinrich Himmler, Reichsführer-SS and concentration camp overseer, a report listing "Jews Executed," August-November. The precise number of those executed: 363,211.

included one created at the time [Figure 7C, cachet 1641] and another made months before but postmarked on December 7 [Figure 7D, cachet 3782].

Other areas had been attacked, including nearby Marine and Army airfields and (within 24 hours) the Philippines and Wake Island, to name only American possessions. But the devastation of the Pacific Fleet was the overwhelming military fact.

Figures 7E (cachet 717) and 7F (cachet 7802) were created for December 8, when the United States formally declared war on Japan. A phrase about the December 7th attack that President Roosevelt used in his war message to Congress— "a date which will live in infamy"—seized the public imagination but could not be rendered into a fighting slogan. Within two weeks "Remember Pearl Harbor" leaped into the public domain, remaining a rallying cry—and an ever-popular slogan on patriotic covers—until the end of the war in the Pacific nearly four years later.

The Japanese moved swiftly and boldly after they crippled the American Fleet at Pearl Harbor on December 7, 1941. Their strategy was to complete the isolation of China and end resistance there, conquer and control the rich resources of Southeast Asia, and subjugate the Philippines, the Dutch East Indies, and the islands of Oceania. They would then build their formidable empire behind the barriers of the Indian and Pacific Oceans. The carefully planned "Oriental Blitzkrieg" began immediately after Pearl Harbor. "It was totally unexpected; Allied commanders had speculated over whether the Nipponese would attack the Philippines, Hong Kong, Malaya, the Dutch East Indies, or Hawaii. No one dreamed that they would lunge simultaneously toward *all* of them, and overwhelm all in twenty-one weeks, at negligible cost to themselves."[11]

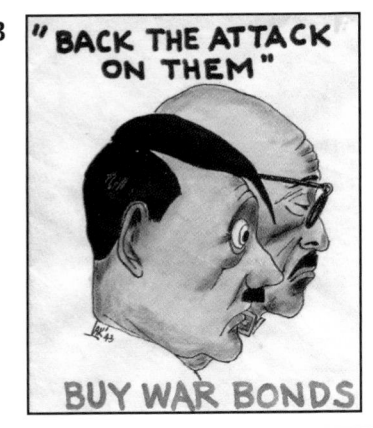

Figure 10. Backing the attack with war bonds (interest-bearing bonds redeemable by the U.S. Treasury) in 1943. American symbols: the Minute Man of the American Revolution and King Kamehameha of Hawaii. A, Cachet 8187. B, Cachet 845. C, Cachet 8021.

The Philippines were invaded on December 10. Guam was seized the same day. Wake Island, the most important outpost between Oahu and Guam, fell after two weeks of stubborn resistance. Hong Kong was occupied on Christmas Day and on the day after New Year's Manila surrendered. On February 15 Singapore also fell after the Japanese scored a quick, devastating rout of British forces in the Malay peninsula. Soon after the fall of Singapore, *Time* magazine was writing that "this was the worst week of the war. . . . Now, as in 1864, the fate of the nation was in the balance."

Throughout Japan small Rising Sun flags were being stuck into maps of Asia and the Pacific to mark the swath cut by the Imperial armed forces. A popular song caught the public mood: "More victory news on the radio! I can't sit still—the excitement, the joy. Aren't our men superb, divine heroes in action."

For months General Douglas MacArthur, Commanding General, U.S. Army Forces, Far East, led a doomed defense against Japanese forces in the mountains and jungles of Bataan on the Philippine island of Luzon. With the fall of the Philippines certain, and the Malay peninsula and Dutch East Indies in Japanese hands, Australia itself lay in the path of the conquering Japanese—and Australia had long since "sent its young men to fight [General Rommel's Afrika Corps] in the North African desert. . . . Something had to be done to still the sense of panic that was developing throughout the entire Southwest Pacific area, and it had to be done quickly."[12]

On March 17, America learned that MacArthur had been smuggled out of the blockaded island fortress of Corregidor and had arrived in Australia. In his first statement there he vowed: "I came through and I shall return." Americans and Australians acclaimed this pledge of eventual offensive action. "America's military altar was bare of other icons that year," and MacArthur became an instant national hero. Interestingly, this canonization "was a direct consequence of the stand on Bataan and Corregidor—the only battle he ever lost, and, as of then, the worst defeat in the history of U.S. arms."[13]

Swept up in the hero-worship, residents of a rural area of south central West Virginia petitioned to have a new fourth class post office established and named for the general. The United States Post Office Department quickly obliged and on March 26, 1942, the Third Assistant Postmaster mailed a postal card announcing forthcoming establishment of the post office. "In consideration of the significance of this name," the card proclaimed, "a special postmark containing the words 'First Day Cover,' in the canceling bars, will be applied to philatelic covers on the opening date." Never before in the United States had there been such national postal recognition for the opening of a post office.

There were 135,056 pieces of mail serviced with the "First Day Cover" cancel at the new MacArthur, West Virginia, post office on April 15, 1942. This total rivaled the number of first day covers (with "First Day of Issue" cancellations) of commemorative stamps in that era. Nearly 60 different cacheted covers

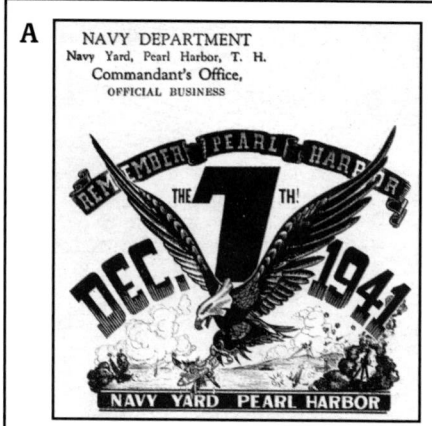

Figure 11. Cachets of illustrated envelopes issued by the Commandant's Office at Navy Yard, Pearl Harbor, mailed on first and second anniversaries of the attack on Pearl Harbor. A, Envelope postmarked December 7, 1942. There is a mixture of symbols: in the right corner the USS *Arizona* is sinking, while the American eagle clutches two Japanese warships. "Remember Pearl Harbor" is the explicit message. B, Envelope postmarked December 7, 1943. American forces are on the move, bursting out of the "December / 7" explosion: the Pearl Harbor remembrance is implicit: The determined sailor strides across the Pacific, leading the attack. The screaming eagle carries his weapon—war bonds—in his talons.

the common cause of destroying the enemies who have challenged the cause of Freedom."[14]

Sports talk and images were ingrained in American life, so the sentiment expressed in a patriotic cover made early in 1942 by Sgt. Arthur C. Christensen was universally grasped. Shown in Figure 9A, the illustration (cachet 10546) signals a visceral post-Pearl Harbor sentiment couched as a sports metaphor: A shaky but determined Uncle Sam, on one knee, is rising from the canvas in a boxing ring. His opponent is not seen in the cachet. There was no need for that. Shouts of "Foul!" rise from the fight crowd. "You can't keep a good man down / We're betting on you, Uncle!" is the ringing message. This was a cachet that could have been produced *only* in the months after Pearl Harbor when Japanese forces were "running wild" in the Pacific.

Another patriotic cover inspired by the events of early 1942 is one published in June of that year by Jacques Minkus of New York City [Figure 9B, cachet 3557]. The cachet shows an embattled American Revolutionary warship and its captain. It is the indomitable John Paul Jones standing on the deck of *Bonhomme Richard*, proclaiming "I have not yet begun to fight!" The storied sea battle between the American ship *Bonhomme Richard* commanded by John Paul Jones and the better-equipped British ship *Serapis* was fought in September 1779. After fiercely pounding the American ship the British captain asked Jones to surrender. Jones later wrote to Benjamin Franklin that "I answered him in the most determined negative," but posterity records an even more determined response by him: "I have not yet begun to fight." Jones succeeded in lashing his damaged vessel to the British ship. After a three hour battle, man-to-man combat, and the loss of nearly half his crew, Jones captured control of *Serapis* minutes before *Bonhomme Richard* sank. ("The scene was dreadful beyond the

were made specifically for the occasion and more than 100 hundred different general purpose patriotic covers were mailed as enclosures to the new post office to obtain the "First Day Cover" postmark.

Ludwig Staehle of New York City transformed a general patriotic cover he had designed for Fleetwood Cover Service into a made-for-the-MacArthur-Post-Office-first-day cover by adding typewritten text. He then addressed the cover to himself, had it mailed from the new post office, and autographed it for his personal collection [Figure 8A, cachet 10045].

Using watercolors, Dorothy Knapp of Rhinebeck, New York, hand painted a portrait of the general surrounded by American symbols [Figure 8B, cachet 2786]. She used similar central vignette elements in her design for a printed cover published for the occasion by Fleetwood Cover Service [Figure 8C, cachet 7632].

In the months after the attack on Pearl Harbor, the mood and themes of patriotic covers reflected the somber war picture in the Pacific. One philatelic writer recorded how events drove changes in wartime envelope art: "The old slogans and designs which portrayed public sentiment a year ago, would not meet the changed conditions of today. Since December 7, 1941, American defenses have been under constant attack by a ruthless enemy. Now we are all united in

Figure 12. Death wishes for Adolph Hitler. A, Cachet 2092. B, Cachet 4533.

reach of language," Jones wrote to Franklin.) Jones's unyielding response became an American legend.[15]

The discouraging war news inspired patriotic cover creators to attempt to define core American values and goals in their cachets. An anonymous artist's emotional defense of American "riches in liberty," expressed in a hand-lettered cachet, is shown in Figure 9C (cachet 3895).

—☆—

An apparently hare-brained American scheme—using land bombers lifting off an aircraft carrier to bomb Tokyo and other Japanese cities—led to the pivotal Battle of Midway in early June 1942 [Figure 9D, cachet 4151]. This battle changed the fortunes of the United States in the Pacific war and changed the tenor of patriotic covers for the rest of the war.

The April 18, 1942, air raid on Japan was conceived as a retaliatory response to Pearl Harbor. Lt. Col. James H. Doolittle led 16 specially modified B-25s from the carrier USS *Hornet* to targets over Tokyo, Kobe, Nagoya, and Yokohama. Though the Doolittle raid did little material damage, it lifted American home front morale by foreshadowing offensive actions to come. The raid also "vividly demonstrated to Japanese military leaders the vulnerability of their home islands through the Midway slot in Japan's defensive perimeter. To all of Yamamoto's already weighty arguments about the attractions of an attack on Midway, the necessity of sealing that slot was now added. Debate ceased in the

Japanese high command about the relative priority of the South or Central Pacific. Both operations would now go forward, straining to the utmost the already tautly stretched resources of the Imperial Navy."[16]

First operation to be put into action: Admiral Yamamoto's plan to occupy Midway Island and menace Hawaii with the threat of invasion. This would force the U.S. Fleet into battle off of Midway—the latest version of the "decisive battle" in the central Pacific that was an inveterate part of Japanese naval doctrine. Admiral Chuichi Nagumo, who so successfully led the attack on Pearl Harbor, now led the carrier force bearing down on Midway.

The plan might have worked, except for the tireless efforts of American cryptanalysts working at Pearl Harbor, the battle leadership of Rear Admiral Raymond A. Spruance commanding Task Force 16, and the intuition of Lt. Commander Wade McCluskey commanding 37 Dauntless dive bombers flying from carrier *Enterprise*. Largely uncoordinated attacks on Japanese carriers by land-based bombers and torpedo bombers had been fended off by Zero fighters without a hit scored on any warship. But the evasion tactics forced on the Japanese carriers prevented more Japanese fighters from being launched, and airborne Zeroes were still near the surface after pouncing on American torpedo bombers when McCluskey—who had changed his group's flight course to follow the wake of a single Japanese destroyer in open waters—discovered the enemy fleet. From the direction of the sun, McCluskey's dive bombers fell upon the Japanese carriers. Within minutes three of four carriers of Admiral Nagumo's Carrier Striking

Figure 13. Rationing ups-and-downs in a 1943 hand painted cover (cachet 8198) by Dorothy Knapp, Rhinbeck, NY.

Force were burning wrecks. The fourth was seriously damaged and scuttled by her crew on the following day. The victory had turned on American dive bombers coming upon Nagumo's fleet at the right moment and losing no time in attacking.

In an interview more than a decade later, Army Chief of Staff General George C. Marshall declared: "The closest squeak and the greatest victory was at Midway. The Navy performance there was magnificent and self-sacrificing to the last degree."[17]

Admiral Yamamoto cancelled the Midway operation and withdrew his forces. His earlier prediction ("I shall run wild for the first six months") had been borne out almost to the day. After Midway, parity in carrier power between Japan the United States was restored but the loss of trained, experienced naval airmen proved insurmountable for Japan. Its military planners had lost their long-sought "decisive battle" and with it the initiative in the Pacific. One historian elegantly summarized the outcome: "At Midway the United States laid aside the shield and picked up the sword, and through all the engagements to follow, never again yielded the strategic offensive."[18]

1943: "BACK THE ATTACK"

The turning point of the war was reached. The German Sixth Army, decimated at Stalingrad, surrendered. Later in the war Hitler acknowledged that Germany's reverses had truly begun with that "breakthrough of Russian armies on the Romanian front on the Don in November 1942." At mid-year

the largest tank battle of the war was fought in central Russia in the region of Kursk; 6,000 German and Soviet armored vehicles struggled for over a week. German forces failed to pinch off the westward bulge the Soviet army had earlier created. After the battle of Kursk, Hitler's army never regained the initiative on the Russian Front. Elsewhere, the Anglo-American North African campaign ended in victory. Sicily was invaded and occupied. Italy was invaded. In June, Reichsführer-SS Himmler recorded: "Responding to my briefing on the Jewish question, the Führer declared that the evacuation of the Jews . . . must be implemented and endured to the end."

The Japanese were slowly driven from their New Guinea positions threatening Australia, and the hellish battle for Tarawa in the Gilbert Islands heralded the American central Pacific offensive that aimed northward to the Marshall and Mariana Islands.

In 1943 the Allied powers seized the offense on nearly all fronts. American illustrated envelopes reflected the change in the strategic situation. Variations on the slogan, "Back the Attack" quickly appeared on patriotic covers. "To hell with defense!! / I'm on the offense!!" shouts a Minute Man running out of a war bond poster onto a battlefield on a patriotic cover by Thornton C. Shaw of Sandusky, Ohio (Figure 10A, cachet 8187).

The war bond theme was reiterated on patriotic covers from many other cities. Arthur Knoll of Hamilton, Ohio, created a water-colored illustrated envelope asking his fellow citizens to "Back the attack on them"—a startled Adolf Hitler and dour Gen. Hideki Tojo (Figure 10B, cachet 845). Knoll used watercolors to produce many of his patriotic covers during the war, most featuring caricatures of war leaders of the Axis and Allied powers.

Only one series of illustrated envelopes mailed from Hawaii during the war was indigenously Hawaiian. This series was published by Etsuo Sayama, who was born in Hawaii of Japanese parents. Educated in Oahu and Japan, Sayama served as an assistant engineer draftsman in the U.S. Army Corps of Engineers throughout the war. One of Sayama's covers was printed in 1943 during the third war loan

Figure 14. Loose talk and its consequences. A, Cachet 65. B, Cachet 3609. C, Cachet 7051.

(war bond drive). With text in English and Hawaiian, the cachet combines elements of the American War for Independence (the Minute Man) and Hawaiian unification (King Kamehameha I). Standing proudly behind them is Uncle Sam (Figure 10C, cachet 8021).

—☆—

War bonds were one of the major topics of American World War II patriotic covers. Indeed, they were the focus of more covers than were devoted to D-Day, or VE Day, or VJ Day, or the Navy, or the Marine Corps, or the Statue of Liberty or the American Flag itself.

Even before Pearl Harbor, President Roosevelt and Secretary of the Treasury Henry Morgenthau realized that the war could not be financed entirely out of current taxes. They wanted to persuade the American people to buy interest-bearing bonds redeemable by the Treasury. In April 1941 Defense Savings Bonds went on sale. Morgenthau went on radio to say that "the question has been: 'What can I do to help?' [Now] it will be possible for everyone—literally everyone—to take part in the National Defense effort."

In 1942 Defense Savings Bonds became War Savings Bonds and an immense effort to sell them began. Each of the eight national war bond drives ("war loans") that were held in just over three years from November 1942 to December 1945 lasted about a month. Thus nearly one-quarter of the wartime period was occupied by feverish activities devoted to meeting the dollar quotas for the bond drives. Three of the war loans overlapped the December 7 Pearl Harbor remembrance date (1942, 1944, 1945), increasing their power.

Figure 11 shows the cachets of official illustrated envelopes printed by the Commandant's Office of the Navy Yard at Pearl Harbor for the first and second anniversaries of the Pearl Harbor attack. The cachet in Figure 11A (cachet 6584), from an envelope postmarked December 7, 1942, has a mixture of symbols. In the right corner USS *Arizona* is exploding and

Figure 15. Interrupted mail sent to sunken transport ship USS *McCawley*. Cachet 7986.

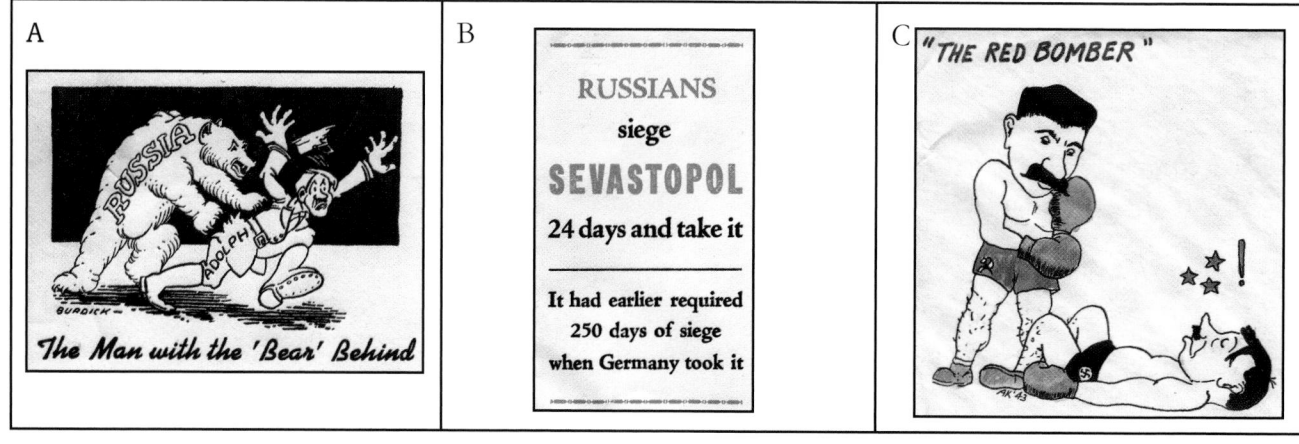

Figure 16. Good news from the Russian Front, 1944. A, Cachet 7633. B, Cachet 6732. C, Cachet 7706.

sinking, while the American Eagle clutches two Japanese warships in its talons. "Remember Pearl Harbor" is the explicit message.

The Navy Yard at Pearl Harbor noted the second anniversary of the attack with a cachet printed in blue on a legal-size penalty envelope (Figure 11B, cachet 1766) . It is a seminal cachet, symbolizing in its many elements the change from defiance and defense to offense. Its message fairly screams "Attack!" The vignette features an American sailor, bayonet at the ready, striding through Pacific waters leading the attack. (Remember, this is an official Naval Department cover.) A warship and a carrier fighter plane are his background supports. A bellicose American eagle flies overhead with a stack of war bonds in his talons, graphically illustrating the people's support for the war effort—and mirroring the nearly universal American belief that war bond purchase was the key to that effort. The central source from which all these elements flow is a land mass over which the words

Figure 17. Confidence in American power, 1944.

"December / 7" are outlined against a bright light. It is the dawning light of a great explosion. The cachet projects American unity, determination, battle-readiness, and power.

Buying bonds demonstrated the unity of the American people and their support for the war effort. The question "What can I do to help?" was repeatedly answered: "Buy bonds." Patriotism got a boost from Hollywood, Madison Avenue, the Treasury Department's War Finance Division, and hundreds of thousands of local drive chairmen throughout the country. War heroes, movie stars, radio personalities, advertising copy writers, and comic book characters tirelessly pleaded with the American people to speed victory by buying bonds. And the people responded magnificently: every war bond drive was oversubscribed.

The award for appearing on more United States patriotic covers than any other wartime personage must go to

Adolf Hitler. This was a reflection of his extraordinary personal impact on world events. Of course these patriotic covers caricatured the German dictator and lambasted his cruelty, ambition, and vanity. And in the end they celebrated his ignominious death. "No one else produced, in a solitary course lasting only a few years, such accelerations in the pace of history," a biographer has written. "No one else so changed the state of the world and left behind such a wake of ruins as he did. It took a coalition of almost all the world powers to wipe him from the face of the earth in a war lasting nearly six years, to kill him—to quote an Army officer of the German resistance—'like a mad dog.'"[19] Of course, death wishes for Adolf Hitler were not lacking on United States patriotic covers published throughout the war [Figure 12A, cachet 2092; Figure 12B, cachet 4533].

—☆—

Many essential goods were rationed, beginning with tires in January 1942. The lack of rubber had become a national crisis: "Japanese conquests in the Far East had gobbled up 97 percent of the nation's rubber supply. . . . The government quickly clamped a freeze on tires, followed by a ban on recapping tires."[20] Rationing of passenger automobiles, typewriters, sugar, and gasoline soon followed.

In 1943 rationing bit even harder. Between February and November of that year most foodstuffs were rationed: meat, shortening and oils, butter, margarine, cheese, processed food, dried fruits, canned milk, jams and jellies. Ration books for these, and more, were issued by the Office of Price Administration (OPA). People applied through the mail for their ration books and received them along with "A Message to Every Ration Book Holder" which told them:

> Your Government is counting on you to help enforce the new regulations by making and keeping this simple pledge—
> *I will accept no rationed foods without giving ration stamps.*
> *I will never pay more than legal prices.*

(Emphasis in original document.)

In the end, Americans endured rationing throughout the war, "grumbling, conniving, sacrificing, and for the most part complying. Compared to the other belligerents, Americans were relatively well off . . . although there were times when items like butter, beef, pork and bacon disappeared entirely. But compared to the average level of peacetime living that most were used to, they underwent hardships."[21]

Dorothy Knapp of Rhinebeck, NY, used watercolors to view of wartime rationing in the illustrated envelope shown in Figure 13 (cachet 8198).

Americans also endured censorship from the time the bombs fell at Pearl Harbor. On December 19, 1941, the Office of Censorship was created. Its Director was authorized "to censor all communications entering or leaving the United States by whatever medium . . . to prevent the transmission of information of value to the enemy." Soon censorship was extended to domestic news media to prevent publication of information that might be of use to the enemy. "The genius of the arrangement was that news censorship was to be voluntary rather than mandatory."[22] Newspapers, magazines, and radio programs voluntarily refrained from disseminating such military information as troop movements or production figures. Even playing of "request numbers on record shows was dropped on the theory that agents might employ them to send code messages," and radio weather reports were discontinued until the fall of 1943, "for fear Axis fliers would be tuned in."[23]

No wonder then that cachets on patriotic covers cautioned against loose speech and dramatically pictured its dire consequences [Figure 14, cachets 65, 3609, and 7051].

—☆—

Patriotic covers were created to record or comment on wartime events; inevitably, some mailed to or from members of the armed forces became entangled in these events. Figure 15 (cachet 7986) shows such a cover. A general purpose patriotic cover created in 1942 (note the "They Shall Not Pass" cachet of that year), it was mailed from Philadelphia on June 9, 1943 to a sailor on transport ship *McCawley*. In the early months of 1943 the ship brought supplies and reinforcements to Guadalcanal.

In mid-June she began preparations for the New Geogia and central Solomons campaign. On June 30 *McCawley* was attacked by Japanese torpedo bombers in Blanche Channel between Rendova and New Georgia Islands. A torpedo hit the engine room of the transport, knocking out all power and killing 15 of her crew. The survivors were pulled clear of the stricken ship by a destroyer, *Ralph Talbot*. A few hours later came the final blow: "The doomed ship was again torpedoed and in 30 seconds she sank in 340 fathoms. The following day it was learned that six motor torpedo boats [U.S. PT-boats] had torpedoed an "enemy" transport in Blanche Channel, after having been informed there were no friendly forces in the area. PTs were then placed directly under Admiral Turner [Richmond Kelly Turner, commander of the Amphibious Force of the Pacific Fleet] and given a liaison officer to keep them informed."[24]

The cover was marked "Returned to Writer." The fate of the sailor to whom it was addressed is unknown.

1944: INVASIONS AND LIBERATIONS

The end of the German and Japanese war machines was assured in 1944. "Fortress Europa" was breached by Allied troops who landed on the beaches of Normandy on June 6 (D-Day) and carried their invasion eastward toward Germany. A summer Russian offensive thrust Soviet troops to the gates of Warsaw and into Hungary. The U.S. Navy and Marines under Admiral Nimitz's command in the central Pacific drove westward until they met General MacArthur's forces swinging north. Taken by American forces in July-August, Saipan and Tinian in the Mariana Islands became home bases for the new B-29 Superfortresses that began bombing Japan later in the year.

Exit, pursued by a bear is the stage direction for the unfortunate Antigonus in Act 3 of *The Winter's Tale*. After that, he is seen no more. Man pursued by bear has been a metaphor for mortal danger ever since. Concrete expression is given in Figure 16A (cachet 7633): Adolf Hitler is "exiting" the scene in panic, the Russian Bear tearing at his backside.

By the beginning of 1944 the military balance on the Russian front had fundamentally shifted. For four months beginning in January, Soviet forces in Ukraine and the Crimea went on an unbroken offensive that destroyed the southern portion of the German armies. In May three Soviet armies converged on Sevastopol, the fortress at the southwestern tip of the Crimea that had been the main Black Sea naval base of the USSR before the German invasion of June 1941. Sevastopol, besieged since that December, fell to German forces in July 1942. Now in May 1944 the positions were reversed. Despite Hitler's demand of his 17th Army commander to hold the fortress to prevent Soviet control of the Black Sea, most of the 17th Army was destroyed and Sevastopol was taken by the Red Army [Figure 16B, cachet 6732].

In the center and northern areas of the Russian Front, the Soviet Byelorussian operation began in June. By mid-summer its forces liberated Minsk and destroyed German Army Group Center, with Soviet forces nearing East Prussia. In twelve days of fighting on this front, "twenty-five divisions with at least 300,000 men had vanished from the German order of battle. The Red Army had shown that conducting Blitzkrieg was no German monopoly and that, in spite of the horrendous losses in the earlier fighting, it had both the means and the ability to drive successfully into a German front that had been held and fortified for many months."[25]

American cachet makers responded to events on the Russian Front with illustrations lauding Soviet accomplishments. Figure 16C (cachet 7706) returns to the boxing metaphor to show Josef Stalin, "The Red Bomber," knocking out Hitler. One way or another, the man pursued by the Russian Bear would be destroyed.

—☆—

"You asked for it" proclaims a caption on an extraordinary cover published by Belles-lettres of Chicago [Figure 17, cachet 10,533]. Mailed in January 1944 (postal markings on the back of the envelope), the cover's all-over cachet features two American eagles swooping down on the surprised and awed figures of Premier Tojo and Adolf Hitler, standing in military uniform, caught with hands on swords. Ruined buildings in the background reflect the destruction they have brought, but may also portend the destruction that will be brought to them. The cover reflects pride in American military power and

Figure 18. Invasions, liberations, and conquests, The Pacific, 1944. A, Cachet 4386. B, Cachet 631. C, Cachet 6775.

confidence in that power simultaneously—the dominating twin eagles—to overcome the two Axis Powers.

"D-Day," an armed forces staff term for the first day of any operation, has gained widest currency for the date of the Allied landings in Normandy in 1944. There were D-Days in the Pacific throughout the year as Allied forces broke through Japan's extended defensive perimeter.

The major expansion of its Pacific fleet in 1943 allowed the U.S. to prosecute a "two-front" war in the Pacific. Central Pacific forces were commanded by Admiral Nimitz; Southwest Pacific forces by General MacArthur. The Marshall Islands, a group of Micronesian Pacific atolls, lay in the Central Pacific. Mandated to Japan after World War I, they were part of Japan's outer defensive perimeter. At the end of January and the first days of February 1944 they became the site of the first U.S. occupation of Japanese soil. Army troops invaded Kwajalein atoll, largest of the Marshall Islands, on February 1. After five days of heavy fighting Kwajalein was secured. Success in the Marshall Islands set the stage for American carrier forces to rampage through the Central Pacific, eventually forcing the Japanese Combined Fleet to withdraw its main forces to Singapore. The cachet shown in Figure 18A (cachet 4386) paid tribute to the sacrifice of the American troops in the Kwajalein campaign.

In the Southwest Pacific, the struggle for New Guinea began in March 1942 when Japanese forces landed along the eastern coast as part of the plan to take the Papuan capital of Port Moresby on the southwestern coast, and to menace Australia. On April 24, 1944, after two years of warfare on the huge island, American forces were able to leapfrog 500 miles north along the coast to Hollandia and Aitape, occupied by the Japanese since April 1942 [Figure 18B, cachet 631]. American coast-hopping advances along the northern shore of New Guinea forced the Japanese to retreat from the southern flank of their defensive perimeter stretching from New Guinea northward to the Caroline and Mariana Islands. The success at Hollandia proved to be an early step in MacArthur's drive towards the Philippines.

The invasions of Saipan, Tinian, and Guam in the Mariana Islands are commemorated in cachet 6775, pictured in Figure 18C.

Invasion day—D-Day—for Saipan was June 15, 1944. It took nearly a month to subdue the Japanese defenders of the rugged island. Toward the end, the war's largest *banzai* charge—an all-out suicidal attack by Japanese infantry advancing *en masse*, often as the last major action of a defeated force—occurred the night of July 6-7. More than 4,300 Japanese bodies were found and buried the next day. With the end of organized resistance on July 9, many Japanese on the island (including civilian families urged on by Japanese troops) jumped to their deaths from Marpi point at the northern tip of the island. Capture of Saipan brought Japan within range of B-29 bombers.

Tinian, which lies just 3 miles from Saipan, was invaded on July 24. Because of its proximity to Saipan, the amphibious operation had an unusual shore-to-shore aspect to it. Organized Japanese opposition was overcome in 12 days, though pockets of resistance were encountered for another three months.

Guam, largest of the Marianas and an American possession since 1898, possessed the only adequate water supply in the Marianas—and the best harbor. It was occupied by the Japanese three days after the attack on Pearl Harbor. D-Day for Guam came two and a half years later, on July 21, 1944. A 55,000-strong American Amphibious Group landed on the island. By August 10 the island was secure, though mopping-up operations continued until the end of the war.

With the conquest of the Marianas, the U.S. Navy had advance bases for operations against the Philippines and the Air Force could begin its strategic air offensive against Japan using airfields from which B-29 bombers flew. It was from Tinian that B-29 bombers delivered the atomic bombs dropped in August 1945 on Hiroshima and Nagasaki.

—☆—

D-Day, June 6, 1944, was the date of "history's greatest amphibious operation," "the mightiest armada ever assembled," "the one most critical event of World War II," "the most difficult and

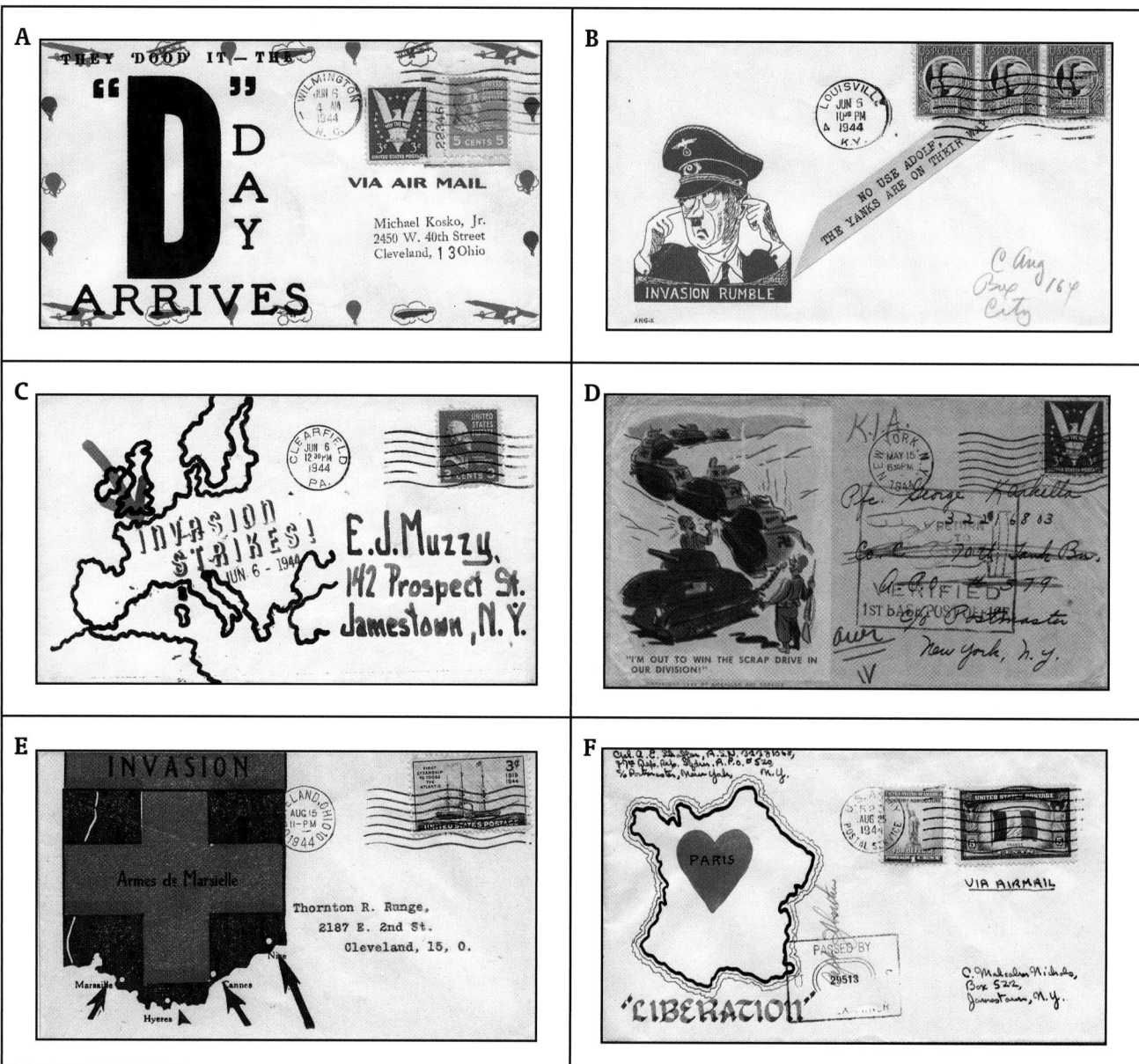

Figure 19. From the invasion of Normandy to the liberation of Paris, June 6 to August 25, 1944. A to D, D-Day covers. A, Cachet 7963. B, Cachet 3844. C, Cachet 3830. D, Cachet 3705. E, Cachet 3820, invasion of Southern France ("Marseille" misspelled in two different ways on cachet). F, Cachet 6100, liberation of Paris.

Figure 20. December 7, 1944, third anniversary of the attack on Pearl Harbor. A, Cachet 4528. B, Cachet 6161. C, Cachet 7269.

complicated operation ever"—all superlatives used to describe the cross-channel invasion of Normandy by Allied forces that came to liberate Western Europe. One more superlative has stuck: "The longest day," involving 5,000 ships, 11,000 sorties by Allied aircraft, and about 154,000 troops who breached the Atlantic Wall. The invasion followed months of bombing of transportation targets in France, amphibious exercises off the British coast, and rising tensions concerning the long-awaited invasion.

It took nearly two months after the initial landings for American forces to cut off the Cotentin peninsula and take Cherbourg in the west, and for British forces to take Caen in the east, but by the end of July Allied armies broke out of Normandy.

A new situation began to form in the summer of 1944: symptoms of disintegration in the German army, "both after the Soviet breakthroughs of late June in the East and the American rupture of the Normandy front at the end of July. . . . There were now mass surrenders alongside instances of garrisons fighting to the bitter end. On both major fronts, very large numbers of German soldiers surrendered; this was an especially novel development on the Eastern Front."[26]

The Normandy invasion was under way by the time people in the United States awakened on June 6. Cachet makers seized the opportunity to have their covers mailed at post offices around the country. A profusion of covers celebrated the D-Day invasion of Normandy [Figures 19A, B, C; cachets 7963, 3844, 3830]. (Figure 19D [cachet 3705] shows a patriotic cover mailed to an American soldier killed in the first days of the Normandy campaign.) The liberation of

French cities followed in the next months [Figures 19E, F; cachets 3820, 6100].

More than 50 patriotics were newly created for D-Day, and hundreds of general purpose patriotics were postmarked and mailed on June 6. One philatelic writer asked if anyone could spare "a copy of any cover that was used for D-Day? I'm trying to see how many different of these I can collect. I'll send whatever you want in exchange."[27]

The demand for D-Day covers has never faded.

—☆—

The war bond theme was again featured on some patriotic covers created for the third anniversary of Pearl Harbor, in part because the sixth war loan running from November 20 to December 16, 1944, was now peaking.

Scheduling the dates of war bond drives around the December 7th anniversary was part of the strategy of the Treasury Department to popularize the drives. The anniversary tie-in was reflected in a cover published by Richard P. Boone of Wilmington, North Carolina, a printer and prolific creator of patriotic covers. "Let's / sock / those / Sons of Heaven / this / December seven! / with war bonds" was the suggestion of the text in his cachet [Figure 20A, cachet 4528].

A hand painted patriotic cover was made by Herman R. Maul of Columbus, Ohio, for the third anniversary of the attack [Figure 20B, cachet 6161]. Staring at a large posted sign that reads "Dec. / 7, /

1941," John Q. Public, a figure reminiscent of many such figures depicted in political cartoons, looks stern and determined as he murmurs to himself: "I won't / forget it."

A motif for the third anniversary of the Pearl Harbor attack was struck by the Sayama patriotic cover shown in Figure 20C (cachet 7269). Featuring a bold "Sunset and Shadows" cachet printed in red, blue, and black, the cover dramatically depicts the doom awaiting Japan. The Rising Sun emblem is now a setting sun that throws the shadow of the Grim Reaper toward the Japanese home islands. In stark black the words, "Dec. 7th / 1941-1944," complete the forceful statement.

1945: UNCOMMON VALOR, UNCONDITIONAL VICTORY

The days of victory finally came in 1945, at great cost. Begun the week before Christmas 1944, Hitler's final counter-offensive in the west, the Ardennes campaign (Battle of the Bulge), killed 19,000 American troops; 15,000 more were captured. But German forces incurred nearly 100,000 casualties as the offensive was routed in January 1945. The Battle of the Bulge depleted German reserves, allowed the winter Russian offensive in the east to achieve an early victory, and hastened the end of the Third Reich. As Anglo-American forces moved eastward, the Russians fought in East Prussia and Hungary and advanced into Austria. In early April the Red

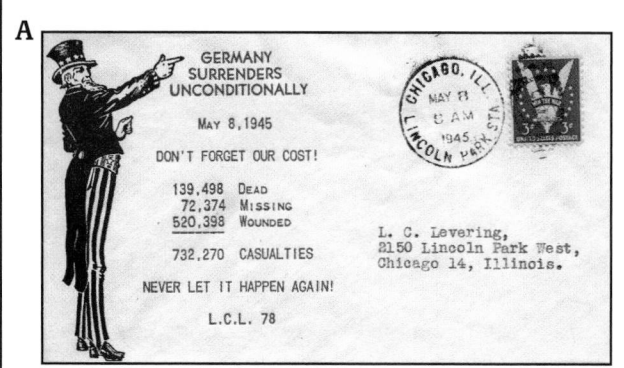

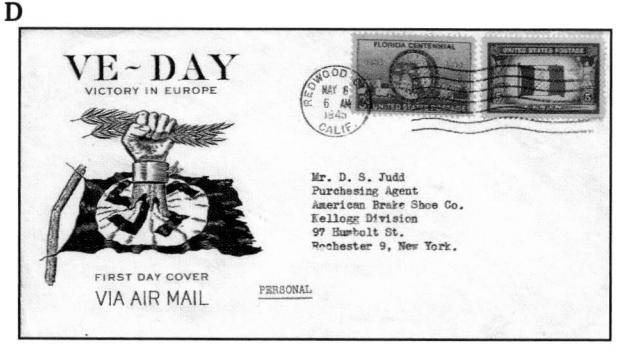

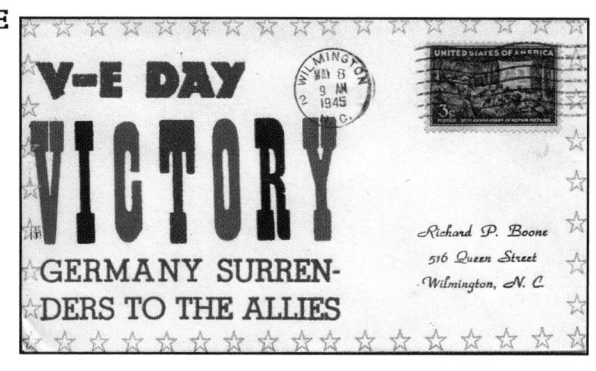

Figure 21. VE Day, May 8, 1945. A, Cachet 2859. B, Cachet 1342. C, Cachet 9339. D, Cachet 9420. E, 9410. F, Cachet 9396.

Army made final preparations for its assault on Berlin. At the same time the Western Allies completed their encirclement of the Ruhr.

In January the Soviets liberated Auschwitz, the largest extermination and concentration camp. A few thousand emaciated prisoners remained alive. Evidence of mass murder at Auschwitz included personal belongings in warehouses of victims: hundreds of thousands of men's suits, 800,000 women's outfits, and 14,000 pounds of human hair. American forces liberated more than 20,000 prisoners at Buchenwald, where thousands more had died of illness, starvation, and ill-treatment. When British forces liberated Bergen-Belsen concentration camp in mid-April, they found thousand of corpses lying unburied on the camp grounds. Most of the 60,000 living prisoners were critically ill with typhus; more than 10,000 died in the next few weeks. British troops burned down the camp to prevent the spread of typhus.[28]

The road to Tokyo was to run through the Philippines, Iwo Jima, and—in the final and greatest land battle of the Pacific War—Okinawa. After the conquest of Okinawa in June and the atomic bombing of Hiroshima and Nagasaki in August, Japan accepted Allied surrender terms.

The end of the war in Europe came into sight in March 1945 when American forces crossed the Rhine, the last major natural obstacle facing them in the battle for Germany.

As Allied armies advanced toward the heart of Germany, cachet makers prepared their VE Day offerings. "It seems that almost everybody has prepared covers for Germany's surrender," wrote John Max Rush in March 1945, "and now they [the covers] may grow musty since it may be a long time before that event occurs."[29] Five divisions of Anglo-American troops had established a bridgehead east of the Rhine even as these cautionary words—based on the sudden reversals of military fortune of the previous months—were published.

Russian forces reached the Berlin outer defenses on April 21. Hitler killed himself in an underground bunker on April 30 and the city surrendered on May 2. Germany surrendered on May 8, and the date was officially proclaimed "Victory in Europe Day" by President Truman and Prime Minister Churchill. This formal end to the war in Europe came one day after General Alfred Josef Jodl, Chief of Operations for the German Armed Forces High Command, signed the instrument of surrender at Allied headquarters in Reims, France. (At the insistence of the Soviet Union the surrender document was ratified in Berlin on May

Figure 22. Events in the Pacific, 1945. A, Cachet 5085. B, Cachet 8481A. C, Cachet 5743. D, Cachet 5744.

9, accounting for the one day difference in anniversary commemorations of VE Day between western nations and Russia.)

In New York City on VE Day, "paper poured out of [Manhattan] windows by the ton, and all over the country whistles sounded, guns boomed, church bells rang, and people went inside the churches for prayers."[30] And the makers of patriotic covers celebrated by shipping all over the country the creations they had been readying for months. Figures of Uncle Sam, the American Eagle, the American Flag, and flags of the United Nations were found in abundance on many of their VE Day covers, as shown in Figures 21A-E (cachets 2859, 1342, 9339, 9420, 9410).

Dorothy Knapp prepared 15 hand painted VE Day covers (including a set of 12 for the overrun European nations). One is shown in Figure 21F (cachet 9396). Symbols abound, both artistic and postal. A female figure standing on a globe of the world rises from draped flags of the United Nations. She holds a laurel wreath in her upraised right hand well above her head. All the other elements of the cachet—the American Eagle, the bold "V", the sword of battle—support this frail figure of victory and peace in Europe. Postal elements have also been carefully chosen: a copy of the Flag of France stamp of the Overrun Countries issue of 1944 has been hand cancelled at the Victory, Vermont post office on VE Day.

—☆—

Casualties mounted in the Pacific as Japanese resistance became ever more fierce. The American re-conquest of the Philippines, begun in late 1944, was capped by the invasion of Luzon in January 1945 and the battle for Manila. Only after large sections of the city were destroyed in street fighting—and some 100,000 Filipino civilians killed, many by unbridled atrocities by Japanese forces—did Japanese resistance collapse. On March 3 Manila was finally liberated. The skillful tactics of delay by General Tomoyuki Yamashita, "his soldiers' willingness to fight to the last breath, and the mounting savagery of combat [had] provided a bitter foretaste of what awaited the Americans to the north on Iwo Jima and Okinawa."[31] (Note over-optimistic "Manila's Liberation / U.S. Forces Enter the Capital of the Philippines—Feb. 4th 1945" in Figure 22A, cachet 5084.)

Marines assaulted Iwo Jima on February 19 [Figure 22B, cachet 8481A]. The small volcanic island, a critical link in Japan's inner defense ring, was conquered after a month of fighting. The battle was fought with "unmatched barbarity. Japanese soldiers stubbornly refused to surrender. Many died the most hideous of deaths, incinerated by flamethrowers that jetted burning gasoline into their bunkers. When the fighting ended at last in late March, only a few hundred Japanese [of the original 21,000 man garrison], most of them wounded, had allowed themselves to be taken prisoner."[32] Marine casualties numbered a third of their force—6,000 killed, over 27,000 wounded. The words of tribute offered by Admiral Nimitz to the Marines in that place have been enshrined with the deeds of the men he eulogized: "On Iwo Jima, uncommon valor was a common virtue."

Next came Okinawa [Figure 22C, cachet 5743], where the defending commander had one main objective: to inflict as many casualties on the invading American force for as long as possible. The Japanese saw that the defense of Okinawa—the central island of the Ryukyus, the group nearest the Japanese home islands—as their final chance to hold off an invasion of the home islands. The emperor's government told his subjects that Okinawa "would be the war's *sekigahara*, its decisive battle. The people were reminded that samurai warriors let 'the enemy cut one's skin to eat his flesh'—that Marines and GIs had been permitted to land so that kamikazes could sink their supporting fleet and isolate them on the island. Certainly they made their greatest effort of the war on Okinawa."[33]

Incessant artillery and mortar fire took their toll on both sides. American Marines and soldiers used napalm bombs, flamethrowers, and flamethrowing tanks to kill Japanese defenders dug into hillsides or hidden in fortified caves. In late June, after ferocious fighting for nearly three months, American forces secured the island [Figure 22D, cachet 5744]. Nearly 40,000 U.S. Marines and soldiers were killed or wounded. The navy sustained another 9,700 casualties on ships, most victims of kamikaze airplane attacks on American warships in Okinawan waters. More than 110,000 Japanese died in the battle. The great effort of the Japanese military was in vain: the American conquest of Okinawa meant that the next amphibious assault would be on the homeland itself.

Operation OLYMPIC, seizure of the home island of Kyushu planned to begin November 1945, was never mounted.

After the atomic bombings of Hiroshima (August 6) and Nagasaki (August 9), Japan offered to surrender (August 10), provided the Emperor and the Imperial Throne remained. The Allied response was: "The authority of the Emperor and the Japanese Government . . . shall be subject to the Supreme

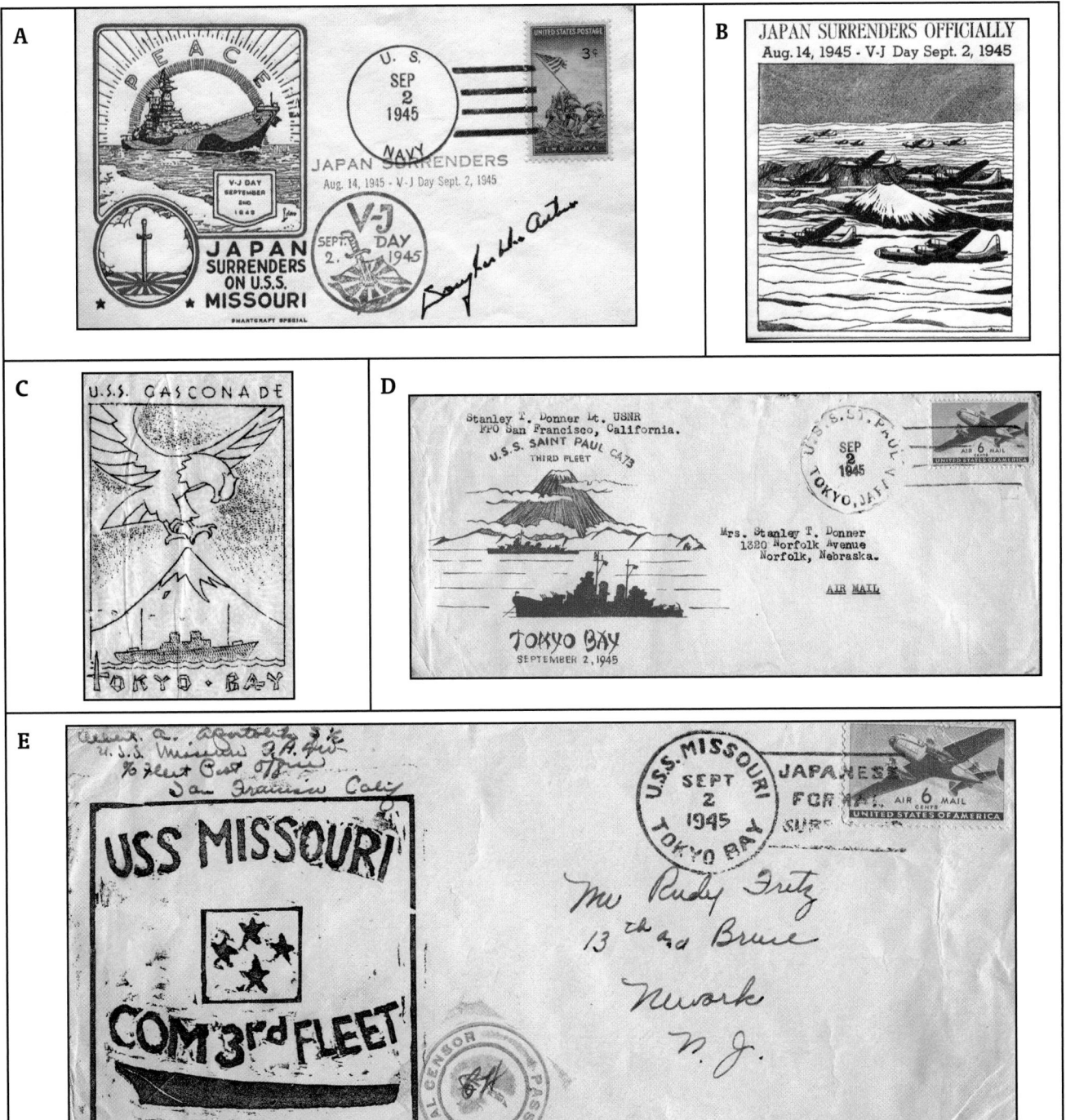

Figure 23. VJ Day, September 2, 1945. A, B: home front cachets. A, Cachet 4028. B, Cachet 4052. C-E: Tokyo Bay cachets. C, Cachet 8593. D, Cachet 8602. E, Cachet 9010.

Commander of the Allied Powers." On August 14 the Japanese accepted the terms. A day later Emperor Hirohito broadcast to his people the news of the surrender. He did not use that term in his speech; only, "the war situation has developed not necessarily to our advantage." He added that "the enemy has begun to employ a new and most cruel bomb," and therefore "our empire accepts the provisions of their Joint Declaration."

After years of war in Asia and the Pacific—after 10 million Chinese died at the hands of Japanese invaders, after a million Japanese military were killed and another million Japanese civilians became casualties, after nearly 100,00 Americans were killed in action or were dead of war-related causes in the Pacific war (and more than twice that number wounded)—after all this, victory and peace had come.

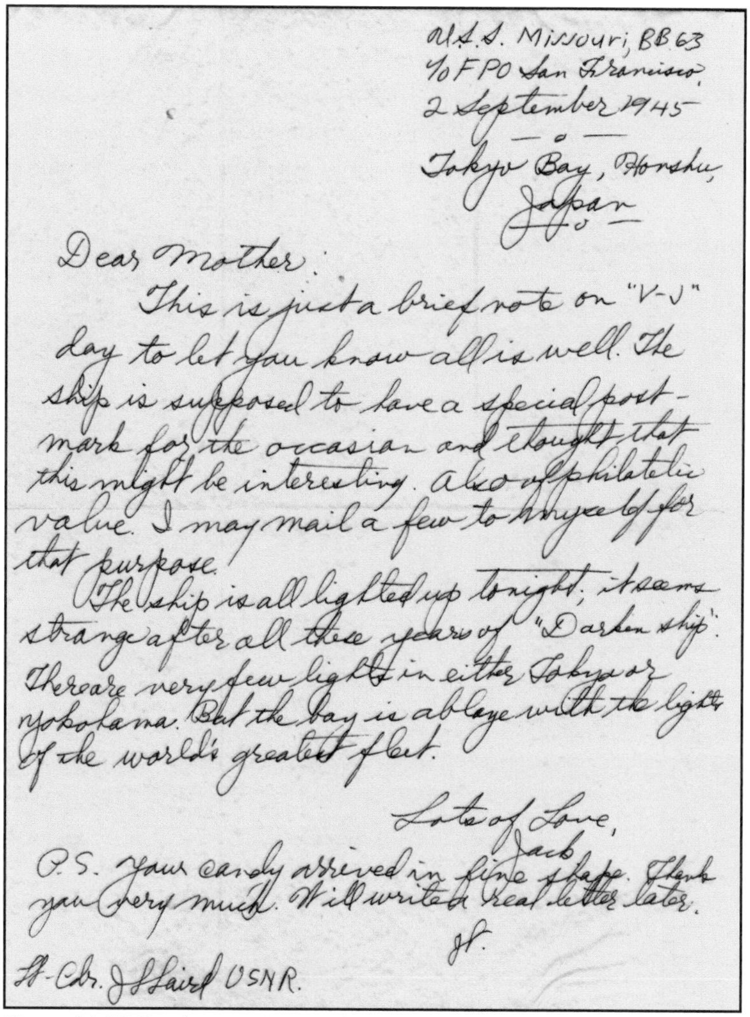
U.S.S. Missouri, BB 63
% FPO San Francisco
2 September 1945
— o —
Tokyo Bay, Honshu,
Japan

Dear Mother:

This is just a brief note on "V-J" day to let you know all is well. The ship is supposed to have a special post-mark for the occasion and thought that this might be interesting. Also of philatelic value. I may mail a few to myself for that purpose.

The ship is all lighted up tonight; it seems strange after all these years of "Darken ship". There are very few lights in either Tokyo or Yokohama. But the bay is ablaze with the lights of the world's greatest fleet.

Lots of Love,
Jack

P.S. Your candy arrived in fine shape. Thank you very much. Will write a real letter later.
JL

Lt-Cdr. J L Laird USNR.

Figure 24. VJ Day letter written to his mother by an officer on USS *Missouri*.

In Washington, DC at 7 p.m. on August 14 President Truman announced that Japan had surrendered. Euphoria greeted the great event. According to Winston Churchill, the end of the cruelest, most destructive war ever occasioned "the greatest outburst of joy in the history of mankind."

In their way the makers of patriotic covers participated in the outburst of joy. There was a great outpouring of VJ Day covers on the evening of August 14 and throughout August 15 to celebrate the acceptance of surrender terms—and then a greater outpouring on September 2, 1945 [Figures 23 A, B; cachets 4028, 4057], the date on which the instrument of surrender was signed on board the flagship of Admiral William Halsey's Third Fleet, the battleship *Missouri*, anchored in Tokyo Bay.

Patriotic covers postmarked between August 28 and September 2 (indeed, for weeks following the signing of the surrender) emanated from many ships of the great flotilla anchored in Tokyo Bay [Figures 23C-D; cachets 8593, 8602], including *Missouri* itself. Figure 23E shows a patriotic cover (cachet 9010) created in the print shop of the battleship and sent home by airmail by a sailor stationed on *Missouri*. Note the "U.S.S. Missouri / Sept 2 1945 / Tokyo Bay" circular date stamp, "Japanese Formal Surrender" 3-line cancel, and naval censor mark.

On board *Missouri* the night of the surrender ceremony a young officer, Lt. Cmdr. John Laird, wrote a letter to his mother [Figure 24]. After briefly mentioning that "the ship is supposed to have a special postmark for the occasion," and conjecturing on the postmark's philatelic value, he closed with these words of pride: "There are very few lights in either Tokyo or Yokohama. But the bay is ablaze with the lights of the world's greatest fleet."

More than 300 different patriotic envelopes made for VJ Day, including those from warships in Tokyo Bay, exploded onto the market. On that note of triumph the days of United States patriotic envelopes of World War II ended.

NOTES and SOURCES

1. Kehr, Ernest A. *The Romance of Stamp Collecting: Notes from the World of Stamps, Stamp Collecting and Stamp Collectors* (New York: Thomas Y. Crowell Company, 1947), p. 19.

2. Ibid.

3. Laurence, Robert. *The George Walcott Collection of Used Civil War Patriotic Covers* (Hanover, Massachusetts: Robert W. Grant, 1975), Introduction to the First Edition.

4. Grant, Robert W. *The Handbook of Civil War Patriotic Envelopes and Postal History* (Hanover, Massachusetts: Robert W. Grant, 1977), p. 1-8.

5. Ibid., pp. 1-1 to 1-2.

6. Ibid., p. 1-10.

7. Billingham, Mrs. Anthony. *America's First Two Years: The Story of American Volunteers in Britain 1939-1941* (London: John Murray and the Pilot Press, 1942), p. 25. Mrs. Billingham was perhaps being discreet in not mentioning that many of the original 240 pilots who joined the Eagle Squadrons before the U.S. entered the war first smuggled themselves into Canada. Yes, there was a time when Americans slipped across the Canadian border to get *into* a war, not *out* of one.

8. Churchill, Winston S. *Their Finest Hour,* volume 2 of the author's six-volume *The Second World War* (Boston: Houghton Mifflin Company, 1949), p. 598.

9. Kennedy, David M. *Freedom from Fear: The American People in Depression and War, 1929-1945* (New York: Oxford University Press, 1999), p. 526.

10. Remarkably, a small advertisement box on page 1 of the January 1942 issue of *Cover News* serves to authenticate this cover. The headline reads: "1941 War Covers—Officially Dated"; and the text of the ad states: "They were mailed on December 7th and have a beautiful embossed historic cachet thereon, franked with obsolete commemoratives—Price 25¢. No cash . . . send one 25¢ defense stamp.—The Cover Specialist—John Mayne."

11. Manchester, William. *American Caesar: Douglas MacArthur 1880-1964* (Boston: Little, Brown and Company, 1978), p. 233.

12. Ibid., p. 251

13. Ibid., p. 307

14. Rush, John Max. "Patriotic Covers," *Cover News,* September 1942, p.4.

15. Isaacson, Walter. *Benjamin Franklin: An American Life* (New York: Simon & Schuster, 2003), p. 390.

16. Kennedy, *Freedom from Fear,* p. 535.

17. Pogue, Forrest C. *George C. Marshall: Ordeal and Hope, 1939-1942* (New York: The Viking Press, 1966), p. 325.

18. Prange, Gordon W., Donald M. Goldstein, and Katherine V. Dillon. *Miracle at Midway* (New York: McGraw-Hill Book Company,1982), p. 397.

19. Fest, Joachim C. *Hitler (*New York: Harcourt Brace Jovanovich, 1973), p. 3.

20. Lingeman, Richard R. *Don't You Know There's a War On?: The American Home Front 1941-1945* (New York: G.P. Putnam's Sons, 1970), p. 235.

21. Ibid., p. 259.

22. Phillips, Cabell. *The 1940s: Decade of Triumph and Trouble* (New York: Macmillan Publishing Co., 1975), pp. 94-95.

23. Lingeman, *Don't You Know There's a War On?*, p. 225.

24. *Dictionary of American Naval Fighting Ships*, Vol. 4 (Washington, DC: Navy Department Office of the Chief of Naval Operations, Naval History Division, 1969), pp. 290-291.

25. Weinberg, Gerhard L. *A World at Arms: A Global History of World War II* (Cambridge, England: Cambridge University Press, 1994), p. 705.

26. Ibid., pp. 705-706.

27. Rush, John Max. "Patriotic Cover Collecting," *Cover News*, August 1944, p. 4. Rush's "Patriotic Cover Collecting" column ran regularly in *Cover News* from November 1942 through May 1945.

28. United States Holocaust Memorial Museum, *Historical Atlas of the Holocaust* (New York: Macmillan Publishing USA, 1996), pp. 166, 208-209.

29. Rush, *Cover News*, March 1945, p. 3.

30. Lingeman, *Don't You Know There's a War on?*, p. 354.

31. Kennedy, *Freedom from Fear*, p. 829.

32. Ibid.

33. Manchester, *American Caesar*, p. 435.

2

The Way They Were

THE AMERICAN cachet makers of World War II included more than 600 individuals and organizations as diverse in their personal histories and geographic distribution as in their talents and techniques. One contemporary observer, writing just three months after the war ended, recalled that they were "men and women in all walks of life. . . . Rich men, poor men, professional men and women, laborers and housewives, all contributed to the great variety of patriotic cover designs. Each one, through individual and often distinctive designs, was able to express his or her personal sentiments or reactions on [sic] either a patriotic, economic, or [military] phase of World War II."[1]

Printing Methods

How did World War II patriotic envelope publishers print the sentiments that informed, inspired, or incited in the name of Country? They employed letterpress and lithography (Greek, "stone writing") as their major printing methods.

Letterpress is a form of relief printing, which involves printing from the raised portion of a plate or printing base. The areas of the plate desired to be left unprinted are removed. Now in relief, the remaining areas are inked, the paper impressed, and the image transferred.[2] This printing technique was used by L.M. "Tex" Edmunds, Fleetwood Cover Service, Herman F. Fluegel, Smartcraft (Edward R. Jordan), and Ludwig W. Staehle, among others.

Drawing on the reminiscences of Paul Hubartt[3] we can learn something of the letterpress printing technique employed with Fluegel cachets. First the image of the artist's drawing was etched in a zinc plate about one-sixteenth of an inch thick, and the plate then fastened (by nails, at that time) to a block of wood that was seven-eighths of an inch thick.

A zinc plate "relief die" of a design by M. Fay Muridge and its final product, a printed cachet on patriotic envelope, are shown in Figures 1A and B.

For cachets printed in five colors—and many Fluegel covers were—five plates were required, one for each color. The zinc plate was then "locked up" in a printing chase, rolled with ink, and pressed firmly against the envelope. "This naturally made an impression in the paper, which went clear through and could be seen (and felt) on the back side of the envelope. In case of a light impression, it may be necessary to hold the envelope sideways and let the light skim across the surface, in order to see the indented lines. When these impression marks are on the back side, you can be sure the cachet was printed by letterpress plates."[4]

This simple "impression marks" test—the presence of plate indentations on the back of the envelope—reveals the letterpress origin of cachets printed in this manner.

Lithographic printing, more commonly used for patriotic cachets, is a form of planographic printing, which does not utilize raised surfaces as in relief printing. Both image and non-image areas are in the same plane. Impression marks are not left on the back side of the envelope.

Figure 1. A, zinc plate used for relief printing of cachet 7148. B, The final product: cacheted, stamped, and postmarked envelope. C, Proof for cachet 10326 by L.M. "Tex" Edmunds. D, The final product: cacheted, stamped, and postmarked envelope.

Over time lithography evolved from making prints off a press that used designs drawn in oily ink on porous stone, with the printing image ink-receptive and the and the nonprinting areas water-receptive. The ink attraction/repulsion principle was still used when porous stone was replaced by a plate treated to accept the ink only where required for printing.[5] This was the offset press technique: the image was first transferred in ink from the lightweight plate (also made of metal but only the thickness of a postal card) to a blanket roller, then from blanket to paper. Hence the image was "offset" onto paper.[6]

Hubartt offered a vivid analogy to illustrate the offset process: "Let's say you have a rubber stamp the shape of a star. Press the star image (with ink on it, of course) against the palm of your hand. Then, while the ink is wet, press your hand against a sheet of while paper. Now you have a star on the paper which has been 'offset' from your hand. Then, while the ink is wet, press your hand against a sheet of paper. The plate never touches the paper. Instead it transfers its image to a rubber 'blanket' (or roller) which contacts the paper as your hand did." Though this description may have oversimplified what happens inside an offset printing press, Hubartt emphasized that his objective was "to illustrate that the cachet was printed by a 'kiss impression' which could in no way leave a visible indentation in the paper."[7]

The high-speed offset press was particularly useful for large press runs and was employed by Jacques Minkus, manager of Gimbels Stamp Department in New York, to print his multicolored wartime patriotic covers in the thousands.

Whether letterpress or lithography was used, printers might check the progress of manufacture by removing prints from the printing base for inspection ("plate proofs"), or check for color that might be other than the final printed color of the cachet ("color trial"), or check for color that was the same as the issued cachet ("color proof").

A color proof on paper of a design by L.M. "Tex" Edmunds, and its printed cachet on patriotic envelope, are shown in Figures 1C and D.

Thermography (Greek, "hot writing") is not a form of printing. It is a technique used in combination with printing to obtain a pattern of raised letters and images. Essentially, after each envelope (or paper) is printed by conventional methods, a fine dust or waxy powder is applied to the wet ink. Some is absorbed and the rest shaken off. Heat is then applied to the printed and powdered envelope, the powder melts and fuses with the ink, and a palpably raised effect of words and image is produced. Thermography was used by a number of patriotic cachet makers, most prominently Walter G. Crosby, whose experience with thermographing covers began in 1930. A brief biography of the man appears in Chapter 3.

Crosby, of San Pedro, CA had been printing and servicing naval covers for many years before producing over 500 wartime patriotic covers, both plain printed and thermographed. To add to the visual effect of many of his covers, Crosby carefully placed a "paste-on" photograph inside a printed border within the cachet. This combination of thermography and pasted-on photograph (always matched to the cachet subject) produced a characteristic "Crosby cover" look.

The five-step Crosby printing and thermographing technique helped Crosby covers earn enduring popularity and assured the cachet maker's reputation in his own time and later. It has been reconstructed by Gene H. Russell as follows:[8]

Step 1: An engraving was made. Black line artwork was converted into a zinc photoengraving and then mounted on a block of wood to make it the height of metal type.

Step 2: Printing. The line engraving block was locked in a letterpress chase and envelopes were hand fed into the press for printing.

Step 3: Applying resin or wax powder. One of these was sprinkled onto the wet cachet and after it was sufficiently absorbed the envelope was tapped to remove unwanted resin.

Step 4: Heating. The envelope was passed through specialized equipment and heated. The resin melted and fused with the ink, and the final printed image stood out in relief and gave the cachet a glistening, "embossed" appearance. (An advantage to the method was that envelopes could be handled or stacked immediately after thermography.)

Step 5: Adding a photograph. As part of some designs, a small black-and-white photograph was glued to the envelope inside a printed frame.

Other printer-publishers experienced in cachet making were able to produce vast numbers of patriotic covers during the war. William S. Linto of Portland, Oregon, worked in the composing room of the *Oregonian*, Portland's largest newspaper, and had a printing press at home on which he created over 1700 wartime patriotics. Richard P. Boone of Wilmington, North Carolina, another printer who was a prolific producer of patriotic covers, published over 500 of them. Bold type faces, a variety of fonts, red and blue (sometimes red or blue) colors, and stock cuts of illustrations marked the lithographed cachets produced by Boone.

"Boone Patriotic Covers In Large Variety, But Very Limited Quantity" headlined a story in *Linn's Weekly Stamp News*.[9] The story noted that "his covers are all printed by himself, the editions are never very large and thus all of them will be scarce in the future. There is something about the covers that make it rather easy to identify them as to their source after one has seen and handled a number of them." The story added that lately "he has been imprinting his name 'Boone,' in small type on the lower corner of each cover," the article continued, "and we commend this practice to all publishers."

Few publishers of patriotic covers heeded this sound advice, as collectors and cataloguers have learned to their sorrow for over five decades. Fortunately the publishers of 95% of the cachets catalogued in Chapter 7 are identified there.

One printer-publisher of wartime patriotics had no background in printing or publishing, and came upon his press by happenstance. James Lewis Lowe recounted his adventure in patriotic covers that began when he was a thirteen year old boy living in Chattanooga, TN. Thanks to his subscription to *Linn's Weekly Stamp News* he learned about patriotic covers in 1943

but had no means of printing them until I visited a one-man print shop near Fourth Ave. and Twenty-third St. in Chattanooga. Fascinated by his shop, I wanted to establish my own but could not afford new equipment. The printer told me that he had on old, broken down, 3"x5" Kelley hand press that he would sell for $5. I managed to save up that amount, purchased the press, had my father to [sic] weld it back together, and set to work producing patriotics, printing over a hundred designs, many of which were merely color varieties. . . . I visited almost every printer in Chattanooga in search of patriotic cuts, i.e., engravings that I could use along with patriotic slogans or quotations. As we say in the south, pickings were slim.[10]

Looking back decades later Lowe recalled that "my patriotics were simple, some rather stupid. In fact, some words were misspelled." But he joined the new Patriotic Cover Exchange Club, became "the proud and patriotic member number 527," and began exchanging a few of his printed patriotics with other collectors. Soon he realized that "my simple designs were in some demand. So I increased production from twenty or thirty to a mailing unused patriotics." All with an old hand press and youthful energy.

Patriotic covers by James Lewis Lowe are illustrated in Figures 2A and B.

The mimeograph was a duplicating machine that made copies of written, drawn, or typed documents from a stencil fitted around an inked drum which pressed its ink through the porous lines of the stencil onto paper. For much of the twentieth century before the invention and ascendancy of the photocopying machine, the mimeograph copier reigned supreme in offices worldwide. The mimeograph also offered personal access to cachet making without the strictures of the printing process.

J. Neal Griffith of Indiana, Pennsylvania, owned a mimeograph machine and used it to produce patriotic covers. He did his own artwork, including hand coloring. A recent article indicated that he "never sold his covers but either gave them to friends and family or exchanged them with other collectors."[11] In addition, Griffith apparently sent his patriotic covers to hometown servicemen.[12] For Griffith, marketing his covers was not the thing. He was one of hundreds of cachet makers who were content to share their sentiments by exchanging

Figure 2. A, B, Patriotic envelopes by James Lewis Lowe. A, cachet 1796. B, Cachet 5800. C, D, Patriotic envelopes by J. Neal Griffith. C, Cachet 2086. D, Cachet 4024.

patriotic envelopes with other wartime collector/cachet makers. Wartime spirit moved them to express their hopes and fears, though their sentiments often outran their talent to express them.

Patriotic covers by J. Neal Griffith are illustrated in Figures 2C and D.

Hand coloring of mimeographed or printed covers, as employed by Griffith and others, is a variant of hand painting. Today the technique is occasionally called "hand tinting."

Most printers of wartime patriotic covers were not identified or publicized by the publishers. Alex R. Hesse of Brooklyn, NY, escaped this anonymity. Well-known before the war for his production of Navy cacheted covers, Hesse worked primarily as a "producer," bringing together "a stable of respected artists, cooperative Navy mail clerks and his own professional printing skills to create some of the most beautiful and sought-after covers in the history of the hobby."[13] Throughout the war Hesse provided printing services to a number of patriotic cover publishers, including Walter Czubay, Herman Fluegel, George Sadworth, Michael Sanders, Smartcraft, and Ludwig W. Staehle. The patriotic covers associated with these publishers—letterpress printed multicolored cachets, envelopes of which sometimes carried naval postmarks stamped by "cooperative Navy mail clerks"—in part owed their high quality to the printing skills of Alex Hesse.

The Market Place, 1: Getting Noticed

During the war George Linn wrote of his contemporary patriotic cover publishers: "The test must be left to the results the dealers get for their efforts. . . . The successful ones are those with the biggest volume of sales and it will always be thus."[14] First they had to get their wares to the marketplace and be noticed. This process took many forms. Some are shown in Figure 3.

Direct advertisement by a wholesaler to dealers was one way to go. Edwin P. Haworth was proprietor of Collector's Surplus of Kansas City, Missouri. He produced his own line of commercially available patriotic envelopes (PentArts covers) and was a key distributor of the cacheted covers of Walter G. Crosby. Figure 3A shows a portion of a letter written

by Haworth to cover dealers, telling them to get their "war zeal up" and "sloganize" the citizenry. Then came his sales pitch: "Crosby . . . has the knack of the thing! Knowing his Naval and First Day covers, . . . we jumped onto him hot-footed to do his duty by us civilians. . . . Unless you know Crosby you wouldn't hope for what he has developed. But we knew Cosby's ability. That's why he has his Set of Patriotic envelopes now ready. That's why we're undertaking their distribution!"

Another way to bring favorable notice was to reproduce as cachets designs produced and advertised by the government.

A portion of a letter from the Adjutant General of the United States, with such a design as its letterhead, is shown in Figure 3B. Six weeks after Pearl Harbor copies of the letter was sent to businesses around the United States asking for their "cooperation in the use of the national slogan 'KEEP 'EM FLYING' for the duration of the war." As part of the letter, the Adjutant General recommended incorporating the slogan or the design "in newspaper, magazine, and other advertising or printed matter."

Cachet makers quickly followed suit. Cachets 4222, 4262, and 4277 containing the "Keep 'em flying" slogan are pictured in the Cachet Catalogue, Chapter 7, as are cachets 4234, 4284, and 4567, which contain variations on the theme (keep 'em diving, frying, or rolling). Also, cachets using the full slogan ("Let's Go! U.S.A. / Keep 'Em Flying!") in various ways are listed as cachets 4574-4577, 4588-4592, 4595, and 4597-4603 in the Cachet Catalogue.

Harry C. Curtiss, proprietor of American Patriotic Press, San Francisco, found another way to sell his patriotic envelopes by directly contacting potential end-users. This is shown in Figure 3C. In a note to E.J. Muzzy in April 1945, Curtiss happily reported that he sent a few of his "Dutch Girl" patriotic envelopes to offices of the Netherlands in San Francisco. The result: "Received an order from the 'Netherland Information Bureau' for 200 'Dutch Girl' covers this morning." He enclosed the note in one of his "Dutch Girl" envelopes (cachet 8359).

In another letter to E.J. Muzzy (Figure 3D), George V. Sadworth, Woodhaven, New York, revealed another way to sell cacheted covers: filling "want lists" of customers and getting the word out to other customers. "I sure had a job digging out most

A

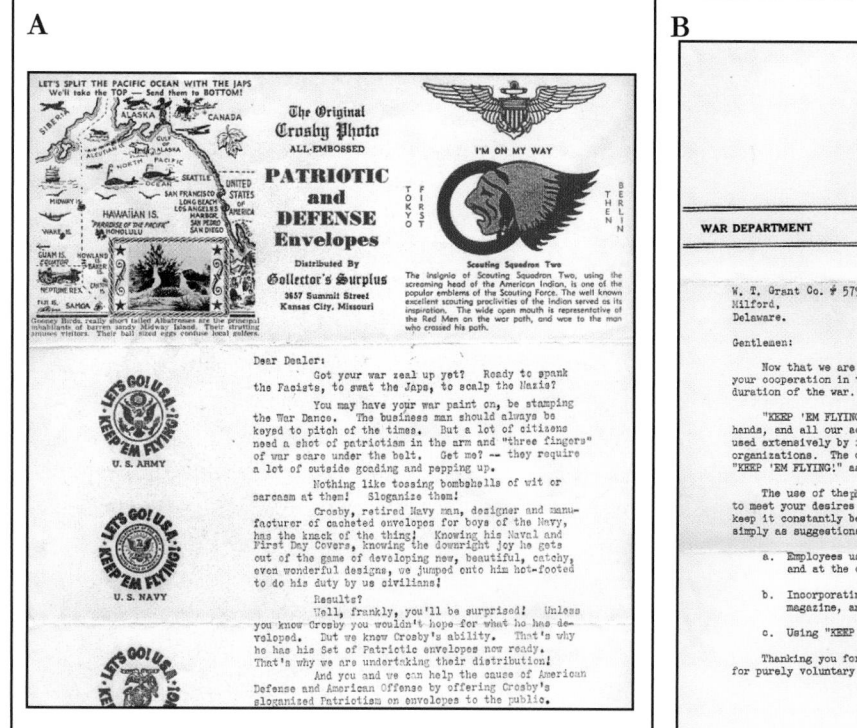

B

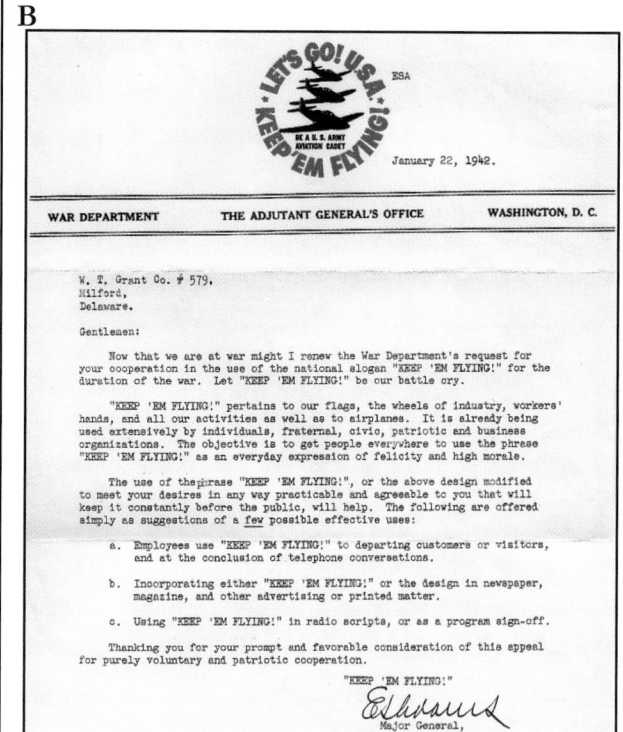

C

D

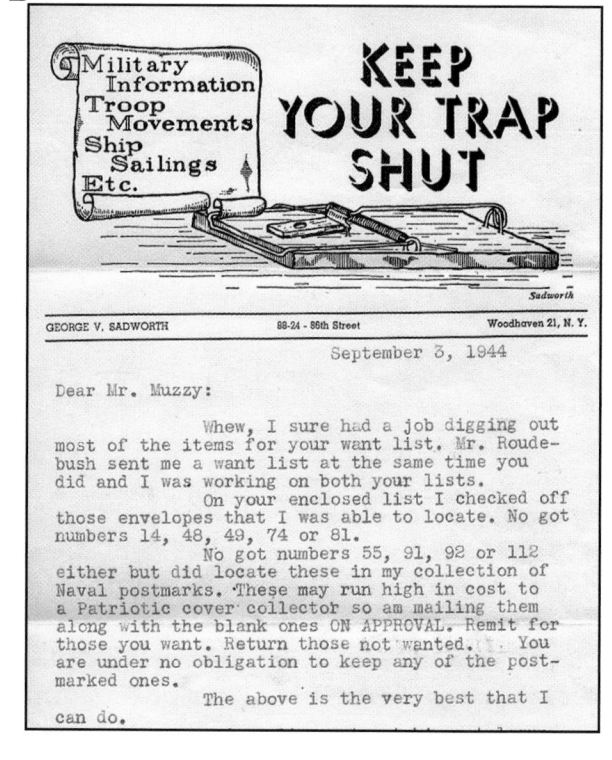

Figure 3. A, Portion of letter from Edwin P. Haworth, Collector's Surplus, to dealers extolling buying and selling Crosby covers. B, Portion of letter from the Adjutant General encouraging use of "Keep 'Em Fyling!" slogan in business and in print. C, A note about successful "Dutch Girl" envelope sale from Harry C. Curtiss to cachet maker E.J. Muzzy, Jamestown, New York. A "Dutch Girl" cover enclosed the note. D, Portion of letter from cachet maker George V. Sadworth, Woodhaven, New York to Muzzy.

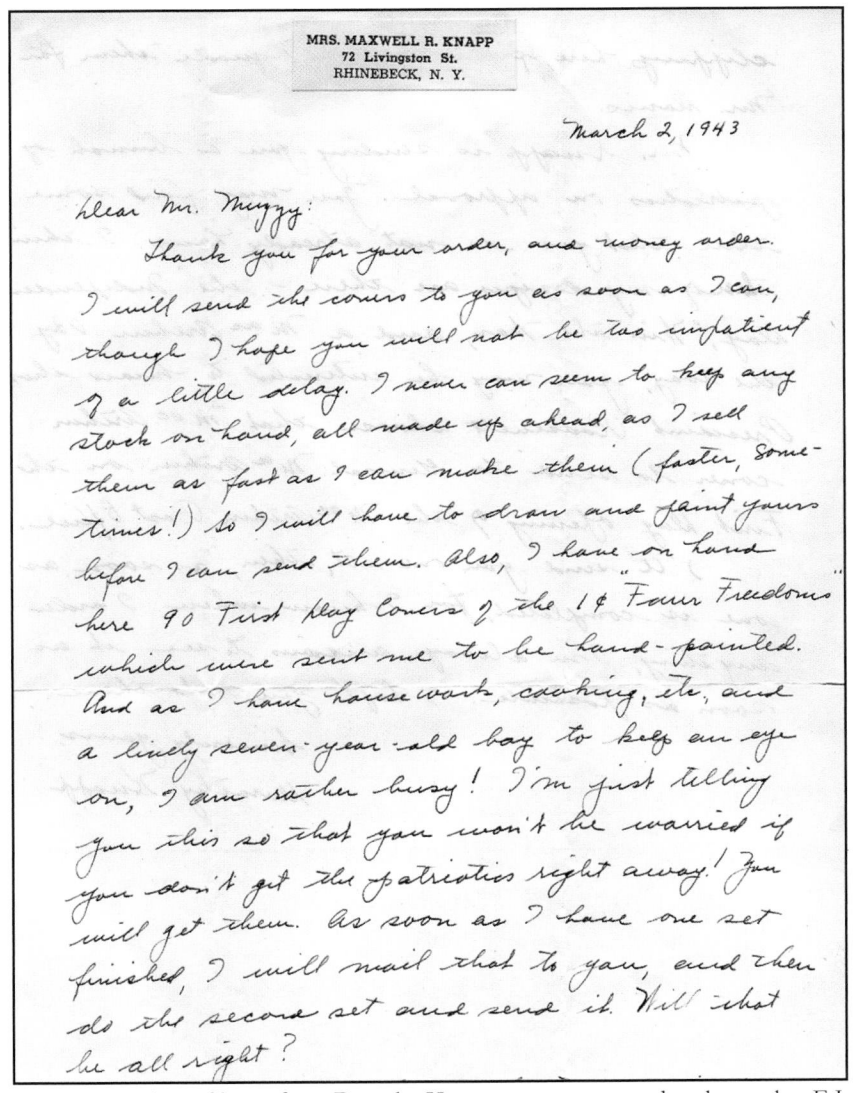

MRS. MAXWELL R. KNAPP
72 Livingston St.
RHINEBECK, N. Y.

March 2, 1943

Figure 4. Portion of letter from Dorothy Knapp to customer and cachet maker E.J. Muzzy, asking his patience in waiting for her hand painted covers to be mailed to him: "I will have to draw and paint yours before I can send them."

In the end the "successful" patriotic envelopes were those that succeeded in communicating across the years to us. Whether commercially prepared in great numbers or personally prepared for mailing to a few friends, they were the patriotic envelopes that withstood the vagaries of artistic taste, political passion, and marketplace demand.

The Market Place, 2: Dorothy W. Knapp— Straight Up, with a Twist

A brief biography of Dorothy W. Knapp is presented in Chapter 3. Tabulated in Chapter 4 are 73 hand painted patriotic cachets designed and published by her. Though this is the largest number of such Knapp cachets yet recorded, the full number is unknown. Did she produce varieties of known cachets that have not yet been recognized? I have catalogued 15 recognizably different cachets made for VE Day and three for VJ Day. There may be others.

We know something of her mailing methods during the war years. She generally pencil-addressed envelopes to herself at her home in Rhinebeck, NY, then re-mailed the completed hand painted envelopes under separate cover to her customers, who paid $1 for each cover.[16]

We also know that Knapp hand painted 12 to 15 sets of first day covers for the National Defense issue of 1940 and similar numbers of hand painted cachets for other first day issues in the 1940s. In fact, "from the 12 to 15 cachets for each issue the demand from collectors quickly ran the production to 50 . . ., a self-imposed number which was the limit Mrs. Knapp thought she could handle."[17] It was conjectured that if she hand painted similar numbers of patriotic cachets, distinguishable varieties would result.

of the items for your want list," he wrote, adding that he was able to find some wanted items only "in my collection of Naval postmarks. These may run high in cost to a Patriotic cover collector so am mailing them along with the blank ones ON APPROVAL. . . . You are under no obligation to keep any of the postmarked ones."[15]

These were some of the ways to bring patriotic envelopes to market. Advertising in philatelic publications, exchanging covers with other cachet makers, or sending covers to George W. Linn to have them listed in his forthcoming *Catalogue of Patriotic Covers of World War II* (published in 1944) were all ways to get noticed.

How busy she was with this work is suggested by a letter she wrote in March 1943 to a customer and fellow cachet maker, E. J. Muzzy. A portion of it is pictured in Figure 4. It begins: "Thank you for your order, and money order. I will send the covers to you as soon as I can, though I hope you will not be too impatient of a little delay. I never can seem to keep any stock on hand, all made up ahead, as I sell them as fast as I can make them (faster, sometimes!) So I will have to draw and paint yours before I can send them."[18]

Also related to her hectic cachet making schedule was the discovery over the last decade of hand painted covers done in her style but with the initials "A.N.C.C." in the left lower corner (rather than "D. Knapp" or no signature at all). That was the first twist in an unfolding story. What was Dorothy Knapp's role in creating these patriotic envelopes? And what is the explanation for these initials?

Some answers were provided by Arthur G. Kroos, Jr., in a three-article series in *First Days*, the Journal of the American First Day Cover Society.[19] The answers were based in part on information in the Universal

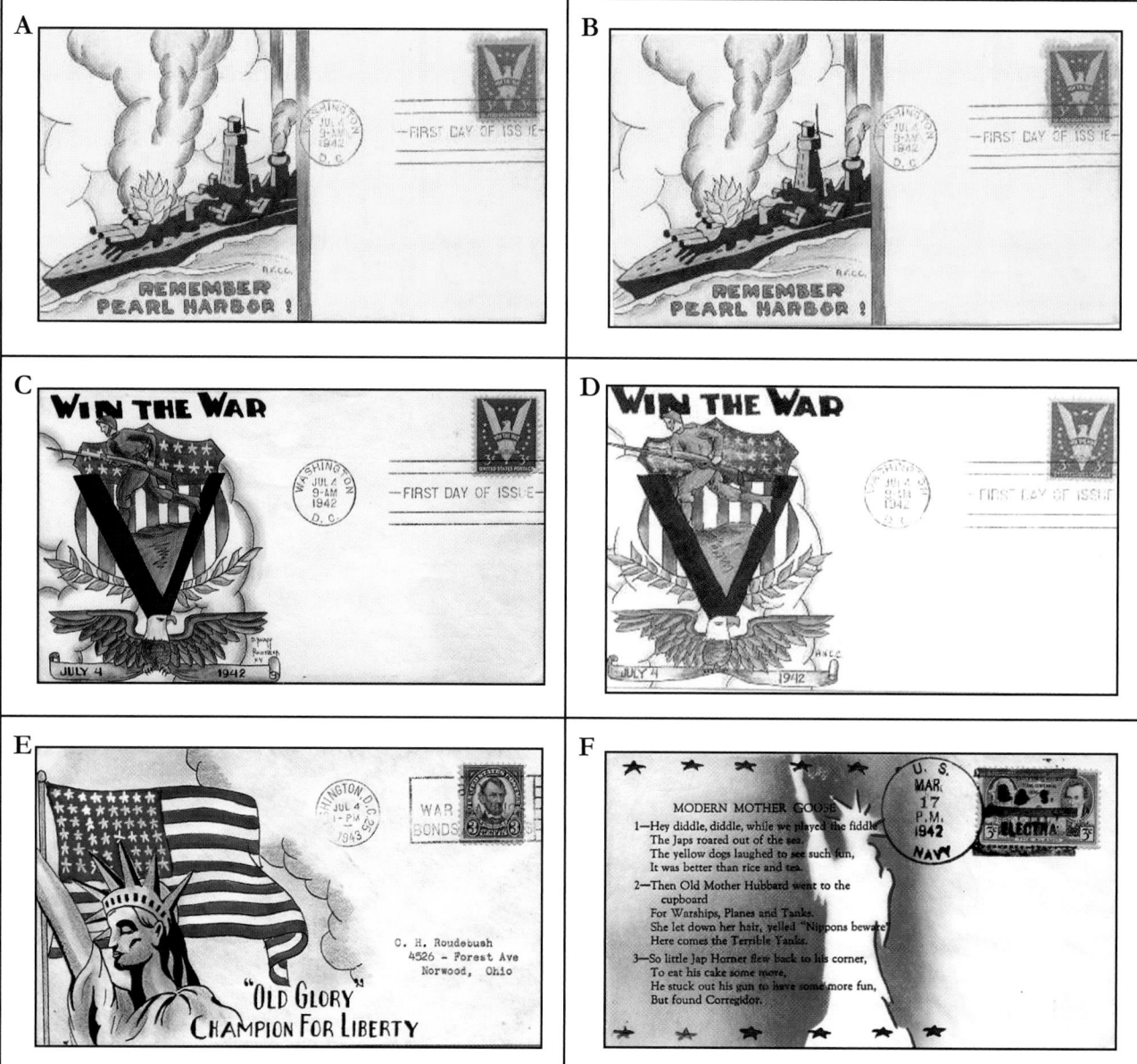

Figure 5. A-D, Dorothy Knapp hand painted covers. A and C contain "D. Knapp" signature. A, Cachet 6539. B and D contain "A.N.C.C." initials. B, C, and D are first day covers and are not listed in the Cachet Catalogue in Chapter 7. E, Cachet 5760, cover in the style of Knapp, but with "W" initialed in the lower left corner. F, cachet 5282, cover by Mae Weigand, Brookln, NY.

Ship Cancellation Society files concerning the cachet making and servicing careers of Louis and Mae Weigand of Brooklyn, New York.

The story began with Louis Weigand, who entered the cacheted cover market in 1936 and sponsored naval event covers cancelled aboard ship. In 1937 he formed his own group, the Associated Naval Cover Collectors (A.N.C.C.). Mae Weigand, his wife, became member #2. Louis wanted to find artists who would hand paint cachets for him and in an advertisement in the A.N.C.C. *Log* wrote, "if you are actually an artist who can draw and paint, there is employment waiting for you. This particularly applies to artists who have experience in cachet work and who have drawn cachets directly on covers."[20]

Sometime in 1941 or 1942, Dorothy Knapp (perhaps in answer to a call for cachet artists) reached an agreement with Louis Weigand. She would continue to design and paint first day cover cachets for her few customers, usually including her name and city to identify her work; in addition, "she would design and hand paint two different cachets for each of the three stamps to be issued in 1942 and then [produce] 20 covers of each cachet for the Weigands to offer their customers."[21]

The Knapp/Weigand working relationship is conclusively demonstrated by the covers illustrated in Figures 5A and B. Figure 5A (cachet 8539) shows an undoubted Dorothy Knapp creation, with her "D.Knapp" signature near the left lower edge of the patriotic envelope. The nearly identical cover in 5B, produced as a first day cover for the Win the War stamp, was designed and hand painted by Knapp but has "A.N.C.C." written above the final "R" in "Remember." It also has an erased penciled address to Weigand in Brooklyn: the Weigands serviced these Knapp-cacheted covers addressed to them and sent the covers to their customers.[22]

Further demonstrating the Knapp/Weigand connection are the first day covers shown in Figures 5C and D. Again, both are Knapp designs, with "D. Knapp" signature (along with erased penciled address to Knapp) in 5C and "A.N.C.C." in 5D.

Then came another twist to the story. For unknown reasons, Louis "decided to discontinue using the initials A.N.C.C. on all cachets he serviced and in their place show Mae's initials "MW" in the lower left corner of the design. These initials were probably added by Mae before Louis serviced them. All are addressed to 'Weigand, 449 E. 43, Bklyn, NY.' *They also found several more artists to assist in designing and hand painting cachets*."[23] [Emphasis added.] It should be noted that a single "W" initial was sometimes used instead of "MW."

A hand painted patriotic cover (cachet 5760) with "W" in the lower left corner is shown in Figure 5E. It is certainly Knapp-like in appearance: the clouds that separate the cachet from the stamped and addressed portion of the envelope are present and the stars in the flag are rendered as in other Knapp patriotic covers. But the face of the Statue of Liberty is heavily shaded and the raised right arm is not well depicted. Was it painted by Knapp, Weigand, or an artist employed by the Weigands "to assist in designing and hand painting cachets"? That is the question shadowing this and some other "W"-signed hand painted patriotic and first day covers.

A hand painted patriotic envelope by Mae Weigand (cachet 5282) is shown in Figure 5F. The silhouetted Statue of Liberty, also found on her numerous covers commemorating flags of the United Nations, is a recurring feature of her patriotic cover work. Her style was a long way from that of Dorothy Knapp. If Mae Weigand was not the hand painting artist "W" who imitated Knapp, who was?

Perhaps when Dorothy Knapp's scattered hand painted patriotic covers are brought together with similar covers serviced by the Weigands—and intensively studied—we will know.

The Market Place, 3:
Weeds

Weeds still grow in the victory garden. Philatelic fakers were at work during the war and for a long time after. Favorite fakery techniques included unauthorized use of handstamps, add-on cachets produced years or decades after the war and, in one known instance at least, a fake Tokyo Bay cancel.

Examples of fraudulent use of a handstamp on patriotic covers can be found on two covers purportedly mailed from Aiea, Hawaii on December 7, 1941, as well as on a number of covers supposedly mailed from Victory, Vermont, on a few significant wartime dates. In the 1970s William Sunner was a Brooklyn, New York resident who was a retired printer, an author of a book on how to win prize contests, and a small-time philatelic hoaxer who made a few war-related covers for fun and profit. His *modus operandi* included underpaying the first-class rate or using a cancelled stamp on one of his newly "cancelled" covers. Figures 6A and B show underpaid covers from Aiea (near Pearl Harbor) postmarked ostensibly at 8 AM, just as the bombs were falling. Sunner had a sense of humor. The two covers commemorate the 154th anniversary of the entrance of the first state, Delaware, into the Union. The cover in 6A implies that a series commemorating the

admission of each state into the Union was forthcoming. Delaware, which entered the Union on December 7, 1787, was conveniently the first—and the last, for no one has ever seen another state so honored in the series.

The anachronistic nature of some postmarks of Victory, Vermont, postmarks has been known for two decades. Pat Herst wrote: "For years, I have had in my 'doubtful' collection a number of covers with postmarks of Victory, VT, which in my opinion cannot be other than fakes."[24]

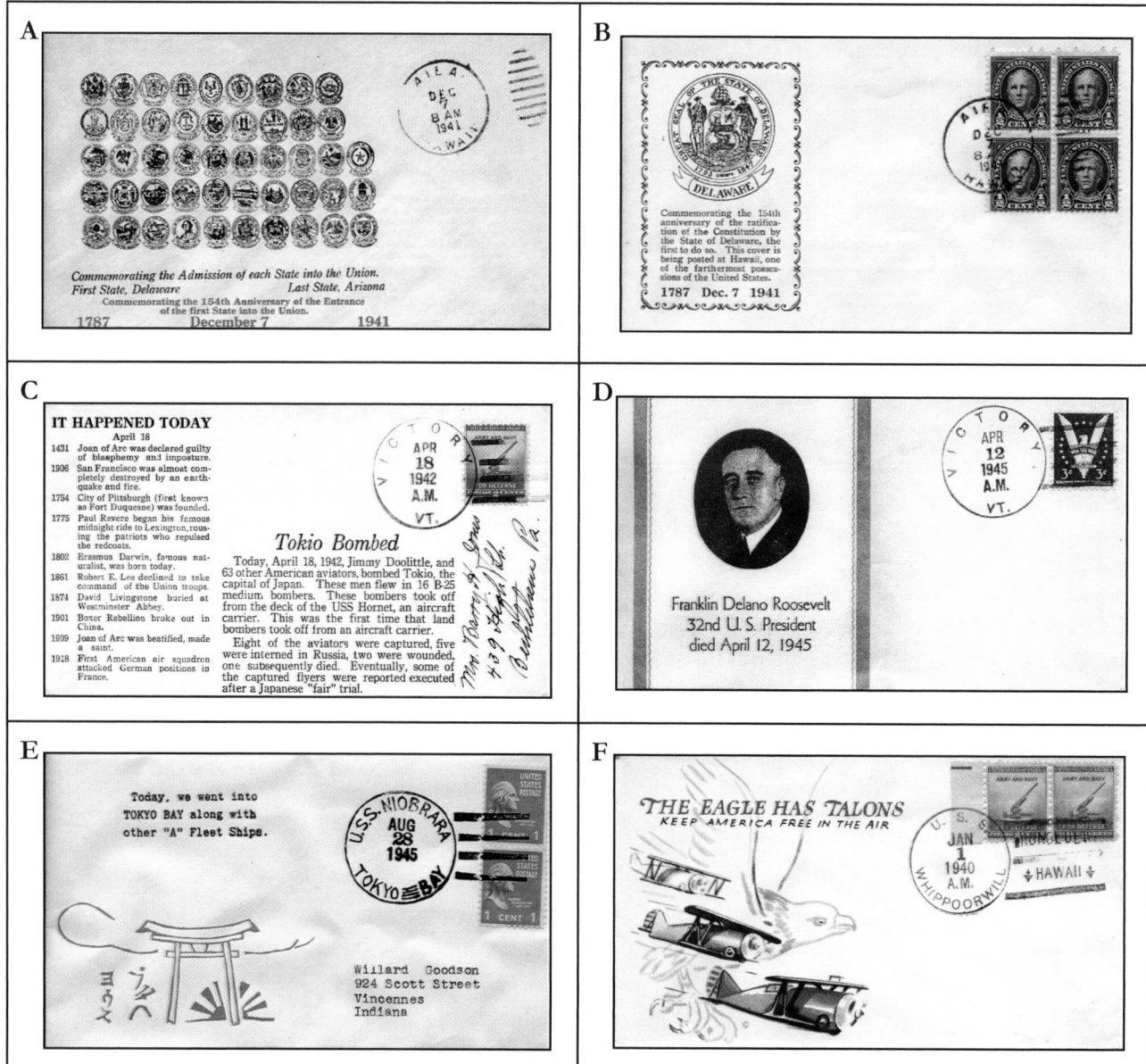

Figure 6. Five weeds and a flower. A & B, Unauthorized use of Aiea, HI, handstamp dated December 7, 1941. C & D, Unauthorized use of Victory, VT, handstamp. E, Fake Tokyo Bay cancel. F, Unchanged year slug on cover postmarked January 1, 1940: stamps and cacheted envelope (cachet 7512) were issued in October 1940.

Two cases of "back-dating by postmark" appear evident in the covers illustrated in Figures 6C and D. The cover in Figure 6C contains statistics about the first bombing raid on Japan (the Doolittle raid) that were not revealed for months or years after the raid. On the cover in 6D marking the death of President Roosevelt the time of day within the circular date stamp (CDS) reads "A.M." But it was early evening when news of the President's death was broadcast. (FDR's death was made public just before 6 PM Eastern time on April 12, 1945. On the East Coast only machine cancels with an evening hour within the CDS are known to be genuine.) The presence of "A.M." within the postmark indicates the likelihood that months or years after the event, the time of its occurrence was not considered by the back-dater.

If you can't get your hands on a postmarking device, why not make your own? That may have been the thought of the creator of the cover illustrated in Figure 6E. USS *Niobrara*, a tanker, arrived at Tokyo Bay on August 30, 1945 to witness the Japanese surrender. It arrived two days *after* the date inscribed on the beautifully-struck fake cancel. Two other Tokyo Bay fake cancels for this vessel, dated September 2 and October 27, 1945 have been recorded in the fifth edition of *Catalog of United States Naval Postmarks*, an excellent source book.[25]

Sometimes a weed is not a weed. A mail clerk can make a mistake and create an innocent postal impossibility. Such was the case for the Minkus patriotic cover illustrated in Figure 6F. The cover was apparently postmarked January 1, 1940 on USS *Whippoorwill*, a minesweeper that saw action in the Pacific throughout the war. But the Minkus envelope was published months later, in October 1940. (Details of Minkus patriotic envelope production are found in Chapter 6.) Also, the two 2¢ antiaircraft gun stamps of the Defense Issue on cover were issued in October 1940. As sometimes happens, the mail clerk on board *Whippoorwill* most likely left the 1940 date slug unchanged on the first day of the new year and a curious new flower— not a weed at all— was now to be found in the victory garden.

NOTES AND SOURCES

1. Miller, Paul J. "Classes & types of patriotics," *Stamps* 53 (11):430, Dec 15, 1945.

2. Wood, Kenneth A. *This is Philately* (Albany, OR: Van Dahl Publications, 1982), p.622.

3. Hubartt, Paul. "Paul Hubartt remembers . . . Fluegel cachets," *First Days* 35 (3):473-476, Jun 1, 1990.

4. Ibid., pp. 474-475.

5. Brett, George. *Philately Printing Methods and Techniques* (State College, PA: Pennsylvania State University, 1985), p. 39.

6. Wood, *This is Philately*, p. 620.

7. Hubartt, "Paul Hubartt remembers," *First Days* 35 (3):475, Jun 1, 1990.

8. Russell, Gene H. "The 'Crosby' Technique," *First Days* 24 (3):84-85, May-Jun 1975.

9. "Boone Patriotic Covers In Large Variety, But Very Limited Quantity," *Linn's Weekly Stamp News*, p. 3, Jun 1, 1944.

10. Lowe, James Lewis. "A boy's adventures into patriotic covers," *Patriotic Patter* 7:1-2, Apr 1996.

11. Zubatsky, David S. "J. Neal Griffith: A biography and catalog of his first day and patriotic cachets," *First Days* 48 (3):11-13, Apr 15, 2003; Part 2, *First Days* 48 (4):23-26, Jun 1, 2003.

12. ———. "J. Neal Griffith," *First Days* 48 (3):12, Apr 15, 2003.

13. Rawlins, R.D. "Alex Hesse, Hall of Fame Selectee," *United Ship Cancellation Society Log* 64 (8):11, Aug 1997.

14. Linn, George W. "Alarmingly atrocious illuminated covers," *Linn's Weekly Stamp News*, p. 4, Jun 4, 1942.

15. Letters and note shown in Figure 3: Author's collection.

16. Patterson, Curtis. "Dorothy W. Knapp — an Update," *First Days* 21 (5):17-19, Sep-Oct 1976.

17. Ibid., p. 18.

18. Letter of Dorothy W. Knapp to Ernest J. Muzzy, March 2, 1943: Author's collection.

19. Kroos, Arthur G., Jr. "The Unknown Weigands, Part I, *First Days* 43 (7):447-451, Sep 1, 1998; Part II, *First Days* 43 (8):575-587, Oct 15, 1998; Part III, *First Days* 43 (9):627-629, Dec 1, 1998.

20. Kroos, "Unknown Weigands, Part I, *First Days* 43 (7):448, Sep 1, 1998.

21. ———. "Unknown Weigands, Part II, *First Days* 43 (8):575-576, Oct 15, 1998.

22. Ibid., pp. 586-587.

23. Ibid, p.579.

24. Herst, Herman Jr. "Victory, Vermont, fakes," *First Days* 31 (2):180-181, Mar 1, 1986. Herst added: "If this Victory, VT, cancel is in private hands, as would appear to be the case, collectors and dealers ought to remember this possibility, as it could be used at any time to make additional fraudulent covers." The actions of a few have cast suspicion on Victory, VT hand cancels that appear on many wartime patriotic covers.

25. Kent, David A., editor in chief. *Catalog of United States Naval Postmarks* (New Britain, CT: Universal Ship Cancellation Society, Fifth Edition, 1997), p. N8.

3

Brief Biographies

THE LIVES of ten wartime cachet makers are briefly recorded in this chapter, along with illustrations of the patriotic envelopes that earned them recognition. Some were skilled designers, some were skilled in selecting designers and manufacturing and distributing patriotic covers, and some recorded wartime events or home front preoccupations. One collected patriotic covers, championed them in his newspaper, and created a national club for their study and exchange.

Modern collecting tastes run to multicolored printed cachets, hand painted cachets, covers recording significant events, and covers that exhibit significant postal usage. The cachets of the ten patriotic cover makers embody these interests, which helps explain their continuing popularity today.

The ten cachet makers are:

Walter G. Crosby, a retired sailor who pioneered thermography and pasted-on photographs on envelopes. Well known for his naval event covers, he often acted as his own designer. R.D. Rawlins noted that envelopes designed and sold by Crosby "may be found for virtually all ships in commission during his era, construction events, port visits, and holiday events."[1]

L.M. "Tex" Edmunds, publicist for the Oklahoma Sheriffs and Peace Officers Association, who published printed multicolored "Gold Star" covers for the Oklahoma City Stamp Club.

Herman Fluegel, retired army officer who published five-color letterpress event covers beginning with D-Day, June 6, 1944.

Dorothy W. Knapp, whose hand painted covers done in watercolors are among the most sought after patriotic covers of World War II.

George W. Linn, who published patriotics before Pearl Harbor to champion American self-defense, used his publication, *Linn's Weekly Stamp News*, to found the wartime Patriotic Cover Exchange Club in 1943, and created the first comprehensive survey of patriotic covers in1944.

William S. Linto, who had his own printing press and his own opinions, and was inexhaustible in the use of the former and irrepressible in the expression of the latter. Linto was by far the most prolific of wartime patriotic cover makers, as might be expected of one who kept his printing press in his den.

Jacques Minkus, who migrated to the United States and built a philatelic empire from a 6-foot stamp counter in a New York department store. His lithographed multicolored patriotics had the widest use internationally of all wartime patriotic covers. Detailed discussion of his patriotic envelopes is recorded in Chapter 5, "Minkus Patriotic Covers: Wartime Journeys."

Etsuo Sayama, Japanese-American who lived in Hawaii, worked as an army engineer, and produced covers reflecting the tangled skein of wartime events on that endangered Pacific territory.

Ludwig W. Staehle, a World War I German army veteran who became a devoted American and used his designing talents to make multicolor cachets extolling the American war effort in World War II.

Capt. Frank E. Teixeira, an American army officer whose unit, the 1st Infantry Division, fought its way from North Africa to Germany. His multicolored event covers were produced after the war.

A photograph or drawing of the designer or publisher is included with each brief biography, together with examples of his or her work.[2]

WALTER G. CROSBY
(1881-1947)

Aprolific cachet maker, Walter G. Crosby produced approximately 600 wartime patriotic cachets. Born in Santa Clara, California, he was a sailor in the United States Navy from the time of the Spanish-American war until his retirement as Chief Gunner's Mate in 1925. While in the service he became a naval cover collector. After retirement he lived in California selling collectibles, including covers. In San Pedro, then Headquarters of the United States Pacific Fleet, Crosby maintained personal contact with naval mail clerks, established a printing shop, and became a pioneer in development and production of cacheted covers.

Crosby initially printed and serviced cacheted covers for naval events and for first days of new postage stamps. When World War II came he turned to patriotic covers, commemorating new military facilities, lampooning Axis leaders, and celebrating the armed forces. The talents of many artists were utilized in making Crosby cachets, and the printed envelopes were sometime sold in bulk to other dealers for their own philatelic operations.[3] The letter shown in Figure 3A in Chapter 2 is evidence of this.

Crosby covers were often thermographed and contained a pasted-on photograph framed within the cachet. Thermography was a technique used in combination with printing to obtain a pleasing pattern of raised words and images. It involved the use of heat in which a waxy powder was melted onto freshly printed cachets and fused with the ink, making the print rise and glisten. The technique, discussed earlier in Chapter 2, was used by a few wartime cachet makers, most prominently Crosby, whose experience with thermographing covers began as early as 1930.

The second common feature of Crosby covers was a small black-and-white photograph glued to the envelope inside a printed frame within the cachet. Crosby scoured books for pictures, made photostats of pictures he needed, and had a photographer "turn out from twenty-five to thirty small negatives the size of those used on [his] covers. These were assembled into sheets about six inches square, which in turn were used to produce sheets of small pictures."[4] Crosby then gave the sheets of small photos to wives of sailors and of local sardine fisherman to cut and paste onto the covers. The working wives "would patiently cut the sheets into individual pictures and paste them onto the covers while their husbands were at sea. The women would return the finished covers to the shop for payment and take a few more boxes home."[5]

The five-step Crosby printing technique helped his covers earn enduring popularity and assured Crosby's reputation among wartime cachet makers. Gene H. Russell's reconstruction of the technique—including thermography to create a pattern of raised letters and images, and addition of a pasted-on photograph inside a printed frame—was described in Chapter 2.

It was the combination of thermography and pasted-on photograph, matched to the cachet subject, that produced the characteristic "Crosby cover" look appreciated by collectors then and now.

Altogether, 479 cachets by Walter G. Crosby —without reference to photographs used—are listed in the cachet catalogue in this book. Adding photo varieties would likely bring the number of Crosby wartime patriotic covers to 600 or more.

These multitudinous varieties deserve their own specialized study.

Walter G. Crosby, ca. 1934

Figure1. Six patriotic covers by Walter G. Crosby illustrating his abiding naval interest and his frequent use of thermography and pasted-on photos. A, Cachet 5669, Navy Day, 1939. B, Cachet 6633 on cover with military post first day cancel. C, Cachet 2261, double cachet, first day, MacArthur, WV, post office. D, Cachet 8504, double cachet, with Crosby's mss. corner card. E, Cachet 5622, Navy Nurse Corps. F, Cachet 8419, Marine Corps, on cover mailed to Alaska, censored in Seattle.

L.M. ("TEX") EDMUNDS
(1891-?)

In June 1941, Tex Edmunds, a member of the Oklahoma City Stamp Club, designed his first cover. Made for the dedication of the New Will Rogers airfield at Oklahoma City, it was elected "King of Cachets" in 1941 by the readers of *Stamps*. The editor of that journal, John J. Haag, wrote of Edmunds's background that he was "an American of Welsh, English and Holland-Dutch ancestry, with several generations of native-born Americans. . . . His father's family helped push the frontiers of our country westward into Ohio, Iowa, and the west. His maternal grandfather was with Commodore Perry, and participated in 'the first landing of Americans in Japan' at Gori-Hama beach, on July 14, 1853."[6]

Of Tex himself, editor Haag wrote that he served as first sergeant of a field artillery replacement battery in World War I, and "is a 'human dynamo' and by profession is a sales-engineer, advertising man contact and public relations man, with stamp and cover collecting as his hobby He is well known as a writer, public speaker, contact man and 'trouble shooter.'"[7]

After his successful debut as cachet maker, Edmunds in the next months published two sets of "Gold Star Covers," patriotic covers sponsored by the Oklahoma City Stamp Club. These multicolored covers, filled with American symbols and containing variations of "Our first duty, defend America!," reflected the fears and hopes around the time of Pearl Harbor.

Edmunds was outraged by "the atrocious manner in which certain designers have persistently misused our flag" and assured prospective purchasers in an advertising flyer that Gold Star Covers "DO NOT VIOLATE THE FLAG CODE OF OUR COUNTRY! They are technically correct, harmoniously colored, fine examples of genuine patriotics; imprinted on a good quality white rag bond envelope. . . . Designed by 'Tex' Edmunds, the drawings have been carefully executed by Edward Henderson, eminent Oklahoma City artist. Expert engravers of the Standard Engraving Co., prepared the color plates, and Alfred E. Samples imprinted the covers. The combined efforts of this group afford collectors an opportunity of acquiring this rarely beautiful set of fascinating GOLD STAR COVERS." Edmunds added that "an interesting historical write-up . . . is inclosed with each cover."

With a few other patriotic covers published in 1942, Edmunds completed his wartime output.

Edmunds's Gold Star Covers continue to be of interest because they are indeed harmoniously colored, crammed with wartime and historical symbols, and often found with late 1941 and early 1942 military postmarks.

Among the envelopes shown here is Gold Star Cover No. 5 (Figure 2C, cachet 5967), mailed from Old Glory, Texas, 10 days before the attack on Pearl Harbor. The American flag—displayed properly, of course—floats serenely in a yellow sky above historic flags of the United States, the Statue of Liberty, and the Minute Man. Also shown (Figure 2D) is Edmunds's "historical write-up" ("I am Old Glory!") on a "stuffer" card found in the envelope.

Thirty-one cachets by Tex Edmunds are listed in the cachet catalogue in this book.

Tex Edmunds, ca. 1941
(from Edmunds wartime letterhead)

Figure 2. Patriotic covers by L.M. ("Tex") Edmunds. A, Cachet 3741, his first cachet, designed for the opening of Will Rogers Field, Oklahoma City; it was crowned "King of Cachets" in 1941. B, Cachet 3754, Memorial Day cover for USS *Houston*, cruiser sunk in the Battle of the Java Sea, February 1942. C, Cachet 5967, saluting American Flags, mailed from Old Glory, Texas. D, Enclosure card for cover shown in C. E , Proof on paper for cachet 10326. F, Cachet 10326. G, Cachet 4438.

HERMAN F. FLUEGEL
(1882-1953)

Born in Baltimore, Herman F. Fluegel became a career soldier in the U.S. Army, attaining the rank of Captain in the Army Corps of Engineers. He served in four wars: the Spanish-American War, the Boxer Rebellion in China, the rebellion in the Philippines, and World War I. In 1939 Fluegel and his wife Ida moved to Washington, DC, where he worked for the Coastal Geodetic Service at the Pentagon. He spent the years of World War II in Washington, and retired to his boyhood home town, Kansas City, Kansas, in 1950..

Fluegel began servicing covers in the early 1930s. His move to Washington in 1939 put him in the right place to obtain timely postmarks for his series of 44 wartime event covers that began on D-Day, June 6, 1944. Many of his cachets were designed by Ludwig W. Staehle (see his biography below); sometimes a "Fluegel Cover" logo was printed below the design, and sometimes only "L.W. Staehle" appeared. Fluegel's D-Day cover (Figure 3A) contained the Staehle logo, as did a similar—and more difficult to find—D-Day cover designed and published by Staehle himself (Figure 9D).

Fluegel was well-acquainted with the chain of designing, printing, and distributing the cacheted envelopes that were already telling the story of the war as Americans saw it. When he published his own patriotic covers he produced the most sought-after series of event covers produced in the United States during the war. The depicted scenes were decorated with maps, flags, and coats of arms, and enhanced by portraits of Allied leaders and views of historic cities and buildings.

In a letter written soon after the end of the war, Fluegel recounted the process of creating his patriotic covers, introducing the subject by saying: "Had I known at the beginning the almost unsurmountable obstacles and difficulties, I would never have undertaken such a task."

He then explained the process: "In producing these War Covers, a supply of envelopes and stamps had to be available for immediate use. The radio was kept going constantly and a group of military and naval personnel (cover collectors) got in touch with each other the moment news was flashed of certain events. . . . I would stamp up the envelopes and rush them to the post office for cancellation. . . . A research was then started for authentic subjects and date to be embodied in the cachet. They were submitted to the artist who made up preliminary sketches. . . . [A] final sketch was made and, upon approval, five to six different color separation drawings had to be made with proper registration of colors. From these en-larged drawings reduced cuts were made. Cuts completed, the cachet was printed on the cancelled envelopes. [Because] each color [took] at least a day to dry, much time was required for this process alone."[8]

One commentator wrote four decades later about Fluegel's patriotic covers: "These early Fluegel cachets have a special richness of quality because they were printed by letterpress, in five and six colors. We don't make cachets like that anymore!"[9]

Forty-four cachets by Herman F. Fluegel are listed in the cachet catalogue in this book.

Herman F. "Cap" Fluegel

Figure 3. Herman F. Fluegel's patriotic covers—many designed by Ludwig W. Staehle—were symbol-packed, multicolored event covers. A, Cachet 3835, Fluegel's first, made for the cross-channel invasion of Normandy. B, Cachet 2775, Invasion of Leyte by American forces. C, Cachet 5151, one of Fluegel's series marking liberation of European capital cities, each postmarked on the day of liberation. D, same cachet, VE Day postmark. E, Cachet 9460, VE Day. F, Cachet 5744. G, Cachet 7460. H, Cachet 6935.

DOROTHY W. KNAPP
(1907-1986)

The artist was born Dorothy Apt in Kingston, New York. She graduated from Skidmore College, Saratoga Springs, New York, in 1929, and became a high school art teacher in Des Moines, Iowa. Eventually she moved to Rhinebeck, New York, to teach there. In 1934 she married Maxwell Knapp, a teacher, stamp collector, and part-time dealer in philatelic covers. Her intention was to become an advertising artist, but, as her son Wally Knapp later wrote, the Depression "changed those plans, as it did so many others in those days. . . . I know that in her later years, as she looked back, she felt a more fulfilling relationship with art through her covers than she would have had through her original plans."[10]

She began her cover-designing career with hand painted (watercolored) cachets for first day covers. M. Douglas Parks wrote that "it was through her husband that E. Milnor Peck of Fleetwood Cover Service learned about her talents as a potential cachet artist. Mr. Knapp sent a hand colored cachet to Mr. Peck and he immediately contacted Mrs. Knapp and asked her to design cachets for him."[11] She began with printed first day covers published for Fleetwood, the first one apparently being for the Kentucky Statehood issue of 1942. Soon she was designing patriotic cachets that were printed during the war by other publishers, including George Richardson of Washington, DC, Charles H. Buckalew of Wilmington, Delaware, and John Max Rush of Asheville, North Carolina—but it was her hand painted covers done in watercolors, necessarily in small quantities, that made her reputation.

Appreciation of Knapp's hand painted patriotics was not long in coming. One fellow cachet maker wrote that Knapp "has 20 beautiful hand-painted covers that have rich color combinations that will add harmonious beauty to any collection. They are exquisite and inspiring and are artistry at its best. Mrs. Knapp has dipped her brush in magic and from the depths of her imagination brought forth beauty that surpasses anything that has been painted on envelopes."[12]

In the last 25 years the hand painted patriotic covers of Dorothy Knapp have achieved "cult" status among collectors of World War II patriotic (and first day) covers. Douglas Parks, in his *Cachet Catalog of Staehle & Knapp*, ruefully noted that "they are so scarce . . . the author has never had an opportunity to obtain them."[13]

Knapp hand painted patriotic covers are recognizable by her "D. Knapp" or "D.W. Knapp" signature at or near the bottom edge of the cachet, though this is not invariable. The signature is usually accompanied by "Rhinebeck, N.Y.," by her graceful letterings with serif "E," "F," and "T," and by her characteristic clouds (or billowing smoke) framing the vignette. When asked about the cloud or smoke placement on the cover, she explained: "It was an easy way to separate or frame off a design from the rest of the envelope."[14]

Knapp's fee for each hand painted patriotic cover was at first 25 cents. As her patriotic and first day covers became more in demand, her fee went to $1. For D-Day, VE Day, and VJ Day covers it was $2.

Seventy-three hand painted cachets by Dorothy Knapp are listed in the cachet catalogue in this book.

Dorothy Knapp, ca. 1976

Figure 4. Designs by Dorothy Knapp. A, cachet 2786, hand painted for opening of MacArthur, WV, post office. B, cachet 7632, printed, same occasion, published by Fleetwood Cover Service. C, cachet 3351, hand painted. D, cachet 5335, printed, published by Fleetwood. E, cachet 2001, hand painted. F, cachet 1812, printed, published by Charles Buckalew, Wilmington, DE. G, cachet 10324, printed, published by George Richardson, Washington, DC. H, cachet 318, printed, published by Fleetwood.

GEORGE W. LINN
(1884-1966)

When it came to patriotic envelopes of World War II, George Ward Linn was a triple threat: he published patriotics, he formed the national Patriotic Cover Exchange Club, and he wrote and published the first comprehensive survey of these envelopes, *Catalogue of Patriotic Covers of World War II*.

Linn was born with printer's ink in his veins. His father, William McAdoo Linn, was the printer-publisher of the Darke County Advocate in Greenville, Ohio, where Linn was born in 1884. In 1893 the family moved to Columbus, where the William M. Linn Printing Company was founded. All four sons of the family worked; George, next to the youngest, "rode a milk truck in the early hours before school. One morning on a 'dump' on West Fifth Avenue, he discovered a cast-off book of stamps. He became an enthusiast almost at once."[15]

Philatelically speaking, Linn never looked back; after completing the tenth grade he worked for a newspaper, returned to his father's print shop, and in 1905 started a mail order stamp business, the George W. Linn Co. In 1911 he printed Linn's Way, the first of several ephemeral house organ/price lists he was to produce. In 1916 Linn researched, wrote, and published his philatelic book, *Mexico—The White and Green Seal Issues of Sonora*, which became a classic work. Linn had become a collector, a dealer, and a student of philately.

In 1920 he took the first step toward publishing a stamp newspaper. *Linn's Stamp News*, a price list sprinkled with commentary, appeared intermittently for the next 5 years. In 1926 he accepted an offer to edit *Weekly Philatelic Gossip*, published in Holton, Kansas, but left after three months because of disagreements with the

George W. Linn, ca. 1950

publisher. When Linn's father died in 1927, George took over the printing company and renamed it the George W. Linn Company. A year later he changed the name to Linprint. The idea of a stamp newspaper was never far from Linn's mind. Throughout 1928 he "traveled to stamp club meetings and exhibitions soliciting advance subscriptions to a new periodical. Vol. 1 No. 1 of *Linn's Weekly Stamp News* appeared on Nov. 5, 1928. The staff consisted of himself plus his wife and daughter, the last of whom addressed the mailing labels by hand."[16]

As *Linn's Stamp News*, the philatelic weekly has survived to this day, prospering particularly after Word War II. Over nearly seven decades it has published more than 3,500 issues. Under the Linprint name the printing company survived until 1942; under this name George W. Linn produced his 25 wartime patriotic covers.

Linn founded the Patriotic Cover Exchange Club in March 1943. The new secretary announced that Linn had "graciously agreed to give his time and space" to the new club. Dues were 25¢ per year. The official journal was (of course) *Linn's Weekly Stamp News,* which cost another 25¢ per year. The new club provided collectors wanted contact with others and a news service to keep them informed.

In 1944 Linn published his *Catalogue of Patriotic Covers of World War II*. This paperbound compendium of all wartime patriotics known to Linn contained 94 pages and cost $1. Most important, publishers for the approximately 3,000 listed covers were named—invaluable documentation for all future patriotic cover cataloguers.

Twenty-five Linprint cachets by George W. Linn are listed in the cachet catalogue in this book.

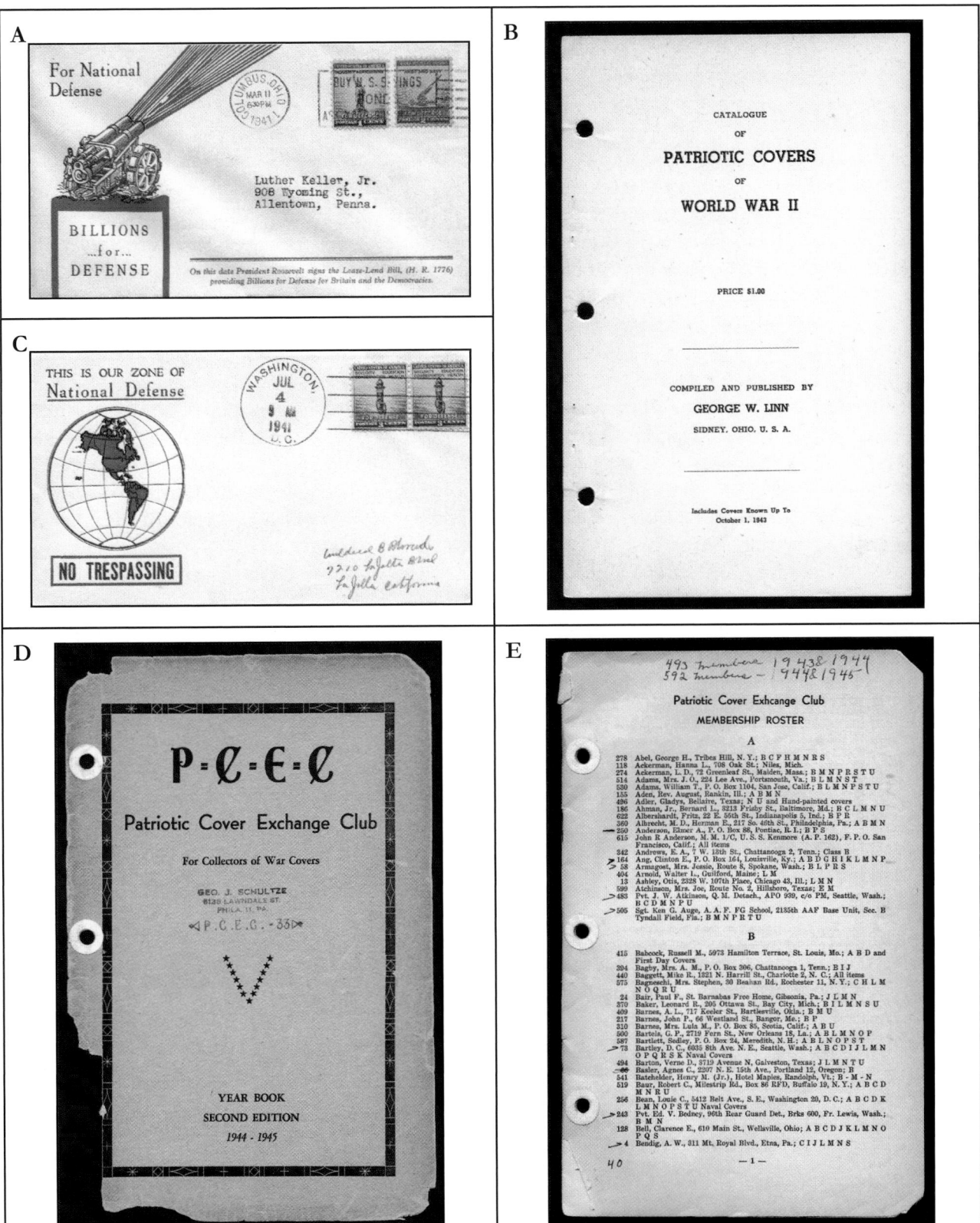

Figure 5. George W. Linn influenced printing and collecting patriotic covers in the United States throughout the war, and his influence on cataloguing patriotics extends to the present. A (Cachet 2408) and C (Cachet 8082), Linprint patriotic covers published by Linn before Pearl Harbor. B, Title page, Linn's *Catalogue of Patriotic Covers of World War II*, published in 1944. D and E, Cover and first page of the 1944-45 year book of the Patriotic Cover Exchange Club, founded by Linn. There were 592 members in 1945.

WILLIAM S. LINTO
(1884-1967)

Linto was angry, opinionated, prejudiced, and jingoistic—and he had his own printing press. During the war he produced over 1700 patriotic covers, more than any other publisher. In his extensive review of Linto cachets in *Naval Cover Cachet Makers Catalog*, R.D. Rawlins wrote that Linto was "one of the most prolific individual producers in America of cacheted covers of all type - naval events, historical, patriotics, political, religious and first day of issue of stamps. A conservative estimate would place the number of different cachets produced by Linto in excess of 5,000 [of all types]."[17]

Born in Yeovil, England, William Stanley Linto emigrated with his family to the United States in 1900. He worked as a compositor for a local newspaper in Gloversville, New York, married in 1907, and in 1913 moved to Portland, Oregon. He worked in the composing room of the Portland *Oregonian* for the next 45 years.

A stamp collector as a boy, Linto returned to the hobby some time after moving to Portland. In the 1920s he acquired a hand-operated printing press and printed cards and announcements in his home for friends. By the middle 1930s he was printing cachets on his home press. Blending his skills and his hobby, Linto became a prolific producer of cacheted covers. Indeed, "nearly all his spare time . . . was spent on this endeavor using his own printing press. All of his cover activities were conducted at home in his den which had been converted from a bedroom."[18]

Linto used his press to record events, denounce politicians, glorify favorite generals, and excoriate perceived enemies of the Republic. The Japanese were an easy editorial target, but Linto carried this to obsession, sometimes assailing Japanese-Americans((as shown in Figures 6G and H).

In about 1935 Linto began identifying each cover by printing on the reverse: "This Cachet Designed / and Sponsored by [or 'This Cachet Sponsored by'] / William S. Linto / 4920 N.E. 16th Ave. /Portland Oregon" [Figure 6B and 6D]. His wartime patriotic covers were identified in this manner. Linto numbered each cachet that he printed, much as an artist might number his prints, and also listed the number of covers issued for that cachet. Because of this numbering and notation system, one observer noted that "Linto covers are fairly easy to track", though "he occasionally lost track of the numbering which caused duplication."[19]

In addition to Linto's erratic count of his patriotic covers, he published some identified by name of subject, as well as "HP" (Historical Patriotic) covers (Figures 6A, B, cachet 4151). These were event covers postmarked at the Navy Atlantic Fleet Service School and were not released from there until the end of the war because the military prohibited servicing souvenir philatelic mail.

Another recognizable feature of some Linto patriotic covers is found in those having a second cachet (a two-line text marking a recent event) added to the right of a previously printed cachet of his (Figure 6F, cachet 3661). In this way hundreds of Linto covers, postmarked on the dates of war events, combined inspiring or inciting statements with event information.

One thousand seven hundred three cachets by William S. Linto are listed in the cachet catalogue in this book.

William S. Linto, 1958

Figure 6. Patriotic covers by William S. Linto. A, Cachet 4151, marking the end of the battle that was the turning point of the Pacific war. B, Identifying markings on the back of cover shown in A. C, Cachet 9505; cover with "Victory" theme was mailed from Victory, VT. D, Identifying markings on the back of cover shown in C. E, Cachet 3664. F, Cachet 3661, with two lines added to cachet shown in E. G (Cachet 4832) and H (Cachet 9938) exemplify Linto's obsession with Japanese-Americans.

JACQUES MINKUS
(1901-1996)

Jacques Minkus was "the man who brought stamps to Main Street," in the words of Arthur Summerfield, Postmaster General in the Eisenhower administration. Minkus was the most widely known patriotic cover maker in the United States.

Born in Lublin, Poland, he was orphaned at age 13 and moved to Germany as a refugee at 1919. In 1926 he moved to France after "I saw the brown shirts beating up the black shirts, bloodying their faces and heads. This was the start of Hitler's rise." A typesetter by trade, Minkus entered into business with his brother, who by then had come to the United States; together they published reprinted Russian and Hebrew classical works. On Sundays in Paris, he found dealers trading in stamps at the Bourse and became a collector himself.

Minkus emigrated to the United States in 1929 and became a publisher of little dictionaries that were sold in chain stores. He soon added low-cost stamp albums and stamp packets to his stock. Then came the entrepreneurial decision that changed his life—and the course of American philately. In 1931 he approached Gimbels Department Store in New York City with the idea of starting a stamp department. "No one really believed I could sell stamps in a department store," he recounted to an interviewer.[20] But his genius for organization and marketing won the day: From a six-foot counter that he leased on a day-to-day basis, Minkus built a philatelic sales and publishing empire that lasted for six decades.

He recalled that "I tackled the job from an energetic merchandizing point of view. I insisted the store support us by giving the stamp department publicity, using the mass media of advertising in major newspapers, such as the *New York Times*. We created a Stamp Club that became a stunning Saturday

event. We had leading personalities of the day from every walk of life. The attendance was usually 250 to 300 people."[21]

By the 1960s Minkus was operating stamp departments in 38 Gimbels department stores across the country.[22]

Minkus published 52 patriotic covers during World War II, beginning with 12 envelopes inspired by announcement of the National Defense stamp issue of October 1940. In an interview years later, he told a philatelic writer: "My inspiration was a deep patriotic feeling, a dedication to the country and a feeling of wanting to . . . help make people aware of what was going on. You may recall that there were a lot of isolationists in this country who were arguing that we didn't have to bother with the rest of the world and that we could live by ourselves."[23] Minkus produced his wartime covers "primarily to promote patriotism, and it was his desire that they be widely used on general correspondence. The envelopes and later accompanying stationery, were thus distributed through Gimbels in New York and Philadelphia to be sold in chain stores, military post exchanges, drug stores and mass distribution outlets. A great deal of effort was also made by Mr. Minkus to have these envelopes canceled at many new military base post offices."[24]

Minkus patriotics achieved the widest circulation of all American patriotics; printings were in the tens of thousands. His patriotic covers, produced by a four-color lithograph process, are easily identified by a tiny logo printed in the right corner on the back of each envelope: "Copyright 1940 [or 1942 or 1943] by Jacques Minkus, New York, N.Y., U.S.A."

All fifty-two cachets by Jacques Minkus are listed in the cachet catalogue in this book.

Jacques Minkus, ca. 1977

Figure 7. Patriotic covers by Jacques Minkus. A, Cachet 84, cover mailed October 8, 1940, before National Defense issue first day. B, Cachet 2683, cover from APO 914, Canton Island. C, Folder with patriotic envelopes, and D, Group of banded envelopes, both for sale in 1942. E, Cachet 7195, cover from APO 25, Solomon Islands. F, Cachet 4812, cover from APO 380, Caserta, Italy. G, Cachet 2686, only known patriotic cover mailed from the USSR.

ETSUO SAYAMA
(1915-?)

Etsuo Sayama viewed the war from a unique perspective—that of an American of Japanese ancestry living in Hawaii.

Sayama, the first of three children, was born in Honolulu to parents who had emigrated from Japan. He was 7 years old when his father died. His mother then returned to Japan with the children. One year later she returned to the U.S. with Etsuo, and married a man who was a stamp and first day cover collector. Sayama's interest in philately was kindled. Later he worked his way through the University of Hawaii, graduating in 1937 with a bachelor's degree in sugar technology. He became an engineering aide for the Construction Quartermaster of the U.S. Army at Hickham Field, Oahu. Soon after the attack on Pearl Harbor, Sayama was transferred to the Drafting Section, U.S. Army Corps of Engineers, located at Punahou School.

As an engineering draftsman and a keen philatelist, Sayama used his drafting skills to design wartime cachets. One reviewer of his patriotic cover work noted that Sayama "produced two distinct types of cachets. One displays a fine-lined draftsman-type drawing and the other is a photo-type with detailed descriptions of a historical event. A friend, an editor of a local newspaper, let him use plates of news pictures for his cachets."[25]

His series of patriotic covers manifested their Hawaiian origin in nearly every cachet. Among Sayama covers redolent of Hawaii were patriotics devoted to: the memory of members of the 100th Infantry Battalion, composed of Japanese-Americans from Hawaii, who gave their lives on the battlefields of Italy, postmarked in Makena ("Memory") (cachet 2704); Kamehameha Day, June 11, 1943 (cachet 4186); Labor Day, September 6, 1943, showing an Hawaiian victory worker, postmarked in Hana

("Work") (cachet 4399); the 'Waikiki Conference' held by President Roosevelt, General MacArthur, and Admiral Nimitz, July 27-29, 1944 (cachet 7835); the abolition of martial law in Hawaii, October 24, 1944 (cachet 5133); Hawaii's quota of 27 million dollars for the 7th War Loan, May 14-June 30, 1945 (cachet 3233), postmarked in Honolulu on the last day of the war bond drive. Five Sayama cachets had victory slogans in English and Hawaiian, including "'Imua, imua a lanakila! / Forward to victory!'" (cachet 3712), and "Sail to / victory / Holo ia / lanakila" (cachet 5962).

Sayama's first patriotic cover (cachet 3230), postmarked December 7, 1942, was created as a memorial to American servicemen who fell in the attack on Pearl Harbor one year earlier. Printed in black, it featured a flag at half staff, three servicemen, and the words: "They shall not have died in vain." The cachet was designed for Sayama by a fellow draftsman, George Cuevas, whose last name appears at the bottom left of the vignette. Later Sayama covers commemorating the second and third Pearl Harbor anniversaries (cachets 6649 and 7269) were mailed on December 7 in 1943 and 1944.

A reviewer recently summed up the theme underlying Sayama's patriotic covers: "It was Sayama's desire to honor the sacrifices made by those who served during the war and to perpetuate [their] rich legacy of hope and courage."[26]

Sayama proudly mailed his covers to collectors from unusual post offices, including Hana, Kanehoe, Kohala, and Pearl City. He traded with other collectors and with servicemen stationed throughout the world, and sometimes sent covers to the mainland purposely to obtain censorship marks.

Thirty-three cachets by Etsuo Sayama are listed in the cachet catalogue in this book.

Etsuo Sayama, 1985

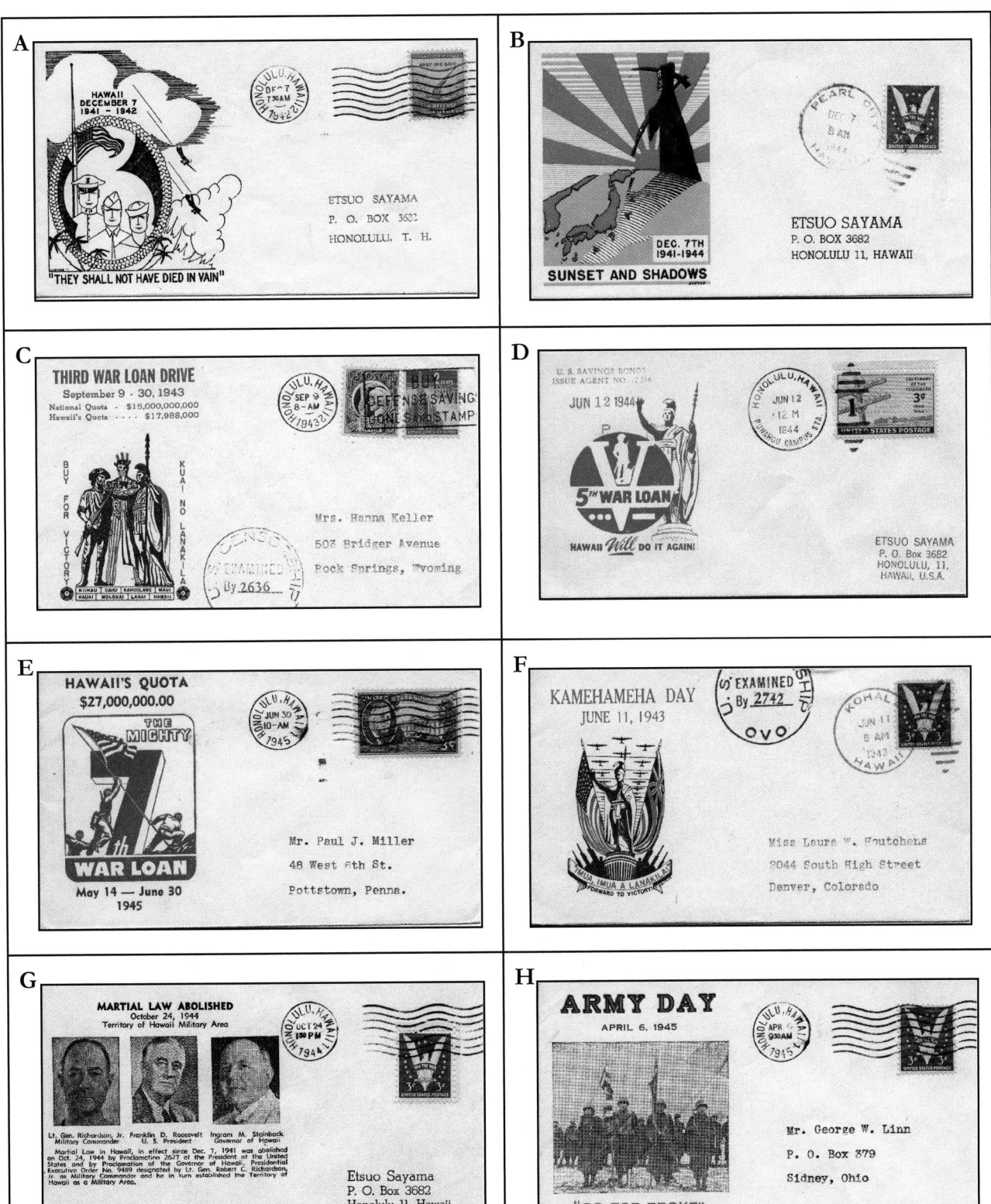

Figure 8. Etsuo Sayama's patriotic covers dealt with themes of wartime Hawaii. A, Cachet 3230, Sayama's first patriotic cover made for the first anniversary of the Pearl Harbor attack. B, Cachet 7269, made for the third anniversary. C (Cachet 8021), D (Cachet 2178), and E (Cachet 3233), made for war bond drives. F, Cachet 4186. G, Cachet 5138. H, Cachet 696, for 442nd Regimental Combat Team, the Army's most decorated unit, composed of Americans of Japanese ancestry from the mainland and Hawaii.

LUDWIG W. STAEHLE
(1893-1967)

Staehle was born in Wurttemberg, Germany. As a youth he showed a flair for designing. He worked as a designer apprentice as a teenager, graduated from a trade school as an interior decorator draftsman, and graduated from a college of fine arts and architectural design at age 20. Drafted into the German army at the beginning of World War I in 1914, Staehle was taken prisoner by the French a year later and served six years as a prisoner of war. He returned home to find his family members sick, old, or dead.

Working as a bank cashier and statistician for a while, Staehle married. In 1927 he emigrated to the United States with his wife and young children. Upon settling in New York City, Staehle became an interior architectural designer, fashioning furniture and interiors for homes, hotels, and theaters. In the early 1930s he began designing cachets for covers celebrating historical events, then cachets for first day covers, mailing them to himself for his own collection. By 1936 he was designing cachets for publishers of first day covers.

Well before Pearl Harbor Staehle, who was proud of his American citizenship, began designing cachets and labels for war-related first day covers and patriotic covers. As one commentator noted, the war provided "an opportunity for his artistic talent to shine especially in the cachet design field."[27] For three consecutive years (1942-1944) he won *Stamps* magazine's "King of Cachets" contest.

Staehle's cachet output during the war was prodigious in both quantity and quality, his peak years coming in 1943 and 1944, when he created about 40 cachets

Ludwig W. Staehle, ca. 1943

each year for wartime events, first days of stamps, and anniversaries of historical feats. His output included 60 patriotic covers he published himself and many more made for other publishers, including Cachet Craft, Czubay, Fleetwood, Fluegel, King's Stamp Club, Minkus, and Smartcraft. These publishers admired the professionalism of his work and placed his designs on their patriotic covers. Collectors admired his multicolored, boldly lettered, richly symbolic designs, and bought the covers. They still admire his designs and buy the covers. Thus, Staehle's preeminence as a cachet designer has been recognized for over sixty years. His covers have retained their freshness and appeal over the decades because of his artistry and the care taken in printing.

In the minds of many collectors of patriotic covers, the names of Ludwig W. Staehle and Herman F. Fluegel are linked. Staehle's designs, with their contrasting colors and strong symbols, were exactly what Fluegel sought for his series of event covers. The series began with an "Invasion Day" cover made for D-Day, June 6, 1944, featuring Generals Eisenhower and Montgomery. Staehle designed this cover for Fluegel and published his own "Invasion Day" cover identical in wording and picture except for the presence of Eisenhower alone in the vignette. This "Ike only" cover must have been made in small numbers, for it is very difficult to find in the philatelic marketplace. The Staehle-Fluegel relationship continued intermittently until the war ended.

Sixty wartime cachets published by Ludwig W. Staehle are listed in the cachet catalogue in this book.

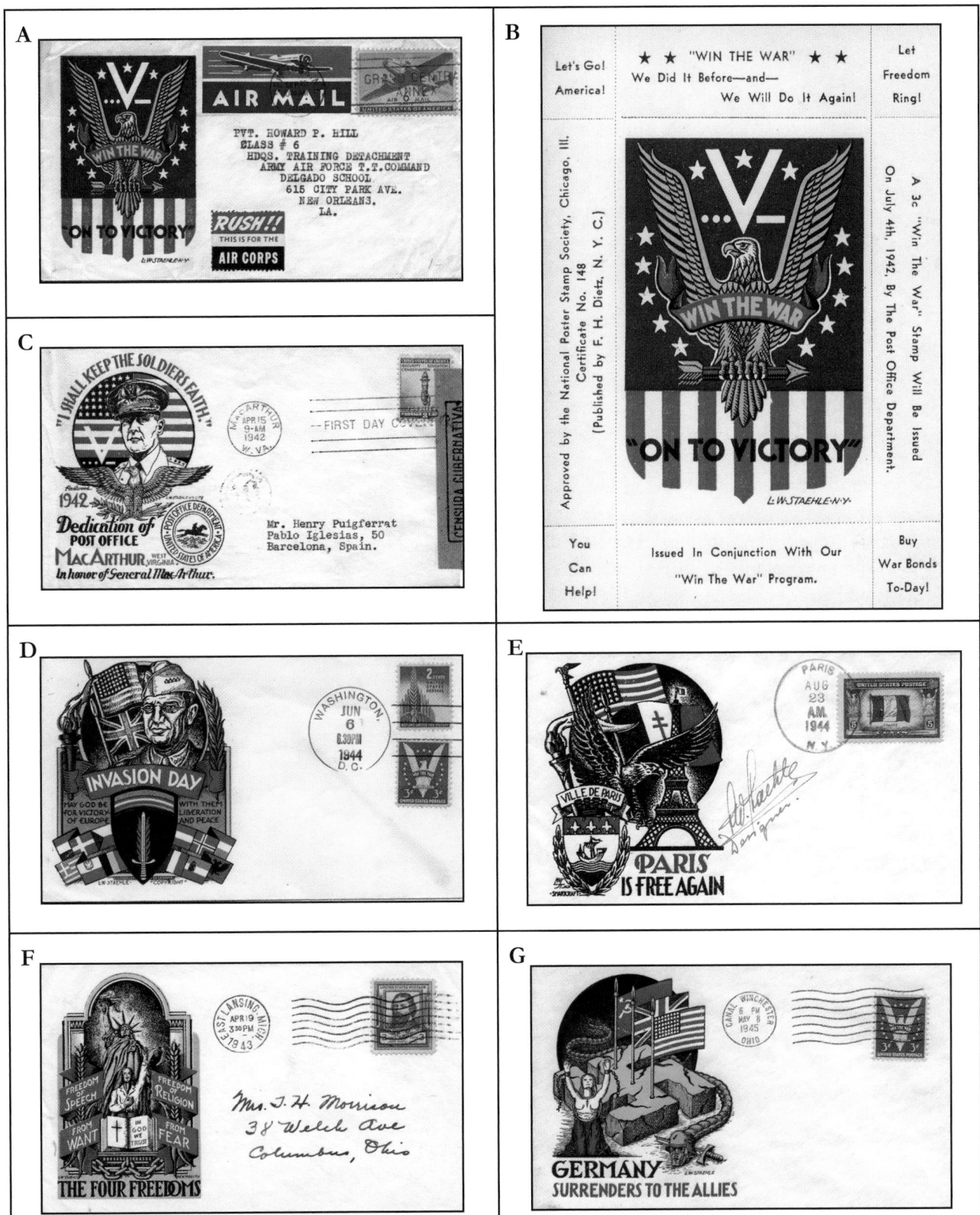

Figure 9. Ludwig W. Staehle's cachet designs were multicolored, boldly lettered, and rich with symbols. A, Cachet 9049, created in 1942 for issuance of the Win the War stamp. B, Adhesive "Poster stamp," one of a series designed by Staehle, published by printer Fred H. Dietz. C, Cachet 3574, first day, MacArthur, WV, post office, published by Fleetwood. D, Cachet 3834 (compare with Staehle-designed Fluegel cover in Figure 4A). E, Cachet 6103, cover signed by Staehle. F, Cachet 2617. G, Cachet 2860.

CAPTAIN FRANK L. TEIXEIRA
(1909-1977)

Frank Loper Teixeira was, as a philatelic writer noted, "first and foremost a military man, philately [following] a close second. Among his many and varied other interests were photography and printing and, when these talents were eventually brought together, they provided the world with an interesting new cachetmaker."[28]

Teixeira was born in Rio de Janeiro, Brazil. After his mother's death when he was a child, he lived with relatives in Spain, Portugal, and France, becoming a stamp collector and in time building a stock of philatelic material. He came to live in New York City upon his father's death when Teixeira was 17 years old. Two years later he enlisted in the U.S. Army, realizing "an ambition that he had developed in childhood as a result of watching a beloved uncle march as a soldier in parades in a Brazilian square."[29] While stationed at Fort Devens, he married in 1941 and lived in nearby Boston.

With the advent of World War II, Teixeira went to Officer Candidate School and eventually served in the 1st Infantry Division in North Africa, Sicily, France, Belgium, and Germany. During the war years he bought covers and related material from patriotic cover makers. As Captain Frank L. Teixeira of the 1st Infantry Division, APO 1, he designed and published four-color event covers related to the war. He published many postwar covers as well.

Teixeira's first patriotic cover, postmarked January 14, 1943, commemorated the Casablanca meeting of President Roosevelt and Prime Minister Churchill. Later covers marked, among other events, D-Day, the liberation of Paris and other European capitals, the crossing of the Rhine, FDR's death, the

Capt. Frank L. Teixeira

atomic bomb, and VE and VJ Days. His corner card, signature as censor, and an APO 1 postmark are almost invariable features of Teixeira's illustrated envelopes, which were franked by his armed forces free mailing privilege or by wartime stamps

A serious problem has arisen concerning the true dates of creation of Teixeira patriotic covers. In 1997 Paul M. Sommers reported finding "two different lettering styles for various cachets in Teixeira's 'Soldier's Free Mail' set."[30] Then in 2004 Sommers disclosed another anomaly: the wrong date on a Teixeira "Russia at war with Japan" cover (July 8, 1945 instead of August 8). A Teixeira flyer for his wartime and post-war covers, apparently released late in 1946 or early 1947, records this error and another for the "Potsdam Conference" cover. Sommers' conclusion: "These two date errors raise a more disconcerting question: Just when did Teixeira actually service his historical covers for events of World War II?"[31] Later in 2004 the same keen-eyed observer produced his conclusive finding of backdating—Teixeira covers franked with stamps issued *after* the cover was supposedly posted. "It is now clear that some of his World War II patriotic event covers were backdated."[32]

Teixeira designed and published 44 wartime patriotic envelopes: 34 marking events, including the liberation of European capital cities, plus 10 of this series (same cachets) franked and postmarked on dates of liberation of European capital cities and then franked and postmarked again on VE Day.

Forty-four cachets published by Frank L. Teixeira are listed in the cachet catalogue in this book.

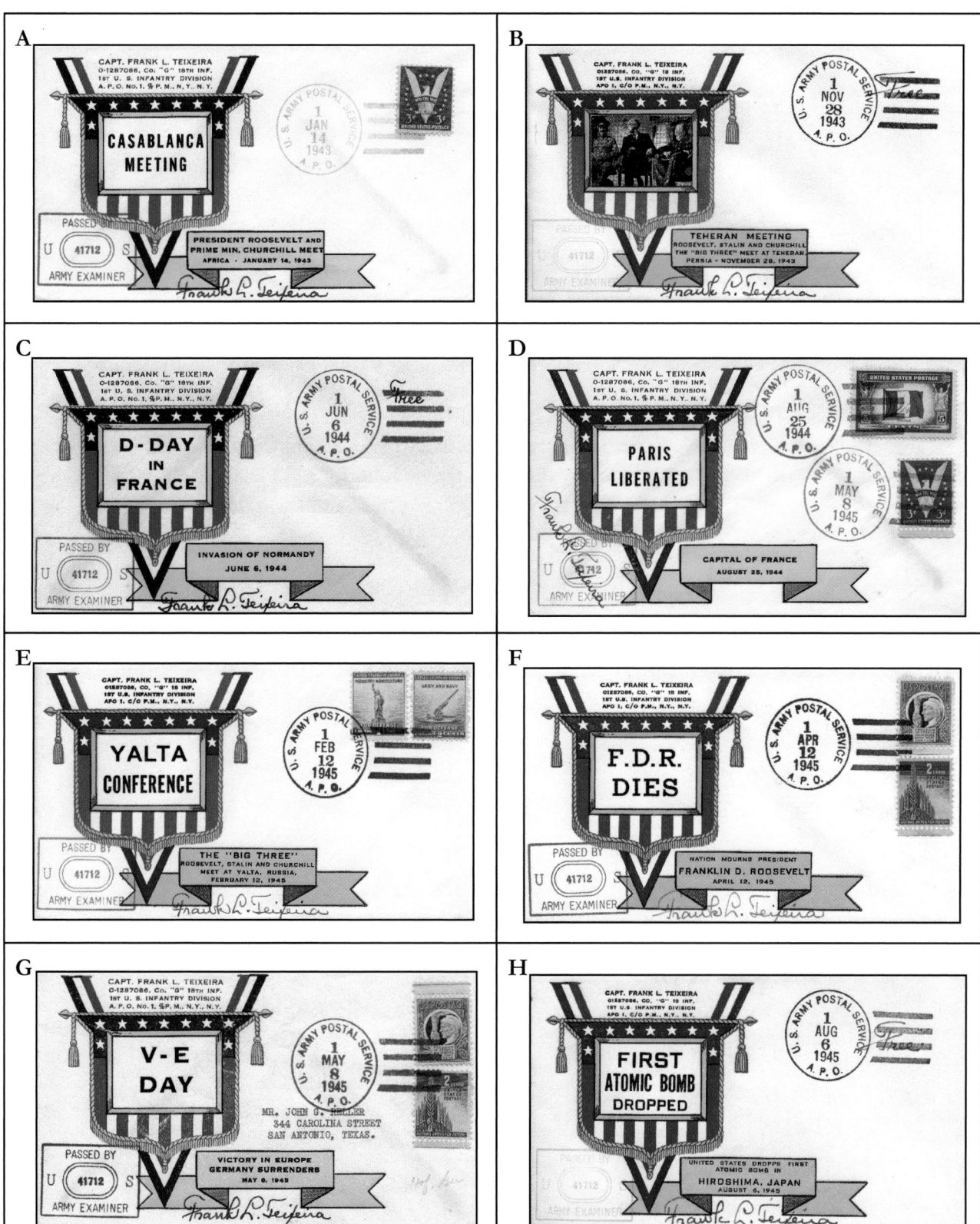

Figure 10. Teixeira cachets, four-color commemorations of wartime events, began with the Casablanca Conference, January 1943. An army officer, Teixeira signed his own covers as censor. A, Cachet 1355. B, Cachet 7311. C, Cachet 1722. D, Cachet 6105 on a cover franked and postmarked on date of liberation of Paris and again on VE Day. Only a single copy has been reported of each of the 11 covers in this double-postmarked Teixeira series. E, Cachet 10485. F, Cachet 2126. G, Cachet 9392. H, Cachet 2220.

NOTES and SOURCES

1. Rawlins, R.D. *Naval Cover Cachet Makers Catalog* (New Britain, CT.: Universal Ship Cancellation Society, 1985), p. C-15.

2. Illustrations of the cachet makers are reproduced with permission as follows:
    For Walter G. Crosby: Stroebel, William H. *Walter G. Crosby, Philatelic Cachet Specialist* (Mesa, Arizona: Burgus Printing Company, 1992), cover illustration; for L.M. "Tex" Edmunds: Edmunds 1942 letterhead (author's collection); for Herman F. Fluegel: Hubartt, Paul. "Paul Hubartt Remembers . . . Fluegel cachets," *First Days* 35 (4):473-476, Jun 1, 1990.
    For Dorothy W. Knapp: Patterson, Curtis. "Dorothy W. Knapp — an update." *First Days* 21 (5):17-19, Sep/Oct, 1976; for George W. Linn: Michael Schreiber, Editor of *Linn's Stamp News*; for William S. Linto: *The Oregonian Masthead* (Portland, Oregon), p. 2, Nov 1958.
    For Jacques Minkus: Monty, Dr. Richard A. *Specialized Catalogue of Jacques Minkus F.D.C.s and Patriotic Cachets* (Stewartsville, New Jersey: F.D.C. Publishing Co., 1977), front cover; for Etsuo Sayama: Ma, Peter. "Etsuo Sayama: The Hawaii cachetmaker of patriotic covers," *First Days* 31 (3):348-354, Apr 15, 1986; for Ludwig W. Staehle: Haag, John J. "1943 'King of Cachets,'" *Stamps* 47:14-15, Apr 1, 1944; for Captain Frank L. Teixeira: Wright, Pat. "Frank Loper Teixeira, Cachetmaker," *First Days* 24 (3):32-33, May-Jun, 1979.

3. Stroebel, William H. *Walter G. Crosby, Philatelic Cachet Specialist* (Mesa, Arizona: Burgus Printing Company, 1992), pp. 2-3.

4. Monty, Richard. "From trite to complex—another look," *American Philatelist* 91:633, August 1977.

5. Ibid.

6. Haag, John J. "King of cachets 1941," *Stamps* 38 (13):447-448, Mar 28, 1942.

7. Ibid.

8. Hubartt, Paul. "Paul Hubartt Remembers . . . Fluegel cachets," *First Days* 35 (4):473-476, Jun 1, 1990.

9. Wright, Patricia. "Fluegel's headache series," *First Days* 31 (3):322-324, Apr 15, 1986.

10. Knapp, Wally. "Dorothy W. Knapp—a fond remembrance," *First Days* 32 (4):408-416, Jun 1, 1987.

11. Parks, M. Douglas. *The Cachet Catalogue of Staehle and Knapp* (Ogallala, Nebraska: M. Douglas Parks, 1981), p. 225.

12. Rush, John Max. "Patriotic covers," *Current Covers and Stamplets* 1 (1):3-4 Sep 14, 1944.

13. Parks, *Cachet Catalogue of Staehle and Knapp*, p. 225.

14. Ibid.

15. Cusick, Allison. *Photo Cachet Catalog—Linprint.* (Stewartsville, New Jersey: FDC Publishing Co., 1976), p. 3.

16. Ibid., p. 4

17. Rawlins, R.D. *Naval Cover Cachet Makers Catalog* (No place given: Universal Ship Cancellation Society, 1985), "L" Section, p.8.

18. Nafziger, Ralph, and Sverid, Richard. "William S. Linto—Oregon cachetmaker," *First Days* 28 (8):1306-1311, 1983.

19. Cohen, Sidney L. "William S. Linto—WWII patriotic covers," *First Days* 31 (2):156-165, Mar 1, 1986.

20. Ilma, Viola. "Interview of the month: Jacques Minkus a colossus," *Stamp Show News* 4 (4):12-13, 57-60, 1978.

21. Ibid.

22. http://www.stamps.org/Almanac/alm_HallofFame_1995-99.htm. In 1997 Minkus was posthumously inaugurated into the American Philatelic Society Hall of Fame.

23. Monty, Dr. Richard A. *Specialized Catalogue of Jacques Minkus F.D.C.s and Patriotic Cachets* (Stewartsville, New Jersey: F.D.C. Publishing Co.), p. 8.

24. Ibid., p.5.

25. Ma, Peter. "Etsuo Sayama: The Hawaii cachetmaker of patriotic covers," *First Days* 31 (3):348-354, Apr 15, 1986.

26. Klug, Janet. "Hawaii's World War II patriotic covers," *Scott's Stamp Monthly* 17 (5):23, Nov 1999.

27. Parks, *Cachet Catalogue of Staehle and Knapp*, p. 1.

28. Wright, Pat. "Frank Loper Teixeira, Cachetmaker," *First Days* 24 (3):32-33, May-Jun, 1979.

29. Ibid.

30. Sommers, Paul M. "Staehle and Teixeira patriotic varieties," *First Days* 42 (8):584-585, Dec 1, 1997.

31. _____. "Date errors on Teixeira patriotic varieties pose vexing question," *First Days* 49 (2):23-25, Mar 1, 2004.

32. _____. "Teixeira: After a few bad dates, we need to talk," *First Days* 49 (6):32-33, Sep 1, 2004.

4

Hand Painted Envelopes

HAND PAINTED COVERS are the quintessence of wartime envelope art. While carrying out their mission of informing, inspiring, or inciting in the name of Country, they also carried on a tradition of hand-drawn envelope adornment that began in the nineteenth century.[1]

A number of media are incorporated in the term "hand painted." Pen and ink (including calligraphy and cartography pens), watercolor with brush, watercolor pen, acrylic, colored pencil, and crayon were all used to create hand painted patriotic cachets on mailing envelopes.

To further define hand painted patriotic cachets: those that were hand painted by the artist are considered to be authentic; later (or even wartime) efforts at coloring in by hand other people's printed cachets are "add-ons" that are not included in the tables or illustrations of this book. Some artists first mimeographed or printed their designs, then hand colored them to complete the work. Authentic expressions of their artists' designs, these "hand tinted" illustrated envelopes (produced by Capt. Richard A. Dannells, J. Neal Griffith, Lannie H. Smith, and others) are included in the table of 832 hand painted cachets at the end of this chapter.

Cachet makers who produced hand painted covers merit special attention. Though hand painted covers constitute only 11.9% of the patriotic covers catalogued in this book (1315 of 11060), interest in them runs disproportionately high. This interest has increased with the passing decades—perhaps because of the vivid designs and colors of cachets, perhaps because of the special talent of some of the artists, or the medium itself, or the uniqueness of each hand painted cachet. Just as documentation of first day covers led to the re-discovery of wartime patriotic covers, an increasing appreciation of hand painted first day covers stimulated the re-discovery and popularity of wartime hand painted patriotic cachets.

Among creators of hand painted cachets were Gladys Adler, Leonard Borkowski, William Clendennen, Everett Klaas, Dorothy W. Knapp, Arthur F. Knoll, Abram LeGallez, and Cpl. A.E. Shaffer. The hand painted patriotic envelopes of these eight cachet makers are tabulated alphabetically by artist in "check lists" in this chapter.

To create her envelope art, Gladys Adler used acrylic over lead pencil, as well as a Crowquill pen (dip-pen) and watercolor pens, to achieve a dramatic effect influenced by the comic-book style of the 1930s and 1940s. Examples of her work are shown in Figure 1.

Leonard Borkowski employed charcoal and colored pencils, a Speedball calligraphy pen, and a Rapidograph cartography pen. "Action lines" abound in his cachets, which are filled with movement of soldiers, airplanes, bombs. These can be seen in his patriotic covers shown in Figure 2.

William Clendennen, used fountain pen with cross-hatching, as well as colored pencil and a Speedball dip-pen. As shown in Figure 3, his cachets are suffused with an earthy humor.

Everett Klaas used a graphic art style, similar to the style seen in product advertisements of the day. Lead pencil drawings underlay the watercolor and fountain pen of his cachet art. Examples of his work are shown in Figure 4.

Dorothy W. Knapp's work was considered in Chapter 2, and her life briefly recounted in Chapter 3. Knapp was a trained artist who used a combination of brush and watercolor pens, as well as fine and thick Crowquill pens. Occasionally, as in the "Axis smasher" and "Sub smasher" cachets shown in Figure 5 C and D, she employed oil pastels as well. Intricate detail, graceful lettering, and billowing clouds framing her design characterize many of her cachets. These "signature" clouds, according to Knapp herself, originally were used "as a means of separating the cachet from the address to the rest of the cover. I didn't exactly know how to blend one into the other and on a couple of first [cachets] I started using the clouds, and it seemed to work, so I guess I just unconsciously kept it up."[2]

When hand painting a cachet for more than one envelope, Knapp "would develop [in ink] a design on scrap paper then pencil the back in order to trace the design onto the envelopes. Next, she would outline [each traced design] in ink, then the sky would be added followed by the clouds, and finally the detail was added to each cover."[3]

Examples of her hand painted cachets are shown in Figure 5, this chapter; in Figures 5A-D, Chapter 2; and in Figures 4A, C, and E, Chapter 3.

Arthur F. Knoll was a gifted commercial caricaturist who used watercolor, fountain pen, and colored pencils to create his cachets. Lead pencil was used as the underlying drawing. Some of his caricature portraits are shown in Figure 6. On some covers, as shown in Figures 6D and E, he used three 1¢ stamps in V-formation to highlight his message.

Abram LeGallez used a variety of techniques to create his cachets. An example is shown in Figure 7B, a mourning cover postmarked on the date of President Roosevelt's death. The pasted-on cachet contains a photograph of a photograph, with a Rapidograph pen used for the black mourning lines. Figure 7D, the VJ Day cover, also features a pasted-on cachet containing a photograph of a photograph, but with a large "V" painted in egg tempera and "Day" inked in with Rapidograph pen. Other LeGallez techniques included windowing the envelope with an X-Acto (or similar) knife and pasting the cachet onto the back of the front portion

of the envelope, facing the viewer. Oil pastels and watered ink were sometimes used in his cachets.

Cpl. A.E. Shaffer's hand painted covers were mailed from his unit at APO 520 (Headquarters of the 15th Air Force at Cerignola, Italy) to collector-friends in the United States. A gifted calligrapher, he used fountain pen with calligraphy tips to create most of his cachets. Four are shown in Figure 8. In the cachet pictured in Figure 8C, Cpl. Shaffer used watercolor for the red star, tempera for the blue, and Rapidograph pen for the middle blue-and-red star.

Little is known of the lives of Adler, a resident of Bellaire, Texas; Borkowski, a commercial artist who lived in Milwaukee; Knoll, of Hamilton, Ohio; and LeGallez, of Slingerlands, New York. Yet their cachet work is becoming well known to collectors.

The 832 hand painted cachets by other artists are arranged alphabetically by artist (from Albrecht through Yontz) in a "check list" at the end of this chapter. Included are those whose work is important but about whose lives little or nothing has been reported (including William J. Batura of Brooklyn, NY, Lannie H. Smith of Houston, and Trudy M. White of Conimicut, RI).

Of Capt. Richard A. Dannells we know only that while at Ft. Bragg, North Carolina, he serviced patriotic covers for a soldier artist "who started a set showing various phases of a soldier's private life. . . . The soldier cut stencils for the outlines and filled in with water colors making an attractive set of 20-25 covers."[4] In a letter to a cachet maker, Capt. Dannells noted that the artist who designed the covers was Pvt. Michael J. Chernovich of the 573rd Field Artillery Battalion, located at Fort Bragg in 1944.[5]

More is known of the life and work of Cécile Cowdery of Long Prairie, MN, whose envelope art went undiscovered by collectors during World War II and is known now only through publication in 1992 of a book about her.[6] Starting June 1942 Cowdery sent letters enclosed in hand painted envelopes addressed to her husband at the 37th Armored Regiment, Pine Camp, NY. Her cachets, drawn with pen and ink or colored pencils, were meant "only to show her husband that she loved and missed him, and with no other purpose in mind."[7] The covers have not appeared in the marketplace, remaining in the hands of the family. Prices listed for her patriotic envelopes are "guesstimates" of market value.

198 HAND PAINTED CACHETS BY GLADYS ADLER

NO.	CACHET TEXT	COLOR	TOPIC	$
68	A corker [handpainted]	Multicolored	Army	D
110	A memory that / shall allways [sic] / live etc. [4/12/45] [handpainted]	Multicolored	FDR	E
140	A prayer / for / in the / service [handpainted]	Multicolored	Relig	C
232	Ach. Himmel / dose / American houzvives [handpainted]	Multicolored	Nazi	D
380	Allied iron ring [handpainted]	Multicolored	Hitle	D
604	Apointments [sic] filled. / Yanks / Russians [handpainted]	Multicolored	Hitle	D
807	Avenged / American flyers murdered [handpainted]	Multicolored	Event	D
821	B / 29 [printed on giant bee stinging head of Japanese officer] [handpainted]	Multicolored	Japan	D
963	Berlin / Tokyo / then / home [handpainted]	Multicolored	Home	D
964	Berlin [in quotes] / Defeatism [handpainted]	Multicolored	Hitle	D
1005	Blockade [handpainted]	Multicolored	Japan	D
1026	Bombing raids [handpainted]	Multicolored	Japan	D
1160	Buy a / bond / we will / do [handpainted]	Multicolored	WAC	D
1161	Buy a / bond / We will / do our part. [handpainted]	Multicolored	WAC	D
1351	Careless talk / costs / lives [handpainted]	Multicolored	Home	D
1390	Christmas / Greetings [Madonna and Child] [handpainted]	Multicolored	Holid	D
1391	Christmas / Greetings [pine branch + oval lantern] [handpainted]	Multicolored	Holid	C
1392	Christmas / Greetings [ribbon + rectangular lantern] [handpainted]	Multicolored	Holdi	C
1413	Cleaning house / I'll soon be home [handpainted]	Multicolored	Japan	D
1717	Dawn at last [handpainted]	Multicolored	ORN	D
1720	D-Day "worries" [handpainted]	Multicolored	Hitle	D
1779	Deep / in / the / heart / of / Texas [handpainted]	Multicolored	Army	C
1781	Deep in the heart of / 36th Division / Texas [handpainted]	Multicolored	Army	E
1782	Deep in the heart of / Texas [handpainted]	Multicolored	Home	E
1788	Defeat. [handpainted]	Multicolored	Japan	D
1821	Delivering / the goods [handpainted]	Multicolored	Navy	D
1894	Do your part / help / win / the / war [handpainted]	Multicolored	Shiel	D
2012	Eagle swooping, trailing 4 stars [handpainted]	Multicolored	Eagle	C
2020	Eat. Drink. / Be merry. / For tomorrow / you may / die. [handpainted]	Multicolored	Hitle	D
2172	Feed em bonds / They will lay the eggs [handpainted]	Multicolored	Air	D
2187	Fight- / work- / save [handpainted]	Multicolored	VforV	D
2198	Fighting / to free / the peoples [handpainted]	Multicolored	EagSh	D
2314	Flowers / for / der Fuehrer / "War stamps" [handpainted]	Multicolored	Ordna	D
2376	For complete / victory / in / 1945 [handpainted]	Multicolored	Japan	D
2550	France [Marianne in ball & chain, U.S. soldier with rifle & keys] [handpainted]	Multicolored	ORN	D
2584	Free / the / world [handpainted]	Multicolored	Liber	D
2620	Freedom / of speech / from fear. Want. Or religion [handpainted]	Multicolored	Flag	D
2623	Freedom / or / slavery / ? [eagle landing] [handpainted]	Multicolored	Eagle	D
2631	Freedom [in wing of eagle] [handpainted]	Multicolored	EagSh	D
2632	Freedom [in wing of eagle] [red & white vertical stripes in shield] [handpainted]	Multicolored	EagSh	D
2751	Gen. MacArthur / has just begun on the / "Rising Sun" [handpainted]	Multicolored	Japan	D
2812	General MacArthur [bust of MacArthur over "V"] [handpainted]	Multicolored	Mac	D
2833	Germans / quit! / War with / Japan / V-J Day / lest you / forget [handpainted]	Multicolored	VEDay	D
2880	Gettin [sic] / stronger [handpainted]	Multicolored	Uncle	D
2894	Give / hospitalized / GIs / war / victims / relief / overseas etc. [handpainted]	Multicolored	RedCr	C
2895	Give / in 1945. [handpainted]	Multicolored	RedCr	D
2915	Give more / in 1944. [handpainted]	Multicolored	RedCr	D
3108	Grant us / thy peace [handpainted]	Multicolored	Relig	C
3134	Greetings [candle and holly] [handpainted]	Multicolored	Holid	C
3135	Greetings [dog with ribbon collar] [handpainted]	Multicolored	Holid	C
3136	Greetings [poinsettia] [handpainted]	Multicolored	Holid	C
3349	He's / back / again [handpainted]	Multicolored	VJDay	D
3427	Holiday wishes [handpainted]	Multicolored	Holid	D
3618	If we / don't / relax / now [handpainted]	Multicolored	Winst	D
3644	If you don't write / you're wrong [handpainted]	Multicolored	Army	C
3671	I'll be / back in a flash. [handpainted]	Multicolored	Army	D
3805	Inflation / Make / your / $$ / have / more / cents [handpainted]	Multicolored	Home	D
3839	Invasion road / to Nip land / China / Okinawa [handpainted]	Multicolored	Army	D
3840	Invasion road / to Nip land / China / Okinawa [handpainted]	Multicolored	Army	D
3873	Island to island [sic] / fleet with fleet / In Tokyo we / meet. [handpainted]	Multicolored	Eagle	E
3874	Island to island / fleet with fleet / In Tokyo we / meet. [handpainted]	Multicolored	Eagle	D
3906	It won't / be long / now. [handpainted]	Multicolored	Japan	D
3938	It's a / 3 pin / alley [handpainted]	Multicolored	Axis	D
3999	Jan. / 01 [sands of time, holly, ribbon] [handpainted]	Multicolored	Holid	C
4018	Jap hands grabbed the fats / we used to import. / "Save used fats now" [handpainted]	Multicolored	Japan	C
4086	Japs are / snakes / bonds / are stakes [handpainted]	Multicolored	Uncle	D
4166	Just about ready for the hammer [handpainted]	Multicolored	Army	D

NO.	CACHET TEXT	COLOR	TOPIC	$
4192	Keep / em / flying [eagle & flag] [handpainted]	Multicolored	EagFl	D
4193	Keep / em / flying [eagle & shield] [handpainted]	Multicolored	EagSh	D
4223	Keep em / flying [eagle diving] [handpainted]	Multicolored	Eagle	D
4224	Keep em / flying [eagle with flag] [handpainted]	Multicolored	EagFl	D
4225	Keep em / flying [eagle, no flag] [handpainted]	Multicolored	Eagle	D
4230	Keep e'm [sic] / flying [eagle landing] [handpainted]	Multicolored	Eagle	D
4306	Keep him on the run [handpainted]	Multicolored	Hitle	D
4311	Keep it / flying / buying [flag, war bonds pennant] [handpainted]	Multicolored	Flag	D
4361	Keep your / boots / working / in /[handpainted]	Multicolored	Hitle	D
4365	Keep your sleeves rolled up / untill [sic] the / job is done [handpainted]	Multicolored	Uncle	C
4439	Lest you / forget / Pearl Harbor [Christmas candles] [handpainted]	Green, red	Holid	C
4440	Lest you forget [graveside cross, helmet, "G.I. Joe"] [handpainted]	Multicolored	Army	D
4575	Let's go! / U.S.A. / Keep / 'em flying! []handpainted]	Multicolored	Air	D
4604	Let's go, / US ["US" letters 63mm high] [handpainted]	Multicolored	Home	D
4747	Lieut. Gen. / Jonathan Wainwright. [handpainted]	Multicolored	Gener	D
4748	Lieut. Gen. / Mark W. Clark [handpainted]	Multicolored	Gener	D
4811	Look to the / future, guard it / "well." [handpainted]	Multicolored	Eagle	D
4818	Looking after / the / stars and stripes [handpainted]	Multicolored	Eagle	D
4889	Lucky 7th / Let's not / gamble / with / victory [handpainted]	Multicolored	Bonds	E
5063	Make him / swallow / that bond. [handpainted]	Multicolored	Japan	D
5231	Merry / Christmas / Happy / New Year [handpainted]	Multicolored	Holid	D
5234	Merry / Christmas [holly, lamp, ribbon] [handpainted]	Multicolored	Holid	D
5236	Merry / Xmas / V [handpainted]	Multicolored	Holid	D
5250	Merry. / Christmas. [snow-covered cottage, pine cones] [handpainted]	Multicolored	Holid	D
5487	Nineteen forty-five [handpainted]	Multicolored	Axis	D
5505	Nineteen forty-four [1944] [Mary, Joseph, Jesus] [handpainted]	Multicolored	Holid	D
5509	Nineteen forty-four [1944]. [handpainted]	Multicolored	Axis	D
5514	Nineteen forty-three [1943] / V / Merry Xmas [handpainted]	Multicolored	Holid	D
5551	No. / 3. [handpainted]	Multicolored	Musso	E
5552	No. 1. [handpainted]	Multicolored	Hitle	E
5553	No. 2. [handpainted]	Multicolored	Japan	E
5838	One down - two to go [handpainted]	Multicolored	UncAx	C
6140	Peace / on / Earth/ Good / will / toward / Men... [handpainted]	Multicolored	Holid	D
6382	Quit cluttering up my / floor with your junk. [handpainted]	Multicolored	Japan	D
6422	Rats / fight fiercest when / "cornered" [handpainted]	Multicolored	Axis	D
6484	Re'mber "Pearl" / Harbor? [handpainted]	Multicolored	Pearl	D
6485	Rember [sic] "Pearl" / Harbor. [handpainted]	Multicolored	Pearl	D
6510	Remember / Pearl / Harbor [colors vary] [handpainted]	Multicolored	Pearl	D
6709	Ruin / Holding back the guillotine [handpainted]	Multicolored	Hitle	D
6753	Sacrifice / "but not our" / freedom [handpainted]	Multicolored	Flag	D
6881	Season's / greetings [poinsettia] [handpainted]	Multicolored	Holid	C
6996	Shall wave / "in honor" / again. [handpainted]	Blue, red	ORN	D
7158	Southern Cross / Philippines [bombers in shape of cross] [handpainted]	Multicolored	Phili	D
7172	Speed them back / WAC's [handpainted]	Multicolored	WAC	D
7290	T kio / Biak / Mariannas [sic] / Truk [handpainted]	Multicolored	Japan	D
7307	Task / Force / 58 / war [handpainted]	Multicolored	Navy	D
7347	Thanksgiving / Day. 1944. [handpainted]	Multicolored	Holid	D
7392	The / big / V / means / we [handpainted]	Multicolored	VforV	D
7576	The grandest / thing in this / world is a / clear conscious [sic] [handpainted]	Multicolored	Uncle	D
7609	The knock-out / war loan [arm in shape of a "7"] [postmarked 6/29/45] [handpainted]	Multicolored	Japan	D
7613	The last round / up. [handpainted]	Multicolored	Japan	D
7836	The Wallop Poll [handpainted]	Multicolored	Axis	D
8118	This war / isnt [sic] won [handpainted]	Multicolored	Japan	D
8211	To Tokyo / we go [handpainted]	Multicolored	Army	D
8290	Tokyo bound. [handpainted]	Multicolored	Armed	D
8426	U.S. [handpainted]	Multicolored	Flag	C
8446	U.S. Army [13 stars in wreath above eagle, shield] [handpainted]	Multicolored	EagSh	C
8448	U.S. Army [in ribbon held in eagle's beak] [handpainted]	Multicolored	EagSh	D
8473	U.S. landings / To Tokyo / we go [handpainted]	Multicolored	Armed	D
8568	U.S.A. [across chest of strong man] [handpainted]	Multicolored	Hitle	D
8571	U.S.A. [across top of shield, below eagle] [handpainted]	Multicolored	EagSh	D
8572	U.S.A. [on shield, under eagle] [handpainted]	Multicolored	EagSh	D
8576	U.S.A. [under eagle, shield, flags] [handpainted]	Multicolored	EagSh	C
8678	Unconditional / surrender [handpainted]	Multicolored	Ally	D
8684	Underground [determined man with lamp and rifle] [handpainted]	Multicolored	ORN	D
8725	United / we fight [handpainted]	Multicolored	Armed	D
8959	United... / ...we fight [handpainted]	Multicolored	Armed	D
8963	Unity / V / victory ["V" 64 mm high] [handpainted]	Multicolored	VforV	D
8981	USA [7 stars inside "S"] [no picture] [handpainted]	Multicolored	Home	D
8983	USA [below eagle, shield, and banners] [handpainted]	Multicolored	EagSh	D
8984	USA [diagonal, letters 42mm high] [handpainted]	Multicolored	Home	D

NO.	CACHET TEXT	COLOR	TOPIC	$
8986	USA [on shield] [handpainted]	Multicolored	EagSh	D
9023	V ...- / for victory [handpainted]	Multicolored	VforV	D
9057	V ...- [inside outline of shield] [handpainted] [postmarked 5/8/45]	Multicolored	VforV	E
9060	V / -- / for victory [handpainted]	Multicolored	VforV	D
9062	V / -- for / Victory / ...- [reddish pink cross] [handpainted]	Multicolored	VforV	D
9063	V / -- for / Victory / ...- [yellow cross] [handpainted]	Multicolored	VforV	D
9068	V / ...- / ...- / Victory [handpainted]	Multicolored	VforV	D
9094	V / ...- / Victory ["...-" and "Victory" across "V"] [handpainted]	Multicolored	VforV	D
9166	V / for victory [handpainted]	Multicolored	ShieV	D
9226	V / V / ...- / Victory / insures / freedom [handpainted]	Multicolored	VforV	D
9266	V ["V" 75 mm tall] [soldier saluting] [handpainted]	Multicolored	Army	D
9273	V [75 mm tall] [left arm of "V": white stars; right arm: blue field, red & white stripes] [hp]	Multicolored	Air	C
9280	V [below saluting soldier] [handpainted]	Multicolored	Army	D
9424	V—for / victory / ...- [handpainted]	Multicolored	Relig	D
9635	Victory. / Hats off to our armed forces. [handpainted]	Black, red	VEDay	E
9748	War / bonds / keep it / flying / buying [flag, war bonds pennant] [handpainted]	Multicolored	Flag	D
9857	We / "must" / do all we / "can" [handpainted]	Multicolored	Uncle	D
9858	We / "must" / do all we / "can" [handpainted]	Multicolored	Uncle	D
9868	We / shall / see / you / through [handpainted]	Multicolored	Army	D
9962A	We have a war / to win [picture similar to cachet 4086] [handpainted]	Multicolored	Uncle	D
9992	We need used / fats / to cook their / goose [handpainted]	Multicolored	Axis	D
10064	Wear one of these / or "do a war job" [handpainted]	Multicolored	Women	D
10102	We're / all behind / you! [handpainted]	Multicolored	Eagle	D
10287	Win the / peace [eagle's head pink] [handpainted]	Multicolored	EagFl	E
10288	Win the / peace [eagle's head white] [handpainted]	Multicolored	EagFl	E
10289	Win the / peace [handpainted]	Multicolored	EagFl	E
10461	Worries [in quotes] [handpainted]	Multicolored	Hitle	E
10539	You birds / follow / me [handpainted]	Multicolored	Eagle	D
10544	You can share in the / invasion! [ms., black ink] + flag [handpainted]	Multicolored	Flag	C
10564	You shall / have work / when you / return / Uncle [handpainted]	Multicolored	Uncle	D
10566	You Tojo's friend / if you don't buy / war bonds [handpainted]	Multicolored	Japan	D
10623	You're needed / in the army [handpainted]	Multicolored	WAC	C
10665	^^Airplane, bomber, with flag [handpainted]	Multicolored	Air	C
10679	^^Angel standing between two large Christmas candles [handpainted]	Multicolored	Holid	C
10684	^^Baby in diapers wearing top hat and bow tie, carrying baton [handpainted]	Multicolored	Holid	D
10696	^^Bear as clown, with balloons, dancing, blowing horn at New Year's [handpainted]	Multicolored	Holid	D
10698	^^Black boy wearing cap, selling newspapers [no text on newspaper] [handpainted]	Multicolored	VEDay	D
10701	^^Bomber flying in front of flag [handpainted]	Multicolored	Flag	D
10713	^^Dog wearing high hat and bow tie, clock near midnight, confetti, toy horn [handpainted]	Multicolored	Holid	D
10728	^^Eagle flying, blank scroll between wings and in front of shield [handpainted]	Multicolored	EagSh	C
10729	^^Eagle flying, holding blank scroll in beak [handpainted]	Multicolored	Eagle	C
10731	^^Eagle holding blank scroll in its talons [handpainted]	Handpainted	Eagle	C
10736	^^Eagle on shield [small eagle, large shield] [handpainted]	Multicolored	EagSh	D
10758	^^Eagle with wings spread, alighting [handpainted]	Multicolored	Eagle	D
10837	^^Hirohito caricature [without "No. 2."] [handpainted]	Multicolored	Japan	E
10840	^^Hitler caricature [without "No. 1."] [handpainted]	Multicolored	Hitle	E
10893	^^Mussolini caricature [without "No. / 3."] [handpainted]	Multicolored	Musso	E
10909	^^Sailboat and tropical island with one tree [handpainted]	Multicolored	Hawai	C
10910	^^Sailboat and tropical island with two trees [handpainted]	Multicolored	Hawai	D
10924	^^Santa Claus face [handpainted]	Multicolored	Holid	C
10925	^^Santa Claus face as clown, laughing [handpainted]	Multicolored	Holid	C
10926	^^Santa Claus face with phone [handpainted]	Multicolored	Holid	C
10930	^^Shepherd, flock, and Christmas Star [handpainted]	Multicolored	Holid	C
10931	^^Shield and anchor [handpainted]	Multicolored	Shiel	C
10960	^^Soldier on phone, back to viewer, thinking of wife and baby [handpainted]	Multicolored	Army	C
10968	^^Soldier smiling, face and helmet shadowed [handpainted]	Multicolored	Army	C
10980	^^Soldier with helmet, head tilted up slightly [handpainted]	Multicolored	Army	C
10984	^^Soldier with rifle inside ship steering wheel, anchor [handpainted]	Multicolored	Armed	C
11007	^^Statue of Liberty encircled by red, white, blue ribbon [handpainted]	Multicolored	Liber	D
11044	^^Virgin and Child with Joseph [handpainted] [postmarked 12/25/44]	Multicolored	Holid	D

Figure 1. Hand painted patriotic covers by Gladys Adler, Bellaire, Texas. A (cachet 5552), B (cachet 5553), and C (cachet 5551), feature America's Public Enemies #1, 2, and 3. D, cachet 9094. E, cachet 1005. F, cachet 10566. G, cachet 2632, postmarked on VE Day. H, cachet 7307, postmarked on VJ Day.

46 HAND PAINTED CACHETS BY LEONARD BORKOWSKI

NO.	CACHET TEXT	COLOR	TOPIC	$
663	Are you in / step with / the 4th war / loan drive? [handpainted]	Multicolored	Bonds	D
828	Back home again / in dear old Utica [handpainted]	Multicolored	Army	D
913	Be my / valentine / Adolf! / Himmel? / Where / is mine etc. [handpainted]	Multicolored	Hitle	D
1013	Blood plasma / saved his life. [handpainted]	Multicolored	Blood	D
1029	Bombs over Berlin. [handpainted]	Multicolored	Air	D
1101	Buck [sic] the Japs - / right of [sic] / the map ...- [handpainted]	Multicolored	Japan	D
1113	Build the weapons / to sink the Nips. [handpainted]	Multicolored	Air	D
1145	Buy / U.S. / war / bonds [handpainted]	Multicolored	Air	D
1190	Buy bonds for victory! [handpainted]	Multicolored	Bonds	D
1239	Buy war / bonds / victory / in 44 / The picnic is my etc. [handpainted]	Multicolored	Home	D
1727	D-Day / turns into / V ...- / Days / It will soon / come etc. [handpainted]	Multicolored	Symb+	D
1861	Did you / give a pint / of blood yet— / to save etc. [handpainted]	Multicolored	Blood	D
1896	Do your part and buy U.S. war bonds ...- [handpainted]	Multicolored	Japan	D
2396	For God and country. / We serve ...- [handpainted]	Multicolored	EagSh	D
3325	Here is an Easter egg / for Tojo and Hitler. [handpainted]	Multicolored	Axis	D
3637	If you can't fight / then don't strike! [handpainted]	Multicolored	Army	D
3958	It's patriotic / to save your / drops of / kitchen fat [handpainted]	Multicolored	Axis	D
4198	Keep / the / war / bonds [handpainted]	Blue, red	Uncle	D
4305	Keep him going ...- [handpainted]	Multicolored	Army	D
4446	Let em have it. / Back em up. [handpainted]	Multicolored	Armed	D
4519	Let's / finish / the / job. [handpainted]	Multicolored	UncV	D
5491	Nineteen forty-four [1944] / Bang / there / goes / Tokyo [handpainted]	Multicolored	Air	D
5623	O' / show me the / way to / Berlin [handpainted]	Multicolored	Armed	D
5795	On their way to Tokyo [handpainted]	Green	Armed	D
5829	One / down / and / two / to / go / Springfield / Armory ...- etc. [handpainted]	Multicolored	Axis	D
6182	Philippines / Jap soon / to lose it's [sic] / stepping stone... [handpainted]	Multicolored	Japan	D
6218	Play ball with Uncle / Sam / To / win / the / war / buy U.S. etc. [handpainted]	Multicolored	Home	D
6645	Remember to / buy / that / Victory / bond / to-day! [handpainted]	Multicolored	Bonds	D
6676	Right in ther [sic] Fuehrers face! / This is a salute / to etc. [handpainted]	Multicolored	Hitle	D
7033	Show me the / way to / Berlin [handpainted]	Multicolored	Army	D
7388	The / 3rd / war loan / All / of US [handpainted]	Multicolored	Hitle	D
7726	The road / to Rome [handpainted]	Multicolored	Army	D
7797	The United / Nation [sic] / invasion egg [handpainted]	Multicolored	Hitle	D
7990	They will always / live in our / hearts. [handpainted]	Multicolored	LinWa	D
8170	To / day / fresh / fish / Save / wrapping / paper...- [handpainted]	Multicolored	Home	D
8273	Tokyo / we / have / come / V-J-Day-is-here [handpainted]	Multicolored	VJDay	E
8279	Tokyo [Japanese mouth] Italy [Mussolini's mouth] [3 Axis heads] [handpainted]	Multicolored	Wash	D
8385	Two [2] down, 1 to go. [handpainted]	Multicolored	Axis	D
8975	US Army [soldier shooting at plane] [handpainted]	Multicolored	Army	D
9698	Vot - next? [handpainted]	Multicolored	Uboat	D
9824	Was is / loose? / Com- / ing / inva- / sion / Buy / that etc. [handpainted]	Multicolored	Hitle	D
10122	We-want / Hiro-hi-to! [handpainted]	Multicolored	VJDay	E
10233	While you strike / at home, / our boys strike / at the enemy. [handpainted]	Multicolored	Army	D
10637	Zip your lip.... / to save a ship. [handpainted]	Multicolored	Navy	D
10670	^^Airplanes, 3, B-25 Mitchells, flying right; large bomb falling [handpainted]	Multicolored	Air	D
10738	^^Eagle on shield, head facing right [eagle color: brown] [handpainted]	Multicolored	EagSh	D

Figure 2. Hand painted patriotic covers by Leonard Borkowski, Milwaukee. A, cachet 1145. B, cachet 10233. C, cachet 10637. D, cachet 1013.E, cachet 1029. F, cachet 9698. G, cachet 6504. H, cachet 10122, cover postmarked VJ Day.

23 HAND PAINTED CACHETS BY WILLIAM CLENDENNEN

NO.	CACHET TEXT	COLOR	TOPIC	$
229	Ach! dot Yank 1st Army is bad / Von Rundstedt's 'return!' [handpainted]	Black	Unit	D
573	And me the champion of the block! [in quotes] [hydrant at left] [handpainted]	Black	Japan	D
710	Ask / Santa / for / U.S. War Bonds [handpainted]	Blue, red	Bonds	D
810	Aw don't—every night at camp / they make us turn out the lights! [in quotes] [handpainted]	Multicolored	Army	E
925	Be wise! / Buy bonds and save 'em. [handpainted]	Black	Owl	D
968	Best idea / Maggie / ever had [handpainted]	Multicolored	Home	D
1714	Daily News / Manila / falls! / On to / Tokyo! [handpainted]	Black	Event	D
2394	For gifts / give U.S. war bonds [handpainted]	Multicolored	Holid	D
3397	History repeats [handpainted]	Black	Hitle	D
3411	Hitlers / war / fund / "Fill 'er up for Adolph!" [handpainted]	Black	Dog	D
3978	I've been / itching / to get out / of these [handpainted]	Black	Army	D
5271	Miss America 1944 -- [handpainted]	Black	WAC	D
5470	Next! [handpainted]	Multicolored	Women	E
5609	Now for a long rest if these / foolish mortals will let me. [handpainted]	Multicolored	Antiq	D
6129	Patton's Third Army [handpainted]	Black	Hitle	D
7631	The man of / the hour— [handpainted]	Black	USSR	D
7709	The Red Cross needs your / aid [handpainted]	Multicolored	RedCr	D
7734	The scourge of Europe. [handpainted]	Blue	Hitle	D
7831	The victory girl [handpainted]	Multicolored	Women	D
8670	Uncle Sam's peace terms. [handpainted]	Black	UncAx	E
10258	Why don't you get a war job? [in quotes] [handpainted]	Black	Women	D
10550	You can't sneak out now Adolph! [in quotes] [handpainted]	Black	Hitle	D
10574	You'll soon be out of the picture, Adolph! [in quotes] [handpainted]	Black	Hitle	D

Figure 3. Hand painted patriotic covers by William Clendennen, Port Jervis, New York. A, cachet 8670. B, cachet 3411. C, cachet 5470. D, cachet 10258.

30 HAND PAINTED CACHETS BY EVERETT KLAAS

NO.	CACHET TEXT	COLOR	TOPIC	$
802	Avenge / Pearl / Harbor [handpainted]	Green, red	Pearl	D
827	Back / the/ attack / with / war bonds and stamps [handpainted]	Blue, red	Bonds	C
972	Better / buy / bonds ["B's" interlinked] [no picture] [handpainted]	Blue, red	Bonds	C
1152	Buy / war / bonds / and / stamps / invest in / liberty [handpainted]	Blue, red	Bonds	C
1154	Buy / war / bonds [handpainted]	Blue, red	Bonds	C
1206	Buy extra bonds / 4th / war loan [handpainted]	Blue, red	Bonds	C
2179	Fifth [5th] war loan / V ...- [handpainted]	Multicolored	Bonds	D
2635	Freedom [vertical] / of / speech / and / religion etc. [handpainted]	Multicolored	Torch	C
4234	Keep 'em diving [handpainted]	Blue, red	Air	D
4261	Keep 'em flying [airplane and V] [handpainted]	Blue, red	VforV	D
4550	Let's give / Hitler's / goose-steppers / the bird - / Here's the bird! [handpainted]	Blue, red	Eagle	C
5502	Nineteen forty-four [1944] / The / greatest blow / of all! [handpainted]	Black	Hitle	D
5575	Not rabbits, / Mr. Jap! [airplanes coming out of Uncle Sam's hat] [handpainted]	Multicolored	Air	C
5604	Now / as then / worth / fighting / for / 1776 1944 [handpainted]	Multicolored	Bell	C
5736	Ohio / fights for / freedom [handpainted]	Blue, red	Home	C
6192	Pin 'em back [handpainted]	Multicolored	Japan	D
6855	Say it with / 1944 / V / bombers [handpainted]	Blue, red	Air	D
7061	Sixth [6th] / war / loan [bomb falling on Japanese flag] [handpainted]	Blue, red	Bonds	D
7063	Sixth [6th] / war / loan [bomb falling on Nazi flag] [handpainted]	Multicolored	Bonds	D
7064	Sixth [6th] / war / loan [Minute Man] [handpainted]	Multicolored	Bonds	D
8728	United for / post-war co-operation [handpainted]	Blue, red	UN	C
8986	USA [on bell] [handpainted]	Multicolored	Bell	D
9522	Victory [above eagle and sun] [handpainted]	Multicolored	Eagle	C
9524	Victory [below eagle and stars] [handpainted]	Blue, red	Eagle	C
9531	Victory [eagle alighting onto "Victory," 7 stars about wings]] [handpainted]	Blue, red	Eagle	D
9533	Victory [eagle flying under "Victory," "V" touching right wing] [handpainted]	Blue, red	Eagle	D
9534	Victory [eagle flying under "Victory," in front of sun and rays] [handpainted]	Multicolored	Eagle	D
9750	War / bonds / speed/ victory [handpainted]	Black, yellow	Liber	C
9843	Wastepaper / fights / for / freedom / Save / a bundle etc. [handpainted]	Blue, red	Home	C
10462	Worth / fighting / for [handpainted]	Blue, red	Bell	C

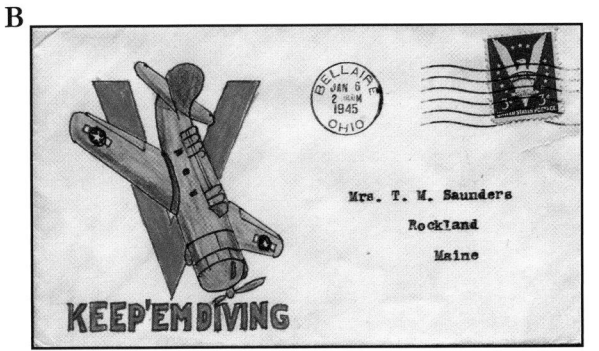

Figure 4. Hand painted covers by Everett Klaas, Bellaire, Ohio. A, cachet 8985. B, cachet 4234. C, cachet 9522. D, cachet 7064.

73 HAND PAINTED CACHETS BY DOROTHY W. KNAPP

NO.	CACHET TEXT	COLOR	TOPIC	$
455	America forever [serviced by Louis & Mae Weigand] [handpainted]	Multicolored	EagFl	G
501*	American Eagle [handpainted] [watercolors=multi, pen & ink=black]	Multi/Black	EagFl	G
502*	American Eagles [handpainted] [watercolors=multi, pen & ink=black]	Multi/Black	Eag+	G
817	Axis / smasher / Army air bases / help / make this / possible [handpainted]	Multicolored	Air	G
1207	Buy his bonds [handpainted]	Multicolored	Uncle	G
1377	Chief of the gremlins / John L. Lewis [handpainted]	Multicolored	Home	G
1423	Coast Guard Cutter Spencer / sinks a sub [all-over cachet] [handpainted]	Multicolored	Coast	H
1726	D-Day / the time / is now! / The invasion has begun— etc. [handpainted]	Multicolored	DDay	I
1802*	Defend America [handpainted] [watercolors=multicolored, pen & ink=black]	Multi/Black	FlLib	G
1828	Democracy/Americanism [handpainted]	Multicolored	Liber	G
2001*	E Pluribus Unum [handpainted] [watercolors=multicolored, pen & ink=black]	Multi/Black	EagFl	H
2106	Everybody / every pay day / 10% [handpainted]	Multicolored	Home	G
2146	Farewell to the pilot / who brought us safely / within etc. [handpainted]	Multicolored	FDR	G
2264	First flag on Mt. Suribachi / was photographed by S/Sgt. Louis R. etc. [handpainted]	Multicolored	Event	G
2340*	Food / for / victory [handpainted] [watercolors=multicolored, pen & ink=black]	Multi/Black	Home	G
2341	Food for freedom [handpainted]	Multicolored	Home	G
2431	For sale / General Patton's dog house / Present owner has etc. [hp]	Multicolored	Patt	G
2658*	Freedom's / lady [above Statue of Liberty, head & shoulder view] [handpainted] [watercolors=multi, pen & ink=black]	Multi/Black	Liber	H
2659	Freedom's lady [below Statue of Liberty, including pedestal] [handpainted]	Multicolored	Liber	G
2786	General Douglas MacArthur / is honored by the opening of etc. [handpainted]	Multicolored	MacFD	I
2902*	Give 'em / both barrels [handpainted] [watercolors=multicolored, pen & ink=black]	Multi/Black	Home	G
3192*	Hands across the sea [handpainted] [watercolors=multicolored, pen & ink=black]	Multi/Black	Ally	G
3266	Heavy [in quotes], heavy hangs over they head" / The next war etc. [handpainted]	Multicolored	Ally	G
3350*	He's / my / Uncle / ! [handpainted] [watercolors=multicolored, pen & ink=black]	Multi/Black	Uncle	H
4227*	Keep 'em / flying [handpainted] [watercolors=multicolored, pen & ink=black]	Multi/Black	Air	G
4266	Keep 'em flying [handpainted]	Multicolored	Air	G
4344*	Keep the sea lanes / open [handpainted] [watercolors=multicolored, pen & ink=black]	Multi/Black	Navy	G
4400	Labor units / for defense / Labor Day [handpainted]	Multicolored	Home	G
4409	Land of the free [handpainted]	Multicolored	Shiel	G
4489*	Let it ring / for ever [handpainted] [watercolors=multicolored, pen & ink=black]	Multi/Black	Bell	H
4692*	Liberty / for all [handpainted] [watercolors=multicolored, pen & ink=black]	Multi/Black	Bell	G
4697	Liberty / is still alive [handpainted]	Multicolored	Liber	G
4773	Light / of / liberty [handpainted]	Multicolored	VforV	G
5145	May / liberty's / torch / shine / forever! [handpainted]	Multicolored	Torch	G
5174*	May liberty's torch / shine forever! [handpainted] [watercolors=multicolored, pen & ink=black]	Multi/Black	Torch	G
6022*	Our navy / guardian of our shores [handpainted] [watercolors=multicolored, pen & ink=black]	Multi/Black	Navy	G
6142	Peace / Sep. 2 1945 / [etc.] / V-J Day etc. [sword pierces flag] [handpainted]	Multicolored	VJDay	I
6143	Peace / Sept. 2 1945 / [etc.] / V-J Day etc. [no sword] [handpainted]	Multicolored	VJDay	I
6215	Planting time is in full swing in the Pacific [handpainted] [monarch size envelope]	Multicolored	Flag	G
6539*	Remember / Pearl Harbor [battleship burning] [handpainted] [watercolors=multicolored, pen & ink=black]	Multi/Black	Pearl	H
6829	Savagery / at its worst - / from now on! [handpainted]	Multicolored	Axis	G
7256	Sub / smasher / Perrin Field / helps make this / possible [handpainted]	Multicolored	Air	G
7355*	That government of the people, / by the people, for the etc. [handpainted] [watercolors=multi, pen & ink=black]	Multi/Black	Linc	H
8081	This is our war! / Join the WAACS [handpainted]	Multicolored	WAC	G
8138	Three [3] years ago / "Wonder where" [etc.] / And / today etc. [handpainted]	Multicolored	Axis	G
8198	To market—to market / Ration / point / range [handpainted]	Multicolored	Home	H
8327	Total blackout? Never! [handpainted]	Multicolored	Liber	G
8481A	U.S. Marines / land on / Iwo Jima and / put the / squeeze on / the Japs [handpainted]	Multicolored	USMC	H
9066	V / "V-E" Day / Germany surrenders / May 8, 1945 / Allied victory etc. [handpainted]	Multicolored	VEDay	I
9123	V / ...- for victory [handpainted] [watercolors=multicolored, pen & ink=black]	Multi/Black	EagV	G
9152*	V / Fight! / for victory [handpainted] [watercolors=multicolored, pen & ink=black]	Multi/Black	Armed	G
9257	V / Wings / for / victory [handpainted]	Multicolored	Air	G
9344	V for victory ["V" 87 mm high] [handpainted]	Multicolored	EagV	G
9396	V-E [in quotes] Day / Allied victory in Europe / V / May 8, 1945 [handpainted]	Multicolored	VEDay	I
9397	V-E Day / Allied victory in Europe / May 8, 1945 [boot, swastika] [handpainted]	Multicolored	VEDay	I
9458A	Victory /Aug. 14, 1945 - Surrender Day / Japan agrees to surrender [handpainted].	Multicolored	VJDay	I
9534A	Victory [flags of U.S. and Albania in front of sun, rays, parting clouds] [handpainted]	Multicolored	VEDay	I
9534B	Victory [flags of U.S. and Austria in front of sun, rays, parting clouds] [handpainted]	Multicolored	VEDay	I
9534C	Victory [flags of U.S. and Belgium in front of sun, rays, parting clouds] [handpainted]	Multicolored	VEDay	I
9534D	Victory [flags of U.S. and Czechoslovakia in front of sun, rays, parting clouds] [handpainted]	Multicolored	VEDay	I
9534	Victory [flags of U.S. and Denmark in front of sun, rays, parting clouds] [handpainted]	Multicolored	VEDay	I
9534F	Victory [flags of U.S. and France in front of sun, rays, parting clouds] [handpainted]	Multicolored	VEDay	I
9534G	Victory [flags of U.S. and Greece in front of sun, rays, parting clouds] [handpainted]	Multicolored	VEDay	I
9534H	Victory [flags of U.S. and Luxembourg in front of sun, rays, parting clouds] [handpainted]	Multicolored	VEDay	I
9534I	Victory [flags of U.S. and Netherlands in front of sun, rays, parting clouds] [handpainted]	Multicolored	VEDay	I
9534J	Victory [flags of U.S. and Norway in front of sun, rays, parting clouds] [handpainted]	Multicolored	VEDay	I
9534K	Victory [flags of U.S. and Poland in front of sun, rays, parting clouds] [handpainted]	Multicolored	VEDay	I

NO.	CACHET TEXT	COLOR	TOPIC	$
9534L	Victory [flags of U.S. and Yugoslavia in front of sun, rays, parting clouds] [handpainted]	Multicolored	VEDay	I
9751	War / U.S. declares war / Dec. 11, 1941 / on Germany and Italy [handpainted]	Multicolored	Event	I
10309	Win the War [4 rows of stars behind eagle] [unsigned] [handpainted]	Multicolored	Eagle	G
10319*	Winged / victory [handpainted] [watercolors=multicolored, pen & ink=black]	Multi/Black	Air	G
10320	Wings / for / victory [handpainted]	Multicolored	ShieV	G
10329*	Wings for victory [handpainted] [watercolors=multicolored, pen & ink=black]	Multi/Black	Air	G

* These illustrated envelopes were produced in two series: 20 numbered multicolored cachets produced by brush and watercolor pens, and 20 numbered black cachets of the same design, including text, produced by pen and ink. The multicolored series was first recorded by Charles W. Martin in *Current Covers and Stamplets* in 1944.[8] In an article introducing patriotic covers in the same issue, John Max Rush also mentioned that "Mrs. Dorothy Knapp of Rhinebeck, New York, has 20 beautiful hand-painted covers. . . ."[9] The pen and ink set was not recorded in *Current Covers and Stamplets*. To my knowledge, this set—all with cancellation dates of January or February 1945, after the appearance of the original article—surfaced publicly when offered for sale in 2005 by Nutmeg Stamp Sales. It is likely that Knapp, who customarily used ink preliminary to adding watercolor details to her design (p. 63), made only one black-ink copy of this set.

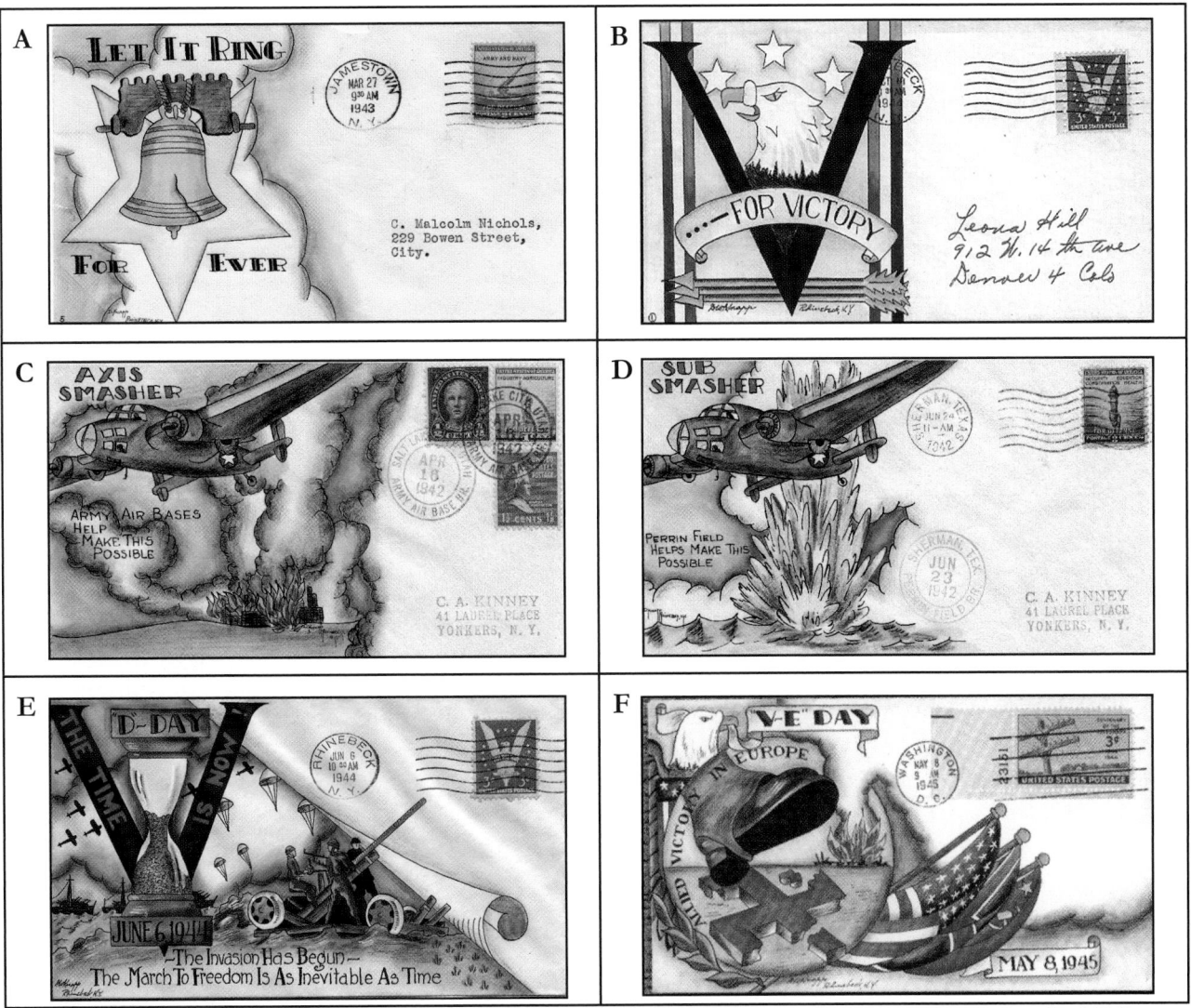

Figure 5. Hand painted patriotic covers by Dorothy W. Knapp, Rhinebeck, New York. A, cachet 4489. B, cachet 9123. C, cachet 817. D, cachet 7256. E, cachet 1726, D-Day. F, cachet 9397, VE Day.

62 HAND PAINTED CACHETS BY ARTHUR F. KNOLL

NO.	CACHET TEXT	COLOR	TOPIC	$
274	Admiral E.J. King [handpainted]	Multicolored	Admir	D
282	Admiral Nimitz [handpainted]	Multicolored	Nim	C
286	Admiral William Leahy [handpainted]	Multicolored	Admir	D
288	Admirtal C.W. Nimitz [handpainted]	Multicolored	Nim	E
845	Back the attack / on them [in quotes] / buy war bonds [handpainted]	Multicolored	Axis	C
868	Back the winners [in quotes] / buy war bonds [handpainted]	Multicolored	Heads	C
1047	Bonds buy bombs / to bomb this bum [in quotes] [handpainted]	Black	Japan	C
1092	Britain's champion / of the people / Earl Lloyd George of Dwyfor [handpainted]	Multicolored	Heads	C
1157	Buy / war bonds / V [FDR, Churchill, Stalin] [handpainted]	Multicolored	Heads	C
1158	Buy / war bonds [FDR, Churchill, Stalin, Hitler, Mussolini] [handpainted]	Multicolored	Heads	C
1250	Buy war bonds / Doolittle [handpainted]	Multicolored	Dool	C
1254	Buy war bonds / for victory / V / "Let's keep America" etc. [handpainted]	Multicolored	Home	C
1617	Commands 1st White Russian Army / Marshal Gregory K. Zhukov [handpainted]	Multicolored	Gener	C
1706	D / Day / June 6th, 1944 [handpainted]	Red	DDay	C
1981	Doug [in quotes] and "Ike" [handpainted]	Multicolored	Mac	D
2270	First lady of the world / "Mme Chiang" / Buy War Bonds [handpainted]	Multicolored	China	C
2708	Gen. "Vinegar Joe" Stilwell [handpainted]	Multicolored	Gener	D
2722	Gen. Ben Lear [handpainted]	Multicolored	Gener	C
2735	Gen. Eisenhower [handpainted]	Multicolored	Ike	D
3202	Happy New Year [in quotes] / 1945 / V [handpainted]	Multicolored	Holid	C
3237	He died before his / Phillipines [sic] were free [in quotes] / President Quezon etc. [hp]	Multicolored	Phili	D
3253	He wants an armistice / Admiral Horthy / of Hungary [handpainted]	Multicolored	Axis	C
3297	Help him come home [in quotes] / K9 Corps / [etc.] / War Bonds / [handpainted]	Multicolored	Unit	C
3314	Help to break it all up [in quotes] / Buy war bonds [handpainted]	Multicolored	Axis	C
3441	Honor to the U.S. Marines / Gen. Alexander Vandergrift [handpainted]	Multicolored	Gener	D
4307	Keep him out / Buy more war bonds [handpainted]	Multicolored	Japan	D
4307A	Keep him out! [in quotes] / buy war bonds [handpainted]	Multicolored	Nazis	D
4335	Keep Rommel on the run. [in quotes] / Buy war bonds [handpainted]	Multicolored	Romm	C
4533	Let's all pull / together [in quotes] / buy war bonds [handpainted]	Black, tan	Hitle	C
4835	Lt. Gen. Alexander Patch [handpainted]	Multicolored	Gener	D
4836	Lt. Gen. Eichelberger [handpainted]	Multicolored	Gener	D
4844	Lt. Gen. Krueger [handpainted]	Multicolored	Gener	D
4846	Lt. Gen. Omar Bradley [handpainted]	Multicolored	Gener	D
4848	Lt. Gen. Patton [handpainted]	Multicolored	Patt	E
4852	Lt.. Gen. Courtney Hodges [handpainted]	Multicolored	Gen	D
4951	Maj Gen. Wedemeyer [handpainted]	Multicolored	Gener	D
4968	Maj. Gen. Parker [handpainted]	Multicolored	Gener	D
5249	Merry Xmas [Santa Claus in helmet across "V" made of holly] [handpainted]	Multicolored	Holid	C
5278	Mitscher [handpainted]	Multicolored	Admir	D
5864	One is helping in / the war effort / the other [in quotes] etc. [handpainted]	Multicolored	Home	C
5935	Our British ally / Air Marshall Tedder [handpainted]	Multicolored	Ally	C
5990	Our French ally / Buy war bonds / Gen. DeGaulle [handpainted]	Multicolored	Ally	D
6213	Plant a / victory garden [handpainted]	Multicolored	Home	C
6433	Rear Adml Joseph J. Clark [handpainted]	Multicolored	Admir	D
6434	Rear Adml. Frederick C. Sherman [handpainted]	Multicolored	Admir	D
6923	Send him down / anytime! [in quotes] / Buy war bonds [handpainted]	Multicolored	Devil	C
6979	Seventh [7th] / war loan / Buy war bonds / Help plant etc. [handpainted]	Multicolored	Bonds	C
7663	The Nazi read only what / Goebbels wants them to [in quotes] etc. [handpainted]	Multicolored	Nazis	C
7706	The Red Bomber [in quotes] [handpainted]	Multicolored	USSR	C
7859	The world's "pain in the neck" / Buy war bonds [handpainted]	Black, red	Hitle	C
7880	Their one objective / V-J Day by etc. [Halsey, Nimitz, Spruance] [handpainted]	Multicolored	VJDay	C
7881	Their one objective / V-J Day by proclamation / in the Pacific [handpainted]	Multicolored	VJDay	C
7956	They both agree it's / the world's best Navy / Our next etc. [handpainted]	Multicolored	FDR	C
8394	Two worn out heels [in quotes] / Buy / war bonds [handpainted]	Black, tan	Axis	C
8477	U.S. Marine Corps / Gen. Alexander Vandegrift [handpainted]	Multicolored	USMC	C
9051	V ...- ["V' 55 mm tall] ["...-" across "V"] [handpainted] [envelope 9 1/2x4 1/8 in.]	Black, red	VforV	C
9330	V [Santa Claus in helmet across "V" made of holly] [handpainted]	Multicolored	Holid	C
9331	V [Santa Claus in helmet across red "V" with holly] [handpainted]	Multicolored	Holid	C
9433	Vice Adm. Marc A. Mitscher / Task Force 58 [handpainted]	Multicolored	Admir	C
9435	Vice Adml. John S. McCain [handpainted]	Multicolored	Admir	D
10055	We won't let the three heels / forget Dec. 7th, 1941 / Buy etc. [handpainted]	Multicolored	Bonds	C
10710	^^DeGaulle, Charles, facing right, Cross of Lorraine behind head [handpainted]	Multicolored	Ally	C

Figure 6. Hand painted patriotic covers by Arthur F. Knoll, Hamilton, Ohio. A, cachet 845. B, cachet 4335, cover postmarked one month after American landings in North Africa. C, cachet 8395, cover postmarked on second anniversary of Pearl Harbor. D, cachet 1250. E, cachet 5864. F, cachet 3202, postmarked on New Year's Day. G, cachet 1617. H, cachet 6979.

28 HAND PAINTED CACHETS BY ABRAM LEGALLEZ

NO.	CACHET TEXT	COLOR	TOPIC	$
319	Air power / to / V...- [handpainted label]	Black	Air	C
320	Air power / to / victory [handpainted label]	Multicolored	Flag+	C
744	Aug. 08, / Russia / 1945 / declares / war on / Japan [handpainted label]	Black, red	Event	C
1095	British / Yanks / Russians/ VE / Day [handpainted label]	Multicolored	VEDay	C
1749	Death / to / German / invaders [handpainted label]	Multicolored	USSR	C
2353	For / freedom / and peace [handpainted label]	Blue, red	ORN	C
2531	Fourth [4th] / war / loan / That / liberty ring etc. [handpainted label]	Multicolored	Bell	C
2679	From the halls of Montezuma / [etc.] / Semper Fidelis [handpainted label]	Black	USMC	C
4007	Jan. 25, / U.S. troops / arrive in / Ireland / 1942. [handpainted label]	Multicolored	Event	C
4026	Japan / strikes at / Hawaii / Dec. 7, 1941 / [etc.] / 3d. anniversary. [handpainted]	Blak, red	Anniv	C
4029	Japan / surrenders / to Allies / Aug 14 / 1945 etc. [handpainted label]	Black, yellow	VJDay	E
4746	Lidice will rise again [in quotes] / V pro Vitezstir etc. [handpainted label]	Blue, red	ORN	C
5082	Manila / taken / Jan. 2, 1942 / Singapore / taken etc. [handpainted label]	Black	Event	C
5853	One hundred fifty-fifth [155th] / anniversary / 1945 [handpainted label]	Multicolored	Coast	C
7361	That the govern- / ment of the people, by / the people [in quotes] etc. [handpainted]	Multicolored	Linc	C
7656	The nation mourns / 1882-1945 [handpainted label with photo of FDR]	Black	FDR	F
8481	U.S. Marines / Iwo Jima [handpainted]	Multicolored	USMC	C
8677	Unconditional / surrender [army, marines, navy symbols] [handpainted]	Multicolored	VEDay	E
9022	V ...- / for / freedom / of speech / religion / from etc. [handpainted label]	Multicolored	Flag	C
9149A	V / E / Day / Unconditional / Surrender [Eisenhower pictured] [handpainted label]	Multicolored	VEDay	E
9185A	V / J / Surrenders to Allies [inside " J"] / Day [handpainted label]	Multicolored	VJDay	E
9253	V / voor victorie / Invaded / but not / conquered [handpainted label 61x45 mm]	Multicolored	ORN	C
9254	V / voor victorie / Invaded / but not / conquered [handpainted label 69x53 mm]	Multicolored	ORN	C
9342	V for sejer / For / freedom / and peace [handpainted label]	Multicolored	ORN	C
9348	V pour la victoire / Occupied / but not / conquered [handpainted label]	Multicolored	ORN	C
9349	V Znamie Turjciestua / Occupied / but not / conquered [handpainted label]	Multicolored	ORN	C
9506	Victory / V za pobeda [handpainted label]	Multicolored	ORN	C
9962	We have / never / lost a / war [handpainted label]	Multicolored	EagSh	C

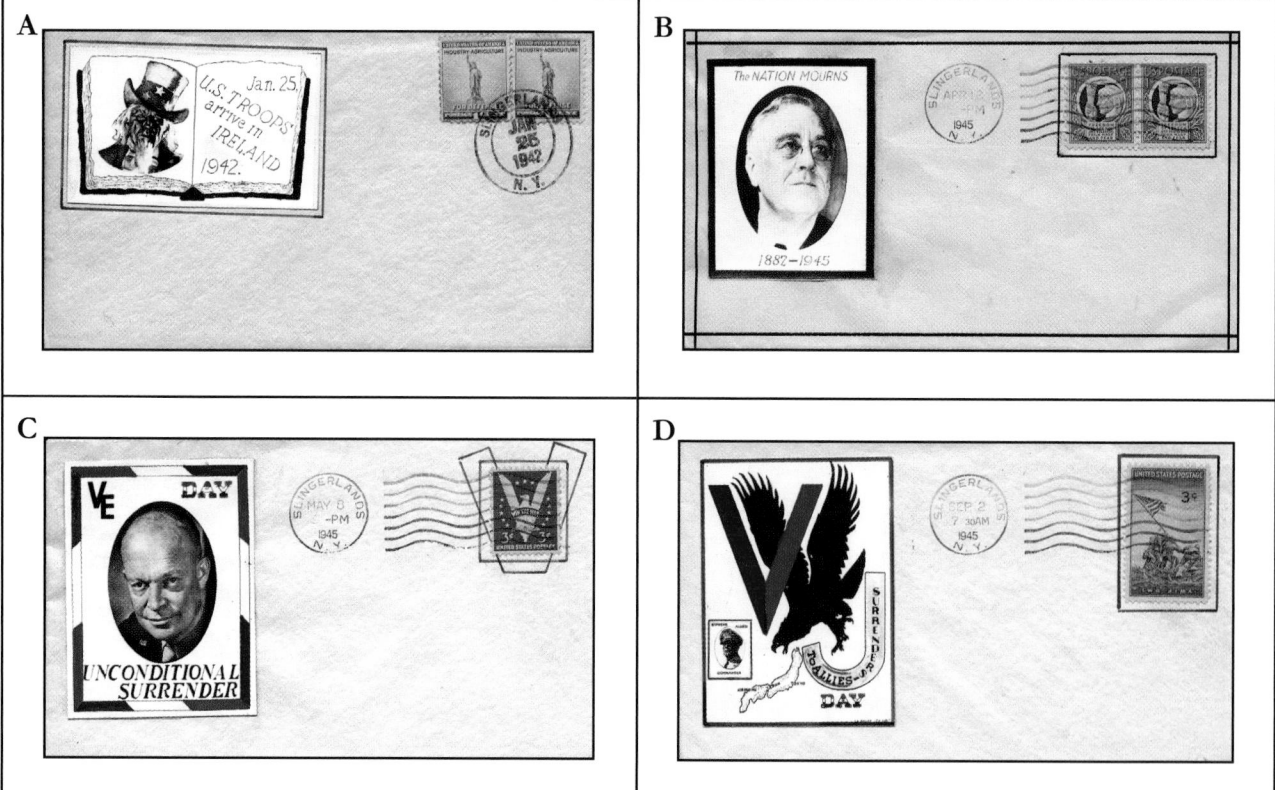

Figure7. Hand painted patriotic covers by Abram LeGallez, Slingerlands, New York. A, cachet 4007, postmarked on date of arrival of first U.S. troops in Great Britain (Northern Ireland) in 1942. B, cachet 7656, postmarked on date of President Roosevelt's death.. C, cachet 9149A, postmarked on VE Day. D, cachet 9185A postmarked on VJ Day.

23 HAND PAINTED CACHETS BY CORPORAL A.E. SHAFFER

NO.	CACHET TEXT	COLOR	TOPIC	$
1340	Capitulation [handpainted]	Multicolored	VEDay	D
1751	Dec. / 07 / 1941 -1943 / two years of war etc. [handpainted]	Black, red	Pearl	C
1758	Dec. 07, 1944 / three years / Italy / Germany / Japan [handpainted]	Blue, red	Pearl	C
1759	Dec. 07, 1944 / three years / now / Japan [handpainted]	Black, red	Pearl	C
1930	Don't be an / "armchair patriot" / Battles / were / never etc. [handpainted]	Black	Home	C
1931	Don't be an / "armchair patriot" [handpainted]	Black	Home	C
2165	Feb. 22, 1945 [handpainted]	Multicolored	Holid	C
2521	Four / freedoms / or / four / slaveries / choose [handpainted]	Blue, red	Unk	C
2843	Germany / Italy / Japan / 1945? [handpainted]	Multicolored	Axis	C
3529	I am an / American [handpainted]	Multicolored	Eagle	C
3775	In this sign we conquer [handpainted]	Blue, red	EagSh	C
3996	Jan 01 1944 / Crush / Germany / this / year [handpainted]	Black, red	Holid	C
6100	Paris / "Liberation" [handpainted]	Multicolored	Event	D
6819	Santa / Maria [in quotes] [handpainted]	Multicolored	Hist	C
7741	The soldier's dream [handpainted]	Multicolored	Home	C
9116	V / ...- [on red and blue star] [handpainted]	Multicolored	VforV	C
9278	V [below cross] [handpainted]	Multicolored	Relig	C
9455	Victory / 1944 [below 3 stars] [handpainted]	Multicolored	Home	C
9456	Victory / 1944 [below 5 stars] [handpainted]	Blue, red	Home	C
9619	Victory valentine [map of U.S.] [handpaintyed]	Multicolored	Map	C
9620	Victory valentine [with heart] [handpainted]	Multicolored	Home	C
10764	^^Eagle, head and neck in profile, outline, [90 mm high, 112 mm wide] [handpainted]	Black	Eagle	C
10905	^^Pumpkin, carved face [handpainted] [orange envelope]	Black, green	Holid	C

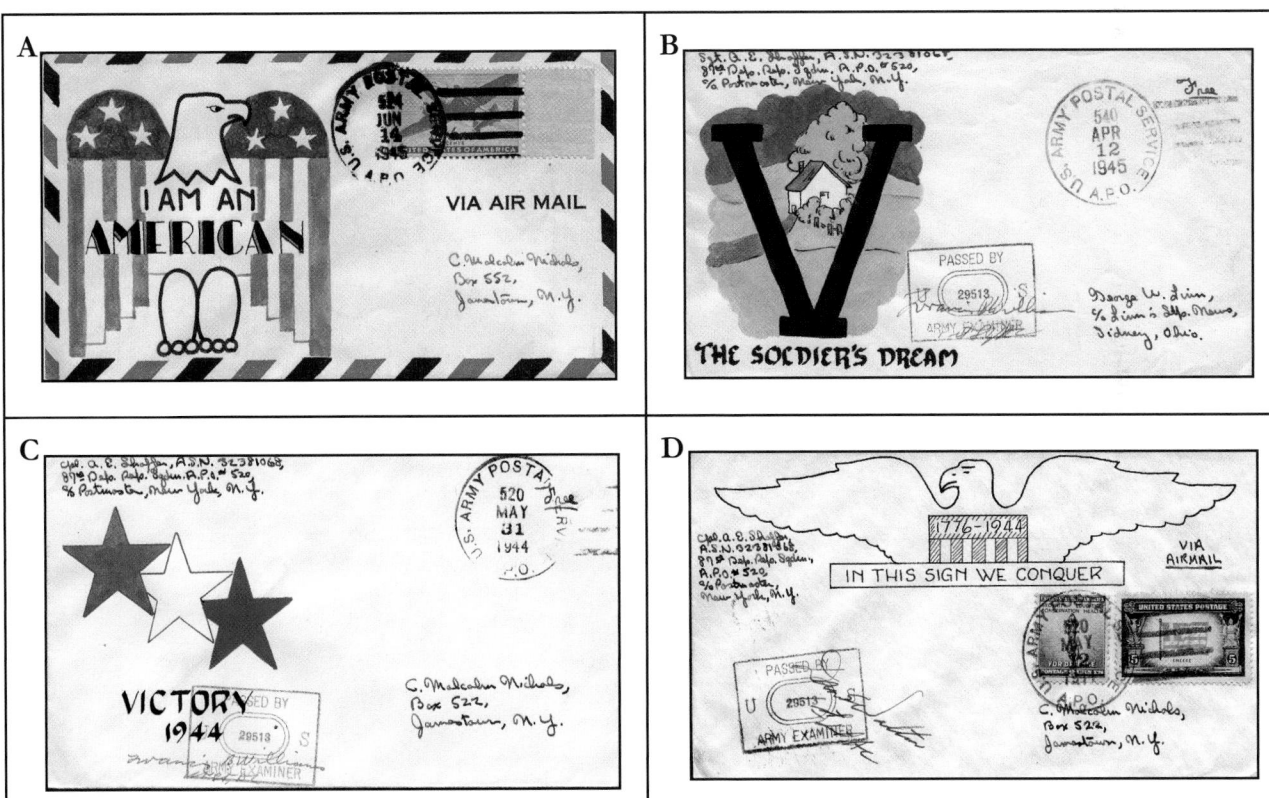

Figure 8. Hand painted patriotic covers by Cpl. A.E. Shaffer, U.S. Army. A, cachet 3529. B, cachet 7741. C, cachet 9455. D, cachet 3775.

832 HAND PAINTED CACHETS BY ALL OTHERS,
ARRANGED ALPHABETICALLY BY ARTIST

PUBLISHER	NO.	CACHET TEXT	COLOR	TOPIC	$
Albrecht	957	Benito the Bumn [sic] / who fed the Italians / more etc. [handpainted]	Unknown	Musso	B
Ander, HJ	10917	^^Sailor smiling, standing near palm, sun behind him [handpainted] [[APO 503, 1/45]	Multicolored	Navy	E
Babcock	4300	Keep freedom ringing / "throughout the world" [handpainted]	Multicolored	Bell	B
Babcock	4317	Keep it waving [in quotes] [handpainted]	Multicolored	Flag	C
Babcock	5772	On / to / victory / V [handpainted]	Multicolored	Air	B
Babcock	5836	One day nearer victory [handpainted]	Multicolored	Home	C
Babcock	7461	The Axis / on its last "leg" now [handpainted]	Multicolored	Map	B
Babcock	8322	Torch of / freedom [text vertical] / Keep it / burning [handpainted]	Multicolored	Torch	B
Babcock	8958	United we will win / Liberty for all [handpainted]	Multicolored	Globe	C
Barnes	10312	Win the war in / '44 / Buy war bonds [handpainted]	Multicolored	Bonds	C
Barwicki	178	A slip of the lip may sink a ship [handpainted]	Multicolored	Uboat	B
Barwicki	832	Back the / attack / Buy more / war bonds [handpainted]	Multicolored	Bonds	C
Barwicki	838	Back the attack / Buy war bonds [handpainted]	Blue, red	Bonds	B
Barwicki	1235	Buy United States war bonds / It's the American way [no picture] [handpainted]	Blue, red	Bonds	B
Barwicki	1258	Buy war bonds / Keep it up! [handpainted]	Multicolored	Air	D
Barwicki	1869	Dishonorable / Jap lost shirt [handpainted]	Multicolored	Japan	B
Barwicki	2263	First Fighter Command [no picture] [handpainted]	Multicolored	Unit	B
Barwicki	3016	God bless America [diagonal text between lines] [no picture] [handpainted]	Multicolored	Home	B
Barwicki	3807	Inseparably united / r U s S I A [handpainted]	Multicolored	Ally	B
Barwicki	3808	Inseparably united / RUSSIA ["U", "S", & "A" in last word are blue, rest is red] [handpainted]	Blue, red	Ally	B
Barwicki	4352	Keep them flying / Buy bonds / Let's go America / Keep them etc. [handpainted`]	Blue, red	Bonds	B
Barwicki	4354	Keep them flying [diagonal] [no picture] [handpainted]	Blue, red	Air	B
Barwicki	4565	Let's go America [diagonal] [no picture] [handpainted]	Blue, red	Home	B
Barwicki	4803	Long may it wave [handpainted]	Multicolored	Flag	C
Barwicki	5746	Okinawa / Japan / Dishonorable / Jap lose shirt [handpainted]	Multicolored	Japan	C
Barwicki	6175	Philippine / Islands [Japanese soldier shot out of a cannon] [handpainted]	Multicolored	Japan	C
BarwickCi	6569	Remember our boys over there / Give to the Red Cross [handpainted]	Red	RedCr	B
Barwicki	9641	Vinegar / Joe [handpainted]	Multicolored	Gener	B
Barwicki	10653	^^Airplane on ground, silhouetted against sky [handpainted]	Black	Air	C
Barwicki	10661	^^Airplane with twin tails [B-25 Mitchell] flying left [handpainted]	Black	Air	B
Barwicki	10668	^^Airplane, twin-bodied, fanciful, shooting at trucks and industrial plant on ground [handpainted]	Multicolored	Air	B
Barwicki	10671	^^Airplanes, 3, B-25 Mitchells, flying upward from USAAF star [handpainted]	Multicolored	Air	B
Barwicki	10673	^^Airplanes, 3, taking off from carrier, flying right [handpainted]	Blue, black	Air	C
Bates	10243	Who is short. [in quotes] [handpainted]	Multicolored	Axis	C
Batura	750	Aug. 14-1945- / -End of Second World War.- [no picture] [handpainted]	Blue	VJDay	D
Batura	2042	Emperor Hirohito issued / a "cease fire order" and etc. [handpainted]	Blue	VJDay	C
Batura	2861	Germany and Italy formally / advised the State Department etc. [handpainted]	Blue	Event	C
Batura	3720	In a new naval / policy as enunciated / by the Secretary of / the United etc. [handpainted]	Multicolored	Event	E
Batura	4037	Japan announced that she is ready / to surrender under etc. [handpainted] [no picture]	Blue	Event	C
Batura	4048	Japan surrendered / unconditionally / Sept. 2 - 1945 [handpainted, pen & ink]	Blue	VJDay	C
Batura	4049	Japan surrendered [in semi-circle] / Sep. 2 - 1945 [handpainted, pen & ink]	Blue	VJDay	C
Batura	4064	Japanes envoy extraordinary to Wash- / ington, Saburo Karusu etc. [typed + handpainted]	Black	Event	F
Batura	5055	Major General, Lewis E. Brereton / left on October 25, 1941 for etc. [handpainted]	Blue, red	Event	D
Batura	5133	Marshal Henri Philippe Petain / was convicted of treason etc. [no picture] [handpainted]	Black	Event	D
Batura	5785	On Sunday Dec. 7 - 1941 / Japan made etc. [UL] [handpainted] [12/7/41 machine cancel]	Blue, red	Event	H
Batura	6304	Pres. Truman / announces / Japan's acceptance / of etc. [no picture] [handpainted]	Black	VJDay	D
Batura	6316	President F.D. Roosevelt / signed / an appropriation measure / adding etc. [handpainted]	Multicolored	Event	E
Batura	6317	President Franklin D. Roosevelt / announced that he etc. [handpainted] [12/3/41]	Unknown	Event	E
Batura	6318	President Harry S. Truman / announced to the U.S. / that etc. [handpainted] [no picture]	Blue	Event	D
Batura	6322	President Truman / announced that hostilities / had ceased. etc. [handpainted] [no picture]	Blue	VJDay	D
Batura	6330	President Truman issued / a new surrender ultimatum / to etc. [handpainted] [no picture]	Blue	Event	C
Batura	6750	Saburo Kurusu, special / Japanese envoy / [etc.] / Nov. 15, 1941. [handpainted]	Black, gold	Event	E
Batura	7165	Speaker of the U.S. House of Representatives / Samuel Rayburn etc. [handpainted]	Black	Event	E
Batura	7477	The Big Four powers agreed / to accept Japan's surrender etc. [handpainted] [no picture]	Blue	Event	D
Batura	7482	The Big Three announced that / Germany will be stripped of etc. [handpainted] [no picture]	Blue	Event	D
Batura	7589	The House of Representatives by a vote / of 224 to 161 etc. [handpainted] [11/28/41]	Black	Event	E
Batura	7693	The President of the / United States of / America etc. [handpainted] [9/20/41]	Multicolored	Event	E
Batura	7736	The second / world war / is over [no picture] [handpainted]	Blue	VJDay	D
Batura	7804	The United States / made a formal declaration etc. [handpainted] [no picture] [12/8/41]	Blue	Event	E
Batura	7806	The United States and Mexico have / reached a friendly etc. [handpainted] [11/19/41]	Black	Event	D
Batura	8551	U.S. troops occupy Surinam, / (Dutch Guiana) Nov. 24, 1941. etc. [handpainted]	Unknown	Event	E
Bayliss	2246	First Day / Nimitz, W. Va. / post office / named in honor of / Admiral etc. [handpainted]	Multicolored	NimFD	C
Bickford	171	A Seabee's liberty dream. [handpainted]	Black	Navy	C
Buxton Mrs	474	American / and / proud of it [allover cachet] [handpainted]	Multicolored	Eagle	D
Buxton Mrs	3729	In defense of liberty [allover cachet] [handpainted]	Multicolored	Air	D

PUBLISHER	NO.	CACHET TEXT	COLOR	TOPIC	$
Buxton Mrs	4407	Land of the free / the U.S.A. [allover cachet] [handpainted]	Multicolored	Map	D
Buxton, D	3528	I am an / American [allover cachet] [handpainted]	Multicolored	Shiel	D
Buxton, D	8031	This America! / Worth a bond each payday? [handpainted] [blue envelope]	Blue, red	Bonds	B
Buxton, D	8575	U.S.A. [under eagle, shield, and 2 chevrons] [handpainted]	Multicolored	EagSh	B
Buxton, D.	322	Air service / U.S.A. [handpainted][envelope 5 3/8x3 3/8 in.]	Multicolored	Armed	B
Card	9788	War loan / 7th / Buy War Bonds / A salute to the Army [handpainted]	Blue, red	Bonds	C
Carpenter	8200	To our fighting / Irish heroes. [handpainted] [envelope 6 7/8x3 15/16 in.]	Multicolored	Home	C
Carter Mrs	6205	Plan now / 1945 / V-garden [handpainted]	Multicolored	Home	C
Conner	3965	It's the monotony that gets me! [handpainted]	Black	Army	B
Conner	10074	We'll be there [small circular logo with tiger head] [handpainted]	Multicolored	Unit	C
Conner	10075	We'll be there [unit insignia, 11th Fighter Squadron] [handpainted]	Multicolored	Unit	C
Cowdery	86	A friend / of yours? / Scentry box [handpainted]	Multicolored	Army	D
Cowdery	102	A handy / little gadget— [in quotes] [handpainted]	Multicolored	Army	D
Cowdery	351	All in / because of / our "all-out" / tactics [handpainted]	Multicolored	Army	D
Cowdery	417	Am I the lucky / one? See what / I got!! [handpainted]	Multicolored	Home	D
Cowdery	563	An' then / what did you / say? [handpainted]	Multicolored	Army	D
Cowdery	570	And I thought / Harry Koester's / bull etc. [burned top, edge] [handpainted]	Multicolored	Ordna	D
Cowdery	580	And then what did the Colonel say / when you told etc. [in quotes] [handpainted]	Multicolored	Army	D
Cowdery	593	Another / problem! [handpainted]	Multicolored	Army	D
Cowdery	809	Aw come on soldier, / just one tall etc. [in quotes] [burned edge] [handpainted]	Multicolored	Army	D
Cowdery	811	Aw! give us / a big smile / soldier - / it etc. [burned edge] [handpainted]	Multicolored	Army	D
Cowdery	997	Black / out! [handpainted]	Multicolored	Army	D
Cowdery	1130	But — / sir, have you noticed that / even the desert has etc. [handpainted]	Multicolored	Army	D
Cowdery	1131	But / "manyana" / never comes!! [handpainted]	Multicolored	Home	D
Cowdery	1746	Dear! dear! / and I thought / you were / one! etc. [handpainted]	Multicolored	Army	D
Cowdery	1838	Depends / on the / individual! [torn at right] [handpainted]	Multicolored	Holid	D
Cowdery	1842	Desert / Sunday [handpainted]	Multicolored	Army	D
Cowdery	1843	Desert waste! [handpainted] [torn envelope]	Multicolored	Army	D
Cowdery	1942	Don't ever / lose that grin / soldier! [burned top, right edges] [handpainted]	Multicolored	Army	D
Cowdery	1975	Don't worry / soldier; / everything / is etc. [burned left edge] [handpainted]	Multicolored	Army	D
Cowdery	1994	Duty and / the beast [in quotes] [burned top edge] [handpainted]	Multicolored	Ordna	D
Cowdery	2044	Empty! [handpainted] [stamp missing]	Multicolored	Army	D
Cowdery	2089	Even in / practice / maneuvers you men / make etc. [burned edge] [handpainted]	Multiucolored	Hitl	D
Cowdery	2110	Everything's / under control / when my soldier's / on the job. [handpainted]	Multicolored	Army	D
Cowdery	2281	Five [5] days / Mrs. Ray R. Cowdery / Long Prairie, Minn. [handpainted]	Multicolored	Home	D
Cowdery	2687	G.I. / army / bathtub! [handpainted]	Multicolored	Army	D
Cowdery	2870	Get a grip, / men - Cowdery's / at the wheel!! [handpainted] [stamp missing]	Multicolored	Army	D
Cowdery	3089	Good night / my love — [in quotes] [burned left edge] [handpainted]	Multicolored	Army	D
Cowdery	3094	Goody - / goody for me, / when (?) this day etc. [burned edge] [handpainted]	Multicolored	Army	D
Cowdery	3155	Gregory - where did you / learn to salute? [in quotes] [handpainted]	Multicolored	Army	D
Cowdery	3203	Hard to / satisfy - / but / all that I want is — [handpainted]	Multicolored	Home	D
Cowdery	3279	Hello darling! / Happy birthday. [handpainted]	Multicolored	Home	D
Cowdery	3332	Here's / how some of / our L.P. boys / look [torn at right] [handpainted]	Multicolored	Army	D
Cowdery	3361	He's still / "squawking" / but / not the etc. [torn at right] [handpainted]	Multicolored	Hitle	D
Cowdery	3363	Hey buddy / how do I get an / outfit etc. [burned top, torn right] [handpainted]	Multicolored	Army	D
Cowdery	3373	Hi! Yo'all in the Army / Merry Christmas! [handpainted]	Multicolored	Holid	D
Cowdery	3438	Honey it's only me / waitin' for you [in quotes] [burned edge] [handpainted]	Multicolored	Home	D
Cowdery	3476	Hot dogs!! / s-i-z-z / wow / ouch papa! [handpainted]	Multicolored	Army	D
Cowdery	3519	Hurry / soldier! / I'm as anxious / as you are! [handpainted]	Multicolored	Army	D
Cowdery	3553	I don't care / if it's 30 below— / or summertime! etc. [top burned] [handpainted]	Multicolored	Home	D
Cowdery	3560	I hear we may get a couple / of extra weeks etc. [burned edge] [handpainted]	Multicolored	Army	D
Cowdery	3587	I think / she's forgetting / me! Only 4 letters / today. [handpainted]	Multicolored	Army	D
Cowdery	3610	If "the pen / is mightier than / the sword" you / should have etc. [handpainted]	Multicolored	Home	D
Cowdery	3676	Im a / WOW! / ("write-often-wife") [handpainted]	Multicolored	Army	D
Cowdery	3677	I'm busy / waitin' for / somebody nice [in quotes] [handpainted]	Multicolored	Army	D
Cowdery	3695	I'm getting / tired so I can / sleep — [in quotes] [handpainted]	Multicolored	Home	D
Cowdery	3696	I'm getting tired so I can / sleep — [in quotes] [handpainted]	Multicolored	Army	D
Cowdery	3699	I'm lonesome for / you too - [burned top edge, torn right edge] [handpainted]	Multicolored	Home	D
Cowdery	3706	I'm so / glad if your / hand is O.K. again! [burned left edge] [handpainted]	Multicolored	Home	D
Cowdery	3882	It can't be so terribly far, soldier — / while etc. [burned edge] [handpainted]	Multicoilored	Army	D
Cowdery	3902	It will / be a red letter / day when etc. [torn right edge] [handpainted]	Multicolored	Army	D
Cowdery	3954	It's me / again hon! [burned left edge] [handpainted]	Multicolored	Army	D
Cowdery	3955	It's men / like you who / will give him etc. [burned top edge] [handpainted]	Multicolored	Hitle	D
Cowdery	3957	It's nice to know / you're always / there. [handpainted]	Multicolored	Army	D
Cowdery	3964	It's the / waiting that's / maddening!! [handpainted]	Multicolored	Army	D
Cowdery	3979	I've gotta get / time off soon / or / else [UR] [burned edge] [handpainted]	Multicolored	Army	D
Cowdery	4177	Just wait!! [handpainted]	Multicolored	Army	D
Cowdery	4792	Lonesome. [handpainted]	Multicolored	Home	D
Cowdery	4817	Lookin' for a / cool, shady spot! [handpainted]	Multicolored	Army	D
Cowdery	5076	Making ends meet / after Xmas! [handpainted]	Multicolored	Army	D

PUBLISHER	NO.	CACHET TEXT	COLOR	TOPIC	$
Cowdery	5077	Mamas' [sic] little helper. [handpainted]	Multicolored	Army	D
Cowdery	5183	Me / with those / "no new letter, / blues" etc. [burned edge] [handpainted]	Multicolored	Home	D
Cowdery	5331	My / "male" makes / good backing! — / and plenty of it. [handpainted]	Multicolored	Army	D
Cowdery	5332	My / chin's / still up / so — / it couldn't / be me!! [handpainted]	Multicolored	Home	D
Cowdery	5334	My / soldier [burned left edge] [handpainted]	Multicolored	Army	D
Cowdery	5543	No one will / get yours. [envelope 4 5/8x3 7/8 in.] [handpainted]	Multicolored	Home	D
Cowdery	5686	Oh! How I / hate to get up in / the morning! [handpainted]	Multicolored	Army	D
Cowdery	5769	On / July / 4th / we salute [handpainted]	Multicolored	Holid	D
Cowdery	6131	Pay call! [handpainted]	Multicolored	Army	D
Cowdery	6239	Plenty of / grit! [handpainted]	Multicolored	Army	D
Cowdery	6274	Poor you! [handpainted]	Multicolored	Army	D
Cowdery	6784	Salute to / you / Pvt. Ray! [burned left, torn right edge] [handpainted]	Multicolored	Army	D
Cowdery	7045	Silence / Don't you love / me any more ? / ? / ? [burned edge] [handpainted]	Multicolored	Army	D
Cowdery	7138	Someday / "they'll" let me / mail it! / ??? / I hope! [burned left edge] [handpainted]	Multicolored	Army	D
Cowdery	7155	Sorry / you're still being / held "incommunicado" [burned edges] [handpainted]	Multicolored	Army	D
Cowdery	7232	Still - / the laugh's on / me - 'cause I don't / know nothin'!! [handpainted]	Multicolored	Home	D
Cowdery	7302	Tank I go home! [handpainted] [torn stamp]	Multicolored	Ordna	D
Cowdery	7313	Tell 'em you're / gonna write [handpainted]	Multicolored	Home	D
Cowdery	7329	Tendin' / strictly to / my / knittin' [handpainted]	Multicolored	Home	D
Cowdery	7353	That first night / on / the desert! [handpainted]	Multicolored	Army	D
Cowdery	7369	That's my letter / buddy! [handpainted]	Multicolored	Army	D
Cowdery	7395	The / dream still / lives! [burned left edge] [handpainted]	Multicolored	Home	D
Cowdery	7398	The / hundreth / time! [burned top left, torn right edge] [handpainted]	Multicolored	Home	D
Cowdery	7415	The / post I'm / tied to! [handpainted] [envelope 5 11/16x3 13/16 in.]	Multicolored	Home	D
Cowdery	7427	The 1943 Prince Charming / has / new use for his / charms! [handpainted]	Multicolored	Army	D
Cowdery	7517	The end of / a swell day [burned left edge] [handpainted]	Multicolored	Army	D
Cowdery	7829	The ups and downs of / army life !! [handpainted]	Multicolored	Army	D
Cowdery	7906	There'll / be two tomorrow / Pvt. Ray! [handpainted]	Multicolored	Army	D
Cowdery	7922	There's always / somethin' nice / about a soldier! [handpainted] [stamp missing]	Multicolored	Army	D
Cowdery	7926	There's only / one soldier / like my / Pvt. [burned left edge] [handpainted]	Multicolored	Army	D
Cowdery	7929	There's one / thing about this / army I'm crazy about! [handpainted]	Multicolored	Home	D
Cowdery	8228	Today, as / always ——— / I / love / you [handpainted]	Multicolored	Home	D
Cowdery	8393	Two outstanding things in my life - etc. [burned right edge] [handpainted]	Multicolored	Home	D
Cowdery	9316	V [height of envelope] [center of envelope] [handpainted] [torn envelope face]	Multicolored	VforV	D
Cowdery	9711	Waitin' for / a green-eyed / soldier. [handpainted] [envelope 4 5/8x3 7/8 in.]	Multicolored	Army	D
Cowdery	9712	Waitin' for / you- soldier! [burned left edge] [handpainted]	Multicolored	Home	D
Cowdery	9784	War games - / Learning to shoot [stamp missing] [handpainted]	Multicolored	Army	D
Cowdery	9785	War games - / nightly gas attack!! [torn at right] [stamp missing] [handpainted]	Multicolored	Army	D
Cowdery	10106	We're as doggone / proud of our / soldier! [burned left edge] [handpainted]	Multicolored	Dog	D
Cowdery	10171	When dreams / are so nice / I'm / just too tired / to think etc. [handpainted]	Multicolored	Home	D
Cowdery	10236	Who caused a / "Feuhrer" / in a hurry? etc. [burned left edge] [handpainted]	Multicolored	Axis	D
Cowdery	10248	Whoopee! Running water / and showers! [handpainted]	Multicolored	Army	D
Cowdery	10342	Wish I / could come / with it, Pvt. Ray! [handpainted]	Multicolored	Home	D
Cowdery	10343	Wish I could / bring it! [stamp missing] [handpainted]	Multicolored	Home	D
Cowdery	10363	With you! [stamp missing] [torn at right] [handpainted]	Multicolored	Home	D
Cowdery	10559	You lick 'em there, soldier / and if it's only with letters etc. [handpainted]	Multicolored	Home	D
Cowdery	10560	You never know what / to expect from this gang! / "Reconnaissance" [handpainted]	Multicolored	Army	D
Cowdery	10563	You really put / "yourself" / into your letters [handpainted]	Multicolored	Army	D
Cowdery	10626	You've / really got / something / there soldier! [handpainted]	Multicolored	Army	D
Cowdery	10697	^^Bird with mistletoe [handpainted]	Multicolored	Holid	D
Cowdery	10898	^^Palm trees against sky [to Pvt. Ray R. Cowdery] [handpainted] [stamp missing]	Multicolored	Army	D
Cowdery	10923	^^Sandman in sky sprinkling sand on army tents below [handpainted] [torn stamp]	Multicolored	Army	D
Cowdery	10948	^^Soldier (Pvt. Ray R. Cowdery) running toward Christmas tree [handpainted]	Multicolored	Army	D
Cowdery	10949	^^Soldier (Pvt. Ray R. Cowdery) sitting on G.I. soap box [handpainted]	Multicolored	Army	D
Cowdery	11009	^^Statue of Liberty in tall oval, yellow flame from torch, yellow stars [handpainted]	Multicolored	Liber	D
Cowdery	11057	^^Woman holding letter and envelope against her cheek [handpainted]	Multicolored	Home	D
Cozart	7220	Station Force ABD Camp Thomas / Davisville, Rhode Island [4 small cachets] [handpainted]	Aqua	Armed	A
Dannells	1676	Count off! [handpainted]	Multicolored	Army	C
Dannells	2027	Eighteenth [XVIII] Corps [under insignia] [handpainted]	Black, blue	Unit	B
Dannells	2033	Eleventh [XI] Corps. [under insignia] [handpainted]	Multicolored	Unit	B
Dannells	2124	Eyes right! [soldier, cap flying off, looking at passing woman] [handpainted]	Multicolored	Army	C
Dannells	2177	Fifth [5th] Div. [below red diamond shoulder sleeve insignia] [handpainted]	Black, red	Unit	B
Dannells	2180	Fifth [5th] war loan drive / "Make it hot for the Japa-Nazi" [handpainted]	Multicolored	Bonds	C
Dannells	2518	Forty-sixth [46th] School Squadron [below insignia] [handpainted]	Multicolored	Unit	B
Dannells	2535	Fourth [4th] Service / Command [under insignia] [handpainted]	Black, blue	Unit	B
Dannells	4943	Mail [soldier leaning on mailbox, dog sitting nearby] [handpainted]	Multicolored	Dog	B
Dannells	5302	MP [on MP's armband]/ Trash [on trash can] [handpainted]	Multicolored	Army	C
Dannells	5521	Ninety-eighth [98th] Div. [under insignia] [handpainted]	Multicolored	Unit	B
Dannells	5522	Ninety-first [91st] Div [under insignia] [handpainted]	Black, green	Unit	B
Dannells	5525	Ninth [IX] Corps. [under insignia] [handpainted]	Multicolored	Unit	B

PUBLISHER	NO.	CACHET TEXT	COLOR	TOPIC	$
Dannells	5854	One hundred fourth [104th] Div. [under insignia] [handpainted]	Multicolored	Unit	B
Dannells	6110	Pass [in hands of whistling soldier] [handpainted]	Multicolored	Army	
Dannells	6893	Second Army [manuscript lettering under numeral insignia] [handpainted]	Black, red	Unit	B
Dannells	6894	Second Army [typed under numeral insignia] [handpainted]	Black, red	Unit	B
Dannells	6975	Seventh [7th.] [under insignia] [handpainted]	Black, red	Unit	B
Dannells	6985	Seventy-second [72nd] Bombardmet [sic] Squadron [under insignia] [handpainted]	Black	Unit	B
Dannells	6986	Seventy-sixth Div. [under insignia] [handpainted]	Multicolored	Unit	B
Dannells	7074	Sixty-sixth [66th] Calvary [sic] Division [under insignia] [handpainted]	Multicolored	Unit	B
Dannells	7120	Soap [on box] [soldier sitting on box, peeling potatoes] [handpainted]	Multicolored	Army	C
Dannells	7121	Soap [soldier sitting on soap box, writing letter to sweetheart] [handpainted]	Multicolored	Army	C
Dannells	8016	Third [3rd] Div. [under insignia] [handpainted]	Black, blue	Unit	B
Dannells	8017	Third [III] Corps [under insignia] [handpainted]	Black, blue	Unit	B
Dannells	8024	Thirty-second [32nd] Div. [under insignia] [handpainted]	Black, red	Unit	B
Dannells	8025	Thirty-seventh [37th] Div. [under insignia] [handpainted]	Black, red	Unit	B
Dannells	8209	To the rear - march! [in quotes] [handpainted]	Multicolored	Army	C
Dannells	8344	Trash [MP looking for soldier hiding in trash can] [handpainted]	Multicolored	Army	C
Dannells	8368	Twenty-eighth [28th] Div. [under insignia] [handpainted]	Black, red	Unit	B
Dannells	8376	Twenty-ninth [29th] Div. [under insignia] [handpainted]	Black, blue	Unit	B
Dannells	8377	Twenty-second [XXII] Corps [under insignia] [handpainted]	Black, blue	Unit	B
Dannells	8378	Twenty-sixth [26th.] [under insignia] [handpainted]	Multicolored	Unit	B
Dannells	8382	Two [2] [numeral insignia of 2nd Army] [handp]	Black, red	Unit	B
Dannells	9530	Victory [diagonal across shield] [eagle standing on shield] [handpainted]	Multicolored	EagSh	C
Dannells	9545	Victory [on shield, diagonally, shield in claws of eagle] [handpainted]	Multicolored	EagSh	C
Dannells	9685	V-J Day! [no picture] [postmarked 9/1/45] [handpainted]	Multicolored	VJDay	C
Dannells	10724	^^Eagle clutching flag in talons [handpainted]	Multicolored	EagFl	B
Dannells	10743	^^Eagle standing on flag, looking bellicose, clouds in background [handpainted]	Multicolored	EagFl	C
Dannells	10835	^^Head of soldier looking up toward left [handpainted]	Multicolored	Army	B
Dannells	10929	^^Sergeant yelling at soldier who has hat in hand [handpainted]	Multicolored	Army	C
Dannells	10952	^^Soldier admiring a woman sitting on ground [handpainted]	Multicolored	Army	C
Dannells	10955	^^Soldier in fatigues, leaning on mop, daydreaming of a woman [handpainted]	Multicolored	Army	C
Dannells	10956	^^Soldier kissing woman, head and shoulders view [handpainted]	Multicolored	Army	C
Dannells	10962	^^Soldier reading love letter, head turned toward viewer, dog behind him [handpainted]	Multicolored	Army	C
Dannells	10963	^^Soldier running left, holding pie, cleaver flying toward head [handpainted]	Multicolored	Army	C
Dannells	10967	^^Soldier sleeping in tent, snoring, feet sticking out toward viewer [handpainted]	Multicolored	Army	C
Dannells	10969	^^Soldier smiling, standing with right thumb up, left hand open [handpainted]	Multicolored	Army	C
Dannells	10972	^^Soldier standing with letter in hands, 2 hearts indicating love [handpainted]	Multicolored	Army	C
Dannells	10973	^^Soldier walking with money in hand, hidden soldier ready to attack him [handpainted]	Multicolored	Army	C
Dannells	10974	^^Soldier with axe in left hand eyeing fallen tree that's crushed his tent [handpainted]	Multicolored	Army	C
Dannells	10976	^^Soldier with full pack, helmet, and rifle, sweaty and tired [handpainted]	Multicolored	Army	C
Dannells	10979	^^Soldier with helmet and rifle, running from a dog chasing him [handpainted]	Multicolored	Army	C
Dannells	10987	^^Soldier, driving Jeep, waving hat in right hand [handpainted]	Multicolored	Army	C
Dannells	10988	^^Soldier, hat flying off head, running toward midair envelope [handpainted]	Multicolored	Army	C
Dannells	10991	^^Soldier, standing, looking at picture of woman in left hand [handpainted]	Multicolored	Army	C
Dannells	11045	^^WAC head and shoulders in profile [handpainted]	Multicolor	WAC	C
Davis, D	1765	Dec. 7th. / 1941 1943 / Two / years / of war / "Remember Pearl Harbor" [handp]	Black	Pearl	C
Davis, D	6220	Please -- / write often [handpainted]	Multicolored	Home	C
Davis, D	7378	The "missing" link / (moved?) [handpainted]	Multicolored	Hitle	B
Davis, D	9394	VE / -Day- [blue "VE" 73 mm high] [handpainted]	Blue, red	VEDay	B
Davis, M	199	A woman's work is from / sun up to sun down. / A sailor's etc. [handpainted]	Multicolored	Navy	B
Doemick	10172	When heel meets "heel". [in quotes] / United / Nations / Hitler [handpainted]	Unknown	UncAx	C
Donaldson	772	August 14, 1945 / Japan surrenders [ink on Butzen winged victory cachet] [hp]	Blue, red	VJDay	B
Dye	11048	^^Warship, "US" on prow; hills+cloud in background [LCI(L)Gp33, 5/8/45] [handp]	Black	VEDay	C
First Day	3719	In a new Naval / policy as / [etc.] / waters adjacent to Iceland. [handpainted]	Multicolored	Uncle	G
Gatens	1052	Bong [handpainted]	Multicolored	Japan	C
Gatens	5692	Oh, how I miss / you tonight [handpainted]	Multicolored	Hitle	C
Gawne	4653	Lettuce / win the war [handpainted]	Black	Home	B
Gielarow	3295	Help drown the rats / Buy bonds and stamps [handpainted]	Multicolored	Axis	C
Glase	9144	V / Day [in shield below eagle] [handpainted]	Multicolored	VJDay	C
Glase	9146	V / Day [on diagonal stripes in shield below eagle] [handpainted]	Multicolored	VJDay	C
Glase	9147	V / Day [on vertical stripes in shield below eagle] [handpainted]	Multicolored	VJDay	C
Glase	9184	V / J / Day [in shield below eagle] [handpainted]	Multicolored	VJDay	C
Glase	9185	V / J / Day [on vertical stripes in shield below eagle] [handpainted]	Multicolored	VJDay	C
Graves	310	Ah ha / Quiet, censor [ink] [handpainted]	Black, red	Home	C
Graves	7325	Ten thousand [10,000] mil [sic] / to Buster [ink] [handpainted]	Multicolored	USMC	C
Graves	7326	Ten thousand [10,000] miles / to / Fremont [civilian with baggage] [ink] [handpainted]	Black	USMC	C
Graves	7327	Ten thousand [10,000] miles / to / Fremont [Marine PFC with baggage] [ink] [handp]	Black	USMC	C
Graves	7328	Ten thousand [10,000] miles / to Freemont [sic] [airplane pulling marine] [ink] [hp]	Multicolored	Air	C
Graves	8323	Toro [in quotes] Jr. [under baby with red bow in hair] [ink] [handpainted]	Black, red	Home	C
Graves	8992	USMC [on blanket of marine daydreaming of red-haired woman] [ink] [handpainted]	Black, red	USMC	C
Griffith	2086	European bombings / Aleutians / The south Pacific etc. [hp] [text typed]	Multicolored	Armed	B

PUBLISHER	NO.	CACHET TEXT	COLOR	TOPIC	$
Griffith	3830	Invasion / strikes / Jun 6 - 1944 [handpainted]	Black, red	DDay	D
Griffith	3911	Italian surrender / today! / Sept. 8, 1943 [handpainted]	Aqua, pink	Event	B
Griffith	6774	Saipan / Aleutians / Casablanca / Rabaul / [etc.] / shall / not have / died in vain. [hp]	Multicolored	Battl	B
Griffith	9790	War loan / VI / Buy bonds and make it / VIctory [hp] [1st day postmark 11/20/44]	Multicolored	Bonds	C
Hadley	824	B-29's / bomb / Tokyo [handpainted]	Black	Japan	B
Hadley	1673	Could I interest / you in a nice line of / tombstones? [allover] [handpainted]	Multicolored	Hitle	D
Hadley	1870	Dishonorable Jap lose shirt [in quotes] [handpainted]	Multicolored	Japan	D
Hadley	2885	GI Joe / Sacred German soil [allover cachet] [handpainted]	Multicolored	Army	D
Hadley	3313	Help to / protect / their future [handpainted]	Multicolored	Home	C
Hadley	3821	Invasion / Berlin / April / 1945 [allover cachet] [handpainted]	Multicolored	Hitle	F
Hadley	5485	Nineteen forty-five [1945] / war fund [handpainted]	Multicolored	RedCr	B
Hadley	6085	Pacific war chart / Unconditional / —surrender / August-14- etc. [handpainted]	Black	Japan	D
Hadley	7373	That's what this war is being fought for... / all us little etc. [handpainted]	Multicolored	Women	C
Hadley	8388	Two down and one to go / Wanted / dead or / alive / Target-Tokio [handpainted]	Multicolored	UncJa	C
Hadley	9697	Von Runstedt's return [in quotes] [handpainted]	Multicolored	Gener	C
Hadley	10518	Yippee! A six hour pass and / there's my etc. [cut-&-pasted cartoon + handpainted]	Multicolored	Army	B
Hannay	9873	We / will / win ["We" red, 'Win" blue] [handpainted] [no picture]	Multicolored	Home	B
Hannay	10369	Work / for / victory ["Work" red, "Victory" blue] [handpainted] [no picture]	Multicolored	Home	B
Hines	2213	Finished / Germany surrenders to the Allies. / May 8th 1945. [handpainted] [pen & ink]	Black	VEDay	D
Holton	9662	V-J Day — / Japan surrender / unconditionally [+ pasted picture] [handpainted]	Red	VJDay	B
Howe	8237	Together to victory [in quotes] [handpainted]	Blue	Uncle	B
Jarrett	6113	Paste the paperhanger - / with waste paper! [handpainted]	Black	Hitle	B
Kirchhofer	4690	Liberty / Church / School [handpainted]	Black	Hitle	C
Klondike	311	Aid our victory - / buy more bonds. [handpainted]	Black	Bonds	C
Klondike	312	Aid the victory— / buy more bonds [handpainted]	Violet	Bonds	B
Klondike	333	Albania will be free again! [handpainted]	Green	ORN	B
Klondike	418	America - England! / Ready / to / strike / at / Europe [handpainted]	Brown	Eagle	B
Klondike	1223	Buy more bonds! [handpainted] [envelope 7 1/2x4 in.]	Brown, green	EagV	B
Klondike	2390	For freedom [vertical text] [handpainted]	Blue	Navy	C
Klondike	3220	Have you / bought your / extra bond / yet? [handpainted]	Red	Bonds	C
Klondike	4530	Lets [sic] make / 194V / our victory year! [handpainted]	Black, blue	VforV	C
Klondike	5486	Nineteen forty-five [194V] [within outline of soldier's head and helmet] [handpainted]	Black	Army	B
Klondike	7003	Sharpen the eagles claws! / Buy plenty of war bonds! [handpainted]	Black	Eagle	C
Klondike	7390	The / America's -- / Gaurdian! [sic] [handpainted]	Black	Globe	C
Klondike	7454	The America's Guardian! [handpainted]	Black	Globe	C
Klondike	7513	The Eagle readies his / brood for Tokyo! [eagle + 5 planes] [handpainted]	Brown	Eagle	C
Klondike	9151	V / E / Germany surrenders! [handpainted]	Multicolored	VEDay	C
Klondike	9350	V...- [two warships, two planes] [handpainted]	Blue	Navy	C
Klondike	9560	Victory ahead - / Guam! Saipan! / Italy! Normandy! / Southern etc. [handpainted]	Blue	Bonds	C
Klondike	9625	Victory! / Our part in the fight for right. [handpainted]	Red	Home	B
Klondike	10011	We see you're right / behind us, folks! / 4th war / loan etc. [handpainted]	Red	Armed	C
Klondike	10512	Yes, / its his / war. / But its / your war / too. [handpainted]	Multicolored	Army	B
Krakora	423	America / land / of the / free [handpainted]	Multicolored	Eagle	C
Krakora	1177	Buy bonds / and set / the / Rising Sun [handpainted]	Multicolored	Japan	B
Krakora	2989	God bless / America [handpainted]	Blue, red	EagSh	C
Krakora	2990	God bless / America [handpainted] [eagle sitting above text]	Blue, red	Eagle	A
Krakora	3530	I am an / American [handpainted]	Blue, red	Shiel	B
Krakora	3767	In service [handpainted]	Blue, red	Home	B
Krakora	4408	Land of the free / U.S.A. [handpainted]	Blue, red	Home	B
Krakora	4701	Liberty / long may it ring [handpainted]	Blue, red	Bell	B
Krakora	4711	Liberty [handpainted]	Blue, red	EagSh	C
Krakora	5749	Old / Glory [handpainted]	Blue, red	Flag	C
Krakora	5994	Our hero / Geen MacArthur [handpainted]	Blue, red	Mac	B
Krakora	6358	Proud / to be an / American [two shields above text] [handpainted]	Blue, red	Shiel	A
Krakora	6425	Ready [all-over cachet] [handpainted]	Blue, red	UncEa	C
Krakora	6516	Remember / Pearl / Harbor [text above picture][handpainted]	Blue, red	Pearl	B
Krakora	7284	Symbol / of / freedom [handpainted]	Blue, red	Liber	C
Krakora	7285	Symbol / of / liberty [Statue of Liberty in front of 5-pointed star] [handpainted]	Blue, red	Liber	B
Krakora	7795	The U.S.A. / Land of the Free [all-over cachet] [handpainted]	Blue, red	Map	B
Krakora	8565	U.S.A. / Wings over America [handpainted]	Blue, red	Air	C
Krakora	8578	U.S.A. [under star, wing, and propellor] [handpainted]	Blue	Armed	A
Krakora	9017	V [upper 2/3 of "V" starts at lower edge] [torch and plane] [handpainted]	Blue, red	VforV	C
Krakora	10073	We'll / show / 'em! [handpainted]	Blue, red	Ordna	B
Krakora	11005	^^Statue of Liberty [upper portion of statue] [handpainted]	Multicolored	Liber	C
Larocque	6701	Roosevelt slept here / [etc.] / Le Chateau / Frontenac in etc. [handpainted]	Multicolored	FDR	D
Lemponen	8162	Time to start / to work / for/ victory [handpainted]	Blue, red	Home	B
Linto	3194	Happy / Thanksgiving [handpainted]	Multicolored	Holid	C
Long	996	Black / market [handpainted]	Multicolored	Home	C
Long	3065	Goering / Ash can [handpainted]	Multicolored	Nazis	C
Long	5430	Nazi werewolves [handpainted]	Multicolored	Hitle	C

PUBLISHER	NO.	CACHET TEXT	COLOR	TOPIC	$
Long	6173	Perpetual / motion [handpainted]	Multicolored	Japan	C
Long	6690	Rome / + / Berlin / + / Tokyo = [handpainted]	Multicolored	Japan	C
Long	8330	Total disaster / Japan / total war [handpainted]	Multicolored	Japan	C
Long	8623	Uncle / Surrender terms [handpainted]	Multicolor	Japan	D
Mack	6065	Out of focus / Greetings / U.S.A. / U.S.A. [handpainted]	Black	Japan	D
Martin	1022	Boil them in oil / save waste fats! [handpainted]	Multicolored	Axis	C
Martin	1216	Buy more bonds - / invest in his future! [handpainted]	Multicolored	Home	C
Martin	1241	Buy war bonds - / put one away for a rainy day - [handpainted]	Black	Dog	B
Martin	1278	Buy war bonds! / Have something to fall back on - [handpainted]	Blue, red	Home	C
Martin	3196	Happy Eastertide / Rose are red - violets are blue - etc. [handpainted]	Multicolored	Holid	B
Martin	3499	How doth the little busy B-29 / improve each shining hour etc. [handpainted]	Multicolored	Japan	B
Martin	3591	I took the / seat of a / [etc.] / I kept / a mother / from etc. [handpainted]	Black	Home	C
Martin	3659	If you're going to / carry tales and / chatter too - the etc. [handpainted]	Multicolored	Home	B
Martin	3702	I'm not buying / war bonds - / because I'm / a pumpkinhead! [handpainted]	Multicolored	Holid	C
Martin	4376	Kitchen help wanted! [handpainted]	Multicolored	Home	C
Martin	5069	Make much more / Keep on producing — [handpainted]	Blue, red	Home	B
Martin	7579	The guy who paid for my rifle - / took it back ! / Buy war bonds— etc. [handpainted]	Black	Army	C
Martin	7890	There are no blue notes in the song / of these birds so etc. [handpainted]	Multicolored	Axis	C
Martin	8078	This is no / bum steer! / It will / be over / quicker / if etc. [handpainted]	Multicolored	Bonds	B
Martin	8114	This slap-happy / Jappy - / took a Marine / for a sappy - etc. [handpainted]	Black	Japan	C
Martin	10063	Wear / it / out / Use / it / up / Make / it do / or do without etc. [handpainted]	Black, green	Home	B
Martin	10345	Witch'll / it be? / Bonds? / or bondage? [handpainted]	Black	Holid	C
Maul	88	A gallant service / WAC [handpainted]	Multicolored	WAC	C
Maul	965	Berlin falls / -Marshal-Zhukov- / planned and executed the etc. [handpainted]	Multicolored	Ally	C
Maul	1760	Dec. 07th 1944 / Third anniversary / Pearl etc. [handpainted below other cachet]	Black	Pearl	C
Maul	6161	Pearl Harbor / Dec. / 7, / 1941 / Third anniversary [handpainted]	Multicolored	Pearl	C
Maul	7418	The / Sad / Sack / G.I. Joe - experience? [handpainted]	Multicolored	Army	C
Maul	10493	Yanks are 50 miles / past the Rhine. / "Ach! Vot a war" / Allies [handpainted]	Multicolored	Hitle	C
McBarrar	7154	Sooo...solly pleese [handpainted]	Multicolored	Japan	C
McKelvey	9575	Victory in / Europe [battleground, olive branch] [handpainted] [2 envelope sizes]	Multicolored	VEDay	C
McKelvey	9576	Victory in / Europe [homeland, planes, olive branch] [handpainted]	Multicolored	VEDay	C
McLaughlin	2882	Getting / there / slow / but / sure! [top center] [handpainted] [APO use]	Blue, tan	Army	C
Meyers	5064	Make him / walk the / plank! / 5th war loan [handpainted]	Multicolored	Japan	C
Meylan	1089	Bringing home / the bacon [in quotes] [handpainted]	Multicolored	USSR	C
Miller	2230	First aid [handpainted]	Multicolored	Army	B
Mitchell	461	America is awake [handpainted]	Multicolored	Antiq	B
Monty	6719	Russan [sic] brake [sic] / pact with / Japan [handpainted]	Multicolored	Japan	C
Muzzy	4078	Jap-O-Lantern [handpainted]	black	Holid	C
Muzzy	9544	Victory [on rag flying from bayonet through German helmet] [handpainted]	Black	VforV	B
Muzzy	10142	What do you / mean / uou / won't / buy / bonds [handpainted]	Black	Bonds	B
Muzzy+Nich	5508	Nineteen forty-four [1944] war fund / Get busy- scratch etc. [handpainted]	Red	RedCr	C
Myers	864	Back the attack! Buy bonds! [vertical text] [handpainted]	Multicolored	Map	C
Myers	970	Best seller [in quotes] / 1944 / revised / edition etc. [handpainted]	Unknown	Japan	B
Myers	1139	Buy / bonds/ and beat / the Axis [handpainted]	Multicolored	Bonds	B
Myers	1168	Buy an extra bond! / My dads [sic] across the pond. etc. [handpainted]	Multicolored	Bonds	B
Myers	1242	Buy war bonds - / put one away for a rainy day - [handpainted]	Multicolored	Bonds	B
Myers	1280	Buy war bonds! have something to fall back on - [handpainted]	Multicolored	Bonds	B
Myers	1375	Chicken? / egg? / I don't know! / war bonds / come first with me. [handpainted]	Multicolored	Chick	B
Myers	1864	Dig up 1/3 more / than you did in '44! [handpainted]	Multicolored	Home	B
Myers	1904	Does this represent / the bond you do not buy? etc. [handpainted]	Blue	Bonds	B
Myers	1924	Don't be a lone wolf! / Get in the fight!! etc. [handpainted] [postmarked Lone Wolf, OK]	Black, yellow	Bonds	C
Myers	2336	Food / fights / for freedom [handpainted]	Multicolored	Home	B
Myers	2916	Give more / in '44 / Red Cross war fund [handpainted] [no picture]	Blue, red	RedCr	B
Myers	3153	Greetings gate! / Don't let these guys celebrate. / Buy etc. [handpainted]	Multicolored	Axis	C
Myers	3186	Halloween / 1944 / Greetings / One year nearer / victory [handpainted]	Black, orange	Holid	C
Myers	3255	He whoo-s wise / buys / war bonds / to have / and / to hold! [handpainted]	Black	Owl	C
Myers	3387	Hirohito / B-29s put him there! / Keep 'em flying! / With etc. [handpainted]	Multicolored	Japan	C
Myers	3498	How doth the little busy B-29 / improve each etc. [handpainted]	Multicolored	Japan	B
Myers	3598	Iceland base / command [handpainted] [envelope 6 3/4x3 3/4 in.]	Unknown	Bases	C
Myers	4006	Jan. 20, 1945 / First 4th term inauguration etc. [postmarked 1/20/45] [handpainted]	Black	FDR	E
Myers	4113	Join the fun--buy ward bonds! [handpainted]	Multicolored	UncAx	C
Myers	4324	Keep letters sailing / they're / etc. / failing! [handpainted]	Blue	Navy	B
Myers	4388	Kwitcherkickin! / our forefathers did without - / sugar - till the etc. [handpainted]	Blue, red	Home	B
Myers	4422	Lead the way! / Buy a bond today [vertical text] [handpainted]	Multicolored	Bonds	B
Myers	5161	May 14 to June 30 / Buy bonds / for / V / o'er the rising sun / 7th War Loan [handpainted]	Multicolored	Bonds	D
Myers	5500	Nineteen forty-four [1944] / One year nearer / victory [handpainted]	Multicolored	Bonds	C
Myers	5834	One away [in quotes]— / yer out! / Mussolini struck out etc. [handpainted]	Multicolored	Musso	B
Myers	5871	Only / 36 / shopping days / for / G.I. Christmas / Deadline = / October 15 [handpainted]	Green, red	Holid	B
Myers	7071	Sixth war loan / Nov. 20 to Dec. 16 / Let's make it etc. [handpainted]	Multicolored	Dog	B
Myers	7081	Slap the Jap / with scrap / To insure a win / save more etc. [handpainted]	Multicolored	Japan	B

PUBLISHER	NO.	CACHET TEXT	COLOR	TOPIC	$
Myers	7082	Slap the Jap / with scrap [handpainted]	Multicolored	Japan	B
Myers	7854	The wise guy / will buy / war bonds / to supply bombs / for the A.A.F. [handpainted]	Black, yellow	Owl	C
Myers	8333	Toughy sez:- / "One way to help / your buddy over there / is to guard [handpainted]	Multicolored	Home	C
Myers	9312	V [eagle with lowered wings, standing on "V"] [handpainted]	Multicolored	EagV	C
Myers	9313	V [eagle with wings superimposed on "V"] [handpainted]	Multicolored	EagV	B
Myers	10092	We'll patch the patches. / And keep bonds till they hatch! / To help etc. [handpainted]	Multicolored	Women	C
Myers	10105	We're a little / old-modish / ...when we invest / our etc. [handpainted]	Multicolored	Bonds	B
Myers	10203	When you or your folks, found refuge here - / this was God's etc. [no picture] handpainted]	Blue, red	Bonds	B
Navy ship	8285	Tokyo Bay! / Japan! [handpainted, lower right] [U.S.S. St. Paul] [Tokyo Bay]	Blue	VJDay	D
Navy ship	9006	USS Colorado - / in Japan [handpainted] [Tokyo Bay]	Black	VJDay	E
Nelson, KE	1283	Buy war savings bonds [handpainted]	Multicolored	Bonds	B
Newton FN	582	And we / demand victory in / Frisco! [handpainted]	Multicolored	UN	C
Newton FN	1065	Breaking through / V / Europe [handpainted]	Multicolored	Armed	C
Newton FN	1991	Dropping the pilot [handpainted]	Multicolored	Winst	C
Newton FN	3254	He who relaxes helps / the Axis. [handpainted]	Multicolored	Home	C
Newton FN	7233	Still puffing away [handpainted]	Multicolored	USSR	C
Newton FN	10222	Where there's smoke there should be some fire! [handpainted]	Multicolored	Japan	C
Nichols	816	Axis / propa- / ganda / plain / balony [handpainted]	Black	Hitle	C
Nichols	1935	Don't be an unwitting Nazi agent! [handpainted]	Black	Home	C
Nichols	7002	Share your rides! [handpainted]	Black	Home	C
Nichols	7270	Superman?? [handpainted]	Black	Hitle	C
Nichols	10170	When day is done! [handpainted]	Multicolored	Hitle	C
Nielsen	7194	Stamp 'em out! [copy of Minkus cachet w/ color, picture variations] [handpainted]	Multicolored	Axis	D
Orlando	10839	^^Hitler behind 8-ball [upper left] [handpainted]	Multicolored	Hitle	B
Parker	94	A good old / American game - / Kicking the / "pigskin" around! [handpainted]	Black	Hitle	B
Parker	113	A move in the / right direction. [handpainted]	Multicolored	Hitle	C
Parker	226	Ach! Der Yanks / ist comming / vunce more again!! [handpainted]	Black, red	Hitle	B
Parker	230	Ach! Du lieber!! / Donner vetter!! / The wolf is on his doorstep! [handpainted]	Multicolored	Hitle	C
Parker	302	After Uncle Sam / gives him the 1-2 / it's 1-2-3-4-5-6-7-/ 8-9-10 etc. [handpainted]	Multicolored	Musso	B
Parker	979	Beware! / Mr. Jap! / We mean / business! [handpainted]	Multicolored	Army	B
Parker	1679	Courage! The Yanks are here!! [handpainted]	Multicolored	Armed	D
Parker	2103	Every night / about this time - / Oh! How I miss you! [handpainted]	Black	Army	B
Parker	2109	Everything Hokay! when you by war / bonds and stamps! [handpainted]	Multicolored	Air	B
Parker	2114	Example of "Der / Master Race". / National Zoo. [handpainted]	Black	Hitle	C
Parker	2869	Get / behinmd / our boys! / Buy / bonds and stamps [handpainted]	Multicolored	Bonds	B
Parker	3098	Got a little / car gem! [handpainted]	Black	Army	B
Parker	3100	Got him where he belongs!! [handpainted]	Multicolored	Hitle	B
Parker	3252	He thinks he has the world / in his grasp; but - / he's behind the "8" ball. [handpainted]	Blue	Hitle	B
Parker	3370	Hey, bud! / How about / investing in a little / freedom today? [handpainted]	Black	Bonds	B
Parker	3397	Hit / him / hard!! / ...-. [handpainted]	Blue	Hitle	B
Parker	3398	Hit 'em hard / And how! / "Give 'im the woiks" [handpainted]	Black	Hitle	B
Parker	3879	It all depends on your / point of view!!!! [handpainted]	Black	Hitle	B
Parker	4162	Just a line home! [handpainted]	Brown, pink	Army	B
Parker	4275	Keep 'em flying! [aviator] [handpainted]	Multicolored	Air	B
Parker	4283	Keep 'em flying!! Kick 'em in the Axis!! [handpainted]	Multicolored	Axis	C
Parker	4418	Latrine General [in quotes] [handpainted]	Multicolored	Army	B
Parker	4568	Let's go U.S.A.! / Keep 'em sending! [handpainted]	Blue	Home	B
Parker	4569	Let's go U.S.A.! / Keep 'em sending! [handpainted] [postmarked 6/6/44]	Multicolored	DDay	D
Parker	4631	Let's put 'em where / they belong. [handpainted]	Blue	Axis	B
Parker	5200	Mein gott!! / Der Yanks / again! / Now commences der / end of etc. [handpainted]	Multricolored	Hitle	C
Parker	5279	Mmmmm! / Ahhhhh! / Home / cooking!! [handpainted]	Blue	Army	C
Parker	5469	Next! / Did you buy yours / today? [handpainted]	Black, blue	Uncle	B
Parker	5524	Ninth / Troop / Carrier / Squadron [handpainted]	Black, blue	Pelic	B
Parker	5687	Oh! how I hate / to get up in / the morning!!! [handpainted]	Black	Army	B
Parker	6372	Put them on the scrap heap! -- where they belong. [handpainted]	Multicolored	Axis	C
Parker	6668	Riding for a downfall, / on a dying horse. [handpainted]	Multicolored	Hitle	B
Parker	6807	Sample of "Der / Master Race" / National Zoo [handpainted]	Multicolored	Hitle	C
Parker	6856	Say, bud! How about / investing in a little / freedom today? [handpainted]	Black	Bonds	B
Parker	6861	Schnicklegrubber / has big / ears for / gossip. / So keep your mouth etc. [handpainted]	Blue	Hitle	B
Parker	7037	Shtop / those / bombs!! / Ve / giff / up! [handpainted]	Multicolored	Axis	C
Parker	7038	Shtop / those bombs!!/ Ve / giff / up! [handpainted]	Black, blue	Axis	B
Parker	7039	Shtop!! / Ve vas only fooling!! / Stamp 'em out!! / Buy war stamps etc. [handpainted]	Multicolored	Axis	C
Parker	7111	So solly! Me fliend!! No wany fight! / Don't believe it! / Knock out etc. [handpainted]	Multicolored	Japan	B
Parker	7134	Some more Nips / gone to roast with / there [sic] honorable etc. [handpainted]	Multicolored	Air	B
Parker	7147	Something to smile / about!!! [handpainted]	Black	Japan	B
Parker	7254	Strike! [bowling ball] [handpainted]	Blue	Axis	B
Parker	7265	Sugar report!! [handpainted]	Black	Army	B
Parker	7464	The Axis gets together [handpainted]	Handpainted	Axis	C
Parker	7765	The tanks / are coming [handpainted]	Black, blue	Ordna	B
Parker	7925	There's nothing hits / the spot like snacks / from home! [handpainted]	Black	Army	B

PUBLISHER	NO.	CACHET TEXT	COLOR	TOPIC	$
Parker	7950	They asked for it! / [etc.] / "Buddies" [handpainted]	Multicolored	Army	C
Parker	9018	V -- for / Victory [2 V's form part of screws closing on Hitler] [handpainted]	Blue	Hitle	B
Parker	9024	V ...- / for Victory [handpainted]	Multicolored	Hitle	B
Parker	9052	V ...- ["V" comes between "..." and "-"] [handpainted]	Multicolored	VforV	B
Parker	9121	V / ...- [with 3 small airplanes] [handpainted]	Blue, red	VforV	B
Parker	9171	V / for Victory! [cross above "V"] [handpainted]	Blue	VforV	B
Parker	9318	V [in quotes] for / Victory Put the / screws /on him [handpainted]	Blue	Hitle	B
Parker	9341	V for ...-/ Victory! [5 planes] [handpainted]	Multicolored	VforV	C
Parker	9425	Via - air mail [handpainted]	Multicolored	Pelic	B
Parker	10091	We'll make him jump to / "Yankee Doodle Dandy" [handpainted]	Multicolored	Japan	B
Parker	10250	Whose [sic] afraid of the big / "bad wolf"? [handpainted]	Multicolored	Japan	B
Parker	10964	^^Soldier saluting [handpainted]	Black	Army	B
Phill, CR	1376	Chickens / for victory / meat / eggs [handpainted]	Multicolored	Chick	B
Pisarof	1841	Der zoopermen / are on der run / Blitzkrieg in reverse [handpainted]	Multicolored	Nazis	C
Pisarof	4082	Japs / Get out / and stay out! / [etc.] / The / Philippines [handpainted]	Black	Phili	B
Price	10606	Your patriotic duty / Fight / infantile / paralysis [handpainted]	Multicolored	Home	B
Price, EK	1171	Buy bonds / 6th war loan / to bomb the Japs [handpainted]	Black, red	Japan	B
Price, EK	2186	Fight / infantile / paralysis / your patriotic duty [handpainted]	Multicolored	Home	B
Price, EK	5396	Naval pursuit [handpainted]	Multicolored	Air	C
Price, EK	6214	Planted in Japan's / black heart. / Tokyo [handpainted]	Black, red	Japan	B
Price, EK	9994	We pinned 'em back / Mr. Jap — [2 varieties, caricature of face] [handpainted]	Multicolored	Japan	B
Price, R	9113	V / ...- [handpainted]	Multicolored	VforV	B
Rayl	2368	For a new life — in a new world [handpainted]	Multicolored	VEDay	D
Rayl	2862	Germany falls / V-Day [handpainted]	Multicolored	VEDay	D
Rayl	2863	Germany falls [handpainted]	Multicolored	VEDay	D
Rayl	10149	What flavor? [in quotes] / I'll take / Manila! [handpainted]	Unknown	UncJa	C
Richards	205	Aachen / surrenders / Oct. 21, 1944 [handpainted]	Black, red	Event	B
Richards	5233	Merry / Christmas [handpainted]	Multicolored	Holid	B
Richards	8982	USA [above eagle] [handpainted]	Multicolored	EagSh	C
Robertson	10511	Yes! Adolph! / Invasion Day! / D [postmarked 06/06/1944] [handpainted]	Blue, red	DDay	C
Rothert	4226	Keep 'em / flying [handpainted] [artist: Chuck Rothert]	Blue	Home	B
Schaefer	10768	^^Eagle, similar to Win-the-War stamp, framed by 3 stars [handpainted]	Blue/Red	Eagle	C
Schirmer	6757	Sad Sack in Normandy. [handpainted]	Black	Army	B
Sharon	9182	V / ictory. / Hats of to our armed forces. [typed text after "V"] [handpainted]	Black, red	VEDay	C
Sharon	9241	V / Victory ["V" 74 mm high, in star] [handpainted]	Black, red	VEDay	C
Sharon	9527	Victory [black letters across red "V," inside 5-pointed star] [handpainted]	Black, red	VEDay	C
Sharon	9548	Victory [script, "V" 87 mm high] [handpainted]	Blue, red	VEDay	C
Shaw	4178	Just waiting for a couple of good yanks!! [handpainted]	Black	Hitle	C
Shaw, TC	344	All fascist / welcome [handpainted]	Unknown	Axis	C
Shaw, TC	722	Atom bombs / thank God. [handpainted]	Black, pink	Atom	E
Shaw, TC	1825	Democracy / welcome / super's [sic] ready. [handpainted]	Multicolored	Japan	B
Shaw, TC	6568	Remember me? I' G.I. Joe --/ Fo't in World War II you know [handpainted]	Red	Army	B
Shaw, TC	9360	V.E. Day. / [etc.] / May 8, 1945 [handpainted on printed cachet]	Black, red	VEDay	B
Shaw, TC	9871	We / welcome / democracy, too. / V ...- / world / wide. [handpainted]	Black, red	Ally	D
Shaw, TC	9872	We / welcome / democracy. / V ...- / worldwide. [handpainted]	Black, red	VforV	C
Shaw, TC	10068	Welcome [handpainted]	Unknown	Hitle	B
Smith, LH	633	April 25, 1945 / Toward United Nations - F.D.R. etc. [handpainted]	Multicolored	Event	C
Smith, LH	741	Attu [handpainted]	Multicolored	Map	C
Smith, LH	743	Aug 24 / 1944 / Bordeaux France / liberated by Allies and etc. [handpainted]	Multicolored	Map	C
Smith, LH	754	Aug. 17, 1943 - Messina falls. [handpainted]	Multicolored	Map	B
Smith, LH	755	Aug. 23, 1944 - Paris liberated by French patriots. Americans and etc. [handpainted]	Multicolored	Map	C
Smith, LH	756	Aug. 24, / 1944 - Nazi Balkan empire crumbles [handpainted]	Multicolored	Map	C
Smith, LH	775	August 17, 1943—Messina falls / to Allies [handpainted]	Multicolored	Map	C
Smith, LH	776	August 17, 1943—Messina falls. [handpainted]	Multicolored	Map	C
Smith, LH	782	August 24, 1944 / Bordeaux France / liberated by Allies etc. [handpainted]	Multicolored	Map	C
Smith, LH	892	Bataan / recaptured / Feb. 17, 1945 / Here's where etc. [handpainted]	Multicolored	Phili	C
Smith, LH	1053	Born / Jan. 30 / 1882 / Died / April 12 / 1945 / Franklin etc. [handpainted]	Multicolored	FDR	C
Smith, LH	1097	British Royal / Navy / Mar. 30 / 1945 / joins stars etc. [handpainted]	Multicolored	Event	C
Smith, LH	1756	Dec. 07, 1941 - Japan made a / treacherous attack on the etc. [handpainted]	Multicolored	Map	C
Smith, LH	1757	Dec. 07, 1941 - The Rising Sun began to / sink in the Pacific [handpainted]	Multicolored	Japan	C
Smith, LH	1763	Dec. 16 1944 / Americans / land on Mindoro / Island in the etc. [handpainted]	Multicolored	Map	C
Smith, LH	2164	Feb. 17, 1945 / United States flag / again / [etc.] / Corregidor etc. [handpainted]]	Multicolored	Anniv	C
Smith, LH	3989	Iwo Jima / Tokyo's "Lookout Island" / Feb. 20 1945 / invaded etc. [handpainted]	Multicolored	Japan	B
Smith, LH	4000	Jan. 04, 1945—Turkey severs relations with Japan [handpainted]	Multicolored	Map	C
Smith, LH	4001	Jan. 10, 1945 - Invasion forces of Gen. Douglas etc. [handpainted]	Multicolored	Map	C
Smith, LH	4002	Jan. 10-20, 1943 - Casablanca Conference, terms agreed / upon etc. [handpainted]	Multicolored	Heads	B
Smith, LH	4004	Jan. 18, 1945 / Warsaw freed / by the Russian / army. etc. [handpainted]	Multicolored	Map	C
Smith, LH	4005	Jan. 19, 1945 - Budapest / capitol [sic] of Hungary etc. [handpainted]	Multicolored	Map	C
Smith, LH	4010	Jan. 26, 1945 - Clark Field captured--richest prize of etc. [postmarked 1/26/45] [hp]	Multicolored	Event	C
Smith, LH	4123	July 04, 1944 — bombing of Saipan! [handpainted]	Multicolored	Air	C

PUBLISHER	NO.	CACHET TEXT	COLOR	TOPIC	$
Smith, LH	4126	July 05, 1943 - Yanks march thru' New Georgia [handpainted]	Multicolored	Map	C
Smith, LH	4128	July 07, 1941 - United States troops occupy Iceland [handpainted]	Multicolored	Map	B
Smith, LH	4130	July 08, 1944 / Occupation of Saipan / marks an important etc. [handpainted]	Multicolored	Map	C
Smith, LH	4131	July 10, 1943 - Allies invade Sicily [handpainted]	Multicolored	Map	C
Smith, LH	4135	July 16, 1945 / Cooking Nippon's goose [Potsdam ultimatum] [handpainted]	Multicolored	Event	C
Smith, LH	4137	July 21 1944 / Yanks recapture Guam [handpainted]	Multicolored	Map	C
Smith, LH	4139	July 25, 1943 - Mussolini was kicked / over the Tyrrhenian etc. [handpainted]	Multicolored	Musso	C
Smith, LH	4143	July 31, 1944 - Famous leaning tower / of Pisa destroyed by etc. [handpainted]	Multicolored	Hist	B
Smith, LH	4149	June 05, 1944 / Fall of Rome, first Nazi capitol [sic] etc. [handpainted]	Multicolored	Axis	C
Smith, LH	4150	June 06, 1944 - Allies land on coast of / France to launch etc. [handpainted]	Multicolored	Map	C
Smith, LH	4152	June 08, 1944 / Bayeaux - first French city to be etc. [handpainted]	Multicolored	ORN	C
Smith, LH	4159	June 27, 1944 / Cherbourg, France / freed of Nazi bondage [handpainted]	Multicolored	Map	C
Smith, LH	4374	Kiska [handpainted]	Multicolored	Map	C
Smith, LH	5089	March / 07th / 1945 / Cologne falls to Allies / Doom of the etc. [handpainted]	Multicolored	Army	C
Smith, LH	5100	March 17, 1942 - Gen. Douglas MacArthur arrives in Australia etc. [handpainted]	Multicolored	Mac	C
Smith, LH	5106	March 26, 1945 / Patton / Berlin [handpainted]	Multicolored	Patt	C
Smith, LH	5108	March 30, 1945 / Negros, last big / Phillipine [sic] island etc. [handpainted]	Multicolored	Map	C
Smith, LH	5139	Masnila freed / Feb. 5th 1945 / 3,700 prisoners liberated [handpainted]	Multicolored	Battl	B
Smith, LH	5155	May 07, / 1945 / Germany / surrenders / unconditionally [handpainted]	Multicolored	Ike	C
Smith, LH	5156	May 08 1945 / V-E Day / proclaimed by / Truman, Churchill etc. [handpainted]	Multicolored	Ally	C
Smith, LH	5163	May 17, 1944 - Myitkyina Burma-airfield captured / by etc. [handpainted]	Multicolored	Map	C
Smith, LH	5466	New Zealand troops / are fighting everywhere / for etc. [handpainted]	Multicolored	Map	C
Smith, LH	5467	New Zealand troops / are fighting on all / fronts for the etc. [handpainted]	Multicolored	Map	C
Smith, LH	5583	Nov. 01, 1944 - Jap navy crushed in / second battle etc. [handpainted]	Multicolored	Battl	B
Smith, LH	5585	Nov. 02, 1944-Korea honored by the United / States for their etc. [handpainted]	Multicolored	Map	C
Smith, LH	5586	Nov. 07, 1942 - Yanks land in Algiers [handpainted]	Multicolored	Map	C
Smith, LH	5591	Nov. 21, 1944 / French soldiers laying / pontoon bridge etc. [handpainted]	Multicolored	Ally	C
Smith, LH	5592	Nov. 24, 1944— Allies / drive for the Rhine [handpainted]	Multicolored	Map	C
Smith, LH	5594	Nov. 28, 1944 - Those / Bee-29's sting again [handpainted]	Multicolored	Japan	C
Smith, LH	5660	Oct. 03, 1944 — Siegfried line broken [handpainted]	Multicolored	Map	C
Smith, LH	5661	Oct. 13 - 1943 - Bagdoglio government / of Italy declares etc. [handpainted]	Multicolored	Map	C
Smith, LH	5662	Oct. 19, 1944 - "By the grace / of God Almighty — / I" etc. [handpainted]	Multicolored	Mac	C
Smith, LH	5663	Oct. 21, 1944 / Aachen - first great German / city falls to Allies. Now the etc. [hp]	Multicolored	Hist	B
Smith, LH	5779	On July 25, 1943 / Benito Mussolini / resigned etc. [handpainted]	Multicolored	Musso	B
Smith, LH	6936	Sept. 03, 1939 - Britain declares war on Germany [handpainted]	Multicolored	Map	C
Smith, LH	6939	Sept. 05, 1944 - The crumbling fortress [handpainted]	Multicolored	ORN	C
Smith, LH	6940	Sept. 08, 1943—The / Casablanca ultimatum / receives its etc. [handpainted]	Multicolored	Map	C
Smith, LH	6941	Sept. 12, 1944 - Yanks / penetrate the Reich [handpainted]	Multicolored	Map	C
Smith, LH	6942	Sept. 18, 1943 - Important Jap base of Lae falls to / Allies [handpainted]	Multicolored	Map	C
Smith, LH	6943	Sept. 21, 1943—Group of Mediterranean islands / occupied etc. [handpainted]	Multicolored	Map	C
Smith, LH	6944	Sept. 27, 1944 - Phillipines [sic] honored / by the United States etc. [handpainted]	Multicolored	Map	B
Smith, LH	7056	Sinking of the Rising Sun [handpainted]	Black, red	Japan	B
Smith, LH	7103	Smoke in der / Fuehrer's eyes / Feb. 3-13 1945 / The Big 3 etc. [handpainted]	Multicolored	Event	C
Smith, LH	7127	Solomon Islands [handpainted]	Multicolored	Map	C
Smith, LH	7476	The big / strike / Berlin / Feb. 5, 1945 / 4000 Allied etc. [handpainted]	Multicolored	Nazis	C
Smith, LH	7729	The Roman / candle [handpainted]	Multicolored	Nazis	C
Smith, LH	8437	U.S. Army / Air Force / Day / Aug. 1, 1907—Wright Bros. etc. [handpainted]	Multicolored	Air	C
Smith, LH	9714	Wake [handpainted]	Multicolored	Map	B
Smith, LH	9717	Wake Island / Seized by the Japs Dec. 24, 1942 [handpainted]	Multicolored	Map	C
Stawuszew	1324	Camp Sibert Ala [with small shield] [handpainted]	Multicolored	Army	B
Stawuszew	6190	Picatinny Arsenal / Dover, N.J. [handpainted] [envelope 7 1/2x3 15/16 in.]	Multicolored	Eagle	D
Stawuszew	7271	Supply Det., Section I / Camp Sibert / Alabama [handpainted]	Multicolored	EagSh	C
Stawuszew	8338	Toward United Nations [handpainted]	Multicolored	Eagle	C
Stawuszew	9521	Victory [above eagle and shield] [handpainted]	Multicolored	EagSh	D
Stawuszew	9673	V-J Day [above eagle holding arrows and olive branch] [handpainted]	Multicolored	VJDay	E
Stawuszew	9674	V-J Day [above flying eagle clutching 3 arrows] [handpainted]	Multicolored	VJDay	D
Stawuszew	10753	^^Eagle with olive branch, arrows [below soldier-publisher's Ccard] [handpainted]	Multicolored	EagSh	C
Steinhardt	59	A beautiful fruit / -but- / no damn good to me. [handpainted]	Multicolored	Uncle	C
Steinhardt	3166	Guaranteed workable / postwar plans. / #1. Rosey the riveter etc. [handpainted]	Multicolored	Women	C
Steinhardt	6370	Put forth thine hand / and take it by the tail / [etc.] / Bible [handpainted]	Multicolored	Japan	C
Steinhardt	6862	Schubert / didn't / finish his / symphony— / damned if / I don't etc. [handpainted]	Multicolored	Uncle	C
Steinhardt	7016	Ship repair unit [handpainted]	Multicolored	Navy	C
Steinhardt	7846	The weapons of our warfare are mighty / through God to the etc. [handpainted]	Multicolored	Relig	C
Steinhardt	9346	V gates - hell - / Just make it V. [handpainted]	Multicolored	Uncle	C
Steinhardt	10229	Which flag / are we / entitled / to wave when / the boys come / home? [handpainted]	Multicolored	Uncle	C
Stoll	361	All out for victory / V [handpainted]	Multicolored	VforV	B
Stoll	2875	Get on the / bondwagon [in quotes] [handpainted]	Multicolored	Bonds	B
Stoll	7891	There are some things / worth fighting for! [handpainted]	Multicolored	Home	B
Stoll	8734	United for war / united in peace [handpainted]	Multicolored	EagSh	B
Stoll	10340	Wipe / out / aggression - greed / and intolerance [handpainted]	Multicolored	Globe	B

PUBLISHER	NO.	CACHET TEXT	COLOR	TOPIC	$
Stoll	10463	Worth / repeating! / Buy / bonds / Buy / bonds [handpainted]	Multicolored	Bonds	C
Stoner	3707	I'm sounding / off for --- [bellowing sergeant, pen & ink] [handpainted]	Black	USMC	B
Sturgill	377	Allied / war machine / Remember / Pearl Harbor / Tokyo, here etc. [handpainted]	Black	VEDay	F
Sturgill	1961	Don't let him down! / European peace / Politicians [handpainted]	Black	VEDay	F
Sturgill	2132	Face saving peace feelers / You haven't quite got the idea etc. [handpainted]	Black	Japan	E
Sturgill	2437	For this we thank thee, Lord [handpainted]	Multicolored	Home	E
Sturgill	3435	Home! [handpainted]	Multicolored	VEDay	F
Sturgill	3669	I'll / surrender / but / [in quotes] etc. / Atomic bombing [handpainted]	Black	Atom	F
Sturgill	3750	In memoriam / They sleep today in other fields etc. [handpainted]	Black	Verse	E
Sturgill	4063	Japan, we hereby / announce our bombing / [etc.] / "Loud speaker" [handpainted]	Black	Japan	E
Sturgill	4066	Japanese Easter egg. / Score of Jap victories / over U.S. etc. [handpainted]	Black	Japan	E
Sturgill	6708	Rub-a-dub-dub, most any day, now / [etc.] / Hon. / Jap fleet [handpainted]	Black	Japan	E
Sturgill	7146	Something else to remember / Russia declares / war etc. [handpainted]	Black	Event	E
Sturgill	7320	Temporary hold / Disaster [handpainted]	Multicolored	Hitle	E
Sturgill	7627	The little boy who got just / what he asked for. [handpainted]	Multicolored	Nazis	E
Sturgill	7982	They raise the / flag again on / Corregidor [handpainted]	Multicolored	Flag	E
Swartz	10704	^^Boy, girl w/ fireworks; U.S. Flag background [7/4/41 postmark] [handpainted]	Multicolored	Holid	B
Swartz	10786	^^Flag, U.S., hanging from yellow window frame [Flag Day, 6/14/41][handpainted]	Multicolored	Flag	B
Swave+Mill	2589	Free France / Patch / Bradley / Patton / "GI" Joe / Ike etc. [handpainted]	Multicolored	Hitle	B
Sweet	2700	Gardens for victory [handpainted] [envelope 7 1/2x3 7/8 in.]	Multicolored	Home	C
Teixeira	5523	Ninety-third [93rd] Division [handpainted]	Black, blue	Army	D
Temple	5	A / merry / American / Christmas [handpainted] [+cut-&-pasted paper]	Multicolored	Holid	C
Temple	71	A date which / will live [in quotes] etc. [handpainted + cut-&-pasted paper]	Black, blue	Pearl	C
Temple	6059	Our wish for / the new year: / Victory / in / 1944 [+ cut-&-pasted paper] [handp]	Multicolored	Holid	C
Trapani	1209	Buy more / war / bonds [handpainted]	Black	Army	C
Unknown	101	A guy can / dream—can't / he? [handpainted]	Multicolored	Unk	B
Unknown	296	Adolph / Little [? words on Mussolini] / Son / of / heaven [handpainted]	Multicolored	Axis	B
Unknown	687	Army / war day / 48 states protect the liberty / 13 colonies won [handpainted]	Red	Army	B
Unknown	739	Attention / Jap war lords / Now that we have captured the etc. [handpainted]	Multicolored	Japan	B
Unknown	757	August 02, 1943 --Yanks capture / Munda [handpainted]	Black, green	Event	B
Unknown	901	Be / alert / remember / Pearl Harbor [handpainted]	Multicolored	EagV	C
Unknown	956	Benito Mussolini, a pompous / guy, / at being a Caesar etc. [handpainted]	Multicolored	Musso	B
Unknown	998	Black out the Rising Sun [handpainted]	Multicolored	Japan	B
Unknown	1192	Buy bonds to keep / the "Stukas" / from our skies [handpainted]	Black	Air	B
Unknown	1296	Buy war stamps and bonds [text diagonal downward] [handp]	Multicolored	Uncle	B
Unknown	1737	Dear Adolph In 1944 / you didn't loose [sic] etc. [4/12/45, FDR's death] [handpainted]	Multicolored	Hitle	D
Unknown	1773	Declaration of war against Japan [typed] [12/8/41] [small handpainted eagle/shield]	Multicolored	Event	C
Unknown	1987	Dreaming / "Oh, to be in New England in the spring." [handpainted]	Black, red	Army	B
Unknown	2032	Eleven overrun / Axis nations [handpainted]	Blue, red	Hitle	B
Unknown	2189	Fight for freedom [handpainted] [no picture]	Blue, red	Home	B
Unknown	2216	Finns shoot / down a / Russian plane. [handpainted] [postmarked 11/13/39]	Blue, red	Air	F
Unknown	2244	First day / MacArthur / Post Office [campaign ribbons, cap, glasses, corn cob pipe] [handpainted]	Multicolored	MacFD	D
Unknown	2321	Flying / circus [in quotes] [vertical] / "King of the heavies" [handpainted]	Multicolored	Globe	C
Unknown	2532	Fourth [4th] Bombardment Squadron / Corregidor / surrenders etc.[pm 05/06/42][hp]	Black, yellow	Event	D
Unknown	2533	Fourth [4th] Bombardment Squadron [handpainted]	Black, yellow	Unit	B
Unknown	2897	Give / war bonds / and stamps! [handpainted]	Multicolored	Holid	C
Unknown	3317	Help. What next! [handpainted]	Multicolored	Hitle	C
Unknown	3541	I bought an extra war bond! [vest button on envelope] [handpainted]	Black	Bonds	C
Unknown	3547	I can't help it if you / are having maneuvers [in quotes] etc. [postmarked Iceland 10/41] [handpainted]	Multicolored	USMC	D
Unknown	3554	I don't care if he is the company mascot / the War Department etc. [handpainted]	Multicolored	Army	C
Unknown	3652	If you like rats / [etc.] / Japs etc. [handpainted] [envelope 9 1/2x4 1/8 in.]	Black	Japan	B
Unknown	3784	Inauguration / first land mail route / [etc.] / Army Postal etc. [handpainted]	Blue, red	Army	D
Unknown	3841	Invasion road / to Nip land / China / Okinawa [handpainted]	Multicolored	Army	B
Unknown	3870	Is that all you can talk about / —military secrets? [in quotes] [handpainted]	Black	Home	B
Unknown	3895	It may cost us / the wealth of our / nation to win this etc. [handpainted]	Black, red	Home	B
Unknown	3929	Italy yeilds [sic] / Unconditional / surrender on / Sept. 8, 1943. [handpainted]	Black, red	Event	B
Unknown	3994	Jaldi! / (hurry!) / [handpainted] [APO 886, Karachi, India]	Multicolored	Ally	C
Unknown	4036	Japan / surrenders [handpainted]	Multicolored	VJDay	C
Unknown	4176	Just wait till Sept. 23. [handpainted]	Black	FDR	B
Unknown	4197	Keep / out / of / the / Buy more bonds [handpainted]	Multicolored	Dog	B
Unknown	4293	Keep 'em rolling [handpainted]	Multicolored	Ordna	B
Unknown	5342	My Easter greetings for '44 / "Let's do more to win this war!" [handpainted]	Multicolored	Holid	B
Unknown	5595	Nov-11th / Armistice / Day [handpainted]	Multicolored	Flag	B
Unknown	5626	O.K. Rembrandt... / where the hell's / our planes! [handpainted]	Multicolored	Air	B
Unknown	5675	Official / VE / Day / yesterday - perhaps etc. [handpainted] [imprint: D.W.M.]	Multicolored	VEDay	B
Unknown	5845	One flag / one country [UL, w/ shield] [handpainted]	Blue, red	Shiel	B
Unknown	6084	Pacific victory / August 14, 1945. [below newspaper headlines] [handpainted]	Black	VJDay	C
Unknown	6145	Peace / VJ / "The Lord will bless / his people with peace" etc. [handpainted]	Multicolored	VJDay	B
Unknown	6157	Pearl Harbor - 7 Dec 41 / V Day / via atomic / [etc.] / 2 Sep 1945 etc. [no picture] [handpainted]	Purple, red	VJDay	B
Unknown	6202	Pisa / falls / to / the Allies / Sept. 2 / 1944 [handpainted]	Multicolored	Event	C

PUBLISHER	NO.	CACHET TEXT	COLOR	TOPIC	$
Unknown	6340	Produce / and / conserve / Share / and / play square / Food / fights etc. [handpainted]	Multicolored	Home	B
Unknown	6507	Remember / Pearl / Harbor [bomb below "Remember"] [handpainted]	Multicolored	Pearl	B
Unknown	6552	Remember / Pearl Harbor [large eagle, small planes] [handpainted]	Multicolored	Pearl	C
Unknown	6621	Remember Pearl Harbor [in quotes] [eagle and soldier] [handpainted]	Black	Pearl	C
Unknown	7110	So solly! / Now you poor / devils hari kari. / V.J. Day. [handpainted]	Multicolored	VJDay	C
Unknown	7216	Starting to-day all cars 35 miles p.h. / A slip / of the lip etc. [handpainted]	Unknown	Axis	C
Unknown	7319	Tell your / Congressman / V / stands for / victory / not / votes etc. [handpainted]	Multicolored	VforV	B
Unknown	7486	The booming roar of a .44 / spelled death to badmen / in etc. [handpainted]	Black	Hitle	B
Unknown	7600	The Japanese believe their / country resulted when a pair etc. [handpainted]	Blue	Japan	B
Unknown	7850	The White House announced / that an "atomic bomb" etc. [handpainted] [no picture]	Blue	Atom	D
Unknown	8392	Two more to / go folks! / Up / and at 'em! / Make / with etc. [handpainted]	Black	Axis	B
Unknown	8567	U.S.A. [above star and 2 chevrons] [handpainted]	Blue	Armed	A
Unknown	8664	Uncle Sammy [in quotes] / says / "Let's all do our / share to insure etc. [handpainted]	Multicolored	Uncle	B
Unknown	9069	V / ...- / 5th / war / loan [handpainted]	Multicolored	Handp	B
Unknown	9150	V / E / Germany surrenders! ["V" 58 mm high] [handpainted]	Black	VEDay	C
Unknown	9389	VE / Day / May 8, 1945 ["V" 47 mm high] [handpainted]	Multicolored	VEDay	C
Unknown	9452	Victory / ...- / V / E ["Victory" on ribbon across "V"] [handpainted]	Blue, red	VEDay	C
Unknown	9454	Victory / ...- [handpainted, ink]	Blue	Torch	B
Unknown	9749	War / bonds / speed / victory [handpainted]	Black, yellow	Liber	B
Unknown	9869	We / shall / win / or / we / shall / die / MacArthur [handp] [imprint: CFN]	Blue, red	MacFD	C
Unknown	10163	Whats a cookin Ernest? [addressed to Ernest J. Muzzy] [cannibal, large pot] [handpainted]	Black	Home	B
Unknown	10382	Work together, win together! [handpainted]	Multicolored	Navy	C
Unknown	10506	Yes indeed / If U think an / Allied second front / is not etc. [handpainted]	Multicolored	Home	C
Unknown	10602	Your name on one / more bond / will mean / one / less / name on etc. [handpainted]	Multicolored	Bonds	C
Unknown	10702	^^Bombs, 3, falling from black airplane, large yellow sun in background [handpainted]	Multicolored	Air	C
Unknown	10740	^^Eagle over shield [eagle black, shield blue, red] [handpainted]	Multicolored	EagSh	C
Unknown	10829	^^Flamethrower scorching backside of Japanese, who is leaping [handpainted]	Multicolored	Japan	C
Unknown	10857	^^Insignia, unknown unit, 2 squares on end, 1 blue, 1 white, brown background [hp]	Multicolored	Unit	B
Unknown	10879	^^MacArthur, General Douglas, full face, eagle and flags behind him [handpainted]	Multicolored	MacFD	D
Unknown	11029	^^Uncle Sam rolling up his sleeves [handpainted]	Multicolored	Uncle	B
Van Alsbur	6631	Remember Pearl Harbor! [text printed black, UR; flag, left, handpainted]	Multicolored	Flag	C
Van Alsbur	7228	Step on it Uncle [in quotes] [handpainted]	Multicolored	Japan	C
Weigand	791	Australia / United Nations [handpainted]	Multicolored	UN	B
Weigand	944	Belgium / United Nations [handpainted]	Multicolored	ORN	B
Weigand	1023	Bolivia / United Nations [handpainted]	Multicolored	UN	B
Weigand	1062	Brazil / United Nations [handpainted]	Multicolored	UN	B
Weigand	1334	Canada / United Nations [handpainted]	Multicolored	UN	B
Weigand	1381	China / United Nations [handpainted]	Multicolored	UN	B
Weigand	1427	Colombia / United Nations [handpainted]	Multicolored	UN	B
Weigand	1694	Cuba / United Nations [handpainted]	Multicolored	UN	B
Weigand	2031	El Salvador / United Nations [handpainted]	Multicolored	UN	B
Weigand	2071	Ethiopia / United Nations [handpainted]	Multicolored	UN	B
Weigand	3109	Great Britain / United Nations [handpainted]	Multicolored	UN	B
Weigand	3666	Il Duce: / "Answer" cried the fascist showman, "emblem of" etc. [handpainted]	Multicolored	Liber	B
Weigand	3667	Il Duce: / When, with fascist ceremonials, / entering etc. [handpainted]	Multicolored	Liber	B
Weigand	3668	Il Duce: / While the bombers / [etc.] / 2—Into that apartment regal etc. [handpainted]	Multicolored	Liber	B
Weigand	3795	India / United Nations [handpainted]	Multicolored	UN	B
Weigand	3863	Iran/ United Nations [handpainted]	Multicolored	UN	B
Weigand	3864	Iraq / United Nations [handpainted]	Multicolored	UN	B
Weigand	4479	Let freedom ring around the world [handpainted]	Multicolored	FlBel	C
Weigand	4899	Luxembourg / United Nations [handpainted]	Multicolored	UN	B
Weigand	5282	Modern Mother Goose / 1-Hey diddle, diddle, while we played etc. [handpainted]	Multicolored	Liber	B
Weigand	5352	Na...-y / 1—A cry of revenge rings out from the sea, / from etc. [handpainted]	Multicolored	Liber	B
Weigand	5465	New Zealand / United Nations [handpainted]	Multicolored	UN	B
Weigand	5471	Nicaragua / United Nations [handpainted]	Multicolored	UN	B
Weigand	5760	Old Glory [in quotes] / Champion for liberty [signed "W": serviced by Louis & Mae Weigand] [hp]	Multicolored	Liber	E
Weigand	6088	Panama / United Nations [handpainted]	Multicolored	UN	B
Weigand	6159	Pearl Harbor / 1—The rosy dawn had scarse [sic] begun. etc. [handpainted]	Multicolored	Liber	B
Weigand	6186	Philippines / United Nations [handpainted]	Multicolored	UN	B
Weigand	6261	Poland / United Nations [handpainted]	Multicolored	UN	B
Weigand	6487	Remember / 3—For the men the Japs / [etc.] / 4—So, remember the men etc. [handpainted]	Multicolored	Verse	B
Weigand	6575	Remember Pearl Harbor / 3—If needed or if asked of us, each man etc. [handpainted]	Multicolored	Pearl	B
Weigand	6722	Russia / United Nations [handpainted]	Multicolored	UN	B
Weigand	6800	Salutes to our boys / 1—They say the Lexington / [etc.] / 2—The etc. [handpainted]	Multicolored	Liber	B
Weigand	7156	South Africa / United Nations	Multicolored	UN	B
Weigand	7616	The Lexington sails on / 1—They say the Lexington / [etc.] / 2—The etc. [handpainted]	Multicolored	Liber	B
Weigand	7617	The Lexington sails on / 3—When the big / [etc.] / 4—Then came the etc. [handpainted]	Multicolored	Liber	B
Weigand	7618	The Lexington sails on / 6—But the old "lex" / [etc.] / 7—As you etc. [handpainted]	Multicolored	Liber	B
Weigand	10442	World situation / 1—Adolph's got a headache / [etc.] / 2—Franko's etc. [handpainted]	Multicolored	Liber	B
Weigand	10632	Yugoslavia / United Nations [handpainted]	Multicolored	ORN	B

PUBLISHER	NO.	CACHET TEXT	COLOR	TOPIC	$
White, TM	180	A soldier's dream, and Hitler's nightmare. [in quotes] [handpainted]	Multicolored	Hitle	F
White, TM	581	And to think, that they / call 'me' a rat!! [in quotes] [handpainted]	Multicolored	Hitle	F
White, TM	1189	Buy bonds for victory [in quotes] / "From our house," etc. [hp] [env. 6 1/2x3 5/8 in.]	Multicolored	Home	D
White, TM	2092	Even vultures / are fussy!! [handpainted]	Multicolored	Hitle	F
White, TM	5132	Mars — Roman god of / war. Stamp him out!! [in quotes] [handpainted]	Multicolored	Antiq	F
White, TM	8613	Uncle / Sam [in quotes, on tag on bird's leg] / Sept. 30, 1942 [handpainted]	Black	Hitle	C
White, TM	8614	Uncle / Sam [in quotes] / Sept. 30, 1942 [handpainted]	Multicolored	Hitle	E
White, TM	8659	Uncle Sam will show 'em! [in quotes] [handpainted] [envelope 5 3/4x3 13/16 in.]	Multicolored	Uncle	F
Wolf, CL	79	A few more bombs will do the job [handpainted]	Multicolored	Unk	B
Wolf, CL	289	Adolf / quits [handpainted]	Black	Hitle	B
Wolf, CL	406	Almost / out [handpainted]	Black	Unk	B
Wolf, CL	416	Am I going / or coming? [handpainted]	Black	Unk	B
Wolf, CL	425	America / must/ stay/ free [handpainted]	Black	Eagle	C
Wolf, CL	545	Americans / can enjoy / Christmas [handpainted]	Multicolored	Holiday	C
Wolf, CL	803	Avenge / Pearl / Harbor [handpainted] [no picture]	Black, red	Pearl	B
Wolf, CL	909	Be foxy / buy / bonds [handpainted]	Black	Bonds	B
Wolf, CL	911	Be grateful / you're an / American [stenciled] [handpainted]	Black, red	Holid	C
Wolf, CL	952	Benito / is / now/ finito [handpainted]	Unknown	Musso	B
Wolf, CL	1170	Buy bonds / 5th / war loan [handpainted]	Black, purple	Bonds	C
Wolf, CL	1179	Buy bonds / There'll / always be a / Christmas [handpainted]	Black, red	Holid	C
Wolf, CL	1205	Buy em by the hatful / war bonds [handpainted]	Multicolored	Bonds	C
Wolf, CL	1393	Christmas / the promise of / permanent peace [stenciled] [handpainted]	Multicolored	Holid	C
Wolf, CL	1419	C'mon / let's / all / fight [no picture] [handpainted]	Multicolored	Home	B
Wolf, CL	1822	Democracy / shall / not / die [handpainted]	Black, red	Home	B
Wolf, CL	1845	Destroy / this / menace [handpainted]	Multicolored	Japan	B
Wolf, CL	1846	Destroy / this menace [handpainted]	Multicolored	Japan	B
Wolf, CL	1916	Don't / be / a / blabber [handpainted]	Multicolored	Home	B
Wolf, CL	1920	Don't / crow / till / it's / over [handpainted]	Multicolored	Home	B
Wolf, CL	1957	Don't hurry! / I'll / wait [handpainted]	Multicolored	Axis	B
Wolf, CL	2018	Easy pickin. [handpainted]	Black	Axis	B
Wolf, CL	2607	Freedom / from / fear [stenciled] [handpainted]	Blue, red	Home	C
Wolf, CL	2608	Freedom / from / want [stenciled] [handpainted]	Blue, red	Home	C
Wolf, CL	2615	Freedom / of / religion [stenciled] [handpainted]	Blue, red	Home	C
Wolf, CL	2618	Freedom / of / speech [stenciled] [handpainted]	Blue, red	Home	C
Wolf, CL	3067	Going down [handpainted]	Multicolored	Japan	B
Wolf, CL	3085	Good news for Adolf / rail / coal / steel / strikes / rubber / planes / ships / bus [hp]	Black, red	Home	C
Wolf, CL	3093	Goodbye Adolf [handpainted]	Multicolored	Hitle	B
Wolf, CL	3234	He / saves / his / bonds / do / you [handpainted]	Blue, red	Uncle	B
Wolf, CL	3504	How soon / ruin [handpainted]	Multicolored	Japan	B
Wolf, CL	3868	Is / Berlin / next? [handpainted]	Black	Hitle	B
Wolf, CL	3931	It's / all / over rat [handpainted]	Black	Hitle	A
Wolf, CL	3973	It's your duty to / 4th / back the attack [handpainted]	Black, purple	Bonds	C
Wolf, CL	4047	Japan suffers / a tomic ache! / Sunday of thanksgiving etc. [handpainted]	Multicolored	Atom	C
Wolf, CL	4544	Let's blow them / off the map [handpainted]	Black, red	Japan	B
Wolf, CL	4647	Let's win / and / then grin [handpainted]	Black, red	Holid	B
Wolf, CL	4936	Made / in / U.S.A. [handpainted]	Black, silver	Axis	B
Wolf, CL	5238	Merry Christmas / Buy / more / war / bonds / Happy New Year [handpainted]	Black, red	Holid	C
Wolf, CL	5495	Nineteen forty-four [1944] / It's victory [handpainted]	Black, red	Home	C
Wolf, CL	6275	Poorer and poorer / are der chances / for / der Fuehrer [handpainted]	Black, red	Hitle	B
Wolf, CL	6710	Rumors [in quotes] [handpainted]	Blue	Army	B
Wolf, CL	6758	Sad words of '43 / 16 / Butter / points per pound [handpainted]	Black	Home	B
Wolf, CL	6759	Sad words of '43 / Closed / for the / duration [handpainted]	Black	Home	B
Wolf, CL	6760	Sad words of '43 / No / beer / today [handpainted]	Black	Home	B
Wolf, CL	6761	Sad words of '43 / Ony one / to a / customer [handpainted]	Black	Home	B
Wolf, CL	6762	Sad words of '43 / Pay / as you / go [handpainted]	Black	Home	B
Wolf, CL	7184	Spots before / his eyes. [handpainted]	Black	Hitle	B
Wolf, CL	7396	The / end / is / near [handpainted]	Black	Hitle	B
Wolf, CL	7927	There's something - / about a soldier. [in quotes] [handpainted]	Black	Army	B
Wolf, CL	8173	To Adolf + Tojo / Roses are red / an' some are pink / We'll etc. [handpainted]	Black, silver	Home	B
Wolf, CL	8238	Tojo / out / Saipan [handpainted]	Black	Japan	B
Wolf, CL	8381	Two / to / go [handpainted]	Blue, red	Axis	B
Wolf, CL	10143	What do you mean - / you won't buy bonds? [handpainted]	Unknown	Army	B
Wolf, CL	10164	What-where-when / 2nd front [handpainted]	Black	Hitle	B
Wolf, CL	10269	Will / Berlin / be / next? [handpainted]	Black	Hitle	B
Wolf, CL	10365	Woe is me / unconditional / surrender / loss of / empire [handpainted]	Unknown	Japan	C
Wolf, CL	10615	Your turn / comes / next [handpainted]	Black	Japan	B
Wolf, RL	5179	May your Xmas / be happy / with victory [handpainted]	Multicolored	Holid	C
Wolf, RL	5876	Only the / beginning [handpainted] / 5th war loan etc. [cut-&-pasted paper]	Black	Japan	C
Wolf, RL	9713	Wake / up / Get ready for the / 6th war / loan [handpainted]	Unknown	Bonds	B
Yontz	723	Atomic bomb. [handpainted]	Multicolored	Atom	D

NOTES and SOURCES

1. Youngblood, Wayne. "Art & envelopes," *American Philatelist* 119 (2):122-126, Feb 2005.

2. Brennan, Jan and John Joseph Brennan. "A chat with Dorothy Wallace Knapp," *First Days* 27 (1):28-36, Jan 1982.

3. Ibid., p. 30.

4. Rush, John Max. "Patriotic covers," *Current Covers and Stamplets* 1 (2):7-8, Oct 1944.

5. Dannells, Capt. Richard A. Letter to A.R. Rowell, Oakland, California, June 23, 1944; author's collection.

6. Berg, Robin. *World War II Envelope Art of Cécile Cowdery* (Lakeville, Minnesota: USM, Inc., 1992).

7. Ibid., p. 9.

8. Martin, Charles W. "Catalogue of hand painted patriotic covers by Mrs. Dorothy W. Knapp," *Current Covers and Stamplets* 1 (1):5-7, Sep 1944. Martin noted enthusiastically: "Here indeed is artistry at its best. These covers show a depth of imagination and a gift of illustration which surpasses anything this writer has seen to date."

9. Rush, John Max. "Patriotic covers," *Current Covers and Stamplets* 1 (1):2-3, Sep 1944. While extolling the artistry of these creations ("Mrs. Knapp has dipped her brush in magic"), Rush displayed an uncanny prescience concerning the significance and possible afterlife of Knapp's patriotic envelopes: "These are for you who love beauty and for all who come after." Other farseeing observations of Rush may be found on pages 91 and 110 (endnote 2), in Chapter 5.

5

From Here To Everywhere:
Postal History

Often collectors shun twentieth century patriotic covers for their philatelic contrivance. World War II patriotics offer no exception. However, with a little search non-philatelic usages can be found that will dress up any war related collection or exhibit that attempts to convey the postal history of the era.
— Louis Fiset[1]

THIS CHAPTER explores the contributions made to postal history by United States patriotic envelopes of World War II.

When, in 2001, the American Philatelic Society created a new Illustrated Mail Division for competitive national philatelic exhibits, it did more than make acceptable the judging and exhibiting of advertising, first day, and patriotic covers. It allowed collectors to think in new ways. Specifically, it allowed collectors and exhibitors of postal history (which in practice commonly means rates, routes, markings, usages, and handling of mail) to think in new ways. And it allowed them to add spice to their exhibits by including examples of illustrated mail—provided they displayed the proper postal history pedigree, of course.

We are only now beginning to see the exhibition fruits of this union of cachet and postal usage.

The early glimmerings of the union were discerned during the war itself. Collectors then were busy coping with the frenzied output of patriotic envelopes. Collecting all they could find, sorting out their designers and publishers, and characterizing types of covers were the preoccupations of many collectors. Some, though, also followed the opening and closing of post offices at army and navy bases when they could discover them. One perceptive philatelic writer, in his "Patriotic Cover Parade" column, noted that the Normandy invasion brought a "deluge of covers from everywhere. Our boys in the invasion . . . mailed many fine covers of historic interest. The collectors in the U.S. were not asleep either. My collection of this date contains many fine cachets with various cancels. But the most interesting are the A.P.O. [Army Post Office] cancels. The boys in France, in Italy, and elsewhere have been wonderful to remember us here at home."[2]

Nearly 60 years later, long after postal history had matured as a collecting interest internationally, inclusion of illustrated mail in national exhibits has opened the "left side" of the envelope to postal history exhibitors, and the mailstream adventures of patriotic envelopes have been re-discovered. These adventures show the workings of wartime domestic and foreign destination surface mail and airmail, and illustrate civilian and military usages of all classes of mail.

Postal history exhibits are often organized around the usages of a single stamp or series of stamps. Using key wartime stamp issues (and "stampless" covers created by the free mail privilege for the armed forces) as an organizing principle is a logical way as well to illustrate postal history aspects of World War II patriotic covers.

Presidential Series of 1938
(The "Prexies")

Between April and December 1938 a new Presidential series of regular postage stamps was issued to replace the series of 1922-1925 that had been in use for well over a decade. Face values of the stamps ranged from the ½¢ Benjamin Franklin to the $5 Calvin Coolidge adhesives.

In service until 1954, the Prexies carried the mail throughout the entire wartime period and found their way onto many a patriotic cover, beginning early in the European war.

First-class mail included letters, cards, matter wholly or partly in writing, typewritten matter mailed sealed against inspection, and mail for which first-class handling was requested. The 3¢ per oz. rate prevailed throughout the war, though there was also a first-class local (intra-city) letter rate of 2¢ per oz. Figure 1A illustrates an example of early wartime usage of the local rate for a patriotic envelope (cachet 2216) by an unknown cachet maker, mailed within

Figure 1. Presidential Series on patriotic covers. A, cachet 2216. B, cachet 1630, mailed on 1st anniversary of Pearl Harbor attack. C, cachet 4724. D, cachet 84. E, cachet 3710, solo use of 18¢ Prexie. F, cachet 2366, airmail from Manus, Admiralty Islands.

Galesburg, IL. It paid the 2¢ carrier post office local rate in November 1939. The rate was paid by the 2¢ John Adams stamp.

More than three years later a patriotic envelope (cachet 1630) produced by an unknown designer commemorated the first anniversary of the attack on Pearl Harbor (Figure 1B). A 3¢ Thomas Jefferson stamp, machine-cancelled in Honolulu, paid the first-class rate. The Honolulu censor handstamp vividly illustrated censorship of outgoing mail from Hawaii.

Third-class mail included merchandise and printed matter weighing no more than 8 oz. (Over 8 oz., such matter went as fourth-class mail.) Figure 1C shows a wrapper (cachet 4724), sealed at the top with a gold star, which unfolded becomes an illustrated advertisement for a "new set of Gold Star patriotics" published in 1942 by "Tex" Edmunds. The wrapper paid 1½¢, the basic third-class single-piece rate per 2 oz. The rate was paid by the 1½¢ Martha Washington stamp.

An example of properly franked third-class, regular (commercial usage), bulk/quantity-discount mail is illustrated in Figure 1D (cachet 84). To qualify for the 1¢ minimum per piece rate it was necessary to mail 200 or more identical pieces (or a total of 20 lbs. of identical pieces) in one mailing. The phrase "Sec. 562, P.L. & R." (Postal Laws & Regulations) was required to be printed or handstamped above or below the postage stamp. The 1¢ rate was paid by two ½¢ Benjamin Franklin stamps (inverted on the cover).

The registry system provided special safeguards for transmission of money and other valuable mail to domestic destinations. For the period through March 25, 1944, the basic registry fee, in additional to regular postage, was 15¢ for indemnity not exceeding $5. The registered first-class cover shown in Figure 1E (cachet 3710) was mailed in February 1943. Postage paid was 18¢: registry fee 15¢ + first-class rate 3¢. The rate was paid with a solo 18¢ Ulysses S. Grant stamp.

Military uses of domestic airmail registered service are found on patriotic covers, such as the Minkus cover illustrated in Chapter 3, Figure 7F (cachet 4812). It was sent on May 7, 1944, after the registry rate change. The mail was rated at 26¢: 20¢ registry + 6¢ airmail (overseas military rate). The envelope was mailed from the 36th General Hospital, APO 380, Caserta, Italy, to "Connersville, NY." But there was "no such post office in state named" (there were two towns named Connersville in the U.S., one in Indiana, the other in Oklahoma), so the cover was stamped "Returned for Better Address" at the APO NY Registry Division, received a "Return to Sender" pointing finger handstamp, and was returned to the soldier in Italy. The cover is a most unusual example of mail addressed to the U.S. returned to a serviceman stationed abroad. Note use of the 20¢ James A. Garfield to pay the registry fee.

The airmail envelope shown in Figure 1F (cachet 2366, by an unknown cachet maker) was mailed in January 1944 from Advance Base Section Drydock (ABSD-2), located at Manus, Admiralty Islands. The sailor who mailed it paid the 6¢ overseas military rate by applying the maximum number of stamps he could use to pay the exact rate—twelve ½¢ Benjamin Franklin stamps, including a margin block of eight stamps.

These illustrated covers are a few of the challenging usages of the Presidential Series of 1938 on World War II patriotic envelopes.

National Defense Issue of 1940

In its official description of U.S. postage stamps, the Post Office Department wrote of the three-stamp National Defense issue: "This series of postage stamps, temporarily replacing the regular issues, was provided to create a general consciousness of the existing threat to our security and focus attention upon the necessity for developing an adequate national defense."[3]

Unlike the complex, multi-valued, and long-lived Prexies, the National Defense Issue was a temporary series created primarily for first-class letter and postcard use. The issue consisted of a 1¢ Statue of Liberty stamp, a 2¢ antiaircraft gun stamp, and a 3¢ uplifted torch stamp, each with "For Defense" printed below the design.

The stamps appeared in October 1940, at a critical juncture following the German conquests of western Europe and over a year before the Japanese attack on Pearl Harbor. In a famous Fireside Chat in December, President Roosevelt forcefully captured the threat to American national security: "If Great Britain goes down, the Axis powers will control the continents of Europe, Asia, Africa, Australasia, and the high seas—and they will be in a position to bring enormous military and naval resources against this hemisphere. . . . We must have more ships, more guns, more planes—more of everything. . . . We must be the great arsenal of democracy."[4]

The first stamps issued in reaction to the war, the National Defense stamps were essentially "patriotic" conceptions. For the next four years they, *and especially the war-related stamps issued after Pearl Harbor*, inspired or complemented the messages of patriotic envelopes.[5]

As American forces began to spread to bases in the Americas, and sometimes beyond, more patriotic covers were being created and more were being mailed to and from these bases. The Defense issue stamps often paid the prevailing rates, creating mailstream memories that delight present-day collectors of World War II postal history.

The first U.S. branch post office established on foreign soil in World War II was established at St. Johns, Newfoundland, on January 15, 1941. Figure 2A illustrates a patriotic cover mailed from the first American overseas army post office on the first day of its operation. The cover (cachet 2242), produced by an unknown cachet maker, is postmarked "American Forces in Newfoundland / Jan 15 / 2 PM

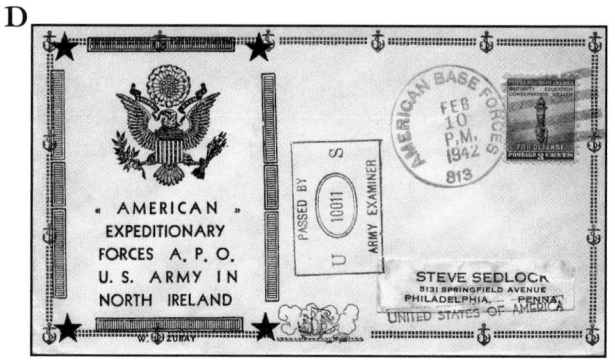

Figure 2. National Defense Issue on patriotic covers. A, cachet 2242, mailed on first day of operation of first overseas APO. B, cachet 8694, mailed on first day of operation of APO 802, Bermuda. C, cachet 5895, mailed on December 7, 1941. D, cachet 478. E, cachet 849. F, cachet 2580, mailed from Milne Bay, New Guinea.

/ 1941." Mailed unsealed, it is franked with the 2¢ antiaircraft gun stamp of the Defense issue.

A series of patriotic envelopes appeared in 1941 celebrating "United / hemisphere defense" and commemorating the opening of American APOs at new bases in the Caribbean and elsewhere. Figure 2B shows such a cover (cachet 8694) from APO 802, Bermuda, noting the opening on April 18, 1941, of "American forces / in Bermuda / Station - New York Post Office / Albert Goldman - Postmaster." Produced by an unknown cachet maker, the cover—like others in the series—bears the autograph of Postmaster Goldman and the name and address of the addressee in calligraphy. The cover is franked with all three Defense Issue stamps; their 6¢ total face value was enough to pay double the first-class rate.

Shown in Figure 2C is a patriotic envelope with a Christmas slogan cancel and singular postmark dated December 7, 1941. Few envelopes, illustrated or otherwise, were legitimately canceled on that Sunday; but John A. Mayne of St. Louis managed to have an envelope stamped with the 2¢ antiaircraft gun stamp, machine-canceled, and mailed to himself as a local letter (clearly denoted by his writing "City" in the address). This memorable piece of postal history was crowned by Mayne's creation of a thermographed cachet (cachet 5895) recalling that day's attack on Pearl Harbor.

The American Expeditionary Forces cover (cachet 478) shown in Figure 2D was produced by Walter Czubay of Astoria, New York, and mailed from the first army post office established in the United Kingdom during World War II. This was APO 813, Victoria Barracks, Belfast, Northern Ireland. It was sent just two months after the attack on Pearl Harbor. The handstamp containing only "813" as the APO descriptor was in use for five months beginning February 4, 1942. The first-class rate was paid by use of the 3¢ uplifted torch stamp.

The first-class rate was again paid by use of the 3¢ uplifted torch stamp on a patriotic cover that is an exemplary piece of little-known but significant wartime postal history. It is shown in Figure 2E. Behind this cover lies the compelling story of war bond drives and the priority accorded American postal communications in World War II.

From November 1942 through December 1945 there were eight national war bond drives (officially named "War Loans"), each lasting about a month.

Thus, nearly one-quarter of the wartime period was occupied by feverish attempts to meet the dollar quotas for the sales of bonds to help finance the war.

Each drive had a slogan or symbol associated with it. The first "Back the Attack" drive was the Third War Loan of September 9-October 2, 1943. As part of its home front activities for the bond drive, the army mounted an exhibit on the grounds of the Washington Monument in Washington, DC, starting the first day of the drive and ending September 26. The exhibit featured a complete Army Post Office field unit conducted entirely by army postal personnel. This working APO at the Washington Monument was an opportunity for American families to see how the mail they exchanged with their loved ones overseas was handled.

The APO exhibit highlighted what the Postmaster General considered the most important task of his Post Office Department: "The expeditious handling of official military and naval mail and seeing to it that our men and women in the armed forces have rapid and uninterrupted postal communication with their families and friends. All other postal problems must be and are subordinated to this one."[6]

The patriotic envelope shown in Figure 2E (cachet 849) was created by the U.S. Army for the APO exhibit at the Washington Monument. It was mailed on the exhibit's opening day, which coincided with the first day of the Third War Loan. The cover contains a "Back the Attack" machine cancel along with the official purple handstamped "Back the Attack" cachet of the Army Postal Service.

Despite being gradually replaced by new war-related stamps in 1942 and 1943, stamps of the Defense Issue continued to be used. An example is shown in Figure 2F. Mailed from APO 703, Milne Bay, New Guinea, in September 1944, this "Japanese Hunting License" cover (cachet 2580) was published by Walter L. Czubay of Astoria, NY. Three 1¢ cent Statue of Liberty stamps of the Defense issue were used to pay the first-class rate (although the soldier sending it could have used his free mailing privilege).

Win the War Stamp of 1942

This was the stamp that launched a thousand ships loaded to the gunwales with mail going nearly everywhere in the world.

Early in 1942 President Roosevelt requested creation of a "war stamp," but one with a difference—no depictions of armed might, no bombers, tanks, cannons, or warships.

An official of the Bureau of Engraving and Printing came upon a poster, "Ships for Victory," created for the United States Maritime Commission. The poster featured the official insignia of the Maritime Commission, a figurative eagle with wings in a "V" position, encircled by 13 stars, with the words "Ships for Victory," on a curved panel imposed on the design. Postmaster General Frank C.

Walker liked the poster design. With the inscription changed to "Win the War," the new design was ready for Presidential review.

FDR made three suggestions: the stamp should be of ordinary, not commemorative, size; it should be "a rich, deep purple, and the eagle should have very little engraving on it so that it will stand out in great contrast to the background"; and it should be issued as a single stamp, not as part of a series.[7]

The President's suggestions were adopted. On July 4, 1942, the 3¢ Win the War Stamp was issued "to symbolize the nation's war effort and victory goal

Figure 3. The Win the War stamp on patriotic covers. A, cachet 4295, mailed twice. B, 6921, "Inter-Island" mail between Marines in the Pacific. C, cachet 8949, from French cruiser *Montcalm*. D, cachet 4200, treaty rate to Peru. E, cachet 9256, patriotic fancy cancel. F, cachet 7031, special delivery.

on the anniversary of American Independence, and to displace, eventually, the 3-cent National Defense stamp."[8]

Over the next three and a half years, 20,642,793,000 Win the War stamps were printed—a production record in such a short time. "Even for an era in which the United States would win global renown for its ability to go from plan to prototype," wrote philatelic journalist Fred W. Baumann decades later, "the 3¢ Win the War stamp was exceptional." Baumann rightly called it the "philatelic foot soldier" of World War II, adding that "few U.S. collectors are unacquainted with it, whatever their ages may be."[9]

Its powerful theme propelled the Win the War stamp into becoming the dominant American postage stamp of its day. Complementing the message conveyed by wartime illustrated envelopes, the Win the War stamp became a favorite choice to pay the postal rate on patriotic covers. Its wartime usages featured an unprecedented variety of postal routes, means of handling and delivering mail, and special mailing situations—all on a worldwide scale. Only now are collectors beginning to fathom the extent of the stamp's wartime postal history.

Military auxiliary markings on a patriotic envelope tell the tragic story of one soldier involved in the cross-Channel invasion of France in June 1944. Chapter 1, Figure 19D illustrates the cover (cachet 3705). With the Win the War stamp paying the first-class letter rate, the cover was mailed on May 15, 1944, to a soldier in the 70th Tank Battalion, stationed in England. Three weeks later, on D-Day, the soldier's unit was in battle on Utah Beach in Normandy. Within days, joined with the 4th Infantry Division, the 70th Tank Battalion was fighting its way across the Cotentin Peninsula toward Cherbourg.

The soldier was killed in action (handwritten "K.I.A." on front of envelope) in the first days of the cross-Channel invasion. His company commander verified his death on June 26 (handwritten notation, back). The envelope was then sent unopened to the 1st Base Post Office in England and returned across the Atlantic to the sender (handstamps, front).

Auxiliary markings, this time civilian in origin, tell the story of a patriotic envelope (cachet 4295) that was mailed and postmarked twice [Figure 3A]. Entering the mailstream maelstrom without a postage stamp in Dubuque on June 30, 1944, it was returned

for postage on July 3rd (handstamps). On July 8, with the Win the War stamp added to pay the first-class letter rate, the envelope was again postmarked and the stamp canceled. A handstamp was added stating, "This is the mail for which you sent postage," and the patriotic cover was on its way to Fairmont, WV.

The patriotic envelope illustrated in Figure 3B has a small "Semper Fidelis" cachet in its upper left corner (cachet 6921). Two Win the War stamps paid the special wartime airmail rate of 6¢ per half ounce for airmail sent to or from members of the U.S. armed forces serving outside the continental United States. In this case, the cover was sent in August 1945 to *and* from members of the armed forces—to a Marine on one Pacific island, from a fellow Marine on a second Pacific island. Hence the handwritten "Inter Island" docketing. The mail traveled from the First Marine Regiment (Infantry), First Marine Division, Okinawa—the Navy No. in the postmark, 12867, indicated the cover was sent through First Marine Division Headquarters—to the Tenth Marine Regiment (Artillery), Second Marine Division, Saipan. Few such inter-island missives survived the war.

Sometimes the Win the War stamp legitimately paid the first-class letter rate for mail from foreign armed forces, including warships. An example is the patriotic envelope (cachet 8949) shown in Figure 3C. There is a story behind this cover mailed from the French cruiser, *Montcalm.*

Soon after Anglo-American troops invaded French North Africa in November 1942, the French scuttled their fleet in Toulon to prevent a German takeover. *Montcalm* was one of a number of French warships that escaped to North Africa and traveled on to the United States. Repaired and modernized in Boston, Philadelphia, or Hampton Roads, they returned to the western Mediterranean in late 1943. *Montcalm* was refitted in Philadelphia. Permitted to use U.S. postal services provided its mail bore U.S. postage, the ship (and others of the French fleet) produced covers handstamped with French ocean service markings and franked with U.S. stamps.

The wartime rate for surface mail to most foreign countries was 5¢ for the first ounce and 3¢ for each additional ounce, but a special treaty rate of 3¢ per ounce prevailed for surface mail to Canada, Mexico, the countries of Central and South America, and

Spain and its possessions. The treaty rate made it inevitable that the Win the War stamp would be found on mail to most or all of these countries. And the ubiquity of patriotic covers made it inevitable that some of them, franked with the Win the War stamp, would be found in civilian mail to these countries. Figure 3D shows such a cover. The Win the War stamp paid the 3¢ treaty surface rate on this patriotic cover (cachet 4200) mailed from Blasdell, NY, to Lima, Peru.

The fancy cancel was supposed to be dead. Its epitaph was sounded in 1934 by the Third Assistant

Postmaster General, who ordered that postage stamps on mail matter must be canceled only with devices and black ink furnished by the Post Office Department. But the spirit of great events prevailed and patriotic fancy cancels—sometimes fashioned to complement patriotic cachets—began appearing on mail soon after Pearl Harbor. An example is shown in Figure 3E, which illustrates a patriotic envelope (cachet 9256) franked with the Win the War stamp. The stamp is canceled with a fancy "V" cancel created and used in Salem, Oregon, by Edwin R. Payne. It is recorded that Payne, "in a purely patriotic

Figure 4. The Allied Nations and Four Freedoms stamps on patriotic covers. A, cachet 10311, local letter rate. B, cachet 5335, postage due. C, cachet 8137, end of the local letter rate. D, cachet 8021, censored from Hawaii. E, cachet 10111, sent airmail to San Francisco, surface to Honolulu. F, cachet 9660A, mailed on VJ Day.

urge, devised a number of patriotic fancy cancelers which he used in his capacity of cancellation clerk in the Salem post office. Eventually the Post Office Department requested that he refrain from using any but official cancelers."[10]

The Win the War stamp also paid the first-class letter portion on mail requiring special services. This is shown in the patriotic envelope (cachet 7031) pictured in Figure 3F. Paying the 10¢ special delivery rate plus 3¢ for first-class handling, the cover was mailed from Ayer, MA, at 6 PM on June 22, 1944, and arrived at the Sampson, NY, post office the next morning (receiving mark on back of envelope).

These are only a few examples in which the singular Win the War stamp complemented the statements made by patriotic envelopes in wartime mailing situations.

Allied Nations and Four Freedoms Postage Stamps of 1943

American entry into the war rendered obsolete the message of the Defense Issue of 1940. Late in 1942 President Roosevelt came across a drawing depicting "an army of uplifted swords marching behind an uplifted palm branch of peace. The president considered the work perfect, for he felt his entire philosophy of peace and cooperation was depicted in the drawing."[11]

On January 14, 1943, the stamp based on that drawing, the 2¢ Nations United for Victory stamp (officially labeled the United Nations stamp,[12] more commonly known as the Allied Nations stamp), was issued to replace the 2¢ National Defense stamp "and as a tribute to the unity with which the liberty-loving nations of the world are marching toward victory over aggressors."[13]

About a month later, on February 12, 1943 (Lincoln's birthday), a new 1¢ Four Freedoms stamp was issued. Its message clearly echoed the "new birth of freedom" promised in Lincoln's Gettysburg Address. This stamp's origins lay in the President's State of the Union address delivered two years earlier, in which he spoke of the four freedoms—freedom of speech and expression, freedom of worship, freedom from want, and freedom from fear—as the foundation of security of the world in the future. The stamp was formally issued "to impress upon the public the necessity of spreading the Four Freedoms throughout the world, and to replace the 1-cent National Defense stamp."[14]

The stamps found use in many mailing situations. One is shown in Figure 4A. The 2¢ Allied Nations stamp paid the local letter rate in Birmingham, MI, on a patriotic envelope (cachet 10311) mailed on the first anniversary of the formation of the women's branch of the Coast Guard, the SPARS. (The name was derived from the motto of the Coast Guard, *Semper Paratus*.) A SPARS label and printed newspaper cut-out are both tied to the cover.

A mailer in Dayton, OH, attempted to pay the local rate on a letter sent to Cambridge City, IN, with results shown in Figure 4B. The underpaid patriotic cover (cachet 5335) was delivered after 1¢ postage due was paid (Cambridge City hand cancel ties postage due stamp).

Paying the first-class letter rate on a patriotic envelope (cachet 8137) shown in Figure 4C are the Allied Nations and Four Freedoms stamps. The cover was machine-cancelled in Honolulu and mailed to the cachet maker in the same city on March 26, 1944. Beginning this date, the local mail rate became a thing of the past, never to return, and the 3¢ letter rate applied to all first-class civilian mail.

Shown in Figure 4D is a patriotic envelope (cachet 8021) postmarked in Honolulu on September 9, 1943, and subject to civil censorship there. (September 9 was the first day of the third of eight national war bond drives, all filled with immense efforts to exceed expected purchases of war bonds: Hawaii and the nation exceeded their respective quotas—$15 billion was the national quota; $18.9 billion was raised.) The 3¢ first-class rate for surface mail from Hawaii to the mainland was paid with the Four Freedoms and Allied Nations stamps.

For the prevailing mainland airmail rate letters between Hawaii and the continental U.S. traveled by air (between mainland cities) and surface (between mainland and Hawaii). Figure 4E pictures a patriotic cover (cachet 10111) franked with three Allied Nations stamps and marked "Air Mail to Coast." The letter traveled by air from Kent, OH, to San Francisco, where it was censored, and then completed its journey to Honolulu as surface mail.

The hand painted patriotic envelope shown in Figure 4F (cachet 9660A) was mailed on VJ Day, September 1945. Eight 1¢ Four Freedoms stamps paid the 8¢ domestic air mail rate that had replaced the 6¢ rateon March 26, 1944. On this occasion, as on other significant occasions of the war, the postage stamps chosen to carry the mail added their own message to that of the VJ Day cachet.

Overrun Countries Commemorative Stamps Issue of 1943-1944

Toward the end of 1942 Ernest A. Kehr, stamp news editor of the *New York Herald Tribune* and personal philatelic advisor to President Roosevelt, was called to meet with the president and discuss a new issue of stamps. Kehr later recalled that the president "advanced the idea of using flags of each of the overrun nations of Europe, printed in their correct colors and set in a frame that included the picture of a phoenix to symbolize regeneration." The president concluded: "It might tell those suffering victims in Europe that we are struggling for their own regeneration." Kehr added, without surprise: "A few months later, the Post Office Department announced that the flag stamps would be issued in honor of the overrun nations of Europe."[15]

The horizontally arranged commemoratives of the Overrun Countries Issue consisted of 13 stamps. Twelve, issued between June and December 1943, honored European nations overrun and occupied by German forces. These included Poland (stamp issued June 22, 1943), Czechoslovakia, Norway, Luxembourg, Netherlands, Belgium, France, Greece, Yugoslavia, Albania, Austria, and Denmark (stamp issued December 7, 1943). Nearly a year later (November 2, 1944) a stamp in the series was issued for Korea, occupied for a half century by Japan.

All of the stamps were of 5¢ denomination. This paid the surface rate for mail to most countries beyond the Western Hemisphere. Unfortunately, many of these were occupied by Axis powers and could receive no mail from the United States.

One student of this issue noted that though " few Overrun Countries stamps penetrated the enemy's heartland, they became favorites of philatelic warriors, who used them frequently on commemorative patriotic as well as first day covers."[16] Often, these "philatelic warriors" were happy to use the multicolored stamps on domestic mail, overpaying the 3¢ rate in order to have Overrun Countries stamps canceled on significant war dates. An example is shown in Figure 5A. This patriotic envelope (cachet 395) proclaimed: "Allies invade the European continent / D-Day / June 6, 1944." A Fort McPherson, GA, hand cancel of that date tied the French flag stamp of the Overrun Countries Issue. Because there was no address and no evidence of erasure of a pencilled address, it is likely that the patriotic cover was serviced at the Fort McPherson post office on a hand-back basis.

Another example of overpaying the first-class rate so an Overrun Countries stamp might be used on a significant date (and complement a cachet message) is shown in Figure 5B. Cachet design and Austrian flag stamp adumbrated the expected cross-Channel invasion as Baby New Year hammered at the forge of Victory on a hand painted patriotic envelope (cachet 10477A) mailed on January 1, 1944.

When Paris was liberated late in August, a hand painted patriotic envelope commemorating the event (cachet 6100) was mailed by a soldier from APO 520, Cerignola, Italy. This airmail cover is shown in Chapter 1, Figure 19D. The soldier-designer used the French flag stamp both to reinforce the message of the cachet and (together with a 1¢ Defense Issue stamp) pay the 6¢ airmail rate.

Incoming mail to servicemen abroad is much more difficult to find than outgoing mail from members of military units back to the United States. Servicemen on the move had little time or opportunity to save their mail. An example of a patriotic envelope (cachet 440) that was mailed overseas to a Marine is shown in Figure 5C. Mailed from Kokomo, IN, in September 1943, the airmail cover went to a member of Marine Air Group 25, Fleet Marine Air Wing, at Navy #131, Noumea, New Caledonia. For good measure, a "Hurry Up! / This is for a / Marine" label was added to the envelope, and was tied by the circular date stamp of the machine cancel. The 5¢ Luxembourg flag stamp and 1¢ Four Freedoms stamp paid the airmail letter rate.

Figure 5D illustrates an example of outgoing mail sent from overseas to the United States is shown in. This patriotic envelope (cachet 4336) was mailed by a sailor on Craft 156 of LCT (Landing Craft, Tank)

Flotilla 5, in Pacific waters in 1945. Two Greek flag stamps of the Overrun Countries Issue overpaid the six cent airmail rate for overseas members of the armed forces by four cents.

The patriotic envelope illustrated in Figure 5E is (cachet 7562) was mailed from Pottstown, PA, to an army officer (and patriotic cover collector) in Camp Maxey, TX. It paid the prevailing eight cent airmail rate with the 5¢ Danish flag stamp and the 3¢ Motion Picture Commemorative stamp issued in 1944.

Why the variations in airmail rates? The domestic airmail letter rate was *six cents per ounce* beginning July 1, 1934. In the midst of the war, on March 26, 1944, the rate increased to *eight cents per ounce*. That is part of the explanation of airmail rate variations, not the whole. Because American forces were beginning to be widely dispersed in 1941, and because this dispersion was accelerated after Pearl Harbor, a special wartime rate of *six cents per half ounce* went into effect on December 25, 1941, for mail sent to or from members of the U.S. armed forces serving outside the continental United States. On October 21, 1942, the special six cent per half ounce rate was extended to mail sent to or from American civilians

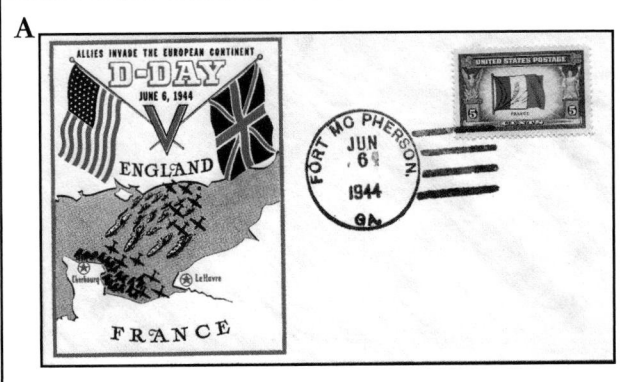

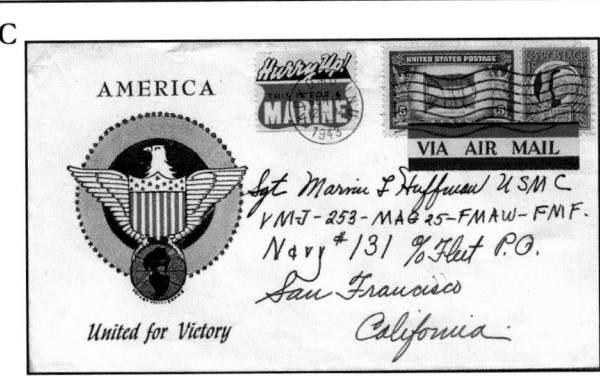

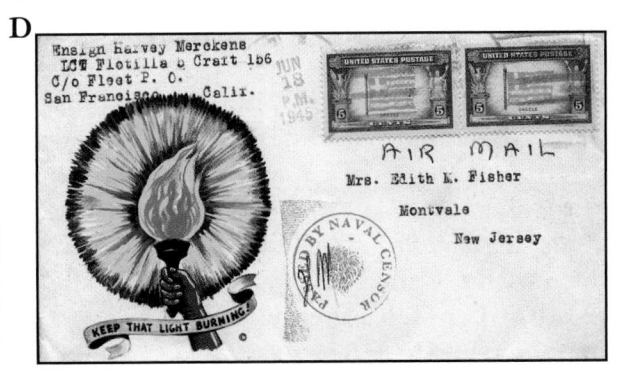

Figure 5. Overrun Countries Series on patriotic covers. A, cachet 395, D-Day. B, cachet 10477A, New Year's Day 1944. C, cachet 440, airmail to a member of Marine Air Group 25, New Caledonia. D, cachet 4336, 6¢ airmail from an LCT in the Pacific. E, cachet 7562, paying 8¢ airmail rate effective March 26, 1944. F, cachet 1966, cover paying surface rate to New Zealand.

served by U.S. military post offices outside the continental United States; and on various dates between 1942 and 1945, the special six cent rate was extended to airmail from some Allied armed forces carried by the U.S. on a space available basis. The special six cent per half ounce airmail rate remained unchanged when the U.S. domestic rate increased to eight cents on March 26, 1944.

There were times of course when an Overrun Countries stamp was used for the purpose formally intended—to pay the one-ounce surface rate to foreign countries. The patriotic cover (cachet 1966) shown in Figure 5F is an example. A 5¢ Norwegian flag stamp paid the surface rate on the cover, mailed in February 1945 from the U.S. to New Zealand.

Iwo Jima Commemorative Stamp Issue of 1945

On February 23, 1945, on top of a hill on Iwo Jima, Associated Press photographer Joe Rosenthal snapped the picture that was to thrill a nation—the raising of the United States flag on Mount Suribachi by five United States Marines and a navy corpsman. A half-century later the son of one of those who raised the flag wrote that something unusual happened to them: "Their collective image, blurred and indistinct, became the most recognized, the most reproduced, in the history of photography. It gave them a kind of immortality—a faceless immortality. The flag raising on Iwo Jima became a symbol of the island, the mountain, the battle, of World War II; of the highest ideals of the nation, of valor incarnate. It became everything except the salvation of the boys who formed it."[17]

Less than five months later the already-iconic image became the central design of a postage stamp commemorating the sacrifice and victory of the Marines on Iwo Jima.[18]

The vertically-arranged Iwo Jima commemorative stamp, printed in "Marine green," was issued on July 11, 1945. The 3¢ stamp became the progenitor of a series of stamps issued to commemorate the achievements of the armed forces in World War II (the Armed Forces Issue of 1945-1946). The other stamps in the series appeared after the war was over.

The war was to last less than eight weeks after the issuance of the Iwo Jima stamp. There was little time

for the stamp to be used in complex mailing situations, but enough time for its message of determination and victory to carry the mail on some fateful final days.

On Iwo Jima, American Marines used bazookas, flamethrowers, and flame-throwing tanks to kill fortified and dug-in Japanese defenders. Tragedy became farce on the hand painted cover (cachet 10829) mailed from San Francisco on July 31, 1945, and shown in Figure 6A. Paying the first-class letter rate, the Iwo Jima stamp provided a sober counterpoint to the "scorched backside" cachet.

A few days after that mailing the first atomic bomb was dropped on Hiroshima. Shown in Chapter 3, Figure 3G, is a patriotic envelope (cachet 7460) commemorating that event. The envelope was hand-cancelled in Washington, DC, on August 6, 1945, the day the first atom bomb was dropped. The Iwo Jima stamp paid the first-class rate and made its statement.

Three days later came the atomic bombing of Nagasaki. Again the Iwo Jima stamp was used, this time on the patriotic envelope (cachet 721) shown in Figure 6B. The stamp was machine-cancelled in Wilmington, NC, on August 9, the day of the bombing.

On August 14, 1945, the Japanese government accepted surrender terms; a day later the Emperor broadcast this to the Japanese people. The war was over. Beginning August 14, the Iwo Jima stamp was used on mail to pay the prevailing rate and to signify victory in the Pacific.

Figure 6C illustrates a patriotic envelope (cachet 9144) that was the first in a series of three (postmarked August 14 and 15 and September 2) that marked the end of the war. An Iwo Jima stamp was tied to the cover by a Reading, PA, machine cancel on each of these dates.

A striking hand painted cover (cachet 722) was sent from cachet maker Thornton C. Shaw of Sandusky, Ohio, to his soldier-son on September 1. The Iwo Jima stamp paid the domestic first-class rate for a letter to a soldier in Iceland. The intense emotion of the cachet reflected the American public's reaction to the sudden end of the war—and a father's relief at learning that his son, who had been anticipating shipment to the Pacific for the planned invasion of Japan, would be spared.

Examples of Iwo Jima stamps carrying the mail on the ultimate VJ Day, September 2, also came from overseas. One emanated from Iwo itself. This is shown in Figure 6E, which illustrates a patriotic envelope (cachet 3738A) mailed first-class to the U.S. by an army officer at APO 86 on Iwo Jima.

Figure 6F shows another VJ Day overseas usage of the Iwo Jima stamp on a patriotic envelope (cachet 9655). A soldier at APO 237, Saipan, Mariana Islands, took this locally-made mimeographed patriotic, applied two Jima stamps to pay the special 6¢ airmail rate for overseas servicemen, and sent the

envelope to—himself. This properly franked, machine-cancelled memento of the end of the war made it safely home from Saipan and has survived into the 21st century.

Transport Plane Airmail Issue, 1941-1944

Early in 1941 President Roosevelt and the Post Office Department decided that a new series of airmail stamps was needed to replace stamps of similar denomination that had been issued at various times since 1926.

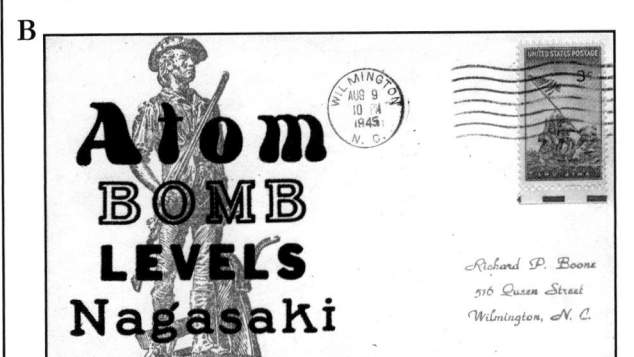

Figure 6. Iwo Jima stamp on patriotic covers. A, cachet 10829. B, cachet 721, atom bombing of Nagasaki. C, cachet 9144. D, cachet 722. E, cachet 3738A, Iwo stamp on cover from APO 86, Iwo Jima, VJ Day. F, cachet 9655, airmail from APO 237, Saipan, Mariana Islands, on VJ Day.

Once the president approved the final common design to be used on the stamps—a version of a 1940s twin-engine transport plane in flight—the stamps were issued in values of 6¢, 10¢, 15¢, 20¢, 30¢, and 50¢ on dates between June 25 and October 29, 1941. A final stamp in the series, denominated 8¢, was issued on March 21, 1944, five days before the domestic airmail rate was increased from six cents to eight cents per ounce.

After December 7, 1941, the stamps of the Transport Plane airmail issue "quickly became the workhorses of U.S. airmail stamps, seeing service on letters and packages all over the world. It was a role they would continue to play until the issuance of new airmail stamps in 1946."[19]

Figure 7A shows a patriotic cover (cachet 10219) mailed to an airman missing in the first days of the Normandy campaign. The officer was a member of the 747th Bombardment Squadron affiliated with the 456th Bombardment Group stationed at Stornara, Italy, at the time of the invasion. As part of the air offensive in Europe, the 747th Bombardment

Figure 7. Stamps of the Transport Plane Airmail Issue on patriotic covers. A, cachet 10219, to an officer in 747th Bombardment Squadron, missing in Normandy invasion. B, cachet 7105, cover mailed from APO 77, Okinawa, two days after completion of battle. C, cachet 3723, cover from USS *Cumberland Sound* , Tokyo Bay, postmarked August 28, 1945. D, cachet 8860. E, cachet 9718, airmail from Puerto Rico, censored in Miami. F, cachet 9974, airmail cover from Pearl Harbor Navy Yard, HI.

Squadron flew missions at Anzio and in the Rome-Arno regions before engaging over Normandy and northern France.

The fate of the intended recipient is recorded on the envelope, which was sent airmail from Columbus, OH, on May 29, 1944. The carmine red 6¢ transport stamp paid the concession airmail rate for mail sent to those serving outside the continental United States. "Missing," handwritten on the front, is partly obscured by a "Verified" handstamp of the 2628 Postal Directory Co. and by the pointing hand "Return to Writer" handstamp. Finally, on the back a U.S. Army Postal Service receiving handstamp at APO 785, Foggia, Italy, was dated "JUN 13, 1944." A straight-line handstamp, "JUN 19 1944," is also recorded on the back, possibly to indicate the date of return by the Army Postal Service. The May 29/June 19 dates bracket the period of engagement at Normandy by the 747th Bombardment Squadron.

The 6¢ transport stamp sometimes paid the airmail rate on letters sent home from battlefields. The patriotic envelope (cachet 7105) illustrated in Figure 7B was mailed from a soldier in the 307th Infantry Regiment, which had been fighting on Okinawa since April 25, 1945. The cover was postmarked at APO 77, Okinawa, on June 25, 1945, two days after the island was finally declared secured.

Two months later, ships of the Third Fleet assembled in Tokyo Bay for the formal Japanese surrender. The postal sections of many ships prepared special cancels and cachets for the occasion. One of them was USS *Cumberland Sound*, a seaplane tender that arrived at Tokyo Bay on August 28 to set up a seadrome for the occupation. Two green cachets adorned the busy patriotic envelope shown in Figure 7C (cachet 3723). A rectangular cachet proclaimed "*In Commemerutione,*" above a small scene of warships in Tokyo Bay backgrounded by Mount Fuji. A circular cachet announced: "First Mail . . . / Entry of Third Fleet / U.S. Navy / Tokyo Bay / Japan." The 6¢ transport stamp was tied to the cover by an August 28, 1945 U.S. Navy cancel.

On September 2 the surrender documents were signed on board the battleship USS *Missouri*. Many ships had special cancels and cachets made for mailing that day, and the 6¢ transport stamp carried them airmail to their mainland destinations. Illustrated in Chapter 1, Figure 23D, is one such patriotic cover (cachet 8602), mailed home by a sailor on USS *Saint Paul*.

The most prized of Tokyo Bay patriotic envelopes (cachet 9010) is illustrated in Chapter 1, Figure 23E. Created in the postal section of the battleship USS *Missouri* and franked with a 6¢ transport airmail stamp, it was mailed home by a sailor on the ship. The cover, used at the site and on the date of the ceremony concluding the war in the Pacific, is the nonpareil of Tokyo Bay patriotic covers. Of this USS *Missouri* patriotic it may be said: You stand alone.

Figure 7D shows a patriotic envelope (cachet 8860) picturing the USS *Houston*, successor to the cruiser of the same name sunk in the Battle of the Java Sea in 1942. The olive green 8¢ transport airplane stamp paid the prevailing airmail rate in effect since March 26, 1944.

The airmail rate between the mainland U.S. and Puerto Rico, the Virgin Islands, and Guantanamo Bay was 10¢ per ½ ounce. (The same rate obtained for airmail within or between Puerto Rico and the Virgin Islands until November 10, 1942, when the rate fell to 6¢ per ounce; intra-Hawaii and intra-Alaska air mail rates were also 6¢ per ounce.[20]) Shown in Figure 7E is a patriotic cover (cachet 9718) that was sent airmail from Puerto Rico to North Ferrisburg, VT on November 28, 1942. It was censored in Miami on its journey northward. A 1942 Christmas seal was tied to the cover by the cancel for the rate-paying purple 10¢ transport airplane stamp.

Figure 7F shows a patriotic envelope (cachet 9974) mailed from the Pearl Harbor Navy Yard. Its destination was Waukegan, Il. The green 20¢ transport airplane stamp paid the airmail rate between Hawaii and the mainland. After a U.S. Navy machine cancel and naval censor handstamp were applied, the cover was on its way across the Pacific.

Other Wartime Issues, 1940-1945

Many other stamps were issued by the United States during the 1939-1945 period, some war-related, some commemorative of people, inventions, or historical events. Eventually they found their way onto patriotic covers, either by design or by coincidence. And nuggets of postal history gold are to be found among the covers. A logical way to review usages of some of these stamps is to organize them chronologically by stamp issuance dates.

Figure 8A shows a patriotic cover (cachet 2884) mailed from San Jose, CA, to Honolulu, HI, on September 27, 1943. The cover, franked with four 10¢ James Whitcomb Riley stamps of the Famous Americans series of 1940, paid double the 20¢ per ½ ounce airmail rate between Hawaii and the mainland, and was censored in San Francisco.

From the interior of Alaska on December 11, 1942, came the censored patriotic cover (cachet 328) illustrated in Figure 8B. It was mailed from the settlement of Shageluk (population 55), located northwest of Anchorage between the Kuskokwim Mountains and the Bering Sea, and addressed to Minneapolis, MN. The 5¢ Chinese Resistance stamp of 1942 overpaid the first-class mail rate by two cents.

A patriotic envelope (cachet 623) designed by Dorothy Knapp for George Richardson is shown in Figure 8C. The 3¢ Centenary of the Telegraph stamp

Figure 8. Other wartime stamp issues on patriotic covers. A, cachet 2884, double-rate airmail to Honolulu, four 10¢ James Whitcomb Riley stamps, Famous Americans series of 1940. B, cachet 328, from Shagaluk, AK, 5¢ Chinese Resistance stamp of 1942.. C, cachet 623, date of FDR's death and Truman's swearing-in., Centenary of the Telegraph stamp of 1944. D, cachet 10429, Philippines stamp of 1944. E, cachet 1257, from Hunt, Idaho, Relocation Center, 3¢ Motion Pictures 50th Anniversary stamp of 1944. F, cachet 6143, Dorothy Knapp hand painted, VJ Day, 5¢ United Nations Conference stamp of 1945.

of 1944 paid the first-class rate on the cover, which was mailed from and to Washington, DC, on April 12, 1945, the date of FDR's death and the swearing-in of Harry Truman as the new President.

On October 20, 1944, American forces invaded Leyte as the first step in the liberation of the Philippines. General Douglas MacArthur proclaimed: "People of the Philippines, I have returned. By the grace of almighty God, our forces stand again on Philippine soil." On that date the patriotic cover (cachet 10429) shown in Figure 8D was mailed from Louisville, KY, to Jamestown, NY. A 3¢ Philippines (Corregidor) stamp appropriately paid the first-class rate. The stamp had been issued just over three weeks earlier, on September 27, 1944. The proximity of the stamp issuance to the Leyte invasion was not by coincidence—plans for the Leyte invasion had been laid months before. From its inception, President Roosevelt "intended the stamp to commemorate the heroic final defense of Corregidor in May 1942. . . . The idea of utilizing a sketch that showed the defenses of Corregidor, especially prior to the landing of U.S. troops to retake the island, appealed to FDR's sense of humor, and he insisted that the central portrait on the new stamp be that depiction of Corregidor."[21]

Finding patriotic covers mailed from Japanese-Americans evacuated from their homes on the west coast to interior relocation camps is a difficult task. The patriotic cover shown in Figure 8E is an example of this hard-to-find breed. It was mailed by an evacuee at the Hunt, Idaho, Relocation Center, on January 26, 1945. The 3¢ Motion Pictures Fiftieth Anniversary stamp of 1944, tied to the cover by the Hunt Relocation Center duplex cancel, paid the first-class rate.

On April 2, 1945, Secretary of State Edward Stettinius, Jr., wrote a memo to President Roosevelt about the forthcoming United Nations Conference on International Organization to be held in San Francisco later that month. He recommended issuance of a series of stamps commemorating the conference before the United Nations charter was to be signed. "Do you approve?" he asked the President.

"FDR not only approved, he called Postmaster General Walker from Warm Springs late that night and informed him that he had been thinking long and hard about the idea. He felt that one stamp should be issued to mark the occasion. 'The design,' he told Walker 'was to be as simple as possible.' He then suggested the wording 'Toward United Nations.' The border he thought should be plain. He approved having a small branch of laurel at the bottom as the sole decorative detail."[22]

Ten days later the president died suddenly. The last official directive he gave to his secretary the afternoon of his death concerned FDR's request to purchase the first United Nations stamp from the postmaster at San Francisco. On April 25, opening day of the Conference and 13 days after FDR's death, the stamp was issued.

Figure 8F shows a hand painted envelope (cachet 6143) by Dorothy Knapp made for VJ Day. The envelope was franked with the 5¢ United Nations Conference stamp, which contained the wording, "Toward United Nations April 25, 1945," with the late president's name added just below the text. A small branch of laurel at the bottom was, as FDR had recommended, the sole decorative detail. A Victory, VT, hand cancel dated September 2, 1945 (with "VJ" replacing the time-of-day slug in the postmark), cancelled the stamp.

Stampless First-Class Mail: The Armed Forces Free Mail Privilege

The United States Congress passed legislation on March 27, 1942, granting the free mail privilege (the "free frank") to members of the U.S. armed forces for "any first-class letter mail admissible to the mails as ordinary mail matter[,] . . . subject to such rules and regulations as the Postmaster General shall prescribe." Among its regulations the Post Office Department ordered that free franked letters and post cards "shall bear in the upper right corner the word 'FREE' and in the upper left corner the name of the sender together with his rank or rating and the designation of the service to which he belongs."[23]

The free mail privilege, which applied only to first-class mail, was put into effect on April 1, 1942. There was an immediate increase in mail volume from members of the armed forces: the Postmaster General noted in his Annual Report for 1942 that "tests prior to [granting of the free franking privilege] indicated mailings from the individual members

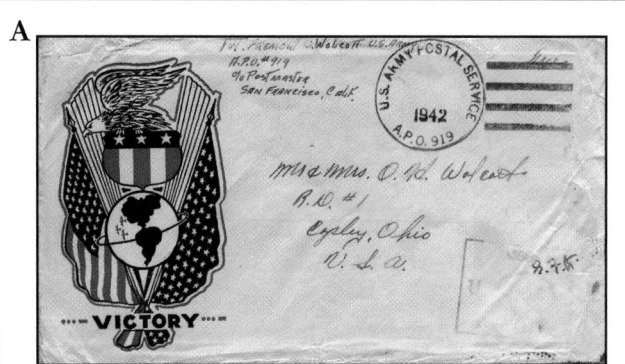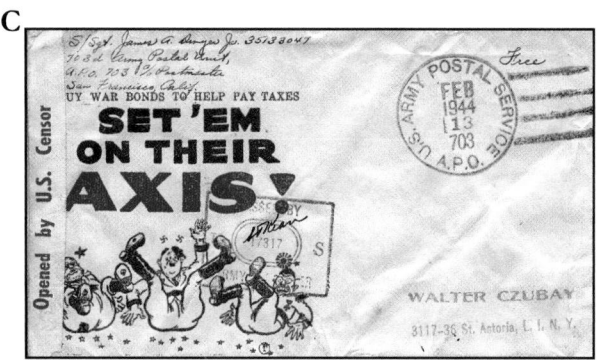

averaged three a week. Since that date the average per man has been more than four and one-half letters."[24]

It did not take long for free-franked military mail to make its postal history mark: surface mail bearing the free frank soon traveled everywhere.

Sometime in 1942—the date slug is missing from the postmark on the envelope—a soldier at APO 919, Bora Bora, Society Islands (French Polynesia), sent home the free-franked patriotic cover (cachet 9450) shown in Figure 9A. A faint army censor handstamp was placed in the lower right corner. A

"Received July 8" handwritten notation on the back indicates that the cover was sent soon after the free franking privilege was granted.

The patriotic envelope shown in Figure 9B (cachet 9706) was mailed free in October 1943 by a member of the Women's Army Corps (WAC) at their training center at Fort Leavenworth, Kansas. Initially called the Women's Army Auxiliary Corps (WAAC) the unit was authorized on May 14, 1942, after Army Chief of Staff George C. Marshall insisted that "I want a woman's corps right away and I don't want

Figure 9. Armed forces free franked first-class mail. A, cachet 9450, mailed from APO 919, Society Islands, French Polynesia. B, cachet 9706, from WAC Training Center, Fort Leavenworth, KS. C, cachet 1277, mailed from APO 703, New Guinea. D, cachet 1415, From Lt. Gen. Alexander M. Patch, Seventh Army commander, APO 758, Marseille, France. E, cachet 2325, from APO 627, Hqs. Fourteenth Air force, Kunming, China. F, cachet 7142, from Espiritu Santo, New Hebrides, with for-profit "Free" label.

any excuses." On July 14, 1943, the women's unit became the Women's Army Corps (WAC), a regular contingent of the army. At its peak strength in April 1945 the Women's Army Corps had 5,746 officers and 93,542 enlisted women. Nearly 10,000 WACs served in the European Theater of Operations and 6,000 more went to the Southwest Pacific. During the war 181 WACs died.

The free-franked patriotic envelope (cachet 1277) shown in Figure 9C was mailed on February 13, 1944, by a soldier serving in the 703rd Army Postal Unit at APO 703, Milne Bay, New Guinea. An army censor tape re-sealed the left edge of the envelope. A "FEB 25 1944" receiving notation on the back indicates that the mail bag containing the cover received airmail treatment from New Guinea: armed forces mail from remote areas of the Pacific traveled by whatever means were available at the time. Mail from New Guinea to Long Island traveling entirely by ship and truck (or train) would not have completed the journey in 12 days.

Two months after the U.S. Seventh Army invaded Southern France in August 1944, its commanding officer, Lt. General Alexander M. Patch, Jr., sent a free-franked patriotic envelope (cachet 1415) to a friend in College Park, GA. The cover is shown in Figure 9D. It was self-censored and mailed from APO 758, Headquarters of the Seventh Army, Marseille, France, by General Patch. His name, rank, and return address; addressee information; censor signature; and "Free" in the right upper corner were all written in the general's hand.

Shown in Figure 9E is a free-franked patriotic envelope (cachet 2325) mailed by Sgt. Wayne Coffin from APO 627, Kunming, China, to his wife. Sgt. Coffin was an aerial photographer (and patriotic cover collector) serving with the 16th Combat Camera Unit, stationed at the Headquarters of the 14th U.S. Air Force, Kunming. The 14th Air Force was commanded by Lt. Gen. Claire L. Chennault of "Flying Tiger" fame. Upon receiving a small supply of these "Flying Tiger" Chennault covers in July 1945, Sgt. Coffin brought them to the general for signing, then mailed the autographed covers, marked "Free," to his wife in Chicago.

As mentioned earlier, among its regulations establishing the armed forces free mailing privilege, the Post Office Department ordered that free franked letters and post cards "shall bear in the upper right corner the word 'FREE'. . . ." It did not specifically order that the word be handwritten by the sender. "Creative uses of 'Free' in the right upper corner of the envelope emerged quickly. As another form of envelope art the fancy free frank was a natural complement to the patriotic cachet, and patriotic cover publishers, freelance printers, and enterprising members of the armed forces all got into the act."[25]

A few of these last produced and sold at some military posts a printed "Postage Free for Victory" adhesive label meant to replace service members' handwritten "Free." The Third Assistant Postmaster General, administrator of postal financial matters, declared that letters bearing these stickers were not acceptable for mailing. Some in the armed forces viewed the ban as a challenge—or knew nothing about it—and dodged the proscription. And another episode in postal history was written.

The patriotic envelope (cachet 7142) shown in Figure 9F was mailed on December 13, 1944, by an airman at Navy 140, Pallikulo Airfield, Espiritu Santo, New Hebrides. A "Postage Free for Victory" label was placed in the right upper corner in place of a handwritten "Free," and was duly cancelled with a handstamp navy cancel. The cover, passed by the naval censor, went on its way to mainland USA. It serves today as another example of the American serviceman's ability to find novel ways to interpret regulations, postal or otherwise.

NOTES and SOURCES

1. Fiset, Louis. "Non-Philatelic Patriotic Covers," *The Prexie Era* (newsletter of the USSS/BIA 1938 Presidential Era Study Group) 31:9-10, Winter 2005.

2. Rush, John Max. "Patriotic Cover Parade," *Western Stamp Collector* 19 (21):5, Jan 10, 1945. Rush's astonishing ability to see beyond the moment was attested by his writing in the same article: "patriotic covers have become the interpreters of this war period of emotion and great suffering, quite as much as any other pictorial or graphic art." Present-day collectors and exhibitors of patriotic envelopes of World War II may find inspiration in this.

3. United States Post Office Department. Postage Stamps of the United States: An Illustrated Description of all United States Postage and Special Service Stamps Issued by the Post Office Department from July 1, 1847, to December 31, 1963. (Washington, DC: United States Government Printing Office, 1964), p. 103.

4. Kennedy, David M. *Freedom from Fear: The American People in Depression and War, 1929-1945* (New York: Oxford University Press, 1999), pp. 468-469.

5. I am grateful to Louis Fiset who, in discussing this chapter, emphasized the complementarity of patriotic envelopes and the patriotic stamps issued to honor our involvement in the war.

6. *Annual Report of the Postmaster General for the Fiscal Year Ending June 30, 1943* (Washington, DC: United States Government Printing Office, 1944), p. 2.

7. Baur, Brian C. *Franklin D. Roosevelt and the Stamps of the United States 1933-1945* (Sidney, Ohio: Linn's Stamp News, Amos Press, Inc., 1993), p. 275.

8. United States Post Office Department. *Postage Stamps of the United States*, p. 106.

9. Baumann, Fred W. "Win the War stamp issued 50 years ago," *Linn's Stamp News*, July 20, 1992, p. 10.

10. Loso, Foster W., and Heyliger de Windt. *20ᵗʰ Century U.S. Fancy Cancelations* (Wolfeboro, New Hampshire: Foster W. Loso and Heyliger de Windt, 1952), p. 149.

11. Baur, *Roosevelt and the Stamps of the United States*, p. 281.

12. United States Post Office Department. *Postage Stamps of the United States*, p. 106.

13. Ibid.

14. Ibid., p. 107.

15. Kehr, Ernest A. *The Romance of Stamp Collecting: Notes From the World of Stamps, Stamp Collecting and Stamp Collectors* (New York: Thomas Y. Crowell Company, 1947), pp. 262-263

16. Lawrence, Ken. "The Overrun Countries Stamps of 1943 and 1944," in Sherman, Lawrence (ed.) *The United States Post Office in World War II* (Chicago: The Chicago Collectors Club, 2002), p. 276.

17. Bradley, James, with Ron Powers. *Flags of our Fathers* (New York: Bantam Books, 2000), p. 3.

18. Bahry, Ted. "Uncommon valor: U.S. Marines and the Iwo Jima stamp," *American Philatelist* 109 (2):135-141, February 1995.

19. Baur, *Roosevelt and the Stamps of the United States*, p. 270.

20. Davis, G.H. *The Transports* (Reston, VA: The Bureau Issues Association, Inc., 1999), pp. 51-52. On p. 52 Davis states that "an example of any one of the three . . . described 6¢ rates [intra-Hawaii, intra-Alaska, and between Puerto Rico and the Virgin Islands] is rare." On the same page one of these outstanding usages is shown—a copy of a Minkus patriotic cover sent airmail from San Juan, PR, to Frederikstad, St. Croix, franked with a 6¢ transport stamp paying the inter-islands airmail postage.

21. Baur, *Roosevelt and the Stamps of the United States*, p. 308.

22. Ibid., p. 319.

23. Martorelli, Richard, "Free Surface Mail," in Sherman, *United States Post Office in World War II*, pp. 167-173.

24. *Annual Report of the Postmaster General for the Fiscal Year ended June 30 1942* (Washington, DC: United States Government Printing Office, 1942), p. 6.

25. Sherman, Lawrence. "The Price of a 'Free' Stamp," in Sherman, *United States Post Office in World War II*, pp. 174-179.

6

Wartime Journeys
of Minkus Patriotic Envelopes

OF ALL American illustrated envelopes produced during World War II, Minkus patriotic covers were the most well-traveled. Two factors contributed to this: the onrush of events from 1940 through the attack on Pearl Harbor in December 1941, and the readiness of Jacques Minkus, creator and manager of "Gimbels Famous Stamp Department." (See Chapter 3 for a brief biography of Minkus.)

American desire to avoid being dragged into another European war was challenged by the German Wehrmacht's conquests in 1940 and the air war over Great Britain (the Battle of Britain) between August and October that year. As anti-Hitler sentiment grew, isolationist/interventionist political battle lines were sharply drawn.

While negotiating his "Bases-for-Destroyers" deal to help Britain, President Roosevelt decided that one of his next domestic moves would be to issue new postage stamps to further educate his fellow countrymen. The president "wanted a series of stamps to replace the current regular stamps then in use. He specifically wanted stamps that would help focus the attention of the American people on the need for a strong national defense."[1] Using a White House letterhead, FDR sketched out for a Post Office Department representative his idea for a series of three stamps that had the words "For Defense" printed at the bottom of each.

The Post Office issued its three National Defense stamps on October 16, 1940. Not coincidentally, this was Registration Day, the date on which all men 21 to 36 years of age began registering for the "draft" under the new National Conscription Act, marking the first "peacetime" draft in American history.

The First Series of Minkus Patriotic Covers, October 1940 (12 Covers)

In the days before the Post Office issued its three National Defense stamps Minkus published a series of 12 illustrated envelopes for use as first day covers and patriotic covers.

Over time Minkus expressed two motivations for producing his first series of illustrated envelopes. Soon after they appeared he commented: "Our people are particularly conscious now of their liberty, and prouder than ever to be Americans. They say so and express it in every possible manner, and we, therefore, decided to bring out these cachet designs for use on personal as well as first-day-cover use."[2] Three decades later he added that he wanted "to help make people aware of what was going on. You may be aware that there were a lot of isolationists in this country who were arguing that we didn't have to bother with the rest of the world and we could live by ourselves."[3]

Minkus, who had seen at first hand the rise of Hitler's National Socialists in Germany, was ready to blow his philatelic trumpet to wake up America.

Soon a large "Gimbels Famous Stamp Department" advertisement offered this first set of Minkus patriotic envelopes for sale by mail: 12 first day covers for $1.00; 120 un-serviced patriotic envelopes also for $1.00. The ad proclaimed: "It's an American idea! It's a great idea! . . . Patriotic envelopes were used during the Civil War. Today they're more appropriate than ever."[4] This was the beginning of Minkus's campaign to make his illustrated envelopes broadly available to Americans everywhere—civilian or soldier, at home or abroad.

Even before Pearl Harbor, American forces began to spread to foreign places in the Western Hemisphere. Minkus was ready for their overseas deployment.

In September 1940, the Bases-for-Destroyers deal with Britain went into effect. The United States obtained rights to bases in the Caribbean that would prove invaluable for defense of the Panama Canal and the Atlantic coast in case of war with Germany.

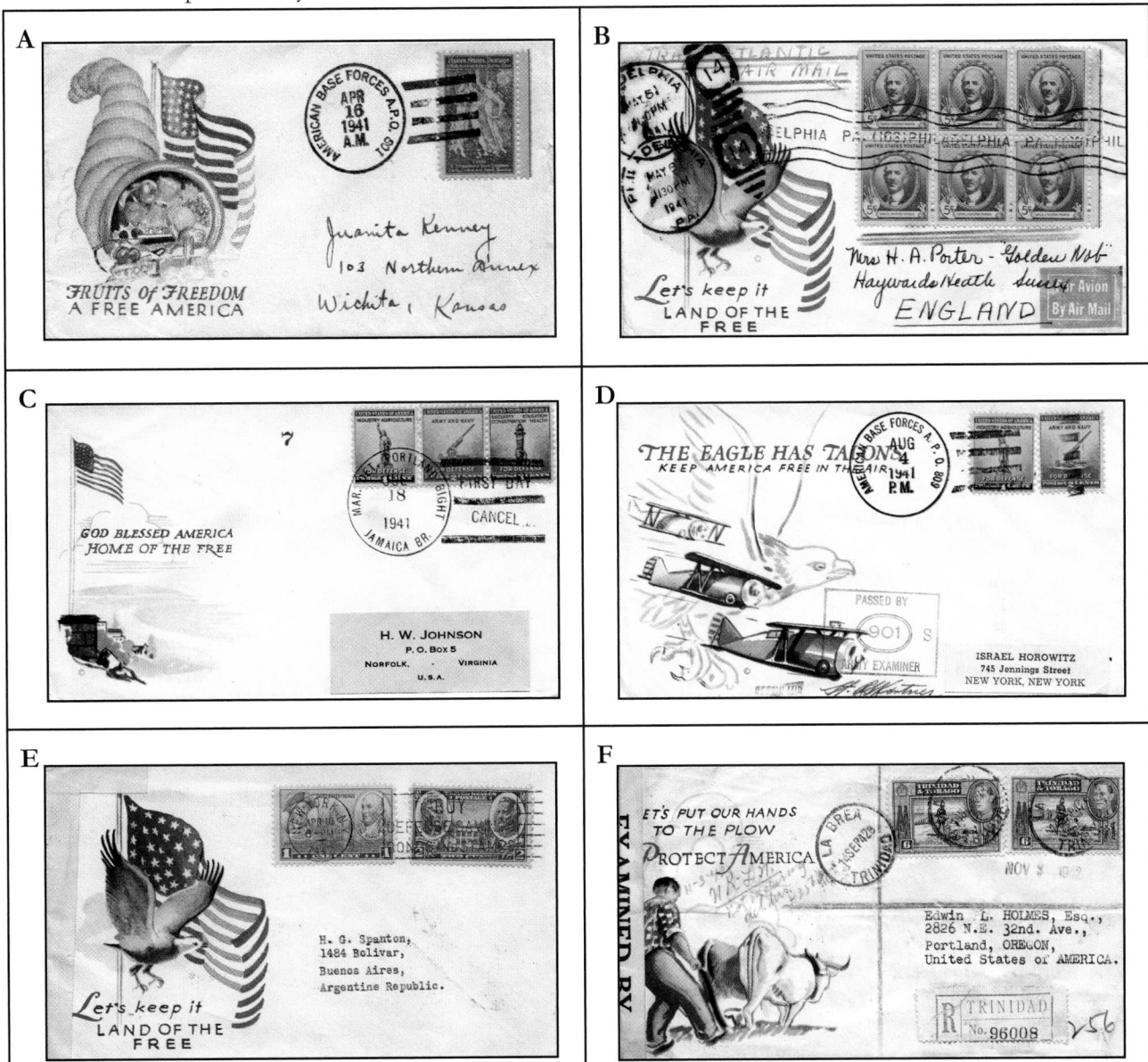

Figure 1. First series of Minkus covers, produced in 1940. A, Cachet 2683, from APO 801, St. Johns, Newfoundland, the first overseas U.S. APO in World War II, postmarked April 16, 1941, first day of operation. B, Cachet 4615, airmail to England, May 1941; 30¢ paid by six 5¢ Samuel Chester French stamps of the Famous Americans series of 1940. C, Cachet 3050, July 18, 1941, first day, Marine detachment postal facility, Portland Bight, Jamaica. D, Cachet 7512, from APO 809, Narsarssuak, Greenland, August 1941. E, Cachet 4615, surface rate to Argentina, April 1942. F, Cachet 4633, registered mail from Trinidad, September 1942.

(Separate from that deal the United States obtained similar rights to bases in Newfoundland and Bermuda as outright "gifts.")

The Bases-for-Destroyers deal was "the first definite reaction by the Roosevelt Administration to a precarious situation which the American people in general were not yet willing to face," wrote Samuel Eliot Morison. "Preconceptions from another era, hatred of war, suspicion of European propaganda and other trends of thought . . . prevented public

opinion from demanding anything forthright or drastic in their own defense, such as cutting off war supplies from Japan, or backing Britain to the limit."[5]

Minkus lost no time in servicing—and advertising—his patriotic envelopes from the new army post offices, naval operating bases, and Marine detachment post offices as they began operating in 1941. "Gimbels patriotic envelopes mailed from the new Naval and Military Bases established by the U.S. Forces in the Western Hemisphere," offered one

Figure 2. Second series of Minkus covers, produced in 1942. A, Cachet 2686, airmail to Marine Air Group 25, Navy No. 131, Noumea, New Hebrides. B, Cachet 2921, airmail from USS *Raleigh*, cruiser convoying ships in the Aleutian Islands and keeping ocean clear between Kiska and Attu in late 1943. C, Cachet 3710, from APO 603, Belem, Brazil. D, Cachet 4336, airmail with mixed franking from White Horse, Yukon. E, Cachet 7885, from Marine Air Group 12, Navy No. 145, Guadalcanal, Solomon Islands. F, Cachet 8730, to an officer in the U.S. Navy Armed Guard aboard merchant vessel SS *Stephen Douglas*.

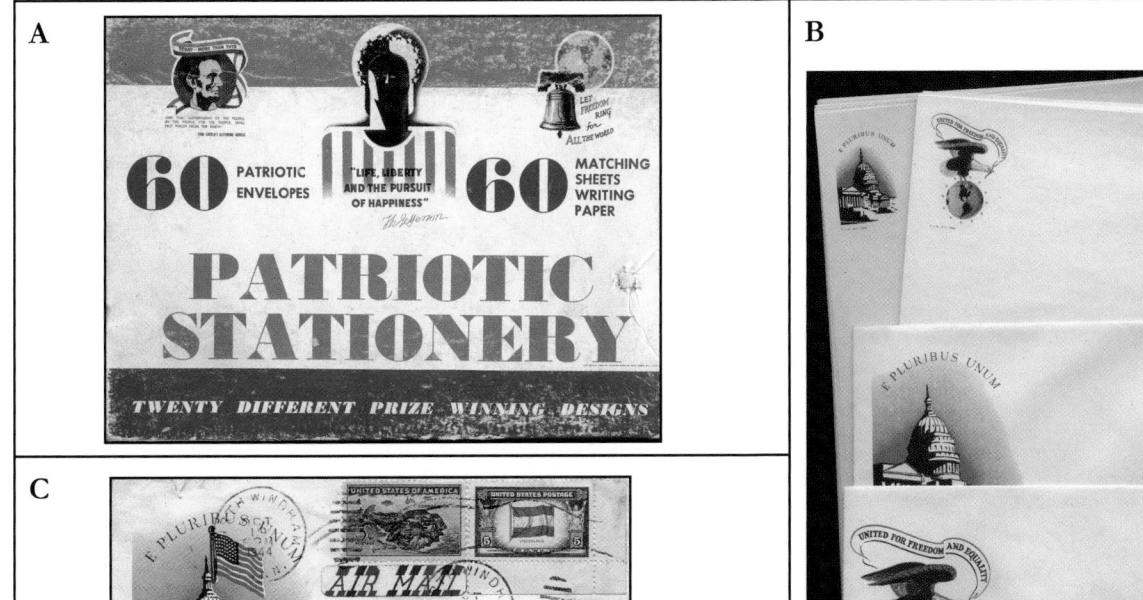

Figure 3. Minkus envelopes and matching stationery, 1942. A, Box of 60 envelopes ("twenty different prize winning designs") with matching stationery. B, Selected contents of box shown in A. C, Cover with a design shown in B (cachet 2000 with a pasted-on flag label added atop the Capitol building), sent airmail to Jamaica, British West Indies, in 1944.

Gimbels advertisement. "Sixteen different, including Iceland, Greenland, Bermuda, Newfoundland, British Guiana, Antigua and others for - - - $1.60."[6]

This was the first wave of Minkus patriotic covers sent to and from overseas.

Examples of international and overseas usages of the first series of Minkus patriotic covers are shown in Figure 1.

The Second Series of Minkus Patriotic Covers, June 1942 (20 Covers)

After Pearl Harbor, and particularly after the series of 20 published in 1942, a flood of Minkus covers engulfed the world. Where American armed forces, diplomats, and civilians went, Minkus covers followed.

Minkus's energetic marketing was on display in the events leading to production of his patriotic covers in June 1942. He proclaimed a nation-wide contest for new patriotic cachet designs. Defense bonds and philatelic books were awarded to

Figure 4. Designs for illustrated envelopes that won first prize in Gimbels wartime contests. A, Herbert Christy's design (cachet 4768), 1942. B, William J. Numeroff's design (cachet 100), 1943.

contestants who best carried out the patriotic theme of the contest and whose artwork was best adaptable and suitable for reproduction on envelopes meant to be mailed. There were 5 judges: Albert Goldman, postmaster of New York City; Maj. Gen. James A. Ulio, Adjutant General of the U.S. Army; Leopold Arnaud, Dean of Architecture at Columbia University and President of the School Art League; Lt. Cmdr. McClelland Barclay, nationally known illustrator (now a naval officer); and Harry Lindquist, publisher of *Stamps* magazine.

The first prize, a $50 war bond, was won by Herbert Christy of New York, NY, for his design depicting "Life, liberty / and the pursuit / of happiness / Th. Jefferson" (cachet 4768).

The headline for a two-page advertisement in June 1942 declared that "Gimbels presents with pride a new series of patriotic envelopes emblazoned with 20 prize-winning designs in color. . . . *Use them for every letter you write!*" [Emphasis in original.] The text added that the designs "won awards in our country-wide contest. There are twenty designs in all. They were chosen for excellence of design, for forcefulness of sentiment. . . . Use them when you write to the folks back home. Use them to write to the boys at camp. Use them and tell the world you're an American—standing behind the boys who are fighting. . . ."[7] Matching stationery was made to complement the envelopes. Both were sold at the Gimbels stores in New York and Philadelphia.

To spread the idea that envelopes with patriotic cachets should be used for mail generally, not only for philatelic use, Minkus sent boxes of envelopes and matching stationery to Congressmen, radio commentators, and newspapers. Gimbels Department store was so pleased with the response that they devoted an entire Broadway window to a display of the patriotic envelopes and stationery over the 4th of July weekend. Four-color lithographed Minkus covers by the tens of thousands were disseminated throughout the United States and army and navy posts abroad, and collectible usages proliferated.

More dramatic in color, broader in theme, and more extensively advertised than the designs of 1940 (the country was now at war and everyone was involved), the second series of Minkus envelopes was a hit with the public. By September 1942 an imposing million and a half of this group had reportedly been sold.[8]

Examples of international and overseas usages of the second series of Minkus patriotic covers are shown in Figure 2, and a box with envelopes and matching stationery is shown in Figure 3.

In the 1940s a stamp business having its counters on the street floor of Gimbels Department store on 34th street in mid-Manhattan squarely met the three guiding principles of real estate: location, location, location. For many New Yorkers, and for an army of wartime visitors, Gimbels was a main shopping destination—and waiting for their arrival as they entered the store were stamp department counters arrayed with gifts for family members, including boxes of "patriotic envelopes emblazoned with 20 prize-winning designs in color. . . *Use them for every letter you write!"*

The Third Series of Minkus Patriotic Covers, June 1943 (20 Covers)

This final series appeared in June 1943. Again there was a well-publicized nationwide contest for the best designs to illustrate envelopes. The judges were the previously mentioned notables except for the New York City postmaster, who was replaced by James M. Mead, United States Senator from New York. The announced theme of the contest was an idea expressed by President Roosevelt: "We fight to retain a great past—and we fight to gain a greater future." The first prize, a $100 war bond, was won by William J. Numeroff of Brooklyn, NY for his design depicting "A great past / A greater future" (cachet 100).

The designs that won first prize in the Gimbels contests of 1942 and 1943 are shown in Figure 4.

Again there were several printings, with variations in the copyright mark on the front of the envelope, small differences in cachet size, and distinct color varieties. Minkus featured a box of 60 envelopes and 60 sheets of paper for $1 in a full page advertisement in *Linn's*: "No more inspiring, eye compelling covers have rolled off the presses! Here they are . . . as stirring as the columns of blue jackets in a Navy Day parade—as breath-taking as the Stars and Stripes unfurled against a Fourth of July sky! Use them for your patriotic covers. Use them for every letter you write. Make your mail—every bit of it—talk. Make it talk turkey on the utter annihilation of the Axis!"[9] And in an advertisement in *Stamps*: "A memorable Christmas present for everyone on your list! Gimbels new patriotic envelopes. . . are done in blazing color. . . . Buy yourself a half a dozen boxes and tie them up in crisp white tissue and scarlet ribbons!"[10]

With American armed forces now numbering in the millions training in the United States, deployed to every continent except Antarctica, and sailing the seven seas, the final series of Minkus patriotic covers was on its way to the world and back again.

Figure 5 illustrates international and overseas usages of Minkus's third series of patriotics.

Varieties and Usages

The 52 patriotic envelopes published by Minkus were far from the largest number produced by a single publisher, but they were the most widely

Figure 5. Third series of Minkus covers, produced in 1943. A, Cachet 1612, airmail to a member of the Naval Armed Guard on SS *Stephen A. Douglas*, merchant ship in Mediterranean waters. B, Cachet 2370, airmail from USS *Pursuit*, mine-sweeper in Pacific waters in October 1943. C, Cachet 3896, surface mail to Australia. D, Cachet 4508, registered mail from British Field Post Office 518, Benghazi, Libya. E, Cachet 8102, free-franked mail from USS *Sangay*, ammunition ship returning from Marshall Islands, March 1944. E, Cachet 8956, to Quebec.

available, commonly used, and universally known of all; and for most people who were not wartime collectors, Minkus covers were *the* patriotic covers of the war. Their multiple uses at home and abroad place them today among the most interesting and collectible of patriotic envelopes, because they illustrate wartime postal history—mainland army postmarks, overseas army post office and naval postmarks, naval operating base and Marine detachment cancels (early in the war only), military and civilian auxiliary markings, censor markings, Navy Armed Guard mail, and foreign origin and destination covers.

Moreover, printings of Minkus patriotics were in the tens of thousands, necessitating employment of different printers to meet the demand: numerous variations in cachet size, color, and copyright symbols resulted. Figure 6 records a few examples.

Current availability of Minkus patriotic envelopes places them among the least costly of those published during World War II.

For all these reasons, there is no better place to start a collection of World War II patriotic envelopes than with the 52 created by Jacques Minkus—in all their variety and with all their worldwide usages.

A checklist of the three series of Minkus patriotic envelopes is found in Table 1. The cachets are alphabetically arranged within each series. The checklist includes the name of designer (when known) and topic of each cachet (see explanation of "Cachet Topic" in Chapter 7).

Figure 6. Color and printing varieties in cachets of second and third Minkus series. A and B, cachet 463: eagle and top band are blue in A, red in B. C and D, cachet 8217: shade, copyright symbol, and print varieties. E and F, cachet 6062: color varieties.

Table 1. The Three Series of Minkus Patriotic Covers

First Series, October 1940 (12 Covers)

NO.	CACHET TEXT	DESIGNER	CITY	STATE	TOPIC
84	A free America / with malice / toward none - justice to all.	Unknown	--	--	EagSh
2683	Fruits of freedom / a free America	Unknown	--	--	Flag
2913	Give me liberty / or give me death	Unknown	--	--	FlLib
3049	God blessed America / A two ocean navy / to protect it	Unknown	--	--	Navy
3050	God blessed America / Home of the free	Unknown	--	--	Flag
3051	God blessed America / We'll protect it	Unknown	--	--	Flag
4615	Let's keep it / land of the / free	Unknown	--	--	EagFl
4633	Let's put our hands / to the plow / protect America	Unknown	--	--	Home
4771	Life, liberty, happiness / Defend your heritage	Unknown	--	--	Flag
7512	The eagle has talons / Keep America free in the air	Unknown	--	--	Air
8735	United in defense / of freedom	Unknown	--	--	Armed
10364	Without freedom / liberty dies	Unknown	--	--	FlLib

Second Series, June 1942 (20 Covers)

NO.	CACHET TEXT	DESIGNER	CITY	STATE	TOPIC
463	America needs your help [copyright "C" red or blue, w/, w/o serifs]	Herbert Christy	New York	NY	Eagle
1415	Clear / the / tracks! [copyright "C" w/, w/o serifs	Ralph Fabri	New York	NY	Axis
1901	Do your share for freedom / and victory will be ours [copyright "C" w/, w/o serifs]	Ludwig W. Staehle	New York	NY	VforV
2000	E Pluribus Unum [copyright "C" w/, w/o serifs]	Herbert Christy	New York	NY	Home
2686	Full speed ahead / to victory!	Herbert Christy	New York	NY	Home
2921	Give them the tools / to finish the job [copyright "C" w/, w/o serifs]	Unknown	--	--	Ordna
3557	"I have not yet begun to fight" / John Paul Jones	Unknown	--	--	Hist
3710	I'm working with / Uncle Sam!	Unknown	--	--	Uncle
4336	Keep that light burning! [Copyright "C" w/, w/o serifs]	Unknown	--	--	Torch
4441	Let / freedom / ring for / all the world [copyright "C" w/, w/o serifs	Unknown	--	--	Bell

4516	Let's / beat 'em / 48 / different ways [Copyright "C" w/, w/o serifs]	Jack W. Acampa	The Bronx	NY	Home
4682	Liberty / above all - for all [copyright "C" w/, w/o serifs]	Unknown	--	--	Liber
4768	"Life, liberty / and the pursuit / of happiness" / Th. Jefferson [Copyright "C" varies]	Herbert Christy	New York	NY	Liber
5576	"Not so fast, / Adolf!" [copyright "C" w/, w/o serifs]	Unknown	--	--	Hitle
5773	On / to victory / for liberty! [copyright "C" w/, w/o serifs] [colors vary]	Ludwig W. Staehle	New York	NY	Lib+
7195	Stamp 'em out! [copyright "C" w/, w/o serifs]	G. Michelson	Bayside	NY	Axis
7885	Then and now ••• — / sailing for victory [Copyright "C" w/, w/o serifs]	Unknown	--	--	Navy
8217	Today •• More than ever / and that government of the people, / by the people etc. [w/, w/o copyright "C"]	Unknown	--	--	Linc
8730	United for freedom and equality [copyright "C" w/, w/o serifs, or no "C"]	Unknown	--	--	Eagle
8732	United for victory [copyright "C" w/, w/o serifs]	Harry E. Stickler	Brooklyn	NY	VforV

Third Series, June 1943 (20 Covers)

NO.	CACHET TEXT	DESIGNER	CITY	STATE	TOPIC
100	A greater future / a great past	William Numeroff	Brooklyn	NY	Home
1612	Coming / soon! / A smash hit	Unknown	--	--	Axis
2370	For all nations	Unknown	--	--	EagSh
2619	Freedom / of speech / from fear / from want / of religion / Atlantic Charter ["Atlantic Charter" in tiny print]	Max Gimpel	New York	NY	Symb
2622	Freedom / of speech / of worship/ from want / from fear	Herbert Christy	New Rochelle	NY	Women
3896	"It shall be done"	Herbert Christy	New Rochelle	NY	Axis
4497	Let there be light	Gustav Michelson	Bayside	NY	Liber
4508	Let us keep / freedom / ringing / throughout the world	Walter Bollendonk	Jackson Heights	NY	Bell
4657	Liberation / from Nazi terror will come / through our victory	Ludwig W. Staehle	New York	NY	Torch
4812	Look to the future / Guard it well [colors vary]	Jack Weiss	Astoria	NY	Armed
5811	On to victory / for liberty [colors vary]	Unknown	--	--	Lib+
6031	Our pledge / ....liberty and / justice for all	Jack Weiss	Astoria	NY	Torch

6062	Ours.... / an heroic / past / and / a glorious / future [colors vary]	Jack Weiss	Astoria	NY	Armed
7701	The ramparts we watch	Unknown	--	--	Home
8102	This is worth fighting for [colors vary]	Gustav Michelson	Bayside	NY	Home
8956	"United we stand!" / Conquer we must when our cause it is just etc. [Copyright position varies]	Herbert Christy	New Rochelle	NY	Armed
9980	We must do all we can!	Ralph Fabri	New York	NY	Bonds
10032	We will gain the / inevitable triumph [w/, w/o copyright "C"]	Unknown	--	--	Antiq
10044	"We will sacrifice anything but our freedom"	Herbert Christy	New York	NY	Uncle
10395	Working for / victory / V	Harold Silverman	New York	NY	Home

A Preliminary Census

Sixty years have passed since the illustrated envelopes so confidently produced and so strenuously marketed by Jacques Minkus completed their postal journeys. They once whizzed about the world performing their part in the most important wartime task of the Post Office Department, "seeing to it that our men and women in the armed forces have rapid and uninterrupted postal communication with their families and friends."[11] Now they await study of the role they played in American postal history of World War II.

This chapter presents a modest proposal for beginning this study—a census of extant Minkus patriotic covers illustrating their international and overseas usages during the war. It seemed then that Minkus covers were ubiquitous. Where indeed did they go, and when? What postal services were required? And what are the current values, listed as retail price ranges, for international and overseas usages (including U.S. territories and possessions) of Minkus covers?

The preliminary census presented in Table 2 is a step in the study of Minkus covers in wartime postal history—an essential baby step forward.[12]

Table 2. International and Overseas Usages of Minkus Patriotic Envelopes in World War II: A Preliminary Census

NO.	CACHET TEXT	COLOR	TOPIC	$[13]
84	**A free America / with malice / toward none - justice to all. [1st Series]**	Multicolored	EagSh	A
	1. Foreign origin surface mail, civilian usage. From: El Salvador, censored in New Orleans, May 1942.			B
	2. Foreign destination surface mail, Western Hemisphere. To: Georgetown, British Guiana, unclaimed, January 1941.			B
100	**A greater future / a great past [3rd Series]**	Multicolored	Home	A
	Domestic surface mail, first-class civilian usage. To: U.S. Naval Training Center, Armed Guard, Gulfport, Mississippi..			B
463	**America needs your help [copyright "C" red or blue, w/, w/o serifs] [2nd Series]**	Multicolored	Eagle	A
	1. Domestic airmail, military usage. From: APO 230, Weimar, Germany, c/o Postmaster New York, May 1945.			C
	2. Domestic surface mail, free-franked military usage. From: 103rd Infantry, APO 43, Manila, Philippines, June 1945.			C

1415   **Clear / the / tracks! [copyright "C" w/, w/o serifs] [2ⁿᵈ Series]**   Multicolored Axis   **A**
  1. Domestic airmail, military usage. From: LCT Flotilla 5, Craft 156, c/o FPO San Francisco, June 1945.   **B**
  2. Domestic surface mail, first-class military usage. From: Lt. Gen. Alexander M. Patch, Jr., HQ. 7th Army, APO 758 (Marseille, France), October 1944.   **E**

1612   **Coming / soon! / a smash hit [3ʳᵈ Series]**   Multicolored Axis   **A**
  Domestic surface mail, first-class civilian usage. To: U.S. Naval Armed Guard, SS *Stephen A. Douglas*, March 1945.   **C**

1901   **Do your share for freedom / and victory etc. [copyright "C" w/, w/o serifs] [2ⁿᵈ Series]**   Multicolored VforV   **A**
  1. Domestic airmail, military usage. From: LCT Flotilla 5, Craft 156, c/o FPO San Francisco, June 1945.   **B**
  2. Foreign destination surface mail, Africa and Middle East. To: South Africa, 4 oz. rate, 14¢, paid, returned to sender by censor, 1944.   **C**

2000   **E Pluribus Unum [copyright "C" w/, w/o serifs] [2ⁿᵈ Series]**   Multicolored Home   **A**
  Foreign destination airmail, Western Hemisphere. To: Kingston, Jamaica, British West Indies, October 1944, 10¢ paid.   **B**

2370   **For all nations [3ʳᵈ Series]**   Multicolored EagSh   **A**
  1. Domestic airmail, civilian usage. To: U.S. Naval Armed Guard, SS *Stephen A. Douglas*, FPO New York, January 1945.   **C**
  2. Domestic airmail, military usage. From: USS *Pursuit* (minesweeper), FPO San Francisco, October 1943. Illustration: Figure 5A.   **D**

2619   **Freedom / of speech / from fear / from want / of religion / Atlantic Charter [3ʳᵈ Series]**   Multicolored Symb   **A**

2622   **Freedom / of speech / of worship / from want / from fear [3ʳᵈ Series]**   Blue, red   Women   **A**
  Domestic airmail, civilian usage. To: U.S. Naval Armed Guard, SS *Stephen A. Douglas*, FPO New York, October 1944.   **C**

2683   **Fruits of freedom / a free America [1ˢᵗ Series]**   Multicolored Flag   **A**
  1. Domestic surface mail, military usage. From: APO 801, St. Johns, Newfoundland, April 16, 1941, first day of operation of first American overseas APO in WWII. Illustration: Figure 1A.   **D**
  2. Domestic surface mail, USMC usage. From: First Marine Division, Fleet Marine Force, April 26, 1941, first day of operation.   **C**
  3. Domestic surface mail, military usage. From: APO 809, Narsarrsuak, Greenland, August 1941.   **B**
  4. Domestic surface mail, military usage. From: APO 801-C, Stephenland, Newfoundland, October 1941.   **B**
  5. Domestic surface nail, military usage. From: APO 801-B, Fort Peperell, Newfoundland, November 1941.   **B**
  6. Foreign origin surface mail. From: Lapa, Brazil, March 1942. American Embassy, Rio de Janeiro, Consular Section, receiving handstamp on back.   **C**
  7. Foreign origin surface mail. From: Surinam (Netherlands Guiana), March 1942. Censored in Surinam and New York City.   **B**
  8. Domestic surface mail, first-class military usage. From: APO 914, Canton Island, May 1942.   **C**
  9. Domestic surface mail, free-franked. From: Fleet Air Wing No. 6, Seattle, August 1943.   **B**

2686   **Full speed ahead / to victory! [copyright "C" w/, w/o serifs] [2ⁿᵈ Series]**   Multicolored Home   **A**
  1. Foreign origin surface mail, civilian usage. From: Moscow, Russia, with Moscow Foreign Section handstamps, Soviet and US censor tapes, January 1944. Only recorded WWII US patriotic mailed from USSR. Illustration: Chapter 2, Figure 7G.   **G**
  2. Domestic airmail, military usage. From: LCT Flotilla 5, Craft 156, c/o FPO San Francisco, June 1945.   **B**
  3. Domestic airmail, civilian usage. To: VMJ-253, Marine Air Group 25, Fleet Marine Air Wing, Navy #131 (Noumea, New Caledonia), ? date, 1943. Illustration: Figure 2A.   **B**

2913   **Give me liberty / or give me death [1ˢᵗ Series]**   Multicolored   FlLib   **A**

     1. Domestic surface mail, USMC usage. From: Marine Detachment, Antigua, Leeward Islands, May 1941.   **B**

     2. Domestic surface mail, military usage. Frm: Guantanamo Bay, Cuba, July 1941.   **B**

     3. Domestic surface mail, naval usage. From: Naval Operating Base, Bermuda, July 1941.   **B**

     4. Domestic surface mail, military usage. From: APO 801-A, Argentia, Newfoundland, July 1941.   **B**

     5. Domestic surface mail, military usage. From: APO 809, Narsarssuak, Greenland, August 1941   **B**

     6. Foreign origin surface mail. From: Port-of-Spain, Trinidad, censored, September 1941.   **C**

     7. Domestic surface mail, military usage. From APO 807, British Guiana, September 1941.   **B**

     8. Domestic surface mail, military usage. From: APO 801, St. Johns, Newfoundland, October 1941.   **B**

     9. Domestic surface mail, military usage. From: APO 801-C, Stephenland, Newfoundland, October 1941.   **B**

     10. Domestic surface mail, military usage. From: APO 801-D, Quidi Vidi, Newfoundland, October 1941.   **B**

     11. Domestic surface mail, USMC usage. From: Marine Detachment, Georgetown, British Guiana, Nov 1941. Censored at US Naval Air Base, British Guiana.   **B**

2921   **Give them the tools / to finish the job [copyright "C" w/, w/o serifs] [2ⁿᵈ Series]**   Multicolored   Ordna   **A**

     1. Domestic airmail, civilian usage. To: 310 Flight School, APO 986, Amchitka Island, Alaska, November 1943.   **B**

     2. Domestic airmail, naval usage. From: USS *Raleigh*, c/o FPO San Francisco, December 1943. Illustration: Figure 2B.   **C**

     3. Domestic surface, first-class civilian usage. To: U.S. Naval Armed Guard, SS *Stephen A. Douglas*, FPO New York, February 1945.   **C**

     4. Domestic airmail, naval usage. From: LCT Flotilla 5, Craft 156, c/o FPO San Francisco, June 1945.   **B**

3049   **God blessed America / a two ocean navy / to protect it [1ˢᵗ Series]**   Multicolored   Navy   **A**

     1. Domestic surface mail, military usage. From APO 801-A, Argentia, Newfoundland, May 21, 1941, first day of APO operation.   **D**

     2. Domestic surface mail, USMC usage. From: First Marine Brigade (Provisional), Iceland, September 1941.   **C**

     3. Domestic surface mail, military usage. From: APO 801-D, Quidi Vidi, Newfoundland, October 1941   **B**

     4. Foreign origin surface mail. From: Port of Spain, Trinidad, opened by censor December 1941.   **C**

     5. Domestic surface, free-frank military usage. From: USS LCI (L) 9, infantry landing craft, large, December 1942.   **C**

3050   **God blessed America / home of the free [1ˢᵗ Series]**   Multicolored   Flag   **A**

     1. Domestic surface mail, military usage. From: APO 803, Port-of-Spain, Trinidad, June 1941.   **B**

     2. Domestic surface mail, USMC usage. From: Marine Detachment, Portland Bight, Jamaica, July 18, 1941, first day of operation. Illustration: Figure 1C.   **D**

     3. Domestic surface mail, USMC usage. From: Marine Detachment, Portland Bight, Jamaica, October 1941.   **B**

     4. Domestic surface mail, military usage. From: Marine Detachment, Georgetown British Guiana, November 1941.   **B**

     5. Domestic surface mail, military usage. From: APO 801-B, Fort Peperell, Newfoundland, November 1941.   **B**

     6. Domestic surface mail, military usage. From: APO 801-C, Stephenland, Newfoundland, October 1941.   **B**

3051   **God blessed America / we'll protect it! [1ˢᵗ Series]**   Blue, red   Flag   **A**

     1. Domestic surface mail, military usage. From: APO 809, Narsarsuak, Greenland, August 1941.   **B**

2. Domestic surface mail, military usage. From: APO 801-A, Argentia, Newfoundland, October 1941 — B

3. Domestic surface mail, military usage. From: APO 801-D, Quidi Vidi, Newfoundland, October 1941. — B

4. Domestic surface mail, USMC usage. From: Marine Detachment, Argentia, Newfoundland, July 1941. — B

5. Domestic surface mail, USMC usage. From: First Marine Brigade (Provisional), Iceland, October 1941. — C

6. Domestic surface mail, military usage. From: APO 810, Baldurshagi, Iceland, October 1941. — B

7. Domestic surface, free-frank military usage. From: APO 368, Foggia, Italy, June 1944 (D-Day). — C

3557 "I have not yet begun to fight" / John Paul Jones [2ⁿᵈ Series] Multicolored Hist A

1. Foreign origin surface mail. From: Juarez, Mexico, ? date, ? year. Censored in El Paso, Texas. — C

2. Domestic airmail, military usage, double rate with two 3¢ postage due stamps added. From: APO 942, Anchorage, c/o Postmaster, Seattle, November ? year. — C

3. Domestic airmail, military usage. From: LCT Flotilla 5, Craft 156, c/o FPO San Francisco, June 1945. — B

3710 I'm working with / Uncle Sam! [2ⁿᵈ Series] Multicolored Uncle A

1. Foreign origin surface mail. From: Quebec, August 1943, with Canadian seal. — B

2. Domestic airmail, military usage. From: LCT Flotilla 5, Craft 156, c/o FPO San Francisco, June 1945. — B

3. Domestic airmail, military usage. From: 1153rd Army Air Force Base Unit, APO 603, Belem, Brazil, c/o Postmaster Miami, July 1945. Illustration: Figure 2C. — C

3896 "It shall be done" [3ʳᵈ Series] Multicolored Axis A

1. Domestic airmail, civilian usage. To: 21st Naval Construction Battalion, FPO San Francisco, with forwarding branch marking, NYC, July 1943. — D

2. Foreign destination surface mail, South Pacific. To: Newcastle, New South Wales, Australia, November 1943. Illustration: Figure 5B. — C

3. Domestic surface mail, first-class military usage. From: 31st Signal Construction Battalion, APO 466 (Jorhat, Assam, India), c/o PM, New York, January 1945. Illustration: Figure 5C. — C

4336 Keep that light burning! [copyright "C" w/, w/o serifs] [2ⁿᵈ Series] Multicolored Torch A

1. Foreign origin airmail. From: White Horse, Yukon, mixed franking, February 1944. Illustration: Figure 2D. — D

2. Domestic airmail, military usage. From: LCT Flotilla 5, Craft 156, c/o FPO San Francisco, June 1945. — B

3. Domestic airmail, civilian usage, U.S. Possessions. From: San Juan, Puerto Rico, to Frederikstad, St. Croix, Virgin Islands, December 26, 1942. 6¢ Inter-Island airmail rate. — D

4441 Let / freedom / ring / for / all the world [copyright "C" w/, w/o serifs] [2ⁿᵈ Series] Multicolored Bell A

1. Foreign destination airmail. To: Toronto, August 1942. — B

2. Foreign destination surface mail, Europe. To: Newboro, Limerick, Ireland, October 1942. Irish censor handstamp. — C

3. Foreign destination surface mail, South Pacific. To: Christchurch, New Zealand, 5¢ paid May 12, 1945. — B

4. Foreign origin surface mail. From: Nanaimo, British Columbia, May 8, 1945 (VE Day). — C

4497 Let there be light [3ʳᵈ Series] Multicolored Liber A

1. Domestic surface mail, free-franked naval usage. From: 91ˢᵗ Construction Battalion, c/o FPO San Francisco, March 1944. — C

2. Domestic surface mail, free-franked military usage. From: 2628 Hospital Section, APO 698, Caserta, Italy, January 1945. — B

4508 Let us keep / freedom / ringing / throughout / the world [3ʳᵈ Series] Multicolored Bell A

1. Domestic surface mail, military usage. From: 135ᵗʰ Infantry Div., APO 34, Caserta, Italy, December 1943. — B

	2. Foreign origin registered surface mail. From: British Field Post Office 518, Benghazi, Libya, to U.S. via APO 816, Cairo, April 1944. Ilustration: Figure 5D.		D
	3. Domestic surface mail, first-class civilian usage. To: US Naval Armed Guard, SS *Stephen A. Douglas*, December 1944.		B
	4. Domestic surface mail, first-class civilian usage. To: US Naval Armed Guard, SS *Stephen A. Douglas*, January 1945.		C
4516	**Let's / beat 'em / 48 / different ways [copyright "C" w/, w/o serifs] [2ⁿᵈ Series]**	**Multicolored Home**	**A**
	1. Foreign destination surface mail, registered, return receipt, South Pacific. To: Napier, New Zealand, censored in San Francisco, 25¢ paid, Sep 1942.		D
4615	**Let's keep it / land of the / free [1ˢᵗ Series]**	**Multicolored EagFl**	**A**
	1. Foreign destination airmail, Europe. To: Haywards Heath, Sussex, England, 30¢ paid, May 1941. Illlustration: Figure 1B.		B
	2. Domestic surface mail, military usage. From: APO 803, Port-of-Spain, Trinidad, October 1941.		B
	3. Domestic surface mail, military usage. From: APO 801, St. Johns, Newfoundland, October 1941.		B
	4. Domestic surface mail, military usage. From: APO 801-C, Stephenland, Newfoundland, October 1941.		B
	5. Foreign destination surface mail, Western Hemisphere. To: Buenos Aires, Argentina, 3¢ paid, April 1942. Censored in New York City. Illustration: Figure 1E.		B
	6. Domestic airmail, military usage. From: 725ᵗʰ Ordnance, APO 25, New Caledonia, December 1944.		B
4633	**Let's put our hands / to the plow / protect America [1ˢᵗ Series]**	**Multicolored Home**	**A**
	1. Domestic surface mail, military usage. From: APO 807, British Guiana, September 1941		B
	2. Domestic surface mail, military usage. From: APO 803, Port-of-Spain, Trinidad, October 1941.		B
	3. Domestic surface mail, naval usage. From: Naval Operating Base, Bermuda, November 1941.		B
	4. Domestic surface mail, military usage. From: APO 809, Narsarrsuak, Greenland, August 1941.		B
	5. Domestic surface mail, first-class military usage. Postmarked Marine Corps, Midway Island , with Marine censor marking, March 22, 1942.		C
	6. Foreign origin surface mail. From unknown city, Bolivia, March 1942.		C
	7. Foreign origin surface registered mail. From: La Brea, Trinidad, September 1942. Censored in New York City. Illustration: Figure 1F.		C
4657	**Liberation / from Nazi terror will come / through our victory [3ʳᵈ Series]**	**Blue, red** **Torch**	**A**
4682	**Liberty / above all - for all [copyright "C" w/, w/o serifs] [2ⁿᵈ Series]**	**Multicolored Liber**	**A**
4768	**"Life, liberty / and the pursuit / of happiness" etc. [copyright "C" varies] [2ⁿᵈ Series]**	**Blue, red** **Liber**	**A**
	1. Foreign destination airmail, Western Hemisphere. To: Half Way Tree, Jamaica, British West Indies, 10¢ paid, June 1943. Censored, unknown place.		C
	2. Domestic airmail, civilian usage. To: 310ᵗʰ Flight School, APO 986, Amchitka Island, Alaska, c/o Postmaster Seattle, December 1943.		B
	3. Domestic airmail, military usage. From: LCT Flotilla 5, Craft 156, c/o FPO San Francisco, June 1945.		B
4771	**Life, liberty, happiness / defend your heritage [1ˢᵗ Series]**	**Multicolored Flag**	**A**
	1.Domestic surface mail, military usage. From: APO 801-A, Argentia, Newfoundland, July 1941.		B
	2. Domestic surface mail, USMC usage. From: Fourth Defense Battalion, Fleet Marine Force, October 1941.		B
	3. Domestic surface mail, naval usage. From: Naval Operating Base, Bermuda, November 1941.		B
	4. Domestic airmail, military usage. From: APO 698, Algiers, August 1943.		B
4812	**Look to the future / guard it well [colors vary] 3ʳᵈ Series]**	**Multicolored Armed**	**A**
	1. Domestic surface mail, free-franked military usage. From: 135ᵗʰ Infantry Division, APO 34, Caserta, Italy, December 1943		B

2. Domestic registered airmail, military usage. From: 36th General Hospital, APO 380, Capua, Italy, May 1944, 26¢ paid (20¢ registered + 6¢ airmail), returned from U.S. to military sender in Europe "for better address." Illustration: Chapter 2, Figure 7F.   D

3. Domestic airmail, first-class civilian usage. To: US Naval Armed Guard, SS *Stephen A. Douglas*, FPO New York, January 1945.   C

4. Domestic airmail, first-class civilian usage. To: US Naval Armed Guard, SS *Stephen A. Douglas*, FPO New York, March 1945.   C

5576 "Not so fast, / Adolf!" [copyright "C" w, w/o serifs] [2nd Series]   Multicolored Hitle A

Domestic airmail, military usage. From: LCT Flotilla 5, Craft 156, c/o FPO San Francisco, June 1945.   B

5773 On / to victory / for liberty! [copyright "C" w, w/o serifs] [colors vary] [2nd Series] Multicolored Lib+ A

1. Domestic airmail, military usage. From: LCT Flotilla 5, Craft 156, c/o FPO San Francisco, June 1945.   B

2. Foreign destination registered surface mail, Western Hemisphere. To: Ottawa., 14¢ paid, February 1943.   C

5811 On to victory / for liberty [colors vary] [2nd Series]   Multicolored Lib+ A

Foreign destination airmail, western hemisphere. To: Kingston, Jamaica, 10¢ paid, March 1944.   C

6031 Our pledge / ....liberty and / justice for all [3rd Series]   Multicolored Torch A

1.. Domestic surface mail, first-class military usage. From: 135th Infantry, APO 34, Caserta, Italy), c/o PM New York, December 1943.   B

2. Domestic surface mail, first-class civilian usage. To: US Naval Armed Guard, SS *Stephen A. Douglas*, c/o FPO, New York, December 1944.   C

3. Domestic surface mail, first-class military usage. From: 135th Infantry, APO 34 (Caserta, Italy), c/o Postmaster, New York.   B

6062 Ours .... / an heroic / past / and / a glorious / future [colors vary] [3rd Series] Multicolored Armed A

Domestic surface mail, first-class civilian usage. To: US Naval Armed Guard, SS *Stephen A. Douglas*, FPO New York, November 1944.   C

7195 Stamp 'em out! [copyright "C" w/, w/o serifs] [2nd Series]   Multicolored Axis A

1. Domestic airmail, military usage. From: LCT Flotilla 5, Craft 156, c/o FPO San Francisco, June 1945.   B

2. Domestic airmail, military usage. From: 725th Ordnance, APO 25, Guadalcanal, Solomon Islands , c/o Postmaster, San Francisco, April 1943. Illustration: Chapter 2, Figure 7E.   B

7512 The eagle has talons / Keep America free in the air [1st Series]   Blue, red   Air   A

1. Domestic surface mail, military usage. From: APO 809, Narsarssuak, Greenland, August 1941. Illustration: Figure 1D.   B

2. Domestic surface mail, military usage. From: APO 801-D, Quidi Vidi, Newfoundland, October 1941.   B

3. Domestic surface mail, military usage. From: APO 804, Ft. Simonds, Jamaica, November 17, 1941, first day of operation of APO.   C

7701 The ramparts we watch [3rd Series]   Multicolored Home A

7885 Then and now •••— / sailing for victory [copyright "C" w/, w/o serifs] [2nd Series]   Multicolored Navy A

1. Domestic airmail, USMC usage. From: Marine Air Group 12, Navy No. I45, Koli Point, Guadalcanal, Solomon Islands, September 1943. Illustration: Figure 2E.   C

2. Foreign origin surface mail. From: Baile Atha Cliath (Dublin), Ireland, November 1943.   C

3. Foreign destination surface mail, Western Hemisphere. To: Buenos Aires, Argentina, 6¢ paid, June 1944. Censored in New York City.   C

4. Domestic surface mail, first-class civilian usage. To: US Naval Armed Guard, SS *Stephen A. Douglas*, FPO New York, December 1944.   C

5. Foreign destination airmail, Western Hemisphere. To: Mandeville, Jamaica, British West Indies, 10¢ paid, September 1945.   C

8102 This is worth fighting for [colors vary] [3rd Series]   Multicolored Home A

Domestic surface mail, naval usage, free-franked. From: USS *Sangay*, c/o FPO San Francisco, March 1944. Illustration: Figure 5E.   C

8217	Today •• more than ever / And that government of etc. [w/, w/o copyright "C"] [2nd Series]	Multicolored	Linc	A
	Foreign destination surface mail. To: Upton Noble, Bath, England, 5¢ paid, January 1943, British censor tape.			C
8730	United for freedom and equality [copyright "C" w/, w/o serifs, or no "C"] [2nd Series]	Multicolored	Eagle	A
	1. Domestic surface mail, military usage. From: 135th Infantry, APO 34, Caserta, Italy, November 1943.			B
	2. Domestic surface mail, first-class civilian usage. To: US Naval Armed Guard, SS *Stephen A. Douglas*, FPO New York, March 1945. Illustration: Figure 2F.			C
8732	United for victory [copyright "C" w/, w/o serifs] [2nd Series]	Multicolored	VforV	A
	Foreign origin surface mail. From: Havana, October 1943.			C
8735	United in defense / of freedom [1st Series]	Multicolored	Globe	A
	1. Foreign origin surface mail. From: Coober Pedy, Australia, January 1941.			C
	2. American possession surface mail. From: Fort Davis, Canal Zone, April 4, 1941, first day, American forces in Republic of Panama.			C
	3. Domestic surface mail, military usage. From: APO 810, Baldurshagi, Iceland, October 1941.			C
	4. Domestic surface mail, military usage. Large "U.S. Navy" rectangular cancel + circular naval censor handstamp, December 1941.			B
	5. Foreign origin surface mail. From: Port-au-Prince, Haiti, March 1942. Censored in Port-au-Prince and New York City.			C
	6. Foreign origin surface mail. From: Cayenne, French Guiana, April 1942. Censored in French Guiana and New York City.			C
8956	"United we stand!" / Conquer we must etc. [copyright position varies] [3rd Series]	Multicolored	Armed	A
	Foreign destination surface mail, western hemisphere. To: Quebec, January 1944. Illustration: Figure 5F.			B
9980	We must do all we can! [3rd Series]	Multicolored	Bonds	A
	1. Domestic airmail, civilian usage. To: US Naval Armed Guard, SS *Stephen A. Douglas*, FPO, c/o FPO New York, September 1944.			C
	2. Domestic airmail, naval usage. From: Naval Air Station Dispensary, Navy No. 30, Maui, Hawaii, c/o FPO San Francisco, October 1944.			C
	3. Domestic airmail, civilian usage. To: US Naval Armed Guard, SS *Stephen A. Douglas*, c/o FPO New York, ? Date, 1944, backstamped "CPNY".			D
10032	We will gain the / inevitable triumph [w/, w/o copyright "C"] [3rd Series]	Blue, red	Antiq	A
	Domestic airmail, special delivery, July 1944 and September 1944, 18¢ paid.			B
10044	"We will sacrifice anything but our freedom" [cachet height 64 or 66 mm [3rd Series]	Multicolored	Uncle	A
	Domestic surface mail, civilian usage. To: USS YMS-111 (motor mine sweeper), c/o FPO New York, February 1944.			B
10364	Without freedom / liberty dies [1st Series]	Multicolored	FlLib	A
	1. Domestic surface mail, military usage. From: USS *Schley*, October 1940.			B
	2. Domestic surface mail, naval usage. From: Naval Operating Base, Bermuda, various dates, July and November 1941.			B
	3. Domestic surface mail, military usage. From: APO 803, Port-of-Spain, Trinidad, various dates, September and October 1941.			B
	4. Domestic surface mail, military usage. From: APO 801, St. Johns, Newfoundland, August 1941.			B
10395	Working for / victory / V [3rd Series]	Multicolored	Home	A

NOTES and SOURCES

1. Baur, Brian C. *Franklin D. Roosevelt and the Stamps of the United States 1933-1945* (Sidney, Ohio: Linn's Stamp News, Amos Press, Inc., 1993), p. 259.

2. "Patriotic envelopes produced by Gimbels," *Cover News* 4 (6):1, Jan 1941.

3. Monty, Dr. Richard A. *Specialized Catalogue of Jacques Minkus F.D.C.s and Patriotic Cachets* (Stewartsville, New Jersey: F.D.C. Publishing Co., 1977), p. 8.

4. "Gimbels famous stamp department patriotic envelopes," *Cover News* 4 (5):4, Dec 1940.

5. Morison, Samuel Eliot. *The Battle of the Atlantic 1939-1943* (Volume I of Morison's *History of United States Naval Operations in World War II*) (Boston: Little, Brown and Company, 1947), p. 35.

6. "For your philatelic friends or your own collection," *Stamps* 37:378, Dec 13, 1941.

7. "Stamped with America's approval Gimbels presents with pride a new series of patriotic envelopes emblazoned with 20 prize-winning designs in color," *Stamps* 39 (12):414-415, June 20, 1942.

8. Hollister, Paul. "Gimbel's World War II patriotics," *Western Stamp Collector* 39:10, Nov 27, 1965.

9. "For your patriotic covers as well as every single letter you write! Gimbels new patriotic envelopes," *Linn's Weekly Stamp News* :7, Nov 11, 1943.

10. "A memorable Christmas present for everyone on your list! Gimbels new patriotic envelopes," *Stamps* 45 (12):400, Dec 18, 1943.

11. *Annual Report of the Postmaster General for the fiscal year ending June 30, 1943* (Washington, DC: United States Government Printing Office, 1944), p. 2.

12. More than a quarter-century ago Dr. Richard A Monty laid the groundwork for later studies of Minkus patriotic envelopes with his *Specialized Catalogue of Jacques Minkus F.D.C.s and Patriotic Cachets* (see note 3). His landmark work was published at a time when Minkus patriotics were scorned as "too common" (thus uninteresting), or simply ignored. It was at Monty's urging that Ben Blumenthal, general manager of Minkus publications in 1976, searched for and unearthed the names of the designers of many of the second and third series of Minkus covers—thirty years after the fact. For many neophyte collectors (myself included) the book's section on army post offices, with illustrations of APO postmarks used on the first series of Minkus covers, opened the door to the splendors of wartime postal history.

13. Values are expressed as retail price ranges. The standard range for postally used Minkus patriotic covers in clean, undamaged condition is A=$3-6. Minkus covers of special interest (foreign origin or destination, special services required, unusual auxiliary markings, etc.) are valued higher: B=$7-15, C=$16-30, D=$31-60,E=$61-125, F=$126-250, and G=$251-500. Values for Minkus and all other patriotic covers are explained in detail in Chapter 7.

7

Cachet Catalogue

READERS of the predecessor volume, *United States Patriotic Covers of World War II,* will be familiar with the descriptive idiosyncracies of the cachet catalogue. New readers should profit from explanations (with examples) of the six categories listed for every recorded cachet: Cachet Number, Text (or description of illustration where there is no text), Color, Topic, Publisher, and Value.

CACHET NUMBER

This catalogue lists more than 11,060 different examples of United States envelope art created during World War II. The cachets—illustrations and inscriptions that decorate the envelopes—are arranged alphabetically and numbered consecutively. Thus cachet text "A / day" is No. 1 in the catalogue and "Zip your lip... /", the last cachet with text, is No. 10637. Cachets that have no text are placed after "Z" cachets and have "^^" symbols at the beginning of the description of the illustration. Thus "^^Aircraft carrier with 5 planes in air," a description of the cachet illustration, is listed as cachet 10638, and "^^Womens Army Corps insignia," the description of the last cachet, is No. 11060.

The use of numbers allows quick reference to the catalogue from chapters which discuss or illustrate cachets of selected publishers, including hand painted cachets discussed in Chapter 4.

Table 1. Differentiating Cachets: Line Break

No.	Cachet Text
6509	Remember / Pearl / Harbor [bomb dropping] [upper left]
6510	Remember / Pearl / Harbor [colors vary] [handpainted]
6511	Remember / Pearl / Harbor [dagger]
6512	Remember / Pearl / Harbor [first word around blue circle with white stars]
6521	Remember / Pearl Harbor
6522	Remember / Pearl Harbor - [the Spirit of '75]
6540	Remember / Pearl Harbor [clock at upper left]
6541	Remember / Pearl Harbor [eagle and flag]
6542	Remember / Pearl Harbor [first word arches over flag and two stars]
6572	Remember Pearl Harbor
6573	Remember Pearl Harbor .. December 7, 1941 / Farewell to the U.S.S. etc.
6574	Remember Pearl Harbor / [etc.] / Buy war stamps and bonds [thermographed]
6575	Remember Pearl Harbor / 3——If needed or if asked of us, each man etc. [handpainted]

Table 2. Differentiating Cachets: Punctuation

No.	Cachet Text
8	A / salute / to / Adolph / Hitler / Chancellor / of / Germany etc.
9	A / salute / to / Hirohito / son of heaven / emperor of Japan etc.
10	A / salute / to / mining / producing / the / dress / and / minerals / for / victory
11	A / salute / to the day when the world / will again enjoy etc.
12	A / salute / to: / Comdr. / Norman / Miller / (one man task force) etc.
13	A / salute / to: / Ernie / Pyle / who has been 29 months over- / seas etc.
161	A salute to / Mrs. T.F. Sullivan etc. [thermographed]
162	A salute to / Wm. B. Owens etc. [thermographed]
163	A salute to all / who are serving / to etc. [thermographed]
164	A salute to Ernie Pyle / beloved scribe of all GI's / The famous etc.

Numbers printed in **bold italics** indicate cachets illustrated at the end of each alphabetical section of the catalogue.

CACHET TEXT (OR DESCRIPTION OF CACHETS THAT HAVE NO TEXT)

Six principles underlie the arrangement of cachets in this catalogue:

1. Alphabetization. Cachets are arranged alphabetically by first word of text. Cachet illustrations that have no text are listed after the "Z" cachet texts and are arranged alphabetically by first word of description of the illustration.

2. Line Separation. To differentiate between cachets with the same text but with a different number of lines of text, or a different break in lines of text, a slash ("/") is used at each line break.

"Remember Pearl Harbor," the popular slogan that appeared on wartime cachets, was rendered in three ways—as three lines ("Remember / Pearl / Harbor"), two lines ("Remember / Pearl Harbor"), and as one line ("Remember Pearl Harbor").

Figure 1 shows cachet catalogue examples of the line break affecting the sequence of these cachet texts. There are two important features in the "Cachet Text" column: line separation affects alphabetical ordering, and descriptions in brackets serve as points of issue, sometimes distinguishing between cachets with identical text but different illustrations. The many uses to which these points of issue are put throughout the catalogue are discussed as the sixth principle, below.

3. Punctuation. After alphabetization and line break, cachets are further arranged by differences in punctuation that may distinguish between otherwise identical texts. This differentiation by punctuation (:) combined with line break ("/") is demonstrated by cachet catalogue examples shown in Figure 2.

4. Shortening text by deleting words from the end. The first lines of an extended text are included in the cachet text entry and "etc." added where the text has been truncated. Enough of the text is included to identify the cachet. All but one of the cachet texts already shown in Figure 2 are examples of shortening of the text (with retention of its individuality).

5. Shortening text by deleting words in the middle. The middle portion of an extended text has sometimes been deleted to accommodate to the allotted space of the "Cachet Text" column. In this case the missing text is indicated by "/ [etc.] /" in place of the deleted middle portion of text. Table 3 shows examples of this from the cachet catalogue. All preserve the unique characteristics of the text that allow for quick cachet identification.

6. Description in brackets of patriotic cover "points of issue" (cachet features or attributes, envelope colors and sizes). Bracketed information is important! Table 4 shows a number of these points of issue, typical of the many that are bracketed throughout the catalogue. These points are essential to:

Discriminate between covers having the same cachet text (cachets 6507, 6512, 6517).

Indicate unusual arrangements or positions of the text (cachets 1051, 6517).

Table 3. Shortening Text by Deleting Words in Middle

No.	Cachet Text
5397	Naval Training School / [etc.] / Harvard University etc. [env. 5 ½x4 in.]
5421	Navy Department / [etc.] / Remember / Pearl Harbor! December 7, etc. [thermographed]
5463	New regular / 8 cent air mail / [etc.] / ...Doolittle
5536	No man is worth his salt who is not / [etc.] / 10-9-'44———Yanks cut off etc.
6463	Red Cross blood plasma / [etc.] / Blood transfusion in the etc. [thermographed]
6464	Red Cross Blood Plasma / [etc.] / U.S. naval hospital ship etc. [thermographed]

Highlight features of the cover unrelated to the cachet (cachets 2599, 5397).

Emphasize a cover's special interest or special value (cachets 9006, 9007).

Throughout the catalogue, thermographed or hand painted cachets have that fact noted in brackets. "Thermographed" is spelled out where space allows; otherwise, it is abbreviated as "thermogr," "thermo," or "therm." Similarly, "handpainted" is spelled out as a single word where space allows or is abbreviated as "handpaint," "handp," or (in particularly tight spots) "hp."

CACHET COLOR

The color of every listed cachet is listed when known by me. If the color is not known, "Unknown" is listed in the Color column. Cachets having more than two colors are listed as "Multicolored."

Publishers sometimes produced patriotic covers with more than one color scheme, creating cachet color varieties that collectors, ever striving for completion, continue to pursue. These color varieties are noted in the catalogue. The various states of color of each cachet are listed in the Color column of the row listing the cachet. In this way the collector, holding any patriotic cover in his or her hand, can consult a single page and learn the known color states of the cachet.

The full color of each cachet is spelled out wherever possible; when not, abbreviations are used. *Color Abbreviations.* Examples found in the catalogue are:

Aqua: Aquamarine
Bk: Black
Bu: Blue
Br: Brown
Gd: Gold
Gn: Green
Gy: Gray
Ma: Magenta
Multi: Multicolored
Pi: Pink
Pu: Purple
O: Orange
R: Red
Sp: Sepia tones
S: Silver
Vi: Violet
Y: Yellow

Cachet color combinations. The many color combinations used for patriotic cachets are recorded in the catalogue. *Slash marks ("/") are used to separate two or more different states of color of a cachet; a comma separates the two colors of a bicolored cachet.* (Many publishers favored a blue and red color scheme; combined with a white envelope this produced a patriotic red, white, and blue effect.)

Examples found in the catalogue include:

Aqua/Red: Some cachets aquamarine, others red.

Bicolor var: Cachet known in a variety of two-color states.

Bk, Or: Bi-colored cachet, black and orange.

Bk, O/R/S: Cachet known in three states: black and orange, red only, and silver only.

Bk, R/Bu,Red: Cachet known in two states: black and red, and blue and red.

Blue: Cachet known only in blue.

Blue, red: Most common two-color combination. The white of the envelope contributes to the overall red, white, and blue effect.

Blue-1: Double cachet cover (by Walter G. Crosby) with far left cachet in blue.

Gd-2: Double cachet cover (Crosby) with near left cachet in gold.

Table 4. Cover Points of Issue [in brackets]

No.	Cachet Text
161	A salute to / Mrs. T.F. Sullivan etc. [thermographed]
1051	Bonds keep her there, / buy more today [text vertical]
2599	Freedom / and / liberty / will be / restored / to ... / Greece [colored envelopes]
2755	Gen. MacArthur announced / the complete liberation / of etc. [typed] [no picture]
2757	Gen. MacArthur, Supreme Allied / Commander for Japan etc. [pen & ink] [no picture]
5397	Naval Training School / [etc.] / Harvard University etc. [env. 5 ½x4 in.]
6507	Remember / Pearl / Harbor [bomb below "Remember"] [handpainted]
6512	Remember / Pearl / Harbor [first word around blue circle with white stars]
6517	Remember / Pearl / Harbor [text runs diagonally] [ship exploding]
6718	Run-Tojo-run / We're gonna set / your rising sun [with map of Pacific islands]
9006	USS Colorado - / in Japan [handpainted] [Tokyo Bay]
9007	USS Delta / Occupational force——Tokyo Bay [postmarked 8/31/45] [Tokyo Bay]

Multi var: Cachet known in a variety of multicolored states. Unknown: Cachet existence known, color unknown.

Catalogued examples of these color abbreviations and combinations are shown in Table 5. Interpreting the color scheme of some of the entries in this table:

Cachet 21 is found in black and red as well as black and brown, and cachet 129 is found in blue and red as well as red and silver.

Cachet 232 has three or more colors and therefore is listed as a multicolored cachet.

Cachet 2681 is bicolored in blue and red.

Cachet 2682 is found in any of four colors: black, blue, gold, or green.

Cachet 2761 has a known text but its color is unknown.

Cachet 2762 is bicolored in brown and gray.

Cachets 2790 and 2791 are "double cachets" found on legal-size envelopes; the former has a blue cachet at far left and a gold cachet at near left. The latter's two cachets are both blue.

CACHET TOPIC

By word or picture every patriotic cover expresses an idea, and sometimes more than one. The "Topic" column of the cachet catalogue tries to capture the salient idea of every listed cachet. The vast number of artists, printers, and publishers involved in producing patriotic covers assured the appearance of an astonishing variety of cachet topics. Catalogue space

limited the Topic column to one topic for each cachet. This limitation only serves to emphasize the variety of wartime subjects that preoccupied cachet makers, collectors, and the nation.

Today's topical (thematic) collectors can expect to find something of use when they explore World War II patriotic covers—themes from Alaska to Hawaii, from aircraft to German submarines, from chickens to dogs and owls and pigeons (and eagles of course), from medical people to Minute Men, from the Red Cross to women's branches of the armed forces, and on and on.

Here is a listing of over 100 topics on wartime cachets, arranged alphabetically. The word or abbreviation (up to 5 letters) is written as it appears in the Topic column of the catalogue, followed by a brief explanation.

Topics: Abbreviations and Explanations.

AJA: Americans of Japanese ancestry
Admir: Admiral(s) of U.S. Navy
Air: Aircraft
Alask: Alaska
Ally: Wartime ally of the United States
Anniv: Anniversary of a significant event
Antiq: Antiquity
Armed: U.S. armed forces
Army: U.S. Army
Atom: Atomic bomb
Axis: Axis power(s)

Table 5. Color Abbreviations and Combinations

No.	Cachet Text	Color
21	A / salute / to: / Major / George E. / Preddy / of Greensboro, N.C., etc.	Bk,R/Bk,Br
232	Ach. Himmel / dose / American houzvives [handpainted]	Multicolored
2681	From the halls of Montezuma to the shores of / [etc.] / U.S. Marine Corps etc.	Blue, red
2682	From Tripoli to the Halls / of the Montezumas [in quotes]	Bk/Bu/Go/Gn
2761	Gen. Mark Clark / 12-8-'44———Yank armor / near Saarbrucken	Unknown
2762	Gen. Marshall	Brown, grey
2790	General Douglas MacArthur / Some etc. First etc. [double cachet] [thermographed]	Blue-1, Gd-2
2791	General Douglas MacArthur / Some etc. First etc. [double cachet] [thermographed]	Blue-1 & 2

Bases: Base(s) leased from Great Britain
Battl: World War II battle
Bell: Liberty Bell
Blood: Blood donation
Bonds: U.S. war savings bonds

Chick: Chicken
China: Country in Asia
Chute: Parachute; paratrooper; parachutist
Coast: U.S. Coast Guard
Conc: Concentration camp

DDay: D-Day: Allied invasion of Europe
Devil: The Devil
Dog: The animal
Dool: Colonel (Later General) James Doolittle

EagFl: Eagle + U.S. Flag
EagSh: Eagle + U.S. Shield
EagV: Eagle + V (for Victory)
Eagle: Eagle as symbol of the United States
Event: Wartime event (with same date postmark)

FDR: President Franklin Delano Roosevelt
FlBel: U.S. Flag + Liberty Bell
FLLib: U.S. Flag + Statue of Liberty
FlMin: U.S. Flag + Minute Man
FlSh: U.S. Flag + Minute Man
Flag: U.S. Flag
Flag+: U.S. Flag + 2 or more other symbols
FlagV: U.S. Flag + V

Gener: General(s) of U.S. Army
Globe: Globe of the world

HST: President Harry S. Truman

Hawai: Hawaii
Heads: Heads of State
Hero: World War II war hero
Hist: Historical figures, events
Hitle: Adolph Hitler
Holid: Major holiday occurring during the war
Home: Wartime home front

Ike: General Dwight D. Eisenhower

Japan: Japanese figures, armed forces

Lib+: Statue of Liberty + other symbols
Liber: Statue of Liberty
Linc: Abraham Lincoln
LinWa: Lincoln and George Washington
Mac: General Douglas MacArthur
MacFD: First Day, MacArthur WV post office
Map: Map of war zone or other significant area
Marsh: General George C. Marshall
Medal: Military medal(s)
Medic: Medical people; military medicine
Merch: U.S. Merchant Marine
Minut: Minute Man
Musso: Benito Mussolini

Navy: U.S. Navy, ships, personnel
Nazis: Nazi leaders, German officers, troops
NeuNa: Post-Pearl Harbor neutral nation(s)
Neutr: U.S. neutrality before Pearl Harbor
Nim: Admiral Chester W. Nimitz
NimFD: First day, Nimitz WV post office
Nurse: Military nurse (s)
ORN: Overrun nations
Ordna: Tanks, artillery, other ordnance
Owl: The bird

Patt: General George S. Patton
Pearl: Pearl Harbor and its anniversaries
Phili: Philippine Islands
Pigeo: Pigeons, Army pigeon service
Pyle: Ernie Pyle, war columnist, author

RedCr: Red Cross
Relig: Religious scenes, symbols, sentiments
Romm: General Erwin Rommel, Afrika Corps

Shiel: Shield of the United States
ShieV: Shield of the United States + V
Skull: Human skull
Sp'76: Spirit of 1776
SPARS: Women's branch of Coast Guard (from *Semper Paratus*)
Symb+: Two or more different symbols

Torch: Torch of Liberty

UN: United Nations
USMC: United States Marine Corps
USSR: Union of Soviet Socialist Republics
Uboat: German submarine (U.S. submarines are listed under "Navy")
UncAx: Uncle Sam and Hitler or Axis leaders
UncJa: Uncle Sam and Japanese figure(s)
Uncle: Uncle Sam
UncV: Uncle Sam and V
Unit: U.S. military unit, large or small
Unk: Unknown

VEDAY: Victory in Europe Day; day of German capitulation
VJ DAY: Victory over Japan Day
Verse: Poetry, rhyme, or doggerel
VforV: V for Victory

WAC: Women's Army Corps
WASP: Women's Airforce Service Pilots
WAVES: Women''s Reserve, U.S. Navy
Wash: George Washington
Winst: Prime Minister Winston Churchill
Women: Women as theme or subject of cachet

CACHET PUBLISHER

In the "Publisher" column of the catalogue are listed 662 people, companies, or government agencies responsible for production and distribution of patriotic covers in World War II.

Some publishers were artists or printers who created and distributed their own work. Others published the creations of others, overseeing cachet design and cover production, advertisement, and distribution. A few artists (including Dorothy Knapp and Ludwig Staehle) sometimes published their own work and sometimes were commissioned by others to design cachets for patriotic covers.

Enough space has been allotted in the column to identify each publisher uniquely. Separate publisher and publisher imprint catalogues listing full names of publishers, their cities and states, and the imprints or logos they used, may be found in the next two chapters.

VALUE ($)

Values in this catalogue are retail price ranges in U.S. dollars for postally used patriotic covers in clean, undamaged condition. They reflect recent dealer selling prices, current dealer price lists, and published auction results.

Values are given for the basic patriotic cover. Inherent in assigned values are methods of production (hand painted, thermographed, multicolored), popularity of cachet maker among collectors, and special dates (date of Pearl Harbor attack, December 7, 1941; D-Day; date of President Roosevelt's death; VE Day; VJ Day) or place (Tokyo Bay) of usage. All these are part of the "basic" nature of the cover. Other cover elements or usages may enhance or detract from these basic values. This is clearly reflected in market transactions. Since all attempts to standardize the monetary amount of such variations have been futile, no attempt will be made here.

It is important though to alert readers to those cover elements and usages that affect value. Factors enhancing patriotic cover value include:

- Foreign destinations
- Censor and other auxiliary marks
- Fancy patriotic cancels
- Interrupted mail (including "Return to Sender," multiple re-addressed, and casualty mail)

- Special mail services, including registered and special delivery mail
- Mail to or from significant people of the war
- Autographs on cover of significant wartime people
- Mail between overseas military personnel
- Combat mail

Again, how much each of these factors enhances value varies in the marketplace. An arbitrary standardization will not be essayed here.

There are of course factors that detract from patriotic cover value. These include:

- Roughly opened or torn envelopes
- Absence of back flap
- Creased envelopes
- Anything that renders a domestic cover less than "clean"
- Unauthorized or fraudulent use of hand cancels and back-dating of cachets to mark historic events (when detected, these may render the covers valueless except as specimens for study or comparison)

"Add-on" cachets raise a special problem A certain degree of event cachet back-dating was inevitable during the war. Envelopes were first stamped and addressed, then postmarked on the date of the event and mailed (or handed back by a mail clerk). Only then was the cachet generally added, since obtaining the proper date of cancellation was paramount and designing and printing took time. Cachet makers took days or weeks to produce cachets that fit the event. By convention such covers are "of the period," though back-dated (the cachets were not prepared on the exact date of the event). They were and are accepted as genuine event covers and their cachets are not considered "add-ons."

In contrast, printing or hand painting a cachet months, years, or in some cases decades after an event in order to inflate the value of a postally used cover was and is an unacceptable philatelic practice. Such "add-on" patriotic cachets are usually shunned by the discerning collector, but there are exceptions.

Chief among the exceptions are the event covers of Captain Frank L. Teixeira, which almost certainly were created after the war, possibly in the 1946-1947 period. Both the cachets and the postmarking of some of his covers appear to have been post-war artifacts. This was discussed earlier, in the brief biography of Captain Teixeira in Chapter 3. So far, the marketplace has not reacted negatively to these attractively designed four-color covers, in part because they have been on the market in small numbers for over five decades.

Table 6 lists valuations used in this catalogue. As mentioned, the value of each patriotic cover is given a price range and assigned a letter grade from A through I in the "Value" column. Covers ranked "A" are valued in the $3 to $6 dollar range, those ranked "B", $7-$15, and so on through those ranked "I" which are valued at greater than $1,000. Covers given an "X" ranking are unpriced because suspicion of fraud is strong.

––––

POINTS TO REMEMBER

Numbers in *bold italics* indicate cachets illustrated at the end of each alphabetical section of the cachet catalogue.

Identically worded three-, two-, and one-line cachets are arranged in that order. Thus, "Remember / Pearl / Harbor is listed first, then "Remember / Pearl Harbor," then "Remember Pearl Harbor." Another example: "A / salute / to" is followed by "A / salute to," then by "A salute to."

When cachet text is shortened from the end, "etc." is added.

When the middle portion of text is deleted, missing text is indicated by "/ [etc.] /" between the first and last portions of cachet text.

"Thermographed" may be abbreviated as "thermogr," "thermo," or "therm" as exigencies of space require; "handpainted" may similarly be shortened to "handpaint," "handp" or "hp."

A slash mark ("/") separates two or more different states of color of a cachet; a comma separates the colors of a bicolored cachet. "Multicolored" cachets have at least three colors. Explanations of color abbreviations are located in the Cachet Color section of this introduction to the catalogue.

Topic abbreviations are listed and explained in the Cachet Topic section.

Values are retail price ranges in U.S. dollars for patriotic covers in clean, undamaged condition.

Important exceptions exist for patriotic envelopes whose condition was affected by war conditions. Valuations begin at "A" ($3 to $6) and range up to "I" (greater than $1,000). An "X" valuation indicates that a cover is unpriced because it is suspicious or fraudulent.

Table 6. Cover Values

Value	*Price Range*
A	$ 3 - 6
B	$ 7 - 15
C	$ 16 - 30
D	$ 31 - 60
E	$ 61 - 125
F	$ 126 - 250
G	$ 251 - 500
H	$ 501 - 1000
I	$ >1000
X	Unpriced: Suspicious or fraudulent cover

CACHET TEXT BEGINNING WITH "A"

NO.	CACHET TEXT	COLOR	TOPIC	PUBLISHER	$
1	A / day / [etc.] / Yank troops re-enter / the Philippines. / Oct. 20, 1944	Red	Event	Threl+Thar	B
2	A / good / steer / the Victory Loan etc.	Unknown	Bonds	Eichenlaub	A
3	A / happy / new / year [each word diagonal] / 1945 [vertical] / Greetings etc.	Blue, red	Holid	Unknown	B
4	A / happy / new year	Multicolored	Holid	Linto	B
5	A / merry / American / Christmas [handpainted] [+cut-&-pasted paper]	Multicolored	Holid	Temple	C
6	A / merry Christmas / and a / happy new year	Multicolored	Flag	Linto	B
7	A / merry Christmas / and etc.	Unknown	Holid	Porto-serv	B
8	A / salute / to / Adolph / Hitler / Chancellor / of / Germany etc.	Black, green	Hitle	Kosko	A
9	A / salute / to / Hirohito / son of heaven / emperor of Japan etc.	Brown,	Japan	Kosko	A
10	A / salute / to / mining / producing / the / dress / and / minerals / for / victory	Red	Home	Garland	A
11	A / salute / to the day when the world / will again enjoy etc.	Blue, red	Flag	Muzzy	B
12	A / salute / to: / Comdr. / Norman / Miller / (one man task force) etc.	Blue, red	Hero	Boone	A
13	A / salute / to: / Ernie / Pyle / who has been 29 months over- / seas etc.	Bk,R/Bu,Red	Pyle	Boone	B
14	A / salute / to: / Fighting / First / Infantry / Army patch #1. / etc.	Black,	Unit	Boone	A
15	A / salute / to: / Gen. George / (Old Blood and Guts) / Patton and / all etc.	Blue, red	Patt	Boone	B
16	A / salute / to: / George / Ray / Tweed / of California for surviving etc.	Bk,R/Gn,O	Hero	Boone	A
17	A / salute / to: / Lieut. / Samuel / Wallace / Magill / No junior officer etc.	Blue, red	Hero	Boone	A
18	A / salute / to: / Lieut. / Van T. / Barfoot / of Carthage, Miss., / who etc.	Black, red	Hero	Boone	A
19	A / salute / to: / Lt. Col. / Francis / Gabreski etc.	Blue, red	Hero	Boone	A
20	A / salute / to: / Lt. Louis A. / Johnson etc.	Unknown	Hero	Nelson, KE	A
21	A / salute / to: / Major / George E. / Preddy / of Greensboro, N.C., etc.	Bk,R/Bk,Br	Hero	Boone	A
22	A / salute / to: / Major / James / Howard etc.	Bu,R/Gn,O	Hero	Boone	A
23	A / salute / to: / Major / Thomas B. / McGuire / of Ridgewood, N.J., etc.	Blue, red	Hero	Boone	A
24	A / salute / to: / Major John L. Smith / United States Marines etc.	Blue, red	Hero	Boone	A
25	A / salute / to: / Pfc. / Joseph / Muckton / of Carteret, N.J., to etc.	Green, red	Hero	Boone	A
26	A / salute / to: / Private / Earl / McAllister / (of the Canadian Army) etc.	Blue, red	Hero	Boone	A
27	A / salute / to: / Sgt. / Alexander / Drabik etc.	Blue, red	Hero	Boone	A
28	A / salute / to: / Sgt. John C. Squires / of Louisville, Ky., etc.	Blue, red	Hero	Boone	A
29	A / salute / to: / the / "Rangers" / the Rangers are home, 199 of them etc.	Green, red	Unit	Boone	A
30	A / salute / to: / the / "Red / Devils" / Story of valor seldom etc.	Green, red	Unit	Boone	A
31	A / salute / to: / the / heroes of / Bastogne / Brig. Gen. A.C. McAuliff etc.	Green, red	Hero	Boone	A
32	A / salute to / Capt. "Smoky Joe" Foss / United States Marine Corps etc.	Blue, red	Hero	Boone	A
33	A / salute to / Capt. A.W. Wermuth / In four months of etc.	Blue, red	Hero	Boone	A
34	A / salute to / Capt. Don S. Gentile / of Piqua, Ohio, who is etc.	Blue, red	Hero	Boone	A
35	A / salute to / Capt. Herman Bottcher / led American forces that split etc.	Blue, red	Hero	Boone	A
36	A / salute to / Capt. Richard I. Bong / of Poplar, Wisc., has shot down etc.	Blue, red	Hero	Boone	A
37	A / salute to / Capt. Robert S. Johnson / of Lawton, Okla., who etc.	Blue, red	Hero	Boone	A
38	A / salute to / Captain Charles Davis / Capt. Davis was with infantry etc.	Blue, red	Hero	Boone	A
39	A / salute to / Colonel John R. Kane / Col. Kane was the leader etc.	Blue, red	Hero	Boone	A
40	A / salute to / Commando Technical Sergeant / Charles E. Kelly etc.	Unknown	Hero	Boone	A
41	A / salute to / Corp. Barney Ross / Knocked off 22 Japs in etc.	Blue, red	Hero	Boone	A
42	A / salute to / Corporal Al Schmid / United States Marines etc.	Blue, red	Hero	Boone	A
43	A / salute to / Douglas Munro, Seaman 1c / Officer in charge of 24 etc.	Blue, red	Hero	Boone	A
44	A / salute to / Lieut. A.J. Brassfield / of Missouri who knocked etc.	Blue, red	Hero	Boone	A
45	A / salute to / Lieut. Robert W. Hanson / of Newtonville, Mass. etc.	Blue, red	Hero	Boone	A
46	A / salute to / Lt. Cmdr. C.C. Kirkpatrick / holder of three Navy etc.	Blue, red	Hero	Boone	A
47	A / salute to / Lt. Col. Francis Gabreski etc.	Unknown	Hero	Boone	A
48	A / salute to / Maj. James Howard of St. Louis, Mo., who dived etc.	Blue, red	Hero	Boone	A
49	A / salute to / Major Doolittle / and the gallant men who etc.	Blue, red	Dool	Boone	B
50	A / salute to / Major John L. Smith / United States Marines / who etc.	Blue, red	Hero	Boone	A
51	A / salute to / Sgt. John Basilone, USMC / for extraordinary heroism etc.	Blue, red	Hero	Boone	A
52	A / salute to / submarine Pompano / the Pompano, victor over at etc.	Black, blue	Navy	Boone	A
53	A / salute to / the Allied Air Force / for the Bismarck Sea victory etc.	Blue, red	Air	Boone	A
54	A / salute to / the Pacific Fleet / for knocking 'ell out of the etc.	Blue, red	Navy	Boone	A
55	A / salute to / the U.S. Sub Patrols / for their splendid work etc.	Blue, red	USsub	Boone	A
56	A / soldier's / message / Though I am far away from you tonight, my dear etc.	Blue, red	Verse	McGovern	A
57	A / sure / hit! [in quotes]	Black	Navy	Lupton	A
58	A / Younkerite / in the / Service reports to	Black	Army	Temple	A
59	A beautiful fruit / -but- / no damn good to me. [handpainted]	Multicolored	Uncle	Steinhardt	C
60	A blot against / [etc.] / Japan / Hawaii / attacked etc. [postmarked 12/7/41]	Blue, red	Event	Unknown	F

NO.	CACHET TEXT	COLOR	TOPIC	PUBLISHER	$
61	A bright blue service star rests in my heart, / there I feel etc. [no picture]	Blue	Verse	Abel	A
62	A buddy-study kit [envelope 7 1/2x5 1/2 in.]	Blue,red	Relig	Bible Med	B
63	A buzzard smelled an awful stink—— / 'twas Hitler dead——that's no lie. etc.	Purple	Verse	Rush	A
64	A careless word / ...another cross	Brown	Army	Yontz	A
65	A careless word / ...another cross [thermographed]	Gold	Army	Yontz	B
66	A congressional act of / 1942 stabilized wages / [etc.] / Jan. 1, 1941—— etc.	Multicolored	Home	Linto	B
67	A congressional act of / 1942 stabilized wages / and prices. Now just etc.	Multicolored	Home	Linto	B
68	A corker [handpainted]	Multicolored	Army	Adler	D
69	A crushed nation can / rise and fight again / France [thermographed]	Blue, red	ORN	Staehle	C
70	A date to remember: / a black / day for / America! etc. [no picture]	Blue, red	Pearl	Boone	A
71	A date which / will live [in quotes] etc. [handpainted + cut-&-pasted paper]	Black, blue	Pearl	Temple	C
72	A day / bonds buy bombs / Yank troops re-invade / the Philippines	Red	Japan	Threl+Thar	A
73	A defense stamp a day / will help buy a gun / for the man who's away etc.	Blue, red	Bonds	Brenn	A
74	A donkey was seeking her son one day / that had strayed to the German etc.	Green	Verse	Rush	A
75	A donor's prayer / when this deep red blood etc.	Blue, red	Blood	Lawrence	A
76	A famous day for / pro-Nazi Irish!	Unknown	Unk	Linto	B
77	A famous day for / pro-Nazi Irish! / 3-17-'45--Stettin falls / to Russians	Unknown	Event	Linto	B
78	A feather / merchant [thermographed]	Red	Merch	Greenlee	A
79	A few more bombs will do the job [handpainted]	Multicolored	Unk	Wolf, CL	B
80	A first / cruise / cutie / with / second / cruise / ideas! [in quotes]	Black	Navy	Lupton	A
81	A free America / means keeping / all Huns and / Japs out!	Gd/Gn/Gd,V	Home	Linto	B
82	A free America / means keeping / all Huns and / Japs out! / 9-2-'44——Finns etc.	Multicolored	Event	Linto	B
83	A free America / means keeping / all Huns and / Japs out! / 9-8-'44——Yanks etc.	Multicolored	Event	Linto	B
84	A free America / with malice / toward none - justice to all.	Multicolored	EagSh	Minkus	A
85	A free France, for the / free French! / Thanks to the Yanks, / and British too!	Bk/Gn/R	Map	Carter	A
86	A friend / of yours? / Scentry box [handpainted]	Multicolored	Army	Cowdery	D
87	A G.I.'s dream of how to pay off the war debt.	Bk/Bu/Br	Hitle	Carter	A
88	A gallant service / WAC [handpainted]	Multicolored	WAC	Maul	C
89	A gem / among the stars	Unknown	Unk	Ang	A
90	A ghost steps out of a jungle green / His eyes are sad at the things etc.	Multicolored	Verse	McCluney	B
91	A GI wish / Sitting on my G.I. bed / my G.I. hat upon etc. [thermographed]	Blue, red	Verse	Baur	A
92	A glimpse into his future	Multicolored	Hitle	Peer	B
93	A goat and a skunk went out in the sun / to play in a field of roses; etc.	Brown	Verse	Rush	A
94	A good old / American game - / Kicking the / "pigskin" around! [handpainted]	Black	Hitle	Parker	B
95	A good smack where it counts	Multicolored	Gener	Peer	B
96	A good week / Madagascar / and / New Caledonia / occupied / and / 21 Jap etc.	Red	Event	Fidelity	B
97	A grand old bird / Don't let it down [colored envelopes]	Blue, red	Eagle	McElroy	A
98	A great nation / A great defense! [Army seal + flag] [thermographed]	Blue	Armed	Crosby	B
99	A great nation! / A great defense! [Army seal + eagle, shield] [thermographed]	Blue/Gold	Armed	Crosby	B
100	A greater future / a great past	Multicolored	Home	Minkus	A
101	A guy can / dream——can't / he? [handpainted]	Multicolored	Unk	Unknown	B
102	A handy / little gadget—— [in quotes] [handpainted]	Multicolored	Army	Cowdery	D
103	A happy New Year / 1945 / greetings / peace etc.	Unknown	Holid	Czubay	A
104	A hard nut - but cracking / U.S.——Britain / Russia / V	Black, green	Ally	Griffith	A
105	A jeep or a peep / we're on top of the heap etc.	Blue, red	Unk	Quigley	B
106	A letter today	Blue	Flag	Huss	A
107	A look at the beast below / is sufficient / reason / why we / should etc.	Green	Japan	Linto	B
108	A man's size job is / done by each WAC etc. [thermographed]	Unknown	WAC	Czubay	B
109	A man's size job is / done by each WAVE etc. [thermographed]	Unknown	WAVE	Czubay	B
110	A memory that / shall allways [sic] / live etc. [4/12/45] [handpainted]	Multicolored	FDR	Adler	E
111	A message to Hitler / A man without a country / is like a horse without etc.	Black	Hitle	Abel	A
112	A monkey posed before Hitler's frame / He thought it a mirror, you see; etc.	Red	Verse	Rush	A
113	A move in the / right direction. [handpainted]	Multicolored	Hitle	Parker	C
114	A nation mourns / its leader / End of mourning period. [postmarked 5/14/45]	Black	FDR	Richardson	D
115	A nation mourns / its leader / Funeral Washington, D.C. [postmarked 4/14/45]	Black	FDR	Richardson	D
116	A nation mourns / its leader / Interment Hyde Park, N.Y. [postmarked 4/15/45]	Black	FDR	Richardson	D
117	A nation mourns / its leader [postmarked 4/12/45]	Black	FDR	Richardson	F
118	A nation mourns! / Franklin Delano Roosevelt etc. [no picture]	Unknown	FDR	Levering	D
119	A nation's pride / aircraft carrier	Blue	Navy	Neal	A
120	A nation's pride / battleship	Blue	Navy	Neal	A
121	A nation's pride / cruisers	Blue	Navy	Neal	A
122	A nation's pride / sub chaser	Blue	Navy	Neal	A

NO.	CACHET TEXT	COLOR	TOPIC	PUBLISHER	$
123	A nation's pride / submarine	Blue	USsub	Neal	A
124	A nation's pride / the convoy	Blue	Navy	Neal	A
125	A navy second / to none [3 planes flying to right] [postmarked before 12/07/1941]	Red	Air	Unknown	C
126	A new GI gets into the war	Multicolored	Atom	Peer	B
127	A paper war! / Every soldier needs it——from / his draft card etc. [no picture]	Black, green	Home	Davis, Ray	A
128	A permanent eclipse of the Rising Sun / is predicted [etc.]. Italy etc.	Unknown	Japan	Runge	A
129	A permanent eclipse of the Rising Sun / is predicted etc. / Aleutians / V	Bu,R/R,Silv	Japan	Runge	A
130	A permanent eclipse of the Rising Sun / is predicted etc. / Coral Sea / V	Unknown	Japan	Runge	A
131	A permanent eclipse of the Rising Sun / is predicted etc. / Gilbert Is. / V	Gold, red	Japan	Runge	A
132	A permanent eclipse of the Rising Sun / is predicted etc. / Marshall Is. / V	Gold, red	Japan	Runge	A
133	A permanent eclipse of the Rising Sun / is predicted etc. / Midway / V	Multicolored	Japan	Runge	A
134	A permanent eclipse of the Rising Sun / is predicted etc. / New Britain / V	Gold, red	Japan	Runge	A
135	A permanent eclipse of the Rising Sun / is predicted etc. / New Guinea / V	Blue, red	Japan	Runge	A
136	A permanent eclipse of the Rising Sun / is predicted etc. / Solomon Is. / V	Blue, red	Japan	Runge	A
137	A permanent eclipse of the Rising Sun / is predicted in the near future	Multicolored	Japan	Runge	A
138	A permanent eclipse of the Rising Sun / is predicted in the near future. / V	Bu,Y/O,Red	Japan	Runge	A
139	A pin-up for civilians etc.	Multicolored	Unk	Trans-Miss	A
140	A prayer / for / in the / service [handpainted]	Multicolored	Relig	Adler	C
141	A real American / General Douglas MacArthur [thermographed]	Blue/Brown	Mac	Sadworth	B
142	A red letter day / in / American history / Germany / surrenders	Blue, red	VEDay	Card	B
143	A red letter day / in / American history / May 8, 1945 / Germany / surrenders	Blue, red	VEDay	Card	B
144	A reminder! / You have / a date / at the / Blood Bank- / The wounded can't etc.	Blue, red	Blood	Eichenlaub	A
145	A Roman holiday [in quotes] [envelope 6 9/16x3 11/16 in.]	Black	Axis	Belles-let	D
146	A salute / to / Captain Allen Wood etc.	Blue, red	Hero	Levering	A
147	A salute / to GI Joe / in the / US Army [thermographed]	Unknown	Army	Czubay	B
148	A salute / to the / American / woman [thermographed]	Unkown	Women	Baur	A
149	A salute / to the day when the world / will again enjoy / "Peace on earth" etc.	Blue, red	Flag	Nichols	B
150	A salute from the civilians / to our etc. [no picture]	Gold	Unk	Price, R	A
151	A salute to - / Cpl. Ken Miller, / first PCEC member (376) / to give etc.	Bk,S/Gn,Gd	Army	Phill, CR	A
152	A salute to / "Jamestown's own" / Co. E, 174th Infantry / "The Fenton" etc.	Multicolored	Unit	Nichols	B
153	A salute to / Albania / We won't forget / Good Friday / of 1939	Multicolored	ORN	Cachet Cra	B
154	A salute to / Colin Kelly / first American pilot etc. [thermographed]	Blue, green	Hero	Baur	B
155	A salute to / Ernie Pyle / beloved scribe of all GI's / The famous etc.	Black/Green	Pyle	Gustafson	B
156	A salute to / Greece / Freedom shall come!	Multicolored	ORN	Cachet Cra	B
157	A salute to / James Powers etc. [thermographed]	Unknown	Hero	Baur	B
158	A salute to / Lt Col Richard Kenny etc. [thermographed]	Unknown	Hero	Baur	B
159	A salute to / Lt John Murphy etc. [thermographed]	Unknown	Hero	Baur	B
160	A salute to / Mike Murphy / first American to / shoot a Jap.	Green, red	Japan	Baur	B
161	A salute to / Mrs. T.F. Sullivan etc. [thermographed]	Unknown	Hero	Baur	B
162	A salute to / Wm. B. Owens etc. [thermographed]	Unknown	Hero	Baur	B
163	A salute to all / who are serving / to etc. [thermographed]	Unknown	Unk	Yontz	B
164	A salute to Ernie Pyle / beloved scribe of all GI's / The famous etc.	Blue	Pyle	Gustafson	B
165	A salute to our / fighting Navy	Blue	Navy	Schlichte	A
166	A salute to the American way of living	Bk/Blue,Red	Flag	Smith, AD	A
167	A salute to the fighting / American Indians etc.	Bicolor	Unk	Cox	A
168	A salute to the Navy! / safe and sure etc.	Unknown	Navy	Schlichte	A
169	A salute to, / Edwin O'Hara etc. [thermo] [env. 6 1/2x3 5/8, 9 1/2x4 3/16 in.]	Green, red	Hero	Baur	B
170	A salute to, / Lt. Col. Mike Murphy / First American glider etc. [thermographed]	Blue, green	Hero	Baur	B
171	A Seabee's liberty dream. [handpainted]	Black	Navy	Bickford	C
172	A setting son of the Rising Sun [kicking mule]	Black	Japan	Cornell	B
173	A shadow over the Rising Sun	Multicolored	Japan	Peer	B
174	A ship a day keeps the Japs away	Blue, red	Japan	Quigley	B
175	A slip of the lip / may sink a ship / Old etc.	Bicolor	Unk	Fabian	A
176	A slip of the lip / may sink this ship / keep them etc. [thermographed]	Blue	Navy	Yontz	B
177	A slip of the lip / may sink this ship / the enemy is etc. [thermographed]	Blue	Navy	Yontz	B
178	A slip of the lip may sink a ship [handpainted]	Multicolored	Uboat	Barwicki	B
179	A slip of your lip / may sink a ship	Unknown	Navy	Kosko	A
180	A soldier's dream, and Hitler's nightmare. [in quotes] [handpainted]	Multicolored	Hitle	White, TM	F
181	A soldier's prayer / by Private Allan Osborne / O Lord to thee on bended etc.	Black,	Verse	Carpenter	A
182	A song for our banner, the watchword etc.	Blue, red	Unk	Card	A
183	A souvenir / from the / United States forces / in Australia [cachet at right]	Blue, red	EagFl	Unknown	B
184	A steel trap for Hirohito	Multicolored	Japan	Peer	B

NO.	CACHET TEXT	COLOR	TOPIC	PUBLISHER	$
185	A step in the / right direction [in quotes]	Blue	Japan	Lawrence	A
186	A strong / navy - a strong / nation	Black	Navy	Coll Surp	A
187	A strong Navy / 1939 1939 / Greeting from the Asiatic Fleet / A strong nation	Green	Navy	Graf	C
188	A sure bet / War bonds / 7th etc.	Bicolor	Bonds	Eichenlaub	A
189	A sure sign	Bicolor	Unk	Carter	A
190	A symbol of our faith	Bicolor	Unk	Carter	A
191	A taste of his own medicine	Black/Green	USSR	Talburt	A
192	A toast to the health / of the Japanese navy / "Bottoms up" / sez U.S.N.	Bu,R/Blue	Japan	Harrington	A
193	A traditional 'man-o'-war' [envelope 6 3/4x3 7/8 in.]	Sepia tones	Navy	Belles-let	C
194	A tribute to the / shore patrol - who / do such [in quotes] etc. [thermographed]	Black/Blue	Navy	Crosby	B
195	A two ocean fleet / buy/ defense / stamps / buy /defense etc. [thermographed]	Black	Navy	Crosby	B
196	A verse in the Bible / reads: / "An eye for an eye. A tooth for a tooth." etc.	Green, silver	Relig	Linto	B
197	A verse in the Bible / reads: / [etc.] / 4-21-'45——Allies / capture Bologna	Green, silver	Event	Linto	B
198	A victorious / 1945 / V [handpainted]	Multicolored	Holid	Nelson, KE	B
199	A woman's work is from / sun up to sun down. A sailor's etc. [handpainted]	Multicolored	Navy	Davis, M	B
200	A wonderful / week / We bomb them / at Cologne / and Ruhr etc. [no picture]	Red	Event	Fidelity	B
201	A word to the wise / is sufficient / Buy more / war stamps / and bonds	Blue, red	Bonds	Kosko	A
202	A.E.F. second / ...- front / 10 Nov 1942 / U.S. Forces occupy / Arzew etc.	Blue, red	Event	First Day	D
203	A.F.R.T.C. / Fort Knox, Ky. [on water tank, soldier in tank in foreground]	Blue	Ordna	Unknown	A
204	A.P.O. 802 Branch / American Base Forces / located aboard U.S.A.T. etc. [thermo]	Gold	Ship	Czubay	D
205	Aachen / surrenders / Oct. 21, 1944 [handpainted]	Black, red	Event	Richards	B
206	Aachen falls / A / Oct 20, 1944 etc. [no picture]	Unknown	Event	McCluney	B
207	Above all / for all / victory / for liberty [thermographed]	Blue	Dove	Boothroyd	A
208	Above all in peace or war	Green, red	Eagle	Carpenter	A
209	Abraham / Lincoln / February 12	Unknown	Linc	Linto	B
210	Abraham Lincoln / "Fondly do we hope, fervently / do we pray, that this" etc.	Blue, red	Linc	Linprint	A
211	Absence makes the / war grow longer	Gn,Bk/R,Bk	Home	Runge	A
212	Absenteeism / and / labor trouble / are etc. [no picture]	Red	Home	Rowe	A
213	Absenteeism / helps the enemy / work etc.	Blue, red	Home	Kosko	A
214	Absenteeism is not Americanism	Black	Home	Runge	A
215	Absentees / help the / Japanese / Work etc. [no picture] [env. 6x3 1/4 in.]	Blue, red	Home	Kosko	A
216	Absolute / unconditional / surrender / [etc.] / 9-12-'44——Yankee columns etc.	Multicolored	Event	Linto	B
217	Absolute / unconditional / surrender / for Nazis / and Japs	Gold, silver	Flag	Linto	B
218	Accidents help the Axis / I want to help etc.	Blue	Axis	Burdick	A
219	Accidents help the Axis / Keep etc.	Purple	Home	Burdick	A
220	Accidents help the Axis / That's funny! / That's the job / I was telling etc.	Red	Home	Burdick	A
221	Accidents help the Axis / Then I says - Lissen, / chum, you can't pinch etc.	Red	Home	Burdick	A
222	Ace of Spades of Marine Scouting Squadron Two / Last of the etc. [thermographed]	Blue/Red	USMC	Crosby	B
223	Ach Fritz, we overshot our mark?	Red	Chute	Ang	A
224	Ach himmel / I pult / de zipper unt not der ripcord! etc.	Blue	Hitle	Fertig	B
225	Ach! der time has come the valrus / said to t'ink of many t'ings. [in quotes]	Bk/Br/Gn	Hitle	Smith, A	A
226	Ach! Der Yanks / ist comming / vunce more again!! [handpainted]	Black, red	Hitle	Parker	B
227	Ach! dose Yankees can't / hit a thing, can dey, / herr etc. [thermographed]	Red	Axis	Yontz	B
228	Ach! dose Yankees can't hit a thing / can dey herr etc. [thermographed]	Red	Axis	Yontz	B
229	Ach! dot Yank 1st Army is bad / Von Rundstedt's 'return!' [handpainted]	Black	Unit	Clendennen	D
230	Ach! Du lieber!! / Donner vetter!! / The wolf is on his doorstep! [handpainted]	Multicolored	Hitle	Parker	C
231	Ach!! wot / a war / noddings / but defeat. [in quotes] [thermographed]	Blue	Hitle	Sadworth	B
232	Ach. Himmel / dose / American houzvives [handpainted]	Multicolored	Nazi	Adler	D
233	Achieve victory through co-operation / Back the attack etc. [thermographed]	Bicolor var	Bonds	Czubay	B
234	Act now on that etc. [envelope 8 11/16x3 5/8 in.]	Unknown	Unk	ITE Circui	B
235	Action!! / Action!! / Our lawmakers must / examine the etc. [no picture]	Multicolored	Home	Linto	B
236	Add a star to your crown / The army needs etc.	Blue, red	Unk	Boone	A
237	Adding strength / to our fighting forces / Women's Army etc. [thermographed]	Purple	WAC	Sadworth	B
238	Adieu / United Nations / Peace / Conference / San Francisco, Calif.	Multicolored	UN	Anti-Pacif	B
239	Adm. "Bull" / Halsey's flagship / U.S.S. / Missouri / where / Japs etc.	Grey, silver	VJDay	Linto	C
240	Adm. "Bull" / Halsey's flagship / U.S.S. / Missouri etc. / 9-2-'45--Censor on etc.	Grey, silver	VJDay	Linto	C
241	Adm. / Ernest / J. King	Unknown	Admir	Linto	B
242	Adm. / Kinnel / "Guilty of / what?"	Gold, sepia	Admir	Linto	B
243	Adm. / Richmond / K. Turner	Gold, sepia	Admir	Linto	B
244	Adm. / Richmond / K. Turner / 6-30-'45--Truman's new etc.	Gold, sepia	Event	Linto	B
245	Adm. / Sir Bertram / "Dynamo" / Ramsay / [etc.] / 1-9-'45——Yanks land / on etc.	Multicolored	Admir	Linto	B
246	Adm. / Sir Bertram / "Dynamo" / Ramsay / Killed in / plane crash / Jan. 2, '45	Multicolored	Admir	Linto	B

NO.	CACHET TEXT	COLOR	TOPIC	PUBLISHER	$
247	Adm. / Sir Bruce / Frasier	Unknown	Admir	Linto	B
248	Adm. / William D. / Leahy	Unknown	Admir	Linto	B
249	Adm. / William D. / Leahy / 1-8-'45——Von Rundstedt / retreats on west front	Unknown	Event	Linto	B
250	Adm. / Wm. F. / Halsey	Unknown	Admir	Linto	B
251	Adm. / Wm. F. / Halsey / 11-18-'44——Allied planes attack / another German etc.	Unknown	Event	Linto	B
252	Adm. A.J. / Hepburn	Multicolored	Admir	Linto	B
253	Adm. A.J. / Hepburn / 12-24-'44——V-bombs visit / northern England	Multicolored	Event	Linto	B
254	Adm. C.W. / Nimitz / He plans far / too / [etc.] / 10-29-'44——Bulgarian etc.	Multicolored	Nim	Linto	B
255	Adm. C.W. / Nimitz / He plans far / too well for / dirty Japs	Gold, sepia	Nim	Linto	B
256	Adm. Chester W. Nimitz	Unknown	Nim	Linto	B
257	Adm. Chester W. Nimitz	Blue	Nim	Unknown	A
258	Adm. Chester W. Nimitz / 12-8-'44——Yanks win back etc.	Unknown	Event	Linto	B
259	Adm. Darlan captured at Algiers	Unknown	Event	Linto	B
260	Adm. Darlan murdered	Unknown	Event	Linto	B
261	Adm. Kimmel	Unknown	Admir	Linto	B
262	Adm. R.E. Ingersoll	Unknown	Admir	Linto	B
263	Adm. R.E. Ingersoll / 12-15-'44——MacArthur / lands on Mindoro	Unknown	Event	Linto	B
264	Adm. Raymond A. Spruance	Black	Admir	Huss	A
265	Adm. Sir Bruce Frasier	Unknown	Admir	Linto	B
266	Adm. W.F. / Halsey / busy sending / [etc.] / 10-21-'44——Yanks capture etc.	Unknown	Event	Linto	B
267	Adm. W.F. / Halsey / busy sending / the Japs down / to Davy Jones	S,Vi/Bk,Gn	Admir	Linto	B
268	Adm. William D. Leahy	Unknown	Admir	Linto	B
269	Adm. Wm. F. Halsey	Unknown	Admir	Linto	B
270	Admiral Chester W. Nimitz / Commander of U.S. forces in the Pacific	Blue	Nim	Huss	A
271	Admiral Chester W. Nimitz / Commander-in-chief / [etc.] / V-J Day etc. [thermographed]	Blue, red	VJDay	Crosby	B
272	Admiral Chester W. Nimitz / Commander-in-chief of the etc. [thermographed]	Blue, red	Nim	Crosby	B
273	Admiral Chester W. Nimitz / destroyer of Jap fleet [thermographed]	Blue	Nim	Unknown	B
274	Admiral E.J. King [handpainted]	Multicolored	Admir	Knoll	D
275	Admiral Ernest J. King / Commander-in-chief of the U.S. Fleet etc.	Black	Admir	Pacific	A
276	Admiral Ernest J. King / Commander-in-chief of the etc. [thermographed]	Blue, red	Admir	Crosby	B
277	Admiral Ernest J. King [colored envelopes]	Bk/Bu/Br	Admir	Huss	A
278	Admiral Halsey	Black/Blue	Admir	Huss	A
279	Admiral Kimmel / wants trial / [etc.] / 5-26-'44——Yanks drive Huns out of etc.	Multicolored	Event	Linto	B
280	Admiral Kimmel / wants trial held! / Who is holding it / up, and why? [no picture]	Gold, silver	Admir	Linto	B
281	Admiral King [VJ Day cancel]	Black	Admir	Southworth	B
282	Admiral Nimitz [handpainted]	Multicolored	Nim	Knoll	C
283	Admiral Nimitz [VJ Day cancel]	Black	Nim	Southworth	B
284	Admiral R.R. Waesche / Commandant of the Coast Guard [VJ Day cancel]	Black	Admir	Southworth	B
285	Admiral William D. Leahy / Chief of Staff to the etc. [thermographed]	Blue, red	Admir	Crosby	B
286	Admiral William Leahy [handpainted]	Multicolored	Admir	Knoll	D
287	Admiral, tell Joey I'll meet him at 9! [in quotes] [w/, w/o stars] [blue envelope]	Multicolored	Navy	Amer Art	A
288	Admirtal C.W. Nimitz [handpainted]	Multicolored	Nim	Knoll	E
289	Adolf / quits [handpainted]	Black	Hitle	Wolf, CL	B
290	Adolf / the Axis has-been / all washed up!	Blue, red	Hitle	Boone	A
291	Adolf / the superman... / "all washed up!"	Bicolor var	Hitle	Boone	A
292	Adolf Hitler / his last territorial demand———	Black, red	Hitle	Carpenter	A
293	Adolf thinks so too	Multicolored	Hitle	Peer	B
294	Adolf: / the super - man: / all washed up!	Blue, red	Hitle	Boone	A
295	Adolf's generosity [in quotes] / Honorable Uncle Sam please to etc.	Blue	Uncle	Citret	A
296	Adolph / Little [? words on Mussolini] / Son / of / heaven [handpainted]	Multicolored	Axis	Unknown	B
297	African victory / May - 1943 / On to Berlin	Brown,	Event	Linto	B
298	African victory day	Unknown	Event	Linto	B
299	After 3 years / 'Ell's a-poppin' / for Mussolini / air etc. [thermographed]	Multicolored	Musso	Boone	A
300	After 3 years / 'Ell's a-poppin' / for Mussolini / Pante etc. [thermographed]	Multicolored	Musso	Boone	A
301	After 3 years / 'Ell's a-poppin' / for Mussolini [thermographed]	Multicolored	Musso	Boone	A
302	After Uncle Sam / gives him the 1-2 / it's 1-2-3-4-5-6-7-/ 8-9-10 etc. [handpainted]	Multicolored	Musso	Parker	B
303	After victory [in parentheses] / And grant us, Lord, the grace to bring etc.	Rust	Home	Neal	A
304	After victory... / one world / united with everlasting peace	Blue, red	Globe	Smith, W	A
305	Again / again / again / and / again / wishing you / Yuletime / greetings	Multicolored	Holid	Linto	B
306	Again, again and again / ———F.D.R. / [etc.] / 10-19-'44——MacArthur's boys etc.	Gold, green	Event	Linto	B
307	Again, again and again / F.D.R. / [etc.] / 7-24-'44——Soviets 50 miles etc.	Gold, green	Event	Linto	B
308	Again, again and again / ———F.D.R., Boston, Oct. 30, 1940- / "Your boys" etc.	Gold	Home	Linto	B

NO.	CACHET TEXT	COLOR	TOPIC	PUBLISHER	$
309	Ah dream las' night / dat a baahr wuz on mah tracks——— / he like ' etc.	Black	Hitle	Andrews	A
310	Ah ha / Quiet, censor [ink] [handpainted]	Black, red	Home	Graves	C
311	Aid our victory - / buy more bonds. [handpainted]	Black	Bonds	Klondike	D
312	Aid the victory——— / buy more bonds [handpainted]	Violet	Bonds	Klondike	C
313	Aim straight for the heart of Japan	Red	Japan	Davis, Ray	A
314	Air Corps V ...- / "Mission accomplished" [thermographed]	Blue, red	Air	Von Los	B
315	Air Corps V ...- / "The Robot" [thermographed]	Blue, red	Air	Von Los	B
316	Air Force / Army Navy / United States armed forces / Marines / keep on etc.	Multicolored	Armed	Unknown	A
317	Air might of the allies / Germany / air-conditioning / Jerry-land	Gray, red	Air	Andrews	B
318	Air power / avenger in war / trail-blazer in peace [artist: Knapp]	Blue, red	Air	Fleetwood	B
319	Air power / to / V ...- [handpainted label]	Black	Air	LeGallez	C
320	Air power / to / victory [handpainted label]	Multicolored	Flag+	LeGallez	C
321	Air Raid / Protection Service [upper left]	Blue, red	Home	Unknown	A
322	Air service / U.S.A. [handpainted][envelope 5 3/8x3 3/8 in.]	Multicolored	Armed	Buxton, D.	B
323	Air service / U.S.A. [thermographed]	Purple	Air	Krakora	A
324	Airmail speeds / America to / victory [colored envelopes]	Blue, red	Eagle	Poppenger	A
325	Al Smith compared / Roosevelt to Lincoln / Who did Lincoln / ever etc.	Multicolored	FDR	Linto	B
326	Al Smith said ... / "No matter how thin you slice it" etc. [no pict] [10/26/39]	Black	Home	Unknown	B
327	Alas! How many lie beneath a / starlit sky. / And freedom's flag afloat etc.	Blue, red	Verse	Brenn	A
328	Alaska dog team post / From. / To	Green	Alask	Muridge	B
329	Albania / Albania was invaded by Axis troops (Italian) / April 7, 1939	Black/Blue	ORN	Cliff	A
330	Albania [JWC imprint]	Blue, red	ORN	Clifford	A
331	Albania [Lowry imprint]	Black	ORN	Lowry	A
332	Albania [Runge imprint]	Bicolor var	ORN	Runge	A
333	Albania will be free again! [handpainted]	Green	ORN	Klondike	C
334	Algiers - May 30, 1943 / Gen. Charles de Gaulle etc.	Unknown	Event	Linto	B
335	All / glory to / God / [etc.] / Japs planned / [etc.] / 6-3-'44———Nazi, etc.	Multicolored	Event	Linto	B
336	All / glory to / God / for our / [etc.] / 8-31-'40———Airliner crashed at etc.	Multicolored	Anniv	Linto	B
337	All / glory to / God / for our / free / America	Multicolored	Flag	Linto	B
338	All / glory to / God / for our / free / America / Japs planned / world etc.	Multicolored	Japan	Linto	B
339	All / out / for / victory	Blue, red	Unit	Cozart	A
340	All / out / for / victory [sihouette of soldier with rifle in center]	Blue, red	Armed	Sanders	A
341	All / out / for / victory [V ...- in center, with or without Sanders imprint]	Blue, red	Armed	Sanders	A
342	All aboard! / 3rd victory / bond loan / drive / now / on	Multicolored	Bonds	Linto	B
343	All aboard! / 3rd victory / bond loan / drive / now / on / Dec. 7, 1941, a date etc.	Multicolored	Bonds	Linto	B
344	All Americans are happy that you / have swept the enemy from [in quotes] etc.	Red	Mac	Brenn	B
345	All but / rubbed out!	Black	Hitle	Burdick	A
346	All fascist / welcome [handpainted]	Unknown	Axis	Shaw, TC	C
347	All fighting for / freedom of speech / freedom of religion / freedom etc.	Gn/R/Bu,Re	Armed	Cozart	A
348	All for freedom / 1776 1812 / 1846 1863 / 1898 1917 / today!	Blue, red	Hist	Brenn	A
349	All for one / one for all	Blue	Air	Carter	A
350	All Germany / surrenders [postmarked 5/8/45]	Blue, red	VEDay	Boone	B
351	All glory / to God! / He has given us / the victory! / praise Him / forever!	Bronze, gold	VJDay	Linto	B
352	All hail the / US Marines / Victory on Iwo	Blue, red	USMC	Boone	A
353	All in / because of / our "all-out" / tactics [handpainted]	Multicolored	Army	Cowdery	D
354	All Japs can think to / say etc.	Unknown	Japan	Linto	B
355	All night in——— / and beans / for breakfast! / Good old / U.S. Navy [thermographed]	Blue	Navy	Crosby	B
355A	All out / for victory [V ...- in center]	Blue, red	Armed	Sanders	A
356	All out for defense / Christmas, Fla / Dec etc.	Bicolor	Holid	Unknown	A
357	All out for V... / O!, how we cried / when etc. [env. 6 1/2x3 5/8, 7 1/2x4 in.]	Green	Home	Abel	A
358	All out for victory	Blue	Women	Huss	A
359	All out for victory / Capt. / Colin / Kelly etc. [with copyright "C"]	Multicolored	Hero	Cachet Cra	A
360	All out for victory / Capt. / Colin / Kelly etc. [without copyright "C"]	Multicolored	Hero	CachetCra	A
361	All out for victory / V [handpainted]	Multicolored	VforV	Stoll	B
362	All out for victory!	Blue, red	EagV	Grandy	A
363	All out war / means we're all in the fight! / do etc. [blue picture]	Blue, red	Ordna	Richardson	A
364	All out war / means we're all in the fight! / do etc. [red picture]	Blue, red	Ordna	Richardson	A
365	All right! / all right! / lets see you do / the bear-act / Adolf / ?	Multicolored	Hitle	Borkowski	C
366	All roads lead to / Tokyo and Berlin!	Bu/R/Violet	Ordna	Ander, EA	A
367	All showed their colors! / The first American soldier to kill etc. [no picture]	Gold, silver	Hero	Linto	B
368	All Slovakia is / liberated by / Red troops [thermographed]	Unknown	Event	Boone	B
369	All together / work or fight / for victory	Bu/R/Bu,Re	VforV	Richardson	A

NO.	CACHET TEXT	COLOR	TOPIC	PUBLISHER	$
370	All together / work! fight! [picture red or blue]	Blue, red	VforV	Richardson	A
371	All together now! / put 'em down and / [etc.] / 1-16-'45——Allies renew etc.	Multicolored	Axis	Linto	B
372	All together now! / put 'em down and / keep 'em down!	Multicolored	Axis	Linto	B
373	All washed up!	Red	Hitle	Peters	A
374	All washed up! / and no place to go!	Bicolor	Unk	Dale	A
375	All-Americans / for any year [artist: Rich Shaw]	Black/Red	Armed	Christens	A
376	Allied / terms / of / unconditional / surrender / Look, Adolf! two loop-holes	Black	Hitle	Talburt	A
377	Allied / war machine / Remember / Pearl Harbor / Tokyo, here etc. [handpainted]	Black	VEDay	Sturgill	F
378	Allied / western / front / Russian / counter / offensives / ouch! [colors vary]	Multicolored	Hitle	Peer	B
379	Allied chiefs proclaim full / V / victory / as all Germany / surrenders etc.	Multicolored	VEDay	Boone	B
380	Allied iron ring [handpainted]	Multicolored	Hitle	Adler	D
381	Allied planning strategy / Cassino	Multicolored	Unk	Gatens	B
382	Allied ships proclaim full / victory etc. [no picture]	Unknown	VJDay	Boone	B
383	Allied Victory in Europe	Blue, red	VEDay	Huss	A
384	Allied victory in Europe [engraved]	Blue, red	VEDay	Heckman	D
385	Allies / invade / Japan	Blue, red	VJDay	Boone	B
386	Allies / take / Augusta / sweep onward [thermographed]	Blue	Event	Boone	B
387	Allies capture / Tunis and Bizerte / complete Axis route [sic] etc.	Green, silver	Event	Linto	B
388	Allies capture Belogorod	Unknown	Event	Linto	B
389	Allies capture Quineville	Unknown	Event	Linto	B
390	Allies have run the / "foxhuns" to their / lairs! / Give 'em the works!	Gold, green	Nazis	Linto	B
391	Allies have run the / [etc.] / 9-6-'44——Americans storm / across Moselle	Multicolored	Event	Linto	B
392	Allies hit / Nazis at / Naples [no picture]	Unknown	Event	Boone	B
393	Allies invade Italy	Unknown	Event	Linto	B
394	Allies invade Sicily	Unknown	Event	Linto	B
395	Allies invade the European continent / D-Day / June 6, 1944 / V etc.	Multicolored	DDay	Unknown	D
396	Allies invade Tunisia	Unknown	Event	Linto	B
397	Allies push through Sicily	Unknown	Event	Linto	B
398	Allies strike / France / Tuesday June 6th 1944 [no picture]	Blue	DDay	Boone	B
399	Allies strike by / sea towards / Rome / mighty amphibious etc. [no picture]	Blue, red	Event	Boone	B
400	Allies take port of / Cherbourg [no picture]	Red	Event	Boone	B
401	Allies take Sicily	Unknown	Event	Linto	B
402	Allies take South Italy	Unknown	Event	Linto	B
403	Allies vs. Axis / Ball one——Philippines, Pearl Harbor / Ball two——Wake, etc.	Red	VJDay	Brenn	B
404	All-out / production / his V for / victory [colored envelopes]	Multicolored	Uncle	Poppenger	A
405	Almanac reading / 1945 / There will be an eclipse of etc. [no picture]	Blue	Bonds	Price, R	A
406	Almost / out [handpainted]	Black	Unk	Wolf, CL	B
407	Along the street / there comes / a blare etc. [envelope 7 1/2x4 in.]	Unknown	Unk	Turner	A
408	Alphabet of democracy / America / Britain / China / Dutch / referred to etc.	Multicolored	Flag	Advertiser	B
409	Altho, I've never met you / (chances are I never will) / your etc.	Blue	Verse	Lawrence	A
410	Always / ready / to / fight / Crowing cock insignia of the U.S.S. etc. [thermographed]	Red	Navy	Crosby	B
411	Always / victorious	Blue, red	Flag	Carpenter	A
412	Always on top	Multicolored	Flag	Ang	A
413	Always prepared [in quotes] / United States Coast Guard / 1790 [thermographed]	Blue	Coast	Sadworth	B
414	Always ready! [thermographed]	Unknown	Unk	Crosby	B
415	Am I / sorry / that I / stood / by for Jake! [in quotes]	Black	Navy	Lupton	A
416	Am I going / or coming? [handpainted]	Black	Unk	Wolf, CL	B
417	Am I the lucky / one? See what / I got!! [handpainted]	Multicolored	Home	Cowdery	D
418	America - England! / Ready / to / strike / at / Europe [handpainted]	Brown	Eagle	Klondike	D
419	America / ...yesterday / ...today / ...and forever!	Blue	EagFl	Neal	A
420	America / America has never / lost a etc. [no picture]	Unknown	Unk	Unknown	A
421	America / fights on and works / on to defeat Japan [artist: Staehle]	Blue, red	Japan	Cachet Cra	B
422	America / is not just a certain area of / land but a principle etc. [no picture]	Blue, red	Bonds	Boone	A
423	America / land / of the / free [handpainted]	Multicolored	Eagle	Krakora	C
424	America / love it or leave	Unknown	Unk	Globe	A
425	America / must / stay / free [handpainted]	Black	Eagle	Wolf, CL	C
426	America / must be first in the air / unless and until etc. [colored envelopes]	Multicolored	Air	Poppenger	A
427	America / our / America; is our life, our hope, etc. [shield only]	Multicolored	Shiel	Amer Pat	A
428	America / our / America; is our life, our hope, etc. [eagle varies] [4 lines]]	Multicolored	EagFl	Amer Pat	A
429	America / our / America; is our life, our hope, etc. [eagle varies] [6 lines]]	Multicolored	EagFl	Amer Pat	A
430	America / our / America; is our life, our hope, etc. [eagle varies] [8 lines]]	Multicolored	EagFl	Amer Pat	A
431	America—— / the arsenal of / democracy [in quotes] / on March 11, 1941, etc.	Multicolored	Home	Advertiser	B

NO.	CACHET TEXT	COLOR	TOPIC	PUBLISHER	$
432	America / the friend to all peaceful / nations -- the enemy to etc.	Purple	Liber	Neal	A
433	America / the land / of / liberty / equality / and / justice / for all etc.	Blue, red	EagFl	Linprint	A
434	America / the land of / liberty [11 blue stars top and bottom]	Blue, red	Liber	Davis, Ral	A
435	America / the land of / liberty [13 red stars top and bottom]	Blue, red	Liber	Davis, Ral	A
436	America / the land of / liberty [no stars]	Blue, red	Liber	Davis, Ral	A
437	America / the land of / liberty [w/ blue stars forming box around text]	Blue, red	Liber	Davis, Ral	A
438	America / the land of the brave / the home of the free etc.	Bicolor	Unk	Baur	A
439	America / to keep our liberty / sacred, / we must always be awake, / and etc.	Blue, red	Liber	Unknown	A
440	America / united for victory	Multicolored	EagSh	Neal	A
441	America / will always be / the land of etc.	Blue, red	Unk	Davis, Ral	A
442	America always [shield on flap] [envelope 5 3/8x3 3/8 in.]	Unknown	Shiel	Unknown	A
443	America at war / inaugurates / Franklin D. Roosevelt etc. [postmarked 1/20/45]	Blue	FDR	Heckman	E
444	America at war / inaugurates / Harry S. Truman etc. [postmarked 4/12/45]	Blue	HST	Heckman	E
445	America at war / mourns / Franklin D. Roosevelt etc. [postmarked 4/12/45]	Black	FDR	Heckman	F
446	America at war / re-elects / Franklin D. Roosevelt etc. [postmarked 11/7/44]	Red	FDR	Heckman	D
447	America first	Blue	Eagle	Krakora	B
448	America first / Franklin Delano Roosevelt / World War II President [thermogr]	Blue	FDR	Crosby	C
449	America first / now and forever [thermographed]	Blue, red	EagFl	Neal	A
450	America for Americans / liberty and justice for all	Violet	EagFl	Neal	A
451	America for peace / U.S.A.	Blue, red	Home	Krakora	A
452	America for us / Out where etc. [envelope 7 1/2x4 in.]	Unknown	Unk	Unknown	A
453	America forever	Green	Eagle	Abel	A
454	America forever [envelope 5 3/4x3 3/4 in.]	Multicolored	Unk	Dime	A
455	America forever [handpainted]	Multicolored	EagFl	Weigand	C
456	America forever [under shield] [upper left]	Blue, red	Shiel	Dime	A
457	America hails the capture / of Corregidor by General / MacArthur's troops.	Blue, red	Event	Boone	B
458	America holds high / the torch of liberty	Blue	Liber	Neal	A
459	America is a democracy etc. [no picture]	Unknown	Unk	Levering	A
460	America is awake	Blue, red	Flag	Smith, W	A
461	America is awake [handpainted]	Multicolored	Antiq	Mitchell	B
462	America is not / free till they / are freed! / Wake Island etc. [colored envelopes]	Blue, red	USMC	Poppenger	A
463	America needs your help [copyright "C" red or blue, w/, w/o serifs]	Multicolored	Eagle	Minkus	A
464	America our America / is our life, our hope, / our happiness, for a etc.	Multicolored	EagFl	Amer Pat	A
465	America speed up!	Green, red	Home	Fleetwood	B
466	America Victorious / honors / the United States / Army	Red	Army	Heckman	A
467	America will never [vertical] / become a party to any plan for partial victory!	Blue	HST	Davis, Ray	B
468	America!	Black	Home	Temple	A
469	America! / Make us free! / Do not let us down!	Blue	ORN	Lohr	A
470	America! / One nation indivisible	Blue, red	EagSh	Mission	A
471	America! / where / liberty and justice / ...for all / prevails [no picture]	Green, red	Home	Boone	A
472	America.. / will / always / fight for / liberty! [no picture]	Black	Home	Wolf, CL	A
473	American -- / and proud of it.	Gold,red	Eagle	Unknown	B
474	American / and / proud of it [allover cachet] [handpainted]	Multicolored	Eagle	Buxton Mrs	D
475	American / and / proud of it!	Blue, red	Eagle	Kosko	A
476	American / and / Russian / patrols etc. [no picture]	Unknown	Event	Threl+Thar	B
477	American / and proud of it	Blue, red	Unk	McCluney	A
478	American / expeditionary / forces A.P.O. / U.S. Army in / North / Ireland	Blue	Army	Czubay	D
479	American / heritage / freedom	Blue, red	EagFl	Smith, W	A
480	American / labor / is the important etc. [cut-&-pasted paper] [yellow envelope]	Black	Home	Temple	B
481	American / Naval heroes / Admiral David Dixon Porter, U.S.N. / captured etc.	Blue, red	Hist	Lupton	A
482	American / Naval heroes / Admiral David Farragut, U.S.N. / on flagship etc.	Blue, red	Hist	Lupton	A
483	American / Naval heroes / Admiral George Dewey, U.S.N. / flagship U.S.S. etc.	Blue, red	Hist	Lupton	A
484	American / Naval heroes / Captain John Paul Jones, U.S.N. / commanded etc.	Blue, red	Hist	Lupton	A
485	American / Naval heroes / Captain Stephen Decatur, U.S.N. / "My" etc.	Blue, red	Hist	Lupton	A
486	American / Naval heroes / Commodore John Barry, U.S.N. / commanded etc.	Blue, red	Hist	Lupton	A
487	American / Naval heroes / Commodore MacDonough, U.S.N. / the hero etc.	Blue, red	Hist	Lupton	A
488	American / Naval heroes / Commodore Schley, U.S.N. / commanded flagship etc.	Blue, red	Hist	Lupton	A
489	American / Naval heroes / Rear Admiral Robert D. Evans, U.S.N. etc.	Blue, red	Hist	Lupton	A
490	American / Naval heroes / Rear Admiral W.T. Sampson, U.S.N. / Spanish- etc.	Blue, red	Hist	Lupton	A
491	American / Red Cross	Black, red	RedCr	Huss	A
492	American [in quotes] / ends with / "I can"	Blue, red	Unk	Bell	A
493	American [vertical text]	Bu,S/Bu,Gol	Minut	Linto	B

NO.	CACHET TEXT	COLOR	TOPIC	PUBLISHER	$
494	American [vertical text] / 9-13-'40——Buckingham Palace / bombed by etc.	Blue, silver	Ally	Linto	B
495	American and Japanese war / Remember the U.S.S. Panay etc. [thrmographed]	Red	Navy	Crosby	C
496	American Base Forces / A.P.O. 256 / U.S. Army Postal etc. [thermographed]	Red	Army	Czubay	D
497	American Base Forces / A.P.O. 918 / U.S. Army Postal etc. [thermographed]	Black	Army	Czubay	D
498	American base forces / U.S. army postal service	Blue	Bases	Czubay	C
499	American by birth / a soldier by choice / an actor by accident / and etc.	Blue, orange	Army	Rohaly	A
500	American defense / United States / Destroyer mail etc. [thermographed]	Bu/Br/Gold	Navy	Sadworth	B
501	American Eagle [handpainted]	Multicolored	EagFl	Knapp	G
502	American Eagles [handpainted]	Multicolored	Eag+	Knapp	G
502A	American Forces / in Newfoundland / changed to / American Forces / A.P.O. 801Branch etc. [thermo]	Red	Bases	Czubay	E
503	American goods are burned at Daw- / son Creek / [etc.] / Aug. '44-- Paris etc.	Multicolored	Event	Linto	B
504	American goods are burned at Daw- / son Creek, B.C., because they can etc.	Gold, silver	Home	Linto	B
505	American half-track	Black	Ordna	Huss	A
506	American heroes / of World War II / Gen. Eisenhower led the North Africa etc.	Red	Ike	Shane	A
507	American patriots / W.W. II / Colin Kelly etc.	Unknown	Hero	Linto	B
508	American patriots / World War II / Colin Kelly sank first Jap ship etc.	Gold, silver	Hero	Linto	B
509	American people / unfair to Japan! / They buy war bonds / and stamps	Green,	Japan	Schust	A
510	American production / United Nations determination / Mein / Kampf	Blue/Red	Nazis	Donaldson	A
511	American Red Cross / angels of mercy / blood plasma / blood donated at etc.	Multicolored	Blood	Fleetwood	B
512	American Red Cross / blood plasma / Give, that others may live [upper left]	Blue, red	Blood	Grimsland	B
513	American Red Cross / blood plasma / our blood etc.	Unknown	Blood	Unknown	A
514	American Red Cross / charterd by Congress / to relieve and prevent etc.	Blue, red	Home	Risinger	A
515	American symbol / of liberty / [etc.] / 12-27-'43——Big German battleship etc.	Multicolored	Event	Linto	B
516	American symbol / of liberty which / [etc.] / 12-27-'43--Big German battleship etc.	Multcolored	Event	Linto	B
517	American symbol / of liberty which / we all cherish	Bu,Gd/Pu,S	Bell	Linto	B
518	American war leaders / Adm / Chester W. / Nimitz	Bk/Bu/Pu	Nim	Coll Surp	A
519	American war leaders / Adm / Ernest J. / King	Bk/Bu/Pu	Admir	Coll Surp	A
520	American war leaders / Adm. / William F. / Halsey	Bk/Bu/Pu	Admir	Coll Surp	A
521	American war leaders / Gen. / Dwight D. / Eisenhower	Bk/Bu/Pu	Ike	Coll Surp	A
522	American war leaders / Gen. / George C. / Marshall	Bk/Bu/Pu	Marsh	Coll Surp	B
523	American war leaders / Gen. Douglas MacArthur	Bk/Bu/Pu	Mac	Coll Surp	B
524	American war leaders / Lt Gen / Jacob L. Devers	Bk/Bu/Pu	Gener	Coll Surp	A
525	American war leaders / Lt. Gen. / Mark W. / Clark	Bk/Bu/Pu	Gener	Coll Surp	A
526	American war leaders / Lt. General / Joseph Stilwell	Bk/Bu/Pu	Gener	Coll Surp	A
527	American war leaders / Maj Gen. / Claire L. / Chennault	Bk/Bu/Pu	Gener	Coll Surp	A
528	American women in war / Army / Nurse / Corps.	Black	Nurse	Coll Surp	A
529	American women in war / Col. / Oveta Culp / Hobby —— / leader of the WACS	Black	WAC	Coll Surp	A
530	American women in war / Col. / Ruth / Cheney / Streeter / -Chief of etc.	Black	WomM	Coll Surp	A
531	American women in war / Col. Florence / A. / Blanchfield / ——Army etc.	Black	Nurse	Coll Surp	A
532	American women in war / Lieut. / Comdr. / Dorothy C. / Stratton—— etc.	Black	SPARS	Coll Surp	A
533	American women in war / Lieut. / Comdr. / Mildred / Helen / McAfee etc.	Black	WAVE	Coll Surp	A
534	American women in war / The SPARS	Black	SPARS	Coll Surp	A
535	American women in war / The WACS	Black	WAC	Coll Surp	A
536	American women in war / The WAVES	Black	WAVE	Coll Surp	A
537	American women in war / U.S. Marine / Corps Women's / Reserve	Black	WomM	Coll Surp	A
538	American-educated / Japs appear "dumb" / [etc.] / 9-2-'45——Halsey wanted etc.	Unknown	VJDay	Linto	B
539	American-educated / Japs appear "dumb" / what a reflection on our etc.	Silver	AJA	Linto	B
540	Americanism / is the "Ism" / [etc.] / 7-29-'44——Yanks capture Coutances! etc.	Multicolored	Event	Linto	B
541	Americanism / is the "ism" / to fight for	Gn, S/Purple	Uncle	Linto	B
542	American-Japanese war / Remember the USS Panay etc. [thermographed]	Red	Japan	Crosby	B
543	American-Japanese war / the battle of the Coral Sea etc. [thermographed]	Blue	Navy	Crosby	B
544	Americans / awake / ! / Liberty's / at stake [envelope 7 1/2x4 in.]	Blue, red	Flag+	Fleetwood	C
545	Americans / can enjoy / Christmas [handpainted]	Multicolored	Holid	Wolf, CL	C
546	Americans / captured / 25,000 / Italians / and etc. [no picture] [green envelope]	Red, silver	Event	Linto	B
547	Americans' heritage—— / freedom	Blue, red	Flag	Smith, W	A
548	Americans! / buy / more / bonds / to set / the / rising scum!	Blue, red	Bonds	Boone	A
549	Americans, awake! / Are you going to / [etc.] / Leif Erickson day / first etc.	Multicolored	Hist	Linto	B
550	Americans, awake! / Are you going to / permit yellow Jap / rats to roam etc.	Gold, purple	AJA	Linto	B
551	Americas [sic] manhood between / the ages of 20 and 44 etc. [no pict] [pen/ink]	Blue	Home	Batura	D
552	Americas [sic] manhood between / the ages of 20 and 44, etc. [thermographged]	Blue	Event	Unknown	D
553	America's freedom / shall live forever	Blue, red	Unk	Baur	A
554	America's heritage—— / Freedom	Blue, red	Unk	Smith, W	A

NO.	CACHET TEXT	COLOR	TOPIC	PUBLISHER	$
555	America's position is / now definite! / We must defeat / Hitler and all etc.	Gold, green	VforV	Linto	B
556	America's prayer for / invasion day / "Almighty and most merciful /God," etc.	Black	Event	Fidelity	B
557	America's stamp collectors / are aiding Uncle Sam / War savings stamps etc.	Red	Bonds	Unknown	A
558	Amsterdam / liberated / Capital of Netherland / May 5, 1945	Multicolored	Event	Teixeira	D
559	Amsterdam / liberated / Capital of Netherland / May 5, 1945 [5/5 + 5/8/45 pmarks]	Multicolored	Event	Teixeira	F
560	An extinct superman [Schicklgruber] [thermographed]	Black	Hitle	Sadworth	B
561	An' I get / paid for / this! / This is the best part of navy life. When etc.	Black	Navy	Lupton	A
562	An idle word / may sell his life / mum is the word / on military matters	Blue, red	USMC	Richardson	A
563	An' then / what did you / say? [handpainted]	Multicolored	Army	Cowdery	D
564	ANC [Army Nurse Corps] [thermographed]	Unknown	Nurse	Czubay	B
565	And / the / time / is / now / [etc.] / 11-25-'44——Yank subs sink 37 etc.	Multicolored	Event	Linto	B
566	And / the time / is / now [in quotes] / 6th / war / loan	Multicolored	Bonds	Linto	B
567	And as ye would / that men should / do etc.	Unknown	Unk	Hillerich	A
568	And don't you forget it / Americans may die - but / America will never die	R/Bu,Orange	Home	Runge	A
569	And I / thought / her husband / was still / in China!	Black	Navy	Lupton	A
570	And I thought / Harry Koester's / bull etc. [burned top, edge] [handpainted]	Multicolored	Ordna	Cowdery	D
571	And it's only the beginning / ——only the beginning....!	Blue	Japan	Lawrence	A
572	And keep him safe. -- Amen.	Blue	Home	Unknown	A
573	And me the champion of the block! [in quotes] [hydrant at left] [handpainted]	Black	Japan	Clendennen	D
574	And me the champion of the block. [in quotes] [hydrant at right]	Black	Dog	Clendennen	B
575	And ne'er shall the sons of Colum- / bia be slaves, while the etc. [no picture]	Gold, silver	Verse	Linto	B
576	And ne'er shall the sons of the Colum- / bia / [etc.] / 10-13-'44——Pope etc.	Multicolored	Event	Linto	B
577	And pass the / ammunition	Blue/Red	Ordna	Richardson	A
578	And remember—— / no blackout!	Black	Home	Lupton	A
579	And the star spangled banner in triumph etc.	Unknown	Unk	Eichenlaub	A
580	And then what did the Colonel say / when you told etc. [in quotes] [handpainted]	Multicolored	Army	Cowdery	D
581	And to think, that they / call 'me' a rat!! [in quotes] [handpainted]	Multicolored	Hitle	White, TM	F
582	And we / demand victory in / Frisco! [handpainted]	Multicolored	UN	Newton FN	C
583	And you / can take a little / off the top / why don't you / get a haircut, / Tex? etc.	Red	Army	Burdick	A
584	Animals are savage / by instinct. Huns / [etc.] / 8-10-'44——Le Mans falls etc.	Multicolored	Event	Linto	B
585	Animals are savage / by instinct. Huns / and Japs by / malicious choice.	Gold, silver	Axis	Linto	B
586	Anniversary / today is a double etc. [thermographed]	Unknown	Unk	Boone	A
587	Announcing / the sixth / war loan drive etc.	Unknown	Bonds	Kosko	A
588	Annual cruise / Oregon / Naval/ reserves / Nineteen forty [no picture]	Multicolored	Navy	Linto	B
589	Another / American ace! etc. [label + blue "Victory" border]	Multicolored	Hero	Unknown	B
590	Another / American ace! etc. [label + red "Victory" border]	Multicolored	Hero	Unknown	A
591	Another / American ace! etc. [label + red "Win the War" border]	Multicolored	Hero	Unknown	B
592	Another / message from / London! [postmarked London, Indiana] [yellow envelope]	Black	Home	Unknown	A
593	Another / problem! [handpainted]	Multicolored	Army	Cowdery	D
594	Another day coming up	Multicolored	Japan	Peer	B
595	Another pair to help over there [in quotes] etc. [thermographed]	Red	Navy	Federal	A
596	Answer / the / Red Cross / call / now / March 1943	Unknown	RedCr	Linto	B
597	Anti air craft [colored envelopes]	Black/Blue	Army	Huss	A
598	Anti tank gun [colored envelopes]	Blue	Ordna	Huss	A
599	Anti-aircraft / artillery / shooting for victory	Blue, red	Ordna	Kosko	A
600	Anti-aircraft V...- / "star gazers" [thermographed]	Brown, red	Ordna	Von Los	B
601	Anybody / seen that / Jap navy / ? / Ask "Davey Jones"!!	Blue	Japan	Lawrence	A
602	APA-51 / U.S.S. Sheridan / Tokyo / 2 Sept. '45 [Tokyo Bay]	Unknown	VJDay	Navy ship	D
603	Apes in American zoos / are in cages, but Japs / are running loose! / Why?	Bk,Gd/Pu,G	AJA	Linto	B
604	Apointments [sic] filled. / Yanks / Russians [handpainted]	Multicolored	Hitle	Adler	D
605	Appeasement / gave us / Pearl Harbor / Men and materials etc. [no picture]	Blue, red	Pearl	Threl+Thar	A
606	Appeasement fails! / Treat Japs as Japs! / Send them to honorable ancestors	Bu,Br/Multi	Japan	Linto	B
607	Appeasement policy / delays the victory!	Silver	Flag	Linto	B
608	Appeasement policy / delays the victory! / 5-10-'44--CIO wins Mont- etc.	Unknown	Event	Linto	B
609	Apply the principles of our / democracy / [etc.] / 6-15-'44-- Rommel's forces take etc.	Multicolored	Event	Linto	B
610	Apply the principles of our / democracy to American / people as well as to etc.	Gold, green	Home	Linto	B
611	Apres la guerre fini!	Blue	Unk	Foster	A
612	April / 26th / 1945 / GI Joe meets Ivan / American 69th Division makes etc.	Multicolored	Event	Fluegel	C
613	April 02, 1945 / Byrnes revealed to Con- / gress etc.	Unknown	Event	Linto	B
614	April 05, 1945 / Austria / Vienna invaded / Russia flaunts Japan	Blue, tan	Event	Fidelity	B
615	April 07, 1945 / a fateful day for the Japs / Japanese / cabinet resigns etc.	Multicolored	Event	Fluegel	C
616	April 09, 1942 / Bataan falls / April 9, 1943 etc.	Unknown	Hist	Linto	B

NO.	CACHET TEXT	COLOR	TOPIC	PUBLISHER	$
617	April 09, 1942 / Bataan falls / April 9, 1943 etc. [thermographed]	Unknown	Phili	McCluney	A
618	April 09, 1942 / Japs captured / Bataan peninsula [no picture]	Brown,	Event	Linto	B
619	April 10 1945 / Vienna / the capital of / Austria was liberated etc.	Multicolored	Event	Fluegel	C
620	April 10, 1945 / Yanks take Hannover / [etc.] / 4-10-'45--Yanks driven etc.	Unknown	Event	Linto	B
621	April 10, 1945 / Yanks take Hannover etc.	Unknown	Event	Linto	B
622	April 12 / 1945 / In memory of our great etc. [thermogr] [postmarked 4/12/45]	Multicolored	FDR	Smartcraft	E
623	April 12, 1945 / 7:09 p.m. / Harry S. Truman / sworn in as / President etc.	Blue	HST	Richardson	E
624	April 12th / 1945/ In memory of our great President etc. [postmarked 4/12/45]	Blue, red	FDR	Staehle	E
625	April 14, 1942 / Pro-German Pierre Laval etc.	Unknown	Event	Linto	B
626	April 16, 1945 / First Army flanks Liepzig; 7th breaks etc. [typed, cut-and-pasted paper]	Black	Event	Unknown	B
627	April 17 - first anniversary / of U.S. air raids on etc. [cut-&-pasted paper]	Blue, red	Event	Temple	C
628	April 18, 1942 / U.S. Air Force, under / Col. J.H. Doolittle, / bombed Tokyo!	Gold, silver	Dool	Linto	C
629	April 19, 1945 / U.S. First Army etc.	Unknown	Event	Linto	B
630	April 20, 1945 / Lt.-Gen. Patton makes / German civilians view, as etc.	Gold, green	Patt	Linto	B
631	April 24, 1944 / We invade / Hollandia / Dutch / New Guinea [no picture]	Black	Event	Fidelity	B
632	April 25 1945 June 25 / United Nations Conference / San Francisco etc.	Multicolored	Event	Fluegel	C
633	April 25, 1945 / Toward United Nations - F.D.R. etc. [handpainted]	Multicolored	Event	Smith, LH	C
634	April 25, 1945 / United Nations / [etc.] / 4-25-'45——Woodruff's 24th Div. etc.	Multicolored	Event	Linto	B
635	April 25, 1945 / United Nations / Conference / opened in San Francisco etc.	Multicolored	UN	Linto	B
636	April 25, 1945 / Yanks meet Reds / 2nd Lt. Wm. D. Robertson, etc.	Gold, silver	Event	Linto	B
637	April 28, 1945 / Italian patriots / kill Mussolini!	Multicolored	Event	Linto	B
638	April 28, 1945 / Italian patriots / kill Mussolini! / 4-28-'45--Japs deliberately at- etc.	Multicolred	Event	Linto	B
639	April 29, 1945 / Allies capture Venice / [etc.] / 4-29-'45-- U.S. Flag etc.	Unknown	Event	Linto	B
640	April 29, 1945 / Allies capture Venice / [etc.] / 4-29-'45-- U.S.-Brit-China etc.	Unknown	Event	Linto	B
641	April 29, 1945 / Allies capture Venice etc.	Unknown	Event	Linto	B
642	April 29, 1945 / The long-defended / Philippines capital, / Baguio, fell etc.	Multicolored	Event	Linto	B
643	April 30, 1945 / Munich falls / to Yanks / [etc.] / 4-30-'45--Reds raise / their flag etc.	Multicolored	Event	Linto	B
644	April 30, 1945 / Munich falls / to Yanks / Italian conquest / ended!	Gold, silver	Event	Linto	B
645	Arch-Nazi-criminal / Goering given royal / treatment! / Shall we also give etc.	Multicolored	Flag	Linto	B
646	Are 3,500,000 / clerks required / to run our / government? [no picture]	Pink, silver	Home	Linto	B
647	Are people queer? / Some crab / [etc.] / 2-18-'44——Pres. Roosevelt vetoes etc.	Multicolored	Event	Linto	B
648	Are people queer? / Some crab / [etc.] / 2-18-'44——Yankees sink a Japanese etc.	Multicolored	Event	Linto	B
649	Are people queer? / Some crab because they have / to go without things etc.	Gold, pink	Home	Linto	B
650	Are they getting it? / Well!! / they asked for it.	Blue, red	Axis	Carpenter	A
651	Are we at war for / the benefit of / plunderers?	Bu,Gd/Bu,S	Armed	Linto	B
652	Are we at war for / the benefit of / plunderers? / Armistice Day etc.	Multicolored	Holid	Linto	B
653	Are we at war for / the benefit of / plunderers? / Pearl Harbor was etc.	Multicolored	Pearl	Linto	B
654	Are we to have —— "Four Freedoms?" / Have we been fooled etc. [yellow envelope]	Black	FDR	Shaw	B
655	Are you "victory happy"? / bear down!	Blue, red	Unk	Kosko	A
656	Are you / doing etc. [label + blue "Victory" border]	Multicolored	Home	Unknown	B
657	Are you / doing etc. [label + red "Victory" border]	Multicolored	Home	Unknown	A
658	Are you / doing etc. [label + red "Win the War" border]	Multicolored	Home	Unknown	B
659	Are you cosily / comfortable? / Please, don't forget / those in the service	Pink, russet	Home	Linto	B
660	Are you doing / all you can / for / V / victory	Unknown	VforV	Levering	A
661	Are you doing all you can / for / V / victory	Unknown	VforV	Levering	A
662	Are you doing your part?	Multicolored	Shiel	McCluney	A
663	Are you in / step with / the 4th war / loan drive? [handpainted]	Multicolored	Bonds	Borkowski	D
664	Are you in the fight? etc. [envelope 8 11/16x3 5/8 in.]	Unknown	Unk	ITE Circui	B
665	Are you in there pitchin'?	Bk/Bu/Gn/P	Home	Smith, AD	A
666	Are you saving scrap? / Metal and rubber / no matter how small / Uncle Sam etc.	Black, gold	Home	Linto	B
667	Are you weary? / So are those in the service! / [etc.] / 2-21-'44--65 Jap ships etc.	Multicolored	Event	Linto	B
668	Are you weary? / So are those in the service! / Fight! etc. [2 color var.]	Multicolored	Home	Linto	B
669	Area D-3 / Medical Department / [etc.] / Save fuel for defense [thermographed]	Black	Navy	Unknown	B
670	Armchair patriotism / will not win / the war! / and don't forget to buy etc.	Gold	Bonds	Linto	B
671	Armistice / Day / Eleven / November	Multicolored	Holid	Linto	B
672	Armistice / Day [1944]	Blue/Red	Holid	Unknown	B
673	Armistice / signed November 11, 1918 / for what?	Multicolored	Holid	Linto	B
674	Armistice Day / 21st anniversary	Blue, red	Holid	Gabel	A
675	Armistice Day / Less [sic] we forget / 11 / November [no picture]	Unknown	Holid	Baur	A
676	Armistice Day / November 11, 1943 / Thank God / [etc.] / What a price was etc.	Multicolored	Holid	Linto	B
677	Armistice Day / November 11, 1943 / Thank God you have lived in / a free etc.	Multicolored	Holid	Linto	B
678	Armistice Day / the "last shot"	Multicolored	Holid	Unknown	A

NO.	CACHET TEXT	COLOR	TOPIC	PUBLISHER	$
679	Armistice Day / twenty fifth anniversary / 1918 - 1943 / "Bonds will" etc.	Black, red	Holid	Zunks	B
680	Armistice Day [Doughboy]	Multicolored	Holid	Ioor	A
681	Armistice Day [Gen. Foch]	Multicolored	Holid	Ioor	A
682	Armistice Day [Gen. Pershing]	Multicolored	Holid	Ioor	A
683	Armistice Day [in quotes] / greetings from / Merchant Marine / Marines etc.	Green	Holid	Unknown	A
684	Arms for victory [on front] / Our country etc. [on back] [env. 9 1/2x4 1/8 in.]	Unknown	Home	Cadillac	C
685	Arms for victory [on front] / Our country etc. [on back] [env. 9 1/2x4 1/8 in.]	Blue, red	Home	Pontiac	D
686	Arms for victory [on front] / Our country etc. [on back] [env. 9 1/2x4 1/8 in.]	Unknown	Home	Saginaw	C
687	Army / war day / 48 states protect the liberty / 13 colonies won [handpainted]	Red	Army	Unknown	B
688	Army accepts B-19 / Nov. 19, 1941	Blue, red	Event	First Day	B
689	Army Air Base / Let's go! U.S.A. / Keep 'em flying! / Perrin Field, Texas	Blue, red	Air	Edmunds	C
690	Army Air Forces [text length, 2.5 cm; diameter of circle, 2.2 cm] [Alaska APO]	Red	Air	Conner	C
691	Army Air Forces [text length, 4.9 cm; diameter of circle, 4.0 cm] [Alaska APO]	Blue	Air	Conner	C
692	Army Air Forces Technical School / Keesler Field, Mississippi	Blue	Air	Army	A
693	Army airways communications system etc. [thermographed]	Unknown	Unk	Czubay	A
694	Army and Navy turn back, from / [etc.] / 5-24-'44——Roosevelt announces etc.	Unknown	Event	Linto	B
695	Army and Navy turn back, from etc.	Unknown	Unk	Linto	B
696	Army day / April 6, 1945 / "Go for broke" / 442nd Combat Team	Blue, red	Unit	Sayama	B
697	Army Day / April 7, 1941	Green	Army	Woodbury	A
698	Army heroes / established 1802 / United States Military Academy etc.	Blue, red	Army	Grimsland	B
699	Army navy & marine naval & air stations established on etc. [thermographed]	Bronze	Bases	Czubay	C
700	Army of the United States / Let's go! U.S.A. / Keep 'em etc. [thermographed]	Blue/Red	Army	Crosby	B
701	Army of the United States [thermographed]	Red	Air	Crosby	B
702	Army of the United States [various photographs pasted on] [thermographed]	Black, red	Army	Crosby	B
703	Arrival of H.M.S. Modasa / Flagship, convoy of 70 / vessels from Liverpool etc.	Blue	Event	Unknown	D
704	Artillery V ...- / "Mobile death" [thermographed]	Bu,R/Gn,Re	Ordna	Von Los	A
705	As Bishop Angus Dun prayed etc. [no picture]	Unknown	Unk	Levering	A
706	As Bishop Anjus [sic] Dun prayed etc. [no picture]	Unknown	Unk	Levering	A
707	As he fought to save the union, / we now fight to save the world.	Green/Red	Linc	Jarrett	B
708	As the best egg for a nest-egg, / buy a war bond——buy a batch. etc. [no picture]	Green	Bonds	Carpenter	A
709	As told to the Marines at Bou / gainville etc.	Blue, red	USMC	Brenn	A
710	Ask / Santa / for / U.S. War Bonds [handpainted]	Blue, red	Bonds	Clendennen	D
711	Ask God / to help / United / Nations / to early / victory / and the etc.	Unknown	Relig	Linto	B
712	Ask yourself, "What / have I done to help / speed" etc. [w/, w/o L.C.L. imprint]	Blue, red	Uncle	Levering	A
713	Assure / them / equipment / Keep / industries / moving!	Gold	Ordna	Linto	B
714	Astonishing! / The "sovereign" people's / [etc.] / 9-3-'44——Finns again etc.	Multicolored	Event	Linto	B
715	Astonishing! / The "sovereign" people's / President is "amazed" to / learn etc.	Multicolored	FDR	Linto	B
716	At Christmas play and / make good cheer etc.	Unknown	Holid	Phill, CR	A
717	At dawn Sunday / Dec. 7th, 1941 / Japan without warning etc. [no pict] [posted12/8/41]	Blue, red	Pearl	Fleetwood	C
718	At last! / our government is / learning you can- / not treat Japs like etc.	Gold, silver	AJA	Linto	B
719	Athens / liberated / Capital of Greece / October 14, 1944	Multicolored	Event	Teixeira	D
720	Athens / liberated / Capital of Greece / October 14, 1944 [10/14/44 + 5/8/45 pmarks]	Multicolored	Event	Teixeira	F
721	Atom / bomb / levels / Nagasaki [thermographed] [postmarked 8/9/45]	Black, red	Atom	Boone	E
722	Atom bombs / thank God. [handpainted]	Black, pink	Atom	Shaw, TC	E
723	Atomic bomb. [handpainted]	Multicolored	Atom	Yontz	D
724	Atomic bombs / "Now we'll have some peace" [thermographed]	Black	Atom	Sadworth	D
725	Atomize bomb / the Japs for a / quick victory!	Gold/Green	Atom	Linto	D
726	Atomize bomb / the Japs for a / quick victory! / 8-10-'45 Kumamoto "greets" etc.	Multicolored	Event	Linto	D
727	Attack! / Sacrifice——the privilege of free men etc. [label + printed border]	Multicolored	Army	Artists	B
728	Attackers of Westwall / Brig Gen / Gordon P. Saville / -- / Twelfth Tactical etc.	Bk/Bu/Red	Gener	Coll Surp	A
729	Attackers of Westwall / Brig Gen / Otto P. Weyland / - Nineteenth etc.	Bk/Blue/Red	Gener	Coll Surp	A
730	Attackers of Westwall / Brig Gen / Richard E Nugent - / Twenty-ninth / Tactical etc.	Bk/Blue/Red	Gener	Coll Surp	A
731	Attackers of Westwall / Brig. Gen / Gordon P. Saville -- / Twelfth Tactical / Air etc.	Blue/Red	Gener	Coll Surp	A
732	Attackers of Westwall / Gen / Lesley J McNair - / Gave his life / in etc.	Bk/Blue/Red	Gener	Coll Surp	A
733	Attackers of Westwall / Lieut Gen / Courtney H / Hodges - / Commanding etc.	Bk/Blue/Red	Gener	Coll Surp	A
734	Attackers of Westwall / Lieut. Gen / George S Patton—— / Commanding etc.	Bk/Blue/Red	Patt	Coll Surp	B
735	Attackers of Westwall / Lieut. Gen / William H. / Simpson - / Commanding etc.	Bk/Blue/Red	Gener	Coll Surp	A
736	Attackers of Westwall / Lieut. Gen. / Alexander M. Patch - / Commanding etc.	Bk/Blue/Red	Gener	Coll Surp	A
737	Attackers of Westwall / Maj. Gen / Elwood R. Quesada / - Ninth Tactical etc.	Bk/Blue/Red	Gener	Coll Surp	A
738	Attackers of Westwall / Maj. Gen. / Hoyt S. / Vandenburg - / Commanding etc.	Bk/Bu/Red	Gener	Coll Surp	A
739	Attention / Jap war lords / Now that we have captured the etc. [handpainted]	Multicolored	Japan	Unknown	B
740	Attention, FBI! / Who are the people in the / U.S.A. now championing / the etc.	Multicolored	AJA	Linto	B

NO.	CACHET TEXT	COLOR	TOPIC	PUBLISHER	$
741	Attu [handpainted]	Multicolored	Map	Smith, LH	C
742	Attu Island recaptured	Unknown	Event	Linto	C
743	Aug 24 / 1944 / Bordeaux France / liberated by Allies and etc. [handpainted]	Multicolored	Map	Smith, LH	C
744	Aug. 08, / Russia / 1945 / declares / war on / Japan [handpainted label]	Black, red	Event	LeGallez	C
745	Aug. 10, 1945, / Japs send / peace terms / [etc.] / 8-10-'45——Kumanoto etc.	Gold, green	Event	Linto	B
746	Aug. 10, 1945, / Japs send / peace terms / to Allies	Gold, green	Event	Linto	B
747	Aug. 11, 1945, / Allies send / counter terms / [etc.] / 8-11-'45——Japs lose etc.	Unknown	Event	Linto	B
748	Aug. 11, 1945, / Allies send / counter terms / to Japs	Gold	Event	Linto	B
749	Aug. 12, 1942 / Churchill and / Stalin meet in / Moscow [no picture]	Brown,	Event	Linto	B
750	Aug. 14-1945- / -End of Second World War.- [no picture] [handpainted]	Blue	VJDay	Batura	D
751	Aug. 14th 1945 / Japan capitulates / In this solemn moment let us give etc.	Multicolored	VJDay	Fluegel	C
752	Aug. 15, 16, 17, 18, 19, 20, 21, ??? / Oh! so sorry —— no etc. [thermographed]	Purple	Japan	Crosby	B
753	Aug. 15. 16. 17, 18, 19, 20, 21, ??? / Oh! so sorry —— no understand etc.	Purple	Japan	Crosby	B
754	Aug. 17, 1943 - Messina falls. [handpainted]	Multicolored	Map	Smith, LH	B
755	Aug. 23, 1944 - Paris liberated by French patriots. Americans and etc. [handpainted]	Multicolored	Map	Smith, LH	C
756	Aug. 24, / 1944 - Nazi Balkan empire crumbles [handpainted]	Multicolored	Map	Smith, LH	C
757	August 02, 1943 --Yanks capture / Munda [handpainted]	Black, green	Event	Unknown	B
758	August 04, 1943 / Russians captured Orel	Unknown	Event	Linto	B
759	August 04th / United / 1790 / States / Coast / 1944 / Guard / Ballad etc.	Red	Coast	Boone	A
760	August 05, 1943 / Allies captured / Munda etc.	Unknown	Event	Linto	B
761	August 06, 1945 / U.S. new atomic etc. [postmarked 8/6/45]	Green	Atom	Linto	F
762	August 07, 1944 / Yanks enter Brest / Soviets on Nazi soil etc. [no picture]	Black	Event	Fidelity	B
763	August 07, 1945 / Japan admits / 1st atom buster / left etc. [no picture]	Black,	Event	Fidelity	C
764	August 08, 1945 / Russia / at war with / Japan / Truman / is etc. [no picture]	Blue, red	Event	Fidelity	B
765	August 09, 1945 / Nagasaki "given" / no. 2 / atomic bomb	Black, gold	Atom	Linto	E
766	August 10, 1945 / Japan / surrender / offer is / considered etc. [no picture]	Orange	Event	Fidelity	B
767	August 10, 1945 / Japs send / peace terms / to Allies	Unknown	Event	Linto	B
768	August 10, 1945 / Japs send / peace terms / to Allies / 8-10-'45——Kumanoto etc.	Unknown	Event	Linto	B
769	August 11, 1945 / Allies send / counter terms / [etc.] / 8-11-'45 Japs lose etc.	Multicolored	Event	Linto	B
770	August 11, 1945 / Allies send / counter terms / to Japs	Multicolored	Event	Linto	B
771	August 14, 1945 / Japan bows / in defeat to / the Allies!	Multicolored	VJDay	Linto	C
772	August 14, 1945 / Japan surrenders [ink on Butzen winged victory cachet] [hp]	Blue, red	VJDay	Donaldson	B
773	August 14, 1945 / Victory - Day / Truman / announces etc. [no picture]	Blue, red	VJDay	Fidelity	C
774	August 17, 1943 / Allies take / Sicily! [no picture]	Blue, gold	Event	Linto	B
775	August 17, 1943——Messina falls / to Allies [handpainted]	Multicolored	Map	Smith, LH	C
776	August 17, 1943——Messina falls. [handpainted]	Multicolored	Map	Smith, LH	C
777	August 18, 1945 / Fourteen nations / end censorship	Multicolored	Event	Linto	B
778	August 19, 1945 / Today Nips will get / [etc.] / 8-19-45——This day will be etc.	Gold, green	Event	Linto	B
779	August 19, 1945 / Today Nips will get instructions / from Gen. MacArthur etc.	Gold, green	Event	Linto	B
780	August 22, 1942 / Brazil / at war / We do well / Solomon and etc. [no picture]	Red	Event	Fidelity	B
781	August 23, 1944 / Romania / quit [sic] Axis / French and Huns / battle in Paris	Rust, silver	Event	Linto	B
782	August 24, 1944 / Bordeaux France / liberated by Allies etc. [handpainted]	Multicolored	Map	Smith, LH	C
783	August 25, 1944 / Paris liberated! / Romania declares / war on Reich!	Multicolored	Event	Linto	C
784	August 27, 1945. First landing / [etc.] / Atsugi Field, Tokyo, Japan! [typed] [w/cachet 7445]	Black	Event	Unknown	E
785	August 28, 1943 / Russians again / capture Kharkov [no picture]	Brown,	Event	Linto	B
786	August 29, 1945 / Pearl Harbor blame / put on Marshall! etc. [no picture]	Purple	Event	Linto	B
787	August report / 1943 / Russia advancing / Denmark / resists etc.	Blue, red	Event	Griffith	B
788	Aunt Jenny's / Garden Club / Garden / for victory [brown envelope 6x4 3/8 in.]	Green	Home	Aunt Jenny	D
789	Aus gespielen [in quotes] / [Hitler, hands in pocket, at shore] / "Yes," etc.	Black	Hitle	Donaldson	A
790	Aus gespielen [in quotes] / [Hitler, on Nazi flag, hands up] / "Yes," etc.	Black	Hitle	Donaldson	A
791	Australia / United Nations [handpainted]	Multicolored	UN	Weigand	B
792	Australians / invade / Borneo [thermographed]	Unknown	Event	Boone	B
793	Australians take Finschafen	Unknown	Event	Linto	B
794	Austria	Blue, red	ORN	Clifford	A
795	Austria / and the world will celebrate the / 125th birthday of etc.	Multicolored	Holid	Staehle	C
796	Austria / Following an ultimatum from Berlin, March 11, 1938, Dr. Kurt etc.	Black	ORN	Ander, CS	A
797	Austria / Schubert / Johann Strauss / Beethoven / Brahms / Haydn / Mozart	Black	ORN	Lowry	A
798	Austria / will be / free / again!	Multicolored	ORN	Cachet Cra	B
799	Avenge / December 7 [label + blue "Victory" border]	Multicolored	Pearl	Unknown	B
800	Avenge / December 7 [label + red "Victory" border]	Multicolored	Pearl	Unknown	B
801	Avenge / December 7 [label + red "Win the War" border]	Multicolored	Pearl	Unknown	B
802	Avenge / Pearl / Harbor [handpainted]	Green, red	Pearl	Klaas	D

NO.	CACHET TEXT	COLOR	TOPIC	PUBLISHER	$
803	Avenge / Pearl / Harbor [handpainted] [no picture]	Black, red	Pearl	Wolf, CL	B
804	Avenge / Pearl Harbor / Philippines etc.	Unknown	Pearl	Davis, Ral	A
805	Avenge / Pearl Harbor / Smash that Jap [thermographed]	Blue, red	Bonds	Yontz	B
806	Avenge Pearl Harbor——buy war bonds today! [label + printed border]	Multicolored	Pearl	Artists	B
807	Avenged / American flyers murdered [handpainted]	Multicolored	Event	Adler	D
808	Avoid / this / Conserve / your gas	Green, silver	Home	Linto	B
809	Aw come on soldier, / just one tall etc. [in quotes] [burned edge] [handpaint]	Multicolored	Army	Cowdery	D
810	Aw don't——every night at camp / they make us etc. [in quotes] [handpainted]	Multicolored	Army	Clendennen	E
811	Aw! give us / a big smile / soldier - / it etc. [burned edge] [handpainted]	Multicolored	Army	Cowdery	D
812	Aw, it was / nothin! [in quotes] [blue envelope]	Multicolored	Navy	Amer Art	A
813	Awake / Americans / protect / states' right	Gold, gree	Fla	Lint	B
814	Awkwitcherbelliakin / there's a war on [no picture][thermographed]	Black/Red	Home	McCluney	A
815	Axe the Axis	Black	Axis	Temple	A
816	Axis / propa- / ganda / plain / balony [handpainted]	Black	Hitle	Nichols	C
817	Axis / smasher / Army air bases / help / make this / possible [handpainted]	Multicolored	Air	Knapp	G
818	Axis war lords / That was well thought out on the part / of the Allies etc.	Multicolored	Axis	Andrews	B

Cover Values (from Table 6, p. 136)

Value	Price Range
A	$ 3 - 6
B	$ 7 - 15
C	$ 16 - 30
D	$ 31 - 60
E	$ 61 - 125
F	$ 126 - 250
G	$ 251 - 500
H	$ 501 - 1000
I	$ >1000
X	Unpriced: Suspicious or fraudulent cover

13

A SALUTE TO:

★ ERNIE PYLE ★

Who has been 29 months overseas among the fighting men of the United Nations and who has wrote over 700,000 words about all the boys for us here at home.

A SPLENDID JOB—WELL DONE.

64

A CARELESS WORD

... ANOTHER CROSS

88

A GALLANT SERVICE

WAC

90

A ghost steps out of a jungle green.
His eyes are sad at the thing he's seen.
His voice is low as you hear it sigh.
"Are YOU willing to LEND? ...
I was willing to die."

E. E. Puls
156 E Frank St
Birmingham, Michigan

117

A NATION MOURNS ITS LEADER

RICHARDSON

138

V

A Permanent Eclipse of the Rising Sun is Predicted in the Near Future.

180

C. Malcolm Nichols
Jamestown
Box 552   N.Y.

"A soldier's dream... and Hitler's night-mare."

264

Adm. Raymond A. Spruance

270

ADMIRAL CHESTER V. NIMITZ
Comander of U.S. Forces in the Pacific

287

"ADMIRAL, TELL JOEY I'LL MEET HIM AT 9!"

COPYRIGHT 1942 BY AMERICAN ART SERVICE

340

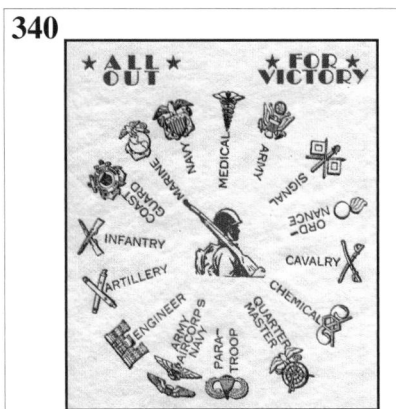

341

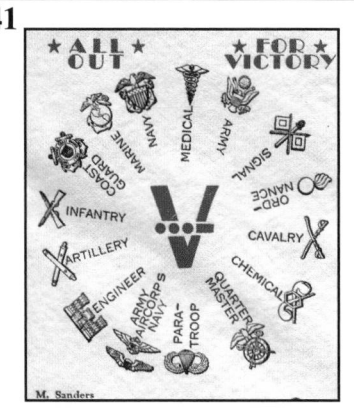

355A

360

384

455

484

528

559

581

619

623

663

696

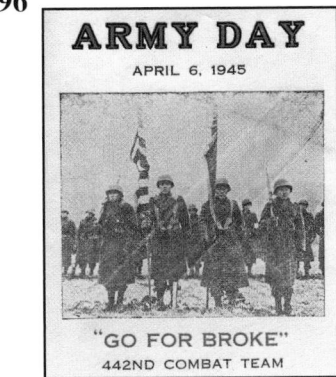

718

722

773

810

CACHET TEXT BEGINNING WITH "B"

NO.	CACHET TEXT	COLOR	TOPIC	PUBLISHER	$
819	B / 29 / And it's only the beginning——only the beginning....!	Blue	Japan	Lawrence	A
820	B / 29 [plane dropping bomb on a Japanese] [thermographed]	Black	Japan	Lawrence	B
821	B / 29 [printed on giant bee stinging head of Japanese officer] [handpainted]	Multicolored	Japan	Adler	D
822	B-19 / Initial flight of / world's largest airplane etc. [env. 9 1/2x4 1/8 in.]	Blue, Red	Air	Unknown	E
823	B-29 / The bees / are swarming, / Mr. Tojo! [cachet colors vary]	Multicolored	Japan	Peer	B
824	B-29's / bomb / Tokyo [handpainted]	Black	Japan	Hadley	B
825	B-29's again / hit / Tokio! / Do you want to see more / bulletins like etc.	Orange, red	Home	Lowell	B
826	B-29's bomb / Japan / today, June 15 [no picture]	Blue, red	Event	Boone	B
827	Back / the/ attack / with / war bonds and stamps [handpainted]	Blue, red	Bonds	Klaas	D
828	Back home again / in dear old Utica [handpainted]	Multicolored	Army	Borkowski	D
829	Back in the / Philippines	Unknown	Unk	Davis, Ral	A
830	Back our boys / with war bonds	Unknown	Bonds	Cox	A
831	Back the / attack / buy bonds	Purple	Bonds	Burdick	A
832	Back the / attack / Buy more / war bonds [handpainted]	Multicolored	Bonds	Barwicki	C
833	Back the / attack! / Buy bonds! [Minute Man] [thermographed]	Blue, red	Bonds	Unknown	B
834	Back the / attack! / Buy bonds! [two soldiers at front line]	Blue, red	Bonds	Unknown	A
835	Back the attack / bring / on / Nazi etc. [various pictures, same text]	Unknown	Unk	Baur	A
836	Back the attack / buy bonds [various pictures, same text]	Blue, red	Bonds	Kosko	A
837	Back the attack / buy war bonds	Blue, red	Bonds	Kosko	A
838	Back the attack / Buy war bonds [handpainted]	Blue, red	Bonds	Barwicki	B
839	Back the attack / buy war bonds! [thermographed]	Red	Ordna	Crosby	B
840	Back the attack / give em hell [airplane] [thermographed]	Green, red	Air	McCluney	A
841	Back the attack / give em hell [infantry]	Bu,Gn/Bu,Y	Armed	McCluney	A
842	Back the attack / give em hell [tank in combat]	Blue, red	Ordna	McCluney	A
843	Back the attack / keep em flying / over Tokyo [thermographed]	Blue	Eagle	Burdick	A
844	Back the attack / on the / Fortress Europe / buy war bonds [no picture]	Red	Bonds	Bendig	A
845	Back the attack / on them [in quotes] / buy war bonds [handpainted]	Multicolored	Axis	Knoll	C
846	Back the attack / third victory war loan / monument grounds unit etc.	Red	Bonds	Czubay	C
847	Back the attack / third victory war loan etc. [no picture]	Unknown	Bonds	Czubay	A
848	Back the attack / third war loan	Blue	Bonds	Artcraft	A
849	Back the attack / Washington DC Sept. 9-26 1943 / Buy bonds / U.S. Army etc.	Purple	Ordna	U.S. Army	A
850	Back the attack [in quotes] / on land, sea and air / buy bonds	Blue, red	Ordna	Sanders	A
851	Back the attack [in quotes] / with victory bonds	Bu/Bu,Red	Bonds	Runge	A
852	Back the attack [in quotes] / with war bonds	Bu/Bu,Red	Bonds	Runge	A
853	Back the attack [three soldiers with rifles, advancing]	Black/Blue	Army	Huss	A
854	Back the attack at all times, / Don't wait for a drive, / So etc. [no picture]	Red	Verse	Ang	A
855	Back the attack! / buy / war / bonds / and let etc.	Unknown	Bonds	Boone	A
856	Back the attack! / buy / war bonds	Unknown	Bonds	Dime	A
857	Back the attack! / buy / war bonds	Black	Bonds	McFarland	A
858	Back the attack! / buy war bonds [thermographed]	Black	Bonds	Czubay	B
859	Back the attack! / buy war bonds [thermographed]	Black	Bonds	McFarland	A
860	Back the attack! / buy war bonds! / unite / for / action [thermographed]	Red	Bonds	Crosby	B
861	Back the attack! [envelope 6 3/4x3 7/8 in.]	Unknown	Unk	Klondike	B
862	Back the attack! [in quotes] / "Buy bonds!"	Blue, red	Shiel	Smith, W	A
863	Back the attack! [two soldiers in moving jeep]	Black/Brown	Army	Huss	A
864	Back the attack! Buy bonds! [vertical text] [handpainted]	Multicolored	Map	Myers	C
865	Back the boys in service. / Buy more war bonds. [orange env. 5 1/8x4 4 1/8 in.]	Black	Armed	Lee	B
866	Back the boys in service. / Buy more war bonds. [pink env. 5 7/8x4 3/16 in.]	Black	Armed	Lee	B
867	Back the liberation / and invasion / Buy more / bonds [thermographed]	Red	Uncle	Sadworth	C
868	Back the winners [in quotes] / buy war bonds [handpainted]	Multicolored	Heads	Knoll	C
869	Back them up with bonds	Blue, red	Armed	Ang	A
870	Back to Hades / son of He - -.	Blue, red	Japan	Harrington	A

NO.	CACHET TEXT	COLOR	TOPIC	PUBLISHER	$
871	Back Uncle Sam / and / Red Cross [Uncle Sam with nurse; other figures vary]	Black/Red	Uncle	Cozart	A
872	Back Uncle Sam / and / the Red Cross	Bk/Br/Red	Uncle	McFarland	A
873	Back Uncle Sam / with war bonds [with/without RDNC imprint; star colors vary]	Blue, red	Uncle	Davis, Ral	A
874	Back up our / fighting / forces	Blue, red	Bonds	Kosko	A
875	Back up our boys / in the service! / They are fighting / for you! [no picture]	Gd,Gn/Multi	Home	Linto	B
876	Back us up / with bonds and bombs etc.	Unknown	Bonds	Eichenlaub	A
877	Backyard vacations / will be a treat. / [etc.] / 7-10-'45——U.S. planes etc.	Gold	Event	Linto	B
878	Backyard vacations / will be a treat. / Try it! / Earn the gratitude / of etc.	Gold	Flag	Linto	B
879	Bad luck / for the / Axis / 6th / war / loan	Black	Bonds	Wolf, CL	A
880	Ban on fraternization / with Germans lifted for / U.S. etc. [typed] [no pict]	Black	Event	Batura	C
881	Bases leased for 99 years / [etc.] / 801-D / Quidi Vidi Newfoundland branch	Black	Bases	Czubay	D
882	Bases leased for 99 years / [etc.] / A.P.O. 801-B / Newfoundland branch	Black	Bases	Czubay	D
883	Bases leased for 99 years / [etc.] / A.P.O. 806 / Antigua B.W.I. branch	Black	Bases	Czubay	D
884	Bases leased for 99 years / [etc.] / A.P.O. 808 / Remember Pearl Harbor	Red	Bases	Czubay	D
885	Bases leased for 99 years / [etc.] / American Base Forces A.P.O. 802	Black/Red	Bases	Czubay	D
886	Bases leased for 99 years / [etc.] / First Day Postal Service [thermographed]	Black/Green	Bases	Czubay	D
887	Bases leased for 99 years / [etc.] / First Marine Brigade in Iceland etc.	Unknown	Bases	Czubay	D
888	Bases leased for 99 years / [etc.] / For national defense [thermographed]	Black	Bases	Czubay	D
889	Bases leased for 99 years / [etc.] / Trinidad B.W.I. branch	Red	Bases	Czubay	D
890	Bataan / "They were / expendable"	Black	Army	Coll Surp	A
891	Bataan / falls to General MacArthur etc. [no picture]	Unknown	Event	Boone	B
892	Bataan / recaptured / Feb. 17, 1945 / Here's where etc. [handpainted]	Multicolored	Phili	Smith, LH	C
893	Bataan! / We're on the road back	Multicolored	Unit	McCluney	A
894	Battle front soldiers / depend on / home front soldiers	Red, silver	Home	Linto	B
895	Battle front soldiers / depend on / home front soldiers / 4-23-'44——Yank etc.	Multicolored	Event	Linto	B
896	Battle ground / War is ended Peace and / [etc.] / Hell / Hitler! etc.	Purple, red	VEDay	Czubay	C
897	Battle in Africa won / by Allied forces! / Von Arnim captured / May 12, 1943	Unknown	Event	Linto	B
898	Battleships / blast Palau [thermographed]	Unknown	Event	Boone	B
899	Battleships will speed us to victory [thermographed]	Bk/Br/Green	Navy	Sadworth	B
900	Be "up to date" / in '44 / Join the "25" club	Orange/Black	Home	McFarland	A
901	Be / alert / remember / Pearl Harbor [handpainted]	Multicolored	EagV	Unknown	C
902	Be / wise / Buy war / bonds and stamps	Green	Bonds	Larocque	A
903	Be / wise / Buy war bonds	Blue, red	Owl	Card	A
904	Be alert!	Black/Brown	Army	Huss	A
905	Be an American	Blue, red	Home	Krakora	A
906	Be careful / what you say! / [etc.] / 11-30-'44——Yanks donate to 'Davy' etc.	Multicolored	Event	Linto	B
907	Be careful / what you say! / Enemies are allowed to / roam free in our midst!	Multicolored	Minut	Linto	B
908	Be careful! / the end / is near / the end of your / rope——Tojo!	Blue	Japan	Peters	A
909	Be foxy / buy / bonds [handpainted]	Black	Bonds	Wolf, CL	B
910	Be glad you're alive / in forty-five / and work like sin etc. [no picture]	Blue/Red	Home	Unknown	A
911	Be grateful / you're an / American [stenciled] [handpainted]	Black, red	Holid	Wolf, CL	B
912	Be loyal to our flag / always and all ways	Blue, red	Flag	Hunt	A
913	Be my / valentine / Adolph! / Himmel? / Where / is mine etc. [handpainted]	Multicolored	Hitle	Borkowski	D
914	Be not misled / with false / [etc.] / 8-5-'44——Stilwell's troops cross etc.	Multicolored	Event	Linto	B
915	Be not misled / with false / rumors! / We have yet / to win etc. [no picture]	Gold, green	Home	Linto	B
916	Be on guard- / watch your speech. / Don't spread rumors	Bu, red/Black	Home	Runge	A
917	Be on the alert / America / keep them up there	Bu, red	Air	Harrington	A
918	Be on the alert / America / keep them up there [distance between lines 1&2 varies]	Bk/Bu/Br/Pu/R	Air	Harrington	A
919	Be patriotic! / Help kill the / black market! / Accept no etc. [no picture]	Black	Home	Kosko	A
920	Be prepared! / national defense	Blue, red	Uncle	Grandy	A
921	Be smart——act dumb / hear no- see no- speak no- / military secrets	Bu/Gn/Green	Home	Davis, D	A
922	Be thrifty! / for / V / save more! / waste paper, fats and tin	Blue, red	UncV	Myers	A
923	Be wise / buy war bonds	Bicolor	Bonds	Card	A
924	Be wise! / Americanize!	Gold, silver	Home	Linto	B

NO.	CACHET TEXT	COLOR	TOPIC	PUBLISHER	$
925	Be wise! / Buy bonds and save 'em. [handpainted]	Black	Owl	Clendennen	D
926	Be with them at every mail call [in quotes]	Green	Armed	Foster	A
927	Beans —— / an' more / beans!	Black	Navy	Lupton	A
928	Beat down / the Huns / then talk!	Unknown	Flag	Linto	B
929	Beat down / the Huns / then talk! / 11-24-'44——U.S. and French / units etc.	Unknown	Event	Linto	B
930	Beat the Axis / help get tanks / for the Yanks / win the war	Blue, red	Ordna	Lemponen	A
931	Beauty and the beast / VJ / Day / Japan surrenders today [thermographed]	Multicolored	VJDay	Crosby	C
932	Beauty and the beast / VJ Day / Japan surrenders to the etc. [thermographed]	Multicolored	VJDay	Crosby	C
933	Beauty and the beast / VJ Day / Japan surrenders today [3 words blue] [thermo]	Multicolored	VJDay	Crosby	C
934	Beauty and the beast / VJ Day / Japan surrenders today [3 words red] [thermo]	Multicolored	VJDay	Crosby	C
935	Beauty and the beast / VJ Day [thermographed]	Multicolored	VJDay	Crosby	C
936	Beethoven's Symphony No. V / V [thermographed]	Blue, gold	VforV	Unknown	B
937	Behind the dimout / lights etc. [on back] [envelope 6 3/4x3 3/4 in.]	Unknown	Unk	Boston Ed	B
938	Behind the eight ball! [colored envelopes]	Blue, red	Axis	Poppenger	A
939	Belgium / Belgium was invaded by Germany in May 1940, in violation etc.	Bk/Bu/R	ORN	Cliff	A
940	Belgium / Belgium was invaded by Germany in May, 1940 in violation / of etc.	Blue	ORN	Ander, CS	A
941	Belgium / Freedom	Black, red	ORN	Clifford	A
942	Belgium / shall / be free / again	Multicolored	ORN	Unknown	A
943	Belgium / shall / be free / again [artist: Staehle]	Blue, red	ORN	Cachet Cra	B
944	Belgium / United Nations [handpainted]	Multicolored	ORN	Weigand	B
945	Belgium [Lowery imprint]	Black	ORN	Lowry	A
946	Belgium [Runge imprint]	Bk/Bk,Orange	ORN	Runge	A
947	Belgium [thermographed] [artist: Staehle]	Multicolored	ORN	Smartcraft	C
948	Belgium shall / rise again / Antwerp, N.Y., U.S.A. / salutes Antwerp etc.	Black	ORN	Rameco	B
949	Belgrade / liberated / Capital of / Yugoslavia etc. [10/16/44 + 5/8/45 pmarks]	Multicolored	Event	Teixeira	F
950	Belgrade / liberated / Capital of Yugoslavia / October 16, 1944	Multicolored	Event	Teixeira	D
951	Believe it or not / no man is / indispensable, / he only thinks etc.	Brown	Eagle	Abel	A
952	Benito / is / now / finito [handpainted]	Unknown	Musso	Wolf, CL	B
953	Benito / Mussolini / super / facist [sic] / space reserved etc. [D&C imprint]	Bk/Bu/Red	Axis	Donaldson	A
954	Benito / Mussolini / super / facist [sic] / space reserved etc. [JLH imprint]	Black	Axis	Hillerich	A
955	Benito and Adolph / got kicked in the can. / The next is etc. [thermographed]	Red	Verse	Sadworth	B
956	Benito Mussolini, a pompous / guy, / at being a Caesar etc. [handpainted]	Multicolored	Musso	Unknown	B
957	Benito the Bumn [sic] / who fed the Italians / more etc. [handpainted]	Unknown	Musso	Albrecht	B
958	Benj. Franklin: one of / America's etc. [picture varies] [thermographed]	Unknown	Hist	Phill, CR	A
959	Berlin / falls / Nazi surrender / in Italy and W. Austria etc. [no picture]	Black	Event	Fidelity	B
960	Berlin / here we come! [airplane colors vary]	Multicolored	Air	Amer Pat	A
961	Berlin / invaded / April 21, 1945 [no picture]	Black, red	Event	Fidelity	B
962	Berlin / Rhur Valley / Nazi power / dams released by allied bombs / Our etc.	Black, blue	Axis	Andrews	B
963	Berlin / Tokyo / then / home [handpainted]	Multicolored	Home	Adler	D
964	Berlin [in quotes] / Defeatism [handpainted]	Multicolored	Hitle	Adler	D
965	Berlin falls / -Marshal-Zhukov- / planned and executed the etc. [handpainted]	Multicolored	Ally	Maul	C
966	Berlin falls / to the etc.	Unknown	Event	Thr+Bu+Tha	B
967	Berlin invaded / April 21, 1945 [no picture]	Black, red	Event	Fidelity	B
968	Best idea / Maggie / ever had [handpainted]	Multicolored	Home	Clendennen	D
969	Best performer of the year / out- / standing / double / cross etc.	Blue	Axis	Citret	A
970	Best seller [in quotes] / 1944 / revised / edition etc. [handpainted]	Unknown	Japan	Myers	B
971	Betsy Ross / 1777 / Making of the first American flag. [imprint red or blue]	Blue, red	Hist	Brenn	A
972	Better / buy / bonds ["B's" interlinked] [no picture] [handpainted]	Blue, red	Bonds	Klaas	C
973	Better think it over! / War bonds are the / best / buy / in / paper etc.	Bu,R/Pu,R	Bonds	Boone	A
974	Better to buy bonds / than to wear them	Green	Bonds	Ryscover	A
975	Between you and me - / and the lamp-post [in quotes] / the enemy is etc.	Brown	Home	Harmer	A
976	Beware Mr. Jap / our avenging eagle / is drawing closer.	Blue/Purple	EagSh	Harrington	A
977	Beware Mr. Jap / our eagle of vengeance / is drawing closer!!	Blue, red	EagSh	Harrington	A
978	Beware! / Do not patronize / Black Markets / It is sabotage! [no picture]	Multicolored	Home	Linto	B

NO.	CACHET TEXT	COLOR	TOPIC	PUBLISHER	$
979	Beware! / Mr. Jap! / We mean / business! [handpainted]	Multicolored	Army	Parker	B
980	BGen Claude A. Larkin	Unknown	Gener	Linto	B
981	BGen Don Carleton	Unknown	Gener	Linto	B
982	BGen Dunckel	Unknown	Gener	Linto	B
983	BGen Frederick Castle	Unknown	Gener	Linto	B
984	BGen Richard C. Sanders	Unknown	Gener	Linto	B
985	BGen William Hoge	Unknown	Gener	Linto	B
986	BGen William S. Lawton	Unknown	Gener	Linto	B
987	Bible School Park / New York / "Keep 'em flying" [thermogr] [colored envelopes]	Blue, red	Relig	Bible	D
988	Big / Sale / a $25.00 bond for $18.75	Black	Bonds	Littlefiel	A
989	Big 3 [in quotes] meeting / July 17 1945 Aug. 1	Multicolored	Event	Fluegel	C
990	Big Four / peace conference / San Francisco / California, U.S.A. / April etc.	Black, green	Event	Ioor	B
991	Big Three Conference / Truman Stalin Churchill / Potsdam, Germany / July etc.	Blue, red	Event	Unknown	B
992	Bill of Rights / Sesquicentennial December 15, 1941 / "A Bill" etc. [gold envelope]	Blue, red	Home	Alden	C
993	Billions for defense / Our home - our land / our liberty	Blue, red	Liber	Linprint	A
994	Birth of Old Glory / June 14, 1776 [thermographed]	Blue, red	Flag	Baur	A
995	Bizerte / and Tunis / captured / by allies etc. [no picture] [thermographed]	Red	Event	Boone	B
996	Black / market [handpainted]	Multicolored	Home	Long	C
997	Black / out! [handpainted]	Multicolored	Army	Cowdery	D
998	Black out the Rising Sun [handpainted]	Multicolored	Japan	Unknown	B
999	Blast / Hitler / buy / war / savings / certificates	Unknown	Hitle	Unknown	A
1000	Blast 'em out of the sky!	Blue, red	Ordna	Dime Store	A
1001	Blast the Axis now / and make sure of / permanent peace! etc. [no picture]	Gold	Axis	Linto	B
1002	Blitz all 'isms / with / Americanism! / [etc.] / "Victory with a vengeance" / There etc.	Multicolored	Lib+	Edmunds	D
1003	Blitz all 'isms / with / Americanism! / [etc.] / Maintain American traditions	Multicolored	Flag+	Edmunds	D
1004	Blitz all 'isms / with Americanism / Our / first / duty / [etc.] / victorious!	Multicolored	Flag+	Edmunds	D
1005	Blockade [handpainted]	Multicolored	Japan	Adler	D
1006	Blood / donors / needed! / Thousands of blood donors are / needed each etc.	Black, red	Blood	Limoges	A
1007	Blood / is / needed / now! / Will you donate blood? [colored envelopes]	Multicolored	Blood	Linto	B
1008	Blood / plasma / proved / its value / Will you / share?	Unknown	Blood	Linto	B
1009	Blood / sweat and / tears / 1942 [envelope 6 3/4x3 7/8 in.]	Blue, red	Map	Belles-let	D
1010	Blood donors / have helped make it / possible to save / 99 out of every etc.	Blue, red	Blood	Lowell	A
1011	Blood donors needed / for the men at the front / Call Red Cross etc.	Bicolor var	Blood	Limoges	A
1012	Blood donors needed! / A pint of your blood can save a / wounded soldier etc.	Black, red	Blood	Limoges	A
1013	Blood plasma / saved his life. [handpainted]	Multicolored	Blood	Borkowski	D
1014	Blood plasma / saves lives / Have you given a pint yet?	Brown, green	Blood	Lowell	A
1015	Blood plasma / the blood plasma stamp etc.	Black	Blood	Cliff	A
1016	Blood plasma [thermographed]	Unknown	Blood	Unknown	A
1017	Blot him out!	Blue, red	Japan	Boone	A
1018	Blot him out! / Allies / invade / Japan	Blue, red	VJDay	Boone	A
1019	Blot him out! / Russia / declares / war etc. [thermographed]	Blue, red	Japan	Boone	A
1020	Bluer and bluer / day by / day / it gets / for / Der Fuehrer!	Black, blue	Hitle	Wolf, CL	A
1021	Bluntly expressing the / American attitude in his talks etc. [typed] [no picture]	Black	Event	Batura	C
1022	Boil them in oil / save waste fats! [handpainted]	Multicolored	Axis	Martin	C
1023	Bolivia / United Nations [handpainted]	Multicolored	UN	Weigand	B
1024	Bombardier	Black	Air	Huss	A
1025	Bombing of Jap fleet in the / [etc.] / "If the Japanese / fleet won't " etc.	Multicolored	Event	Fluegel	C
1026	Bombing raids [handpainted]	Multicolored	Japan	Adler	D
1027	Bombs / for / rats / Hitler / Tojo	Multicolored	Axis	Lawrence	A
1028	Bombs away	Unknown	Unk	Carter	A
1029	Bombs over Berlin. [handpainted]	Multicolored	Air	Borkowski	D
1030	Bombs recognize / Hitler and / [etc.] / 7-24-'44——Yanks holding / firm on Guam	Unknown	Event	Linto	B
1031	Bombs recognize / Hitler and spare / him!	Unknown	Event	Linto	B
1032	Bonds / built them	Blue/Green	Bonds	Threl+Thar	A

NO.	CACHET TEXT	COLOR	TOPIC	PUBLISHER	$
1033	Bonds / built them / buy more bonds / keep etc.	Unknown	Bonds	Threl+Thar	A
1034	Bonds / built them / the Third Fleet etc.	Unknown	Bonds	Threl+Thar	A
1035	Bonds / built them [thermographed]	Blue/Green	Bonds	Threl+Thar	A
1036	Bonds / buy / bombs	Bu/R/Yellow	Japan	Threl+Thar	A
1037	Bonds / buy / bombs / Todays headache [etc.] / Italy declares war / on Japan	Red/Yellow	Event	Threl+Thar	B
1038	Bonds / buy / bombs / Todays headache [etc.] / Marines go ashore / on Iwo Jima	Red/Yellow	Event	Threl+Thar	B
1039	Bonds / buy / bombs / V-J Day / Japan signs surrender / pact aboard the etc.	Black, red	VJDay	Threl+Thar	B
1040	Bonds / buy / bombs / Yank troops / are back in / Manila	Red/Yellow	Event	Threl+Thar	B
1041	Bonds / buy / bombs [envelope 7 1/2x3 15/16]	Unknown	Japan	Threl+Thar	B
1042	Bonds / keep / her / there / buy / more / today	Bu/Br/Gn/O/R	Liber	Jarrett	A
1043	Bonds / you buy 'em / Bombs / I'll drop 'em	Blue/Brown	Air	Huss	A
1044	Bonds bought now / will buy a home later.	Black	Bonds	Littlefiel	A
1045	Bonds buy / bombers / [etc.] / Waves / release a / man for sea etc. [thermographed]	Blue	WAVES	Czubay	B
1046	Bonds buy / grenades [colored envelopes]	Black	Army	Huss	A
1047	Bonds buy bombs / to bomb this bum [in quotes] [handpainted]	Black	Japan	Knoll	C
1048	Bonds buy grenades	Blue	Army	Huss	A
1049	Bonds in action [picture of gunner in plane]	Unknown	Bonds	Carter	A
1050	Bonds in action [picture of tank]	Green, red	Bonds	Ang	A
1051	Bonds keep her there, / buy more today [text vertical]	Bu/Br/Gn/O/R	Liber	Jarrett	A
1052	Bong [handpainted]	Multicolored	Japan	Gatens	C
1053	Born / Jan. 30 / 1882 / Died / April 12 / 1945 / Franklin etc. [handpainted]	Multicolored	FDR	Smith, LH	C
1054	Borneo invaded / Munich falls to / 7th etc. [thermographed]	Unknown	Event	Boone	B
1055	Both doing / their part	Black	Unk	McFarland	A
1056	Both doing / their part	Bk/Bu/Red	Symb+	Cozart	A
1057	Both doing their part	Red	Symb+	Cozart	A
1058	Both filled up now / Benito etc.	Unknown	Axis	Donaldson	A
1059	Boy, oh boy, / they sure will / be preserved / when we get / through with 'em!	Red	Axis	Barnes	A
1060	Boys and girls / we got 'em on / [etc.] / Commemorating "Bill of Rights" etc.	Multicolored	Hist	Linto	B
1061	Boys and girls / we got 'em on / the run! Now / give 'em the / works!!	Multicolored	Hitle	Linto	B
1062	Brazil / United Nations [handpainted]	Multicolored	UN	Weigand	B
1063	Brazil declares / war / on Japan today [thermographed]	Unknown	Event	Boone	B
1064	Break ceiling prices / get around etc.	Unknown	Unk	Boone	A
1065	Breaking through / V / Europe [handpainted]	Multicolored	Armed	Newton FN	C
1066	Breathes there a man with soul etc.	Unknown	Unk	McCluney	A
1067	Brig. Gen. / Arnold J. / Funk etc.	Unknown	Gener	Linto	B
1068	Brig. Gen. / Frank A. / Allen Jr. etc.	Unknown	Gener	Linto	B
1069	Brig. Gen. / William / Hoge etc.	Unknown	Gener	Linto	B
1070	Brig. Gen. Claude A. / Larkin	Unknown	Gener	Linto	B
1071	Brig. Gen. Frederick / Castle	Unknown	Gener	Linto	B
1072	Brig. Gen. Richard C. / Sanders	Unknown	Gener	Linto	B
1073	Brig.-Gen. / Clif / Andrus	Unknown	Gener	Linto	B
1074	Brig.-Gen. / Clif / Andrus / 2-9-'45——Nazis now bend / to the Allies' will	Unknwon	Event	Linto	B
1075	Brig.-Gen. / Don / Carleton	Gold, silver	Gener	Linto	B
1076	Brig.-Gen. / Don / Carleton / 1-7-'45——Yank ships / shell Luzon	Unknown	Event	Linto	B
1077	Brig.-Gen. / Dunckel	Multicolored	Gener	Linto	B
1078	Brig.-Gen. / Frederick / Castle / [etc.] / 2-6-'45——Reds smash / Nazi barrier	Unknown	Event	Linto	B
1079	Brig.-Gen. / Frederick / Castle / killed in / action. / Belgium	Unknown	Gener	Linto	B
1080	Brig.-Gen. / Hanford / MacNider	Gold, sepia	Gener	Linto	B
1081	Brig.-Gen. / Lewis C. / Beebe / [etc.] / 8-21-'45——Nagasaki now a / desert etc.	Unknown	Atom	Linto	D
1082	Brig.-Gen. / Lewis C. / Beebe / captured by / Japs in the / Philippines, 1942	Unknown	Gener	Linto	B
1083	Brig.-Gen. / Luther S. / Smith	Gold, sepia	Gener	Linto	B
1084	Brig.-Gen. / William S. / Lawton	Gold, green	Gener	Linto	B
1085	Brig.-Gen. / William S. / Lawton / 11-23-'44——French / storm Strasbourg	Unknown	Event	Linto	B
1086	Bright stars and stripes / will etc.	Blue, red	Unk	Ander, EA	A

NO.	CACHET TEXT	COLOR	TOPIC	PUBLISHER	$
1087	Bring / On / Nazi / Defeat / Sooner [first letters form the acronym "Bonds"]	Blue, red	Bonds	Lemponen	A
1088	Bring / on / nips / defeat / sooner	Blue, red	Bonds	Gustafson	B
1089	Bringing home / the bacon [in quotes] [handpainted]	Multicolored	USSR	Meylan	C
1090	Bringing up reserves on the home front	Brown	Home	Neal	A
1091	Britain declared / war on the Tokio / government. / Dec. 8 -1941- [pen & ink]	Blue, red	Event	Batura	D
1092	Britain's champion / of the people / Earl Lloyd George of Dwyfor [handpainted]	Multicolored	Heads	Knoll	C
1093	British / New Guinea / Let's split the Pacific ocean etc. [thermographed]	Blue, red	Armed	Crosby	B
1094	British / seize / Taranto / Germans take Rome [no picture]	Multicolored	Event	Boone	B
1095	British / Yanks / Russians/ VE / Day [handpainted label]	Multicolored	VEDay	LeGallez	C
1096	British invade / Greece / enter Patras —— etc. [no picture] [thermographed]	Green	Event	Boone	B
1097	British Royal / Navy / Mar. 30 / 1945 / joins stars etc. [handpainted]	Multicolored	Event	Smith, LH	C
1098	Brussels / liberated / Capital of Belgium / September 4, 1944	Multicolored	Event	Teixeira	D
1099	Brussels / the capital of / Belgium was liberated / by British-Canadian etc.	Multicolored	Event	Fluegel	C
1100	Bryansk, Salerno, Smolensk, / victories to remember. etc.	Blue, red	Minut	Griffith	A
1101	Buck the Japs - / right of [sic] / the map ...- [handpainted]	Multicolored	Japan	Borkowski	D
1102	Budapest / liberated / February 13, 1945 [no picture]	Black, red	Event	Fidelity	B
1103	Buddha and the dragon——the / symbols of a fighting nation / China etc.	Blue	China	Unknown	A
1104	Buddies [vertical] / Hannigan / Hague / [etc.] / 10-14-'44——Reds and Nazis etc.	Multicolored	Event	Linto	B
1105	Buddies [vertical] / Hannigan / Hague / Kelly / Hopkins / Hillman etc.	Gold, silver	Home	Linto	B
1106	Bugs [in quotes] Baer says: / [etc.] / 8-30-'44——Ploesti falls to Reds! etc.	Multicolored	Event	Linto	B
1107	Bugs [in quotes] Baer says: / Moscow could have / won the war on / victory etc.	Gold, green	Ally	Linto	B
1108	Build / friendships / not warships / for national / defense [no picture]	Black	Neutr	Johnson, C	B
1109	Build morale / on the / home front	Black	Home	Cox	A
1110	Build morale / on the / home front	Green	Home	Larocque	A
1111	Build morale / on the / home front	Blue/Brown	Home	Harrington	A
1112	Build morale / on the / 'home front'	Blue, red	Uncle	Card	A
1113	Build the weapons / to sink the Nips. [handpainted]	Multicolored	Air	Borkowski	D
1114	Built / like / a / boot / but / ruled by a heel	Unknown	Musso	Baur	A
1115	Bulgaria / orders / Germans / ousted	Red, tan	Event	Boone	B
1116	Bullets know no name or creed / Smith / Kelly / Muller/ Wan Lee etc.	Magenta	Hero	Davis, D	A
1117	Bulls eye / We'll get / an "E" [thermographed]	Blue	Navy	Crosby	B
1118	Bums away!	Blue, red	Axis	Mid States	A
1119	Bund members / win in court! / Opinion rendered by Judge Hall etc.	Blue, silver	Home	Linto	B
1120	Bundles / for Tokio [bomber dropping bombs]	Blue, red	Air	Unknown	A
1121	Bundles for Hitler [envelope 6x3 1/2 in.]	Blue, red	Hitle	Powers	A
1122	Bunk fatigue	Black	Armed	Lupton	A
1123	Bureaucracy / breeds / dissension / [etc.] / Pearl Harbor was attacked etc.	Multicolored	Event	Linto	B
1124	Bureaucracy / breeds / dissension / For better government etc. [2 color varieties]	Multicolored	Minut	Linto	B
1125	Bureaucratic / system is driving / us around / [etc.] / Fourth war bond drive	Multicolored	Bonds	Linto	B
1126	Bureaucratic / system is driving / us around / in circles. etc. [no picture]	Gold, silver	Home	Linto	B
1127	Burst asunder the chains / throw open the doors. / etc. [typed]	Black	Verse	Shaffer, A	A
1128	Business dollars / seem to get more / [etc.] / 5-31-'44——Yankee bombers etc.	Unknown	Event	Linto	B
1129	Business dollars / seem to get more con- / sideration than etc. [no picture]	Gold, silver	Home	Linto	B
1130	But —— / sir, have you noticed that / even the desert has etc. [handpainted]	Multicolored	Army	Cowdery	D
1131	But / "manyana" / never comes!! [handpainted]	Multicolored	Home	Cowdery	D
1132	Butcher boys / They lived on Iwo Jima / And also in Japan / Now when etc.	Red	Japan	Abel	A
1133	Button / your / lip! / loose talk can cost lives	Black	Home	Oregon Hob	A
1134	Buy / be / foxy / bonds [postmarked Fox, KY]	Black	Bonds	Unknown	B
1135	Buy / bonds ["Buy" is vertical] [no picture]	Gold, silver	Bonds	Linto	B
1136	Buy / bonds and more bonds / We'll etc.	Unknown	Bonds	Eichenlaub	A
1137	Buy / bonds! / and stamp out the / Axis; buy Christmas seals! / and etc.	Unknown	Holid	Stanard	A
1138	Buy / bonds! / keep it / waving!	Blue, red	Flag	Smith, W	A
1139	Buy / bonds/ and beat / the Axis [handpainted]	Multicolored	Bonds	Myers	B
1140	Buy / defense / bonds / Nothing etc. [envelope 9 1/2x4 1/8 in.]	Unknown	Bonds	Consolidat	B

NO.	CACHET TEXT	COLOR	TOPIC	PUBLISHER	$
1141	Buy / defense bonds and stamps! / Remember etc. [envelope 9 1/2x4 1/8 in.]	Unknown	Bonds	Garfield	B
1142	Buy / for / victory / Kuai / no / lanakila / Niihau Oahu Kahoolawe Maui etc.	Blue, red	Uncle	Sayama	B
1143	Buy / more bonds / for early victory	Blue/Red	Bonds	Richardson	A
1144	Buy / those / bonds / and stamps / to-day! / 1918 1942 / Armistic Day etc.	Blue, red	Flag	Dietz	A
1145	Buy / U.S. / war / bonds [handpainted]	Multicolored	Air	Borkowski	D
1146	Buy / United / States / war / bonds / and / let 'em hatch etc. [no picture]	Green/Red	Bonds	Boone	A
1147	Buy / United / States / war / bonds / and let etc. [no picture]	Red	Bonds	Boone	A
1148	Buy / United States / war / bonds / and / stamps	Blue, red	Bonds	Risinger	A
1149	Buy / United States / war / bonds etc.	Black	Bonds	Stamp Rev	A
1150	Buy / United States war/ savings etc. [envelope 9 1/2x4 1/8 in.]	Unknown	Bonds	Psychiana	B
1151	Buy / US war bonds / and etc. [envelope 9 1/2x4 1/8 in.]	Unknown	Bonds	Peoples	B
1152	Buy / war / bonds / and / stamps / invest in / liberty [handpainted]	Blue, red	Bonds	Klaas	C
1153	Buy / war / bonds [envelope 9 1/2x4 1/8 in.]	Black	Bonds	Daily News	B
1154	Buy / war / bonds [handpainted]	Blue, red	Bonds	Klaas	C
1155	Buy / war / bonds and / keep / 'em	Black	Bonds	Unknown	A
1156	Buy / war bonds / and / stamps [with or without Sanders imprint]	Blue, red	Bonds	Sanders	A
1157	Buy / war bonds / V [FDR, Churchill, Stalin] [handpainted]	Multicolored	Heads	Knoll	C
1158	Buy / war bonds [FDR, Churchill, Stalin smiling; Hitler, Mussolini sweating] [handpainted]	Multicolored	Heads	Knoll	C
1159	Buy / war stamps / war bonds / to keep / America free	Unknown	Bonds	Davis, Ral	A
1160	Buy a / bond / we will / do [handpainted]	Multicolored	WAC	Adler	D
1161	Buy a / bond / We will / do our part. [handpainted]	Multicolored	WAC	Adler	D
1162	Buy a bond and build a / battleship / Keep them / rolling / by / buying bonds	Purple	Bonds	Peters	A
1163	Buy a bond for Easter etc.	Green	Holid	Abel	A
1164	Buy a lot of bonds / to buy a lot of bombs / to bomb a lot of bums ...-	Black	Bonds	Stefun	A
1165	Buy a share / in the / USA / live to enjoy it / another day—— in / victory	Blue, red	Bonds	Boone	A
1166	Buy a share in / America / $25.00 for $18.75!	Blue, red	Bonds	Boone	A
1167	Buy a war bond today / buy another etc.	Unknown	Bonds	Davis, Ral	A
1168	Buy an extra bond! / My dads [sic] across the pond. etc. [handp]	Multicolored	Bonds	Myers	B
1169	Buy bonds / "and help delouse the universe"	Black	Axis	Donaldson	A
1170	Buy bonds / 5th / war loan [handpainted]	Black, purple	Bonds	Wolf, CL	B
1171	Buy bonds / 6th war loan / to bomb the Japs [handpainted]	Black, red	Japan	Price, EK	C
1172	Buy bonds / America! / Churchill [thermogrpahed]	Blue, red	Heads	Boone	A
1173	Buy bonds / America! / Democracy must / and shall be / preserved!	Blue, red	Uncle	Boone	A
1174	Buy bonds / America! / The birthday etc. [Liberty or Uncle Sam]	Blue, red	Bonds	Boone	A
1175	Buy bonds / America! / Victory over Hiterism / in Nineteen and forty-four	Blue, red	Bonds	Boone	A
1176	Buy bonds / America! / Yanks, Reds etc. [thermographed]	Blue, red	Unk	Boone	A
1177	Buy bonds / and set / the / Rising Sun [handpainted]	Multicolored	Japan	Krakora	B
1178	Buy bonds / bonds / bonds / bonds / bonds etc.	Blue	Uncle	Burdick	A
1179	Buy bonds / There'll / always be a / Christmas [handpainted]	Black, red	Holid	Wolf, CL	B
1180	Buy bonds / today and / prevent / slavery / tomorrow! [no picture]	Gold	Bonds	Linto	B
1181	Buy bonds / today and / prevent / weeping / tomorrow! [no picture]	Multicolored	Bonds	Linto	B
1182	Buy bonds / today for / victory / tomorrow! [no picture]	Multicolored	Bonds	Linto	B
1183	Buy bonds [Hitler, Japanese figure flattened; buildings in ruins behind them]	Green	Bonds	Burdick	A
1184	Buy bonds [sailor with semaphore flags] [thermographed]	Unknown	Bonds	Sadworth	B
1185	Buy bonds [thermographed]	Red	Bonds	Hillerich	A
1186	Buy bonds and keep them!	Blue	Uncle	Vermond	A
1187	Buy bonds for / Uncle Sam [thermographed]	Bu,R/Gn,Red	Bonds	Phill+Cox	A
1188	Buy bonds for Christmas gifts / and help Santa defy tradition, / by etc.	Green, red	Holid	Carter	A
1189	Buy bonds for victory [in quotes] / "From our house," etc. [hp] [env. 6 1/2x3 5/8 in.]	Multicolored	Home	White, TM	D
1190	Buy bonds for victory! [handpainted]	Multicolored	Bonds	Borkowski	D
1191	Buy bonds to bomb bums.	Black	Bonds	Unknown	A
1192	Buy bonds to keep / the "Stukas" / from our skies [handpainted]	Black	Air	Unknown	B
1193	Buy bonds to win / the peace	Multicolored	Flag	Linto	B
1194	Buy bonds to win / the peace / Navy Day——27-10-'43	Unknown	Event	Linto	B

NO.	CACHET TEXT	COLOR	TOPIC	PUBLISHER	$
1195	Buy bonds to win / the peace / Navy Day——Oct. 27, 1943	Multicolored	Bonds	Linto	B
1196	Buy bonds up / to the hilt / and secure / [etc.] / Navy Day——27-10-'43	Multicolored	Bonds	Linto	B
1197	Buy bonds up / to the hilt / and secure / your reward / in victory	Multicolored	Bonds	Linto	B
1198	Buy bonds! / and stamp out the / Axis! / Buy Christmas seals! / and stamp etc.	Green, red	Bonds	Stanard	A
1199	Buy bonds. / United States Navy / Ex scienta tridens [thermographed]	Bk/Br/Red	Bonds	Phill, CR	A
1200	Buy defense / bonds and / stamps	Blue	Bonds	Northern O	D
1201	Buy defense bonds / keep 'em flying	Blue, red	Bonds	Risinger	A
1202	Buy defense bonds / keep 'em rolling etc. [no picture]	Unknown	Bonds	Shaw, MM	A
1203	Buy 'em and / keep 'em / war / bonds [no picture]	Orange/Red	Bonds	Cox	A
1204	Buy 'em and / keep 'em war / bonds	Green	Bonds	Phill, CR	A
1205	Buy em by the hatful / war bonds [handpainted]	Multicolored	Bonds	Wolf, CL	C
1206	Buy extra bonds / 4th / war loan [handpainted]	Blue, red	Bonds	Klaas	D
1207	Buy his bonds [handpainted]	Multicolored	Uncle	Knapp	G
1208	Buy more / bonds / for our / America [stenciled]	Multicolored	Bonds	Wolf, CL	B
1209	Buy more / war / bonds [handpainted]	Black	Army	Trapani	C
1210	Buy more / war bonds / and stamps / Support the etc. [label + printed border]	Multicolored	Bonds	Artists	B
1211	Buy more / war bonds and stamps / Hand up your etc. [label + printed border]	Multicolored	Bonds	Artists	B
1212	Buy more / war bonds and stamps / Put your heart etc. [label + printed border]	Multicolored	Bonds	Artists	B
1213	Buy more / war bonds and stamps / Smash the etc. [label + printed border]	Multicolored	Bonds	Artists	B
1214	Buy more / war bonds! / keep it ringing etc.	Unknown	Bonds	Davis, Ral	A
1215	Buy more bonds	Blue	Bonds	Huss	A
1216	Buy more bonds - / invest in his future! [handpainted]	Multicolored	Home	Martin	C
1217	Buy more bonds / and keep 'em [envelope 6x3 1/2 in.]	Black	Bonds	Peters	A
1218	Buy more bonds / Fifth [etc.] / let 'em hatch	Blue, red	Bonds	Boone	A
1219	Buy more bonds / Fifth [etc.] / V / 5th war loan / ...-	Blue, red	Bonds	Boone	A
1220	Buy more bonds / to keep them flying	Blue, red	Bonds	Davis, Ral	A
1221	Buy more bonds [vertical] / Put / something / more than / this away for etc.	Blue, red	Bonds	Boone	A
1222	Buy more bonds!	Blue, red	Bonds	Boone	A
1223	Buy more bonds! [handpainted] [envelope 7 1/2x4 in.]	Brown, green	EagV	Klondike	B
1224	Buy more war bonds / hasten another etc.	Unknown	Bonds	Hill	A
1225	Buy more war bonds / V / ...- / for etc. [Total cachet height 71 or 76 mm]	Black	Bonds	McFarland	A
1226	Buy more war bonds / V / ...- / for-victory / bonds buy block busters	Black	VforV	Cozart	A
1227	Buy more war bonds and stamps / Take a smash at etc. [label + printed border]	Multicolored	Bonds	Artists	B
1228	Buy more war bonds and stamps / War bonds etc. [label + printed border]	Multicolored	Bonds	Artists	B
1229	Buy more war bonds now / for future security too! [no picture]	R/Gd,Green	Bonds	Cox	A
1230	Buy more war bonds now / for future security, too!	Black	Bonds	Phill, CR	A
1231	Buy seals / write V-mail / first day cover / Nov. 27, 1944	Blue, red	Home	Unknown	A
1232	Buy seals buy bonds / greetings / 1943	Unknown	Bonds	Unknown	A
1233	Buy stamps and bonds / Victory / ...- / We will / win this / war etc.	Blue, red	Eag+	Unknown	A
1234	Buy U.S. / bonds and / stamps / Inflation	Brown/Red	Bonds	Burdick	A
1235	Buy United States war bonds / It's the American way [no picture] [handpainted]	Blue, red	Bonds	Barwicki	B
1236	Buy US defense bonds - Remember Pearl etc. [no picture] [env. 9 1/2x4 1/8 in.]	Unknown	Unk	MacMillan	B
1237	Buy US defense savings bonds [no picture]	Unknown	Bonds	Conn Light	A
1238	Buy war / bonds / for / victory	Green	Bonds	Ohio Bell	D
1239	Buy war / bonds / Victory / in 44 / The picnic is my etc. [handpainted]	Multicolored	Home	Borkowski	D
1240	Buy war bonds	Blue/Brown	Bonds	Huss	A
1241	Buy war bonds - / put one away for a rainy day - [handpainted]	Black	Dog	Martin	B
1242	Buy war bonds - / put one away for a rainy day - [handpainted]	Multicolored	Bonds	Myers	B
1243	Buy war bonds / a salute to the / Army Air Force	Blue, red	Air	Card	A
1244	Buy war bonds / a salute to the / Coast Guard	Blue, red	Coast	Card	A
1245	Buy war bonds / a salute to the / Marine Corps	Blue, red	USMC	Card	A
1246	Buy war bonds / a salute to the / Naval Air Force	Blue, red	Bonds	Card	A
1247	Buy war bonds / a salute to the Army	Blue, red	Army	Card	A
1248	Buy war bonds / a salute to the Navy	Bu/Bu,Red	Bonds	Card	A

NO.	CACHET TEXT	COLOR	TOPIC	PUBLISHER	$
1249	Buy war bonds / and the Axis will go to the	Red	Devil	Runge	A
1250	Buy war bonds / Doolittle [handpainted]	Multicolored	Dool	Knoll	C
1251	Buy war bonds / every pay day / Let's double / our quota [man above text, pointing]	Brown	Bonds	Phill, CR	A
1252	Buy war bonds / every pay day / Let's double / our quota [no flags above text]	Br/Gold/Red	Bonds	Cox	A
1253	Buy war bonds / every pay day / Let's doublle / our quota [flags above text]	Brown/Red	Bonds	Phill, CR	A
1254	Buy war bonds / for victory / V / "Let's keep America" etc. [handpainted]	Multicolored	Home	Knoll	C
1255	Buy war bonds / for victory!	Blue, red	Bonds	Ander, EA	A
1256	Buy war bonds / God bless / America!	Blue, red	Bonds	Ander, EA	A
1257	Buy war bonds / it could be a ticket home for your son [env. 6x3 1/2 in.]	Green	Bonds	Davis, Ray	A
1258	Buy war bonds / Keep it up! [handpainted]	Multicolored	Air	Barwicki	D
1259	Buy war bonds / keep us flying	Blue	Air	Goodfellow	B
1260	Buy war bonds / portrait of a patriot [envelope 6x3 1/2 in.]	Violet	Bonds	Davis, Ray	A
1261	Buy war bonds / saving money - saving lives [envelope 6x3 1/2 in.]	Black	Bonds	Davis, Ray	A
1262	Buy war bonds / season's greetings	Unknown	Bonds	Runge	A
1263	Buy war bonds / stop inflation; aid your nation [envelope 6x3 1/2 in.]	Blue	Bonds	Davis, Ray	A
1264	Buy war bonds / they are worth fighting for	Black/Brown	Navy	McFarland	A
1265	Buy war bonds / they are worth fighting for	Black/Brown	Army	McFarland	A
1266	Buy war bonds / they are worth living for	Red	Ordna	McFarland	A
1267	Buy war bonds / they are worth working for	Brown	Army	McFarland	A
1268	Buy war bonds / this kind of action etc. [envelope 6x3 1/2 in.]	Unknown	Bonds	Davis, Ray	A
1269	Buy war bonds / USA [thermographed]	Unknown	Bonds	Dye	B
1270	Buy war bonds / with the money you / can make or save with / this etc.	Black	Bonds	Kelsey	B
1271	Buy war bonds [airmail envelope]	Green	Bonds	Anderson	A
1272	Buy war bonds [small sihouettes in profile, Washington and Lincoln]	Red	LinWa	Unknown	A
1273	Buy war bonds [thermographed]	Unknown	Bonds	McCluney	A
1274	Buy war bonds to / keep America free	Green	Home	McFarland	A
1275	Buy war bonds to / keep the air free	Purple	Air	McFarland	A
1276	Buy war bonds to / keep the Navy in action	Blue	Bonds	McFarland	A
1277	Buy war bonds to help pay taxes / set 'em / on their / Axis! [thermographed]	Blue, red	Bonds	Czubay	A
1278	Buy war bonds! / Have something to fall back on - [handpainted]	Blue, red	Home	Martin	C
1279	Buy war bonds! / keep 'em flying	Blue, red	Bonds	Speede	A
1280	Buy war bonds! have something to fall back on - [handpainted]	Multicolored	Bonds	Myers	B
1281	Buy war bonds. / And the Axis will go to the / Italy has gone etc. [Haynes corner card]	Black, red	Devil	Haynes	A
1282	Buy war bonds. / And the Axis will go to the [Runge corner card]	Red	Devil	Runge	A
1283	Buy war savings bonds [handpainted]	Multicolored	Bonds	Nelson, KE	B
1284	Buy war savings stamps and bonds [envelope 5 1/2x3 1/4 in.]	Blue, red	Bonds	Unknown	A
1285	Buy war stamps & bonds ...- / send the Axis to the	Red	Devil	Runge	A
1286	Buy war stamps & bonds ...- / Send the Axis to the [flag above text]	Bu,O/Bu,Red	Devil	Runge	A
1287	Buy war stamps & bonds ...- [no flag above text]	Red	Bonds	Runge	A
1288	Buy war stamps & bonds / and the Axis etc.	Brown	Devil	Runge	A
1289	Buy war stamps & bonds [flag above text]	Blue, red	Bonds	Runge	A
1290	Buy war stamps and bonds / [etc.] / Serving in the United States Nany [thermogr]	Black	Bonds	Crosby	B
1291	Buy war stamps and bonds / help put / 'em in / the jug / [thermographed]	Blue/Red	Axis	Crosby	B
1292	Buy war stamps and bonds / Win the war / Serving in / Navy [thermographed]	Blue	Bonds	Crosby	B
1293	Buy war stamps and bonds / Win the war / United States Navy [thermographed]	Blue	Bonds	Crosby	B
1294	Buy war stamps and bonds / Win the war / US Marines etc. [thermographed]	Unknown	Bonds	Crosby	B
1295	Buy war stamps and bonds / Win the war [thermographed]	Blue/Purple	Bonds	Crosby	B
1296	Buy war stamps and bonds [text diagonal downward] [handp]	Multicolored	Uncle	Unknown	B
1297	Buy your / liberty with / victory / bonds	Multicolored	Bonds	Linto	B
1298	Buy your / liberty with / victory / bonds / Navy Day——Oct. 27, 1943	Multicolored	Navy	Linto	B
1299	Buy your full share / in America	Blue, red	Bonds	Quigley	B
1300	Buy your share / of bonds	Blue, red	Bonds	Burdick	A
1301	Buy your share of freedom today / buy war bonds [envelope 6x3 1/2 in.]	Brown	Bonds	Davis, Ray	A
1302	Buy-buy bonds, buy-buy stamps etc.	Unknown	Bonds	Tijerina	A

NO.	CACHET TEXT	COLOR	TOPIC	PUBLISHER	$
1303	Buying U.S. savings / bonds is your way / of saying / keep America / free	Gold, red	Eagle	Linto	B
1304	Buys bonds / the down payment on / our freedom was made etc.	Blue, red	Bonds	Griffith	A
1305	BuyWarBondsBuyWarBonds / Not your fiurst chance / that's gone by etc. [no pict]	Black	Bonds	Myers	A
1306	By next spring I have been / president etc.	Purple	Unk	McFarland	A
1307	By the driven snow-white / and the living [in quotes] etc. [thermographed]	Multicolored	Flag	Andrews	B
1308	By the old love we'll receive them etc.	Blue	Navy	Carpenter	A
1309	By the rude bridge that arched the flood / their flag to [in quotes] etc.	Blue, red	Verse	Grandy	A
1310	By way of sug- / gestion to long / distance users / "I'll" etc. [brown envelope]	Green	Home	Ohio Bell	D
1311	Byrnes says: / draft 4-F's. / [etc.] / 1-12-'45——Yanks and / British meet etc.	Multicolored	Event	Linto	B
1312	Byrnes says: / draft 4-F's. / And why not the / useless thousands / in the etc.	Gold, silver	Flag	Linto	B

Cover Values (from Table 6, p. 136)

Value	Price Range
A	$ 3 - 6
B	$ 7 - 15
C	$ 16 - 30
D	$ 31 - 60
E	$ 61 - 125
F	$ 126 - 250
G	$ 251 - 500
H	$ 501 - 1000
I	$ >1000
X	Unpriced: Suspicious or fraudulent cover

825

849

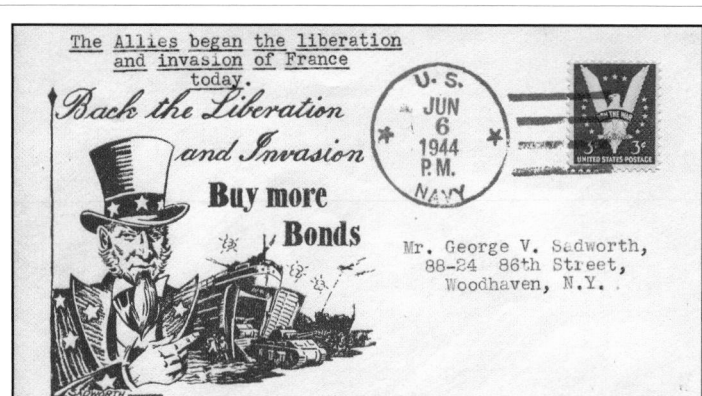

867

935

953

987

1004

1009

1046

1047

1092

1101

1113

1142

1212

1213

1228

CACHET TEXT BEGINNING WITH "C"

NO.	CACHET TEXT	COLOR	TOPIC	PUBLISHER	$
1313	C.B.I. [China-Burma-India Theater insignia, UL] [envelope 6x3 1/2 in.]	Blue, red	Unit	Army	D
1314	Cairo Conference leaders [envelope 6 3/4x3 7/8 in.]	Black	Heads	Belles-let	C
1315	California here I come [in quotes]	Multicolored	UN	Peer	B
1316	Call / your floor / boys! / Pisa / get it etc. [env. 9 1/2x4 1/8 in.]	Black, brown	Musso	Barg	C
1317	Called to "arms" / my definition of a / kiss is a report to / head-quarters	Black	Army	Lupton	A
1318	Calling / all / dollars / Turn them into bonds [no picture]	Gold, silver	Bonds	Linto	B
1319	Calling / all nurses / Uncle Sam needs you [envelope 5 9/16x3 9/16 in.]	Unknown	Nurse	Baur	A
1320	Calling all / Americans! / Enroll in the / 8th victory bond drive	Gold, silver	Bonds	Linto	B
1321	Calling all absentees	Black, red	Home	Andrews	B
1322	Calling all nurses [envelope 5 9/16x3 9/16 in.]	Unknown	Nurse	Baur	A
1323	Calling America to action	Blue	Navy	Robertson	A
1324	Camp Sibert Ala [with small shield] [handpainted]	Multicolored	Army	Stawuszew	B
1325	Campaign slogans / of F.D.R. / 1932——The Forgotten Man. / 1936——Finish etc.	Silver	FDR	Linto	C
1326	Can a Jap / be a real / American? [no picture]	Gd,Gn/Gd,S	AJA	Linto	B
1327	Can he run / fast enough? / [etc.] / Commemorating "Bill of Rights" Day etc.	Multicolored	Hist	Linto	B
1328	Can he run / fast enough? / Will his pal / wait for him?	Multicolored	Axis	Linto	B
1329	Can Nazis take it? / Could they ever? / They can dish it out.	Multicolored	Nazis	Linto	B
1330	Can we return / Abe Lincoln's idea of / government in America?	Multicolored	Eagle	Linto	B
1331	Can you look / at this slimy / [etc.] / Dillon S. Meyer, WRA, must be etc.	Multicolored	AJA	Linto	B
1332	Can you look / at this slimy / beast and for- / get Dec. 7, / 1941, and etc.	Multicolored	Japan	Linto	B
1333	Can you remember / Roosevelt's 1932 / campaign speeches? etc. [no picture]	Unknown	FDR	Linto	B
1334	Canada / United Nations [handpainted]	Multicolored	UN	Weigand	B
1335	Canada at war	Multicolored	Ally	King's	C
1336	Canol Project / [etc.] / 3-2-'42——Japs report sinking U.S.S. but she came etc.	Multicolored	Anniv	Linto	B
1337	Canol Project / to cost $25,000,000 / but is upward from / $130,000,000 etc.	Multicolored	Home	Linto	B
1338	Can't refuse call to duty / FDR	Red	FDR	Unknown	B
1339	Canteen service / Veterans of Foreign Wars / of the etc. [envelope 6x3 1/2 in.]	Blue	Armed	VFW	A
1340	Capitulation [postmarked 5/5/45, date of premature wire report] [handpainted]	Multicolored	VEDay	Shaffer, A	D
1341	Capitulation Day [caps] / The United Nations triumph / over Nazi Germany [engraved]	Blue, red	VEDay	Heckman	D
1342	Capitulation Day [script] / The United Nations triumph / over Nazi Germany [engraved]	Blue, red	VEDay	Heckman	D
1343	Capt. / Colin / Kelly / Jr. / Colin P. Kelly, Jr., etc. [env. 5 3/8x3 7/16 in.]	Blue	Hero	Unknown	A
1344	Capt. / of the / head [thermographed]	Black	Navy	Atwell	B
1345	Capt. / Robert / Prince / [etc.] / 2-24-'45——Yanks free 2000 / prisoners etc.	Unknown	Event	Linto	B
1346	Capt. / Robert / Prince / one of 3 / liberators of / Cabanabuan prison etc.	Unknown	Hero	Linto	B
1347	Capt. Arthur W. Wermuth	Brown	Hero	Huss	A
1348	Capt. Robert Prince	Unknown	Unk	Linto	B
1349	Captain Colin Kelly, Jr., sinks the / [etc.] / Haruna [env. 6 3/4x3 7/8 in.]	Multicolored	Hero	Belles-let	D
1350	Captain Colin P. Kelly / of the Army, who gave his life etc. [colored envelopes]	Multicolored	Hero	Poppenger	A
1351	Careless talk / costs / lives [handpainted]	Multicolored	Home	Adler	D
1352	Carry on! / That's the wish of / our departed chief / and the full desire etc.	Gold, purple	FDR	Linto	B
1353	Carrying more / than his share / of the load—— / what are you doing to etc.	Black/Blue	Army	Ang	A
1354	Casablanca meeting / Occupation of Tunisia / [etc.] / Review of 1943	Multicolored	Event	Staehle	C
1355	Casablanca meeting / President Roosevelt and / Prime Min. Churchill / [etc.] / Africa - January 14, 1943	Multicolored	Event	Teixeira	D
1356	Cash money "locked in" your etc. [envelope 6 3/4x3 3/4 in.]	Blue	Bonds	Bartley	A
1357	Cash money / "locked in" your pocket / isn't the key to winning etc.	Blue	Home	Quigley	B
1358	Cassino / Formia / fall to etc. [no picture]	Multicolored	Event	Boone	B
1359	Cassino to Yanks	Unknown	Event	Linto	B
1360	Cast away the / arms of hate / and misery, / uphold etc. [Liberty colors vary]	Multicolored	Liber	Amer Pat	A
1361	Ceilings—— / prices / wages	Gold, silver	Home	Linto	B
1362	Ceilings—— / prices / wages / 6-27-'44——Yanks capture the / vital port of etc.	Unknown	Event	Linto	B
1363	Champions of / freedom	Red	Hist	Boone	A

NO.	CACHET TEXT	COLOR	TOPIC	PUBLISHER	$
1364	Change / ego for / efficiency! / [etc.] / 10-19-'44——MacArthur's boys etc.	Multicolored	Event	Linto	B
1365	Change / ego for / efficiency! / [etc.] / 7-20-'44——Hitler and group etc.	Multicolored	Event	Linto	B
1366	Change / ego for / efficiency! / Nov. 7, 1944	Gold, silver	Home	Linto	B
1367	Chaperone of the deep [envelope 6 3/4x3 7/8 in.]	Brown	Event	Belles-let	C
1368	Charles de Gaulle	Blue, gold	Heads	Runge	A
1369	Chattanooga, Tennessee / dynamo for ... / victory etc. [env.9 1/2x4 1/8 in.]	Gn/Bu, red	Home	Andrews	C
1370	Chattanooga, Tennessee / dynamo for... / victory	R,Bu/R,Gn	Home	Andrews	A
1371	Chemical warfare service / 4.2 mortar [thermographed]	Green	Army	DeLeuze	A
1372	Cherbourg / in our hands / "D" Day + 20 [rubber stamp with cachet 3397]	Red	Event	Unknown	C
1373	Cherbourg / surrenders / Fierce Soviet / offensive; / Vitebsk falls [no picture]	Blue, red	Event	Fidelity	B
1374	Chiang Kai-Shek	Unknown	Heads	Runge	A
1375	Chicken? / egg? / I don't know! / war bonds / come first with me. [handpainted]	Multicolored	Chick	Myers	B
1376	Chickens / for victory / meat / eggs [handpainted]	Multicolored	Chick	Phill, CR	B
1377	Chief of the gremlins / John L. Lewis [handpainted]	Multicolored	Home	Knapp	G
1378	Chin up, eyes front and smile etc.	Unknown	Unk	Quigley	B
1379	China—— / Roosevelt's / political / [etc.] / 9-13-'44——Yanks down 200 etc.	Multicolored	Event	Linto	B
1380	China—— / Roosevelt's / political / spanking / ground	Gold, silver	Flag	Linto	B
1381	China / United Nations [handpainted]	Multicolored	UN	Weigand	B
1382	China fights for / freedom / Dr. Sun Yat-Sen / founder of etc. [colored envelopes]	Multicolored	China	Poppenger	A
1383	Chinese soldiers are paid / 30c a month! / But / [etc.] / Navy Day——27-10-'43	Multicolored	Navy	Linto	B
1384	Chinese soldiers are paid / 30c a month! / But think of the fun / they etc.	Gold/Multi	China	Linto	B
1385	Chow! [soldier running with eating utensils in hand] [env. 7 1/2x3 7/8 in.]	Brown	Army	Unknown	A
1386	Christ is vital all the time / especially now!	Unknown	Relig	Linto	B
1387	Christ walking on the waters [postmarked 12/25/42]	Green	Relig	Unknown	B
1388	Christmas / cheer .... / Ring out ye bells! / May peace be / everywhere forever!	Multicolored	Holid	Linto	B
1389	Christmas / greetings / United States Navy [thermographed]	Unknown	Navy	Sadworth	B
1390	Christmas / Greetings [Madonna and Child] [handpainted]	Multicolored	Holid	Adler	D
1391	Christmas / Greetings [pine branch + oval lantern] [handpainted]	Multicolored	Holid	Adler	C
1392	Christmas / Greetings [ribbon + rectangular lantern] [handpainted]	Multicolored	Holdi	Adler	C
1393	Christmas / The promise of / permanenet peace [stenciled] [handpainted]	Multicolored	Holid	Wolf, CL	C
1394	Christmas 1944 / help wipe out the Axis	Unknown	Holid	Lowell	A
1395	Christmas bells - / Victory bells / May they bring a just and lasting peace / to etc.	Red, sepia	Holid	Unknown	A
1396	Christmas greetings / a sincere wish / may you find / war bonds / among etc.	Green	Holid	Davis, D	A
1397	Christmas greetings / from / Penasse, Minnesota / Santa's first stop! etc.	Multicolored	Holid	Zunks	B
1398	Christmas greetings / from Sugar Land Texas 1944. / Buy bonds!- / So that etc.	Green, red	Holid	Zunks	B
1399	Christmas greetings / Liberty for all, / peace on earth and / good will etc.	Multicolored	Holid	Staehle	C
1400	Christmas greetings / Liberty for all, peace on / earth and good will etc.	Multicolored	Holid	Staehle	C
1401	Christmas greetings / peace on earth!	Unknown	Holid	Davis, Ral	A
1402	Christmas greetings from Victory, Vermont	Red	Holid	Unknown	A
1403	Churchill	Red, silver	Heads	Runge	A
1404	Churchill - Roosevelt confer	Unknown	Hist	Linto	B
1405	Churchill addressed Congress	Unknown	Hist	Linto	B
1406	Churchill addressed joint session of etc.	Unknown	Hist	Linto	B
1407	Churchill and FDR meet at sea	Unknown	Hist	Linto	B
1408	Churchill and Stalin meet in Moscow	Unknown	Hist	Linto	B
1409	Churchill in Washington	Unknown	Hist	Linto	B
1410	Cigarettes hard / to get? / U.S. / [etc.] / 6-14-'45——Aussies / take Brunei	Multicolored	Event	Linto	B
1411	Cigarettes hard / to get? / U.S. bonds will / be a better buy!	Gold, green	Bonds	Linto	B
1412	Civil liberties groups / are urging Japs to go / to Michigan and Ohio etc.	Pink, blue	AJA	Linto	B
1413	Cleaning house / I'll soon be home [handpainted]	Multicolored	Japan	Adler	D
1414	Cleaning up the Saar basin	Multicolored	Army	Peer	B
1415	Clear / the / tracks! [copyright "C" w/, w/o serifs]	Multicolored	Axis	Minkus	A
1416	Cleveland Cover Club / Fifth Annual Exhibition / Victory etc. [thermographed]	Red	Eagle	Cleveland	B
1417	Clover-leaf Division / 1944 / Italy / 1945	Blue	Unit	Unknown	A

NO.	CACHET TEXT	COLOR	TOPIC	PUBLISHER	$
1418	Clytie spark chasers	Blue	Navy	Carpenter	A
1419	C'mon / let's / all / fight [no picture] [handpainted]	Multicolored	Home	Wolf, CL	B
1420	Coal miners ordered back	Unknown	Event	Linto	B
1421	Coal will maek / it hot for the /Axis / Buy U.S. war bonds [env. 9 1/2x4 3/16 in.]	Black	Bonds	Valley	B
1422	Coast Guard / The U.S. Coast Guard, fourth arm of our fighting forces, was etc.	Purple	Coast	Ander, CS	A
1423	Coast Guard Cutter Spencer / sinks a sub [all-over cachet] [handpainted]	Multicolored	Coast	Knapp	H
1424	Coat of arms / of the free / state of Bremen / we invade it / and etc.	Blue, red	Event	Fidelity	B
1425	Cologne / opposition is / liquidated. / Over the Rhine / go the / Nazi / enemy.	Black, red	Event	Griffith	B
1426	Cologne is taken / [etc.] / March 5, 1945	Multicolored	Event	Teixeira	D
1427	Colombia / United Nations [handpainted]	Multicolored	UN	Weigand	B
1428	Colonel / Paul W. / Tibbets, Jr. / [etc.] / 8-7-'45——B-29s blast etc.	Gold, green	Atom	Linto	D
1429	Colonel / Paul W. / Tibbetts, Jr. / pilot of B-29 / "Enola Gay" etc. [8/7/45]	Gold, green	Atom	Linto	D
1430	Columbia, / the gem of the ocean. / A two-ocean navy / second to none!	Blue/Red	Flag	Apnew	A
1431	Columbus / discovers America / October 12, 1492 / 1942 / Keep America etc.	Multicolored	Holid	Staehle	C
1432	Columbus / sesqui-cuarto / centennial / 1492-1942 etc. [thermographed]	Black	Holid	Crosby	B
1433	Columbus Day / Columbus / Day / Oct. 12th. / 1941	Blue	Holid	Graf	A
1434	Columbus discovered America / October 12, 1492 / We aim to etc. [no picture]	Multicolored	Home	Linto	B
1435	Columbus sesqui-cuarto centennial / October / 12th etc. [thermographed]	Black	Holid	Crosby	B
1436	Com. Eli T. Reich / 8-26-'44——China and Russia etc.	Unknown	Event	Linto	B
1437	Com. Eli T. Reich / Commander of / U.S.S. Sealion / which sank Jap etc.	Unknown	Navy	Linto	B
1438	Combat insignia 001 [37th Pursuit Squadron] [label + printed border]	Multicolored	Air	Robbins	C
1439	Combat insignia 002 [Scouting Squadron VS-72] [label + printed border]	Multicolored	Globe	Robbins	C
1440	Combat insignia 003 [Bombing Squadron VB-6] [label + printed border]	Multicolored	Air	Robbins	C
1441	Combat insignia 004 [62nd Pursuit Squadron] [label + printed border]	Multicolored	Air	Robbins	C
1442	Combat insignia 005 [Bombing Squadron VB-3] [label + printed border]	Multicolored	Air	Robbins	C
1443	Combat insignia 006 [Torpedo Squadron VT-2] [label + printed border]	Multicolored	Air	Robbins	C
1444	Combat insignia 007 [Scouting Squadron VS-42] [label + printed border]	Multicolored	Air	Robbins	C
1445	Combat insignia 008 [Torpedo Squadron VT-5] [label + printed border]	Multicolored	Air	Robbins	C
1446	Combat insignia 009 [45th Air Base Squadron] [label + printed border]	Multicolored	Air	Robbins	C
1447	Combat insignia 010 [Scouting Squadron VS-2] [label + printed border]	Multicolored	Air	Robbins	C
1448	Combat insignia 011 [Scouting Squadron VS-5] [label + printed border]	Multicolored	Air	Robbins	C
1449	Combat insignia 012 [Scouting Squadron VS-6] [label + printed border]	Multicolored	Air	Robbins	C
1450	Combat insignia 013 [23rd Pursuit Squadron] [label + printed border]	Multicolored	Air	Robbins	C
1451	Combat insignia 014 [Bombing Squadron VB-2] [label + printed border]	Multicolored	Air	Robbins	C
1452	Combat insignia 015 [Fighting Squaadron VV-3] [label + printed border]	Multicolored	Air	Robbins	C
1453	Combat insignia 016 [Fighting Squadron VF-71] [label + printed border]	Multicolored	Air	Robbins	C
1454	Combat insignia 017 [15th Observation Squadron] [label + printed border]	Multicolored	Air	Robbins	C
1455	Combat insignia 018 [Jacksonville Air Station] [label + printed border]	Multicolored	Air	Robbins	C
1456	Combat insignia 019 [Scouting Squadron VS-41] [label + printed border]	Multicolored	Air	Robbins	C
1457	Combat insignia 020 [Fighting Squadron VF-2] [label + printed border]	Multicolored	Air	Robbins	C
1458	Combat insignia 021 [Fighting Squadron VF-72] [label + printed border]	Multicolored	Air	Robbins	C
1459	Combat insignia 022 [Fighting Squadron VF-6] [label + printed border]	Multicolored	Air	Robbins	C
1460	Combat insignia 023 [Torpedo Squadron VT-3] [label + printed border]	Multicolored	Air	Robbins	C
1461	Combat insignia 024 [Scouting Squadron VS-71] [label + printed border]	Multicolored	Air	Robbins	C
1462	Combat insignia 025 [Fighting Squadron VF-42] [label + printed border]	Multicolored	Air	Robbins	C
1463	Combat insignia 026 [Eagle Squadron] [label + printed border]	Multicolored	Air	Robbins	C
1464	Combat insignia 027 [Scouting Squadron VS-3] [label + printed border]	Multicolored	Air	Robbins	C
1465	Combat insignia 028 [Fighting Squadron VF-41] [label + printed border]	Multicolored	Air	Robbins	C
1466	Combat insignia 029 [56th Pursuit Squadron] [label + printed border]	Multicolored	Air	Robbins	C
1467	Combat insignia 030 [Bombing Squadron VB-5] [label + printed border]	Multicolored	Air	Robbins	C
1468	Combat insignia 031 [38th Bombardment Group] [label + printed border]	Multicolored	Air	Robbins	C
1469	Combat insignia 032 [Torpedo Squadron VT-6] [label + printed border]	Multicolored	Air	Robbins	C
1470	Combat insignia 033 [67th, 68th, 69th Pursuit Sqdrns] [label + printed border]	Multicolored	Air	Robbins	C
1471	Combat insignia 034 [94th Pursuit Squadron] [label + printed border]	Multicolored	Air	Robbins	C

NO.	CACHET TEXT	COLOR	TOPIC	PUBLISHER	$
1472	Combat insignia 035 [45th Pursuit Squadron] [label + printed border]	Multicolored	Air	Robbins	C
1473	Combat insignia 036 [Marine Fighting Squadron 221] [label + printed border]	Multicolored	USMC	Robbins	C
1474	Combat insignia 037 [4th Photographic Squadron] [label + printed border]	Multicolored	Eagle	Robbins	C
1475	Combat insignia 038 [503rd Parachute Battalion] [label + printed border]	Multicolored	Chute	Robbins	C
1476	Combat insignia 039 [75th Squadron] [label + printed border]	Multicolored	Air	Robbins	C
1477	Combat insignia 040 [Util. Unit U.S.S. Saratoga] [label + printed border]	Multicolored	Navy	Robbins	C
1478	Combat insignia 041 [50th Pursuit Squadron] [label + printed border]	Multicolored	Air	Robbins	C
1479	Combat insignia 042 [79th Bombardment Squadron] [label + printed border]	Multicolored	Air	Robbins	C
1480	Combat insignia 043 [94th Squadron] [label + printed border]	Multicolored	Air	Robbins	C
1481	Combat insignia 044 [16th Bombardment Wing] [label + printed border]	Multicolored	Air	Robbins	C
1482	Combat insignia 045 [Fighting Squadron VF-5] [label + printed border]	Multicolored	Air	Robbins	C
1483	Combat insignia 046 [108th Observation Squadron] [label + printed border]	Multicolored	Air	Robbins	C
1484	Combat insignia 047 [6th Reconn. Squadron] [label + printed border]	Multicolored	Air	Robbins	C
1485	Combat insignia 048 [Naval Air Sta., Pensacola] [label + printed border]	Multicolored	Air	Robbins	C
1486	Combat insignia 049 [46th Bombardment Group] [label + printed border]	Multicolored	Air	Robbins	C
1487	Combat insignia 050 [Jackson Air Base] [label + printed border]	Multicolored	Air	Robbins	C
1488	Combat insignia 051 [United States Mosquito Fleet] [label + printed border]	Multicolored	Navy	Robbins	C
1489	Combat insignia 052 [Los Angeles Bomber] [label + printed border]	Multicolored	Air	Robbins	C
1490	Combat insignia 053 [133rd Field Artillery Battalion] [label + printed border]	Multicolored	Army	Robbins	C
1491	Combat insignia 054 [36th Field Artillery] [label + printed border]	Multicolored	Ordna	Robbins	C
1492	Combat insignia 055 [504th Milit. Police Battn] [label + printed border]	Multicolored	Army	Robbins	C
1493	Combat insignia 056 [63rd Signal Battalion] [label + printed border]	Multicolored	Army	Robbins	C
1494	Combat insignia 057 [62nd Signal Battalion] [label + printed border]	Multicolored	Army	Robbins	C
1495	Combat insignia 058 [36th Signal Battalion] [label + printed border]	Multicolored	Army	Robbins	C
1496	Combat insignia 059 [11th Naval Dist. Sect. Base] [label + printed border]	Multicolored	Navy	Robbins	C
1497	Combat insignia 061 [251st Coast Artillery] [label + printed border]	Multicolored	Ordna	Robbins	C
1498	Combat insignia 062 [1st Defense Bttn., Fleet Marine] [label + printed border]	Multicolored	USMC	Robbins	C
1499	Combat insignia 063 [22nd Pursuit Squadron] [label + printed border]	Multicolored	Air	Robbins	C
1500	Combat insignia 064 [U.S.S. Hornet] [label + printed border]	Multicolored	Navy	Robbins	C
1501	Combat insignia 065 [126th Observation Squadron] [label + printed border]	Multicolored	Air	Robbins	C
1502	Combat insignia 066 [Pomona Bomber] [label + printed border]	Multicolored	Air	Robbins	C
1503	Combat insignia 067 [5th Reconn. Squadron] [label + printed border]	Multicolored	Air	Robbins	C
1504	Combat insignia 068 [204th Coast Artillery] [label + printed border]	Multicolored	Army	Robbins	C
1505	Combat insignia 069 [Alaska Defense Command] [label + printed border]	Multicolored	Navy	Robbins	C
1506	Combat insignia 070 [609th Tank Destroyer Bttn.] [label + printed border]	Multicolored	Army	Robbins	C
1507	Combat insignia 071 [31st Pursuit Squadron] [label + printed border]	Multicolored	Air	Robbins	C
1508	Combat insignia 072 [16th Reconn. Squadron] [label + printed border]	Multicolored	Air	Robbins	C
1509	Combat insignia 073 [77th Bombardment Squadron] [label + printed border]	Multicolored	Air	Robbins	C
1510	Combat insignia 074 [Bat'ry "B", 202nd Artill.] [label + printed border]	Multicolored	Army	Robbins	C
1511	Combat insignia 075 [121st Air Observ. Sqdrn.] [label + printed border]	Multicolored	Air	Robbins	C
1512	Combat insignia 076 [U.S.S. Blue] [label + printed border]	Multicolored	Navy	Robbins	C
1513	Combat insignia 077 [2nd Btn., 134th Med. Regt.] [label + printed border]	Multicolored	Medic	Robbins	C
1514	Combat insignia 078 [34th Combat Engineers] [label + printed border]	Multicolored	Army	Robbins	C
1515	Combat insignia 079 [Btry "A", 98th Field Art.] [label + printed border]	Multicolored	Army	Robbins	C
1516	Combat insignia 080 [21st Bombardment Squadron] [label + printed border]	Multicolored	Air	Robbins	C
1517	Combat insignia 081 [7th Bombardment Squadron] [label + printed border]	Multicolored	Air	Robbins	C
1518	Combat insignia 082 [Anti-tank Co., 101st Inf.] [label + printed border]	Multicolored	Army	Robbins	C
1519	Combat insignia 083 [74th Field Artill. Battn.] [label + printed border]	Multicolored	Army	Robbins	C
1520	Combat insignia 084 [Mine Division 19] [label + printed border]	Multicolored	Navy	Robbins	C
1521	Combat insignia 085 [754th Tank Battalion] [label + printed border]	Multicolored	Ordna	Robbins	C
1522	Combat insignia 086 [43rd Bombardment Group] [label + printed border]	Multicolored	Air	Robbins	C
1523	Combat insignia 087 [H.M.S. Illustrious] [label + printed border]	Multicolored	Navy	Robbins	C
1524	Combat insignia 088 [1st Marine Brigade] [label + printed border]	Multicolored	USMC	Robbins	C
1525	Combat insignia 089 [Free French "Lone Eagle"] [label + printed border]	Multicolored	Air	Robbins	C

NO.	CACHET TEXT	COLOR	TOPIC	PUBLISHER	$
1526	Combat insignia 090 [1st Defense Bttn., 3rd Div.] [label + printed border]	Multicolored	Army	Robbins	C
1527	Combat insignia 091 [Battery "D", 114th Artill.] [label + printed border]	Multicolored	Army	Robbins	C
1528	Combat insignia 092 [751st Tank Battalion] [label + printed border]	Multicolored	Ordna	Robbins	C
1529	Combat insignia 093 [2nd Signal Armored Battn.] [label + printed border]	Multicolored	Army	Robbins	C
1530	Combat insignia 094 [124th Division] [label + printed border]	Multicolored	Army	Robbins	C
1531	Combat insignia 095 [Losey Field Int'cept. Sqdn] [label + printed border]	Multicolored	Air	Robbins	C
1532	Combat insignia 096 [421st Coast Battalion] [label + printed border]	Multicolored	Army	Robbins	C
1533	Combat insignia 097 [40th Bombardment Group] [label + printed border]	Multicolored	Air	Robbins	C
1534	Combat insignia 098 [St. Thomas Submarine Base] [label + printed border]	Multicolored	USsub	Robbins	C
1535	Combat insignia 099 [Anti-tank Co., 16th Inf.] [label + printed border]	Multicolored	Army	Robbins	C
1536	Combat insignia 100 [32nd Pursuit Squadron] [label + printed border]	Multicolored	Air	Robbins	C
1537	Combat insignia 102 [71st Pursuit Squadron] [label + printed border]	Multicolored	Air	Robbins	C
1538	Combat insignia 103 [Aer'cal, U.S.S. Albemarle] [label + printed border]	Multicolored	Navy	Robbins	C
1539	Combat insignia 104 [U.S.S. Pelias] [label + printed border]	Multicolored	Navy	Robbins	C
1540	Combat insignia 108 [79th Pursuit Group] [label + printed border]	Multicolored	Air	Robbins	C
1541	Combat insignia 109 [482nd Ordnance Company] [label + printed border]	Multicolored	Ordna	Robbins	C
1542	Combat insignia 110 [31st Observation Squadron] [label + printed border]	Multicolored	Air	Robbins	C
1543	Combat insignia 111 [Advance Carrier Trg. Gp.] [label + printed border]	Multicolored	Air	Robbins	C
1544	Combat insignia 112 [Fl. "B", Air Corps Trg.] [label + printed border]	Multicolored	Air	Robbins	C
1545	Combat insignia 113 [Company "F", 114th Inf'try] [label + printed border]	Multicolored	Army	Robbins	C
1546	Combat insignia 114 [U.S.S. Pegasus] [label + printed border]	Multicolored	Navy	Robbins	C
1547	Combat insignia 115 [Btry "A", 165th Field Art.] [label + printed border]	Multicolored	Ordna	Robbins	C
1548	Combat insignia 116 [57th Signal Battalion] [label + printed border]	Multicolored	Army	Robbins	C
1549	Combat insignia 119 [15th Transport Squadron]] [label + printed border]	Multicolored	Chute	Robbins	C
1550	Combat insignia 120 [California State Guard] [label + printed border]	Multicolored	Army	Robbins	C
1551	Combat insignia 122 [55th School Sqdrn, Air] [label + printed border]	Multicolored	Air	Robbins	C
1552	Combat insignia 124 [9th Naval Dist., Reserve] [label + printed border]	Multicolored	Navy	Robbins	C
1553	Combat insignia 125 [RCAF Station, Dartmouth] [label + printed border]	Multicolored	Air	Robbins	C
1554	Combat insignia 128 [307th Pursuit Squadron] [label + printed border]	Multicolored	Air	Robbins	C
1555	Combat insignia 129 [38th Bombardment Squadron] [label + printed border]	Multicolored	Air	Robbins	C
1556	Combat insignia 130 [73rd Evacuation Hospital] [label + printed border]	Multicolored	Medic	Robbins	C
1557	Combat insignia 132 [331st School Sqdrn, ACAFS] [label + printed border]	Multicolored	Air	Robbins	C
1558	Combat insignia 133 [92nd Reconnaissance Troop] [label + printed border]	Multicolored	Army	Robbins	C
1559	Combat insignia 136 [Flt. "D", Wireless, RNZAF] [label + printed border]	Multicolored	Army	Robbins	C
1560	Combat insignia 137 [125th Observation Squadron] [label + printed border]	Multicolored	Air	Robbins	C
1561	Combat insignia 140 [59th Ordnance Company]] [label + printed border]	Multicolored	Ordna	Robbins	C
1562	Combat insignia 141 [90th Signal Battalion] [label + printed border]	Multicolored	Army	Robbins	$
1563	Combat insignia 142 [Aviation Repair Unit 1] [label + printed border]	Multicolored	Air	Robbins	C
1564	Combat insignia 144 [Hq 604th Tank Destr Battn] [label + printed border]	Multicolored	Ordna	Robbins	C
1565	Combat insignia 146 [13th Sqdr., Brit. Avia. Course] [label + printed border]	Multicolored	Air	Robbins	C
1566	Combat insignia 147 [Regt. Commun., 66th Armor] [label + printed border]	Multicolored	Army	Robbins	C
1567	Combat insignia 150 [Texas Defense Guard Air] [label + printed border]	Multicolored	Air	Robbins	C
1568	Combat insignia 151 [Midland Flying School] [label + printed border]	Multicolored	Air	Robbins	C
1569	Combat insignia 152 [Annette Island Artillery] [label + printed border]	Multicolored	Ordna	Robbins	C
1570	Combat insignia 154 [Luke Field Flying School] [label + printed border]	Multicolored	Air	Robbins	C
1571	Combat insignia 155 [47th Bombardment Squadron] [label + printed border]	Multicolored	Air	Robbins	C
1572	Combat insignia 158 [17th Transport Squadron] [label + printed border]	Multicolored	Air	Robbins	C
1573	Combat insignia 162 [67th Bombardment Squadron] [label + printed border]	Multicolored	Air	Robbins	C
1574	Combat insignia 163 [Hqs. Sqdrn., 28th Group] [label + printed border]	Multicolored	Air	Robbins	C
1575	Combat insignia 165 [48th Pursuit Squadron] [label + printed border]	Multicolored	Air	Robbins	C
1576	Combat insignia 167 [Hqs. Corps Area Svc. Comm.] [label + printed border]	Multicolored	Air	Robbins	C
1577	Combat insignia 170 [32nd Airship Ptrl. Sqdrn.] [label + printed border]	Multicolored	Air	Robbins	C
1578	Combat insignia 176 [92nd Sqdrn. Flying School] [label + printed border]	Multicolored	Air	Robbins	C
1579	Combat insignia 177 [41st Bombardment Squadron] [label + printed border]	Multicolored	Air	Robbins	C

NO.	CACHET TEXT	COLOR	TOPIC	PUBLISHER	$
1580	Combat insignia 179 [Fifth Signal Company] [label + printed border]	Multicolored	Army	Robbins	C
1581	Combat insignia 180 [Bttry "K", 3rd Coast Art.] [label + printed border]	Multicolored	Ordna	Robbins	C
1582	Combat insignia 181 [Med. Detach. 121st Artill.] [label + printed border]	Multicolored	Medic	Robbins	C
1583	Combat insignia 185 [Ellington Field Detachment] [label + printed border]	Multicolored	Air	Robbins	C
1584	Combat insignia 186 [57th Air Base Squadron] [label + printed border]	Multicolored	Air	Robbins	C
1585	Combat insignia 189 [Coast Guard Air Station] [label + printed border]	Multicolored	Air	Robbins	C
1586	Combat insignia 191 [342nd Bombardment Squadron] [label + printed border]	Multicolored	Air	Robbins	C
1587	Combat insignia 201 [Bombing Squadron VB 8] [label + printed border]	Multicolored	Air	Robbins	C
1588	Combat insignia 202 [A.A.F. Tech. Training Command] [label + typed border]	Multicolored	Air	Robbins	C
1589	Combat insignia 207 [Patrol Squadron VP 32] [label + printed border]	Multicolored	Air	Robbins	C
1590	Combat insignia 208 [Observation Squadron VO-4] [label + printed border]	Multicolored	Air	Robbins	C
1591	Combat insignia 210 [Patrol Squadron VP 1] [label + printed border]	Multicolored	Air	Robbins	C
1592	Combat insignia 211 [Patrol Squadron VP 23] [label + printed border]	Multicolored	Air	Robbins	C
1593	Combat insignia 213 [Auxiliary Squadron VJ 3] [label + typed border]	Multicolored	Air	Robbins	C
1594	Combat insignia 215 [3rd Pursuit Squadron] [label + typed border]	Multicolored	Air	Robbins	C
1595	Combat insignia 218 [72nd Bombardment Squadron] [label + typed border]	Multicolored	Air	Robbins	C
1596	Combat insignia 222 [Company A, 802nd Signal Service] [label + typed border]	Multicolored	Army	Robbins	C
1597	Combat insignia 231 [Consol. Mess Co., Ft. Monmouth] [label + typed border]	Multicolored	Army	Robbins	C
1598	Combat insignia 239 [77th Pursuit Squadron] [label + typed border]	Multicolored	Air	Robbins	C
1599	Combat insignia 241 [7th Bombardment Squadron] [label + typed border]	Multicolored	Air	Robbins	C
1600	Combat insignia 242 [44th Reconnaissance Squadron] [label + printed border]	Multicolored	Air	Robbins	C
1601	Combat insignia 243 [55th Pursuit Squadron] [label + printed border]	Multicolored	Air	Robbins	C
1602	Combat insignia 245 [4th Fighter Comm. Sgnl. School] [label + printed border]	Multicolored	Air	Robbins	C
1603	Combat insignia 246 [356th Bombardment Squadron] [label + printed border]	Multicolored	Air	Robbins	C
1604	Combat insignia 247 [Signal Corps Pigeon Corps] [label + printed border]	Multicolored	Pigeo	Robbins	C
1605	Combat insignia 248 [Finance Department, Fort Monmouth] [label + typed border]	Multicolored	Army	Robbins	C
1606	Come / V-Day / will you be / proud of your / war effort? [pink envelope]	Black	VforV	Temple	A
1607	Come across / war bonds / 7th war loan drive / May 14 - June 30 - 1945	Green, brown	Bonds	Eichenlaub	A
1608	Come across / war bonds / 7th war loan drive / May 14 - June 30, 1945	Green, brown	Bonds	Eichenlaub	A
1609	Come down / to earth! / [etc.] / 7-15-'44——Yanks capture / 21 French villages	Unknown	Event	Linto	B
1610	Come down / to earth! / An over-op- / timistic view / can etc. [no picture]	Silver	Home	Linto	B
1611	Come in / on fifth / war bond / drive!	Blue, silver	Bonds	Linto	B
1612	Coming / soon! / a smash hit	Multicolored	Axis	Minkus	A
1613	Coming / victory	Unknown	Unk	Phill, CR	A
1614	Coming soon / total / black-out / for Hitler and / his gang	Black	Air	Neal	A
1615	Coming soon! / (we / hope) / Germany's new / secret weapon etc. [no picture]	Blue/Red	Axis	Boone	A
1616	Commando tactics, dear!	Green	Home	Ang	A
1617	Commands 1st White Russian Army / Marshal Gregory K. Zhukov [handpainted]	Multicolored	Gener	Knoll	C
1618	Commemorating / the 20th anniversary / of the signing of the / Armistice etc.	Red	Holid	Shane	B
1619	Commemorating / the construction of / the first / Army tank / Rome etc.	Blue	Ordna	Unknown	A
1620	Commemorating the "four freedoms" / [etc.] / freedom [beach landing] [thermo]	Green	Armed	Crosby	B
1621	Commemorating the "four freedoms" etc. [Lincoln] [thermographed]	Unknown	Hist	Crosby	B
1622	Commemorating the "four freedoms" etc. [Statue of Liberty] [thermographed]	Unknown	Liber	Crosby	B
1623	Commemorating the / cessation of hositilities, the U.S. etc. [8/14/45 Navy postmark]	Red	VJDay	Navy	D
1624	Commemorating the / cessation of hositilities, the U.S. etc. [8/15/45 Navy postmark]	Blue	VJDay	Navy	D
1625	Commemorating the / cessation of hositilities, the U.S. etc. [8/16/45 Navy postmark]	Blue	VJDay	Navy	D
1626	Commemorating the / national defense etc.	Black	Unk	Allen	A
1627	Commemorating the / occupation of / Paris, France / by etc. [typed, ink border]	Black	Event	Batura	D
1627A	Commemorating the admission of each state into the Union. / First state, Delaware etc.	Blue, red	Hist	Sunner	X
1628	Commemorating the 210th an- / niversary of the birth of Haym / Salomon etc.	Orange	Hist	Unknown	A
1629	Commemorating the dedication / of the / MacArthur West Virginia / Post etc.	Unknown	MacFD	Postmaster	H
1630	Commemorating the first anniversary of the / treacherous attack on Pearl etc.	Red	Hero	Unknown	A
1631	Commemorating the first anniversary of the / treacherous attack on Pearl etc.	Red	Pearl	Unknown	A
1632	Commemorating the flag / raising of Iwo Jima [attack on peak] [thermographed]	Bicolor var	USMC	Crosby	B

NO.	CACHET TEXT	COLOR	TOPIC	PUBLISHER	$
1633	Commemorating the flag / raising of Iwo Jima [Lt. Gen. Smith] [thermographed]	Bicolor var	USMC	Crosby	B
1634	Commemorating the flag / raising of Iwo Jima [map of island] [thermographed]	Bicolor var	USMC	Crosby	B
1635	Commemorating the flag / raising of Iwo Jima [MC bulldogs] [thermographed]	Bicolor var	USMC	Crosby	B
1636	Commemorating the flag / raising of Iwo Jima [MC insignia] [thermographed]	Bicolor var	USMC	Crosby	B
1637	Commemorating the nations / overrun etc. [photo labels] [thermographed]	Unknown	ORN	Crosby	B
1638	Commemorating the principles etc. For defense etc. [double cachet] [thermo]	Red-1, Blue-2	USMC	Crosby	D
1639	Commemorating the principles of / "the United Nations" etc. [thermographed]	Red	USMC	Crosby	B
1640	Commemorating the United ? Nations' crusade etc.	Unknown	UN	Linto	B
1641	Commemorative mailing / "Japan attacks," etc. [postmarked 12/7/41]	Blue	Event	First Day	F
1642	Commissioned / United States Ship / Aaron Ward / [etc.] / Remember Pearl Harbor	Blue	Navy	Unknown	A
1643	Commodore / V.H. / Schaeffer	Unknown	Navy	Linto	B
1644	Commodore / V.H. / Schaeffer / 1-22-'45——Yanks bomb / Okinawa Island	Unknown	Event	Linto	B
1645	Comrades the joyous time / is ours, for the triumphal etc. [text colors vary]	Multicolored	Flag	Amer Pat	A
1646	Comrades?	Multicolored	Axis	Peer	B
1647	Confederate Memorial Day / 1865 May 10th 1944 / Remember the Blue and the Gray	Blue, red	VforV	Boone	A
1648	Confidentially / Gen. Doolittle [envelope 9 1/2x4 1/8]	Blue, red	Dool	Unknown	D
1649	Congress at last really / is waking / [etc.] / 12-28-'44——Yanks trap Huns etc.	Multicolored	Event	Linto	B
1650	Congress at last really / is waking up. They now / know they etc. [no picture]	Gold, pink	Home	Linto	B
1651	Congress can solve the / man-power shortage easy / Simply etc. [no picture]	Multicolored	Home	Linto	B
1652	Congress proclaimed / existence of a state of / "war" between etc. [pen & ink]	Blue, red	Event	Batura	D
1653	Congressional override veto of nonstrike bill	Unknown	Event	Linto	B
1654	Congressional Record / March 12, 1943 / shipped etc.	Unknown	Home	Linto	B
1655	Connubial dispute, period / [etc.] / 8-20-'44——French battle Nazis in etc.	Unknown	Event	Linto	B
1656	Connubial dispute, period / by Ethel etc.	Unknown	Event	Linto	B
1657	Conserve gas! / V / Let the highways / work for victory! / American	Multicolored	Minut	Linto	B
1658	Conserve gas! / V / Let the highways / work for victory! / Justice	Multicolored	Minut	Linto	B
1659	Consistency! / our boys fighting / [etc.] / 1-26-'42——Amer. Expeditionary etc.	Unknown	Anniv	Linto	B
1660	Consistency! / our boys fighting / Japs in the Pacific / Japs running etc.	Bronze, black	AJA	Linto	B
1661	Cooked goose - a la Russian [in quotes]	Black	Hitle	Donaldson	A
1662	Cooked goose - ala Russian [in quotes]	Black/Brown	Hitle	Donaldson	A
1663	Cookie-pushing parties/ was the new technique / for dodging diplomatic etc.	Gold, silver	Ally	Linto	B
1664	Copenhagen / liberated / capital of Denmark / May 5, 1945	Multicolored	Event	Teixeira	D
1665	Copenhagen / liberated / capital of Denmark etc. [5/5/45 + 5/8/45 pmarks]	Multicolored	Event	Teixeira	F
1666	Coral Sea battle	Unknown	Hist	Linto	B
1667	Correct time / any time / is the right / time to write / -to- / G.I. etc.	Blue, red	Home	Davis, D	A
1668	Corregidor	Black	Phili	Coll Surp	A
1669	Corregidor / is ours again / May 6th 1942——February 17th 1945 / Victory etc.	Multicolored	Phili	Fluegel	C
1670	Corregidor / Thou rugmged rocky fortress / guardian of Manila Bay / Your epic etc.	Blue, red	Verse	Wallace	A
1671	Corregidor needs no comment / from me. Through the bloody [in quotes] etc.	Blue, red	Phili	Brenn	A
1672	Cosmetics - ve iss in a mess - Adolf [envelope 6 3/4x3 7/8 in.]	Unknown	Unk	Belles-let	C
1673	Could I interest / you in a nice line of / tombstones? [allover] [handpainted]	Multicolored	Hitle	Hadley	D
1674	Could it be - / the War Department is / [etc.] / 12-23-'44——Draft quotas etc.	Multicolored	Event	Linto	B
1675	Could it be—— / The War Dept. is in- / viting another / Pearl Harbor / by etc.	Gold, silver	Flag	Linto	B
1676	Count off! [handpainted]	Multicolored	Army	Dannells	C
1677	Courage and perseverance have / [etc.] / 10-12-'44——Yanks drop 3500 / tons etc.	Multicolored	Event	Linto	B
1678	Courage and perseverance have a / magnetic talisman before etc. [no picture]	Pi,S/ Gn,S	Hist	Linto	B
1679	Courage! The Yanks are here!! [handpainted]	Multicolored	Armed	Parker	D
1680	Cover them over with beautiful / flowers etc.	Unknown	Unk	Brenn	A
1681	Crippled in action, H.M.S. 'Formidable' / seeks haven for repairs / in etc.	Blue, red	Event	First Day	C
1682	Crippled in action, H.M.S. 'Furious' / seeks haven for repairs / at etc.	Blue, red	Event	Unknown	C
1683	Crissy's poem / There, little / [etc.] / 10-27-'41——Pres. Roosevelt said: etc.	Multicolored	FDR	Linto	B
1684	Crissy's poem / There, little citizen, / don't you cry; / The O.P.A. will etc.	Multicolored	Flag	Linto	B
1685	Crossed / fingers / will / not / win war!	Gold, green	Home	Linto	B
1686	Crossed / fingers / will not / win war! / 3-29-'45——Yanks 185 / miles from etc.	Gold, green	Event	Linto	B

NO.	CACHET TEXT	COLOR	TOPIC	PUBLISHER	$
1687	Crossing the seas to all / lands	Unknown	Unk	Symbols	B
1688	Crow! and / justly so, over / [etc.] / 8-17-'44——Gen. Patton's / forces streak for Paris	Gold, green	Event	Linto	B
1689	Crow! and / justly so, over our / courageous / fighting / forces!	Gold,Gn/Gn,S	Chick	Linto	B
1690	Cruisers destroyers / gunboats tenders etc. [circumscribing naval picture]	Black	Navy	Unknown	A
1691	Crush / in '44	Green	Hitle	Davis, D	A
1692	Crushed by the powers of / right, Japan, like the / object below, by etc.	Black, red	Japan	Carpenter	A
1693	Crying towel / just a bunch of cry-babies!	Red	Axis	Barnes	A
1694	Cuba / United Nations [handpainted]	Multicolored	UN	Weigand	B
1695	Current Covers and Stamplets / Wish / [etc.] / Slogans help- / But actions win.	Green, red	Holid	Runge	A
1696	Curtains / for / Mussolini / 1945 / forgetting etc.	Black	Musso	Hyde	A
1697	Curtains [in quotes] / for / Mussolini etc. [envelope 9 7/16x4 1/16 in.]	Black	Home	Hyde	B
1698	Czecho / slovakia / the republic of Czechosolvakia etc.	Bk/Bu/Red	ORN	Cliff	A
1699	Czechoslovakia	Brown	ORN	Runge	A
1700	Czechoslovakia / freedom lives on etc.	Unknown	ORN	Runge	A
1701	Czechoslovakia / Lidice	Black	ORN	Lowry	A
1702	Czechoslovakia / Patton invades / We take Leipsig / Ernie Pyle dies on Ie	Blue, brown	Event	Fidelity	B
1703	Czechoslovakia [flag, star, plane, rifles, helmets]	Blue, red	ORN	Clifford	A
1704	Czechoslovakia [thermographed]	Unknown	ORN	Smartcraft	B
1705	Czechoslovakia regains / freedom / Prague, Neb., U.S.A., / salutes etc.	Blue	VEDay	Rameco	B

Cover Values (from Table 6, p. 136)

Value	Price Range
A	$ 3 - 6
B	$ 7 - 15
C	$ 16 - 30
D	$ 31 - 60
E	$ 61 - 125
F	$ 126 - 250
G	$ 251 - 500
H	$ 501 - 1000
I	$ >1000
X	Unpriced: Suspicious or fraudulent cover

1321

1340

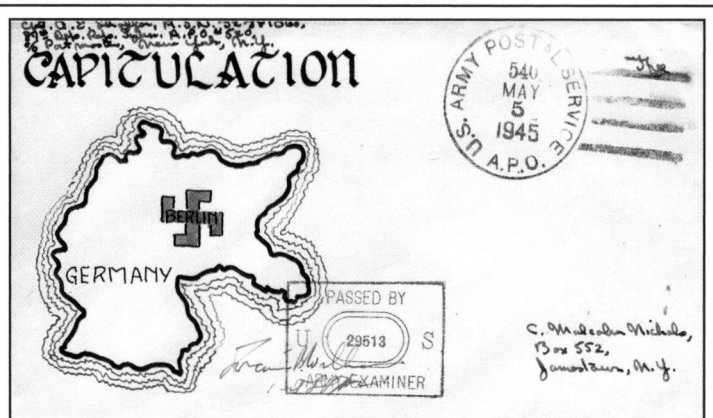

1342

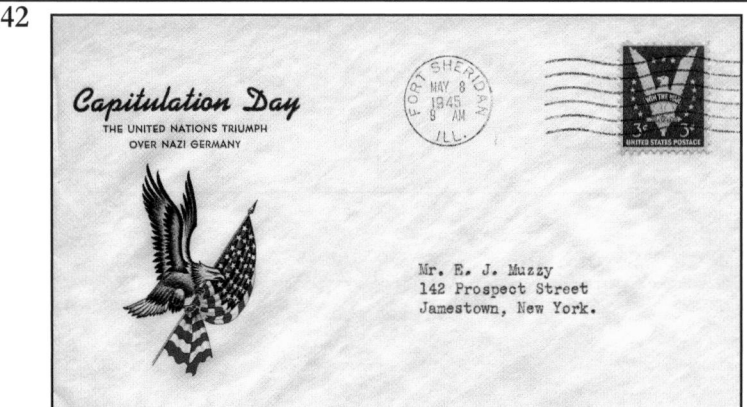

1353

1376

1398

1415

1427

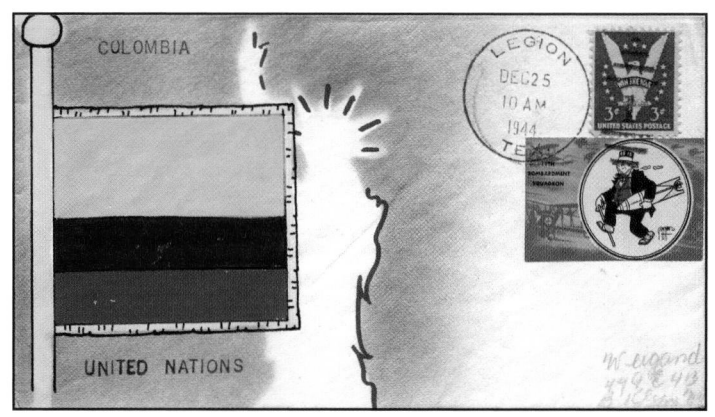

1442
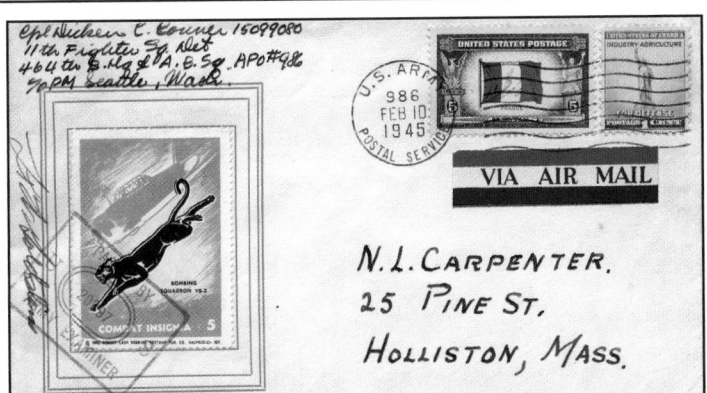

1521

1612

COMING SOON!
A SMASH HIT

1623
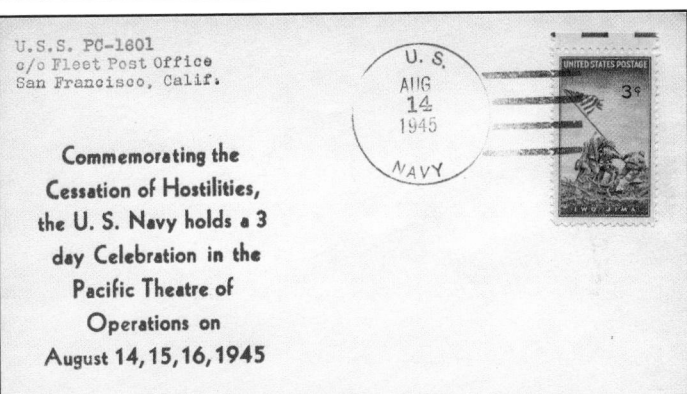

1667

CORRECT TIME

ANY TIME
IS THE RIGHT
TIME TO WRITE
-TO-
G. I. JANE
G. I. JOE

1673

1676

1695

Current Covers & Stamplets
Wish you a Merry Christmas,
and Happy New Year

Slogans Help-

But Actions Win.

1702

CZECHOSLOVAKIA

PATTON INVADES
We take Leipsig
Ernie Pyle dies on Ie

CACHET TEXT BEGINNING WITH "D"

NO.	CACHET TEXT	COLOR	TOPIC	PUBLISHER	$
1706	D / Day / June 6th, 1944 [handpainted] [postmarked 06/06/44]	Black, red	DDay	Knoll	C
1707	D / Day / The road to Berlin is the only road ahead. [no picture]	Red	DDay	Runge	B
1708	D / Day / The world has waited for this / day, June 6th, 1944. etc. [no picture]	Red	DDay	Unknown	B
1709	D / Day is / here / Their lives / are in it! etc. [no picture]	Blue, red	DDay	Threl+Thar	B
1710	D / Day is / here / Their lives / are in it! etc. [no picture] [thermographed]	Blue, red	DDay	Threl+Thar	B
1711	D [in quotes] Day / American and Allied / troops, after many / months of etc.	Blue	DDay	Fidelity	B
1712	D Day is here / Deliverance / from / oppression	Blue, red	DDay	Lowell	B
1713	D Day is here / Despair / defeat / doom / for you —— Mr. Hitler	Black, gold	DDay	Lowell	B
1714	Daily News / Manila / falls! / On to / Tokyo! [handpainted]	Black	Event	Clendennen	D
1715	Daniel in the lion's den [postmarked 12/25/42]	Brown	Relig	Unknown	B
1716	Darling - gee / I'm glad you're / back from sea! / We'll make the / most etc.	Black	Home	Lupton	A
1717	Dawn at last [handpainted]	Multicolored	ORN	Adler	D
1718	Dawn of a new freedom [thermographed]	Multicolored	VEDay	McCluney	B
1719	Day by day it gets / bluer and bluer / for der Fuehrer	Black, blue	Hitle	Temple	B
1720	D-Day "worries" [handpainted]	Multicolored	Hitle	Adler	D
1721	D-Day / day of doom / for / the hordes of Hell / day of deliverance / for etc.	Black, gold	DDay	McCluney	B
1722	D-Day / in / France / Invasion of Normandy / June 6, 1944	Multicolored	DDay	Teixeira	D
1723	D-Day / is coming - / Schickelgruber!	Brown/Orange	Hitle	Schust	A
1724	D-Day / is coming / here! / Normandy etc.	Multicolored	DDay	Schust	B
1725	D-Day / is here! / Normandy invaded / June 6, 1944 / Southern France etc.	Unknown	Hitle	Schust	A
1726	D-Day / the time / is now! / The invasion has begun—— etc. [handpainted]	Multicolored	DDay	Knapp	I
1727	D-Day / turns into / V ...- / Days / It will soon / come etc. [handpainted]	Multicolored	Symb+	Borkowski	D
1728	D-Day / We, too, must do something / Back the attack! / Buy etc. [thermographed]	Red	DDay	Czubay	C
1729	D-Day [in quotes] / invasion prayer / Almighty God, our heavenly Father, etc.	Green, red	DDay	Linto	C
1730	D-Day is here / deliverance / from / oppression	Unknown	DDay	Lowell	B
1731	D-Day is here / despair / defeat / doom etc.	Unknown	DDay	Lowell	B
1732	Dead Germans / are still bad / Germans but / better dead!	Gold	Flag	Linto	B
1733	Dead Japs can fight no more! / Dead Japs can torture no etc. [no picture]	Black	Japan	Anti-Pacif	A
1734	Dead or alive? / If yo is or if yo aint / please tell us Mr. Hitler? etc.	Red	Hitle	Abel	A
1735	Dead! / Yes! they had plans / changed by Uncle Sam	Bicolor var	Axis	Linto	B
1736	Dealing / destruction / devastating / doom etc. [thermographed]	Unknown	Unk	McCluney	A
1737	Dear Adolph In 1944 / you didn't loose [sic] etc. [4/12/45, FDR's death] [handpainted]	Multicolored	Hitle	Unknown	D
1738	Dear Mom—— / Thanks for the cookies. The one I [in quotes] etc. [yellow envelope]	Multicolored	Army	Amer Art	A
1739	Dear Mom, / Don't worry, we'll do / the job!	Blue, red	Symb+	Fleetwood	B
1740	Dear Mom: / It's not easy for us to write letters, / but please ask all etc.	Multicolored	Flag+	Linto	B
1741	Dear Mom: / Sherman once said "War was hell" / But how could he have etc.	Purple	Armed	Abel	A
1742	Dear Mom: / Today I bagged / a Jap plane with your / kitchen fats etc.	Black/Blue	Home	Johns Cov	A
1743	Dear Mom——Ever thinking of you [in quotes]—— etc. [env. 6 3/4x3 7/8 in.]	Sepia tones	Home	Belles-let	C
1744	Dear Santa / Please add / Adolph to / your etc.	Unknown	Unk	Runge	A
1745	Dear Son / Glad to hear / victory will etc.	Unknown	Home	Baur	A
1746	Dear! dear! / and I thought / you were / one! etc. [handpainted]	Multicolored	Army	Cowdery	D
1747	Death / to / fascism / and / Nazism [no picture]	Black, orange	Axis	Threl+Thar	A
1748	Death / to / fascism / and / Nazism [no picture] [thermographed]	Black, orange	Axis	Threl+Thar	A
1749	Death / to / German / invaders [handpainted label]	Multicolored	USSR	LeGallez	C
1750	Death to the German invaders!	Black, red	USSR	Schust	A
1751	Dec. / 07 / 1941 -1943 / two years of war etc. [handpainted]	Black, red	Pearl	Shaffer, A	C
1752	Dec. / 7 / 1944 / Remember Pearl Harbor [envelope 8 7/8x3 3/4]	Blue	Pearl	Unknown	B
1753	Dec. 01, 1942 / Gas / rationing / is / nationwide [no picture]	Black/Blue	Event	Fidelity	B
1754	Dec. 02, 1943 / 17 Allied ships sunk / by Germans at / Bari, Italy [no picture]	Multicolored	Event	Linto	B
1755	Dec. 02, 1943 / 17 Allied ships sunk / by Germans at / Bari, Italy [no picture]	Multicolored	Event	Linto	B
1756	Dec. 07, 1941 - Japan made a / treacherous attack on the etc. [handpainted]	Multicolored	Map	Smith, LH	C
1757	Dec. 07, 1941 - The Rising Sun began to / sink in the Pacific [handpainted]	Multicolored	Japan	Smith, LH	C

NO.	CACHET TEXT	COLOR	TOPIC	PUBLISHER	$
1758	Dec. 07, 1944 / three years / Italy / Germany / Japan [handpainted]	Blue, red	Pearl	Shaffer, A	C
1759	Dec. 07, 1944 / three years / now / Japan [handpainted]	Black, red	Pearl	Shaffer, A	C
1760	Dec. 07th 1944 / Third anniversary / Pearl etc. [handpainted below other cachet]	Black	Pearl	Maul	C
1761	Dec. 11, 1941 / Pres. Roosevelt / declared / war / on etc. [back-dated]	Gold, rose	Axis	Linto	B
1762	Dec. 11, 1941 / U.S.A. / at / war / with / Germany / and Italy [on card]	Blue, red	Event	Fidelity	C
1763	Dec. 16 1944 / Americans / land on Mindoro / Island in the etc. [handpainted]	Multicolored	Map	Smith, LH	C
1764	Dec. 17, 1943 / Gen. Kruger's forces / smashed ashore at / Arawe in a full etc.	Multicolored	Map	Smith, LH	B
1765	Dec. 7th. / 1941 1943 / Two / years / of war / "Remember Pearl Harbor" [handp]	Black	Pearl	Davis, D	C
1766	December / 07 / War / bonds / Navy Yard Pearl Harbor [env. 9 1/2x4 1/8 in.]	Blue	Symb+	Navy	B
1767	December / 07th 07th / Remember / 07th 07th etc. [no picture]	Unknown	Pearl	Baur	A
1768	December 07, 1941 / Japs / sneak-attack / Pearl Harbor etc. [back-dated]	Green, rose	Pearl	Linto	X
1769	December 08, 1941 / War / declared on / Japs / by Pres. Roosevelt [back-dated]	Green, rose	Japan	Linto	X
1770	December 11, 1941 / Hitler in Berlin / Mussolini in Rome etc. [no picture]	Blue, red	Event	Jackson	C
1771	December 16, 1944 / Hans surprised the / Yanks with counter- / attack on etc.	Unknown	Event	Linto	B
1772	December 26, 1941 / Churchill addressed a / joint session of the etc.	Unknown	Event	Linto	B
1773	Declaration of war against Japan [typed] [12/8/41] [small handpainted eagle/shield]	Multicolored	Event	Unknown	C
1774	Decoration Day is the most / beautiful of our holidays——the / grim etc.	Blue, red	Holid	Brenn	B
1775	Dedicated to that force of enlightenment and / conservation that will etc.	Black	Home	Allen	A
1776	Dedicated to U.S. heroes on all fronts [picture left, text lower right]	Blue, red	Eagle	Neal+Harv	A
1777	Dedication / To every individual in America who etc. [label + printed border]	Multicolored	Eagle	Parkinson	B
1778	Dedication of / post office / Nimitz, W. Va. / in honor etc. [thermographed]	Multicolored	NimFD	Smartcraft	C
1779	Deep / in / the / heart / of / Texas [handpainted]	Multicolored	Army	Adler	C
1780	Deep in our hearts / the valor / of / Bataan [colored envelopes]	Blue, red	Uncle	Poppenger	A
1781	Deep in the heart of / 36th Division / Texas [handpainted]	Multicolored	Army	Adler	E
1782	Deep in the heart of / Texas [handpainted]	Multicolored	Home	Adler	E
1783	Deep sea fish [envelope 6 3/4x3 7/8 in.]	Brown	Navy	Belles-let	C
1784	Defeat / the Axis / [etc.] / Surrender [env. 6 1/2x3 5/8, 9 7/16x4 1/8 in.]	Multicolored	VforV	Ever Ready	B
1785	Defeat / the Axis / V / Work for etc. [env. 6 1/2x3 5/8, 9 7/16x4 1/4 in.]	Multicolored	VforV	Ever Ready	B
1786	Defeat! [repeated 16 times in circle around a bust of Hitler]	Blue, red	Hitle	Boone	A
1787	Defeat! [repeated 16 times in circle around a bust of Japanese officer]	Blue, red	Japan	Boone	A
1788	Defeat. [handpainted]	Multicolored	Japan	Adler	D
1789	Defend / America ! [eagle with wings inside large V]	Bk,R/Bu,R/Gn	EagV	Lowe	A
1790	Defend / America [eagle alighting onto text] [draped flag at left]	Bu,Gd/Gn,Gd	EagFl	Amer Pat	A
1791	Defend / America [eagle alighting onto text] [no draped flag at left]	Bu,Gd/Gn,Gd	Eagle	Amer Pat	A
1792	Defend / America [eagle landing on ribbon with text] [env. 7 1/2x3 7/8 in.]	Green, yellow	Eagle	Curtiss, H	A
1793	Defend / America [no picture] [envelope 6x3 1/2 in.]	Blue, red	Home	Powers	A
1794	Defend / America! [swastika on rattlesnake]	Bu,R/Bu,Y	Axis	Lowe	A
1795	Defend / America! [swastika on rattlesnake]	Bk,Gn/Bk,Y	Axis	Lowe	A
1796	Defend / America! [swastika on rattlesnake]	Bk,Bu/Bu,Gn	Axis	Lowe	A
1797	Defend / American / freedom etc. [envelope 6 3/4x3 3/4 in.]	Black	Uncle	Acme Fast	B
1798	Defend Alaska...buy defense stamps & bonds! / Three Alaska belles [thermogr]	Gold	Alask	Crosby	B
1799	Defend Alaska...buy defense stamps and bonds / Mt. Iliamna and Mt. Redoubt etc.	Silver	Alask	Crosby	B
1800	Defend America	Red	Eagle	Boone	A
1801	Defend America / by aiding England	Blue, red	Flag	Norona	A
1802	Defend America [handpainted]	Multicolored	FlLib	Knapp	G
1803	Defend America [no picture] [envelope 6x3 1/2 in.]	Blue, red	Home	Powers	A
1804	Defender of liberty	Blue, red	Symb+	Lowe	A
1805	Defender of liberty [eagle, Liberty Bell, soldier]	Multicolored	Symb+	Fleetwood	B
1806	Defending a great nation / United States / [etc.] / Keep 'em flying [thermographed]	Green	Navy	Sadworth	B
1807	Defending a great nation / United States / aircraft carrier [thermographed]	Bk/Bu/Green	Navy	Sadworth	B
1808	Defending a great nation / United States / aircraft carrier [thermographed]	Multicolored	Navy	Sadworth	B
1809	Defense force / section base / Tompkinsville [thermographed]	Red	Armed	Unknown	B
1810	Dejected / you say? / Wait for / the / finish!	Bicolor var	Axis	Linto	B
1811	Delaware / Greetings / to the blue hen's chicks	Blue	Armed	Buckalew	C

NO.	CACHET TEXT	COLOR	TOPIC	PUBLISHER	$
1812	Delaware / The blue hen / greets her / chicks! [artist: Dorothy Knapp]	Blue, red	Armed	Buckalew	D
1813	Deliver / us / from / evil [in quotes] / Their etc. [label + printed border]	Multicolored	ORN	Artists	B
1814	Deliver us / from evil [in quotes] / For peace etc. [label + printed border]	Multicolored	ORN	Artists	B
1815	Deliver us from evil / War bonds will remove this etc. [label + printed border]	Multicolored	ORN	Artists	B
1816	Deliver us from evil [in quotes] / "Protective" etc. [label + printed border]	Multicolored	ORN	Artists	B
1817	Deliver us from evil [in quotes] / Defend your etc. [label + printed border]	Multicolored	Home	Artists	B
1818	Deliver us from evil [in quotes] / Destroy the etc. [label + printed border]	Multicolored	Nazis	Artists	B
1819	Deliver us from evil [in quotes] / Eradicate the etc. [label + printed border]	Multicolored	Nazis	Artists	B
1820	Deliver us from evil [in quotes] / Her liberation etc. [label + printed border]	Multicolored	Conc	Artists	B
1821	Delivering / the goods [handpainted]	Multicolored	Navy	Adler	D
1822	Democracy / shall / not / die [handpainted]	Black, red	Home	Wolf, CL	B
1823	Democracy / still / lives	Black, purple	Uncle	Wolf, CL	A
1824	Democracy / still / lives / Germany surrenders [last line, cut-&-pasted paper]	Black, purple	VEDay	Wolf, CL	B
1825	Democracy / welcome / super's [sic] ready. [handpainted]	Multicolored	Japan	Shaw, TC	B
1826	Democracy must / and shall be / preserved!	Blue, red	Uncle	Boone	A
1827	Democracy must and / shall be preserved	Blue	Eag+	Lowell	A
1828	Democracy/Americanism [handpainted]	Multicolored	Liber	Knapp	G
1829	Democratic National Chairman / Robert E. Hannegan / of etc. [typed] [no picture]	Black	Event	Batura	B
1830	Denmark / overrun / but not forever / it shall be free again.	Blue, red	ORN	Cachet Cra	B
1831	Denmark / the kingdom of Denmark etc.	Bk/Bu/R	ORN	Cliff	A
1832	Denmark [Clifford imprint]	Blue, red	ORN	Clifford	A
1833	Denmark [Lowry imprint]	Black	ORN	Lowry	A
1834	Denmark [Runge imprint]	Red	ORN	Runge	A
1835	Denmark freed! / Gen. Eisenhower announces: etc. [UL, ink manuscript] [5/4/45]	Blue	ORN	Sprague	B
1836	Department of Michigan / Jewish War Veterans of etc. [env. 9 1/2x4 1/8 in.]	Blue	Wash	Jewish Vet	C
1837	Department of the Navy / Bureau of Navigation [envelope 5 5/8x4 3/8 in.]	Multicolored	Navy	Curt-Teich	A
1838	Depends / on the / individual! [torn at right] [handpainted]	Multicolored	Holid	Cowdery	D
1839	Der only cure / for / der Fuehrer! / knock / him / for etc. [hanging rope]	Black, blue	Hitle	Wolf, CL	A
1840	Der only cure / for / der Fuehrer! / knock / him / for etc. [rope + Hitler]	Black, blue	Hitle	Wolf, CL	A
1841	Der zoopermen / are on der run / Blitzkrieg in reverse [handpainted]	Multicolored	Nazis	Pisarof	C
1842	Desert / Sunday [handpainted]	Multicolored	Army	Cowdery	D
1843	Desert waste! [handpainted] [torn envelope]	Multicolored	Army	Cowdery	D
1844	Destination / Tokyo!	Multicolored	Air	McCluney	A
1845	Destroy / this / menace [handpainted]	Multicolored	Japan	Wolf, CL	B
1846	Destroy / this menace [handpainted]	Multicolored	Japan	Wolf, CL	B
1847	Destroy this / loathsome / beast! / How? / Buy U.S. / bonds!	Multicolored	Japan	Linto	B
1848	Detachment B / First Defense Battalion / Fleet Marine Force etc. [thermographed]	Black	USMC	Czubay	C
1849	Detroit race riot	Unknown	Event	Linto	B
1850	Devil's disciple	Blue/Green	Nazis	Talburt	A
1851	Devil's disciple	Green	Unk	McCluney	A
1852	Diamond Head crater / an American fortress	Green	Hawai	Lupton	A
1853	Dick-take-him / Poor Musso, he is sick again / and thinks that he will etc.	Black	Musso	Abel	A
1854	Dictators cannot / bear free speech! / [etc.] / Do your part to / ax the Axis!	Blue, red	UncAx	Boone	A
1855	Dictators cannot / bear free speech! Government of the / people, by the etc.	Blue, red	Uncle	Boone	A
1856	Did democracy / fade out / [etc.] / 01-28-'44——Russians take Leningrad etc.	Multicolored	Event	Linto	B
1857	Did democracy / fade out / [etc.] / 12-27-'43——Big German battleship / etc.	Blue, brown	Event	Linto	B
1858	Did democracy / fade out with / the "New Deal"? / What became etc. [no picture]	Blue, Gold	Home	Linto	B
1859	Did I ever show you my stamps, Winnie? [in quotes]	Black/Blue	Heads	Unknown	A
1860	Did someone mention the Japanese 'Diet'?	Multicolored	Japan	Peer	B
1861	Did you / give a pint / of blood yet—— / to save etc. [handpainted]	Multicolored	Blood	Borkowski	D
1862	Did you notice how fast our / Congressional bodies acted / to over-ride etc.	Pink, silver	Home	Linto	B
1863	Dig down, brother etc. [envelope 8 11/16x3 5/8 in.]	Unknown	Unk	ITE Circui	B
1864	Dig up 1/3 more / than you did in '44! [handpainted]	Multicolored	Home	Myers	B
1865	Dillon S. Myer thinks he / is the social up-lifter for etc. [no picture]	Multicolored	AJA	Linto	B

NO.	CACHET TEXT	COLOR	TOPIC	PUBLISHER	$
1866	Dillon S. Myer's Jap attitude re- / minds you of the "America First" etc.	Unknown	AJA	Linto	B
1867	Dinosaur of destiny [envelope 6 3/4x3 7/8 in.]	Unknown	Unk	Belles-let	C
1868	Discharage [sic] medal	Unknown	Unk	Jessop	A
1869	Dishonorable / Jap lost shirt [handpainted]	Multicolored	Japan	Barwicki	B
1870	Dishonorable Jap lose shirt [in quotes] [handpainted]	Multicolored	Japan	Hadley	C
1871	Dismember / the kraken! / Russia / Italy	Black, red	Axis	Runge	A
1872	Dismember / the kraken! Russia / Italy	Bicolor var	Axis	Runge	A
1873	Dismember the German kraken / Russian drive / Allied drive	Blue, red	Axis	Runge	A
1874	Dispense all red tape / in the war program / Give idlers and etc. [no picture]	Gold, silver	Home	Linto	B
1875	District of Columbia / [etc.] / Alaska / Pickup and deliver enroute [thermographed]	Multicolored	Air	Crosby	B
1876	Dive bombers [VJ Day cancel]	Black	Air	Southworth	B
1877	Do all you can / to keep alive / the flame of freedom / in 1945	Multicolored	Torch	Griffith	A
1878	Do it / now! / Donate blood / for our / fighting men	Bu/Br/Gn/Red	Blood	Jarrett	A
1879	Do not chatter / military matter	Bu/Br/Gd/Gn/	Home	Cox	A
1880	Do not relax now!! / We must win / this war first!! /. And etc. [no picture]	Gold, silver	Bonds	Linto	B
1881	Do the best you can / with what you have / today.	Multicolored	Relig	Linto	B
1882	Do you / save / your / bonds? [colored envelopes]	Black	Bonds	Unknown	A
1883	Do you / want to be / Hitler's and / Hirihito's [sic] / goat? / Buy bonds!	Multicolored	Bonds	Linto	B
1884	Do you / want to be taxed to pay / for subsidies / ?	Blue, gold	Home	Linto	B
1885	Do you expect to hang / around long, Adolf?	Black/Blue	Hitle	Davis, Ray	A
1886	Do you know / that... / the Japs are licked / Today is / "V-J" Day	Green/Purple	VJDay	Schulze	B
1887	Do you like old chestnuts? / How about / [etc.] / 3-30-'44——Reds capture etc.	Multicolored	Event	Linto	B
1888	Do you like old chestnuts? / How about this one? / Do not change horses etc.	Multicolored	Flag	Linto	B
1889	Do you want barbarous / Japs for / [etc.] / 4-27-'45——Yanks battle with etc.	Green, silver	Event	Linto	B
1890	Do you want barbarous / Japs for neighbors? / Remember the tortures etc.	Green, silver	AJA	Linto	B
1891	Do you want peace? / Then remove the causes of war - / or etc. [brown envelope]	Black	Relig	Shaw, TC	A
1892	Do your best to help the war—— / so we'll reach this objective in '44	Brown	Axis	Lawrence	A
1893	Do your part / for / victory [1 star or 7 stars]	Bk/Bu/Br/Gn/	EagV	Cozart	A
1894	Do your part / help / win / the / war [handpainted]	Multicolored	Shiel	Adler	D
1895	Do your part / work or fight [no picture]	Unknown	Home	Ang	A
1896	Do your part and buy U.S. war bonds ...- [handpainted]	Multicolored	Japan	Borkowski	D
1897	Do your part for / liberation / buy bonds	Blue, red	Bonds	Kosko	A
1898	Do your patriotic / duty willingly, to- / day, just like this etc. [color varieties]	Multicolored	Bonds	Linto	B
1899	Do your post war / planning etc. [envelope 8 11/16x3 5/8 in.]	Unknown	Unk	ITE Circui	B
1900	Do your share / keep on buying bonds [Lincoln, Washington, or Uncle Sam shown]	Blue, red	Bonds	Risinger	A
1901	Do your share for freedom / and victory etc. [copyright "C" w/, w/o serifs]	Multicolored	VforV	Minkus	A
1902	Does Japan get all of this——no! / "Remember Pearl" etc. [map] [thermographed]	Blue	Symb+	Crosby	B
1903	Does Japan get all this? No!! [map] [thermographed]	Gold/Red	Symb+	Crosby	B
1904	Does this represent / the bond you do not buy? etc. [handp]	Blue	Bonds	Myers	B
1905	Does Walter "I-love-me" / Winchell / [etc.] / 6-15-'44——Rommel's forces etc.	Multicolored	Event	Linto	B
1906	Does Walter "I-love-me" / Winchell think he is the / only patriot in / America?	Blue, gold	Home	Linto	B
1907	Dog collar rates top "A" / [etc.] / 1-21-'45——Yanks take / Tarlac, Luzon etc.	Unknown	Event	Linto	B
1908	Dog collar rates top "A" / priority! / Boy! What would collar / on a cow etc.	Unknown	Home	Linto	B
1909	Doing double duty / Gas serves / - the home front etc. [env. 6x3 1/16 in.]	Blue	Home	Ohio Fuel	D
1910	Doing our part for victory / U.S. submarines [thermographed]	Blue/Red	USsub	Sadworth	B
1911	Doing their bit for victory! / keep them rolling	Unknown	Armed	Davis, Ral	A
1912	Donald Duck, mascot of the Naval Air Station / is looking forward etc. [thermogr]	Green	Navy	Crosby	B
1913	Donate / some blood for wounded / now!	Multicolored	Blood	Linto	B
1914	Donate / some blood for wounded / now! / [etc.] / 9-27-'44——British "Lost" etc.	Multicolored	Event	Linto	B
1915	Donate a pint of blood / to a serviceman etc.	Blue, red	Blood	Ander, EA	A
1916	Don't / be / a / blabber [handpainted]	Multicolored	Home	Wolf, CL	B
1917	Don't / be hyp- / notized / by Axis propo- [sic] / ganda, / Buy war stamps & bonds	Brown	Home	Runge	A
1918	Don't / bla / rumors	Unknown	Home	Speede	A
1919	Don't / call / [etc.] / vital war use [no picture]	Black	Home	Mich Bell	B

NO.	CACHET TEXT	COLOR	TOPIC	PUBLISHER	$
1920	Don't / crow / till / it's / over [handpainted]	Multicolored	Home	Wolf, CL	B
1921	Don't / rumors	Blue, red	Home	Speede	A
1922	Don't be / a back yard / general [in quotes]	Black	Uncle	Stoll	A
1923	Don't be / a back yard / general [in quotes]	Multicolored	Uncle	Stoll	C
1924	Don't be a lone wolf! / Get in the fight!! etc. [hp] [pmarked Lone Wolf, OK]	Black, yellow	Bonds	Myers	C
1925	Don't be a Nazi! / Be American...invest in war bonds!	Black, red	Nazis	Cochran	B
1926	Don't be a slave! / make your money work / for you! Buy war bonds!	Green, red	Bonds	Speede	A
1927	Don't be a spare / be a SPAR [thermographed]	Multicolored	SPARS	McCluney	A
1928	Don't be a squanderbug etc. [envelope 8 11/16x3 5/8 in.]	Unknown	Unk	ITE Circui	B
1929	Don't be a sucker!! / invest in war bonds!	Green, red	Bonds	Cochran	A
1930	Don't be an / "armchair patriot" / Battles / were / never etc. [handpainted]	Black	Home	Shaffer, A	C
1931	Don't be an / "armchair patriot" [handpainted]	Black	Home	Shaffer, A	C
1932	Don't be an old / financial wall flower. / Waltz out your dough—— etc.	Blue, red	Bonds	Quigley	B
1933	Don't be an old financial wall flower. / Waltz etc. [envelope 6 3/4x3 3/4 in.]	Blue	Bonds	Quigley	B
1934	Don't be an ostrich! / buy bonds for nest / eggs, and freedom!	Black	Bonds	Davis, D	A
1935	Don't be an unwitting Nazi agent! [handpainted]	Black	Home	Nichols	C
1936	Don't be fooled with / OPA- / [etc.] / Dec. 7, 1941, a date etc. [no picture]	Multicolored	Pearl	Linto	B
1937	Don't be fooled with / OPA-Administration's / subsidy plan. etc. [no picture]	Multicolored	Home	Linto	B
1938	Don't blow it / oh workman or scholar / hang on to your dollar etc.	Green, violet	Verse	Threl+Thar	A
1939	Don't destroy waste paper / Save our scrap / to etc. [env. 9 1/2x4 1/8 in.]	Black, red	Home	Mono Svc	C
1940	Don't disappoint the / [etc.] / 12-6-'44——Civil War going / on now in Greece!	Unknown	Event	Linto	B
1941	Don't disappoint the / the [sic] Devil. Give him / all the Jap rats / You etc.	Bicolor var	Devil	Linto	B
1942	Don't ever / lose that grin / soldier! [burned top, right edges] [handpainted]	Multicolored	Army	Cowdery	D
1943	Don't fence me in	Blue	Unk	Foster	A
1944	Don't fence me in [in quotes] / to Frisco conference / Russia	Multicolored	USSR	Peer	B
1945	Don't fence me in [thermographed]	Bicolor var	Hitle	Ang	A
1946	Don't flash this unless you mean it.	Bk,Bu/Bu,Red	VforV	Ang	A
1947	Don't forget / to buy a bunch of bonds etc. [no picture]	Green/Blue,	Bonds	Smith, W	A
1948	Don't forget the / boys over there / this Christmas [env 6 3/4x3 7/8 in.]	Unknown	Holid	Klondike	B
1949	Don't forget the / loyal service of / [etc.] / 11-3-'44——Antwerp now ready etc.	Multicolored	Event	Linto	B
1950	Don't forget the / loyal service of / the / AWVS	Multicolored	FlLib	Linto	B
1951	Don't forget the boys / in uniforms——they are / doing the etc. [no picture]	Silver/Gd,S	Armed	Linto	B
1952	Don't forget the boys / over there	Unknown	Unk	Baur	A
1953	Don't forget to write / to the boys who fight.	Black	Army	Unknown	A
1954	Don't forget: / to buy a bunch of bonds / to buy a bunch of bombs etc.	Blue, red	Shiel	Smith, W	A
1955	Don't grumble or growl / about your taxes—— / Think what you'd pay etc.	Blue	Home	Lawrence	A
1956	Don't hang up here, the fighting is down below.	Brown	Chute	Ang	A
1957	Don't hurry! / I'll / wait [handpainted]	Multicolored	Axis	Wolf, CL	B
1958	Don't jump, Mr. 4F / Working is fighting, too!	Blue, red	Home	Eichenlaub	A
1959	Don't just scratch! / dig right in, and buy war bonds	Blue, red	Bonds	Runge	A
1960	Don't let him / down now!	Unknown	Unk	Boone	A
1961	Don't let him down! / European peace / Politicians [handpainted]	Black	VEDay	Sturgill	F
1962	Don't let the Axis hypnotize you / buy war etc. [man, woman left or right]	Bicolor var	Bonds	Runge	A
1963	Don't let them down / buy bonds and keep 'em	Green/Red	Armed	Jarrett	A
1964	Don't relax——keep building / for national defense / A strong Navy etc. [thermographed]	Green	Navy	Sadworth	B
1965	Don't spend rashly. / Fight inflation.	Bk/Blue/Red	Home	Carter	A
1966	Don't talk about / ship cargoes / careless talk / costs lives	Blue, red	VforV	Lowell	A
1967	Don't telephone / during / air raid alarms etc. [no picture]	Black	Home	NY Tel Co	B
1968	Don't travel unless / absolutely / necessary / It may etc. [no picture]	Green	Home	Rowe	A
1969	Don't tread / on me [snake, 4 stars]	Unknown	Hist	Runge	A
1970	Don't tread on me [number of stars in battle standards and color of oval vary]	Bicolor var	Hist	Runge	A
1971	Don't tread on me [snake, 12 stars + 1 large star, all in oval]	Bk,Y/Bu,Red	Hist	Runge	A
1972	Don't tread on me [snake, 12 stars + eagle, no oval]	Blue, red	Hist	Runge	A
1973	Don't type your troubles etc. [eagle and shield]	Unknown	EagSh	Dailey	A

NO.	CACHET TEXT	COLOR	TOPIC	PUBLISHER	$
1974	Don't type your troubles etc. [eagle on perch]	Unknown	Eagle	Dailey	A
1975	Don't worry / soldier; / everything / is etc. [burned left edge] [handpainted]	Multicolored	Army	Cowdery	D
1976	Doolittle did it once. / He can do it again if you do more	Blue, red	Dool	Quigley	B
1977	Double dealing / U.S. tries to bring / [etc.] / 9-18-'44——U.S. patrol etc.	Multicolored	Event	Linto	B
1978	Double dealing / U.S. tries to bring / Argentina to time / England makes etc.	Multicolored	Flag	Linto	B
1979	Doubly wise man / There was a man in our town and / he knew what was etc.	Green, red	Verse	Threl+Thar	A
1980	Doubt is but fog, / however thick. / Faith is light, / however dim.	Multicolored	Relig	Linto	B
1981	Doug [in quotes] and "Ike" [handpainted]	Multicolored	Mac	Knoll	D
1982	Down below / is the Imperial Jap fleet etc.	Green	Japan	Abel	A
1983	Down the road to Tokyo and / Berlin etc.	Unknown	Unk	Brenn	A
1984	Down under / we're kicking / the Jap etc. [envelope 9 1/2x4 1/8 in.]	Unknown	Unk	Barg	C
1985	Down under / we're kicking / the Jap skin / in place of / the pig skin!	Unknown	Japan	James	B
1986	Draft age lowered to 18	Unknown	Event	Linto	B
1987	Dreaming / "Oh, to be in New England in the spring." [handpainted]	Black, red	Army	Unknown	B
1988	Dreaming / of you / every / night! [in quotes]	Black	Armed	Lupton	A
1989	Dreaming / of you! [in quotes]	Multicolored	Armed	Lupton	A
1990	Drop it! / Axis / aggression [colored envelopes]	Multicolored	Axis	Poppenger	A
1991	Dropping the pilot [handpainted]	Multicolored	Winst	Newton FN	C
1992	Duck, boys, duck!! / Thank God you don't / [etc.] / Leif Erikson Day etc.	Multicolored	Hist	Linto	B
1993	Duck, boys, duck!! / Thank God you don't have to / duck! All you have to etc.	Multicolored	Bonds	Linto	B
1994	Duty and / the beast [in quotes] [burned top edge] [handpainted]	Multicolored	Ordna	Cowdery	D
1995	Duty comes / first! [with or without 4 stars, top and bottom] [blue envelope]	Multicolored	Navy	Amer Art	A
1996	Duty loyal / first to serve	Unknown	Unk	Baur	A
1997	Duty, honor, country [in quotes] etc. [env. 6 15/16x3 15/16 in.]	Sepia tones	Hero	Belles-let	C

Cover Values (from Table 6, p. 136)

Value	Price Range
A	$ 3 - 6
B	$ 7 - 15
C	$ 16 - 30
D	$ 31 - 60
E	$ 61 - 125
F	$ 126 - 250
G	$ 251 - 500
H	$ 501 - 1000
I	$ >1000
X	Unpriced: Suspicious or fraudulent cover

1707

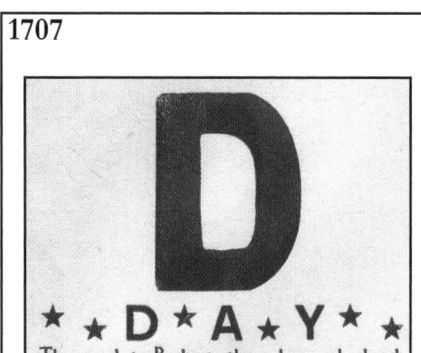

1727

1729

"D-DAY"

INVASION PRAYER

ALMIGHTY GOD, our Heavenly Father, especially do we pray for thy continued presence with our forces, giving them strength and courage, and granting them the Victory. We do not covet nor wish to kill. We want only PEACE! Thy will! Amen!

Richard Lee Wolf
325 Lindenwood Ave.,
Akron, 1, Ohio

1749

1751

DEC. 7 1941 - 1943

Two years of War

ITALY GERMANY JAPAN

1762

DEC. 11. 1941
U.S.A.
AT
WAR
WITH
GERMANY
AND ITALY

BUY DEFENSE SAVINGS BONDS AND STAMPS

Lewis W. Haskell Jr.,
Postmaster,
Auburn, Maine.

1778

Dedication of
POST OFFICE
NIMITZ, W. VA.
In Honor of Admiral Nimitz

1788

1811

1812

1844

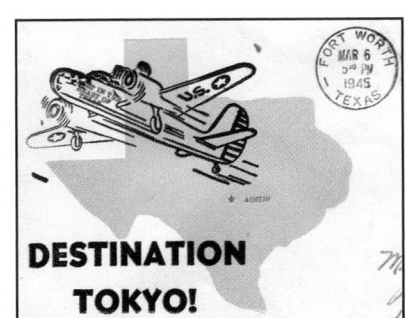

1886

1892

1901

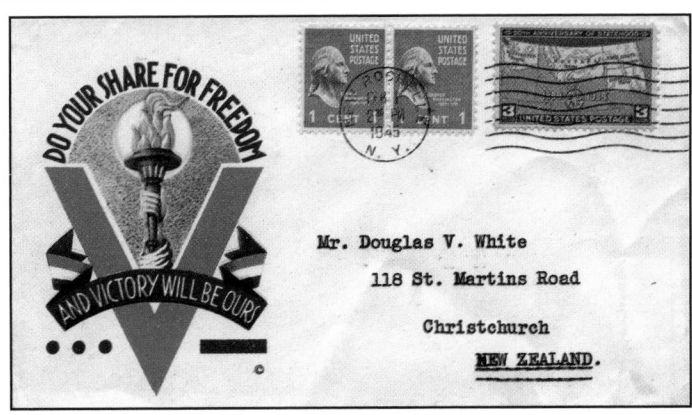

1903

1931

CACHET TEXT BEGINNING WITH "E"

NO.	CACHET TEXT	COLOR	TOPIC	PUBLISHER	$
1998	E Pluribus Unum	Unknown	Unk	Lohr	A
1999	E Pluribus Unum	Blue	Unk	Cabot	A
2000	E Pluribus Unum [copyright "C" w/, w/o serifs]	Multicolored	Home	Minkus	A
2001	E Pluribus Unum [handpainted]	Multicolored	EagFl	Knapp	H
2002	E.S. / R.A.F. [upper left] [blue envelope 7 1/2x3 7/8 in.]	Blue	Eagle	Unknown	H
2003	Each little error / gives etc. [label + red "Win the War" border]	Multicolored	Home	Unknown	B
2004	Each little error / gives etc.[label + blue "Victory" border]	Multicolored	Home	Unknown	B
2005	Each little error / gives etc.[label + red "Victory" border]	Multicolored	Home	Unknown	B
2006	Each little error / gives our / enemies / more / time!	Multicolored	Home	Amer Art	A
2007	Each penny digs the Axis / grave a little deeper [+ war bond Minute Man symbol]	Blue, red	Flag	Nichols	B
2008	Each stamp you buy will do its bit etc. [no picture]	Unknown	Home	Lowe	A
2009	Eager beaver / Eager beaver / invention no. 2: / "kick-in-the- / pants" etc.	Black/Blue	Home	Phill, CR	A
2010	Eagle on crossed rifle, sword, and lance	Blue	Eagle	Unknown	A
2011	Eagle standing on shield, ribbon through shield	Blue, red	EagSh	Krakora	A
2012	Eagle swooping, trailing 4 stars [handpainted]	Multicolored	Eagle	Adler	C
2013	Early Americans in full dress	Blue, red	Home	Brenn	A
2014	Easter	Blue	Holid	Brenn	A
2015	Easter / April 13	Multicolored	Holid	Linto	B
2016	Easter / greetings [chicks, flags, flowers, bunny]	Blue	Holid	Brenn	A
2017	Easter / greetings [eagle, flags, flowers]	Blue	Holid	Brenn	A
2018	Easy pickin. [handpainted]	Black	Axis	Wolf, CL	B
2019	Eat that! [envelope 6 7/8x4 in.]	Multicolored	Hitle	Unknown	B
2020	Eat. Drink. / Be merry. / For tomorrow / you may / die. [handpainted]	Multicolored	Hitle	Adler	D
2021	Eddie Rickenbacker / Great American ace aviator of World Wars I and II	Black	Hero	Pacific	B
2022	Edict is / sounded to / Japan [bicolor varieties]	Black, red	Event	Boone	B
2023	Edward / Kennedy / AP correspondent / He gave us the / news of surrender etc.	Sepia, silver	Army	Linto	B
2024	Edward J. Abel, 42141678	Black	Army	Abel	B
2025	Eighteen dollars seventy-five cents [$18.75] / will buy 25 dollar's [sic] etc.	Gold, green	Bonds	Linto	B
2026	Eighteen eighty-two [1882]-1945 / Roosevelt / F.D. Roosevelt etc.	Unknown	FDR	Linto	D
2027	Eighteenth [XVIII] Corps [under insignia] [handpainted]	Black, blue	Unit	Dannells	B
2028	Eighty thousand [80,000] enemy trapped / Cape Bon	Unknown	Hist	Linto	B
2029	Eisenhower / the name that heads etc.	Unknown	Ike	Runge	A
2030	Eisenhower announces / Nazis surrender etc. [thermographed]	Blue, red	VEDay	Boone	B
2031	El Salvador / United Nations [handpainted]	Multicolored	UN	Weigand	B
2032	Eleven overrun / Axis nations [handpainted]	Blue, red	Hitle	Unknown	B
2033	Eleventh [XI] Corps. [under insignia] [handpainted]	Multicolored	Unit	Dannells	B
2034	Eleven-thirty [11:30] a.m. / Eisenhower / in / Washington / June 18 / 1945	Blue, red	Ike	Fidelity	B
2035	Eliminate this / hideous / monster! / Just invest / in Uncle's / bonds!	Bicolor var	Japan	Linto	B
2036	Elliott Roosevelt's / dog given priority in / air transportation / over etc.	Unknown	FDR	Linto	B
2037	Ell's a-poppin' / for Hitler today / War bonds will make it hotter	Blue, red	Hitle	Boone	A
2038	Emblem / [etc.] / Let's / face / [etc.] / 2-17-'41——Four-year etc. [3 cachets]	Multicolored	Anniv	Linto	B
2039	Emblem / [etc.] / Let's / face / it / and with a smile. etc. [2 cachets]	Multicolored	Flag	Linto	B
2040	Emblem / of / justice, / freedom, / liberty, / equality, / America! [1 cachet]	Multicolored	Flag	Linto	B
2041	Emergency cargo ship / for British government/ Venture / launched / Sept. 27 1941	Black	Event	Unknown	C
2042	Emperor Hirohito issued a / a "cease fire order" and etc. [no picture] [handpainted]	Blue	VJDay	Batura	C
2043	Empire Occupation Forces - Japan [U.S.S. WV Ccard, cancel, 9/2/45] [Tokyo Bay]	Black	VJDay	Navy ship	E
2044	Empty! [handpainted] [stamp missing]	Multicolored	Army	Cowdery	D
2045	Encourage youths / to join / [etc.] / 11-1-'44——British land on southwest etc.	Multicolored	Event	Linto	B
2046	Encourage youths / to join the / Civil Air Patrol / Cadet Corps	Multicolored	Uncle	Linto	B
2047	Enemies will flee / by the etc.	Multicolored	Air	Amer Pat	A
2048	Enemy ears are listening / If you tell where he's going, / he may never etc.	Blue, red	Armed	Lowell	A
2049	Engineers	Brown	Armed	Huss	A
2050	Engineers / "miracle workers" [with or without V ···–] [thermographed]	Blue, red	Armed	Von Los	B

NO.	CACHET TEXT	COLOR	TOPIC	PUBLISHER	$
2051	Engineers / For Freedom's sake	Black, green	Army	Cozart	A
2052	England / Factories, sold out / to Germany, point their / deadly product etc.	Black	ORN	Coll Surp	B
2053	Enlighten children! / Better to nauseate our / children now with the etc.	Multicolored	Flag	Linto	B
2054	Enlist in the / volunteer port / [etc.] / 11-6-'44——U.S. bombers / raid etc.	Multicolored	Event	Linto	B
2055	Enlist in the / volunteer port / security force / ···–	Multicolored	FlLib	Linto	B
2056	Enlist your dog / for defense!	Brown	Dog	Huss	A
2057	Entering the domain of Neptunus Rex [Fleet emblem] [thermographed]	Red	Navy	Crosby	B
2058	Entering the domain of Neptunus Rex [Navy emblem] [thermographed]	Blue	Navy	Crosby	B
2059	Entering the domain of Neptunus Rex [Seabees emblem] [thermographed]	Unknown	Navy	Crosby	B
2060	Equality [vertical]	Gd,Vi/Gn,Vi	Minut	Linto	B
2061	Equality [vertical] / 8-31-'40——Airliner crashed at / Lovettsville, Va. 21 etc.	Multicolored	Minut	Linto	B
2062	Equality! Where? / June 8, 1945 / Pres. Truman says etc. [no picture]	Multicolored	Home	Linto	B
2063	Eradicate Huns' love / for the sword / with the / sword [no picture]	Red, silver	Nazis	Linto	B
2064	Ernie / Pyle / Brave / Men / Guam. (AP) Ernie Pyle / the GI's columnist etc.	Black/Red	Pyle	Brenn	B
2065	Ernie Pyle	Unknown	Pyle	Linto	B
2066	Ernie Pyle / famous war / correspondent / and G.I.'s / friend, killed by etc.	Sepia, violet	Pyle	Linto	B
2067	Ernie Pyle / killed in action / A better understanding	Black	Pyle	Davis, D	B
2068	Ernie Pyle / the best known and most loved etc.	Blue/Red	Pyle	Brenn	B
2069	Ernie Pyle / We will have won this war etc.	Purple/Red	Pyle	Brenn	A
2070	Eternal vigilance / is the / price of liberty [in quotes] etc.	Blue, red	Hist	Boone	A
2071	Ethiopia / United Nations [handpainted]	Multicolored	UN	Weigand	B
2072	European aces / Capt. / John T. Godfrey / age 22 / (Woonsocket, R.I.) / 8th Air etc.	Black	Hero	Coll Surp	A
2073	European aces / Capt. Henry W. Brown / age 21 / (Arlington, Va) / 9th Air Force etc.	Black	Hero	Coll Surp	A
2074	European aces / Col. Glenn E. Duncan / age 25 / (Houston, Tex) / etc.	Blue	Hero	Coll Surp	A
2075	European aces / Col. Glenn E. Duncan / age 25 / (Houston, Tex.) etc.	Blue	Hero	Coll Surp	A
2076	European aces / Col. Hubert Zemke, / age 31 / (Missoula, Mont) / 8th Air Force	Black	Hero	Coll Surp	A
2077	European aces / Col. Hubert Zemke, / age 31 / (Missoula, Mont) etc.	Black/Blue	Hero	Coll Surp	A
2078	European aces / Lt. Col. / David C. Schilling / age 26 / (Travers City,) etc.	Black	Hero	Coll Surp	A
2079	European aces / Lt. Col. Francis S. Gabreski / age 25 / (Oil City, Pa.) / 8th Air etc.	Black	Hero	Coll Surp	A
2080	European aces / Lt. Col. John C. Meyer / age 25 / (Forest Hills, N.Y.) etc.	Bk/Bu/Pu	Hero	Coll Surp	A
2081	European aces / Maj. / Duane W. Beeson / (Boise, Idaho) etc.	Black/Blue	Hero	Coll Surp	A
2082	European aces / Maj. / Fred J. / Christensen, Jr. / age 22 etc.	Black	Hero	Coll Surp	A
2083	European aces / Maj. George E. / Preddy, / age 25 / (Greensboro, N.C.) etc.	Black	Hero	Coll Surp	A
2084	European Aces / Maj. John S. Gentile - age 22 / (Piqua, Ohio) etc.	Black/Blue	Hero	Coll Surp	A
2085	European aces / Maj. Robert S. Johnson, / age 25 / (Lawton, Okla) etc.	Black/Purple	Hero	Coll Surp	A
2086	European bombings / Aleutians / The south Pacific etc. [hp] [text typed]	Multicolored	Armed	Griffith	B
2087	Europe's D-Day - June 6, 1944 / but look etc. [no picture]	Unknown	DDay	Abel	B
2088	Even he / bought / bonds	Black	Bonds	Burdick	A
2089	Even in / practice / maneuvers you men / make etc. [burned edge] [handpainted]	Multicolored	Hitl	Cowdery	D
2090	Even tho our boys are / [etc.] / 8-6-'44——Yanks take Brittany! / Nazis try etc.	Multicolored	Event	Linto	B
2091	Even tho our boys are / doing a magnificent job / the "sovereign" people's etc.	Gold, green	FDR	Linto	B
2092	Even vultures / are fussy!! [handpainted]	Multicolored	Hitle	White, TM	F
2093	Eventually	Blue, red	Axis	Hill	A
2094	Ever onward!	Blue, red	Unk	Mission	A
2095	Ever watchful and alert / defending for us / our liberties	Black/Blue	Navy	Harrington	A
2096	Every "floating" dollar supports the enemy-- / Keep putting yours etc.	Blue	Bonds	Quigley	A
2097	Every bond / means another etc.	Blue	Bonds	Burdick	A
2098	Every bond you buy / is a nail etc.	Blue, red	Flag	Kosko	A
2099	Every day is moveing [sic] day to me!	Black, red	Hitle	Lowe	A
2100	Every fire / is sabotage / today! / [etc.] / Columbus Day——Oct. 12, '43 etc.	Multicolored	Event	Linto	B
2101	Every fire / is sabotage / today! / Prevent fires	Gd,Gn/Gn,S	Home	Linto	B
2102	Every fire / is sabotage / today! / Prevent fires	Green, purple	Home	Linto	B
2103	Every night / about this time - / Oh! How I miss you! [handpainted]	Black	Army	Parker	B
2104	Every payday / buy / V / war / bonds etc. [no picture]	Unknown	Bonds	Leonhard	A

NO.	CACHET TEXT	COLOR	TOPIC	PUBLISHER	$
2105	Every portion of our country finds the / most commanding [in quotes] etc.	Blue, red	Hist	Boone	A
2106	Everybody / every pay day / 10% [handpainted]	Multicolored	Home	Knapp	G
2107	Everything considered / where would you prefer / [etc.] / 7-4-'44——Chinese etc.	Multicolored	Event	Linto	B
2108	Everything considered / where would you prefer / to live? America? etc.	Multicolored	Ordna	Linto	B
2109	Everything Hokay! when you by war / bonds and stamps! [handpainted]	Multicolored	Air	Parker	B
2110	Everything's / under control / when my soldier's / on the job. [handpainted]	Multicolored	Army	Cowdery	D
2111	Evidently freedom is not / intended for / [etc.] / 8-5-'44——38 Jap ships etc.	Unknown	Event	Linto	B
2112	Evidently freedom is not / intended for the fighting / forces!! / Congress etc.	Unknown	Home	Linto	B
2113	Evil backed by force / may prevail for a time / yet / right and truth etc.	Multicolored	Liber	Lowell	A
2114	Example of "Der / Master Race". / National Zoo. [handpainted]	Black	Hitle	Parker	C
2115	Exit gangster / number one	Green	Musso	Neal	A
2116	Extra / ! / Berlin falls, city in flames / and ruins. Tokio you are next	Green	Event	Abel	B
2117	Extra / Buy extra / war bonds / Paris hails Allied army! etc. [colored envelopes]	Black, red	Event	Temple	C
2118	Extra / Buy extra / war bonds / Warsaw falls to Red Army!!!!!! etc. [pink envelope]	Black	USSR	Temple	B
2119	Extra / Buy extra / war bonds / Warsaw liberated, January etc. [colored envelopes]	Black	Event	Temple	C
2120	Extra! / Japan / defeated / surrenders	Blue, red	VJDay	Kosko	B
2121	Extra! / Japan / surrenders	Green, red	VJDay	Kosko	B
2122	Eyes on the alert / the Coast Guard	Multicolored	Coast	Amer Pat	A
2123	Eyes right! [in quotes] [yellow envelope]	Multicolored	Army	Amer Art	A
2124	Eyes right! [soldier, cap flying off, looking at passing woman] [handpainted]	Multicolored	Army	Dannells	C

Cover Values (from Table 6, p. 136)

Value	Price Range
A	$ 3 - 6
B	$ 7 - 15
C	$ 16 - 30
D	$ 31 - 60
E	$ 61 - 125
F	$ 126 - 250
G	$ 251 - 500
H	$ 501 - 1000
I	$ >1000
X	Unpriced: Suspicious or fraudulent cover

2000

2001

Don Buxton,
760 Caledonia,
Dubuque,
Iowa.

2002

2020

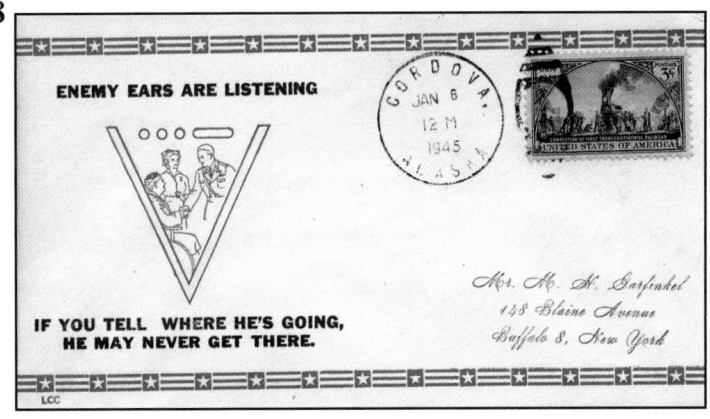

EAT. DRINK.
Be Merry.
For Tomorrow
you MAY
DIE.

2034

11.30 A. M.

EISENHOWER

IN

WASHINGTON

June 18

1945

2048

ENEMY EARS ARE LISTENING

IF YOU TELL WHERE HE'S GOING,
HE MAY NEVER GET THERE.

2050

Engineers

"Miracle Workers"

2070

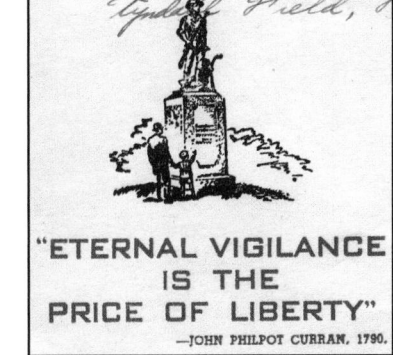

"ETERNAL VIGILANCE
IS THE
PRICE OF LIBERTY"
—JOHN PHILPOT CURRAN. 1790.

2074

2080

2085

2092

2093

2120

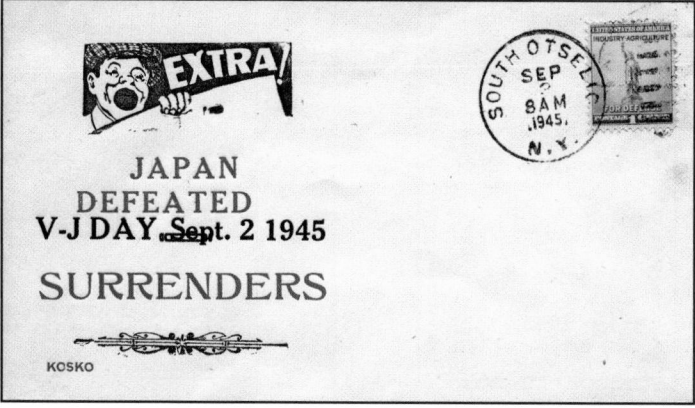

2123

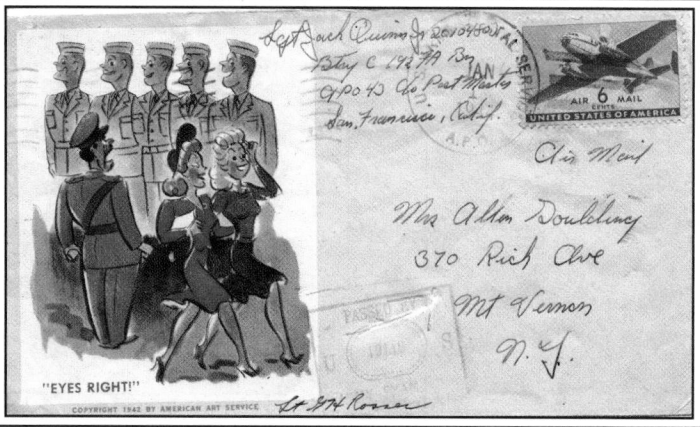

2124

CACHET TEXT BEGINNING WITH "F"

NO.	CACHET TEXT	COLOR	TOPIC	PUBLISHER	$
2125	F.D.R. / Clipper / round trip / U.S. / to / Africa etc. [no picture]	Blue, red	Event	Fidelity	B
2126	F.D.R. / dies / Nation mourns President / Franklin D. / [etc.] / April 12, 1945	Multicolored	FDR	Teixeira	F
2127	F.D.R. / Stalin / Churchill / agree on 3 fronts / [etc.] / Tehran [no picture]	Black, red	Event	Fidelity	B
2128	F.D.R. / Stalin / Churchill / Black Sea 2-7-45 [no picture]	Black, red	Event	Fidelity	B
2129	F.D.R.——1932 / "We must guard against / monopoly" / Today we have more etc.	Unknown	FDR	Linto	B
2130	F.D.R.——1932 / "We must guard against" / [etc.] / 10-19-'44——Tokyo reports etc.	Unknown	Event	Linto	B
2131	F.R.S. Normandie, / seized at anchorage / by U.S. May 16, 1941.	Blue	Event	Unknown	C
2132	Face saving peace feelers / You haven't quite got the idea etc. [handpainted]	Black	Japan	Sturgill	E
2133	FADM Ernest King	Unknown	Admir	Linto	B
2134	Fairfax / Corps of Engineers —— U.S. Army / on the job etc. [thermographed]	Red	Army	Sadworth	B
2135	Faith [in quotes] [mother, son, flag, airplanes]	Blue	Home	Huss	A
2136	Faith [with or without Huss imprint on back]	Blue	Symb+	Huss	A
2137	Faith hope / and charity / with prayer / are especially needed in / these etc.	Gold, silver	Relig	Linto	B
2138	Faith lost in / OPA / They do not / [etc.] / 1-1-'45——Byrnes urges etc.	Multicolored	Home	Linto	B
2139	Faith lost in / OPA / They do not / keep their word	Multicolored	Flag	Linto	B
2140	Fala / Don't kick my dog around!	Black	Dog	Gantz	A
2141	Fall in! / we're on the march / our goal is / victory	Multicolored	Armed	Ever Ready	A
2142	False report of / Jap surrender by etc. [thermographed]	Unknown	VJDay	Boone	B
2143	Fancy having some / of these things / [etc.] / Victory fleet day etc.	Multicolored	Navy	Linto	B
2144	Fancy having some / of these things fall- / ing around you! / How about etc.	Multicolored	Bonds	Linto	B
2145	Far away from the USA / serving etc.	Unknown	Armed	McCluney	A
2146	Farewell to the pilot / who brought us safely / within etc. [handpainted]	Multicolored	FDR	Knapp	G
2147	Fascism or democracy? / [etc.] / 1-18-'45——Japs lose 24 more / ships in etc.	Unknown	Event	Linto	B
2148	Fascism or democracy? / Drew Pearson——Sun., Jan. 14—— / quoting Hannigan etc.	Unknown	Flag	Linto	B
2149	Fascist / regime is / dissolved etc. [thermographed]	Unknown	Event	Boone	B
2150	Father's Day June 17 / [etc.] / There'll be home bonds etc.	Red	Bonds	Burdick	A
2151	Fats that once went down the / drain / Saves [sic] our soldiers scars etc.	Blue, red	Verse	Brenn	A
2152	FDR and Churchill meet in Quebec	Unknown	Event	Linto	B
2153	FDR and Giraud meet in D.C.	Unknown	Event	Linto	B
2154	FDR signs tax bill	Unknown	FDR	Linto	B
2155	FDR-Churchill-Chiang Kai Shek meet	Unknown	Event	Linto	B
2156	Fear / speech / press / religion / the four freedoms	Unknown	Unk	Baur	A
2157	Fear want / religion speech / Let freedom ring!	Multicolored	Globe	Cachet Cra	A
2158	Fearless / Democratic / Reliable / FDR [thermographed]	Unknown	FDR	Crosby	B
2159	Feather your nest with / war bonds	Black/Blue	Bonds	Huss	A
2160	Feb. 04th / 1945 / Manila / Freedom / rings again for the / Philippines etc.	Multicolored	Symb+	Fluegel	C
2161	Feb. 04th to 12th 1945 / The Yalta Conference [thermographed]	Multicolored	Heads	Unknown	C
2162	Feb. 14, 1943 / Russians captured / Rostov [no picture]	Blue, gold	Event	Linto	B
2163	Feb. 17, 1942 / Singapore / surrendered / to Japs [no picture]	Brown, green	Event	Linto	B
2164	Feb. 17, 1945 / United States flag / again / [etc.] / Corregidor etc. [handpainted]]	Multicolored	Anniv	Smith, LH	C
2165	Feb. 22, 1945 [handpainted]	Multicolored	Holid	Shaffer, A	C
2166	Feb. 24, 1942 / U.S. planes raid / Wake Island [no picture]	Multicolored	Event	Linto	B
2167	Feb. 28, 1942 / United Nations / defeated in / Java Sea battle [no picture]	Multicolored	Event	Linto	B
2168	February 13, 1945 / Nichols airfield and / Cavite now controlled / by MacArthur's etc.	Gold, silver	Event	Linto	B
2169	February 18, 1945 / We secure / our positions / on / Iwo etc. [no picture]	Red, yellow	Event	Fidelity	B
2170	February 23, 1945 / Turkey / wars / Germany / and Japan etc. [no picture]	Blue, red	Event	Fidelity	B
2171	February 25, 1945 / Egypt at war / (its Premier assassinated) etc. [no picture]	Blue, red	Event	Fidelity	B
2172	Feed em bonds / They will lay the eggs [handpainted]	Multicolored	Air	Adler	D
2173	Feed the flame of freedom etc.	Blue, red	Unk	Garfinkel	A
2174	Feeding the fishes! [in quotes]	Black	Navy	Lupton	A
2175	Fewer and fewer / grow the / days of / Der Fuehrer!	Multicolored	Hitle	Wolf, CL	A
2176	Field Marshall Montgomery	Blue, gold	Ally	Runge	A
2177	Fifth [5th] Div. [below red diamond shoulder sleeve insignia] [handpainted]	Black, red	Unit	Dannells	B
2178	Fifth [5th] war loan / Hawaii will do it again!	Red	VforV	Sayama	B
2179	Fifth [5th] war loan / V ··· [handpainted]	Multicolored	Bonds	Klaas	D
2180	Fifth [5th] war loan drive / "Make it hot for the Japa-Nazi" [handpainted]	Multicolored	Bonds	Dannells	C
2181	Fifth [5th] year of Chinese / resistance etc.	Black	China	Wash Stamp	A
2182	Fifth Marines / First Marine Division / Fleet Marine Force / First Day etc.	Black	USMC	Czubay	D
2183	Fifth war loan / Another war loan drive etc.	Unknown	Bonds	Abel	A

NO.	CACHET TEXT	COLOR	TOPIC	PUBLISHER	$
2184	Fifty [50] yrs / serving America / entertainment / and news / now serving etc.	Blue, red	Home	Poppenger	A
2185	Fifty thousand / planes for / national defense / Masters of / the air....	Blue, red	Air	Linprint	A
2186	Fight / infantile / paralysis / your patriotic duty [handpainted]	Multicolored	Home	Price, EK	C
2187	Fight- / work- / save [handpainted]	Multicolored	VforV	Adler	D
2188	Fight bombs with fog [no picture] [envelope 9 1/2x4 1/8 in.]	Blue, red	Home	Fog	C
2189	Fight for freedom [handpainted] [no picture]	Blue, red	Home	Unknown	B
2190	Fight for victory [thermographed]	Blue/Red	Eagle	Farnam	A
2191	Fight it out / on this line / Gear yourself in etc. [label + printed border]	Multicolored	Home	Artists	B
2192	Fight the war / and build the country etc.	Black	China	Farnam	A
2193	Fight, / give and / live for / [etc.] / 9-13-'40——Buckingham Palace etc.	Multicolored	Anniv	Linto	B
2194	Fight, / give and / live for / God and / America	Gold/Gd,S	Flag	Linto	B
2195	Fightin' words! etc. [slogans vary, series of 12]	Blue, red	Uncle	Levering	A
2196	Fighting / for liberty! [6 stars at top]	Black, red	Armed	Davis, Ral	A
2197	Fighting / for victory! [11 stars at top]	Black, red	Armed	Davis, Ral	A
2198	Fighting / to free / the peoples [handpainted]	Multicolored	EagSh	Adler	D
2199	Fighting for / freedom's sake [symbol of branch of service]	Unknown	Armed	Cozart	A
2200	Fighting for / victory! [13 stars at top]	Unknown	Unk	Davis, Ral	A
2201	Fighting for liberty	Unknown	Unk	Davis, Ral	A
2202	Fighting for victory [w/, w/o copyright "C"] [fingers make "V" above heads]	Blue, red	Armed	Cachet Cra	A
2203	Fighting for you and me	Unknown	Unk	Ang	A
2204	Fighting Marines [in quotes] / 2nd. Marine Division [thermographed]	Red, yellow	USMC	Crosby	B
2205	Fighting Squadron [includes space for label] [thermographed]	Unknown	Air	Sadworth	B
2206	Fighting Squadron 3	Black	Armed	McCluney	A
2207	Fighting watchdogs / at home and overseas / [etc.] / Coast / Guard etc.	Blue, red	Coast	Bean	A
2208	Fill it up / I said! / Nixsky! / No more / gas for / you, / Adolf!	Black	Hitle	Roberts	A
2209	Final victory / Americans / don't quit etc.	Unknown	Unk	Lowell	A
2210	Final victory / The Rising Sun was permanently / eclipsed by an atom.	Multicolored	VJDay	Runge	B
2211	Finis! / World War II [no picture] [overprinted diagonally on other cachets]	Green	VJDay	Muzzy	B
2212	Finis! / World War II [picture: amphibious landing or soldier on train]	Green	VJDay	Muzzy	B
2213	Finished / Germany surrenders to the Allies. / May 8th 1945. [handpainted] [pen & ink]	Black	VEDay	Hines	D
2214	Finished! / Look at 'em!! / U.S. war bonds and stamps / will finish the etc.	Multicolored	Axis	Linto	B
2215	Finished! / Three tyrants sought to rule / the world / Look at 'em!!	Multicolored	Axis	Linto	B
2216	Finns shoot / down a / Russian plane. [handpainted] [postmarked 11/13/39]	Blue, red	Air	Unknown	F
2217	Fire away	Unknown	Unk	Hillerich	A
2218	Fire away [thermographed]	Unknown	Unk	Ang	A
2219	Firepower for Eisenhower [thermographed]	Unknown	Ike	McCluney	A
2220	First / atomic bomb / dropped / United States dropps [sic] first etc. [8/6/45]	Multicolored	Atom	Teixeira	E
2221	First / Cavalry Divison / Leyte / Luzon [artist: Knapp]	Black, red	Symb+	Buckalew	C
2222	First / cover / Keep / U.S.A. / out of war / Write your etc. [postmarked 9/39]	Multicolored	Neutr	Butzen	F
2223	First / dictator to fall / Benito Mussolini / Mussolini resigned / as etc.	Blue, red	Musso	Boone	A
2224	First / win / the / victory / [etc.] / Navy Day——Oct. 27, 1943	Multicolored	Navy	Linto	B
2225	First / win / the / victory / then the / peace! [multicolor varieties]	Multicolored	VforV	Linto	B
2226	First / win / the / war [stenciled]	Black, red	Home	Wolf,CL	A
2227	First [1st] / D-Day / Anniversary / One year ago today / Allies invaded etc.	Multicolored	Anniv	Teixeira	D
2228	First [1st] post office named in honor Gen. MacArthur / MacArthur etc. (in circle) [UL]	Black	MacFD	Unknown	C
2229	First [1st] U.S. Infantry Division / [etc.] / Algeria / Tunisia / Sicily etc.	Multicolored	Unit	Teixeira	C
2230	First aid [handpainted]	Multicolored	Army	Miller	B
2231	First American serviceman / to lose both hands and / feet in battle. World War II etc.	Blue, red	Hero	Layne	B
2232	First American soldier killed at Hawaii / Robert Niedzwiecki was the etc.	Red	Pearl	Unknown	A
2233	First anniversary / of / D / Day is / here / heir lives / are etc. [no picture]	Blue, red	DDay	Threl+Thar	B
2234	First anniversary / Pearl Harbor / attack / 1941-1942 [with other cachets]	Blue/Magenta	Pearl	Navy Yard	B
2235	First anniversary of the declaration of war [typed] [12/8/42]	Black	Home	Sievert	B
2236	First anniversary of the declaration of war against Japan [typed] [12/8/42]	Black	Home	Sievert	B
2237	First anniversary of the yellow / swine's vicious attack on / Pearl Harbor etc.	Multicolored	Pearl	Linto	B
2238	First anniversary U.S. declaration of war / against Japan 12-8-41 [UL] [typed]	Black	Pearl	Unknown	B
2239	First Cavalry Division	Black, gold	Unit	McCluney	A
2240	First Cavalry Division / enters / Manila	Multicolored	Event	McCluney	B
2241	First Cavalry Division / enters Manila	Multicolored	Event	McCluney	B
2242	First day / BPO / Newfoundland	Purple	Bases	Unknown	D
2243	First day / in commission [thermographed]	Blue, red	Navy	Sadworth	B
2244	First day / MacArthur / Post Office [campaign ribbons, cap, glasses, corn cob pipe] [hp]	Multicolored	MacFD	Unknown	D
2245	First day / new post office / MacArthur / Raleigh county / [etc.] / cancelation	Blue, red	MacFD	Sanders	C

NO.	CACHET TEXT	COLOR	TOPIC	PUBLISHER	$
2246	First Day / Nimitz, W. Va. / post office / named in honor of / Admiral etc. [handp]	Multicolored	NimFD	Bayliss	C
2247	First day / postal service / Rifle range, MCB, San Diego, Calif. [thermogr]	Red	USMC	Crosby	B
2248	First day / War-time Saving / February 9, 1942 etc. [env. 9 1/2x4 1/8 in.]	Unknown	Event	Unknown	B
2249	First Day cancelation / Atlantic Amphibious Force (equipped etc.) [thermo]	Blue, red	Flag	Smith, W	B
2250	First Day cancellation / Post Office, Camp Pendleton / [etc.] / Corps [thermographed]	Red	USMC	Crosby	B
2251	First day cancellation / Post office, Camp Pendleton, Oceanside, etc. [thermographed]	Red	USMC	Crosby	B
2252	First day cancellation at / ——MacArthur, Raleigh County—— / 1942 etc.	Black	MacFD	Unknown	C
2253	First day cover in honor of General Douglas MacArthur etc. [at lower edge]	Blue, red	MacFD	Unknown	C
2254	First day Jap sub cover / Jap two-man submarine / captured over etc. [thermogr]	Blue, red	Japan	Crosby	B
2255	First day Jap sub cover / Japanese two-man sub etc. [thermographed]	Green, red	Japan	Crosby	B
2256	First day mail service / at MacArthur, W. Va. / April 15, 1942 / America etc.	Black, blue	MacFD	Zunks	C
2257	First day post office dedication / in honor of etc. [with date] [thermographed]	Bu/R/Blue,Re	MacFD	Crosby	C
2258	First day post office dedication / in honor of etc. [without date] [thermographed]	Bk/Bu/Gn/R/	MacFD	Crosby	C
2259	First day post office dedication / MacArthur, etc. [3 line heading] [thermographed]	Bu/Gd/R	MacFD	Crosby	C
2260	First day post office dedication / MacArthur, etc. [4 line heading] [thermographed]	Bu, R/Gd/Si	MacFD	Crosby	C
2261	First day post office etc. General Douglas etc. [double cachet] [thermographed]	Pur-1, gold-2	MacFD	Crosby	E
2262	First draft number / 158 / They shall not pass / On etc. [postmarked 10/29/40]	Multicolored	Event	Linprint	D
2263	First Fighter Command [no picture] [handpainted]	Multicolored	Unit	Barwicki	B
2264	First flag on Mt. Suribachi / was photographed by S/Sgt. Louis R. etc. [handpainted]	Multicolored	Event	Knapp	G
2265	First God / then our / America	Unknown	Liber	Linto	B
2266	First in war - first in peace / first in the hearts / of our countrymen.	Blue, red	Wash	Ander, EA	A
2267	First in war / first in peace / first in the hearts / of our countrymen.	Blue, red	Symb+	Ander, EA	A
2268	First in war in peace / first in etc. [thermographed]	Unknown	Wash	Baur	A
2269	First in war. First in peace. / First in the hearts of his countrymen. [thermographed]	Blue, red	Wash	Baur	A
2270	First lady of the world / "Mme Chiang" / Buy War Bonds [handpainted]	Multicolored	China	Knoll	C
2271	First line of defense / United States Navy [thermographed]	Br/Green	Navy	Crosby	B
2272	First line of defense / United States Navy / U.S. Marines, etc. [thermographed]	Red	USMC	Crosby	B
2273	First Marine Division / Fleet Marine Force / U.S. Marine Corp. etc. [thermographed]	Red	USMC	Czubay	C
2274	First Marines / First Marine Division / Fleet Marine Force / first day etc.	Black	USMC	Czubay	D
2275	First Marines / First Marine Division / Fleet Marine Force / First etc. [thermographed]	Black	USMC	Czubay	D
2276	First official / MacArthur Day / June 13, 1942	Unknown	Mac	Unknown	B
2277	First peacetimer drawing / for selective military etc. [on cacheted cover]	Black	Event	Unknown	B
2278	First to fight	Black	USMC	Lupton	A
2279	First victory then peace forever [engraved]	Red	VforV	Huss	B
2280	First woman in American Army / Deborah Sampson Gannett / [etc.] / 1781 etc.	Black	Women	Unknown	A
2281	Five [5] days / Mrs. Ray R. Cowdery / Long Prairie, Minn. [handpainted]	Multicolored	Home	Cowdery	D
2282	Five [5] years war with Japan / 1937 / 1942 / "Fight the war" etc.	Multicolored	China	Fleetwood	B
2283	Five star launchings / [etc.] / Dionne / quintuplets / of Canada etc. [thermographed]	Blue, red	VforV	Unknown	B
2284	Flag day / at Old Glory, Texas / June 14th, 1941 / "Let's defend it"	Blue, red	Flag	Zunks	B
2285	Flag day / June 14 [postmarked 6/14/41]	Multicolored	Flag	Linto	B
2286	Flag day / June 14th / Be American etc.	Unknown	Flag	Unknown	A
2287	Flag Day / June 14th / Betsy Ross House, Arch / Street, Philadelphia, Pa.	Blue, red	Flag	Ioor	A
2288	Flag day / June fourteenth [flag being sewn or crossed flags]	Blue, red	Flag	Ioor	A
2289	Flag Day [in quotes] / [etc.] / A.P.O. No. 801 A / Newfoundland [6/14/41] thermo]	Unknown	Bases	Hutnick	C
2290	Flag Day [in quotes] / [etc.] / A.P.O. No. 803 A / Trinidad [6/14/41] thermo]	Unknown	Bases	Hutnick	C
2291	Flag day rites / A great nation! / A great defense! [6/14/40] [thermographed]	Blue, red	Flag	Unknown	B
2292	Flag of free	Purple	Flag	Dime	A
2293	Flag of freedom / long may it wave	Blue	Flag	Abel	A
2294	Flag of the free / Fight to keep it free.	Blue, red	Flag	Unknown	A
2295	Flag of the free heart's hope etc.	Blue, red	Flag	Card	A
2296	Flag of the free. / Fight to keep it free.	Blue, red	Flag	Unknown	A
2297	Flag raising over Berlin / On July 4, 1945, the / American flag was etc.	Multicolored	Flag	Fluegel	C
2298	Flash / Germany / surrenders [broadcaster in V]	Blue, red	VEDay	Lowell	C
2299	Flash / Japan surrenders [broadcaster in V]	Unknown	VJDay	Lowell	C
2300	Flash / No matter what / [etc.] / Allies drop paratroops into Netherlands [colored envs.]	Black	Event	McCluney	C
2301	Flash / No matter what / [etc.] / Yanks invade Okinawa Jima in the Ryukyus etc.	Black	Event	Temple	C
2302	Flash / no matter what / the news: buy more / [etc.] / Germany surrenders!	Black	VEDay	Temple	B
2303	Flash! / Germany / surrenders	Blue, red	VEDay	Brenn	B
2304	Flash! / Germany / unconditionally / surrenders!	Blue, red	VEDay	Brenn	B
2305	Flash! / Japan / surrenders!	Blue, red	VJDay	Brenn	B
2306	Flash! / Japan / unconditionally / surrenders!	Blue, red	VJDay	Brenn	B
2307	Flash! / Japan surrenders!	Blue, red	VJDay	Brenn	B

NO.	CACHET TEXT	COLOR	TOPIC	PUBLISHER	$
2308	Flash!! / Hitler's Europe / invaded!! [Portland, Oregon postmark 6/6/44]	Gold, silver	DDay	Linto	C
2309	Fleet Adm. / Ernest / King / 3/1/'45——Yanks land / on Palawan Island	Unknown	Admir	Linto	B
2310	Florence / land / of the / Renaissance / emerges as / Nazi / control / ends	Aqua, red	Event	Griffith	B
2311	Florida centennial / 1845 1945 / [etc.] / Commemorating / V-J Day etc.	Blue, red	VJDay	Unknown	B
2312	Florida centennial / 1845 1945 / World War II is over / Japan surrenders etc.	Blue, red	VJDay	Unknown	B
2313	Flotilla 28 / Somewhere / with the Navy	Blue	Navy	Unknown	B
2314	Flowers / for / der Fuehrer / "War stamps" [handpainted]	Multicolored	Ordna	Adler	D
2315	Fly high with / Let's go! USA / keep 'em etc. [thermographed]	Red	Unk	Crosby	B
2316	Fly high with the / U.S. Army [thermographed]	Red	Air	Crosby	B
2317	Fly high with the / U.S. Navy [thermographed]	Unknown	Unk	Crosby	B
2318	Fly high with the U.S.M.C. / [etc.] / Second Marine Division, Camp etc. [thermogr]	Red	USMC	Crosby	B
2319	Fly high with the U.S.M.C. / Let's go! U.S.A. etc. [thermographed]	Red	USMC	Crosby	B
2320	Fly high, sky high / with / United States Air Force etc. [thermographed]	Gold	Air	Crosby	B
2321	Flying / circus [in quotes] [vertical] / "King of the heavies" [handpainted]	Multicolored	Globe	Unknown	C
2322	Flying / for victory	Blue, red	Air	Davis, Ral	A
2323	Flying / steel V ···– / The Robot [thermographed]	Unknown	Unk	Von Los	B
2324	Flying again over Manila	Unknown	Flag	Ang	A
2325	Flying Tiger [in quotes] Chennault [thermographed]	Brown	Gener	Crosby	B
2326	Flying to victory / with the U.S. / Air Corps	Green	Eagle	Neal	A
2327	Follow me	Bu,R/Bu,Si	Army	Cozart	A
2328	Follow me	Blue, red	Army	Unknown	A
2329	Follow our [flag] earn your [wings] / support the [army] and the [navy] etc.	Blue, red	Symb+	Boothroyd	A
2330	Fondly do we hope, / fervently do we pray, that the mighty etc.	Multicolored	Linc	Grifith	A
2331	Fondly do we hope, fervently do we pray etc.	Unknown	Unk	Baur	A
2332	Food / fights / for / freedom / Grow / [etc.] / Make gardens etc. [no picture]	Unknown	Home	Carpenter	A
2333	Food / fights / for / freedom / Grow more for '44 [no picture]	Green, red	Home	Carpenter	A
2334	Food / fights / for / freedom / More / [etc.] / Make gardens etc. [no picture]	Multicolored	Home	Carpenter	A
2235	Food / fights / for / freedom / More victory gardens / in 1944 [no picture]	Green, purple	Home	Carpenter	A
2336	Food / fights / for freedom [handpainted]	Multicolored	Home	Myers	B
2337	Food / for freedom	Gold, silver	Home	Linto	B
2338	Food / for freedom / ——9-9-'44——Yanks clearing way / to the Philippines	Multicolored	Event	Linto	B
2339	Food fights for freedom	Bk/Bu/R	Armed	Smith, AD	A
2340	Food for / victory [handpainted]	Multicolored	Home	Knapp	G
2341	Food for freedom [handpainted]	Multicolored	Home	Knapp	G
2342	Food for victory.	Blue, red	Home	Baur	A
2343	Food is / ammunition. / Use it sparingly! [no picture]	Black	Home	Phill, CR	A
2344	Food is a weapon / Don't waste it! / Buy wisely-cook carefully-eat it all	Green/Violet	Home	Linto	B
2345	Footholds. / France	Multicolored	UncAx	Adler	D
2346	For / American liberty / then, now and / the future	Blue, brown	Bell	Carpenter	A
2347	For / buy more war bonds [fingers form V]	Blue, red	VforV	Boone	A
2348	For / buy more war bonds [Statue of Liberty]	Blue	Liber	Harrington	A
2349	For / defense / navy / army	Black	Armed	Allen	A
2350	For / defense / Security / Education / Conservation / Health	Black	Home	Unknown	A
2351	For / democracy	Blue, red	Air	Clifford	A
2352	For / freedom / and / your own / welfare / buy / more / United etc. [no picture]	Gn,R/Black	Bonds	Unknown	B
2353	For / freedom / and peace [handpainted label]	Blue, red	ORN	LeGallez	C
2354	For / future / fun / the Victory Loan etc.	Green, orange	Bonds	Eichenlaub	A
2355	For / liberty	Blue, red	Liber	Clifford	A
2356	For / national defense / in the / Atlantic and Pacific / with a two ocean / navy/ We don't mean / maybe	Blue, red	Navy	Linprint	A
2357	For / V ···– / victory / and a greater etc. [no picture]	Unknown	VforV	Harrington	A
2358	For / V ···– / victory [no picture]	Blue, red	VforV	Unknown	A
2359	For / V / ···– / buy / war bonds [no picture]	Blue, red	Bonds	Boone	A
2360	For / victory / buy / United / States etc. [envelope 9 1/2x4 1/8 in.]	Black	Bonds	Pacif G&E	B
2361	For / victory / buy / US etc. [on back] [envelope 6x3 1/2 in.]	Unknown	Bonds	Sears	A
2362	For / victory / buy / war bonds [no picture] [brown envelope]	Unknown	Bonds	Ohio Bell	D
2363	For / victory / keep / 'em / flying	Blue, red	Air	Threl+Thar	A
2364	For / victory / keep / 'em / flying! / V	Blue, red	Air	Krakora	A
2365	For / victory [no picture]	Unknown	Bonds	Runge	A
2366	For / victory! [planes in formation form "V"] [thermographed]	Blue, red	Air	Unknown	A
2367	For a / 100% / fighter / fool-proof etc. [envelope 6 3/4x3 3/4 in.]	Unknown	Unk	Quigley	B
2368	For a new life —— in a new world [handpainted]	Multicolored	VEDay	Rayl	D
2369	For a safe return	Red	Home	Buxton	A

NO.	CACHET TEXT	COLOR	TOPIC	PUBLISHER	$
2370	For all nations	Multicolored	EagSh	Minkus	A
2371	For America, Americanism!	Unknown	Home	Linto	B
2372	For American liberty / then, now and the future	Blue	Wash	Foster	A
2373	For American liberty / then, now, the future	Blue	Wash	Foster	A
2374	For Americans / one flag / [etc.] / 9-23-'44——Manila blasted again by etc.	Unknown	Event	Linto	B
2375	For Americans / one flag / one "ism" / Americanism [multicolor varieties]	Multicolored	Flag	Linto	B
_2376_	For complete / victory / in / 1945 [handpainted]	Multicolored	Japan	Adler	D
2377	For defense / [etc.] / Let's keep 'em flying	Unknown	Air	Knight	A
2378	For defense / buy / United / States / savings / bonds / and etc. [env. 9 1/2x4 1/8]	Black, gold	Minut	D.C. Penal	B
2379	For defense / buy / United / States / savings / bonds / and stamps	Green/Red	Minut	Ohio Bell	D
2380	For defense / buy / United / States / savings / bonds / and stamps	Blue	Minut	Unknown	A
2381	For defense / buy / United / States / savings / bonds / and stamps / on etc.	Blue, red	Unk	Risinger	A
2382	For defense / buy / United / States / savings etc. [thermographed]	Unknown	Unk	Crosby	B
2383	For defense / buy / United / States etc.	Unknown	Bonds	Parrott	A
2384	For defense / buy / United / States etc. [envelope 9 1/2x4 1/8 in.]	Blue	Bonds	U.S. Treas	B
2385	For defense / buy / United etc.	Blue	Unk	Commercial	B
2386	For defense / buy / United States / savings etc.	Brown	Bonds	Smith, W	A
2387	For defense / Security / Education	Black	Home	Allen	A
2388	For defense of / a great nation / the United States Navy / "Men" etc. [thermographed]	Purple	Navy	Sadworth	B
2389	For defense of a / great democracy / U.S. submarines [thermographed]	Green	USsub	Sadworth	A
2390	For freedom [vertical text] [handpainted]	Blue	Navy	Klondike	D
2391	For freedom of the seas! / keep etc. [two styles of lettering] [colored envs.]	Multicolored	Navy	Poppenger	A
2392	For freedom's sake / victory / we will win	Bk/Gn/R	EagV	McFarland	A
2393	For freedom's sake / we must win or / we will perish [thermographed]	Blue, red	EagV	Yontz	B
2394	For gifts / give U.S. war bonds [handpainted]	Multicolored	Holid	Clendennen	D
_2395_	For God Prince of Peace for country [w/, w/o symbol explanation on back]	Multicolored	Relig	Bohemian	A
2396	For God and country. / We serve ···– [handpainted]	Multicolored	EagSh	Borkowski	D
2397	For humanity and freedom / America will never fail. [eagle above text]	Gold, green	Eagle	Amer Pat	A
2398	For humanity and freedom / America will never fail. [various flag arrangements]	Multicolored	Flag	Amer Pat	A
2399	For justice and / freedom	Bu/Gn/R	Ordna	Cozart	A
2400	For justice and / freedom	Brown	Unk	McFarland	A
2401	For liberty / and peace on earth / buy war bonds	Green, red	Holid	Lowell	A
2402	For liberty / and peace on earth etc. [picture: Wise men or cross]	Unknown	Unk	Clifford	A
2403	For liberty [picture: soldier or sailor]	Black/Red	Armed	Harrington	A
_2404_	For life, liberty and / pursuit of the Axis / United States Navy etc. [thermographed]	Blue, red	Navy	Sadworth	B
2405	For myself, I do not want to run / FDR	Brown	FDR	McFarland	B
2406	For national / defense / Billions / ...for... / defense	Blue, red	Ordna	Linprint	A
2407	For national / defense / Billions / [etc.] / defense / Remember Pearl Harbor!	Blue, red	Pearl	Linprint	B
2408	For national / defense / Billions / [etc.] / On this date etc. [3/11/41]	Blue, red	Event	Linprint	C
2409	For national defense / [etc.] / First Marine Brigade / in Iceland [thermographed]	Unknown	USMC	Sadworth	C
2410	For national defense / a strong / [etc.] / "We're in it" etc. [thermographed]	Green	Navy	Sadworth	B
2411	For national defense / a strong navy second to none etc. [thermographed]	Green	Navy	Sadworth	B
2412	For national defense / Embarkation Station / [etc.] / First day etc. [thermographed]	Red	Home	Unknown	D
2413	For national defense / The United States battleship / U.S. Navy [thermographed]	Blue	Navy	Sadworth	B
2414	For national defense / U.S. Navy [thermographed]	Blue	Navy	Sadworth	B
_2415_	For national defense / U.S. submarines [size of 1st line varies] [thermographed]	Bu/Gd/Red	USsub	Sadworth	B
2416	For national defense / United States / Marine etc. [1st line 39 mm] [thermographed]	Blue, red	USMC	Crosby	B
2417	For national defense / United States / Marine etc. [1st line 59 mm] [thermographed]	Blue, red	USMC	Crosby	B
_2418_	For national defense / United States Marine Corps / on land etc. [thermographed]	Blue, red	USMC	Sadworth	B
2419	For national defense / USS Flusser etc. [thermographed]	Bu/Gn/R	Navy	Sadworth	B
2420	For national defense / USS Griffin etc. [thermographed]	Bu/Gn/R	Navy	Sadworth	B
2421	For national defense / USS Grudgeon etc. [thermographed]	Bu/Gn/R	Navy	Sadworth	B
2422	For national defense / USS Helena etc. [thermographed]	Bu/Gn/R	Navy	Sadworth	B
2423	For national defense / USS Holland [thermographed]	Bu/Gn/R	Navy	Sadworth	B
2424	For national defense / USS New York [thermographed]	Bu/Gn/R	Navy	Sadworth	B
2425	For national defense / USS Seawolf etc. [thermographed]	Bu/Gn/R	Navy	Sadworth	B
2426	For national defense / with / Wendell Willkie / for President	Blue, red	Flag	Unknown	B
2427	For national security / American Base Forces / A.P.O. - No. 803	Purple	Bases	Bean	B
2428	For national security / let's go - U.S.A. / V Keep 'em Floating!	Black	Navy	Bean	A
2429	For our darling flag we sing etc.	Unknown	Flag	Card	A
2430	For protection, buy war bonds	Blue	Bonds	Haynes	A
2431	For sale / General Patton's dog house / Present owner has etc. [hp]	Multicolored	Patt	Knapp	G

NO.	CACHET TEXT	COLOR	TOPIC	PUBLISHER	$
2432	For services / rendered	Unknown	Armed	Dis Am Vet	A
2433	For the / defense / of / America	Blue, red	Flag	Linprint	A
2434	For the lack of blood / many suffering GI's / will die. Make your etc. [env. 7 1/2x4 in.]	Blue, red	Blood	Levering	A
2435	For the speedy liberation of the brave / [etc.] / A real American etc. [thermographed]	Red	Mac	Sadworth	B
2436	For this we fight / with all our might	Unknown	Unk	Carter	A
2437	For this we thank thee, Lord [handpainted]	Multicolored	Home	Sturgill	E
2438	For thrills / help dispose of / Japs and Huns / Buy bonds	Unknown	Flag	Linto	B
2439	For tomorrow's peace / buy war bonds / today	Gd,S/Multi	Bell	Linto	B
2440	For us here at home, don't spend as you / roam. / Buy bonds and keep etc.	Orange	Verse	Carpenter	A
2441	For victory	Bk/Bu/R	EagV	Cozart	A
2442	For victory - buy U.S. bonds and stamps [center cachet] [env. 5 9/16x3 9/16 in.]	Blue, red	Flag	Smith, W	B
2443	For victory / ··· -	Bu/Bu,Red	VforV	Unknown	A
2444	For victory / ··· - / buy / more / war / bonds etc. [env. 6 3/4x3 7/8 in.]	Blue, red	Uncle	Belles-let	C
2445	For victory / 160th A.A.F. Base Unit (F.C.) / Langley Field, Va. [thermogr]	Red, silver	Air	Unknown	A
2446	For victory / and peace	Unknown	Unk	Ang	A
2447	For victory / blood / sweat / tears / and your money / in war bonds!	Blue, red	Flag	Brenn	A
2448	For victory / buy / United States / war bonds / and / stamps	Red	Bonds	Boone	A
2449	For victory / buy / United / States war etc.	Red	Bonds	Klotzbach	A
2450	For victory / buy / United / States / Bonds etc. [flag above text] [env. 7 1/2x4 in.]	Multicolored	Bonds	Ang	A
2451	For victory / buy / United / States / defense / bonds / stamps	Blue, red	Bonds	Jensen	A
2452	For victory / buy / United / States / defense etc. [cachet frame hgt 75 mm]	Blue	Bonds	Jensen	A
2453	For victory / buy / United / States / war / bonds / and / stamps	Red	Bonds	Boone	A
2454	For victory / buy / United / States / war etc. [cachet height 23 mm]	Black	Bonds	DeHart	A
2455	For victory / buy / United / States / war etc. [cachet height 23 mm]	Black	Bonds	Stefun	A
2456	For victory / buy / United / States / war etc. [cachet height 26 mm]	Black	Bonds	Diamond	A
2457	For victory / buy / United / States / war etc. [cachet height 29 mm]	Blue	Bonds	Rankin	A
2458	For victory / buy / United / States / war etc. [cachet height 29 mm]	Black	Bonds	Linn	A
2459	For victory / buy / United / States / war etc. [cachet height 30 mm]	Black	Bonds	Amer Naval	A
2460	For victory / buy / United / States / war etc. [cachet height 42 mm, on back]	Black	Bonds	Western	B
2461	For victory / buy / United / States / war etc. [cachet height 53 mm]	Black	Bonds	Mott+Wood	B
2462	For victory / buy / United / States / war etc. [cachet height 53 mm]	Blue	Bonds	Cox	A
2463	For victory / buy / United / States / war etc. [cachet height 66 or 67 mm]	Blue	Bonds	Wayne	A
2464	For victory / buy / United / States / war etc. [cachet hgt 26 mm] [env. 8 7/8x3 7/8 in.]]	Black	Bonds	U.S. Treas	B
2465	For victory / buy / United / States / war etc. [envelope 8 11/16x3 5/8 in.]	Unknown	Bonds	ITE	B
2466	For victory / buy / United / States / war etc. [text height 22 mm]	Black	Bonds	Stamp Rev	A
2467	For victory / buy / United / States / war etc. [text height 23 mm]	Black	Bonds	Dahl	A
2468	For victory / buy / United / States / war etc. [text height 23 mm]	Black	Bonds	First Nat	A
2469	For victory / buy / United / States etc. [envelope 9 1/2x4 1/8 in.]	Black	Bonds	Acme Fast	A
2470	For victory / buy / United / States etc. [envelope 9 1/2x4 1/8 in.]	Black	Bonds	Detroit Ed	A
2471	For victory / buy / United etc. [all over cachet, on back] [env. 7 1/2x4 in.]	Unknown	Bonds	Hinrichs	B
2472	For victory / buy / United States / war bonds / and / stamps	Blue	VforV	Unknown	A
2473	For victory / buy / US / war / bonds / stamps [envelope 7 1/2x3 15/16 in.]	Unknown	Bonds	Penn-Harr	A
2474	For victory / buy a share in / America / Bonds buy ships	Blue, red	Bonds	Amer Naval	B
2475	For victory / buy etc. [thermogr] [env. 5 7/8x4 7/8, 6 1/2x4 11/16 in.]	Black	Bonds	U.S. Treas	B
2476	For victory / buy more war bonds	Blue, red	Flag	Abel	A
2477	For victory / buy US war / savings bonds etc. [envelope 6 3/4x3 3/4 in.]	Multicolored	Bonds	Amer Pat	A
2478	For victory / buy US war / savings etc. [no picture]	Unknown	Bonds	Simionescu	A
2479	For victory / don't let the Axis hypnotize you / buy a war bond today	Unknown	Bonds	Runge	A
2480	For victory / Naval Air Sta. / Jax, Florida. [thermographed]	Silver	Air	Czubay	B
2481	For victory / produce and act to win the race	Unknown	Home	Runge	A
2482	For victory / remember Munich——act now!	Unknown	Unk	Runge	A
2483	For victory / Sect. B, 3013 A.A.F.B.V. / Deming, New Mex. [thermo]	Red, silver	Air	Unknown	A
2484	For victory / Suppy [sic] Det., Section 1 / Camp Sibert, Ala. / Free [thermographed]	Green, silver	Air	Czubay	B
2485	For victory / V / ··· - / God bless America / Love it or / leave it! etc.	Red	FlagV	Unknown	A
2486	For victory / V / team work	Unknown	Unk	Baur	A
2487	For victory / We can... / We will.. / We must.	Blue, red	Home	Krakora	A
2488	For victory / We won't forget etc.	Brown	Unk	Runge	A
2489	For victory ["V" height 25 mm, other text 5 mm] [paratrooper descending]	Blue	Chute	Krakora	B
2490	For victory [··· - and eagle above text]	Red	Eagle	Runge	A
2491	For victory [··· - and flag above text]	Blue, red	Flag	Runge	A
2492	For victory [fingers form V above text]	Multicolored	VforV	Ang	A
2493	For victory [picture: U.S. flag, allied flags, or eagle]	Red	Unk	Runge	A

NO.	CACHET TEXT	COLOR	TOPIC	PUBLISHER	$
2494	For victory [service emblems above text]	Unknown	Armed	Dailey	A
2495	For victory and world peace	Gold	FDR	Carpenter	B
2496	For victory and world peace / 1882-1945	Gray	FDR	Carpenter	B
2497	For victory liberty and honor / we can / we must / we will win! [thermographed]	Blue	Torch	Yontz	B
2498	For victory liberty and honor [with or without frame of stars] [thermographed]	Blue	Torch	Yontz	B
2499	For victory! / Buy war bonds	Blue	Bonds	Unknown	A
2500	For victory! ["V" height 92 mm]	Blue, red	VEDay	Runge	B
2501	For your own safety / and / the war etc.	Unknown	Unk	Kosko	A
2502	For your own safety / and / the war etc. [env. 5 1/8x4 1/8, 5 7/8x4/1/8 in.]	Unknown	Unk	Kosko	A
2503	Fore! Let's put etc. [label + red "Win the War" border]	Multicolored	Home	Unknown	B
2504	Fore! Let's put etc.[label + blue "Victory" border]	Multicolored	Home	Unknown	B
2505	Fore! Let's put etc.[label + red "Victory" border]	Multicolored	Home	Unknown	B
2506	Forest fires / Japs could start them / [etc.] / 7-16-'45——This is 7th etc.	Multicolored	Event	Linto	B
2507	Forest fires / Japs could start them / but you etc.	Green, silver	Home	Linto	B
2508	Forestall inflation / buy war bonds	Black	Ordna	Ander, EA	B
2509	Forget politics! / War problems / come first! [no picture]	Multicolored	Home	Linto	B
2510	Formula for success / in Washington etc.	Unknown	Home	Linto	B
2511	Fort Huachuca / Arizona	Multicolored	Unit	Unknown	B
2512	Fort Mills / Corregidor / Island / surrenders / May 6, 1942 [no picture]	Black	Event	Fidelity	B
2513	Fortress Europa / trembles / It's [sic] towers bombed / the clock around etc.	Blue, red	Axis	Griffith	A
2514	Fortress Europe? / starting to shake, crack and crumble. [gray envelope]	Green, yellow	Nazis	Baur	B
2515	Forty-fourth [44th] / United States Army / In all things prepared	Aqua/Red	Unit	Army	B
2516	Forty-fourth [44th] [under insignia]	Blue, yellow	Unit	Dannells	B
2517	Forty-seven [47] [on pennant] [U.S.S. Rutland] [Tokyo Bay]	Gray, red	VJDay	Navy ship	E
2518	Forty-sixth [46th] School Squadron [below insignia] [handpainted]	Multicolored	Unit	Dannells	B
2519	Forward to / V ··· - / victory / in 1944 [w/, w/o Card imprint] [no picture]	Blue, red	VforV	Card	A
2520	Forward to victory	Multicolored	EagV	Dime	A
2521	Four / freedoms / or / four / slaveries / choose [handpainted]	Blue, red	Unk	Shaffer, A	C
2522	Four freedoms / freedom of speech etc. [thermographed]	Blue, red	Unk	Grimsland	B
2523	Four freedoms / will that, some day / [etc.] / 2-18-'44——U.S. 9th Air etc.	Multicolored	Event	Linto	B
2524	Four freedoms / Will that, some day / soon, include freedom etc. [no picture]	Multicolored	Home	Linto	B
2525	Four freedoms [in quotes] / our present to the world	Unknown	Unk	Runge	A
2526	Fourteen ninety-two [1492] / That fellow Columbus / [etc.] / 1942 / Now we etc.	Black	Home	Unknown	C
2526A	Fourteenth [14th] Provisional Marine Co. / Fleet Marine Force etc. [pmarked 1st Mar. Brig. Prov.] [thermo]	Blck	USMC	Unknown	D
2527	Fourth (last) day / 23rd annual convention. / [etc.] / Buy / defense / bonds	Blue, red	Bonds	Unknown	B
2528	Fourth / war bond / drive / 1-1-'44——55,000 tons of bombs / dropped on etc.	Black, blue	Event	Linto	B
2529	Fourth / war bond / drive [no picture]	Black, blue	Bonds	Linto	B
2530	Fourth / war bond / drive opens / If you can't drop bombs etc. [no picture]	Blue	Bonds	Boone	A
2531	Fourth [4th] / war / loan / That / liberty ring etc. [handpainted label]	Multicolored	Bell	LeGallez	C
2532	Fourth [4th] Bombardment Squadron / Corregidor / surrenders etc.[pm 05/06/42][hp]	Black, yellow	Event	Unknown	D
2533	Fourth [4th] Bombardment Squadron [handpainted]	Black, yellow	Unit	Unknown	B
2534	Fourth [4th] coal strike ended	Unknown	Home	Linto	B
2535	Fourth [4th] Service / Command [under insignia] [handpainted]	Black, blue	Unit	Dannells	B
2536	Fourth [4th] term inauguration / President / of the / United States etc.	Silver	FDR	Czubay	E
2537	Fourth [4th] war loan / buying a / bond is no / sacrifice [stenciled]	Black	Bonds	Wolf, CL	B
2538	Fourth [numeral] / time / 1945 / January 20th	Red	FDR	Staehle	E
2539	Fourth anniversary / September 28, 1943 / For / freedom's / sake / buy war etc.	Bk,O/Bu,Red	Bonds	Zunks	B
2540	Fourth war loan / January-February 1944	Blue, red	Bonds	Smith, W	A
2541	France	Black	ORN	Lowry	A
2542	France	Unknown	ORN	Runge	A
2543	France	Blue, red	ORN	Clifford	A
2544	France / "Forward / with God" / for / liberty	Blue, red	ORN	Cachet Cra	B
2545	France / a salute to you by the / red /etc.	Unknown	ORN	Hill	A
2546	France / almost / cleared / of Nazis / France	Black, red	ORN	Fidelity	B
2547	France / joins / United / Nations	Black	Event	Fidelity	B
2548	France / Liberty equality fraternity	Unknown	ORN	Runge	A
2549	France / Paris revolts / Marseilles free / Roumania quits	Blue, red	Event	Fidelity	B
2550	France [Marianne in ball & chain, U.S. soldier with rifle & keys] [handpainted]	Multicolored	ORN	Adler	D
2551	France libre / A salute to Paris / from Paris, N.Y. / on day of liberation	Black	Event	Unknown	B
2552	France libre / A salute to Paris etc.	Black	ORN	Rameco	B
2553	Franklin / Delano / Roosevelt / [etc.] / Great men etc. [postmarked 4/12/45]	Black, blue	FDR	Griffith	F
2554	Franklin / Delano / Roosevelt / 1882-1945	Black	FDR	Allen	B

NO.	CACHET TEXT	COLOR	TOPIC	PUBLISHER	$
2555	Franklin D / Roosevelt etc. [picture: FDR]	Gn/Pu/Red	FDR	Cliff	B
2556	Franklin D / Roosevelt etc. [picture: Hyde Park Home of FDR]	Gn/Pu/Red	FDR	Cliff	B
2557	Franklin D / Roosevelt etc. [picture: Warm Springs, Georgia, Home of FDR]	Gn/Pu/Red	FDR	Cliff	B
2558	Franklin D / Roosevelt etc. [picture: White House]	Gn/Pu/Red	FDR	Cliff	B
2559	Franklin D. Roosevelt / former President of the United States	Black	FDR	Pacific	B
2560	Franklin D. Roosevelt / January 30th, 1882 / [etc.] / The only thing we etc.	Black	FDR	Cozart	B
2561	Franklin D. Roosevelt / little White House etc.	Unknown	FDR	Fleetwood	B
2562	Franklin D. Roosevelt / memorial / the / 4 / freedoms	Blue, red	FDR	Cachet Cra	B
2563	Franklin D. Roosevelt / our wartime President / died etc. [postmarked 4/12/45]	Black	FDR	Ander, EA	E
2564	Franklin D. Roosevelt / President / of the / United etc. [typed] [no picture]	Black	FDR	Batura	C
2565	Franklin D. Roosevelt etc. [no picture]	Unknown	FDR	Levering	B
2566	Franklin D. Roosevelt, / Hyde Park's / [etc.] / laid to rest etc. [postmarked 4/15/45]	Black	FDR	Levering	D
2567	Franklin Delano Roosevelt / [etc.] / He passed this way [in quotes]	Black, yellow	FDR	Unknown	B
2568	Franklin Delano Roosevelt / 1882 - 1945 [picture: FDR; border: red, blue stars]	Multicolored	FDR	Unknown	B
2569	Franklin Delano Roosevelt / 1882-1945 [picture: White House or NY or GA home]	Multicolored	FDR	Poppenger	B
2570	Franklin Delano Roosevelt / 32nd U.S. President / died April 12, 1945 [4/12/45]	Gold, silver	FDR	Linto	X
2571	Franklin Delano Roosevelt / In memoriam / 1882-1945	Multicolored	FDR	Ioor	B
2572	Franklin Delano Roosevelt / Jan. 30, 1882 - April 12, 1945 [postmarked 4/12/45]	Black	FDR	Fidelity	F
2573	Franklin Delano Roosevelt—— / President of the United States [in quotes]	Sepia tones	FDR	Belles-let	C
2574	Franklin Delano Roosevelt 1882-1945	Black	FDR	Puls	B
2575	Franklin Delano Roosevelt etc. [envelope 6 3/4x3 7/8 in.]	Black	FDR	Belles-let	C
2576	Free / France / fights / on / United / to stamp out the Axis [env. 6 1/8x3 5/8]	Green, red	ORN	Runge	A
2577	Free / France / Following the capitulation of the government of France etc.	Blue/Red	ORN	Ander, CS	A
2578	Free / open / season / [etc.] / For victory B A qualified hunter [thermogr]	Brown	Japan	Czubay	B
2579	Free / open / season / [etc.] / Hunter signed up until victory. [thermographed]	Brown	Japan	Czubay	B
2580	Free / open / season / [etc.] / Imperial Japanese Service [thermographed]	Br/Gn/O/R	Japan	Czubay	B
2581	Free / open / season / [etc.] / Signed sealed and deliver. [thermo] [env. 9 3/8x4 1/8]	Red	Japan	Czubay	B
2582	Free / open / season / [etc.] / Signed sealed and deliver. [thermographed]	Br/Gn/O/R	Japan	Czubay	B
2583	Free / So solly!! [picture: shell bouncing off head of Japanese] [thermogr]	Blue	Japan	Sadworth	B
2584	Free / the / world [handpainted]	Multicolored	Liber	Adler	D
2585	Free / with the compliments of / all United States war bond buyers [thermographed]	Blue	Japan	Sadworth	B
2586	Free [picture: balloon raising Hitler aloft] [envelope 6x3 1/2 in.]	Multicolored	Hitle	Coward-McC	A
2587	Free [picture: shell bouncing off head of Japanese] [thermographed]	Blue	Japan	Sadworth	B
2588	Free [picture: soldier's head] [envelope 6x3 1/2 in.]	Black, orange	Armed	Coward-McC	A
2589	Free France / Patch / Bradley / Patton / "GI" Joe / Ike etc. [handpainted]	Multicolored	Hitle	Swave+Mill	B
2590	Free France / Patch / Bradley / Patton / "GI" Joe / Ike etc. [thermographed]	Blue	Hitle	Swave+Mill	B
2591	Free men fight with more / than guns etc.	Unknown	Unk	Lowell	A
2592	Free speech / What does it mean? / Upton Close forced / off NBC network etc.	Black, gold	Flag	Linto	B
2593	Freedom	Blue, red	EagSh	Clifford	A
2594	Freedom - liberty - justice / for all / America / My country, 'tis etc. [thermogr]	Bu/Br/Gd/R	EagFl	Crosby	B
2595	Freedom / "E pluribus unum"	Brown	Symb+	Brenn	A
2596	Freedom / ...and a / renewed / courage / of the / Vikings etc. [colored envelopes]	Blue, red	ORN	Poppenger	A
2597	Freedom / and / liberty / to the / armed / forces	Blue	Armed	Sadworth	B
2598	Freedom / and / liberty / to the / armed / forces / V / Day	Blue	VEDay	Sadworth	B
2599	Freedom / and / liberty / will be / restored / to... / Greece [colored envelopes]	Blue, red	ORN	Poppenger	A
2600	Freedom / -and / peaceful years / ahead / for / Denmark [colored envelopes]	Blue, red	ORN	Poppenger	A
2601	Freedom / Czechoslovakia / again will / cast off etc. [colored envelopes]	Blue, red	ORN	Poppenger	A
2602	Freedom / for the / liberty / loving / people / of / France [colored envelopes]	Blue, red	ORN	Poppenger	A
2603	Freedom / for which / Albert I / led [etc.] / Belgium [colored envelopes]	Blue, red	ORN	Poppenger	A
2604	Freedom / forever	Blue, red	EagSh	Unknown	A
2605	Freedom / forever / the Victory Loan etc.	Unknown	Unk	Eichenlaub	A
2606	Freedom / from / facism [sic] / and / slavery / for / Albania [colored envelopes]	Blue, red	ORN	Poppenger	A
2607	Freedom / from / fear [stenciled] [handpainted]	Blue, red	Home	Wolf, CL	C
2608	Freedom / from / want [stenciled] [handpainted]	Blue, red	Home	Wolf, CL	C
2609	Freedom / from fear of invasion / [etc.] / for / Jugoslavia [colored envelopes]	Blue, red	ORN	Poppenger	A
2610	Freedom / from Japanese / bondage and / slavery / for / Korea [colored envs.]	Blue, red	ORN	Poppenger	A
2611	Freedom / from the / evils of / German / [etc.] / Austria [colored envelopes]	Blue, red	ORN	Poppenger	A
2612	Freedom / from the Japanese / [etc.] / for the / Philippines [colored envs.]	Blue, red	Phili	Poppenger	A
2613	Freedom / it's [sic] light / must again / shine on / Poland [colored envs.]	Blue, red	ORN	Poppenger	A
2614	Freedom / Liberation day today / Germany surrenders [text upper left, allover cachet]	Br,R/Gn,R/Red	VEDay	Czubay	C
2615	Freedom / of / religion [stenciled] [handpainted]	Blue, red	Home	Wolf, CL	C
2616	Freedom / of / speech / from / want / [etc.] / The / 4 / freedoms / to etc.	Black, green	Torch	Staehle	C

NO.	CACHET TEXT	COLOR	TOPIC	PUBLISHER	$
2617	Freedom / of / speech / from / want / freedom / of / [etc.] / The four freedoms	Multicolored	Liber	Staehle	C
2618	Freedom / of / speech [stenciled] [handpainted]	Blue, red	Home	Wolf, CL	C
2619	Freedom / of speech / from fear / from want / of religion / Atlantic Charter	Multicolored	Heads	Minkus	A
2620	Freedom / of speech / from fear. Want. Or religion [handpainted]	Multicolored	Flag	Adler	D
2621	Freedom / of speech / of religion / from want / from fear / Four / freedoms [artist: Knapp]	Blue, red	Eag+	Goldstein	B
2622	Freedom / of speech / of worship / from want / from fear	Blue, red	Women	Minkus	A
2623	Freedom / or / slavery / ? [eagle landing] [handpainted]	Multicolored	Eagle	Adler	D
2624	Freedom / our heritage	Blue, red	EagSh	Mission	A
2625	Freedom / ours to preserve / ours to enjoy / ours to transmit	Blue, red	Flag	Carpenter	A
2626	Freedom / rings again / Manila's liberation / [etc.] Feb. 4th 1945 [thermographed]	Blue, red	Event	Smartcraft	C
2627	Freedom / shall reign	Blue, red	Unk	Baur	A
2628	Freedom / to / live / in / peace / [etc.] / Luxemburg [colored envelopes]	Blue, red	ORN	Poppenger	A
2629	Freedom / U.S. troops invade Manila, Feb. 4, 1945 [thermogr]	Multicolored	Event	Smartcraft	C
2630	Freedom / will / come/ and / [etc.] / for the / Netherlands [colored envelopes]	Blue, red	ORN	Poppenger	A
2631	Freedom [in wing of eagle] [handpainted]	Multicolored	EagSh	Adler	D
2632	Freedom [in wing of eagle] [red & white vertical stripes in shield] [handpainted]	Multicolored	EagSh	Adler	D
2633	Freedom [vertical]	Gold/Bk,Gold	Minut	Linto	B
2634	Freedom [vertical] / 8-31-'40———Airliner crashed at / Lovettsville, Va. 21 etc.	Unknown	Anniv	Linto	B
2635	Freedom [vertical] / of / speech / and / religion etc. [handpainted]	Multicolored	Torch	Klaas	C
2636	Freedom for all	Multicolored	Unk	Dime	A
2637	Freedom for all [crossed American and British flags]	Brown	Flag	Davis, Ray	A
2638	Freedom forever	Multicolored	Shiel	Amer Pat	A
2639	Freedom is the last, best hope of earth. [in quotes] "Let none falter" etc.	Black/Purple	Linc	Carpenter	A
2640	Freedom lives on / in the hearts etc.	Blue, red	Flag	Runge	A
2641	Freedom of / religion / 150 / December 15 etc.	Blue, red	Hist	Fleetwood	B
2642	Freedom of / religion, speech, press / that is what United etc. [no picture]	Gold, silver	UN	Linto	B
2643	Freedom of [sic] / Nazie [sic] / rule / France / Albania / Poland etc.	Blue, red	VEDay	Baur	B
2644	Freedom of religion	Multicolored	Flag	Runge	A
2645	Freedom of religion / speech / press	Unknown	Home	Linto	B
2646	Freedom of speech / and of religion / from want etc. [env. 6 3/4x3 3/4 in.]	Blue, red	Eagle	Sayama	B
2647	Freedom of speech / and religion / from / want / and / fear	Blue, red	FlagV	Sanders	A
2648	Freedom of speech / and religion / from want [in quotes] etc. [colored envelopes]	Blue, red	Eagle	Poppenger	A
2649	Freedom of speech / and religion, / freedom from / want and fear	Green, grey	Torch	Ioor	A
2650	Freedom of speech and / [etc.] / Czechoslovakia	Unknown	ORN	Runge	A
2651	Freedom of speech and religion / that the etc.	Black	Unk	Farnam	A
2652	Freedom of the seas, land, and air! / "History has recorded who fired" etc.	Multicolored	Eag+	Edmunds	D
2653	Freedom of worship / freedom of speech etc. [eagle]	Multicolored	Eagle	Boone	A
2654	Freedom of worship / freedom of speech etc. [no picture]	Multicolored	Home	Boone	A
2655	Freedom then / freedom again	Blue	Home	Carter	A
2656	Freedom under God!	Blue, red	Flag	Mission	A
2657	Freedom, liberty and / justice for all.	Blu, red	Flag	Baur	A
2658	Freedom's / lady [above Statue of Liberty, head & shoulder view] [handpainted]	Multicolored	Liber	Knapp	H
2659	Freedom's lady [below Statue of Liberty, including pedestal] [handpainted]	Multicolored	Liber	Knapp	G
2660	French fleet joins allies	Unknown	Event	Linto	B
2661	French scuttle fleet	Unknown	Event	Linto	B
2662	Friendly words! / "Put it there, Ivan" / It will be recorded for history etc.	Blue, red	Event	Levering	B
2663	From / perishable blood / to / life-saving plasma / The etc. [artist: Staehle]	Multicolored	Blood	Smartcraft	C
2664	From / to [soldier in foxhole]	Green	Army	Scott+Conn	B
2665	From / to [soldier pointing to himself]	Brown	Army	Unknown	A
2666	From / Uncle / Sam [envelope 6 3/4x3 7/8 in.]	Purple	Japan	Foster	A
2667	From a soldier overseas [in quotes] / So you're sick of the way etc. [no picture]	Black/Red	Verse	Boone	A
2668	From Des Moines / home of the WAACS etc. [rubber stamp + cut-&-pasted paper]	Blue, red	WAC	Temple	C
2669	From foreign hills and plains, [in quotes] etc. [no picture]	Black	Verse	Carpenter	A
2670	From foreign hills and plains, [in quotes] etc. [picture: church]	Bk/Blue, gold	Verse	Carpenter	A
2671	From foreign hills and plains, [in quotes] etc. [picture: eagle]	Black	Verse	Carpenter	A
2672	From idle words, big bombs grow	Black	Armed	Davis, Ray	A
2673	From Locksley Hall / For I dipt into the future, far as etc. [no picture]	Blue	Verse	Harmer	A
2674	From me / to you [thermographed] [envelope 5 3/4x4 3/4 in.]	Unknown	Unk	Unknown	A
2675	From our rock-bound eastern etc. [no picture]	Unknown	Unk	Carpenter	A
2676	From the / buggy to the / grave etc.	Black	Unk	Runge	A
2677	From the / hearts of the / blood donors / via / The Red etc. [colored envelopes]	Multicolored	Blood	Poppenger	A
2678	From the frying pan / to the battle line	Bk,Gn/Gn,Red	Home	Davis, Ray	A

NO.	CACHET TEXT	COLOR	TOPIC	PUBLISHER	$
2679	From the halls of Montezuma / [etc.] / Semper Fidelis [handpainted label]	Black	USMC	LeGallez	C
2680	From the halls of Montezuma etc.	Red	USMC	Flesch	A
2681	From the halls of Montezuma to the shores of / [etc.] / U.S. Marine Corps etc.	Blue, red	USMC	Cachet Cra	A
2682	From Tripoli to the Halls / of the Montezumas [in quotes]	Bk/Bu/Go/Gn	USMC	Neal	A
2683	Fruits of freedom / a free America	Multicolored	Flag	Minkus	A
2684	Full concern / and deep / responsibilty etc.	Blue, red	Home	Payne, AE	A
2685	Full speed ahead / for victory	Multicolored	Navy	Dime	A
2686	Full speed ahead / to victory! [copyright "C" w/, w/o serifs]	Multicolored	Home	Minkus	A

Cover Values (from Table 6, p. 136)

Value	*Price Range*
A	$ 3 - 6
B	$ 7 - 15
C	$ 16 - 30
D	$ 31 - 60
E	$ 61 - 125
F	$ 126 - 250
G	$ 251 - 500
H	$ 501 - 1000
I	$ >1000
X	**Unpriced: Suspicious or fraudulent cover**

2169

February 18, 1945

We Secure
Our Positions
on

Iwo Jima
(750 miles from Tokyo)
and on

Corregidor

2202

*Dr. W. H. Nelson
50 Hay Street
Subiaco
Western Australia*

2256

First Day Mail Service
AT MacARTHUR, W. VA.
APRIL 15, 1942

America Salutes MacArthur
SPONSORED BY
THE ORIGINAL ORDER OF ZUNKS
The Collector's Society

2259

2260

2261

2262

First Draft Number
158

They Shall Not Pass

*Luther Keller, Jr.
908 Wyoming St.,
Allentown, Penna.*

On this day the numbers to be alotted to Draft Registrants were drawn at Washington, D. C.
The first number being drawn by Secretary of War, Stimson.

2267

FIRST IN WAR
FIRST IN PEACE

FIRST IN THE HEARTS
OF OUR COUNTRYMEN.

2297

2298

2327

2335

Carpenter, Holliston, Mass.

2351

2356

2376

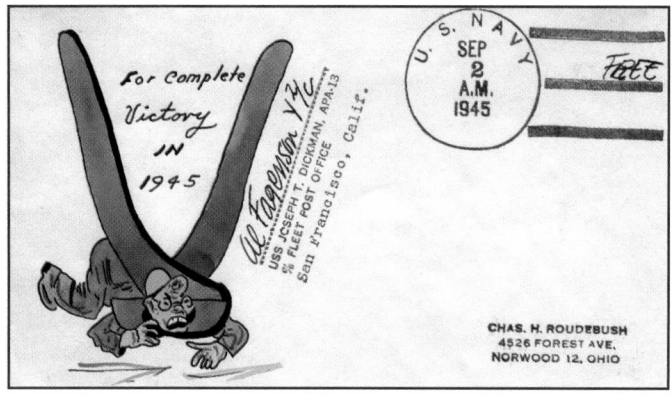

2395

2404

2415

2418

2444

2492

2526A

2621

2652

2685

CACHET TEXT BEGINNING WITH "G"

NO.	CACHET TEXT	COLOR	TOPIC	PUBLISHER	$
2687	G.I. / army / bathtub! [handpainted]	Multicolored	Army	Cowdery	D
2688	G.I. [burned left edge, torn right edge]	Multicolored	Army	Cowdery	D
2689	G.I. Joe [in quotes]	Multicolored	Army	Knoll	D
2690	G.I. Joe [in quotes] is on the go / Back him up / buy etc.	Unknown	Unk	Boone	A
2691	Gals are needed in / the SPARS / [etc.] / 11-21-'44—Nazis S.W. / front etc.	Unknown	Event	Linto	B
2692	Gals are needed in / the SPARS / Interesting careers [no picture]	Gold, silver	SPARS	Linto	B
2693	Gang way / Tokio; / we are heading for / "victory" [text black or gold]	Multicolored	Air	Amer Pat	A
2694	Gang way / Tokyo; / we are heading for / victory	Multicolored	Air	Amer Pat	A
2695	Gangway / fourth war loan / starts today	Black, red	Bonds	Wolf, CL	B
2696	Gang'way / Tokyo; / we're on the right / road to victory.	Multicolored	Air	Amer Pat	A
2697	Gang-way for / victory! / We must win! etc.	Unknown	Unk	Brenn	A
2698	Garden / "Food will win the war and write the peace" / for / victory	Blue, red	Home	Burpee	B
2699	Garden / in / 1945 / for / victory	Blue	VforV	Davis, D	A
2700	Gardens for victory [handpainted] [envelope 7 1/2x3 7/8 in.]	Multicolored	Home	Sweet	C
2701	Gas / wasted / may / mean / lives / lost!	Gold, blue	Home	Linto	B
2702	Gas and oil / vital war / necessity!! / Use only / as needed [multicolor varieties]	Multicolored	Home	Linto	B
2703	Gas, flames and bombs in the modern battles. / Make old-time weapons etc.	Blue, gold	Verse	Carpenter	A
2704	Gave the last full measure of devotion [in quotes] / Makena / In memory etc.	Black, red	AJA	Sayama	B
2705	G'bye folks—it got / too hot for me! / Il Duce resigned / as dictator etc.	Blue, red	Musso	Boone	A
2706	Gen. "Ike" / Eisenhower / top man / Allied / forces	Green, pink	Ike	Linto	B
2707	Gen. "Jimmy" / Doolittle / terror of Tokyo! / General "Jimmy" Doolittle etc.	Black	Hero	Pacific	B
2708	Gen. "Vinegar Joe" Stilwell [handpainted]	Multicolored	Gener	Knoll	D
2709	Gen. / Carl A. / Spaatz / planning now to / put Jap rats out / of their misery	Gold, sepia	Gener	Linto	B
2710	Gen. / Charles / de Gaulle / [etc.] / The / Casablanca / Conference / 1943	Multicolored	Heads	Smartcraft	C
2711	Gen. / H.H. / Arnold / Com. Army / Air Forces	Multicolored	Gener	Linto	B
2712	Gen. / Leslie R. / Groves / atomic bomb / chief [postmarked 8/12/45]	Gold, silver	Atom	Linto	D
2713	Gen. / Mark / Clark	Gn,Red/Gn,Si	Gener	Linto	B
2714	Gen. / Mark / Clark / 12-8-'44—Yanks armor / near Saarbrucken	Multicolored	Event	Linto	B
2715	Gen. / Short / "Guilty of / what?"	Multicolored	Gener	Linto	B
2716	Gen. / Short / "Guilty of / what?" / 12-19-'44—Yanks blunt / German drive	Multicolored	Event	Linto	B
2717	Gen. / Sir Harold / Alexander	Unknown	Gener	Linto	B
2718	Gen. / Sir Harold / Alexander / 12-7-'44—U.S. forces / land at Ormoc	Unknown	Event	Linto	B
2719	Gen. / Thomas / E. Rilea / [etc.] / 2-26-'45—Liberated sections of the etc.	Multicolored	Event	Linto	B
2720	Gen. / Thomas / E. Rilea / Supply Sta. / Australia	Green, purple	Gener	Linto	B
2721	Gen. Anthony McAuliffe	Unknown	Gener	Linto	B
2722	Gen. Ben Lear [handpainted]	Multicolored	Gener	Knoll	C
2723	Gen. Carl A. Spaatz	Unknown	Gener	Linto	B
2724	Gen. Charles de Gaulle / today commuted Marshal etc. [pen & ink] [no picture]	Blue	Event	Batura	D
2725	Gen. Douglas <MacArthur / Commander in the Pacific [thermo]	Blue, red	Mac	Crosby	B
2726	Gen. Douglas MacArthur	Black	Mac	Crockett	B
2727	Gen. Douglas MacArthur	Blue, red	Mac	Ioor	B
2728	Gen. Douglas MacArthur / none better!!	Green	Mac	Linto	B
2729	Gen. Douglas MacArthur / Supreme Commander of Allied Forces in the Pacific	Black	Mac	Pacific	B
2730	Gen. Dwight D. Eisenhower / Supreme Allied Commander in Europe [thermogr]	Blue, red	Ike	Crosby	B
2731	Gen. Dwight D. Eisenhower [thermographed]	Brown	Ike	Sadworth	B
2732	Gen. Dwight Eisenhower / "I consider the Red Cross" etc.	Blue, red	Ike	Brenn	A
2733	Gen. Edwin D. Patrick	Unknown	Gener	Linto	B
2734	Gen. Eisenhower	Unknown	Ike	Runge	A
2735	Gen. Eisenhower [handpainted]	Multicolored	Ike	Knoll	D
2736	Gen. Eisenhower led the etc.	Black	Ike	Unknown	A
2737	Gen. Eisenhower's / comment on the / weather on "D-Day" / "The sun has" etc.	Black, silver	DDay	Linto	B
2738	Gen. Elwood R. Quesada	Unknown	Gener	Linto	B
2739	Gen. Geo. S. Patton / leader of armored advance into Germany	Black	Patt	Pacific	B
2740	Gen. George C. Marshall Gen. Douglas MacArthur [VJ Day cancel]	Black	Marsh	Southworth	B
2741	Gen. George C. Marshall / Chief of Staff [thermographed]	Unknown	Gener	Crosby	B
2742	Gen. H.H. Arnold	Unknown	Gener	Linto	B
2743	Gen. H.H. Arnold / Chief of the Army Air Forces [thermographed]	Unknown	Gener	Crosby	B
2744	Gen. Jonathan Wainwright	Multicolored	Gener	Knoll	D
2745	Gen. Jonathon [sic] M. Wainwright / [etc.] / Tokio Bay, Japan. [thermographed]	Blue, red	VJDay	Crosby	B
2746	Gen. Joseph / "Vinegar" / Stilwell	Unknown	Gener	Linto	B

NO.	CACHET TEXT	COLOR	TOPIC	PUBLISHER	$
2747	Gen. Joseph Stilwell	Unknown	Gener	Linto	B
2748	Gen. MacArthur	Blue, red	Mac	Runge	B
2749	Gen. MacArthur	Multicolored	Mac	Knoll	D
2750	Gen. MacArthur / Admiral Halsey / President Truman / V-J Day	Black	VJDay	Knoll	C
2751	Gen. MacArthur / has just begun on the / "Rising Sun" [handpainted]	Multicolored	Japan	Adler	D
2752	Gen. MacArthur / Philippines / Tokyo / Mac "Sun of Heaven" Arthur	Black/Red	Japan	Harrington	B
2753	Gen. MacArthur announced / [etc.] / liberation / of the Philippine etc. [typed]	Black	Event	Batura	D
2754	Gen. MacArthur announced / Japan's occupation and etc. [pen & ink] [no picture]	Blue	Event	Batura	D
2755	Gen. MacArthur announced / the complete liberation / of etc. [typed] [no picture]	Black	Mac	Unknown	B
2756	Gen. MacArthur says: / "On to / Tokyo" / and we know that etc. [no picture]	Green	Mac	Davis, D	B
2757	Gen. MacArthur, Supreme Allied / Commander for Japan etc. [pen & ink] [no picture]	Blue	Mac	Batura	D
2758	Gen. Malin Craig	Unknown	Gener	Linto	B
2759	Gen. Malin Craig / 7-18-'45——Nazis' fate etc.	Unknown	Event	Linto	B
2760	Gen. Mark Clark	Unknown	Gener	Linto	B
2761	Gen. Mark Clark / 12-8-'44——Yank armor / near Saarbrucken	Unknown	Event	Linto	B
2762	Gen. Marshall	Brown, grey	Gener	Runge	B
2763	Gen. Marshall	Unknown	Marsh	Linto	B
2764	Gen. Marshall	Multicolored	Marsh	Knoll	D
2765	Gen. Marshall / 5-3-'45——British / take Hamburg	Unknown	Event	Linto	B
2766	Gen. Marshall [vertical]	Sepia, silver	Marsh	Linto	B
2767	Gen. McNair / Normandy / July 1944 / In memorial to a great General etc.	Multicolored	Gener	Staehle	C
2768	Gen. Omar Bradley	Unknown	Gener	Linto	B
2769	Gen. Omar Bradley / 4-8-'45——Yanks seize / S.S. death etc.	Unknown	Event	Linto	B
2770	Gen. Short	Unknown	Gener	Linto	B
2771	Gen. Short / 12-19-'44——Yanks blunt etc.	Unknown	Event	Linto	B
2772	Gen. Vandegrift / U.S.M.C. [thermographed]	Black	Gener	Sadworth	B
2773	Gen. Wainwright / is rescued from / Japs etc. [no picture]	Unknown	Event	Boone	B
2774	Gene A. Burris reporting...	Black	Army	Burris	B
2775	General / Douglas MacArthur / Leyte. Oct. 20th 1944. [etc.] U.S. forces etc.	Multicolored	Event	Fluegel	C
2776	General / Douglas MacArthur / V / for victory etc. [thermographed]	Blue, red	Mac	Crosby	B
2777	General / MacArthur / has him / on the run	Blue, red	Japan	Boone	A
2778	General / Montgomery [colored envelopes]	Black/Brown	Gener	Huss	A
2779	General Alexander A. / Vandergrift, Commandant / of the Marine Corps [VJ Day]	Black	Gener	Southworth	B
2780	General Chennault in China——	Bk/Br/Gy	Gener	Huss	A
2781	General Claire Chennault / Commander of the U.S. "Flying Tigers" in China	Black	Gener	Pacific	B
2782	General Douglas MacArthur / Allied / [etc.] / Tokio Bay etc. [thermographed]	Blue, red	VJDay	Crosby	B
2783	General Douglas MacArthur / Allied Commander in the Pacific [thermographed]	Blue, red	Mac	Crosby	B
2784	General Douglas MacArthur / Commanding General etc. [FDR cabinet autographs]	Unknown	Mac	Post Off	H
2785	General Douglas MacArthur / General etc. [thermographed]	Gold	Mac	Crosby	B
2786	General Douglas MacArthur / is honored by the opening of a / post office at etc. [handpainted]	Multicolored	MacFD	Knapp	I
2787	General Douglas MacArthur / is honored / by naming the newly established etc.	Black	Mac	Intercity	B
2788	General Douglas MacArthur / our national hero etc.	Blue	Mac	Butler	B
2789	General Douglas MacArthur / Some etc. First etc. [double cachet] [thermographed]	Blue-1, Red-2	MacFD	Crosby	E
2790	General Douglas MacArthur / Some etc. First etc. [double cachet] [thermographed]	Blue-1, Gd-2	MacFD	Crosby	E
2791	General Douglas MacArthur / Some etc. First etc. [double cachet] [thermographed]	Blue-1 & 2	MacFD	Crosby	E
2792	General Douglas MacArthur / Some people etc. [thermographed]	Multicolored	Mac	Crosby	B
2793	General Douglas MacArthur [engraved]	Black	Mac	Wash Stamp	B
2794	General Douglas MacArthur [envelope 6 3/4x3 7/8 in.]	Sepia tones	Mac	Belles-let	C
2795	General Dwight D. Eisenhower	Black	Ike	Artcraft	B
2796	General Dwight D. Eisenhower / Commander-in-Chief of Allies etc.	Black	Ike	Pacific	B
2797	General Eisenhower	Bk/Bu/Br	Ike	Huss	A
2798	General Eisenhower announces / [etc.] / Germany / [etc.] / V-E Day [thermographed]	Blue, red	VEDay	Boone	B
2799	General Eisenhower announces / victory / as all Germany etc. [thermographed]	Blue, red	VEDay	Boone	B
2800	General Eisenhower announces / victory / as Nazis / give up [thermographed]	Blue, red	VEDay	Boone	B
2801	General George C. / Marshall [VJ Day cancel]	Black	Marsh	Southworth	B
2802	General George S. Patton [VJ Day cancel]	Black	Patt	Southworth	B
2803	General Henry H. Arnold / Chief of Army Air Force [VJ Day cancel]	Black	Gener	Southworth	B
2804	General Joseph W. Stillwell	Black	Gener	Pacific	B
2805	General Lafayette [in quotes]——('Vive la France') etc. [env. 6 3/4x3 3/4 in.]	Sepia tones	Hist	Belles-let	C
2806	General MacArthur	Unknown	Mac	Linto	B
2807	General MacArthur	Black	Mac	Huss	B
2808	General MacArthur	Blue, silver	Mac	Linto	B

NO.	CACHET TEXT	COLOR	TOPIC	PUBLISHER	$
2809	General MacArthur / American war leader	Bk/Bu/Br/Gn	Mac	McFarland	B
2810	General MacArthur / American war leader [envelope 9 3/8x4 1/8 in.]	Red	Mac	McFarland	N
2811	General MacArthur / MacArthur Day June 13, 1942 / V / ...-	Gray, violet	Event	Huss	B
2812	General MacArthur [bust of MacArthur over "V"] [handpainted]	Multicolored	Mac	Adler	D
2813	General Mark W. Clark [VJ Day cancel]	Black	Gener	Southworth	
2814	General of the Army / George C. Marshall	Black	Marsh	Wash Stamp	B
2815	General Sikorski [envelope 6x3 ½ in.]	Black	Gener	Huss	A
2816	General Tadeusz A. Kosciuszko / Polish patriot fought for Amer- / ican etc.	Red	Hist	Czubay	A
2817	General Wladyslaw Sikorski	Black/Purple	Gener	Jancowski	A
2818	Geneva conference / What does / [etc.] / 4-27-'45——Yanks dash / into Austria	Green, purple	Event	Linto	B
2819	Geneva conference / What does it mean to our / boys in prison camps / Use etc.	Gd,S/Gn,Pu	Flag	Linto	B
2820	Gen'l MacArthur / on to Tokyo!	Blue, red	Mac	Davis, Ral	B
2821	Geo VI Rex / Unheralded, Lord Halifax / arrived in U.S. aboard H.M.S. King etc.	Red, violet	Event	First Day	D
2822	George M Cohan / always said / you're a grand old flag [env. 9 1/2x4 1/8 in.]	Blue, red	Flag	Vogel	C
2823	George Washington / 1789 / First President / [etc.] / 1797 etc.	Black, red	Wash	Unknown	A
2824	George Washington / a portrait / [etc.] / in home of William / Patten, Rhinebeck etc.	Blue, sepia	Wash	Unknown	A
2825	George Washington / a portrait / [etc.] / in State Normal School, West Chester etc.	Blue, sepia	Wash	Unknown	A
2826	George Washington / father of the land we love.	Blue, red	Wash	Card	A
2827	George Washington / fought for Americans etc.	Unknown	Wash	Davis, Ral	A
2828	George Washington / Like Washington and our forefathers, we must not etc.	Purple	Wash	Neal	A
2829	German creed: / "Give or and [sic] die" / Our creed: / "Live and let live"	Gold, silver	Ordna	Linto	B
2830	German war machine runs / [etc.] / 3-22-'44——U.S. Navy reported the loss etc.	Unknown	Event	Linto	B
2831	German war machine runs / on ball bearings made by / neutral (?) Sweden	Unknown	Nazis	Linto	B
2832	Germans / flee / Naples [no picture]	Blue, red	Event	Boone	B
2833	Germans / quit! / War with / Japan / V-J Day / lest you / forget [handpainted]	Multicolored	VEDay	Adler	D
2834	Germans / surrender /in Italy [thermographed]	Unknown	Event	Boone	B
2835	Germans / take / Mussolini	Blue, red	Event	Boone	B
2836	Germans admit / Berlin encircled etc. [thermographed]	Unknown	Event	Boone	B
2837	Germans are Nazis / when winning / [etc.] / 6-24-'44 Nazis flee Cherbourg etc.	Unknown	Event	Linto	B
2838	Germans are Nazis / when winning and / murdering! / Forget soft- etc.	Multicolored	Nazis	Linto	B
2839	Germans ask for peace [no picture] [cut-&-pasted paper] [postmarked 5/2/45]	Black	Event	Davis, D	B
2840	Germans capture Rostov	Unknown	Event	Linto	B
2841	Germans sink 17 Allied ships	Unknown	Event	Linto	B
2842	Germans, in Paris, with / their ususal trickery, ask for / 24 etc. [no picture]	Gold, green	Event	Linto	B
2843	Germany / Italy / Japan / 1945? [handpainted]	Multicolored	Axis	Shaffer, A	C
2844	Germany / official / surrender / date / false / surrender etc.	Unknown	VEDay	Boone	B
2845	Germany / Surrender day [postmarked 05/08/45]	Blue, red	Axis	Hill	B
2846	Germany / surrenders / false date [no picture]	Unknown	Event	Boone	B
2847	Germany / surrenders / to the / Allies / General Dwight etc. [thermographed]	Bu,Red/Multi	VEDay	Crosby	B
2848	Germany / surrenders / to the / Allies [no picture]	Multicolored	VEDay	Boone	B
2849	Germany / surrenders / to the / Allies [no picture] [false and official surrender dates]	Blue, red	VEDay	Boone	C
2850	Germany / surrenders / to the / Allies [text in shield]	Bu,Red/Multi	VEDay	Boone	B
2851	Germany / surrenders / to the / Allies [text over Minute Man]	Multicolored	VEDay	Boone	B
2852	Germany / surrenders / to the Allies ["V" 78 mm high]	Blue, red	VEDay	Boone	B
2853	Germany / surrenders / to the Allies [letters 10 mm high] [no picture]	Blue, red	VEDay	Boone	B
2854	Germany / surrenders / to the Allies [letters 3 mm high] [no picture]	Red	VEDay	Boone	B
2855	Germany / surrenders / to the Allies [text in shield]	Blue, red	VEDay	Boone	B
2856	Germany / surrenders / to the Allies [text over flags]	Blue, red	VEDay	Boone	B
2857	Germany / surrenders / to the Allies. [typed cachet]	Black, red	VEDay	Sharon	B
2858	Germany / surrenders / Tokio / destroyed! etc.	Red	VEDay	Burdick	B
2859	Germany / surrenders / unconditionally / May 8, 1945 / Don't forget our cost! etc.	Blue, red	VEDay	Levering	C
2860	Germany / surrenders to the Allies	Multicolored	VEDay	Staehle	C
2861	Germany and Italy formally / advised the State Department etc. [handpainted]	Blue	Event	Batura	D
2862	Germany falls / V-Day [handpainted]	Multicolored	VEDay	Rayl	D
2863	Germany falls [handpainted]	Multicolored	VEDay	Rayl	D
2864	Germany Italy / Japan / Nock [sic] them off——one by one!	Green, red	Axis	Lowe	A
2865	Germany surrenders / The Hitlerites have / been vanquished / Lest we etc.	Blue, red	VEDay	Sanders	B
2866	Germany surrenders / to the Allies / We must win the peace	Red	VEDay	Threl+Thar	B
2867	Germany surrenders to / the Allies / on —— / Eisenhower etc. [thermographed]	Bu,R/Multi	VEDay	Crosby	B
2868	Germany surrenders! / VE	Multicolored	VEDay	Griffith	B
2869	Get / behinmd / our boys! / Buy / bonds / and stamps [handpainted]	Multicolored	Bonds	Parker	B
2870	Get a grip, / men - Cowder's / at the wheel!! [handpainted] [stamp missing]	Multicolored	Army	Cowdery	D

NO.	CACHET TEXT	COLOR	TOPIC	PUBLISHER	$
2871	Get Bataan back / buy / bonds	Orange	Mac	Ohio Bell	D
2872	Get behind the man etc. [envelope 8 11/16x3 5/8 in.]	Unknown	Unk	ITE Circui	B
2873	Get into war work / Help him help you [thermographed]	Blue	Armed	Sadworth	B
2874	Get more victory bond sheets if / your ship is to make port	Blue, red	Bonds	Quigley	B
2875	Get on the / bondwagon [in quotes] [handpainted]	Multicolored	Bonds	Stoll	B
2876	Get this, you folk who want to soak / the Axis on the button. etc.	Blue	Bonds	Temple	A
2877	Get your heart / in America	Blue, red	Bonds	Ander, EA	A
2878	Get your heart / in America / buy war bonds	Unknown	Bonds	Ander, EA	A
2879	Getin' [sic] there / firstest with th' / mostest [in quotes]	Black	Ordna	Wolf, CL	A
2880	Gettin [sic] / stronger [handpainted]	Multicolored	Uncle	Adler	D
2881	Getting / in his / hair	Blue/Red	Hitle	Mutual	A
2882	Getting / there / slow / but / sure! [top center] [handpainted] [APO use]	Blue, tan	Army	McLaughlin	C
2883	Getting the mallet ready for some good heavy slugging	Black	Armed	Smith, DH	A
2884	Getting warm! [text 29, 34, 35, or 40 mm long] [colored envelopes]	Blue, red	UncJa	Poppenger	A
2885	GI Joe / Sacred German soil [allover cachet] [handpainted]	Multicolored	Army	Hadley	D
2886	GI Joe [in quotes] / is on the go / back him up / buy / war / bonds etc.	Blue, red	Torch	Boone	A
2887	Giant B 29's / bomb Japan / US troops / in Saipan / Fierce etc. [no picture]	Blue	Event	Fidelity	B
2888	Gifts of / steel V ...- / from the men of steel [thermographed]	Unknown	VforV	Von Los	B
2889	Gimme that gun! / The guy who lent us the / money etc. [thermographed]	Blue	Armed	Roudebush	A
2890	Girls—ages 22 to 45— who / [etc.] / 10-25-'44—Jap navy given / another etc.	Multicolored	Event	Linto	B
2891	Girls—ages 22 to 45—who / can qualify, are needed in / U.S. Army Nurse Corps	Multicolored	Nurse	Linto	B
2892	Give / 5 / in / '45 pints of blood etc. [thermographed]	Unknown	Blood	Threl+Thar	A
2893	Give / bond / stamp / gifts this Xmas	Unknown	Holid	Phill, CR	A
2894	Give / hospitalized / GIs / war / victims / relief / overseas etc. [handpainted]	Multicolored	RedCr	Adler	C
2895	Give / in 1945. [handpainted]	Multicolored	RedCr	Adler	D
2896	Give / join / generously [thermographed]	Unknown	Unk	Phill, CR	A
2897	Give / war bonds / and stamps! [handpainted]	Multicolored	Holid	Unknown	B
2898	Give according to / your means, not / your meanness.	Multicolored	Relig	Linto	B
2899	Give bond & stamp / gifts this Xmas.	Green, red	Uncle	Phill, CR	A
2900	Give Dillon S. Myer a / real chance / [etc.] / 12-27-'41—Japs bomb Manila etc.	Multicolored	Anniv	Linto	B
2901	Give Dillon S. Myer a / real chance to uplift / the yellow swine! etc.	Green, pink	AJA	Linto	B
2902	Give 'em / both barrels [handpainted]	Multicolored	Home	Knapp	G
2903	Give him / your best	Blue, red	Uncle	Kosko	A
2904	Give him wings! / Buy defense bonds [thermographed]	Unknown	Air	Czubay	A
2905	Give him wings! / Buy war stamps & bonds / a strong / navy etc. [thermographed]	Blue	Bonds	Czubay	A
2906	Give it your / best! [first 3 words placed vertically]	Blue, red	Flag	Smith, W	A
2907	Give it your best! / "Is life so dear, or peace so sweet, / as to be" etc.	Blue, red	Flag	Lemponen	A
2908	Give it your best.	Blue, red	Flag	Ang	A
2909	Give MacArthur and / Doolittle the goods! / They'll mow 'em etc. [no picture]	Brown, purple	Mac	Linto	B
2910	Give me / liberty / or give / me / death [in quotes] / Patrick Henry [no Ccard]	Black/Red	VforV	Morri, EW	B
2911	Give me / liberty / or give / me / death [in quotes] / Patrick Henry [w/Ccard]	Blue/Red	VforV	Morri, EW	C
2912	Give me / liberty, / or give / me death / Patrick Henry / March 23, 1775	Multicolored	Hist	Griffith	A
2913	Give me liberty / or give me death	Multicolored	FlLib	Minkus	A
2914	Give me liberty / or give me death!! [text diagonal, in "V" shape]	Blue	Hist	Unknown	A
2915	Give more / in 1944. [handpainted]	Multicolored	RedCr	Adler	D
2916	Give more / in '44 / Red Cross war fund [handpainted] [no picture]	Blue, red	RedCr	Myers	B
2917	Give now! / give more! / keep your Red Cross etc. [envelope 6x3 1/2 in.]	Black	Home	Peters	A
2918	Give now, more / than ever before.	Blue, red	RedCr	Phill, CR	A
2919	Give the Devil / his due! / [etc.] / 1-15-'45—Hun west "Bulge" / cost etc.	Multicolored	Event	Linto	B
2920	Give the Devil his due! / Send him / Hitler and / Hirohito	Multicolored	Devil	Linto	B
2921	Give them the tools / to finish the job [copyright "C" w/, w/o serifs]	Multicolored	Ordna	Minkus	A
2922	Give to / Red Cross / war fund / United States Army / Nurse Corps / [thermographed]	Unknown	Nurse	Czubay	A
2923	Give to / Red Cross / war fund [thermographed]	Red	Armed	Czubay	A
2924	Give to the / Red Cross	Unknown	RedCr	Linto	B
2925	Give to the / Red Cross / 2-18-'44—U.S. fleet and planes etc.	Unknown	Event	Linto	B
2926	Give today / Red Cross / war fund / When he needs you / most— etc. [no pict.]	Black	RedCr	Unknown	B
2927	Give us / more weapons [label + blue "Victory" border]	Multicolored	Army	Unknown	B
2928	Give us / more weapons [label + red "Victory" border]	Multicolored	Army	Unknown	B
2929	Give us / more weapons [label + red "Win the War" border]	Multicolored	Army	Unknown	B
2930	Give us the / tools	Blue	Unk	Richardson	A
2931	Give us the / tools / Tokio	Red	Unk	Richardson	A
2932	Give us the rest of / Bataan / [etc.] / 2-22-'40—Finland asks Rus- / sia etc.	Multicolored	USSR	Linto	B

NO.	CACHET TEXT	COLOR	TOPIC	PUBLISHER	$
2933	Give us the rest of / Bataan story / [etc.] / Feb. 11, '41—Italy notified etc.	Multicolored	Event	Linto	B
2934	Give us the rest of / Bataan story Army / and Navy officials / are sitting on.	O, purple	Flag	Linto	B
2935	Give war bonds / stamps / as gifts this Christmas	Unknown	Holid	Phill, CR	A
2936	Give! / A pint of your blood / may save a life / Give!etc. [thermographed]	Brown, red	Blood	Von Los	B
2937	Give! / Help / build / the / Shangri-la	Unknown	Navy	Linto	A
2938	Give'n him / both barrels	Black	Air	Wolf, CL	A
2939	Giving 'em a / warm reception	Black	Ordna	Wolf, CL	A
2940	Giving him a real headache	Gold, green	Japan	Peer	B
2941	Giving their best for / Uncle Sam	R,B/R,Gn	Uncle	Cozart	A
2942	Go / and / vote / Nov. / 7	Multicolored	Home	Linto	B
2943	Go / and / vote / Nov. / 7 / 10-6-'44—U.S. 1st starts new / offensive on etc.	Multicolored	Event	Linto	B
2944	Go / and / vote / Nov. / 7 / 8-13-'44—Yanks cut Nazis' / escape route to Paris	Multicolored	Event	Linto	B
2945	Go / get / 'em / America! [colored envelopes]	Blue, red	FagFl	Poppenger	A
2946	Go / to your / blood / donor / center / now!	Vi, silver	Blood	Linto	B
2947	Go / to your / blood donor / center / now! / 8-19-'44—Allies outflank etc.	Unknown	Event	Linto	B
2948	Go ahead, please—— / take day off! [thermographed]	Bk/Bu/Br/Red	Japan	Swave+Mill	A
2949	Go get 'em / marine! / The 3 etc.	Blue	USMC	Herschaft	B
2950	Go straight / with lots of / power at / "yellow vultures"	Blue, red	Eagle	Quigley	B
2951	Go without / so they won't have to / Food is etc. [label + printed border]	Multicolored	Armed	Artists	B
2952	God / bless / America	Blue, red	Holid	Carpenter	A
2953	God / bless / America / envy of all nations / Buy its defense bonds! [thermographed]	Blue, red	FlSh	Crosby	B
2954	God / bless / America / the envy of every nation [w/, w/o serifs] [thermographed]	Blue, red	FlSh	Crosby	B
2955	God / bless / America [thermographed]	Unknown	FlSh	Crosby	A
2956	God / bless / our / freedom [with eagle or star; flag location, size vary]	Multicolored	Flag	Amer Pat	A
2957	God / bless / our / navy	Bk,Gd/Bk,Si	Navy	Linto	B
2958	God / bless / our / navy / 10-27-'44—Capture of Samar	Multicolored	Navy	Linto	B
2959	God / bless / our / navy / 10-27-'44—Yanks sink and / damage over 37 Jap ships	Multicolored	Event	Linto	B
2960	God / speed / our / boys / in their / drive for victory / and etc. [no picture]	Blue	Armed	Unknown	B
2961	God bless / America	Blue	Shiel	Cox	A
2962	God bless / America	Blue, red	EagSh	Linprint	A
2963	God bless / America	Blue, red	Ordna	Ander, EA	A
2964	God bless / America	Blue, red	EagSh	Ander, EA	A
2965	God bless / America	Blue	Bell	Price, R	A
2966	God bless / America	Blue, red	EagSh	Card	A
2967	God bless / America / Allies occupy / Trobriand etc. [thermographed]	Unknown	Event	Boone	B
2968	God bless / America / Allies take / Balikpapan etc. [thermographed]	Unknown	Event	Boone	B
2969	God bless / America / Democracy etc.	Blue, red	Unk	Boone	A
2970	God bless / America / For victory / buy / U.S. / war / bonds	Blue, red	Flag+	Boone	A
2971	God bless / America / For victory / buy / United / States / war / bonds etc.	Blue, red	Minut	Boone	A
2972	God bless / America / I am proud to be etc.	Unknown	Unk	Kosko	A
2973	God bless / America / Keep her free	Blue, red	FlSh	Schust	A
2974	God bless / America / Maj. Bong killed: / Atom / bombs etc. [thermographed]	Blue, red	Atom	Boone	D
2975	God bless / America / Major Boyington etc. [thermographed]	Silver	Event	Boone	B
2976	God bless / America / Munda falls to US / troops etc. [thermographed]	Unknown	Event	Boone	B
2977	God bless / America / Mussolini resigns / as dictator; King / Emanuele takes on etc.	Blue, red	Event	Boone	B
2978	God bless / America / Remember / Pearl / Harbor	Blue, red	Pearl	Boone	A
2979	God bless / America / Russians enter / Poland	Blue, red	Event	Boone	B
2980	God bless / America / Russians enter /	Unknown	Event	Boone	B
2981	God bless / America / Slap the Jap with a war stamp!	Blue, red	Shiel	Ander, EA	A
2982	God bless / America / US downs 123 / Jap etc. [thermographed]	Unknown	Event	Boone	B
2983	God bless / America / We are are proud to / be Americans	Magenta	Flag	Unknown	A
2984	God bless / America [bell at UL, 7 stars at L&R edges, with Minuteman]	Blue, red	Bell	Boone	A
2985	God bless / America [bell at UL, 7 stars at L&R edges, without Minuteman]	Blue, red	Bell	Boone	A
2986	God bless / America [bell at UL, red and blue lines frame envelope]	Blue, red	Bell	Boone	A
2987	God bless / America [bell or Capitol dome at L, in circle of 13 stars]	Blue, red	Bell	Boone	A
2988	God bless / America [envelope 6x3 ½ in.]	Bk/Gr/R	Unk	Schlichte	A
2989	God bless / America [handpainted]	Blue, red	EagSh	Krakora	C
2990	God bless / America [handpainted] [eagle sitting above text]	Blue, red	Eagle	Krakora	B
2991	God bless / America [Liberty bell or ornamental bars]	Blue	Unk	Phill, CR	A
2992	God bless / America [shield & ornamental bars]	Gd,Pu/Pu,S	Shiel	Phill+Cox	A
2993	God bless / America [stars clustered within stripes] [patterned env. 6 1/4x4 1/4 in.]	Black, gold	Shiel	Schlichte	B
2994	God bless / America! / Please speed us / to victory!	Multicolored	Map	Linto	B

NO.	CACHET TEXT	COLOR	TOPIC	PUBLISHER	$
2995	God bless / Buy war bonds / America!	Red	LinWa	Unknown	A
2996	God bless / our freedom [text under 3 flags]	Multicolored	Flag	Amer Pat	A
2997	God bless / our freedom. [text under 1 or 3 flags]	Multicolored	Flag	Amer Pat	A
2998	God bless / the land / where / liberty is / treasured. [text on eagle]	Black, gold	Eagle	Amer Pat	A
2999	God bless / the land / where / liberty is / treasured. [text under 3 flags]	Multicolored	Flag	Amer Pat	A
3000	God bless / the land / where / liberty is / treasured. [text under eagle]	Black, gold	Eagle	Amer Pat	A
3001	God bless / the land where / liberty is treasured [multicolored, various]	Multicolored	Home	Amer Pat	A
3002	God bless America	Blue	EagSh	Foster	A
3003	God bless America	Unknown	Unk	Dime	A
3004	God bless America	Bk,Bu/Multi	Hist	Carpenter	A
3005	God bless America	Blue, red	EagFl	Stanard	A
3006	God bless America	Black/Red	Flag	Unknown	A
3007	God bless America / for victory / keep 'em /etc.	Blue	Unk	Petrasek	A
3008	God bless America / it's great to be an American / etc. [env. 6 1/2x3 5/8 in.]	Blue, red	EagSh	Alden	B
3009	God bless America / it's great to be etc. [env. 6 3/4x3 3/4 in.]	Unknown	Unk	Alpert	A
3010	God bless America / love it / or leave it!	Blue	Unk	Unknown	A
3011	God bless America / Love it or / leave it! / U.S.S. Columbia / is now the gem etc.	Red	Navy	Unknown	A
3012	God bless America / my home sweet home	Black	Unk	Harrington	A
3013	God bless America / one nation, mighty / [etc.] / Armistice Day / 1941 etc.	Blue, red	Holid	Honolulu	B
3014	God bless America / the U.S. Navy / will protect it [thermographed]	Bu/Purple	Navy	Sadworth	B
3015	God bless America / we are proud to be Americans	Purple	Flag	Bartz	A
3016	God bless America [diagonal text between lines] [no picture] [handpainted]	Multicolored	Home	Barwicki	B
3017	God bless America [in quotes]	Blue, red	Flag	Unknown	A
3018	God bless America [in ribbon across USA]	Blue, red	Home	Krakora	B
3019	God bless America [no picture]	Unknown	Unk	Dime	A
3020	God bless America!	Blue	LinWa	Ander, EA	A
3021	God bless America! / for victory / buy / U.S. etc. [Washington w/ flag]	Blue, red	Hist	Ander, EA	A
3022	God bless America! / for victory / buy / U.S. etc. [Washington w/ Lincoln]	Blue, red	LinWa	Ander, EA	A
3023	God bless America! / for victory / buy / U.S. war bonds [with ordnance]	Blue, red	EagSh	Ander, EA	A
3024	God bless America! / for victory / buy / U.S. war bonds [with stars]	Blue, red	EagSh	Ander, EA	A
3025	God bless America! / for victory / buy / U.S. war bonds [without ordnance]	Blue, red	EagSh	Ander, EA	A
3026	God bless America! / for victory / buy / U.S. war bonds [without stars]	Blue, red	EagSh	Ander, EA	A
3027	God bless America! / for victory / buy war bonds [last line with serifs]	Blue, red	Unk	Ander, EA	A
3028	God bless America! / for victory / buy war bonds [last line without serifs]	Blue, red	Unk	Ander, EA	A
3029	God bless America! / for victory / buy war bonds!	Black	Bonds	Unknown	A
3030	God bless America! / for victory! / buy war bonds	Blue, red	Unk	Ander, EA	A
3031	God bless America! / V / ...-	Red	VforV	Ander, EA	A
3032	God bless America! / V / ...- / for victory etc.	Blue, red	VforV	Ander, EA	A
3033	God bless America! [flags above text]	Blue, red	Flag	Mission	A
3034	God bless America! [thermographed]	Blue, red	Flag	Mission	A
3035	God bless daddy	Green	Home	Buxton	A
3036	God bless our army / We march to war / today [typed] [pmark 12/7/41]	Red	Event	Sweet	G
3037	God bless our freedom	Multicolored	Flag	Amer Pat	A
3038	God bless our freedom [text between stars and under 1 flag]	Multicolored	Flag	Amer Pat	A
3039	God bless our freedom [text under 3 flags]	Multicolored	Flag	Amer Pat	A
3040	God bless our freedom [text under shield]	Multicolored	Shiel	Amer Pat	A
3041	God bless our freedom [text under small shield]	Multicolored	Shiel	Amer Pat	A
3042	God bless our freedom.	Multicolored	Flag	Amer Pat	A
3043	God bless our freedom. [text under 3 flags]	Multicolored	Flag	Amer Pat	A
3044	God bless our freedom. [text, in ornamental frame, runs through large shield]	Multicolored	Shiel	Amer Pat	A
3045	God bless the land where / liberty / is treasured [text under 3 eagles]	Multicolored	Eagle	Amer Pat	A
3046	God bless the land where / liberty is treasured. [no picture] [yellow envelope]	Gold	Home	Amer Pat	A
3047	God bless the land where / liberty is treasured. [one flag]	Multicolored	Flag	Amer Pat	A
3048	God bless the land where / liberty is treasured. [three flags]	Multicolored	Flag	Amer Pat	A
3049	God blessed America / A two ocean navy / to protect it	Multicolored	Navy	Minkus	A
3050	God blessed America / Home of the free	Multicolored	Flag	Minkus	A
3051	God blessed America / We'll protect it!	Blue, red	Flag	Minkus	A
3052	God blessed America / with / and justice for all!	Bk/Bu/Br	Liber	Harrington	A
3053	God blessed America / with / and justice for all!	Blue, red	Liber	Harrington	A
3054	God has / made / America / great! / [etc.] / 8-31-'40—Airliner crashed etc.	Multicolored	Anniv	Linto	B
3055	God has / made / America / great! / Keep it / this way	Multicolored	Flag	Linto	B
3056	God has delivered us from / our enemies! / [etc.] / 9-2-'45—Butcher of etc.	Unknown	VJDay	Linto	B

NO.	CACHET TEXT	COLOR	TOPIC	PUBLISHER	$
3057	God has delivered us from / our enemies! / Almighty God we etc. [no picture]	Gold, silver	VJDay	Linto	B
3058	God was / on / our side! / Two atom bombs / set the Rising Sun / Victory	Multicolored	VJDay	Boone	C
3059	God was / on / our side! / V ...- / Two atom bombs / set etc. [thermographed purple]	Multicolored	VJDay	Boone	C
3060	God was / on / our side! / V / ...- / V-J Day / Victory [thermographed purple]	Multicolored	VJDay	Boone	B
3061	God was / on / our side! / Victory	Blue, red	VJDay	Boone	B
3062	God was / on / our side! / V-J Day / Victory [fingers in "V"] [thermo purple]	Multicolored	VJDay	Boone	B
3063	God was / on / our side! / V-J Day / Victory [no finger "V"] [color varieties]	Multicolored	VJDay	Boone	B
3064	God will bless America / if / America gets right with God.	Green, red	Relig	Speede	A
3065	Goering / Ash can [handpainted]	Multicolored	Nazis	Long	C
3066	Goering, Kesselring / surrender to US etc. [thermographed]	Unknown	Event	Boone	B
3067	Going down [handpainted]	Multicolored	Japan	Wolf, CL	B
3068	Going full speed	Red	Eag+	Hillerich	A
3069	Gold Star Covers [2 small cachets under text] / Keep 'em flying! etc. [env. 7 1/2x4 in.]	Black	FlagV	Edmunds	E
3070	Gold Star Covers [2 small cachets under text] / Remember Pearl etc.[env. 7 1/2x4 in.]	Black	FlMin	Edmunds	E
3071	Gone - but not forgotten	Black	Unk	Phill, CR	A
3072	Gone - but not forgotten	Black/Green	Hitle	McCluney	A
3073	Gone but not forgotten / U.S.S. Arizona / sunk by the sons of H---, / War bonds etc.	Black	Navy	Harrington	A
3074	Gone...but——not forgotten!!! / U.S.S. Arizona / But.....a reminder!! etc.	Black	Pearl	Harrington	A
3075	Gone...but——not forgotten!!! / U.S.S. Arizona / We will always etc.	Black/Purple	Pearl	Harrington	A
3076	Gone-but-not forgotten / USS Pigeon etc.	Black/Blue	Navy	Harrington	A
3077	Gone-but-not forgotten / USS Sturtevant etc.	Black	Navy	Harrington	A
3078	Gone-but-not forgotten / We will / [etc.] / USS Panay	Black	Navy	Harrington	A
3079	Good / news! / Buy war bonds	Green	Bonds	Larocque	A
3080	Good fishing ahead / if / you buy / war bonds / every payday	Red	Bonds	Kosko	A
3081	Good Friday / April 7, 1944 / Consider for a moment His / supreme etc.	Multicolored	Relig	Linto	B
3082	Good neighbors [in quotes] / V / ...- / Purchases / of U.S. defense etc.	Multicolored	Bonds	Linto	B
3083	Good neighbors [in quotes] / We will keep / 'em flying / There is no match etc.	Multicolored	Ally	Linto	B
3084	Good news / You can still get / a $25. war bond for / only $18.75!!!	Bu/Gn/Red	Bonds	Threl+Thar	A
3085	Good news for Adolf / rail / coal / steel / strikes / rubber / planes / ships / bus [hp]	Black, red	Home	Wolf, CL	C
3086	Good news from home etc. [label + blue "Victory" border]	Multicolored	Army	Unknown	B
3087	Good news from home etc. [label + red "Victory" border]	Multicolored	Army	Unknown	B
3088	Good news from home etc. [label + red "Win the War" border]	Multicolored	Army	Unknown	B
3089	Good night / my love —— [in quotes] [burned left edge] [handpainted]	Multicolored	Army	Cowdery	D
3090	Good old U.S.N. / All night in - / and beans / for breakfast! [thermographed]	Green	Navy	Crosby	B
3091	Good transportation / tends / for etc.	Unknown	Unk	Southwest	B
3092	Good transportation / tends for / victory [envelope 9 1/2x4 1/8 in.]	Black	Home	Univ Car	B
3093	Goodbye Adolf [handpainted]	Multicolored	Hitle	Wolf, CL	B
3094	Goody - / goody for me, / when (?) this day etc. [burned edge] [handpainted]	Multicolored	Army	Cowdery	D
3095	Gosh! / I forgot to / buy that $25 / [etc.] / 10-7-'44—Fisher Body Co. etc.	Multicolored	Bonds	Linto	B
3096	Gosh! / I forgot to / buy that $25 / [etc.] / 9-29-'44—Allies go into etc.	Multicolored	Event	Linto	B
3097	Gosh! / I forgot to / buy that $25 / war bond for / $18.75	Gd/Gd,Silver	Bonds	Linto	B
3098	Got a little / car gem! [handpainted]	Black	Army	Parker	B
3099	Got 'D' jitters Adolf? [in quotes] / "You haven't seen anything yet!"	Black	Hitle	Donaldson	A
3100	Got him where he belongs!! [handpainted]	Multicolored	Hitle	Parker	B
3101	Gov. Stevenson proclaims Sunday etc.	Unknown	Unk	McCluney	A
3102	Government officials and enter- / [etc.] / 10-31-'44—Yank subs sink / 18 etc.	Unknown	Event	Linto	B
3103	Government officials and enter- / [etc.] / 6-24-'44—Yanks down 5 Jap etc.	Unknown	Event	Linto	B
3104	Government officials and enter- / tainers travel thru special etc. [no picture]	Unknown	Home	Linto	B
3105	G-P answers the call / with / men and bonds [envelope 9 1/2x4 1/8 in.]	Unknown	Home	Garfield	B
3106	Grand opening / Nimitz W. Va. / Post Office [eagle in circle, attacking]	Multicolored	NimFD	Unknown	D
3107	Gran'paw's jinin-up—— / sez you gotta fight skunks with skunks. [in quotes]	Bu/Br/Purple	Home	Boone	A
3108	Grant us / thy peace [handpainted]	Multicolored	Relig	Adler	C
3109	Great Britain / United Nations [handpainted]	Multicolored	UN	Weigand	B
3110	Great leap year / Clark helping Huns leap out of Italy / Stalin helping Huns etc.	Multicolored	Ally	Linto	B
3111	Great men never die for / their spirits live on etc. [Angel]	Multicolored	Shiel	Amer Pat	A
3112	Great men never die for / their spirits live on etc. [Washington]	Multicolored	Wash	Amer Pat	A
3113	Great Seal of the United States / USS Blue etc. [thermographed]	Unknown	Navy	Crosby	B
3114	Great Seal of the United States / USS Case etc. [thermographed]	Unknown	Navy	Crosby	B
3115	Great Seal of the United States / USS Conygham etc. [thermographed]	Unknown	Navy	Crosby	B
3116	Great Seal of the United States / USS Rhind etc. [thermographed]	Unknown	Navy	Crosby	B
3117	Great Seal of the United States / USS Somers etc. [thermographed]	Unknown	Navy	Crosby	B
3118	Great Seal of the United States / USS Vestal etc. [thermographed]	Unknown	Navy	Crosby	B

NO.	CACHET TEXT	COLOR	TOPIC	PUBLISHER	$
3119	Greatest event / of the year! / V ...- victory / Germany surrenders	Blue, red	VEDay	Kosko	B
3120	Greatest single air / raid in history etc. [thermographed]	Unknown	Event	Boone	B
3121	Greece	Black	ORN	Lowry	A
3122	Greece	Blue, red	ORN	Clifford	A
3123	Greece	Blue/Brown	ORN	Runge	A
3124	Greece / 1943	Blue, red	ORN	Unknown	A
3125	Greece / the kingdom of Greece etc.	Bk/Bu/Red	ORN	Cliff	A
3126	Greece [thermographed]	Unknown	ORN	Smartcraft	B
3127	Greece given PC-622	Unknown	Event	Linto	B
3128	Greece shall rise again / Athens, N.Y., U.S.A. salutes / Athens, Greece etc.	Black	ORN	Rameco	B
3129	Greed and wars / go together! [no picture]	Multicolored	Home	Linto	B
3130	Greetings / bonds for Xmas	Green, red	Holid	Kosko	A
3131	Greetings / from / home / folks	Blue, red	Home	Carpenter	A
3132	Greetings / from / the Lone Star state / to / a Texan in the etc. [no picture]	Unknown	Unk	McCluney	A
3133	Greetings / to / Hitler Hirohito / from United Nations	Blue, red	Axis	Baur	A
3134	Greetings [candle and holly] [handpainted]	Multicolored	Holid	Adler	C
3135	Greetings [dog with ribbon collar] [handpainted]	Multicolored	Holid	Adler	C
3136	Greetings [poinsettia] [handpainted]	Multicolored	Holid	Adler	C
3137	Greetings from / Guantanamo Bay, Cuba / U.S. Naval station etc. [thermogr]	Blue/Silver	Navy	Crosby	B
3138	Greetings from / the Seabees / U.S. Navy / Crush the / Japanese etc. [thermogr]	Blue	Navy	Crosby	B
3139	Greetings from / the Seabees / U.S. Navy Construction Battalion / Seabees on etc.	Blue	Navy	Crosby	B
3140	Greetings from / U.S. Navy / Crush the / Japanese / menace! etc. [thermogr]	Blue	Navy	Roudebush	A
3141	Greetings from / U.S.S. Gilmer / [etc.] / A strong / Navy - a etc. [thermographed]	Red	Navy	Crosby	B
3142	Greetings from / Unalaska, Alaska / "Alaska defense center" [thermographed]	Gold	Alask	Crosby	B
3143	Greetings from / US Coast Guard / All night etc. [thermographed]	Unknown	Coast	Crosby	B
3144	Greetings from / US Coast Guard / Crush etc. [thermographed]	Unknown	Coast	Crosby	B
3145	Greetings from / US Marines / Buy war etc. [thermographed]	Red	USMC	Crosby	B
3146	Greetings from / US Merchant Marine Service / Crush etc. [thermographed]	Unknown	Merch	Crosby	B
3147	Greetings from / US Navy / Crush etc. [thermographed]	Unknown	Navy	Crosby	B
3148	Greetings from Alaska / 1942 / Madonna and Child etc. [thermographed]	Red	Alask	Crosby	B
3149	Greetings from Holliston / to those in the service	Green, red	Holid	Carpenter	A
3150	Greetings from the / fleet	Green	Navy	Lupton	A
3151	Greetings from the Fleet / Navy Day 1941	Blue	Navy	Sadworth	B
3152	Greetings from U.S. Coast Guard / All night in - / and beans etc. [thermographed]	Blue	Coast	Crosby	B
3153	Greetings gate! / Don't let these guys celebrate. / Buy etc. [handpainted]	Multicolored	Axis	Myers	B
3154	Greetings, pals, and a hearty cheer etc.	Green	Verse	Rathkamp	A
3155	Gregory - where did you / learn to salute? [in quotes] [handpainted]	Multicolored	Army	Cowdery	D
3156	Grim reality! / Let's do our part!	Unknown	Armed	Linto	B
3157	Grim reality! / Let's do our part! / 2-15-'44——Rooke Island, off south etc.	Unknown	Event	Linto	B
3158	Guadalcanal / "Let 'em have it!"	Black	Armed	Coll Surp	A
3159	Guadalcanal / the Allied forces fought Japs here to a standstill [thermographed]	Blue, green	Armed	Crosby	B
3160	Guadalcanal [vertical, inside "1"] / First Marine Division etc. [therm]	Blue, red	Unit	Unknown	C
3161	Guadalcanal Buna Attu / Gona etc. [thermographed]	Black, red	Armed	McCluney	A
3162	Guadalcanal's Vandegrift	Black/Blue	Gener	Huss	A
3163	Guam / under / Ameriocan / men / Conquest complete	Blue, red	Event	Griffith	B
3164	Guam and / Wake Island are back in the nest	Brown/Red	Eagle	Runge	A
3165	Guam and / Wake Island are back in the nest [envelope 9 1/2x4 1/8 in.]	Blue	Eagle	Runge	B
3166	Guaranteed workable / postwar plans. / #1. Rosey the riveter etc. [handpainted]	Multicolored	Women	Steinhardt	C
3167	Guard / American / liberty!	Unknown	Unk	Davis, Ral	A
3168	Guardian / of / our home	Unknown	Unk	Ehde	A
3169	Guardians of our sea lanes / stepping stones to Tokio	Blue, red	Navy	Carpenter	A
3170	Guardians of the seas / US Navy	Unknown	Navy	Boone	A
3171	Guarding our nation's / future!	Bk/Blue/Red	Flag	Smith, AD	A
3172	Guarding our nation's / future! / The fight for liberty etc.	Red	Flag	Smith, AD	A
3173	Guarding the gateway to America	Blue/Red	Liber	Smith, AD	A
3174	Guess we are truly suckers! "Last week the Rocky Mountain music / etc.	Gold, silver	AJA	Linto	B
3175	Guess we are truly suckers! / [etc.] / 6-30-'44——Chinese rout Japs etc.	Gold, silver	Event	Linto	B
3176	Guess who? [in quotes] [blue envelope]	Multicolored	Navy	Amer Art	A
3177	Gunner's / mate [in quotes] [w, w/o 4 stars upper & lower right] [blue envelope]	Multicolored	Navy	Amer Art	A

2731

2751

2783

2786

2793

2805

2833

2847

2860

2885

2905

2921

2936

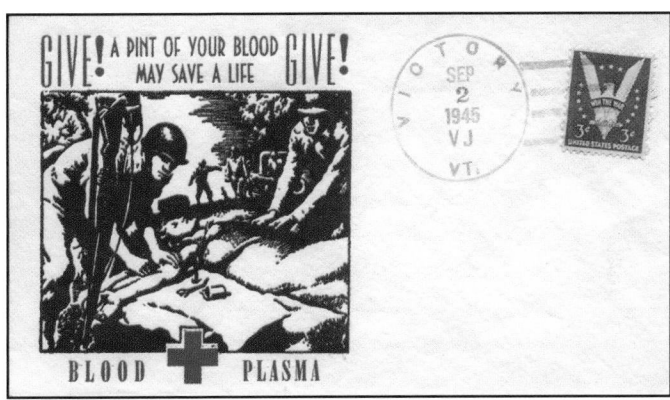

2954

2974

3106

3177

CACHET TEXT BEGINNING WITH "H"

NO.	CACHET TEXT	COLOR	TOPIC	PUBLISHER	$
3178	H hour? / When ? Day Where? / Invasion	Gold, red	DDay	Unknown	B
3179	H.M.S. Illustrious [in quotes] / badly damaged in Malta / arrives in Port etc.	Blue	Event	Unknown	C
3180	H.M.S. Malaya / First British man-of-war / to enter American Navy etc. [thermo]	Blue, red	Ally	Sanders	C
3181	Had enuf? / Nov. 5 / will tell!	Unknown	Home	Linto	B
3182	Half [1/2] / The job is only half done / Don't stop now / Buy more bonds etc.	Red	Bonds	Harmer	A
3183	Half [1/2] / The job is only half done / don't stop now etc.	Red	Bonds	Harmer	A
3184	Halleluiah Manila Halleliuah / for the foot steps of / Yankee etc. [env. 7 1/2x4 in.]	Aqua, black	Phili	Amer Pat	A
3185	Halleluiah Manila Halleliuah / for the foot steps of / Yankee freedom etc.	Multicolored	Phili	Amer Pat	A
3186	Halloween / 1944 / Greetings / One year nearer / victory [handpainted]	Black, orange	Holid	Myers	C
3187	Halloween / October / thirty-one [postmarked 10/31/41]	Multicolored	Holid	Linto	B
3188	Halloween / October thirty-one / Nineteen / forty [postmarked 10/31/40]	Multicolored	Holid	Linto	B
3189	Halsey-Jap-on-knees / Yes, the Japs they have a Navy, / and their men etc.	Red	Navy	Abel	A
3190	Halt / in the name / of humanity. [small or large infantryman]	Multicolored	Army	Amer Pat	A
3191	Handing the boot a line! [in quotes] [thermographed]	Blue	Navy	Lupton	A
3192	Hands across the sea [handpainted]	Multicolored	Ally	Knapp	G
3193	Hans was always slow / at catching on!	Black	Axis	Wolf, CL	A
3194	Happy / Thanksgiving [handpainted]	Multicolored	Holid	Linto	C
3195	Happy days are / coming / when the boys / come marching / home	Orange	Armed	Abel	A
3196	Happy Eastertide / Rose are red - violets are blue - etc. [handpainted]	Multicolored	Holid	Martin	B
3197	Happy family / Jack Sprat was always flat / His wife was always "clean" etc.	Blue, red	Verse	Threl+Thar	A
3198	Happy new year / at Welcome, N.C. / [etc.] / "Invest in America"	Blue, red	Holid	Zunks	B
3199	Happy New Year / at Welcome, N.C. / 1942 / [etc.] / Buy defense bonds!	Blue, red	Holid	Zunks	C
3200	Happy new year / January 1, 1941 / "Liberty and justice for all"	Multicolored	Liber	Hamilton	B
3201	Happy new year / May victory and peace / come to all of us / in 1945	Blue, red	Holid	Lowell	A
3202	Happy New Year [in quotes] / 1945 / V [handpainted]	Multicolored	Holid	Knoll	C
3203	Hard to / satisfy - / but / all that I want is ⸺ [handpainted]	Multicolored	Home	Cowdery	D
3204	Hark! the voice of liberty	Blue	LinWa	Hill	A
3205	Harlingen Army Air Field / Harlingen, Texas [Air Force patch 40 or 58 mm diameter]	Multicolored	Army	Unknown	A
3206	Harry S. / Truman / 1945 Thirty-third etc.	Unknown	HST	Johns Cov	B
3207	Harry S. Truman / takes oath as / new president.	Multicolored	HST	First Day	E
3208	Harry S. Truman sworn in / as 33rd U.S. President	Gold	HST	Linto	C
3209	Hats off / to Fulton Lewis, Jr. / [etc.] / 12-27-'39⸺Earthquake in etc.	Multicolored	Anniv	Linto	B
3210	Hats off / to Fulton Lewis, Jr. / one of the nation's etc. [no picture]	Gold, silver	Home	Linto	B
3211	Hats off to⸺ace pilot / Capt. Don S. Gentile / Piqua, Ohio / Record of etc.	Blue, red	Air	Avy	A
3212	Have / faith / in God / and / victory is assured / He has etc. [colored envelopes]	Gn,S/Multi	Relig	Linto	B
3213	Have / faith in / America [no picture]	Unknown	Unk	Ang	A
3214	Have a heart, / be a true American, / buy more war bonds	Blue, red	Bonds	Harrington	A
3215	Have a heart, / be a true American, / cooperate with etc. [print style varies]	Bk/Bu/Red	Uncle	Harrington	A
3216	Have landed, and have the situation well in hand [in quotes]	Multicolored	USMC	Amer Art	A
3217	Have our boys in / service been in / [etc.] / 5-11-'45⸺Yanks land on etc.	Multicolored	Event	Linto	B
3218	Have our boys in / service been in a / sports event or / terrible war? etc.	Multicolored	Flag	Linto	B
3219	Have we got a navy? / Ask Japan etc. [small or large battleship]	Red/Bu,Red	Navy	McCluney	A
3220	Have you / bought your / extra bond / yet? [handpainted]	Red	Bonds	Klondike	D
3221	Have you enlisted / in the war / on waste?	Gold, silver	Home	Linto	B
3222	Have you ever seen / anything better?	Multicolored	Flag	Linto	B
3223	Have you given aid / to a boy at the / front today / by etc. [no picture]	Green	Blood	Rowe	A
3224	Have you heard / the cry for blood? / How much have you / given? / Can you etc.	Blue, red	Blood	Levering	A
3225	Having a / happy 4th / of July!	Black/Blue	Navy	Lupton	A
3226	Having a swell time at the beach! [in quotes]	Black	Navy	Lupton	A
3227	Having a swell time in Hawaii! [in quotes]	Black	Navy	Lupton	A
3228	Having lots of fun / fish-back riding! [in quotes]	Black	Navy	Lupton	A
3229	Hawaii	Multicolored	Hawai	Unknown	A
3230	Hawaii / December 7 / 1941-1942 / "They shall not have died in vain"	Black	Pearl	Sayama	B
3231	Hawaii / Paradise / of the / Pacific	Green, yellow	Hawai	Unknown	A
3232	Hawaii [thermographed]	Unknown	Hawai	Crosby	B
3233	Hawaii's quota / $27,000,000.00 / the / mighty / 7th / war loan etc.	Green, red	Bonds	Sayama	B
3234	He / saves / his / bonds / do / you [handpainted]	Blue, red	Uncle	Wolf, RL	A
3235	He comes to / break oppression, / to set the etc. [in quotes]	Multicolored	Holid	Griffith	B
3236	He did his bit today / did you? / Buy etc.	Unknown	Bonds	Boone	A
3237	He died before his / Phillippines [sic] were free [in quotes] / President Quezon etc. [hp]	Multicolored	Phili	Knoll	D

NO.	CACHET TEXT	COLOR	TOPIC	PUBLISHER	$
3238	He faces / death / Did you / buy bonds?	Green, silver	Armed	Linto	B
3239	He faces / death / Did you / by bonds? / 6-27-'45——MacArthur an- / nounced etc.	Multicolored	Event	Linto	B
3240	He gave / 100% / What are [etc.] / Are you buying? / Bonds / Fourth war loan	Green, purple	Armed	Threl+Thar	A
3241	He gave / 100% / What are you giving?	Bk/Br/Pu	Armed	Threl+Thar	A
3242	He gave all / Did you give?	Unknown	Unk	Baur	A
3243	He is doing his best! / are / you? / buy bonds / America!	Unknown	Unk	Boone	A
3244	He is fighting! / You keep writing!	Unknown	Armed	Phill, CR	A
3245	He is taking / chances with / death! / You can / buy bonds! etc.	Multicolored	Army	Linto	B
3246	He is the US Army. The etc.	Unknown	Army	Brenn	A
3247	He just loves dessert, Captain, but / you see that [in quotes] etc. [buff envelope]	Multicolored	Armed	Amer Art	A
3248	He needs your support [envelope 9 1/2x4 1/8 in.]	Green/Violet	Uncle	Unknown	B
3249	He says he's so afraid he'll die?	Black	Nurse	Lupton	A
3250	He stands with ever / watchful eye, / o'er all our far- / flung battle lines.	Blue	Uncle	Carpenter	A
3251	He starts with / a smile! What / are you doing / about etc. [multicolor varieties]	Multicolored	Bonds	Linto	B
3252	He thinks he has the world / in his grasp; but - / he's behind the "8" ball. [handpaint]	Blue	Hitle	Parker	B
3253	He wants an armistice / Admiral Horthy / of Hungary [handpainted]	Multicolored	Axis	Knoll	C
3254	He who relaxes helps / the Axis. [handpainted]	Multicolored	Home	Newton FN	C
3255	He whoo-s wise / buys / war bonds / to have / and / to hold! [handpainted]	Black	Owl	Myers	C
3256	He will / guide us to / Victory!	Blue, red	FDR	Davis, Ral	B
3257	He'a comes mi tapedoboat man! [one or two lines for return address] [thermogr]	Black	Navy	Crosby	B
3258	Heading for a rest cure! [in quotes]	Black	Navy	Lupton	A
3259	Health for victory / [etc.] / Roosevelt / 1944 March of Dimes [thermographed]	Blue, red	Flag	Bean	B
3260	Hear not the / cry for peace! / [etc.] / 9-2-'44——Yanks take Pisa! / Huns' etc.	Multicolored	Event	Linto	B
3261	Hear not the / cry for peace! / It's only a / stall for / time!	Multicolored	Flag	Linto	B
3262	Heart Mountain, Wyoming [letters 1 mm high at UL, with barracks and mountain]	Blue	AJA	Unknown	D
3263	Heart Mt., Wyo. [letters 11 mm high] [eagle w/ stars + barracks and mountain]	Blue, silver	AJA	Oka	G
3264	Heavenly Father etc.	Unknown	Relig	Linto	B
3265	Heavier / loan / quotas / HLQ / This is a 100% war, buy more bonds [no picture]	Blue, red	Bonds	Quigley	B
3266	Heavy [in quotes], heavy hangs over they head" / The next war etc. [handpainted]	Multicolored	Ally	Knapp	G
3267	Heed Pres. Truman's / watchword / work, work, work!	Blue, gold	HST	Linto	B
3268	Heel [in quotes] Hitler!! [kicking mule]	Black/Brown	Hitle	Cornell	B
3269	Heil - it's the fuehrer [in quotes]	Black	Hitle	Donaldson	A
3270	Heil - it's the fuehrer	Black	Hitle	Donaldson	A
3271	Heil Hitler, / you can take over any time! [in quotes] / Buy war bonds	Black	Devil	Donaldson	A
3272	Heil Hitler, / you can take over any time! [in quotes] [imprints: AK & ID]	Black	Devil	Donaldson	A
3273	Heil! It's the fuehrer	Black, red	Hitle	Donaldson	A
3274	Hell / Hitler! / Wanted / Schicklegruber / for murder / Free!	Vi/Yellow	Hitle	Czubay	C
3275	Hell / Hitler! / Wanted / Schicklegruber / for murder / Free!	Bu/Br/Gn/Gy	Hitl	Czubay	C
3276	He'll / remember / Pearl Harbor	Unknown	Armed	Dis Am Vet	A
3277	Hell wouldn't have him [in quotes] / "Get out!!" [Musso] [imprints: A.K., I.D.]	Black	Devil	Donaldson	A
3278	Hello Central / G'me France ——- / —— We'll be over	Black	Armed	Wolf, CL	A
3279	Hello darling! / Happy birthday. [handpainted]	Multicolored	Home	Cowdery	D
3280	Hello Tojo! Is you lissinin? / One hundred super flying forts / bomb etc.	Green	Japan	Abel	A
3281	Hello Tokio / for your information etc.	Red	Japan	Abel	A
3282	Hello, iss dot you, Adolf? [in quotes] / Dnieper / Line	Black/Multi	Hitle	Smith, DH	A
3283	Help "US" get the world out of its jam / keep active,, think clearly, work	Blue, red	Unk	Quigley	B
3284	Help / save paper / especially / U.S. war bonds	Unknown	Bonds	Linto	B
3285	Help / save paper / especially / U.S. war bonds [no picture]	Gd/Gd,Purple	Bonds	Linto	B
3286	Help / Uncle / keep / the / heat / on!	Multicolored	Uncle	Linto	B
3287	Help / Uncle / keep / the / heat / on! / 12-10-'44——Yanks 77th / Div. etc.	Multicolored	Event	Linto	B
3288	Help / Uncle Sam / end the war [envelope 6x3 1/2 in.]	Unknown	Uncle	Reuss	A
3289	Help / Uncle Sam / end the war etc. [border: Buy war bonds today] [no picture]	Blue, red	Uncle	Reuss	A
3290	Help / Uncle Sam / end the war victoriously / make the peace etc. [no picture]	Blue, red	Uncle	Reuss	A
3291	Help Britain / "Save the children" [no picture] [envelope 9 1/2x4 1/8 in.]	Unknown	Ally	MacMillan	B
3292	Help buy planes / for "honorable visit" to Tokio [thermographed]	Brown/Red	Air	Sadworth	B
3293	Help defeat Hitler by calling / him by his right name... / Schickelgruber!	Red	Hitle	Temple	A
3294	Help defeat the Axis / For protection etc.	Unknown	Axis	Haynes	A
3295	Help drown the rats / Buy bonds and stamps [handpainted]	Multicolored	Axis	Gielarow	C
3296	Help fill the / reserved space / Buy more war / bonds [colored envelopes]	Black	Axis	Worl	A
3297	Help him come home [in quotes] / K9 Corps / [etc.] / War Bonds / [handpainted]	Multicolored	Unit	Knoll	C
3298	Help keep / prices down! / Use it up——wear it / out——make it do——or etc.	Blue, red	Home	Brenn	A
3299	Help pave / the way to / Berlin - /...Buy - / war bonds	Gray/Green	Armed	Carpenter	A
3300	Help preserve / our liberty / Remember etc.	Brown	Unk	Runge	A

NO.	CACHET TEXT	COLOR	TOPIC	PUBLISHER	$
3301	Help preserve / our liberty.	Black	Wash	Price, EK	A
3302	Help prevent / fire! / the sabotage / [etc.] / Columbus Day——Oct. 12, '43 etc.	Multicolored	Holid	Linto	B
3303	Help prevent / fire! the / sabotage agent / of the enemy! [no picture]	Blue, gold	Home	Linto	B
3304	Help put / 'em in / the jug! / "Remember Pearl Harbor" etc. [thermographed]	Brown	Axis	Crosby	B
3305	Help put / 'em in / the jug! / Buy defense stamps and bonds [thermographed]	Brown	Axis	Crosby	B
3306	Help put / 'em in / the jug! [shades of brown] [thermographed]	Brown	Axis	Crosby	B
3307	Help rationing plans - don't beef, / Ram reports and etc. [envelope 6 3/4x3 3/4 in.]	Blue, red/Blue	Home	Quigley	B
3308	Help set Japan's Rising Sun / with defense bonds	Red	VforV	Fumbarger	B
3309	Help set the rising sun / Yes, the Japanese etc.	Blue	Japan	Brenn	A
3310	Help sponsor a fighting / destroyer / Keep etc.	Blue	Unk	Peters	A
3311	Help Texas win the war / victory if / we work and fight / defeat if / we etc.	Blue, red	Home	McCluney	A
3312	Help Texas win the war / victory if etc. [no picture]	Unknown	Unk	McCluney	A
3313	Help to / protect / their future [handpainted]	Multicolored	Home	Hadley	C
3314	Help to break it all up [in quotes] / Buy war bonds [handpainted]	Multicolored	Axis	Knoll	C
3315	Help win / Buy war bonds	Green, red	Bonds	Kosko	A
3316	Help! / Adolf / help! / You stay / out of / this! / Darn those / little guys!	Pi/Pu/R	Musso	Roberts	A
3317	Help. What next! [handpainted]	Multicolored	Hitle	Unknown	C
3318	Helping / speed victory!	Blue, red	Unk	Davis, Ral	A
3319	Hemisphere defense bases / American Base Forces, Army Post Office - Trinidad	Blue, red	Bases	Smith, W	D
3320	Hemisphere defense bases / First day cancellation / A.P.O. 805 - St. Lucia	Blue, red	Bases	Smith, W	D
3321	Hemisphere defense bases / First day etc. / Marine detachment, Newfoundland	Blue, red	Bases	Smith, W	D
3322	Hemisphere defense bases / First day etc. / Submarine base, Virgin Islands	Blue, red	Bases	Smith, W	D
3323	Her prayers follow you - / (Whistler's 'Mother') [in quotes] [env. 7x4 in.]	Sepia tones	Home	Belles-let	C
3324	Here comes skipper Werve / [etc.] / largest navy in the world always.	Blue	Navy	Werve	A
3325	Here is an Easter egg / for Tojo and Hitler. [handpainted]	Multicolored	Axis	Borkowski	C
3326	Here is President Roosevelt's / comment, which he authorized etc. [no picture]	Red	FDR	Boone	B
3327	Here is to brag! The Yankee flag, that stands at the head of all, and her etc.	Blue	Flag	Carpenter	A
3328	Here is your / Minute Man [Treasury Department Wrapper, 7 15/16x10 15/16 in.]	Black, red	Minut	U.S. Treas	G
3329	Here they are nuts all three, / The half cracked Adolph, and the Japanee etc.	Black	Axis	Donaldson	A
3330	Here we come Japs [in quotes] / U.S. First Army etc.	Blue, red	Japan	Abel	A
3331	Here we enjoy taps! [in quotes]	Black	Armed	Lupton	A
3332	Here's / a letter for —— [envelope 8 7/8x3 7/8 in.]	Multicolored	Army	Porto-Serv	B
3333	Here's / how some of / our L.P. boys / look [torn at right] [handpainted]	Multicolored	Army	Cowdery	D
3334	Here's a letter from Alaska! [thermographed]	Red	Alask	Crosby	B
3335	Here's to old B. and G. / He's full of P. and V. / When someone said etc.	Black	Gener	Rowell	B
3336	Here's to our glorious flag / untarnished, unsullied unbeaten. [therm]	Blue, red	Flag	Baur	B
3337	Heroes / of / America / our / inspiration! [last 2 lines all caps]	Blue, red	LinWa	Brenn	A
3338	Heroes / of / America / our / inspiration! [last 2 lines caps and lower case]	Blue, red	LinWa	Mission	A
3339	Heroes of / steel V ...- / with steel nerves [thermograophed]	Unknown	Unk	Von Los	B
3340	Heroes of the Kasserine	Unknown	Hero	McCluney	A
3341	Heroic Americans / "Betsy Ross was" etc. [#9] [label + printed border]	Multicolored	Hist	Parkinson	B
3342	Heroic Americans / "Genius is about two" etc. [#24] [label + printed border]	Multicolored	Hist	Parkinson	B
3343	Heroic Americans / "Let reverence for the" etc. [#19] [label + printed border]	Multicolored	Linc	Parkinson	B
3344	Heroic Americans / "Liberty and Union, now" etc. [#18] [label + printed border]	Multicolored	Hist	Parkinson	B
3345	Heroic Americans / "O'er the land of the" etc. [#16] [label + printed border]	Multicolored	Hist	Parkinson	B
3346	Heroic Americans / "Resistance to tyrants" etc. [#11] [label + printed border]	Multicolored	Hist	Parkinson	B
3347	Heroic Americans / "Speak softly and carry etc." [#25] [label + printed border]	Multicolored	Hist	Parkinson	B
3348	Heroic Americans / Firmly embedded in the etc. [#2] [label + printed border]	Multicolored	Hist	Parkinson	B
3349	Herr Hitler's dream of reign supreme / is really quite etc. [no picture]	Green	Hitle	Shaw, CF	A
3350	He's / back / again [handpainted]	Multicolored	VJDay	Adler	D
3351	He's / my / Uncle / ! [handpainted]	Multicolored	Uncle	Knapp	H
3352	He's a grand old man / Let's back him up! / Buy war stamps & bonds	Black	Uncle	Richard	A
3353	He's betting his life / You / back him up! / Buy more war bonds	Brown, red	Army	Boone	A
3354	He's betting his life / You / buy more war bonds	Unknown	Unk	Boone	A
3355	He's betting his life / You back him up!	Brown, red	Army	Boone	A
3356	He's my uncle! [envelope 6x3 1/2 in.]	Blue, red	EagUn	Powers	A
3357	He's not thru! / We must / [etc.] / 1-3-'45--Mac's men liberate etc.	Unknown	Event	Linto	B
3358	He's not thru! / We must / continue to / back him!	Unknown	Unk	Linto	B
3359	He's spreading the news / $25 bond for 18.75. [envelope 6x3 1/2 in.]	Black	Bonds	Cox	A
3360	He's spreading the news / Germany surrenders!!! [envelope 6x3 1/2 in.]	Brown, green	VEDay	Cox	B
3361	He's spreading the news / Japan falls!!! [envelope 6x3 1/2 in.]	Unknown	VJDay	Cox	B
3362	He's still / "squawking" / but / not the etc. [torn at right] [handpainted]	Multicolored	Hitle	Cowdery	D
3363	He's their Uncle Sam	Blue	Uncle	Hillerich	A

NO.	CACHET TEXT	COLOR	TOPIC	PUBLISHER	$
3364	Hey buddy / how do I get an / outfit etc. [burned top, torn right] [handpainted]	Multicolored	Army	Cowdery	D
3365	Hey folks! Want / a gift suggestion? etc.	Unknown	Home	Phill, CR	A
3366	Hey you! / Don't quit that war job etc. [thermographed]	Unknown	Home	Baur	A
3367	Hey! / youse guys! / The mail's in! [envelope 8 7/8x3 7/8 in.]	Multicolored	Army	Porto-Serv	B
3368	Hey! got / any mail for —— [Army or Navy] [envelope 8 7/8x3 7/8 or 7 1/4x3 7/8 in.]	Multicolored	Armed	Porto-Serv	B
3369	Hey! that's / my name [envelope 8 7/8x3 7/8 in.]	Multicolored	Army	Porto-Serv	B
3370	Hey, bud! / How about / investing in a little / freedom today? [handpainted]	Black	Bonds	Parker	B
3371	Hey, Mr. Postman, take this one and run! [in quotes] [envelope 7 1/2x3 7/8 in.]	Black	Army	Fertig	B
3372	Hi ya, sailor! / Bet this is the etc. [no picture] [env. 9 1/2x4 1/8 in.]	Unknown	Navy	Meryle	B
3373	Hi! Yo'all in the Army / Merry Christmas! [handpainted]	Multicolored	Holid	Cowdery	D
3374	Hi, buddy / don't / forget / to buy / U.S. / war / bonds	Multicolored	Bonds	Linto	B
3375	Hi, buddy / don't let / your Uncle / Sam down! / Buy U.S. / war bonds!	Multicolored	Bonds	Linto	B
3376	Hi, buddy / have you / purchased / your / U.S. / bonds?	Unknown	Bonds	Linto	B
3377	Hic / Hic / How am I doing? [in quotes]	Black	Unk	Lupton	A
3378	Hide in your shell / but you're next / and doomed for H....[thermographed]	Bk/Bu/Br	Hitle	Ang	A
3379	Hi-folks/ Here's that / overdue / mail for [envelope 8 7/8x3 7/8 in.]	Multicolored	Unk	Porto-Serv	B
3380	High tide and / torpedoes can't / stop the mail / for [env. 8 7/8x3 7/8 in.]	Multicolored	Navy	Porto-Serv	B
3381	High time / somebody wuz / tossin' a line / to [envelope 8 7/8x3 7/8 in.]	Multicolored	Navy	Porto-Serv	B
3382	High-ho! Here's / a letter for [envelope 8 7/8x3 7/8 in.]	Multicolored	Air	Porto-Serv	B
3383	High-ranking Navy and Marine Corps officers who attended the etc. [9/2/45]	Black	VJDay	Southworth	B
3384	Hi-ho, hi-ho / We're off to Tokyo [artist: Rich Shaw]	Bu/Gn/Red	Armed	Christens	A
3385	Himmel! / un blimpen! / Down / qvick! [allover] [yellow env. 7 7/16x3 7/8 in.]	Black	Uboat	Army	C
3386	Hirihito [sic] wants to / be very happy / We can help / Buy bonds [no picture]	Multicolored	Japan	Linto	B
3387	His / road home / Don't block it! [ten envelope]	Black	Navy	Ohio Bell	D
3388	Hirohito / B-29s put him there! / Keep'em flying! / With etc. [handpainted]	Multicolored	Japan	Myers	C
3389	His "end" is inevitable	Brown	UncJa	Lawrence	A
3390	His prayer—— / Please do all you / [etc.] / 2-5-'45——Yanks / take Manila	Unknown	Event	Linto	B
3391	His prayer—— / Please do all you / can over there to / help us fight for etc	Unknown	Armed	Linto	B
3392	His regular face lifting treatment	Multicolored	Japan	Peer	B
3393	His telephone / comes first!	Blue	Army	Ohio Bell	D
3394	His turn / is / coming / next	Blue/Red	Japan	Peters	A
3395	His V for / victory [colored envelopes]	Blue, red	Uncle	Poppenger	A
3396	History in the making / [etc.] / 4th / time / inauguration of F.D. Roosevelt	Bk,R,S/Bu,R,	FDR	Staehle	E
3397	History repeats [handpainted]	Black	Hitle	Clendennen	D
3398	Hit / him / hard!! / ...-. [handpainted]	Blue	Hitle	Parker	B
3399	Hit 'em hard / And how! / "Give 'im the woiks" [handpainted]	Black	Hitle	Parker	B
3400	Hitler / Mussie / Hirohito etc.	Unknown	Axis	Baur	A
3401	Hitler / They thought when he rose a leader / grand, / he would bless his etc.	Bk,R/Bk,Bro	Hitle	Carpenter	A
3402	Hitler and Hell [in quotes] / Hitler called the Devil on the telephone etc.	Red	Hitle	Boone	A
3403	Hitler and the Devil / Hitler called the Devil etc. [lined border]	Bu/O/Red	Hitle	Boone	A
3404	Hitler and the Devil / Hitler called the Devil etc. [no lined border]	Bu/O/Red	Hitle	Boone	A
3405	Hitler claims / the better men, / but, the U.S. Army, / builds supermen!	Bk/Bu/Pu/R	Hitle	Harrington	A
3406	Hitler claims he has / the better men / but, he first has met United etc.	Blue	Army	Harrington	A
3407	Hitler enjoys the / personal political / differences which etc. [no picture]	Gold, silver	Hitle	Linto	B
3408	Hitler-Musso-Tojo / The heavy slugging terrors / on three called strikes etc.	Red	Axis	Buckalew	B
3409	Hitler's "holly" German soil	Multicolored	Hitle	Peer	B
3410	Hitler's / superrace / kaput!	Gold	Hitle	Linto	B
3411	Hitler's / war / fund / "Fill 'er up for Adolph!" [handpainted]	Black	Dog	Clendennen	D
3412	Hitler's Europe [with "Eu" X'd out]	Multicolored	Hitle	Peer	B
3413	Hitler's Europe is invaded / After a long wait of two years, the United etc.	Blue	DDay	Unknown	B
3414	Hitler's mad dog / Help destroy him [thermographed]	Bk/Bk,Y/R,Y	Japan	Sadworth	C
3415	Hitler's mad dog / Help destroy him [thermographed]	Multi/O,Red	Japan	Sadworth	C
3416	Hitler's service / flag	Black/Blue	Hitle	Boone	A
3417	Hitler's service / flag	Black, brown	Hitle	Rush, JM	A
3418	Hitler's subs are presenting / a modern version of... / carrying coals to etc.	Black, green	Navy	Andrews	B
3419	Hitting him where it hurts	Multicolored	UncJa	Peer	B
3420	Hives - hum / for vengeance / U.S. / plane / plants / Swarm Tokio	Bu/Gn/Red	Air	Davis, D	A
3421	Ho! ho! / ho! ho! / "He who laughs / last ——" / Ethiopia / Musso / Africa	Brown	Musso	Roberts	A
3422	Hoarding...? / Our government has huge / quantities of various foods etc.	Multicolored	Home	Linto	B
3423	Hoiman's [in quotes] horn, it ain't / so sweet, / poor "Adolph's" day is etc.	Black/R,Bu	Nazis	Runge	A
3424	Hold high / the torch / of / civilization [colored envelopes]	Blue, red	Torch	Poppenger	A
3425	Hold high the torch of liberty	Blue/Red	Liber	Harrington	A
3426	Hold to the line [in quotes] / to prevent inflation / What line?	Multicolored	Home	Linto	B

NO.	CACHET TEXT	COLOR	TOPIC	PUBLISHER	$
3427	Holiday wishes [handpainted]	Multicolored	Holid	Adler	D
3428	Hollandia / we are here!	Multicolored	Navy	Amer Pat	A
3429	Home / of / freemen [small shield]	Multicolored	Shiel	Amer Pat	A
3430	Home / of / freemen [tall shield and soldier]	Multicolored	Armed	Amer Pat	A
3431	Home / while our men fight abroad / to etc. [no picture]	Unknown	Unk	Phill, M	A
3432	Home of freemen [text in caps across small shield]	Multicolored	Shiel	Amer Pat	A
3433	Home of freemen [text in script across eagle on large shield]	Multicolored	EagSh	Amer Pat	A
3434	Home of the original American	Blue, red	Hist	Brenn	A
3435	Home! [handpainted]	Multicolored	VEDay	Sturgill	F
3436	Hon. golly! / War bonds / dood it! / Pacific strip poker [thermographed]	Blue	UncJa	Unknown	B
3437	Honest fellers, that tattooing was / done before I ever heard of the etc.	Brown	Armed	Neal	A
3438	Honey it's only me / waitin' for you [in quotes] [burned edge] [handpainted]	Multicolored	Home	Cowdery	D
3439	Honor cover / Heroes of the Navy	Multicolored	Navy	Cliff	B
3440	Honor mother / Mothers day [flags]	Black, red	Holid	Brenn	A
3441	Honor to the U.S. Marines / Gen. Alexander Vandergrift [handpainted]	Multicolored	Gener	Knoll	D
3442	Honorable chef is reserving / Japan for dessert. Allied forces / Japan etc.	Black, tan	Japan	Andrews	B
3443	Honorable conferees say / "The Son of Heaven / wants more territory" etc.	Green, red	Japan	Myers	A
3444	Honorable Jap [in quotes] / Hitler's mad dog / Help destroy him [thermographed]	Black, yellow	Japan	Sadworth	C
3445	Honorable request to Jap fleet / "Come out and fight" / Frank Knox etc.	Blue	Japan	Bean	A
3446	Honorably / serving our / nation on all / battlefronts / [etc.] / 1775-1944	R,Gn/S,Gn	USMC	Dale	A
3447	Honoring our armed forces / [etc.] / Liberty Ship -- World War II [therm]	Black, Green	Merch	Crosby	C
3448	Honoring our armed forces / [etc.] / U.S.S. Comfort (AH-6) [therm]	Multicolored	Navy	Crosby	C
3449	Honoring our armed forces / [etc.] / USS Arizona etc. [thermographed]	Unknown	Navy	Crosby	B
3450	Honoring our armed forces / [etc.] / USS Oklahoma etc. [thermographed]	Unknown	Navy	Crosby	B
3451	Honoring our armed forces / [etc.] / USS Utah etc. [thermographed]	Unknown	Navy	Crosby	B
3452	Honoring our armed forces / second to none / US Navy etc. [thermographed]	Unknown	Navy	Crosby	B
3453	Honoring our armed forces / United States Army [thermographed]	Unknown	Army	Crosby	B
3454	Honoring the / US Army / crossing etc.	Brown	Army	Grimsland	B
3455	Honoring the oppressed / [etc.] / Jugoslavia	Unknown	ORN	Runge	A
3456	Honors / to our / courageous / navy etc.	Unknown	Navy	Linto	B
3457	Hoo—— Hoo—— / Take a tip from / "the wise old bird" / Buy and keep etc.	Black, blue	Bonds	Lowell	A
3458	Hoo.. Hoo.. / take a tip from / "the wise old bird" / He still invests etc.	Bk,Gn/Br,Gn	Bonds	Lowell	A
3459	Hoosiers fight on every front etc.	Red	Armed	Price, R	A
3460	Hoot / mon! / $100 / United / States / war / bonds etc. [left border]	Green, red	Bonds	Boone	A
3461	Hoot / mon! / $100 / United / States / war / bonds etc. [no left border]	Gree, red	Bonds	Boone	A
3462	Hoot / mon! / $25.00 / war bonds / now selling for / $18.75 [7 stars]	Green, red	Bonds	Boone	A
3463	Hoot / mon! / $25.00 / war bonds / now selling for / $18.75 [no stars]	Green, red	Bonds	Bone	A
3464	Hoot / mon! / a stamp a day, will keep the Nip / and Hun away.	Black, red	Bonds	Baur	A
3465	Hoot, mon, / save waste paper / save waste fat / save gas and rubber etc.	Black, red	Home	Eichenlaub	A
3466	Hope / liberty / right / Invasion, to etc.	Unknown	Unk	Runge	A
3467	Hope I'm called soon——I'm crazy / to get into a uniform! [in quotes] [blue envelope]	Multicolored	Home	Amer Art	A
3468	Horrors! Horrors!! / U.S. war / bonds will / keep our / women and children etc.	Gold	Bonds	Linto	B
3469	Hospital band in review, Camp Butner, N.C.	Sepia	Medic	Unknown	B
3470	Hospital Corps, U.S.N. / on sea and ashore / Naval Hospital, San Diego etc. [thermo]	Red	Medic	Crosby	C
3471	Hospital Corps, U.S.N. / on sea and ashore / U.S. Navy Hospital Corps etc. [thermo]	Silver	Medic	Crosby	C
3472	Hostilities exist. / There is / no blinking at the fact [in quotes] etc.	Blue, red	FDR	Amer Pat	B
3473	Hostilities exist. / There is no / blinking at the fact [in quotes] etc.	Blue, red	FDR	Amer Pat	B
3474	Hostilities exist. [in quotes] / [etc.] / Tokyo / bombed / so sorry! [thermographed]	Multicolored	Japan	Boone	B
3475	Hot / foot / Sicily / invaded / July 14, 1943	Black, red	Event	Fidelity	B
3476	Hot dogs!! / s-i-z-z / wow / ouch papa! [handpainted]	Multicolored	Army	Cowdery	D
3477	Hot foot	Red	Hitle	Peters	A
3478	Hour of victory / appears near as / Allies send the / terms to Japs! [thermographed]	Blue, red	Event	Boone	A
3479	Housewives! / save / waste etc. [label + blue "Victory" border]	Multicolored	Women	Unknown	B
3480	Housewives! / save / waste etc. [label + red "Victory" border]	Multicolored	Women	Unknown	B
3481	Housewives! / save / waste etc. [label + red "Win the War" border]	Multicolored	Women	Unknown	B
3482	How about / a message / for —— [envelope 8 7/8x3 7/8 in.]	Multicolored	Navy	Porto-Serv	B
3483	How about an all- / out bombing of / Japan? [no picture]	Multicolored	Japan	Linto	B
3484	How about trying this / for size, Adolf?	Black	Hitle	Davis, Ray	B
3485	How am I doing [in quotes]	Black	Unk	Baur	A
3486	How am I doing.	Blue, red	Uncle	Unknown	A
3487	How am I doing? [in quotes] [sailor walking to left]	Black	Navy	Lupton	A
3488	How am I doing? [in quotes] [soldier walking to right]	Black	Army	Lupton	A
3489	How can England expect / [etc.] / 9-21-'44——Halsey's men sink, damage / 37 etc.	Unknown	Event	Linto	B

NO.	CACHET TEXT	COLOR	TOPIC	PUBLISHER	$
3490	How can England expect / India to fight for / England's empire while etc.	Unknown	Ally	Linto	B
3491	How can the war / labor board, di- / vided 8 to 4, / make etc. [no picture]	Multicolored	Home	Linto	B
3492	How could we loose [sic]? / To G.I. Joe / When this war is over etc.	Black	Home	Shaw, TC	A
3493	How do you say / yes [handpainted]	Multicolored	Japan	Wolf, CL	B
3494	How does it feel / to die? / I could tell you - but / it's too etc. [therm]	Multicolored	Army	unknown	A
3495	How does your / situation rank / [etc.] / Victory Fleet Day / September 27 etc.	Multicolored	Home	Linto	B
3496	How does your / situation rank / with this man / in service? / Sure you'll etc.	Multicolored	Bonds	Linto	B
3497	How does your / situation rank / with this man / in service? etc. [color varieties]	Multicolored	Bonds	Linto	B
3498	How doth the little busy B-29 / improve each etc. [handpainted]	Multicolored	Japan	Myers	B
3499	How doth the little busy B-29 / improve each shining hour etc. [handpainted]	Multicolored	Japan	Martin	B
3500	How long will / Churchill and Stalin / continue to run the / United States?	Unknown	Ally	Linto	B
3501	How long will / Churchiull and Stalin / [etc.] / 9-4-'44——Huns called to etc.	Unknown	Event	Linto	B
3502	How much of / this week's pay etc. [envelope 8 11/16x3 5/8 in.]	Unknown	Home	ITE Circui	B
3503	How much the whole world owes to / this historic shrine! Built 1732-1747 etc.	Black	Hist	Clark	A
3504	How soon / ruin [handpainted]	Multicolored	Japan	Wolf, CL	B
3505	How they would / enjoy it	Unknown	Unk	Baur	A
3506	How to come home with / extra red / points! etc. [thermographed]	Unknown	Unk	Threl+Thar	A
3507	How will the / "Masters of Confusion" / in Washington handle / the postwar etc.	Unknown	Home	Linto	B
3508	How will the / "Masters" / [etc.] / 8-24-'44——Yanks reported / at Swiss border	Unknown	Home	Linto	B
3509	How your tax money is used / Curtiss- / [etc.] / 9-13-'40——Buckingham etc.	Multicolored	Anniv	Linto	B
3510	How your tax money is used / Curtiss-Wright Aviation Co. etc. [no picture]	Pink, silver	Home	Linto	B
3511	How's about / war / bonds / as tickets etc.	Unknown	Bonds	Boone	A
3512	Humanity date / United Nations etc. [first line: large caps]	Multicolored	UN	Amer Pat	A
3513	Humanity date / United Nations etc. [first line: small caps]	Multicolored	UN	Amer Pat	A
3514	Huns say they / will fight / [etc.] / 3-12-'45——Zamboanga and / airfield etc.	Unknown	Event	Linto	B
3515	Huns say they / will fight it out / in the sewers! / Right at home!	Unknown	Nazis	Linto	B
3516	Huns seek a peace / based on reason! / [etc.] / 9-19-'44——Yank subs sink etc.	Multicolored	Event	Linto	B
3517	Huns seek a peace / based on reason! / Well, we have the etc. [no picture]	Multicolored	Nazis	Linto	B
3518	Hurry / boost your / bond-buying etc.	Blue, red	Bonds	Kosko	A
3519	Hurry / soldier! / I'm as anxious / as you are! [handpainted]	Multicolored	Army	Cowdery	D
3520	Hyde Park / Franklin Delano Roosevelt etc. [thermographed]	Unknown	FDR	Grimsland	B
3521	Hyde Park home / Place of birth etc.	Blue, red	FDR	Cachet Cra	B

Cover Values (from Table 6, p. 136)

Value	Price Range
A	$ 3 - 6
B	$ 7 - 15
C	$ 16 - 30
D	$ 31 - 60
E	$ 61 - 125
F	$ 126 - 250
G	$ 251 - 500
H	$ 501 - 1000
I	$ >1000
X	Unpriced: Suspicious or fraudulent cover

3202

"HAPPY NEW YEAR"

1945

HAMILTON, OHIO
JAN 1
8-AM
1945

Arthur Knoll
660 Emerson Ave
Hamilton, Ohio

3269

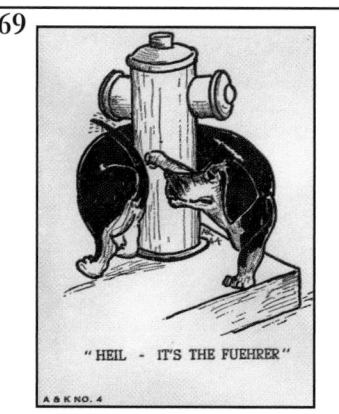

"HEIL - IT'S THE FUEHRER"

A & K NO. 4

3292

HELP BUY PLANES
FOR "HONORABLE VISIT" TO TOKIO

3297

"HELP HIM COME HOME"

K9 CORPS
WAGS

HAMILTON, OHIO
NOV 30
7-AM
1944

Art Knoll
660 Emerson
Hamilton, Ohio.

BUY WAR BONDS

Knoll'44

3328

Here is your

Minute Man

IMPORTANT.—Please enclose this wrapper when sending revised mailing instructions to Minute Man.

619

Mr. Frank X. Monaghan,
Postmaster,
Butte, Montana.

OFFICIAL BUSINESS

TREASURY DEPARTMENT
WAR FINANCE DIVISION
WASHINGTON, D. C.

PENALTY FOR PRIVATE USE TO AVOID
PAYMENT OF POSTAGE, $300

GPO

3335

HERE'S TO OLD B. AND G.
HE'S FULL OF P. AND V.
WHEN SOMEONE SAID
"THERE'S KRAUTS AHEAD"
HE REPLIED "WHO G.A.D.?"

3344

COPR. 1943 R. L. PARKINSON

NO. 18

DANIEL
WEBSTER
1782-1852

LB

HEROIC AMERICANS

"Liberty and Union, now and forever,
one and inseparable!"

3345

3351

3367

3388

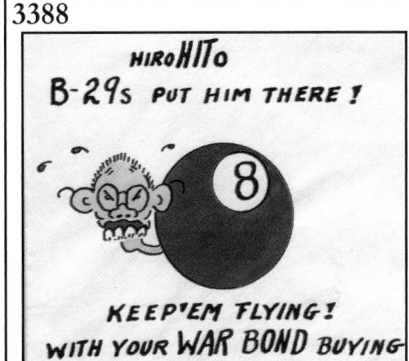

3392

3401

3419

3482

CACHET TEXT BEGINNING WITH "I"

NO.	CACHET TEXT	COLOR	TOPIC	PUBLISHER	$
3522	I / have / returned [in quotes] / U.S. forces under etc. [text dated 10/20/44]	Multicolored	Mac	Staehle	C
3523	I / have / returned [in quotes] / U.S. forces under etc. [text dated 12/15/44]	Multicolored	Mac	Staehle	C
3524	I admired these stripes on a uniform / I saw——so [in quotes] etc. [blue envelope]	Multicolored	Navy	Amer Art	A
3525	I aim to hit! I bet you! [above or below picture] etc. [thermographed]	Blue	Navy	Crosby	B
3526	I am an / American / Isn't it great to be free?	Unknown	Unk	Boone	A
3527	I am an / American / It's great to be an American! [letters vary in coloring]	Blue, red	Unk	Boone	A
3528	I am an / American [allover cachet] [handpainted]	Multicolored	Shiel	Buxton, D	D
3529	I am an / American [handpainted]	Multicolored	Eagle	Shaffer, A	C
3530	I am an / American [handpainted]	Blue, red	Shiel	Krakora	B
3531	I am an American, / and whenever I look up and see / the Stars and Stripes etc.	Blue, red	Flag	Carpenter	A
3532	I am an American——I take pride in my / country the United States of America.	Black, purple	Uncle	Lowe	A
3533	I am going over! / I hope you will / not fail me! / Keep on / buying / bonds!	Multicolored	Bonds	Linto	B
3534	I am leaving now, but I'll be / back. The voice of freedom [in quotes] etc.	Blue, red	Mac	Brenn	B
3535	I am proud / to be an / American	Blue	Unk	Gen Coin	A
3536	I am proud to be / a nephew of the / world's greatest uncle	Blue, red	Uncle	Neal	A
3537	I am voting / for / Tom and John / Are you? / Thomas E. Dewey etc.	Black, sepia	Home	Miner	B
3538	I am with you	Blue, gold	Navy	McGovern	A
3539	I am with you	Bu,Gn/Bu,O	Navy	McGovern	A
3540	I believe in America..its institutions / ..its methods ...its way of etc.	Blue, red	EagFl	Brenn	A
3541	I bought an extra war bond! [vest button on envelope] [handp]	Black	Bonds	Unknown	C
3542	I came . / I saw. / I'm sawdust!	Multicolored	Hitle	Unknown	B
3543	I came through and I returned [in quotes] [thermographed]	Blue	Mac	Crosby	B
3544	I came through and I will return [in quotes] [thermographed]	Blue	Mac	Crosby	B
3545	I came. / I saw. / I'm sawdust! / Another Caesar	Blue, red	Hitle	Dale	A
3546	I can read it, but I can't pronounce it [in quotes] [buff envelope]	Multicolored	Army	Amer Art	A
3547	I can't help it if you / are having maneuvers [in quotes] etc. [pmark Iceland 10/41] [hp]	Multicolored	USMC	Unknown	D
3548	I could have / sworn that I / saw / a torpedo! [in quotes]	Black	Navy	Lupton	A
3549	I demand / unconditional surrender? / Japan surrenders / Atomic bomb etc.	Blue, red	VJDay	Baur	B
3550	I didn't investigate / before I invested! / Now all I have is advice: etc.	O, purple	Bonds	Eichenlaub	A
3551	I do not want war. / I want peace... / a piece of England [in quotes] etc.	Blue, red	Hitle	Smith, W	A
3552	I don't / want 'em!	Blue/Red	Axis	Barnes	A
3553	I don't care / if it's 30 below—— / or summertime! etc. [top burned] [handpainted]	Multicolored	Home	Cowdery	D
3554	I don't care if he is the company mascot / the War Department etc. [handpaint]	Multicolored	Army	Unknown	C
3555	I guess this is the / end	Black	Hitle	Wolf, CL	A
3556	I have / returned / Gen. MacArthur / US troops etc. [thermographed]	Unknown	Mac	Boone	B
3557	I have not yet begun to fight [in quotes] / John Paul Jones	Multicolored	Hist	Minkus	A
3558	I have sworn upon the / altar etc. [5 lines]	Red, silver	Eagle	Boone	A
3559	I have sworn upon the altar, / of God eternal hostility against etc.	Blue, red	Eagle	Boone	A
3560	I hear we may get a couple / of extra weeks etc. [burned edge] [handpainted]	Multicolored	Army	Cowdery	D
3561	I knew it! The same story etc.	Blue, red	Uncle	Carpenter	A
3562	I knew the men of Bataan well and / loved / [etc.] / Gen Douglas MacArthur.	Blue, red	Mac	Baur	B
3563	I know not what course others may / [etc.] / 10-18-'44——Halsey's boys sink etc.	Black, gold	Event	Linto	B
3564	I know not what course others may / take; but as for me, give me liberty etc.	Gy,Gn/Gold	Hist	Linto	B
3565	I only regret / that I have [in quotes] / [etc.] / V-J Day / Japan surrenders	Multicolored	VJDay	Thorpe	C
3566	I only regret / that I have but one life / to lose for [in quotes] etc.	Multicolored	Hist	Thorpe	B
3567	I pay no more than top legal prices / I accept no rationed goods without etc.	Green/Red	Home	Limoges	A
3568	I pay no more than top legal prices etc. [thermogr.] [envelope 7 1/2x4 in.]	Red	Home	Limoges	B
3569	I pledge allegiance / to the flag of the / United States of / America etc.	Multicolored	EagFl	Amer Pat	A
3570	I pledge allegiance the flag of the / United States etc.	Blue, red	Flag	Ang	A
3571	I pledge allegiance to the flag / of the United States of America / and to etc.	Multicolored	Flag	Linto	B
3572	I say boys / are they all like this?	Blue, red	Army	Unknown	A
3573	I shall / return / Gen. Douglas etc.	Black	Mac	Rameco	B
3574	I shall keep the soldiers faith. [in quotes] / 1942 / Dedication / [etc.] / MacArthur. [artist: Staehle]	Blue, red	MacFD	Fleetwood	C
3575	I shall know but one country etc. [plane in level flight or diving]	Unknown	Air	Baur	A
3576	I shall know but one country. I was born etc.	Unknown	Unk	Lowe	A
3577	I shall return / General MacArthur etc.	Unknown	Mac	Lowell	B
3578	I shall return / MacArthur did return etc.	Multicolored	Mac	Phill, CR	B
3579	I shall return [in quotes] / [etc.] / Phillippines [sic] / invaided [sic]	Blue, red	Event	Unknown	B
3580	I shall return [in quotes] / Above the ringing of the bells / and the etc.	Blue	Mac	Lawrence	B
3581	I shall return [in quotes] / General MacArthur / Extra / Extra / Phillippines [sic] etc.	Blue, red	Event	Unknown	B

NO.	CACHET TEXT	COLOR	TOPIC	PUBLISHER	$
3582	I shall return to the Philippines [in quotes]	Black/Purple	Mac	Davis, Ray	B
3583	I shall serve if elected / by etc.	Green	Unk	McFarland	A
3584	I slipped! / Falling! / Musso / Greece	Brown	Musso	Roberts	A
3585	I stand for / freedom and / liberty etc.	Blue, red	Uncle	Levering	A
3586	I therefore believe it is my / duty etc.	Unknown	Unk	Brenn	A
3587	I think / she's forgetting / me! Only 4 letters / today. [handpainted]	Multicolored	Army	Cowdery	D
3588	I thought I'd find my boy friend / here——he's been a kitchen policeman etc.	Black	Army	Deming	A
3589	I told you so! / Italy / Germany / Japan next [envelope 7 1/2x4 in.]	Multicolored	Axis	Baur	A
3590	I told you we could / [etc.] / Germany surrenders [printed + cut-&-pasted]	Black, yellow	VEDay	Wolf, CL	B
3591	I took the / seat of a / [etc.] / I kept / a mother / from etc. [handpainted]	Black	Home	Martin	C
3592	I urge every Filipino to be of / good cheer etc.	Blue, red	EagSh	Brenn	A
3593	I want you to make / the etc.	Black	Unk	Unknown	A
3594	I went to Camp —— —— —— to see / my husband and met the handsomest etc.	Black	Women	Deming	A
3595	I will keep the / soldier's faith [in quotes] / MacArthur	Black/Brown	Mac	Yontz	B
3596	I will return [in quotes] / Today, March 17, 1942 etc.	Orange	Mac	Unknown	B
3597	I won't let / my sweetheart / down etc. [envelope 8 7/8x3 7/8 in.]	Multicolored	Unk	Porto-serv	B
3598	Iceland base / command [handpainted] [envelope 6 3/4x3 3/4 in.]	Unknown	Bases	Myers	C
3599	Iceworms and flapjacks served every noon in the sourdough etc. [on flap]	Blue, red	Alack	Unknown	A
3600	Ickes and Myer Co. / [etc.] / 3-17-'44——Yanks invade Manus Isle, / also etc.	Multicolored	Event	Linto	B
3601	Ices and Myer Co. / Jap custodians / Maybe, soon, we will / have a etc.	Multicolored	AJA	Linto	B
3602	Ickes should make / a good buddy for / Hirohito and Tojo [no picture]	Brown, red	Home	Linto	B
3603	Idiot [in quotes] Hitler / rules a / savage race!	Gold, silver	Hitle	Linto	B
3604	Idle chatter brings disaster	Green	Unk	Davis, Ray	A
3605	Idle gossip sinks ships [75 or 77 mm long] [no picture] [envelope 6x3 ½ in.]	Red	Home	USO	A
3606	Idle gossip sinks ships! / So / button up your lip [picture: aircraft carrier]	Blue, red	Navy	Baur	A
3607	Idle gossip sinks ships! / So / button up your lip [picture: battleship]	Red	Navy	Baur	A
3608	Idle money will / not win the / war! Use it to / buy bonds [no picture]	Gd/Gd,Silver	Bonds	Linto	B
3609	Idle words / sink ships	Blue/Red	Navy	Richardson	A
3610	If "the pen / is mightier than / the sword" you / should have etc. [handpainted]	Multicolored	Home	Cowdery	D
3611	If / you can't / go / across / come / across!! / Buy / bonds.	Black	Bonds	Frye	A
3612	If a man is going to be an etc.	Unknown	Unk	Brenn	A
3613	If Americans permit present / growing tendency to bureau- etc. [no picture]	Gold, green	Home	Linto	B
3614	If it can be used / don't throw it etc.	Unknown	Unk	Brenn	A
3615	If it doesn't help win the war—— / forget it [in quotes]	Black, Brown	EagSh	Altenbernd	A
3616	If it doesn't help win the war—— / forget it [in quotes] [envelope 7 1/2x4 in.]	Black	EagSh	Altenbrand	A
3617	If the hat fits, / wear it!	Black	Women	Christens	A
3618	If we / don't / relax / now [handpainted]	Multicolored	Winst	Adler	D
3619	If we are seriously planning / for peace why prepare / for war ????	Gold	Event	Linto	B
3620	If we get a few more / bureaucrats in Wash- / ington we will etc. [no picture]	Multicolored	Home	Linto	B
3621	If we remain one people, under an efficient / [etc.] / 10-10-'44——Halsey's etc.	Gold, green	Event	Linto	B
3622	If we remain one people, under an efficient / government, etc. [no picture]	Gold	Wash	Linto	B
3623	If ye break faith / with us who die / we shall not sleep. [in quotes]	Multicolored	Holid	Monty	C
3624	If you ! buy war bonds / and save them. [thermographed] [envelope 7x5 in.]	Blue, red	Bonds	Unknown	A
3625	If you are an American / [etc.] / 4-6-'44——Japs wire traps to dead Yanks. etc.	Multicolored	Event	Linto	B
3626	If you are an American / [etc.] / Navy Day——Oct. 27, 1943	Multicolored	Navy	Linto	B
3627	If you are an American / shake hands with yourself	Multicolored	Minut	Linto	B
3628	If you are an American / shake hands with yourself	Multicolored	Flag	Linto	B
3629	If you are good / at angling try / landing some / U.S. Bonds	Gn, S/Multi	Bonds	Linto	B
3630	If you are not active / in / [etc.] / 6-17-'44——Elba Isle now occupied etc.	Unknown	Event	Linto	B
3631	If you are not active / in winning-the-war / efforts please keep / out of etc.	Silver	Liber	Linto	B
3632	If you buy war bonds / and save them [thermographed]	Blue, red	Bonds	Baur	A
3633	If you can't / drive a tank / you can / help build one	Blue	Unk	Peters	A
3634	If you can't / drop one... / invest in one! / Buy bonds / America!	Blue, red	Bonds	Boone	A
3635	If you can't / fly a plane / you can etc.	Red	Unk	Peters	A
3636	If you can't / sail a ship / you can / help build one	Green	Navy	Peters	A
3637	If you can't fight / then don't strike! [handpainted]	Multicolored	Army	Borkowski	C
3638	If you can't go across / come across etc.	Red	Unk	Harrington	A
3639	If you care, buy a share etc. [envelope 8 11/16x3 5/8 in.]	Unknown	Unk	ITE Circui	B
3640	If you do not / want America / "Russianized" / vote for / Dewey!	Black, red	Flag	Linto	B
3641	If you do not / want America / [etc.] / 9-25-'44——Nazis cut line / of etc.	Multicolored	Event	Linto	B
3642	If you don't buy more bonds you undercut / civilization——do you want etc.	Blue, red	Bonds	Quigley	B
3643	If you don't write - / you're wrong!	Blue	Army	Shaw, MM	A
3644	If you don't write / you're wrong [handpainted]	Multicolored	Army	Adler	C

NO.	CACHET TEXT	COLOR	TOPIC	PUBLISHER	$
3645	If you don't write it, no one can read it.	Blue	Army	Davis, Ray	A
3646	If you don't write, you're wrong	Blue	Unk	Christens	A
3647	If you feel like I feel, etc. [no picture] [top, bottom border design varies]	Red	Verse	Brenn	A
3648	If you have skill, apply it. / [etc.] / Victory Fleet Day / September 27, 1943	Multicolored	Navy	Linto	B
3649	If you have skill, apply it. / If you have brains, use them. / If you have etc.	Gd,R/Gn,Red	Minut	Linto	B
3650	If you have to stand / in line pick / [etc.] / 6-4-'45——U.S.S. destroyer etc.	Multicolored	Event	Linto	B
3651	If you have to stand / in line pick the one / selling U.S. Bonds!	Multicolored	Bell	Linto	B
3652	If you like rats / [etc.] / Japs etc. [handpainted] [envelope 9 1/2x4 1/8 in.]	Black	Japan	Unknown	B
3653	If you love / America / give in /etc.	Unknown	Unk	Levering	A
3654	If you must / hoard / put those / war etc. [no picture]	Unknown	Unk	Threl+Thar	A
3655	If you must talk / [etc.] / Marines [brown penalty env. 8 11/16x5 5/8 in.]	Black	USMC	USMC	E
3656	If you patronize black markets / you better hide your face, like / this etc.	Green	Home	Davis, D	A
3657	If you talk / he hears	Black	Hitl	Wolf, CL	A
3658	If you're / either of these etc. [envelope 8 11/16x3 5/8 in.]	Unknown	Unk	ITE Circui	B
3659	If you're going to / carry tales and / chatter too - the etc. [handpainted]	Multicolored	Home	Martin	B
3660	If you're going to / carry tales and / chatter too .. / the place for etc.	Multicolored	Verse	Meyers	C
3661	If... / our military branch / [etc.] / 12-27-'43——Big German battleship etc.	Multicolored	Mac	Linto	B
3662	If... / our military branch / [etc.] / 12-28-'44——Russians take Leningrad etc.	Multicolored	Event	Linto	B
3663	If... / our military branch / of the government / was / [etc.] / for 29 months	Multicolored	Mac	Linto	B
3664	If... / our military branch / of the government / was / [etc.] / MacArthur!	Multicolored	Mac	Linto	B
3665	Ike's strategy beat Huns	Blue, sepia	Ike	Linto	B
3666	Il Duce: / "Answer" cried the fascist showman,"emblem of" etc. [handpainted]	Multicolored	Liber	Weigand	B
3667	Il Duce: / When, with fascist ceremonials, / entering etc. [handpainted]	Multicolored	Liber	Weigand	B
3668	Il Duce: / While the bombers / [etc.] / 2——Into that apartment regal etc. [handpainted]	Multicolored	Liber	Weigand	B
3669	I'll / surrender / but / [in quotes] etc. / Atomic bombing [handpainted]	Black	Atom	Sturgill	F
3670	I'll / take / Manila! [in quotes] [thermographed]	Blue	Uncle	Crosby	B
3671	I'll be / back in a flash. [handpainted]	Multicolored	Army	Adler	D
3672	I'll be glad when this / 'chute shortage is over! [in quotes]	Multicolored	Chute	Amer Art	A
3673	I'll have you fellows / restricted / [etc.] / Greetings from [thermographed]	Blue	Navy	Crosby	B
3674	I'll have you fellows / restricted to your / ship etc. [thermographed]	Unknown	Unk	Crosby	B
3675	I'll sink the / English Navy / .. if they / catch me!	Blue/Purple	Musso	Roberts	A
3676	Im a / WOW! / ("write-often-wife") [handpainted]	Multicolored	Army	Cowdery	D
3677	I'm busy / waitin' for / somebody nice —— [in quotes] [handpainted]	Multicolored	Army	Cowdery	D
3678	I'm buying war bonds / Me worry? / [etc.] / Armed forces etc. [thermographed]	Brown/Green	Armed	Crosby	B
3679	I'm buying war bonds / Me worry? / [etc.] / I joined the U.S. Navy / and quit etc. [thermographed]	Blue/Green	Bonds	Crosby	B
3680	I'm buying war bonds / Me worry? / [etc.] / I'm gonna join the Army [thermographed]	Red	Army	Crosby	B
3681	I'm buying war bonds / Me worry? / [etc.] / I'm gonna join the WAVES [thermogr]	Red	WAVE	Crosby	B
3682	I'm buying war bonds / Me worry? / [etc.] / Join the WACS / by gum! [thermographed]	Green	WAC	Crosby	B
3683	I'm buying war bonds / Me worry? / [etc.] / Join the WACS and etc. [thermographed]	Purple	WAC	Crosby	B
3685	I'm buying war bonds / Me worry? / [etc.] / Join the WAVES / by gum! [thermogr]	Red	WAVE	Crosby	B
3685	I'm buying war bonds / Me worry? / [etc.] / Join the WAVES [thermographed]	Red	WAVE	Crosby	B
3686	I'm buying war bonds / Me worry? / [etc.] / Merchant Marine etc. [thermographed]	Blue	Merch	Crosby	B
3687	I'm buying war bonds / Me worry? / [etc.] / U.S. Navy etc. [thermographed]	Blue	Bonds	Crosby	B
3688	I'm buying war stamps / Me worry? / [etc.] / WACS and quit etc. [thermographed]	Purple	WAC	Crosby	B
3689	I'm doing my bit / and more / What's etc.	Unknown	Unk	Myers	A
3690	I'm doing my bit to / keep them up there!	Blue	Unk	Peters	A
3691	I'm doing my bit to / keep them up there!	Blue	Unk	Sklare	A
3692	I'm doing my bit to / keep them up there!	Blue	Unk	Boland	A
3693	I'm doing my bit, to- / keep them up there!	Br,Bu/Bk/Bu	Air	Harrington	A
3694	I'm doing my share / for Uncle Sam	Multicolored	Uncle	Dime	A
3695	I'm getting / tired so I can / sleep —— [in quotes] [handpainted]	Multicolored	Home	Cowdery	D
3696	I'm getting tired so I can / sleep —— [in quotes] [handpainted]	Multicolored	Army	Cowdery	D
3697	I'm glad that I'm American / I'm glad that I am free! / I etc. [no picture]	Brown, silver	Verse	Linto	B
3698	I'm going to like this town! [in quotes]	Black	Navy	Lupton	A
3699	I'm lonesome for / you too - [burned top edge, torn right edge] [handpainted]	Multicolored	Home	Cowdery	D
3700	I'm lookin' for —— [envelope 8 7/8x3 7/8 in.]	Multicolored	Army	Porto-serv	B
3701	I'm not asking you to do / I'm asking etc.	Unknown	Unk	Lowe	A
3702	I'm not buying / war bonds - / because I'm / a pumpkinhead! [handpainted]	Multicolored	Holid	Martin	B
3703	I'm on my way / Tokyo first / [etc.] / Scouting Squadron Two etc. [thermographed]	Red	Air	Crosby	B
3704	I'm on observation / duty! [in quotes]	Black	Army	Lupton	A
3705	I'm out to win the scrap drive in / our division! [in quotes] [buff envelope]	Multicolored	Army	Amer Art	A
3706	I'm so / glad if your / hand is O.K. again! [burned left edge] [handpainted]	Multicolored	Home	Cowdery	D
3707	I'm sounding / off for --- [bellowing sergeant, pen & ink] [handpainted]	Black	USMC	Stoner	B

NO.	CACHET TEXT	COLOR	TOPIC	PUBLISHER	$
3708	I'm the / head / man now! / "Just made captain of the head!"	Black	Navy	Lupton	A
3709	I'm Tojo... / [etc.] / I'm Adolph... / [etc.] / I'm Benito... etc.	Blue, red	Axis	Boone	A
3710	I'm working with / Uncle Sam!	Multicolored	Uncle	Minkus	A
3711	I'm writing / this while / scrubbing the etc. [env. 8 7/8x3 7/8 in.]	Multicolored	Navy	Porto-serv	B
3712	Imua, imua a lanakila! [in quotes] / Forward to victory!	Blue, red	Home	Sayama	B
3713	In / defense / of / U.S.A. [mimeographed] [on mail from marines in Iceland]	Black	Armed	Unknown	F
3714	In / defense / of / U.S.A. [mimeographed] [on mail from other military posts]	Black	Armed	Unknown	C
3715	In / Italy / and elsewhere / Queen of the battle	Blue, red	Army	Cozart	A
3716	In / memoriam [postmarked 05/30/1943]	Black	Holid	Unknown	B
3717	In 1944 the Yanks / captured territory / [etc.] / 8-31-'44——Yanks advance etc.	Unknown	Event	Linto	B
3718	In 1944 the Yanks / captured territory / in 9 days that re- / quired 24 etc.	Unknown	Armed	Linto	B
3719	In a new Naval / policy as / [etc.] / waters adjacent to Iceland. [handpainted]	Multicolored	Uncle	First Day	G
3720	In a new naval / policy as enunciated / by the Secretary of / the United etc. [handp]	Multicolored	Event	Batura	E
3721	In a rush? Yes!! / but only to buy his / share of war bonds	Blue/R,Bu	Bonds	Harrington	A
3722	In Berlin we shall be [in quotes]	Black, blue	USSR	Schust	A
3723	In commemoration / First mail / U.S.S. Cumberland Sound etc. [8/28/45] [Tokyo Bay]	Green	VJDay	Navy ship	F
3724	In commemoration of a heroic and / courageous / [etc.] / Czecho- / slovakia	Multicolored	ORN	Grandy	A
3725	In commemoration of a heroic and / courageous people. We salute / Belgium	Multicolored	ORN	Grandy	A
3726	In commemoration of a heroic and / courageous people. We salute / Denmark	Blue, red	ORN	Grandy	A
3727	In commemoration of a heroic and / courageous people. We salute / France	Multicolored	ORN	Grandy	A
3728	In commemoration of U.S. armed forces / we salute / The / [etc.] / Marines	Multicolored	USMC	Fluegel	C
3729	In defense of liberty [allover cachet] [handpainted]	Multicolored	Air	Buxton Mrs	D
3730	In defense of liberty [eagles and airplanes]	Blue, red	Home	Krakora	A
3731	In far off Hawaii the time / was 7:55 a.m. December 7th etc. [typed] [12/7/42]	Black	Pearl	Sievert	B
3732	In grateful memory / of / all the boys / who have etc. [envelope 6x3 ½ in.]	Blue, red	Armed	Reuss	A
3733	In his Easter bonnet / is Sergeant Bunny too / sending you his greetings etc.	Purple	Holid	Abel	A
3734	In hoc signo vincimus [in quotes] (in this sign we) etc. [env 6 3/4x3 7/8 in.]	Blue, red	EagV	Belles-let	C
3735	In honor of / United States / Marines / Hail / to the / Leathernecks etc.	Blue, red	USMC	Fleetwood	B
3736	In honor of / United States / Marines / Hail / to the etc. [artist: Knapp]	Blue, red	USMC	Fleetwood	C
3737	In honor of / Women Marines / I've freed a marine / to fight! etc.	Multicolored	USMC	Unknown	C
3738	In honor of the / United States Army.	Blue, gold	Army	Grandy	A
3738A	In honor of United States / Marine Corps. / Iwo Jima stamp / postmarked / [etc.] / on Iwo Jima etc.	Green	VJDay	Unknown	E
3739	In league with the Devil / the yellow menace	Black/Yellow	Japan	Neal	A
3740	In May, 1943 / at Tunis and Bizerte / the Axis hit the dirt etc.	Blue, red	Event	Griffith	b
3741	In memoriam / Dedication / Will Rogers Field / Oklahoma City, Oklahoma etc.	Black	Air	Edmunds	C
3742	In memoriam / Franklin D. Roosevelt / 1882-1945 / There is etc.	Black	FDR	Garfield	B
3743	In memoriam / Franklin D. Roosevelt / 1882-1945 [first line in caps]	Black	FDR	Shaw, MM	B
3744	In memoriam / Franklin D. Roosevelt / 1882-1945 [thermogr] [postmarked 4/12/45]	Multicolored	FDR	Von Los	E
3745	In memoriam / Franklin D. Roosevelt etc. [postmarked 4/12/45]	Black	FDR	Abel	E
3746	In memoriam / Franklin Delano Roosevelt etc.	Black	FDR	Detroit Ed	B
3747	In memoriam / Franklin Delano Roosevelt etc. [mourning cover] [imprint: RLB]	Black	FDR	Unknown	D
3748	In memoriam / Franklin Delano Roosevelt etc. [thermogr] [postmarked 4/12/45]	Black, gold	FDR	Butzen	E
3749	In memoriam / Nov. 1943 / to those who etc.	Unknown	Event	McCluney	B
3750	In memoriam / They sleep today in other fields etc. [handpainted]	Black	Verse	Sturgill	E
3751	In memoriam / to 4 chaplains who lost etc.	Unknown	Hero	Cachet Cra	B
3752	In memoriam / to those / who fell / Salerno / Sept. 1943	R,Y/Bk,Bu	Event	McCluney	B
3753	In memoriam / to those who fell etc.	Unknown	Unk	McCluney	A
3754	In memoriam / U.S.S Houston / [etc.] / Memorial Day, May 30, 1942 etc.	Black	Navy	Edmunds	C
3755	In memoriam / USS Houston etc.	Red	Navy	Christens	A
3756	In memory / Franklin D. Roosevelt / Gone but etc.	Blue	FDR	Abel	B
3757	In memory / Franklin D. Roosevelt / Memorial Day / May 30, 1945 etc. [thermogr]	Blue	FDR	Crosby	B
3758	In memory / of our comrades [thermographed]	Unknown	Unk	Baur	A
3759	In memory / of Roosevelt / April 12, 1945	Black	FDR	Davis, Ral	B
3760	In memory / of the / American fliers / [etc.] / —— the more planes will fly	Black	Air	Huss	A
3761	In memory / of the / American fliers / from Shangri-La / murdered / by etc.	Black	Air	Huss	A
3762	In memory of / Franklin D. Roosevelt	Bk,Bu/Bk,Br	FDR	Runge	B
3763	In memory of / Franklin D. Roosevelt / Memorial Day / May 30, etc. [thermographed]	Blue	FDR	Crosby	C
3764	In omnia paratus / 1 / Algeria / Tunisia / Sicily / France etc. [thermographed]	Multicolored	Unit	Teixeira	D
3765	In omnia paratus / US Army [thermographed]	Unknown	Army	Czubay	B
3766	In peace / America leads!	Gold, silver	Flag	Linto	B
3767	In service [handpainted]	Blue, red	Home	Krakora	B
3768	In solemn reverence to those / who answered the call to duty	Blue, gold	Flag	Linto	B
3769	In the fight for freedom! etc. [top star has 1 or 2 points] [colored envelopes]	Multicolored	Ordna	Poppenger	A

NO.	CACHET TEXT	COLOR	TOPIC	PUBLISHER	$
3770	In the hell of war, that boy you know, / may lie there in the wounded row, etc.	Red	RedCr	Neal+Harv	A
3771	In the name of freedom / they have served etc.	Unknown	Unk	Fleetwood	B
3772	In the Philippines, at Okinawa, / Iwo Jima, Guam, and in fact all etc.	Blue	Japan	Brenn	A
3773	In the ring! / until etc. [second line 43, 46, or 47 mm long] [colored envelopes]	Blue, red	Uncle	Poppenger	A
3774	In this critical moment, I wish again to pledge to / America, in behalf etc.	Purple/Red	Phili	Neal	A
3775	In this sign we conquer [handpainted]	Blue, red	EagSh	Shaffer, A	C
3776	In thought / in action / I am an American Day / May 16th etc. [thermographed]	Blue, red	Flag+	Czubay	B
3777	In to win	Bk/Bu/Brown	Armed	Donaldson	A
3778	In to win / 9th USAAF	Blue	Eagle	Air Force	B
3779	In to win [envelope 7 1/2x4 in.]	Unknown	Unk	Cochran	A
3780	In tribute to the / gallant Marines	Black, violet	USMC	Ioor	A
3781	In Vest [no picture] [envelope 9 1/2x4 1/8 in.]	Unknown	Unk	Sun Valley	B
3782	In you / go! / Japan / Dog / house	Blue/Purple	Ally	Roberts	A
3783	Inauguration / Day / Jan. 20th, 1941 / Washington, D.C. [thermographed]	Blue, red	FDR	Crosby	E
3784	Inauguration / first land mail route / [etc.] / Army Postal etc. [handpainted]	Blue, red	Army	Unknown	D
3785	Inauguration / of Vice President / Harry S. Truman / as the 33rd etc.	Multicolored	HST	Smartcraft	E
3786	Independence / Day / July / 4th [thermographed]	Gold	Holid	Sadworth	B
3787	Independence / Day / July 4, 1945 / a day for renewing our faith etc.	Purple	Holid	Rinker	B
3788	Independence / Day [between concentric circles]	Blue	Uncle	Unknown	A
3789	Independence / Hall / and that government etc. [envelope 7 1/2x4 in.]	Unknown	Hist	Battles	A
3790	Independence / Hall / The cradle of liberty [total cachet height 71 or 75 mm]	Blue, red	Hist	Brenn	A
3791	Independence Day / About / to / explode etc.	Multicolored	Holid	Griffith	A
3792	Independence Day / July 4 / Freedom of / Speech Press / Religion Fear	Blue, red	Holid	Baur	A
3793	Independence day / July 4, 1942	Blue	Holid	Unknown	A
3794	Independence Day / July 4th / 1944 / "A heritage of free people"	Blue, red	Holid	Zunks	B
3795	India / United Nations [handpainted]	Multicolored	UN	Weigand	B
3796	India aroused / Beware Japan / you are treading on dangerous soil	Brown	Japan	Neal	A
3797	Indiana is 100 per / cent in the war.	Bu/Gd/Gn/S	Home	Phill+Cox	A
3798	Indiana's boys fight / on every front. / Back those hoosiers / with bonds!	Blue	Bonds	Price, R	A
3799	Indomitable and courageous.	Blue, red	Wash	Neal	A
3800	Industrial targets in / Nagoya, Osaka, Akashi and Gifu etc. [typed] [no picture]	Black	Event	Batura	C
3801	Industry / agriculture / education / aviation / our national defense	Unknown	Unk	Osborne	A
3802	Industry and agriculture join forces etc.	Black	Home	Allen	A
3803	Infantry / Replacement Training / Center [printed in italics]	Multicolored	Unit	Hannay	A
3804	Infantry Advanced / Replacement Training / Center	Multicolored	Unit	Hannay	A
3805	Inflation / Make / your / $$ / have / more / cents [handpainted]	Multicolored	Home	Adler	D
3806	Inonu, Churchill and FDR meet	Unknown	Heads	Linto	B
3807	Inseparably united / r U s S I A [handpainted]	Multicolored	Ally	Borwicki	B
3808	Inseparably united / RUSSIA ["U", "S", & "A" in last word are blue, rest is red] [handpainted]	Blue, red	Ally	Barwicki	B
3809	Insignia of / the Atomic / Bomb branch / of our / service / Description: etc.	Blue, green	Atom	Linto	C
3810	Inspection? Looks like invasion.	Blue	WAC	Ang	A
3811	Instead of / wishful / thinking / buy bonds	Unknown	Bonds	Linto	B
3812	Insure your future / Save with war bonds [no picture]	Unknown	Bonds	Lupkin	A
3813	Interesting careers / open for gals / [etc.] / 11-20-'44——Sixth war loan etc.	Unknown	Event	Linto	B
3814	Interesting careers / open for gals in the / WAVES [no picture]	Green, silver	WAVE	Linto	B
3815	International progress for / [etc.] / 1-12-'45——Japs lose 25 ships / off etc.	Unknown	Event	Linto	B
3816	International progress for / U.S. will be none if we / continue to appease.	Unknown	Flag	Linto	B
3817	Interned Italians freed	Unknown	Home	Linto	B
3818	Interwoven is the / love of liberty with / every ligament of / the heart.	Blue, red	Flag	Griffith	A
3819	Intestinal fortitude will win / the war	Black	Home	Runge	A
3820	Invasion / Armes de Marseille [postmarked 8/15/44, invasion of southern France]	Multicolored	Event	Runge	C
3821	Invasion / Berlin / April / 1945 [allover cachet] [handpainted]	Multicolored	Hitle	Hadley	F
3822	Invasion / D-Day, June 6th, 1944. / The hour of liberation has struck!	Blue, red	DDay	Zunks	B
3823	Invasion / first day / not to enslave—— / but to bring hope. [Sicily landing]	Multicolored	Event	Runge	B
3824	Invasion / it's a sick beast - / the Nazi kraken	Grey, red	DDay	Runge	B
3825	Invasion / June 6, 1944 / Allies land in northern France [no picture]	Red	DDay	Werve	B
3826	Invasion / keep the fighting front supplied. / Buy war bonds.	Green, red	Flag	Haynes	A
3827	Invasion / never again- / too little / too late! [Sicily landing]	Multicolored	Event	Runge	B
3828	Invasion / not to enslave / but to bring hope	Green, red	DDay	Runge	B
3829	Invasion / of the / European continent / D-Day / June 6th, 1944 / V / ...-	Red	DDay	Unknown	B
3830	Invasion / strikes! / Jun 6 - 1944 [handpainted]	Black, red	DDay	Griffith	D
3831	Invasion / to destroy the Axis dragon	Bk,R/Gn,Red	DDay	Runge	B
3832	Invasion / to destroy the Axis dragon	Bk,Br/Bk,Gn	DDay	Runge	B

NO.	CACHET TEXT	COLOR	TOPIC	PUBLISHER	$
3833	Invasion cover / Allied army / strikes Italy: etc. [no picture] [thermographed]	Red	Event	Boone	B
3834	Invasion day / May God be with them etc. [Eisenhower alone]	Multicolored	DDay	Staehle	E
3835	Invasion day / May God be with them etc. [Eisenhower and Montgomery]	Multicolored	DDay	Fluegel	C
3836	Invasion of France	Brown	DDay	Staehle	C
3837	Invasion of France [Gen. Bradley]	Black	DDay	Staehle	C
3838	Invasion of Germany, / with / Gen. Geo. Patton.	Blue, red	Patt	Baur	B
3839	Invasion road / to Nip land / China / Okinawa [handpainted]	Multicolored	Army	Unknown	B
3840	Invasion road / to Nip land / China / Okinawa [handpainted]	Multicolored	Army	Adler	D
3841	Invasion road / to Nip land / China / Okinawa [handpainted]	Multicolored	Army	Adler	D
3842	Invasion rumble	Black/Red	Unk	Ang	A
3843	Invasion rumble / D-Day, June 6th, 1944 [printed + cut-&-pasted paper]	Unknown	DDay	Ang	C
3844	Invasion rumble / No use Adolf, / the Yanks etc. [printed + cut-&-pasted paper]	Red	DDay	Ang	C
3845	Invasion rumble / The rumble turns to etc. [printed + cut-&-pasted paper]	Black	DDay	Ang	C
3846	Invasion starts / at the bond-booth / [etc.] / Dec., 7, 1941, a date we etc.	Multicolored	Pearl	Linto	B
3847	Invasion starts / at the bond-booth / Italy / down!	Multicolored	Bonds	Linto	B
3848	Invasion starts / at the bond-booth / Italy down!	Multicolored	Bonds	Linto	B
3849	Invasion! / Landing made on French coast / at / 3 a.m. June 6, 1944	Orange	DDay	Roberts	B
3850	Invest / in / victory / buy / bonds	Blue, red	Flag+	Buxton	A
3851	Invest / protect / the heritage of our / children / Buy U.S. war bonds now	Blue	Women	Huss	A
3852	Invest in / America / Buy-buy / buy bonds	Blue, red	Bonds	Ang	A
3853	Invest in freedom!	Blue, red	FlMin	Nichols	B
3854	Invest in liberty / and freedom today etc.	Bu/Br/R	Unk	Harrington	A
3855	Invest in U.S.A. / Buy war bonds	Blue	Bonds	Ander, EA	A
3856	Invest in victory / ...- [envelope 6 9/16x3 11/16 in.]	Blue, red	EagV	Belles-let	C
3857	Invest in victory etc. [envelope 8 11/16x3 5/8 in.]	Unknown	Unk	ITE Circui	B
3858	Invest Ohio's / excess funds in etc.	Blue, red	Home	Payne, AE	A
3859	Invest your stack / Back the attack! etc. [first line diagonal]	Green, red	Bonds	Boone	A
3860	Invest your stack / Back the attack! etc. [first line horizontal]	Green, red	Bonds	Boone	A
3861	Invest your stack! / Back the attack! / Buy war bonds now	Brown, green	Bonds	Boone	A
3862	Invite a / guest of honor / from the service etc.	Black	Home	Deming	A
3863	Iran/ United Nations [handpainted]	Multicolored	UN	Weigand	B
3864	Iraq / United Nations [handpainted]	Multicolored	UN	Weigand	B
3865	Ireland fails / to show / [etc.] / 3-17-'44——Huns still clinging to the etc.	Multicolored	Event	Linto	B
3866	Ireland fails / to show / its appreciation / for U.S. helping / her to etc.	Multicolored	Home	Linto	B
3867	Iron cavalry [in quotes] [envelope 6 3/4x 3 7/8 in. or 6 9/16x3 3/4 in.]	Sepia tones	Army	Belles-let	C
3868	Is / Berlin / next? [handpainted]	Black	Hitle	Wolf, CL	B
3869	Is life so dear, or peace so sweet / as to be etc.	Black	Unk	Allen	A
3870	Is that all you can talk about / ——military secrets? [in quotes] [handpainted]	Black	Home	Unknown	B
3871	Is this patriotism? / Did Curtiss-Wright / [etc.] / Navy Day——27-10-'43	Multicolored	Navy	Linto	B
3872	Is this patriotism? / Did Curtiss-Wright Aviation / Co. etc. [no picture]	Multicolored	Home	Linto	B
3873	Island to island [sic] / fleet with fleet / In Tokyo we / meet. [handpainted]	Multicolored	Eagle	Adler	E
3874	Island to island / fleet with fleet / In Tokyo we / meet. [handpainted]	Multicolored	Eagle	Adler	D
3875	Isn't it great to be an / American [all-over cachet] [shield and ribbon]	Blue, red	Shiel	Krakora	B
3876	Isn't it great to be an / American?	Unknown	Unk	Boone	A
3877	It / still takes / the / Infantry / for etc. [envelope 7 1/2x4 in.]	Black, red	Army	Schirmer	A
3878	It ain't the breeze, lik a dragon's etc.	Green	Unk	Brenn	A
3879	It all depends on your / point of view!!!! [handpainted]	Black	Hitle	Parker	B
3880	It came from the / American lines. / [etc.] / No, Heinie! / Our secret etc.	Unknown	Axis	Linto	B
3881	It cant [sic] happen here! / No? / Insure against this hazard / Buy U.S. etc.	Bu/Brown/Re	Bonds	Cozart	A
3882	It can't be so terribly far, soldier —— / while etc. [burned edge] [handpainted]	Multicolored	Army	Cowdery	D
3883	It happened today / April 18 / 1431 Joan of Arc was etc. [no picture] [backdated]	Black	Event	Unknown	X
3884	It is a tiresome road / but!! - Tokyo lies ahead!	Black	Army	Conner	A
3885	It is my duty to defend my country, if need should arise.	Black, purple	Armed	Lowe	A
3886	It is suggested that / the secret / [etc.] / 9-3-'44——Yanks capture Perl etc.	Multicolored	Event	Linto	B
3887	It is suggested that / the secret plant at / Pasco, Wash., etc. [no picture]	Gold, green	Home	Linto	B
3888	It is the opinion of / that / Uncle Sam, / shall always, / sail the high seas!	Blue	Unk	Harrington	A
3889	It is the opinion of / Uncle Sam , / shall always: / sail the high seas!	Green	Unk	Harrington	A
3890	It is time we take note / of England's attitude! / We fight etc. [no picture]	O, silver	Ally	Linto	B
3891	It is up to us / to safeguard the / liberty those of / 1776 gave us!!	Gold, silver	Liber	Linto	B
3892	It is your patriotic duty as an / American / to buy war bonds	Blue, red	Flag	Boone	A
3893	It is your patriotic duty as an / American! / to buy war bonds	Blue, red	Flag	Boone	A
3894	It makes scents / To market "Black Market" to spend / lots of jack etc.	Black, red	Home	Threl+Thar	A
3895	It may cost us / the wealth of our / nation to win this etc. [handpainted]	Black, red	Home	Unknown	B

NO.	CACHET TEXT	COLOR	TOPIC	PUBLISHER	$
3896	It shall be done [in quotes]	Multicolored	Axis	Minkus	A
3897	It stands for freedom! / Long may it wave!	Blue, red	Flag	Mayo	A
3898	It takes $380,000 to pull a / 1,000-plane air raid on / Germany alone! etc.	Green, red	Bonds	Boone	A
3899	It takes / $7.00 per / second to etc.	Unknown	Unk	Boone	A
3900	It takes lots of money / to provide etc. [env. 6 1/2x3 5/8 or 7 1/2x4 in.]	Green	Armed	Harrington	A
3901	It takes money to provide my outfit / War bonds will provide it!!!	Black/Red	Army	Harrington	A
3902	It will / be a red letter / day when etc. [torn right edge] [handpainted]	Multicolored	Army	Cowdery	D
3903	It will be a glorious day etc.	Unknown	Unk	Brenn	A
3904	It will happen, if we lag a bit	Blue, red	Army	Harrington	A
3905	It will not be long / now when Hitler / and Hirohito will / be glad to etc.	Blue, red	Uncle	Linto	B
3906	It won't / be long / now. [handpainted]	Multicolored	Japan	Adler	D
3907	It won't be long now	Blue	Air	Foster	A
3908	It won't be long now [in quotes] / V [multicolored, various]	Multicolored	Heads	Knoll	B
3909	It won't be long now! / "D" / Day / is on the way! [no picture]	Blue	Home	Boone	A
3910	Italian / fleet sur- / renders / to Allies [no picture]	Red	Event	Boone	B
3911	Italian surrender / today! / Sept. 8, 1943 [handpainted]	Aqua, pink	Event	Griffith	B
3912	Italians / asking / peace / demonstrate in / streets etc. [thermographed]	Red	Event	Boone	B
3913	Italians declare / war / on Germany / Allies etc. [no picture] [thermographed]	Red	Event	Boone	B
3914	Italians surrender Pantelleria	Unknown	Event	Linto	B
3915	Italy / at war with / Germany / Azores / is Allied base etc. [no picture]	Blue, red	Event	Fidelity	B
3916	Italy / invaded / September 3, 1943	Green, red	Event	Fidelity	B
3917	Italy / one down——two to go!	Bu,Purple	Axis	Mayfield	A
3918	Italy / surrenders / September 8, 1943 ["X" through Italian peninsula]	Multicolored	Event	Fidelity	B
3919	Italy / surrenders / September 8th, 1943 [no picture] [thermographed]	Blue, red	Event	Boone	B
3920	Italy / surrenders! / The Italian collapse was / announced September 8th etc.	Blue	Event	Unknown	B
3921	Italy [word upside down] Berlin Tokyo / On to Berlin / [etc.] / Dec. 7, etc.	Multicolored	Pearl	Linto	B
3922	Italy [word upside down] Berlin Tokyo / On to Berlin / and Tokyo [no picture]	Multicolored	Axis	Linto	B
3923	Italy declares war! / October 13th, 1943 / The Italian government, under etc.	Red	Event	Zunks	C
3924	Italy Germany Japan / Hitler etc.	Brown	Axis	Buckalew	B
3925	Italy has gone / Germany & Japan / are next.	Bk,R/Multi	Axis	Runge	A
3926	Italy might fare better at the / big gambling table if she didn't etc.	Blue, gold	Musso	Andrews	A
3927	Italy quits! / September 8th, 1943. / General Eisenhower etc. [no picture]	Blue, red	Event	Zunks	B
3928	Italy surrenders	Unknown	Event	Linto	B
3929	Italy yeilds [sic] / Unconditional / surrender on / Sept. 8, 1943. [handpainted]	Black, red	Event	Unknown	B
3930	It's "K.O." for Tokyo! / Let's go! / Ready! / Aim! etc. [thermographed]	Unknown	Japan	Crosby	B
3931	It's / all / over rat [handpainted]	Black	Hitle	Wolf, CL	B
3932	It's / bye, bye / Hitler / (the chump!) [caps] / if you / buy, buy / bonds!	Blue, red	Hitle	Internat	A
3933	It's / bye, bye / Hitler / (the chump) [italics] / if you / buy, buy / bonds!	Blue, red	Hitle	Internat	A
3934	It's / free / fellers [envelope 6x3 ½ in.]	Black, orange	Armed	Coward-	B
3935	It's / great / to live in America [engraved]	Blue	Liber	Artcraft	B
3936	It's / great / to live in America [with rays emanating from torch] [engraved]	Blue, gold	Liber	Artcraft	B
3937	Its [sic] a blackout / from California [folded cover]	Black	Japan	Unknown	B
3938	It's a / 3 pin / alley [handpainted]	Multicolored	Axis	Adler	D
3939	It's a good / thing cows / can't fly! [in quotes]	Black	Navy	Crosby	A
3940	It's a long trip that we are on etc.	Unknown	Unk	Brenn	A
3941	It's alla / Greek / to me! / How to fight / Musso	Green	Musso	Roberts	A
3942	It's better to park it, / than aid the / black market	Brown	Uncle	Ryscovers	A
3943	It's better to park it, / than aid the / black market	Brown	Uncle	Ryscovers	A
3944	It's dawning! / Give 'em the works!	Multicolored	Axis	Linto	B
3945	It's GI this and GI that / GI haircut [thermographed]	Unknown	Unk	Baur	A
3946	It's great / to be / born / of the / red etc.	Unknown	Unk	Davis, Ral	A
3947	It's great / to be an / American	Blue, red	Flag	Dime	A
3948	It's great / to be an American	Unknown	Unk	Norona	A
3949	It's great to be / an American	Blue, red	Flag	Bean	A
3950	It's great to be / an American	Unknown	Unk	Dime	A
3951	It's great to be / an American [eagle red, blue, or green; text blue]	Bu,R/Gn,Red	EagV	Cozart	A
3952	It's great to be / an American [eagle red, blue, or green; text red]	Bu,R/Gn,Red	EagV	Cozart	A
3953	It's growing late, Adolf	Black	Hitle	Citret	A
3954	It's me / again hon! [burned left edge] [handpainted]	Multicolored	Army	Cowdery	D
3955	It's men / like you who / will give him etc. [burned top edge] [handpainted]	Multicolored	Hitle	Cowdery	D
3956	It's more than a war bond / It's a share in the victory; etc. [no picture]	Red	Bonds	Davis, Ray	A
3957	It's nice to know / you're always / there. [handpainted]	Multicolored	Army	Cowdery	D
3958	It's patriotic / to save your / drops of / kitchen fat [handpainted]	Multicolored	Axis	Borkowski	C

NO.	CACHET TEXT	COLOR	TOPIC	PUBLISHER	$
3959	It's plain horse sense etc. [label + blue "Victory" border]	Multicolored	Home	Unknown	B
3960	It's plain horse sense etc. [label + red "Victory" border]	Multicolored	Home	Unknown	B
3961	It's plain horse sense etc. [label + red "Win the War" border]	Multicolored	Home	Unknown	B
3962	It's still worth / fighting for	Blue	Bell	Barwicki	A
3963	Its stripes of red, eternal dyed etc.	Blue, red	Flag	Card	A
3964	It's the / waiting that's / maddening!! [handpainted]	Multicolored	Army	Cowdery	D
3965	It's the monotony that gets me! [handpainted]	Black	Army	Conner	B
3966	It's them letters - he says / they give him a terrific lift! [in quotes]	Black, blue	Armed	Unknown	A
3967	It's time / to buy bonds	Silver	Bonds	Phillips	A
3968	It's time to / make Japs / say 'Uncle'	Gold, pink	Japan	Linto	B
3969	It's time to ring again [in quotes] [envelope 6 3/4x3 7/8 in.]	Sepia tones	Bell	Belles-let	C
3970	It's up to / us / to win this war etc.	Blue, red	Uncle	Kosko	A
3971	It's wise / it's patriotic / Buy / war bonds [no picture]	Blue, red	Bonds	Kosko	A
3972	It's wise / it's patriotic / buy war bonds!	Unknown	Unk	Brenn	A
3973	It's your duty to / 4th / back the attack [handpainted]	Black, purple	Bonds	Wolf, CL	C
3974	It's your Red Cross / in Nineteen forty-four etc.	Blue, red	RedCr	Brenn	A
3975	It's your war / and mine	Blue/Red	Liber	Richardson	A
3976	It's yours! / it's mine! / let's / make / your / dollar / count etc.	Unknown	Bonds	Harrington	A
3977	It's yours! it's mine! let's make etc.	Black/Brown	Unk	Harrington	A
3978	I've been / itching / to get out / of these [handpainted]	Black	Army	Clendennen	D
3979	I've gotta get / time off soon / or / else [UR] [burned edge] [handpainted]	Multicolored	Army	Cowdery	D
3980	Iwo / Jima / 1945 / [etc.] / In honor of the U.S. Marine Corps	Multicolored	USMC	Staehle	C
3981	Iwo / Jima / captured / U.S. Marines raise / the American flag / on Iwo etc.	Multicolored	Event	Teixeira	D
3982	Iwo / Jima / In honor of the / U.S. Marine Corps.	Blue, red	USMC	Staehle	C
3983	Iwo / Jima / In honor of the / U.S. Marine Corps. [artist: Staehle]	Red, silver	USMC	Smartcraft	C
3984	Iwo / Jima / In honor of the U.S. Marine Corps and / their heroic fight on etc.	Blue, red	USMC	Staehle	C
3985	Iwo / Jima / United States / Marines [thermographed]	Unknown	USMC	Crosby	B
3986	Iwo Jima / "Marines raise Old Glory on Iwo"	Blue, red	USMC	Grimsland	A
3987	Iwo Jima / attacked by 3rd, 4th, & 5th Marines February 19-21st 1945 etc.	Black	USMC	Lowry	A
3988	Iwo Jima / attacked by etc.	Black	USMC	Allen	A
3989	Iwo Jima / Tokyo's "Lookout Island" / Feb. 20 1945 / invaded etc. [handpainted]	Multicolored	Japan	Smith, LH	B
3990	Iwo Jima [Boll imprint]	Blue, red	USMC	Boll	A
3991	Iwo Jima [thermographed]	Unknown	USMC	Crosby	B

Cover Values (from Table 6, p. 136)

Value	Price Range
A	$ 3 - 6
B	$ 7 - 15
C	$ 16 - 30
D	$ 31 - 60
E	$ 61 - 125
F	$ 126 - 250
G	$ 251 - 500
H	$ 501 - 1000
I	$ >1000
X	Unpriced: Suspicious or fraudulent cover

3528

3529

3546

3551

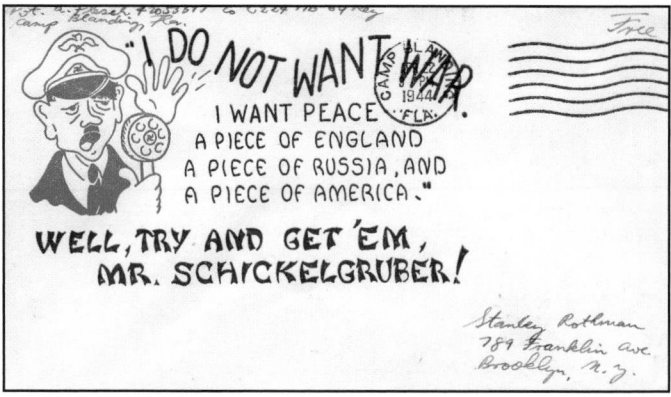

3574

3602

Ickes should make a good buddy for Hirohito and Tojo

3609

3637

3679

3680

3681

3709
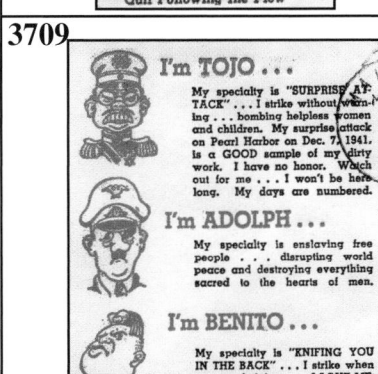

3711

3782

3785

3810

3830

3933

CACHET TEXT BEGINNING WITH "J"

NO.	CACHET TEXT	COLOR	TOPIC	PUBLISHER	$
3992	Jack and Jill / Jack and Jill paid up a bill / a long due obligation. etc.	Black, red	Verse	Threl+Thar	A
3993	Jack-in-the-box / We don't like inflation / it causes alarm. / But if we etc.	Black, orange	Verse	Threl+Thar	A
3994	Jaldi! / (hurry!) / [handpainted] [APO 886, Karachi, India]	Multicolored	Ally	Unknown	C
3995	Jamestown, N.Y. / salutes it's [sic] / 3,500 / men and women etc. [no picture]	Multicolored	Armed	Nelson, KE	B
3996	Jan 01 1944 / Crush / Germany / this / year [handpainted]	Black, red	Holid	Shaffer, A	C
3997	Jan 08, 1945 / Bataan! Corregidor! / We etc. [no picture]	Unknown	Event	McCluney	B
3998	Jan. / 01 [postmarked 1/1/41]	Gold, green	Holid	Linto	B
3999	Jan. / 01 [sands of time, holly, ribbon] [handpainted]	Multicolored	Holid	Adler	C
4000	Jan. 04, 1945——Turkey severs relations with Japan [handpainted]	Multicolored	Map	Smith, LH	C
4001	Jan. 10, 1945 - Invasion forces of Gen. Douglas etc. [handpainted]	Multicolored	Map	Smith, LH	C
4002	Jan. 10-20, 1943 - Casablanca Conference, terms agreed / upon etc. [handpainted]	Multicolored	Heads	Smith, LH	C
4003	Jan. 17th / 1945 / Warsaw / In / commemoration / of the heroic / uprising etc.	Multicolored	ORN	Fluegel	C
4004	Jan. 18, 1945 / Warsaw freed / by the Russian / army. etc. [handpainted]	Multicolored	Map	Smith, LH	C
4005	Jan. 19, 1945 - Budapest / capitol [sic] of Hungary etc. [handpainted]	Multicolored	Map	Smith, LH	C
4006	Jan. 20, 1945 / First 4th term inauguration etc. [pmark 1/20/45] [handpainted]	Black	FDR	Myers	E
4007	Jan. 25, / U.S. troops / arrive in / Ireland / 1942. [handpainted label]	Multicolored	Event	LeGallez	C
4008	Jan. 26, 1830 / 115th anniversary / "Liberty and union, / now and forever," etc.	Multicolored	Hist	Griffith	B
4009	Jan. 26, 1942 / Amer. Exp. Force / landed in / North Ireland [no picture]	Multicolored	Event	Linto	B
4010	Jan. 26, 1945 - Clark Field captured--richest prize of etc. [postmarked 1/26/45] [hp]	Multicolored	Event	Smith, LH	C
4011	January 14 / This cover is issued to com- / memorate the following etc.	Blue, red	Event	Shane	A
4012	January 17, 1945 / Poland / Warsaw recaptured	Blue, green	Event	Fidelity	B
4013	January 17, 1945 / Warsaw and Krakow fall / to Russians	Unknown	Event	Linto	B
4014	Jap [sic] sign / surrender / terms on / this ship / U.S.S. / Missouri etc.	Multicolored	VJDay	Linto	B
4015	Jap balloon / raids	Green	Home	Runge	B
4016	Jap capitulation day / Japan agrees / to unconditional etc. [engraved]	Blue, red	VJDay	Heckman	D
4017	Jap fleet in Solomons	Unknown	Event	Linto	B
4018	Jap hands grabbed the fats / we used to import. / "Save used fats now" [handpainted]	Multicolored	Japan	Adler	C
4019	Jap surrender / envoys land / on Ie island on / way to get sur- / render terms.	Blue, red	Event	Boone	B
4020	Japan / bombed / by / U.S. / Air Force [no picture] [postmarked 4/18/42]	Red	Event	Fidelity	C
4021	Japan / bombed again - hit Sasebo / navy base and steel / city etc. [no picture]	Red	Event	Boone	B
4022	Japan / declares / war / on / U.S.A. / Dec. 7, 1941 [postmarked 12/7/41] [card]	Gold	Pearl	Fidelity	E
4023	Japan / ignores / ultimatum [thermographed]	Unknown	Event	Boone	B
4024	Japan / invaded! / by army of occupation [postmarked 8/28/45]	Multicolored	VJDay	Griffith	D
4025	Japan / rubber / out	Purple	Japan	Foster	A
4026	Japan / strikes at / Hawaii / Dec. 7, 1941 / [etc.] / 3d. anniversary. [handpainted]	Blak, red	Anniv	LeGallez	C
4027	Japan / surrenders / 7:00 p.m. / Eastern War Time [postmarked 8/14/45]	Blue, red	VJDay	Unknown	C
4028	Japan / surrenders / on U.S.S. / Missouri [thermographed]	Blue, red	VJDay	Smartcraft	C
4029	Japan / surrenders / to Allies / Aug 14 / 1945 etc. [handpainted label]	Black, yellow	VJDay	LeGallez	E
4030	Japan / surrenders / to the / Allies / The Axis is axed!	Blue, red	VJDay	Boone	B
4031	Japan / surrenders / to the / Allies / The Axis is axed! / Today is / V-J Day	Blue, red	VJDay	Boone	B
4032	Japan / surrenders / to the / Allies / V-J Day [under newsboy and readers]	Blue, red	VJDay	Boone	B
4033	Japan / surrenders / to the / Allies [circle around text] [thermographed]	Blue, red	VJDay	Boone	B
4034	Japan / surrenders / to the / Allies [shield, Minute Man, or both] [thermographed]	Blue, red	VJDay	Boone	B
4035	Japan / surrenders / to the Allies / Japs quit	Blue, red	VJDay	Boone	B
4036	Japan / surrenders [handpainted]	Multicolored	VJDay	Unknown	C
4037	Japan announced that she is ready / to surrender under etc. [handpainted] [no picture]	Blue	Event	Batura	C
4038	Japan attacks America / Today, December 7, 1941 / at etc. [backdated 12/7/41]	Blue/Red	Pearl	Unknown	X
4039	Japan broadcasts / offer to / surrender to Allies [thermographed]	Blue, red	Event	Boone	B
4040	Japan fears US invasion of homeland	Red	Japan	Abel	A
4041	Japan jittery / over Potsdam / report. They / fear Russian etc. [no picture]	Black	Event	Fidelity	B
4042	Japan next! / What do they mean? / What have our Pacific / forces been etc.	Brown, purple	Flag	Linto	B
4043	Japan quits! / August 10th, 1945. / Japan today told the / world she is etc.	Blue, red	Japan	Zunks	C
4044	Japan signs / peace treaty / Well done / VJ / Day [3 diving planes]	Multicolored	VJDay	Amer Pat	C
4045	Japan signs peace terms / aboard the U.S.S. etc. [env. 9 1/2x4 1/4 in.]	Black	VJDay	Crosby	C
4046	Japan signs peace terms / aboard the U.S.S. etc. [env. as above] [Tokyo Bay]	Black	VJDay	Crosby	E
4047	Japan suffers / a tomic ache! / Sunday of thanksgiving etc. [handpainted]	Multicolored	Atom	Wolf, CL	C

NO.	CACHET TEXT	COLOR	TOPIC	PUBLISHER	$
4048	Japan surrendered / unconditionally / Sept. 2 - 1945 [handpainted, pen & ink]	Blue	VJDay	Batura	C
4049	Japan surrendered [in semi-circle] / Sep. 2 - 1945 [handpainted, pen & ink]	Blue	VJDay	Batura	C
4050	Japan surrenders / [etc.] / 1945 [postmarked 9/10/45] [env. 9 1/2x4 1/8 in.]	Blue, red	NimFD	Crosby	C
4051	Japan surrenders / America avenges / Pearl Harbor [print size, style vary]	Bk/R, yellow	VJDay	Fidelity	B
4052	Japan surrenders / Aug. 14, 1945-V-J Day etc. [env. as above] [Tokyo Bay]	Multicolored	VJDay	Crosby	E
4053	Japan surrenders / Aug. 14, 1945-V-J Day Sept. 2, etc. [env. 9 1/4x4 1/4 in.]	Multicolored	VJDay	Crosby	D
4054	Japan surrenders / Today, September 2, 1945, the President of the etc.	Gray	VJDay	Unknown	B
4055	Japan surrenders / Victory / Thanks to our Army, Navy and / Marine Corps etc.	Red	VJDay	Neal	B
4056	Japan surrenders / VJ Day [thermographed]	Gold	VJDay	Unknown	B
4057	Japan surrenders officially / Aug. 14, 1945 - V-J Day Sept. 2, 1945 [thermographed]	Blue	VJDay	Unknown	C
4058	Japan surrenders unconditionally / Victory [small eagle, "V," 2 flags]	Blue, red	VJDay	Huss	B
4059	Japan surrenders unconditionally / Victory / V / Liberty [thermographed]	Blue, red	Event	Huss	B
4060	Japan surrenders unconditionally / Welcome home fighting forces [Liberty]	Blue, red	VJDay	Huss	B
4061	Japan surrenders unconditionally [above eagle with flag] [thermographed]	Blue, red	VJDay	Huss	B
4062	Japan surrenders unconditionally [above helmeted man giving "V" sign] [thermographed]	Blue, red	VJDay	Huss	B
4063	Japan, we hereby / announce our bombing / [etc.] / "Loud speaker" [handpainted]	Black	Japan	Sturgill	E
4064	Japanes envoy extraordinary to Wash- / ington, Saburo Karusu etc. [typed + handpainted]	Black	Event	Batura	F
4065	Japanese defeated in Midway	Unknown	Event	Linto	C
4066	Japanese Easter egg. / Score of Jap victories / over U.S. etc. [handpainted]	Black	Japan	Sturgill	E
4067	Japanese fleet in / Solomons / Nov. 12, 1942	Unknown	Event	Linto	B
4068	Japanese Fleet in / Solomons / Nov. 12, 1942 [no picture]	S, Purple	Japan	Linto	B
4069	Japanese Navy Day	Green/Red	Navy	Christens	A
4070	Japanese planes attacked / Pearl Harbor / [etc.] / The formal surrender etc.	Black	Event	Unknown	A
4071	Japanese sign surrender / terms aboard U.S.S. Missouri / in etc. [ten envelope]	Red	VJDay	Unknown	B
4072	Japanese sign surrender / terms at Tokyo Bay on / 2 September 1945	Red	VJDay	Unknown	B
4073	Japanese two-man sub / captured over one etc. [thermographed]	Blue/Green	Navy	Crosby	B
4074	Japan's battle cry. / Save / our / skin.	Blue, red	Japan	Baur	A
4075	Japan's homeland / "The Yanks are / comin'!!" / "Iki, waki, konki, sookekki!"	Blue, brown	Japan	Lawrence	B
4076	Japan's new war slogan —— meaning / [etc.] / "Iki, waki, konki, sookekki"	Brown	Japan	Lawrence	A
4077	Japan's traditional / treachery has been / proven again! etc. [no picture]	Multicolored	Pearl	Linto	B
4078	Jap-O-Lantern [handpainted]	black	Holid	Muzzy	C
4079	Jappy your [sic] a sappy / [etc.] / America / sez Luhta [thermographed]	Blue, red	Japan	Luhta	A
4080	Jappy you're a sappy / We worked fought and won / for etc. [no picture]	Red	VJDay	Luhta	B
4081	Japs "peace terms" / to United States etc.	Unknown	Japan	Linto	B
4082	Japs / Get out / and stay out! / [etc.] / The / Philippines [handpainted]	Black	Phili	Pisarof	B
4083	Japs / Quit / August 14, 1945 [thermographed]	Red	VJDay	Mayo	B
4084	Japs / take / Java / March 10, 1942 [no picture]	Blue	Event	Fidelity	B
4085	Japs admit loss of Guadalcanal	Unknown	Event	Linto	B
4086	Japs are / snakes / bonds / are stakes [handpainted]	Multicolored	Uncle	Adler	D
4087	Japs are a common foe / of the whole world! / [etc.] / Dec. 7, 1941, etc.	Multicolored	Pearl	Linto	B
4088	Japs are a common foe / of the whole world! / Russia should etc. [no picture]	Gold, pink	Japan	Linto	B
4089	Japs attack / Dutch Harbor / Jun 4 - 1942 [postmarked 6/4/42]	Blue, red	Event	First Day	E
4090	Japs attack / Midway Island / Jun 4 - 1942 [postmarked 6/4/42]	Blue, red	Event	First Day	F
4091	Japs capture Bataan	Unknown	Event	Linto	C
4092	Japs capture Rangoon	Unknown	Event	Linto	B
4093	Japs defeated in Midway	Unknown	Event	Linto	B
4094	Japs flee / from / Kiska / August 21, 1943 [no picture]	Red	Event	Fidelity	B
4095	Japs have nothing / in common with / Americans! / We should etc. [no picture]	Multicolored	AJA	Linto	B
4096	Japs have plenty / while Americans / are on slim rations / Why? [no picture]	Multicolored	AJA	Linto	B
4097	Japs kill captured Americans / while the yellow Jap rats in etc. [no picture]	Gold, green	AJA	Linto	B
4098	Japs lose 28 ships at Battle of Guadalcanal	Unknown	Event	Linto	B
4099	Japs lose Vella Lavella Isle	Unknown	Event	Linto	B
4100	Japs planned / world domination! / Today foxholes will / look big to them!	Multicolored	Minut	Linto	B
4101	Japs say they will / avenge honorable / defeat of Germans!	Gold, silver	Japan	Linto	B
4102	Japs sign / surrender / terms on / [etc.] / 9-1-'45——Reds clear the / Japs etc.	Multicolored	VJDay	Linto	C
4103	Japs sign / surrender / terms on / this ship / U.S.S. Missouri / "Bull" etc.	Multicolored	VJDay	Linto	C
4104	Japs take Corregidor	Unknown	Event	Linto	C
4105	John L. Lewis / admits defeat...decides / F.D.R. etc. [no picture] [thermographed]	Blue	Event	Boone	B

NO.	CACHET TEXT	COLOR	TOPIC	PUBLISHER	$
4105A	John Paul Jones / Founder of our navy	Green	Hist	Unknown	A
4106	Join / American Red Cross / USS Relief etc.	Red	RedCr	Czubay	C
4107	Join / American Red Cross / USS Solace etc.	Red	RedCr	Czubay	C
4108	Join / CA / PL / Keep America supreme	Unknown	Unk	McCluney	A
4109	Join / the / silence / squad / Keep your eyes etc. [label + printed border]	Multicolored	Home	Artists	B
4110	Join the / silence / squad / to preserve our liberty [label + printed border]	Multicolored	FlLib	Artists	B
4111	Join the / U.S. Navy / crush the / Japanese / menace! etc. [thermographed]	Blue	Navy	Crosby	B
4112	Join the Air Force / and see Tokio [artist: Knapp]	Blue, red	Air	Fleetwood	B
4113	Join the fun--buy ward bonds! [handpainted]	Multicolored	UncAx	Myers	C
4114	Join the Navy——lick the Axis	Blue	Navy	Myers	A
4115	Join the WAC / Put your skill in uniform [cachet size 62x50 mm or 77x63 mm]	Black/brown	WAC	Huss	A
4116	Join the WAVEs [colored envelopes]	Black/blue	WAVE	Huss	A
4117	Join! [thermographed]	Unknown	Unk	Phill, CR	A
4118	Join! [thermographed]	Red	RedCr	Boland	A
4119	Jugoslavia	Brown	ORN	Runge	A
4120	July / 04 / 19 43 / Navy etc. [rubber stamp on "Win the War" Fleetwood cachet]	Red	Holid	Sayama	C
4121	July 04 / Independence / Day / Sign etc.	Unknown	Holid	Kosko	A
4122	July 04, 1776 / The United States / gained etc.	Unknown	Holid	Brenn	A
4123	July 04, 1944 —— bombing of Saipan! [handpainted]	Multicolored	Air	Smith, LH	C
4124	July 04th / 1776	Unknown	Holid	Ioor	A
4125	July 04th / Let us now, more than ever before, / dedicate this day etc. [thermographed]	Blue, red	Holid	Yontz	B
4126	July 05, 1943 - Yanks march thru' New Georgia [handpainted]	Multicolored	Map	Smith, LH	C
4127	July 05, 1943 / Nine Jap ships sunk / and others damaged / in etc. [no picture]	Br,S/Multi	Event	Linto	B
4128	July 07, 1941 - United States troops occupy Iceland [handpainted]	Multicolored	Map	Smith, LH	B
4129	July 08, 1943 / U.S. subs sink / ten more Jap / ships! [no picture]	Brown, silver	Event	Linto	B
4130	July 08, 1944 / Occupation of Saipan / marks an important etc. [handpainted]	Multicolored	Map	Smith, LH	C
4131	July 10, 1943 - Allies invade Sicily [handpainted]	Multicolored	Map	Smith, LH	C
4132	July 10, 1943 / Allied forces, / commanded by Eisenhower, etc. [no picture]	Multicolored	Event	Linto	B
4133	July 11, 1945 / 28,000 veterans of / World War 2, from / Europe etc.	Gold, purple	Flag	Linto	B
4134	July 14, 1945! / "Le jour de gloire / est arrive'!" [UL, handwritten in ink]	Black	Event	Sprague	C
4135	July 16, 1945 / Cooking Nippon's goose [Potsdam ultimatum] [handpainted]	Multicolored	Event	Smith, LH	C
4136	July 16, 1945 / Truman / at Potsdam / to confer / with etc. [no picture]	Blue, red	Event	Fidelity	B
4137	July 21 1944 / Yanks recapture Guam [handpainted]	Multicolored	Map	Smith, LH	C
4138	July 21, 1944 / 45,000 Marines / invade Guam / Japs took it etc. [no picture]	Blue, red	Event	Fidelity	B
4139	July 25, 1943 - Mussolini was kicked / over the Tyrrhenian etc. [handpainted]	Multicolored	Musso	Smith, LH	C
4140	July 26, 1945 / Churchill defeated / Japan / receives / Big 3 etc. [no picture]	Blue, green	Event	Fidelity	B
4141	July 27, 1945 / Japs turn / down Allies' / peace terms	Gold, silver	Event	Linto	B
4142	July 29, 1943 / Ten Jap ships / sunk and four / damaged! [no picture]	Unknown	Japan	Linto	B
4143	July 31, 1944 - Famous leaning tower / of Pisa destroyed by etc. [handpainted]	Multicolored	Hist	Smith, LH	B
4144	June / 04 / 1944 / Rome / falls [no picture]	Red, yellow	Event	Fidelity	B
4145	June 03, 1943 / Roosevelt orders coal / miners back to work [no picture]	Pink, silver	Event	Linto	B
4146	June 04th / 1944 / The fall of / Rome [General Harold Alexander]	Multicolored	Event	Staehle	C
4147	June 04th / 1944 / The fall of / Rome [General Mark Clark]	Multicolored	Event	Staehle	C
4148	June 04th / 1944 / The fall of / Rome [Pope Pius XII]	Multicolored	Event	Staehle	C
4149	June 05, 1944 / Fall of Rome, first Nazi capitol [sic] etc. [handpainted]	Multicolored	Axis	Smith, LH	C
4150	June 06, 1944 - Allies land on coast of / France to launch etc. [handpainted]	Multicolored	Map	Smith, LH	C
4151	June 07, 1942 / Japs defeated in / 3-day battle of / Midway [Navy cancel 6/7/42]	Gold, silver	Event	Linto	D
4152	June 08, 1944 / Bayeaux - first French city to be etc. [handpainted]	Multicolored	ORN	Smith, LH	C
4153	June 11 / 1945 / Borneo / Australian / 7th Division / lands on / Brunei Beach	Multicolored	Event	Fluegel	C
4154	June 12, 1943 / Lampedusa and Linosa / islands surrender to / Allied forces	Unknown	Event	Linto	B
4155	June 20, 1943 / Race riots in / Detroit, Mich.	Unknown	Event	Linto	B
4156	June 21, 1943 / Supreme Court decides / curfew ruling on / Japs necessary	Unknown	AJA	Linto	B
4157	June 22, 1943 / Third coal / strike ended!	Unknown	Event	Linto	B
4158	June 26, 1945 / Truman at the / United Nations conference	Blue, red	Event	Fidelity	B
4159	June 27, 1944 / Cherbourg, France / freed of Nazi bondage [handpainted]	Multicolored	Map	Smith, LH	C
4160	June 30, 1942 / We register eighteen, nineteen / and twenty etc. [no picture]	Green	Event	Fidelity	B
4161	June 30, 1945 / President Truman's new Cabinet / appointees take their etc.	Gold	Event	Linto	B
4162	Just a line home! [handpainted]	Brown, pink	Army	Parker	B

NO.	CACHET TEXT	COLOR	TOPIC	PUBLISHER	$
4163	Just a mild April shower, boys etc. [thermographed]	Unknown	Unk	Crosby	B
4164	Just a pause to honor those who did believe and worked etc. [no picture]	Gold	VEDay	Unknown	B
4165	Just a watchin' for that message / that "the Rising Sun has set.	Blue, red	Home	Carpenter	A
4166	Just about ready for the hammer [handpainted]	Multicolored	Army	Adler	D
4167	Just Another Putrid Scent	Blue, red	Japan	Muz & Nice	B
4168	Just cut yourself short on sugar etc. [no picture]	Red	Home	Foster	A
4169	Just fishing' wont [sic] win / buy war bonds.	Black/brown	Home	Runge	A
4170	Just fishing' won't win / ···– buy war stamps and etc. [env. 6 1/16x3 5/8 in.]	Black, orange	Home	Runge	A
4171	Just fishing' won't win the war / ···– buy war stamps and bonds ···–	Unknown	Home	Runge	A
4172	Just how much sales resistance has he?	Black	NeuNa	Smith, DH	A
4173	Just one hat in the / ring etc.	Unknown	Unk	Runge	A
4174	Just think! You do not have / [etc.] / 6-1-'44 German defenses at Rome etc.	Multicolored	Event	Linto	B
4175	Just think! You do not have / to ask Hitler's permission to listen / to etc.	Multicolored	Armed	Linto	B
4176	Just wait till Sept. 23. [handpainted]	Black	FDR	Unknown	B
4177	Just wait!! [handpainted]	Multicolored	Army	Cowdery	D
4178	Just waiting for a couple of good yanks!! [handpainted]	Black	Hitle	Shaw	C
4179	Just what is liberty?... / Nobody can define liberty satisfactorily. etc.	Blue, red	Torch	Boone	A
4180	Justice [vertical]	Gold, silver	Minut	Linto	B
4181	Justice [vertical] / We don't want war / Neither do we want etc.	Multicolored	Minut	Linto	B
4182	Justice Byrnes / named / price / chief / Alaska / offensive etc. [no picture]	Blue	Event	Fidelity	B
4183	Justice for all	Black	EagSh	McFarland	A
4184	Justice for all	Green/Red	Unk	Cozart	A
4185	Justice will / triumph! / "Victory in '44"	Brown, red	Home	Donaldson	A

Cover Values (from Table 6, p. 136)

Value	*Price Range*
A	$ 3 - 6
B	$ 7 - 15
C	$ 16 - 30
D	$ 31 - 60
E	$ 61 - 125
F	$ 126 - 250
G	$ 251 - 500
H	$ 501 - 1000
I	$ >1000
X	Unpriced: Suspicious or fraudulent cover

4004

4016

4022

4028

4029

4043

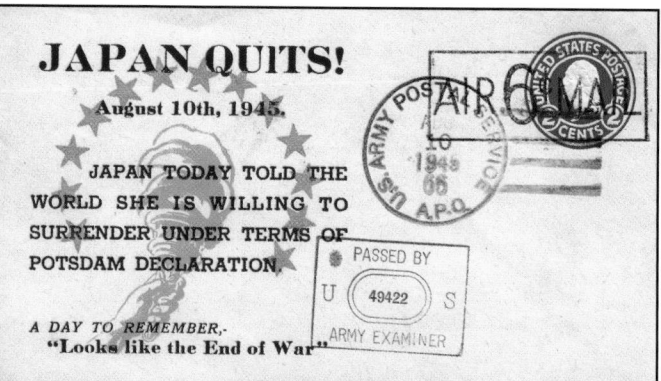

4057

4090

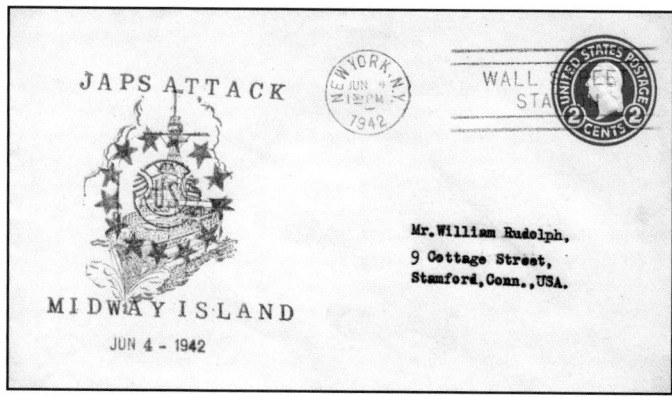

CACHET TEXT BEGINNING WITH "K"

NO.	CACHET TEXT	COLOR	TOPIC	PUBLISHER	$
4186	Kamehameha Day / June 11, 1943 / "Imua, imua a lanakila!" / Forward to etc.	Blue, red	Hawai	Sayama	B
4187	Kamehameha Day / War bond souvenir / June 11, 1943 [env. 8 7/8x3 7/8 in.]	Blue	Hawai	Unknown	C
4188	Kamehameha Day / War bond souvenir / June 11, 1944 [env. 8 7/8x3 7/8 in.]	Blue	Hawai	Unknown	C
4189	Kamrade! / unconditional / surrender / Nazi armies crushed by Allied etc.	Blue	VEDay	Unknown	B
4190	Keep / democracy / on top! / 8-2-'44——Yanks, in swift / drive take Rennes	Multicolored	Event	Linto	B
4191	Keep / democracy / on top! [no picture]	Multicolored	Home	Linto	B
4192	Keep / em / flying [eagle & flag] [handpainted]	Multicolored	EagFl	Adler	D
4193	Keep / em / flying [eagle & shield] [handpainted]	Multicolored	EagSh	Adler	D
4194	Keep / Old Glory flying / keep on buying etc.	Unknown	Unk	Bartz	A
4195	Keep / on / buying / bonds / for / victory [Eagle in V]	Blue, red	EagV	Risinger	A
4196	Keep / our / victory-winning / eagles flying / with purchases / of war etc.	Multicolored	EagV	Linto	B
4197	Keep / out / of / the / Buy more bonds [handpainted]	Multicolored	Dog	Unknown	C
4198	Keep / the / war / bonds [handpainted]	Blue, red	Uncle	Borkowski	D
4199	Keep / your / at her / side [thermographed]	Unknown	Unk	Baur	A
4200	Keep / your / at his / side [thermographed]	Unknown	Unk	Baur	A
4201	Keep / your / bonds / V	Blue, red	Bonds	Boone	A
4202	Keep / your / bonds [no picture]	Green	Bonds	Boone	A
4203	Keep / your trap / shut / don't tell anything / to the Axis rats [thermographed]	Black/Gold	Home	Boothroyd	A
4204	Keep alert, look your responsibilities / straight in the eye etc. [env. 6 3/4x3 3/4 in.]	Black/Blue	Home	Bartley	A
4205	Keep all calls / [etc.] / for war [buff envelope 6 3/4x3 3/4 in.]	Unknown	Home	Mich Bell	B
4206	Keep America / free / do your share / for victory [thermographed]	Blue, red	EagSh	Yontz	B
4207	Keep America free	Blue/Green	Unk	Cozart	A
4208	Keep America free / buy bonds for victory [all caps]	Black	Flag	Littlefiel	A
4209	Keep America free / buy bonds for victory [caps and lower case]	Black	Flag	Littlefiel	A
4210	Keep America free / keep the right to choose / our President etc. [no picture]	Blue	Home	Lemponen	A
4211	Keep America free / keep the right to choose etc. [w/ U.S. President on label]	Blue	Home	Lemponen	B
4212	Keep America free [eagle and ribbon]	Green	Eagle	Cozart	A
4213	Keep America free [text 3 mm below picture]	Black	Home	McFarland	A
4214	Keep America free [text 5 mm below picture]	Black	Home	McFarkand	A
4215	Keep America free in the air / for a righteous / cause	Blue	Air	McFarland	A
4216	Keep America supreme [thermographed]	Green	Air	McCluney	A
4217	Keep bombing Berlin / 'til this goose is cooked [in quotes]	Black	Hitle	Donaldson	A
4218	Keep busy / flatfoot!	Black	Navy	Lupton	A
4219	Keep 'em / dropping / Buy U.S. / war bonds / now!	Black/Blue	Air	Clendennen	B
4220	Keep 'em / dropping / Buy U.S. / war bonds / now!	Blue	Air	Williams	A
4221	Keep 'em / flying / United States / defense bonds	Red	Bonds	Stephens	A
4222	Keep 'em / flying [6 fighter-bombers]	Blue, red	Air	Richardson	A
4223	Keep em / flying [eagle diving] [handpainted]	Multicolored	Eagle	Adler	D
4224	Keep em / flying [eagle with flag] [handpainted]	Multicolored	EagFl	Adler	D
4225	Keep em / flying [eagle, no flag] [handpainted]	Multicolored	Eagle	Adler	D
4226	Keep 'em / flying [handpainted] [artist: Chuck Rothert]	Blue	Home	Rothert	B
4227	Keep 'em / flying [handpainted]	Multicolored	Air	Knapp	G
4228	Keep 'em / in the dark / stop / stop / loose-talk	Black	Japan	Davis, D	A
4229	Keep 'em / sailing! / American ships etc. [envelope 6 3/4x3 3/4 in.]	Blue	Navy	Propeller	A
4230	Keep e'm [sic] / flying [eagle landing] [handpainted]	Multicolored	Eagle	Adler	D
4231	Keep 'em coming etc. [label + blue "Victory" border]	Multicolored	Home	Unknown	B
4232	Keep 'em coming etc. [label + red "Victory" border]	Multicolored	Home	Unknown	B
4233	Keep 'em coming etc. [label + red "Win the War" border]	Multicolored	Home	Unknown	B
4234	Keep 'em diving [handpainted]	Blue, red	Air	Klaas	D
4235	Keep em firing / A good Jap is a dead etc.	Unknown	Japan	Morrison	A
4236	Keep 'em firing / keep on buying ... / bonds [artillery]	Bu,R/Red	Ordna	Risinger	A
4237	Keep 'em firing / keep on buying ... / bonds [machine gun]	Bu,R/Red	Ordna	Risinger	A
4238	Keep 'em firing!	Blue, red	Ordna	Hillerich	A
4239	Keep 'em floating / US / Merchant / Marine	Unknown	Merch	Kosko	A
4240	Keep 'em floating / US / Merchant / Marine [6x4 in.]	Blue, red	Merch	Kosko	A
4241	Keep 'em floating!	Red	Unk	Unknown	A

NO.	CACHET TEXT	COLOR	TOPIC	PUBLISHER	$
4242	Keep 'em flying / "Remember / Pearl / Harbor" / "Slap / the Jap / off the" etc.	Green	UncJa	Unknown	A
4243	Keep 'em flying / and / keep 'em sailing etc.	Blue, red	Unk	Risinger	A
4244	Keep 'em flying / and / keep on buying / bonds - for victory	Blue, red	Air	Risinger	A
4245	Keep 'em flying / buy / bonds - for victory / now	Blue, red	Air	Risinger	A
4246	Keep 'em flying / buy victory bonds / preserve liberty [airplane, Liberty Bell]	Blue, red	Air	Risinger	A
4247	Keep 'em flying / buy war bonds [no picture] [envelope 7 1/2x4 in.]	Unknown	Unk	County	B
4248	Keep 'em flying / don't let him down!	Black	Unk	Hartman	A
4249	Keep 'em flying / Keep 'em rolling / Do your duty / Keep on buying etc. [2 flags]	Blue, red	Flag	Bartz	A
4250	Keep 'em flying / Keep 'em rolling / Do your duty/ Keep on buying etc. [airplane]	Blue, red	Air	Bartz	A
4251	Keep 'em flying / keep it ringing / keep on buying / war bonds & stamps	Blue, red	FlBel	Amer Pat	A
4252	Keep 'em flying / keep on buying ... / bonds [eagle holding flag]	Blue, red	EagFl	Risinger	A
4253	Keep 'em flying / keep on buying ... / bonds [eagle in V]	Blue, red	EagV	Risinger	A
4254	Keep 'em flying / keep on buying ... / bonds [eagle on rock]	Blue, red	Eagle	Risinger	A
4255	Keep 'em flying / keep on buying ... / bonds [eagle with palm branches]	Blue, red	Eagle	Risinger	A
4256	Keep 'em flying / keep on buying ... / bonds [Minute Man]	Blue, red	Minut	Risinger	A
4257	Keep 'em flying / keep on buying ... / bonds [plane flying left]	Blue, red	Air	Risinger	A
4258	Keep 'em flying / keep on buying ... / bonds [plane flying right, parachutes]	Blue, red	Chute	Risinger	A
4259	Keep 'em flying / keep on buying / bonds for victory	Blue, red	UncV	Risinger	A
4260	Keep 'em flying [2 planes dropping bombs]	Blue, red	Air	Powers	A
4261	Keep 'em flying [airplane and V] [handpainted]	Blue, red	VforV	Klaas	D
4262	Keep 'em flying [eagle, flag, airplane, outline map of USA]	Blue, red	EagFl	Smartcraft	B
4263	Keep 'em flying [eagle, shield, 3 planes]	Multicolored	Air	Dime	A
4264	Keep em flying [envelope 7 1/2x3 15/16]	Unknown	Unk	Unknown	A
4265	Keep 'em flying [globe and flags of United Nations]	Blue, red	UN	Cachet Cra	A
4266	Keep 'em flying [handpainted]	Multicolored	Air	Knapp	G
4267	Keep 'em flying [head of aviator]	Blue, red	Air	Cachet Cra	A
4268	Keep 'em flying [in arc inside circle] [airplane and star]	Blue, red	Air	Krakora	A
4269	Keep 'em flying [in quotes] [type style, corner card AAF unit, airplane vary]	Blue	Air	Air Force	A
4270	Keep 'em flying [in quotes][no picture]	Blue	Air	Air Force	A
4271	Keep 'em flying [solid plane or outline of plane]	Blue	Air	Dime	A
4272	Keep 'em flying [three small planes]	Blue	Air	Dime	A
4273	Keep 'em flying [U.S., British flags]	Blue, red	Flag	Quigley	B
4274	Keep 'em flying [upper left, below flag and bomber]	Blue	Air	McCabe	A
4275	Keep 'em flying! [aviator] [handpainted]	Multicolored	Air	Parker	B
4276	Keep 'em flying! [envelope 7 1/2x4 in.]	Multicolored	Unk	Dime	A
4277	Keep 'em flying! [in quotes] / Control of the air was recognized early etc.	Multicolored	Air	Advertiser	B
4278	Keep 'em flying! [kicking mule]	Brown	Axis	Cornell	B
4279	Keep 'em flying! [no picture] [envelope 9 1/2x4 1/8 in.]	Unknown	Air	Philadelph	A
4280	Keep 'em flying! [two planes dropping bombs] [envelope 6x3 1/2 in.]	Blue, red	Air	Powers	A
4281	Keep 'em flying!! / For victory and peace..buy war bonds!	Green, red	Air	Cochran	A
4282	Keep 'em flying!! [planes]	Green, red	Air	Dye	A
4283	Keep 'em flying!! Kick 'em in the Axis!! [handpainted]	Multicolored	Axis	Parker	C
4284	Keep 'em frying [thermographed]	Red	Axis	Crosby	B
4285	Keep em happy	Purple	Unk	Foster	A
4286	Keep 'em happy / Write a letter to a / friend in the service today!	Blue, red	Armed	Smith, W	A
4287	Keep 'em happy with mail! [thermographed]	Black	Armed	Czubay	A
4288	Keep 'em rolin' [sic] with / war bonds	Bk/Purple	Ordna	Lowe	A
4289	Keep 'em rolling - / - keep on buying bonds [tank]	Blue, red	Ordna	Risinger	A
4290	Keep 'em rolling / keep on buying ... / bonds [jeep]	Blue, red	Ordna	Risinger	A
4291	Keep 'em rolling / keep on buying ... / bonds [tank]	Blue, red	Ordna	Risinger	A
4292	Keep 'em rolling / keep on buying ... / bonds [truck]	Blue, red	Ordna	Risinger	A
4293	Keep 'em rolling [handpainted]	Multicolored	Ordna	Unknown	B
4294	Keep 'em sailing / buy more bonds	Unknown	Unk	Chapman	A
4295	Keep 'em sailing / keep on buying ... / bonds [landing craft or speed boat]	Blue, red	Bonds	Risinger	A
4296	Keep 'em smiling / write today [thermographed]	Blue	Unk	Crosby	B
4297	Keep every day / Independence / Day / buy etc.	Blue, red	Eagle	Kosko	A
4298	Keep forging ahead / day by day etc.	Red	Home	Carpenter	A
4299	Keep forging ahead, day by day, / less time our boys will be away.	Red	Home	Carpenter	A

NO.	CACHET TEXT	COLOR	TOPIC	PUBLISHER	$
4300	Keep freedom ringing / "throughout the world" [handpainted]	Multicolored	Bell	Babcock	B
4301	Keep him / goose-stepping! etc. [label + blue "Victory" border]	Multicolored	Hitle	Unknown	B
4302	Keep him / goose-stepping! etc. [label + red "Victory" border]	Multicolored	Hitle	Unknown	B
4303	Keep him / goose-stepping! etc. [label + red "Win the War" border]	Multicolored	Hitle	Unknown	B
4304	Keep him flying!	Blue, red	EagV	Myers	A
4305	Keep him going ···- [handpainted]	Multicolored	Army	Borkowski	D
4306	Keep him on the run [handpainted]	Multicolored	Hitle	Adler	D
4307	Keep him out / Buy more / war bonds [handpainted]	Multicolored	Japan	Knoll	D
4307A	Keep him out! [in quotes] / Buy war bonds [handpainted]	Multicolored	Nazis	Knoll	D
4308	Keep his bayonet / sharp / with / bonds	Bu/Gn/R/Y	Armed	Jarrett	A
4309	Keep his bayonet / sharp / with / bonds / VE	Blue, yellow	VEDay	Jarrett	B
4310	Keep in step / buy bonds / He won't dodge dying.... Don't you dodge buying	Red	Armed	Dale	A
4311	Keep it / flying / buying [flag, war bonds pennant] [handpainted]	Multicolored	Flag	Adler	D
4312	Keep it / under / your hat / the enemy has ears	Blue, red	Uncle	McCluney	A
4313	Keep it / waving [flag and globe]	Blue, red	Flag	Clifford	A
4314	Keep it burning / buy bonds	Blue, red	Unk	Risinger	A
4315	Keep it flying [in quotes] [envelope 7 1/2x3 7/8 in.]	Blue, red	Flag	Unknown	A
4316	Keep it waving [envelope 6 3/4x3 3/4 in.]	Blue, red	Flag	Garfield	A
4317	Keep it waving [in quotes] [handpainted]	Multicolored	Flag	Babcock	C
4318	Keep it waving! [5 flags grouped] [envelope 6 1/8x3 5/8 in. or 6 1/2x3 5/8 in.]	Blue, red	Flag	Garfield	A
4319	Keep it waving! [one flag]	Black	Flag	Davis, Ral	A
4320	Keep its light / bright! / buy a share etc.	Unknown	Torch	Dailey	A
4321	Keep its light / bright! [thermographed]	Blue/Red	Torch	Dailey	A
4322	Keep its light burning bright!	Unknown	Torch	Dailey	A
4323	Keep its light burning! [thermographed]	Unknown	Torch	Dailey	A
4324	Keep letters sailing / they're / etc. / failing! [handpainted]	Blue	Navy	Myers	B
4325	Keep lines clear / for war calls [no picture]	Unk	Home	Mountain	B
4326	Keep me smiling [in quotes] / write today! in quotes] [all caps] [thermographed]	Blue	Navy	Crosby	B
4327	Keep me smiling [in quotes] etc. [caps & lower case; w/, w/o frame] [thermographed]	Blue	Navy	Crosby	B
4328	Keep Old Glory flying / Every day is Flag Day [envelope 9 1/2x4 1/8 in.]	Unknown	Flag	Unknown	A
4329	Keep on buying / bonds - for victory [Minute Man]	Blue, red	Minut	Risinger	A
4330	Keep on writing / to the men who are fighting	Blue, red	Armed	Staehle	B
4331	Keep our / boys out / of foreign / war	Unknown	Neutr	Unk	B
4332	Keep our Air Corps flying / keep faith in etc. [envelope 6 3/4x3 3/4 in.]	Black	Air	Elks	A
4333	Keep our boys moving forward / buy war [thermographed]	Green	Bonds	Sadworth	B
4334	Keep our boys well supplied / with "love pellets" for the / Axis! Buy U.S. etc.	Multicolored	Bonds	Linto	B
4335	Keep Rommel on the run. [in quotes] / Buy war bonds [handpainted]	Multicolored	Romm	Knoll	C
4336	Keep that light burning! [copyright "C" w/, w/o serifs]	Multicolored	Torch	Minkus	A
4337	Keep the / Red Cross / beside etc. [on back] [envelope 6 3/4x3 3/4 in.]	Unknown	RedCr	Bost Ed	B
4338	Keep the home fires burning [in quotes] / [etc.] / Remember etc. [thermographed]	Red	USMC	Crosby	B
4339	Keep the home fires burning [in quotes] / [etc.] / Semper Fidelis [thermographed]	Red	USMC	Crosby	B
4340	Keep the home fires burning [in quotes] / [etc.] / Semper Fidelis [thermographed]	Red	USMC	Crosby	B
4341	Keep the home fires burning [in quotes] / [etc.] / the boys come home. [thermographed]	Blue/Red	Navy	Crosby	B
4342	Keep the home fires etc. Donald Duck, mascot etc. [double cachet] [thermographed]	Red-1, Gn-2	Mac	Crosby	D
4343	Keep the lights bright and the Cascades / white, we won't always have to fight.	Blue, red	Home	Quigley	B
4344	Keep the sea lanes / open [handpainted]	Multicolored	Navy	Knapp	G
4345	Keep the sights on 'em / buy war bonds [brown envelope]	Red	Bonds	Ohio Bell	D
4346	Keep the U.S. out of war / write your Congressman today, to / keep the etc.	Unknown	Neutr	Butzen	D
4347	Keep them / rolling / buy / war bonds	Blue	Unk	Ohio Bell	D
4348	Keep them busy / rolling / buy / war bonds	Blue	Unk	Ohio Bell	D
4349	Keep them floating / With more scrap / for the Jap / now they'll pay / in etc.	Blue	Navy	Carpenter	A
4350	Keep them floating / with more scrap / for the Jap / now they'll pay etc.	Blue	Navy	Carpenter	A
4351	Keep them flying / Berlin is dying	Black/Blue	Unk	Harrington	A
4352	Keep them flying / Buy bonds / Let's go America / Keep them etc. [handpainted]	Blue, red	Bonds	Barwicki	B
4353	Keep them flying / for final victory / ...V- / Remember Pearl etc. [rubber stamps]	Purple	UncV	Unknown	A
4354	Keep them flying [diagonal] [no picture] [handpainted]	Blue, red	Air	Barwicki	B
4355	Keep them rolling / until they hit Berlin	Blue	Unk	Harrington	A
4356	Keep this ape out on a limb [in quotes] / "Hirohito the invincible???"	Black/Brown	Japan	Donaldson	A

NO.	CACHET TEXT	COLOR	TOPIC	PUBLISHER	$
4357	Keep this smile / on good old Uncle / Sam, and the way / is easy. Just buy etc.	Multicolored	Bonds	Linto	B
4358	Keep United States out of war etc. [circles stamp] [blue env.] [mailed 9/39]	Red	Neutr	Unknown	F
4359	Keep writing / while they're / fighting / for / V / V / ···–	Blue, red	Armed	Harrington	A
4360	Keep writing! / Write every day / to the pal in service! [no picture]	Blue	Home	Stefun	A
4361	Keep your / boots / working / in /[handpainted]	Multicolored	Hitle	Adler	D
4362	Keep your appliances / in fightin' form [on back]	Black	Home	Phila Elec	B
4363	Keep your faith in God / now and to the end.... / Please pray Our Father etc.	Multicolored	Relig	Linto	B
4364	Keep your Red Cross / at his side / give! [envelope 6x3 ½ in.]	Black	RedCr	Peters	A
4365	Keep your sleeves rolled up / untill [sic] the / job is done [handpainted]	Multicolored	Uncle	Adler	C
4366	Kelly sinks Jap ship / Colin P. Kelly, etc. [env. 6 1/2x3 5/8 or 6x3 ½ in.]	Orange	Hero	Unknown	A
4367	Kentucky's sons / fight on / every front	Blue, red	Home	Threl+Thar	A
4368	Kentucky's sons / fight on / every front [thermographed]	Blue, red	Home	Threl+Thar	A
4369	Kharkov re-taken / by Germans [rubber stamp with cachet 4080]	Red	Event	Unknown	C
4370	Kicked out! / Tojo / ——(so sorry!)	Blue, red	Japan	Boone	B
4371	Kicked sky high!	Gold, green	Japan	Cox	A
4372	Kinda give it / your personal / attention / will you?	Blue	Army	Unknown	A
4373	King of the Pacific / ruler of the waves [thermographed]	Unknown	Unk	McCluney	A
4374	Kiska [handpainted]	Multicolored	Map	Smith, LH	C
4375	Kiss me again, Betty! [in quotes] [yellow envelope]	Multicolored	Army	Amer Art	A
4376	Kitchen help wanted! [handpainted]	Multicolored	Home	Martin	C
4377	Kitty Hawk Day / [etc.] / Forty years of aviation / "The future depends on you"	Blue, orange	Air	Zunks	B
4378	Knowing the horrors / of this war are you / [etc.] / 11-27-'44——Chutists etc.	Gold, silver	Event	Linto	B
4379	Knowing the horrors / of this war are you / doing / everything etc. [no picture]	Gold, silver	Home	Linto	B
4380	Korea	Black	ORN	Lowry	A
4381	Korea / Chosen / the day of / liberation etc. [thermographed]	Multicolored	ORN	Smartcraft	B
4382	Korea / Korea has been under the yoke etc.	Blue	ORN	Cliff	A
4383	Korea / liberated / After 35 years of / Japanese occupation / Korea is etc.	Multicolored	ORN	Teixeira	D
4384	Korea / The people of Korea will be / free and independent again.	Multicolored	ORN	Cachet Cra	B
4385	Korea shall be free again!	Unknown	ORN	Anderson	A
4386	Kwajalein / Feb / 1944 / "Greater love / hath no man -"	Black, red	Armed	McCluney	B
4387	Kwit yer gripin' / meatless / Tuesday! / gas rationing! / blackouts! etc.	Bk/Br/Gn	Home	Carter	A
4388	Kwitcherkickin! / our forefathers did without - / sugar - till the etc. [handpainted]	Blue, red	Home	Myers	B

Cover Values (from Table 6, p. 136)

Value	*Price Range*
A	$ 3 - 6
B	$ 7 - 15
C	$ 16 - 30
D	$ 31 - 60
E	$ 61 - 125
F	$ 126 - 250
G	$ 251 - 500
H	$ 501 - 1000
I	$ >1000
X	**Unpriced: Suspicious or fraudulent cover**

4186

4198

4206

4222

4234

4262

4277

4284

4305

4306

4307A

4308

4313

4326

4336

4356

4361

4374

4375

4386

CACHET TEXT BEGINNING WITH "L"

NO.	CACHET TEXT	COLOR	TOPIC	PUBLISHER	$
4389	L.-Gen. / Brereton / ⋯ - / ⋯ -	Unknown	Gener	Linto	B
4390	L.-Gen. / Brereton / ⋯ - / ⋯ - / 11-8-'44——Gen. Patton starts / drive etc.	Unknown	Event	Linto	B
4391	L.-Gen. / Jacob L. / Devers	Gold, silver	Gener	Linto	B
4392	L.-Gen. / Jacob L. / Devers / 12-29-'44——Nips claim they attacked / U.S. etc.	Multicolored	Event	Linto	B
4393	Labor Day	Multicolored	Home	Hale	A
4394	Labor Day / at Liberty, N.Y. / For victory - liberty - and honor / 1942	Blue, red	Holid	Zunks	B
4395	Labor Day / at War, W. Va. / September 7th etc. [env. 6 1/2x3 5/8, 6x3 ½ in.]	Blue, red	Holid	Cleveland	A
4396	Labor Day / Sept. 03, 1945 / Birth of a / better era etc.	Unknown	Holid	Linto	B
4397	Labor Day / Sept. 05, 1942 / 174 ships / launched	Unknown	Holid	Linto	B
4398	Labor Day / September / second [postmarked 9/2/40]	Gold, silver	Holid	Linto	B
4399	Labor Day / September 06, 1943 / work for / victory	Blue, red	Hawai	Sayama	B
4400	Labor units / for defense / Labor Day [handpainted]	Multicolored	Home	Knapp	G
4401	Ladies' tailor [in quotes] [envelope 6 9/16x3 3/4 in.]	Sepia tones	Nazis	Belles-let	C
4402	Ladies who labor / shorten / the road / to / victory	Blue, red	Women	Richardson	A
4403	Lafayette we are here! / Chas. E. Stanton July 4, 1917 / History repeats in 1944 etc.	Blue, red	Hist	Griffith	A
4404	Lafayette we are on the way	Blue, red	Map	Hill	A
4405	Lampedusa & Linora Islands surrender	Unknown	Event	Linto	B
4406	Land / of the / free / O say, can you see etc.	Unknown	Unk	Unk	A
4407	Land of the free / the U.S.A. [allover cachet] [handpainted]	Multicolored	Map	Buxton Mrs	D
4408	Land of the free / U.S.A. [handpainted]	Blue, red	Home	Krakora	B
4409	Land of the free [handpainted]	Multicolored	Shiel	Knapp	G
4410	Land sea air	Black	Unk	Kotab	A
4411	Landing made / on Okinawa [rubber stamp with cachet 756]	Aqua	Event	Unknown	C
4412	Last / shell	Black/Brown	Unk	Harrington	A
4413	Last lap to / liberty - Japan!	Green	Japan	Phill, CR	A
4414	Last message from / Corregidor ... (Part Four) etc. [no picture]	Blue/Purple	Phili	Boone	C
4415	Last message from / Corregidor ... (Part One) etc. [no picture]	Blue/Purple	Phili	Boone	C
4416	Last message from / Corregidor ... (Part Three) etc. [no picture]	Blue/Purple	Phili	Boone	C
4417	Last message from / Corregidor ... (Part Two) etc. [no picture]	Blue/Purple	Phili	Boone	C
4418	Latrine General [in quotes] [handpainted]	Multicolored	Army	Parker	B
4419	Laval is / the Judas / of France! / [etc.] / 8-29-'44——Yanks in Reims! etc.	Blue, gold	Event	Linto	B
4420	Laval is / the Judas / of France! [no picture]	Bu,Gd/Gn,Re	ORN	Linto	B
4421	Laval named chief of Vichy govt.	Unknown	Event	Linto	B
4422	Lead the way! / Buy a bond today [vertical text] [handpainted]	Multicolored	Bonds	Myers	B
4423	Lead us from the shadows / of sorrow and fear, etc. [position of text varies]	Multicolored	Liber	Amer Pat	A
4424	Leaky pens cost lives	Bk/Br/Gn/Red	Army	Davis, Ral	A
4425	Leaky pens cost lives	Blue, yellow	Army	Davis, Ral	A
4426	Learn about German / "culture" / [etc.] / 9-5-'44——Reds run wild / over Romania	Unknown	Event	Linto	B
4427	Learn about German / "culture" / in stories written by / Andre Lebarn etc.	Unknown	Nazis	Linto	B
4428	Learn the truth / about wasting your / tax money. Listen to / Fulton Lewis, Jr.	Gold, silver	Home	Linto	B
4429	Learning / Hitler / his / American's / British / Canadian's etc. [no picture]	Blue, red	Hitle	Schirmer	A
4430	Lend yourself / [etc.] / Buy US war bonds	Black	Bonds	Catholic	A
4431	Lend yourself / some money / buy etc. [envelope 9 1/2x4 1/8 in.]	Blue	Bonds	Woodall	B
4432	Less talking / more shooting etc. [on back] [buff envelope]	Black	Unk	Mich Bell	B
4433	Lest we forget / 1918.1944	Unknown	Unk	Boone	A
4434	Lest we forget / our hero dead [thermographed]	Blue, silver	Relig	Yontz	B
4435	Lest we forget / the hell that etc.	Purple	Unk	Christens	A
4436	Lest we forget / the price of freedom paid / with the lives of etc. [thermographed]	Blue, red	Armed	Von Los	B
4437	Lest we forget [in quotes] / 1918 1944	Blue, red	Holid	Boone	A
4438	Lest we forget December 7, 1941 [in quotes] / [etc.] / citizens murdered by Japan!	Multicolored	Pearl	Edmunds	D
4439	Lest you / forget / Pearl Harbor [Christmas candles] [handpainted]	Green, red	Holid	Adler	C
4440	Lest you forget [graveside cross, helmet, "G.I. Joe"] [handpainted]	Multicolored	Army	Adler	D
4441	Let / freedom / ring / for / all the world [copyright "C" w/, w/o serifs]	Multicolored	Bell	Minkus	A
4442	Let 'em have it / buy / extra bonds [envelope 6 9/16x3 3/4 in.]	Sepia tones	Bonds	Belles-let	C
4443	Let 'em have it [in quotes]	Blue, red	Army	Boone	A
4444	Let em have it!	Black	Army	Wolf, CL	A

NO.	CACHET TEXT	COLOR	TOPIC	PUBLISHER	$
4445	Let 'em have it, boys! [in quotes]	Blue, red	Army	McFarland	A
4446	Let em have it. / Back em up. [handpainted]	Multicolored	Armed	Borkowski	D
4447	Let 'em wash up and go home!! [envelope 6x3 ½ in.]	Olive	Armed	Conner	A
4448	Let every man be swift / to hear, slow to speak etc. [italic print]	Blue, gold	Relig	Amer Pat	A
4449	Let every man be swift / to hear, slow to speak etc. [script print]	Blue, gold	Relig	Amer Pat	A
4450	Let every man honor and love / the land etc.	Unknown	Unk	Brenn	A
4451	Let freedom / ring	Blue, red	Bell	Krakora	A
4452	Let freedom / ring forever	Multicolored	Bell	Dime	A
4453	Let freedom ring	Bu,red/Green	Home	Boone	A
4454	Let freedom ring / I have returned / MacArthur [envelope 7 1/2x4 in.]	Blue, red	Mac	McFarland	B
4455	Let freedom ring / I have returned / MacArthur [envelope 7 1/4x4 1/4 in.]	Black	Mac	McFarland	B
4456	Let freedom ring / throughout the world [5 massed flags]	Red	Flag	McFarland	A
4457	Let freedom ring / throughout the world [tank]	Red	Ordna	McFarland	A
4458	Let freedom ring [airplane above text]	Blue	Air	McFarland	A
4459	Let freedom ring [Columbia, eagle, shield above text]	Green	Bell	McFarland	A
4460	Let freedom ring [flag of Albania]	Multicolored	ORN	Ioor	A
4461	Let freedom ring [flag of Austria]	Multicolored	ORN	Ioor	A
4462	Let freedom ring [flag of Belgium]	Multicolored	ORN	Ioor	A
4463	Let freedom ring [flag of Czechoslovakia]	Multicolored	ORN	Ioor	A
4464	Let freedom ring [flag of Denmark]	Multicolored	ORN	Ioor	A
4465	Let freedom ring [flag of France]	Multicolored	ORN	Ioor	A
4466	Let freedom ring [flag of Greece]	Multicolored	ORN	Ioor	A
4467	Let freedom ring [flag of Korea]	Multicolored	ORN	Ioor	A
4468	Let freedom ring [flag of Luxembourg]	Multicolored	ORN	Ioor	A
4469	Let freedom ring [flag of Netherlands]	Multicolored	ORN	Ioor	A
4470	Let freedom ring [flag of Norway]	Multicolored	ORN	Ioor	A
4471	Let freedom ring [flag of Poland]	Multicolored	ORN	Ioor	A
4472	Let freedom ring [flag of Yugoslavia]	Multicolored	ORN	Ioor	A
4473	Let freedom ring [jeeps above text]	Red	Army	McFarland	A
4474	Let freedom ring [MacArthur above text]	Black	Bell	McFarland	A
4475	Let freedom ring [PT-boat above text]	Green	Navy	McFarland	A
4476	Let freedom ring [tank above text]	Red	Bell	McFarland	A
4477	Let freedom ring [tank]	Red	Ordna	McFarland	A
4478	Let freedom ring [warships above text]	Black	Bell	McFarland	A
4479	Let freedom ring around the world [handpainted]	Multicolored	FlBel	Weigand	C
4480	Let freedom ring! [no stars]	Blue/Purple	Home	Cozart	A
4481	Let freedom ring! [position of draped flag at left varies] [env. 6x3 ½ in.]	Multicolored	FlBel	Amer Pat	A
4482	Let freedom ring! [row of 6 stars, cachet height 64 mm]	Blue/Purple	Home	Cozart	A
4483	Let freedom ring! [row of 6 stars, cachet height 69 mm]	Blue/Purple	Home	Cozart	A
4484	Let freedom ring! [text w/ serifs, 45 mm long] [eagle, flag, liberty bell]	Blue, red	EagFl	Poppenger	A
4485	Let freedom ring! [text w/o serifs, 42 mm long] [eagle, flag, bell]	Blue, red	EagFl	Poppenger	A
4486	Let freedom ring! [text w/o serifs, 50 mm long] [eagle, flag, bell]	Blue, red	EagFl	Poppenger	A
4487	Let freedom ring! [text w/o serifs, 55 mm long] [eagle, flag, bell]	Blue, red	EagFl	Poppenger	A
4488	Let freedom shine!	Blue, red	Liber	Grandy	A
4489	Let it ring / for ever [handpainted]	Multicolored	Bell	Knapp	H
4490	Let none but Americans / stand guard to-night! etc.	Black, green	Wash	McCluney	A
4491	Let our lights so shine / [etc.] / 7-6-'44——Yankees sink and / damage 36 etc.	Multicolored	Event	Linto	B
4492	Let our lights so shine / before all people / so spiritual rather / than etc.	Gold, silver	Liber	Linto	B
4493	Let the angel / of mercy / always be / with you [draped flag at left]	Multicolored	Relig	Amer Pat	A
4494	Let the angel / of mercy / always be / with you [w/o draped flag]	Multicolored	Relig	Amer Pat	A
4495	Let them wash up and go home! / Buy more war bonds	Bu/Br/Gn/Red	Army	Conner	A
4496	Let them wash up and go home! / Buy more war bonds	Blue, red	Army	Conner	A
4497	Let there be light	Multicolored	Liber	Minkus	A
4498	Let this be / America's answer [colored envelopes]	Blue, red	Air	Poppenger	A
4499	Let this book be / your guide for / victory!	Gold, silver	Relig	Linto	B
4500	Let this book be / your guide for / victory! / Navy Day——27-10-'43	Multicolored	Navy	Linto	B
4501	Let us ask God to will / [etc.] / 2-16-'42——U-boats attacked Nether- etc.	Unknown	Anniv	Linto	B
4502	Let us ask God to will / the minds of men that / the world may never etc.	Unknown	Relig	Linto	B

NO.	CACHET TEXT	COLOR	TOPIC	PUBLISHER	$
4503	Let us have faith that / right makes might / and in that faith let us to etc.	Gold, silver	Linc	Linto	B
4504	Let us have faith that / right makes might, and in / that faith let us to the end etc.	Blue, red	Linc	Griffith	B
4505	Let us have faith that right makes / [etc.] / 10-8-'44——Halsey's fleet etc.	Multicolored	Event	Linto	B
4506	Let us have faith that right makes / might, and in that faith let us to etc.	Green, silver	Linc	Linto	B
4507	Let us have faith that right makes might; and in that faith etc.	Blue, red	Linc	Baur	A
4508	Let us keep / freedom / ringing / throughout / the world	Multicolored	Bell	Minkus	A
4509	Let us keep it flying [on flap] [envelope 7 1/2x4 in.]	Unknown	Flag	Dime Store	A
4510	Let us not force one / man to "hog" the / White House! / Remember the etc.	Multicolored	FDR	Linto	B
4511	Let us pray / for / an early / a just / and a / lasting / peace [no picture]	Blue	Relig	Rowe	A
4512	Let us raise a standard etc.	Unknown	Unk	Lowe	A
4513	Let us return to / a government / of the people / by the etc. [no picture]	Multicolored	Home	Linto	B
4514	Let your motto be: / "We will put forth every effort / to preserve" etc.	Unknown	Home	Linto	B
4515	Let's —— / down on the / Axis	Brown, green	Axis	Dale	A
4516	Let's / beat 'em / 48 / different ways [copyright "C" w/, w/o serifs]	Multicolored	Home	Minkus	A
4517	Let's / burn the Axis	Black, red	Axis	Dime Store	A
4518	Let's / face / it / and with a smile. / Those in service / have no choice! etc.	Multicolored	Flag	Linto	B
4519	Let's / finish / the / job. [handpainted]	Multicolored	UncV	Borkowski	C
4520	Let's / go! / bond-way / [etc.] / 7th war loan drive——May 14-June 30	Green	Bonds	Davis, D	B
4521	Let's / go! / bond-way / the / right of way / to victory	Bu/Br/Gn/Red	VforV	Davis, D	A
4522	Let's / go! / Keep 'em flying	Multicolored	FlBel	Grandy	A
4523	Let's / go! / V	Multicolored	FlBel	Grandy	A
4524	Let's / go! / V / "Win the war!"	Multicolored	FlBel	Grandy	A
4525	Let's / go! / via dog-team [thermographed]	Blue/Gold	Alask	Crosby	B
4526	Let's / make / 'em / holler / Uncle / ···‒ [plain printing]	Red	UncAx	Yontz	B
4527	Let's / make / 'em / holler / Uncle / ···‒ [thermographed]	Red	UncAx	Yontz	B
4528	Let's / sock / those / Sons of Heaven / this / December seven! / with war bonds	Green	Japan	Boone	A
4529	Lets [sic] go all the way! / for the / U.S.A.	Multicolored	Eagle	Myers	B
4530	Lets [sic] make / 194V / our victory year! [handpainted]	Black, blue	VforV	Klondike	C
4531	Let's all / be / Americans [star-spangled hat in circle]	Blue, red	Home	Krakora	A
4532	Let's all buy bombs / to bomb Berlin / If we all do / we're bound to win	Blue, red	Flag	Price, R	A
4533	Let's all pull / together [in quotes] / Buy war bonds [handpainted]	Black, tan	Hitle	Knoll	C
4534	Let's all pull / together for / victory	Blue, red	VforV	Boone	A
4535	Let's all pull together / Keep 'em rolling / Five Southern etc. [thermographed]	Red	Home	Crosby	B
4536	Let's all pull together for victory! V ···‒ ["V" 55 mm high]	Blue, red	VforV	Boone	A
4537	Let's all pull together for victory! V ["V" 66 mm high]	Blue, red	VforV	Boone	A
4538	Let's all work / for victory	Blue, red	EagFl	Lowell	A
4539	Let's all work / together / for / victory [env. 6 1/2x3 5/8, 9 1/2x4 1/8 in.]	Multicolored	Home	Ever Ready	B
4540	Let's all work for / victory [thermographed]	Red	Eagle	Sadworth	B
4541	Let's be democratic! / [etc.] / 7-17-'44——Yanks drive into / St. Lo and etc.	Unknown	Event	Linto	B
4542	Let's be democratic! / Pass the / White House / plums around	Unknown	Home	Linto	B
4543	Let's be thankful / Germany surrenders! / Today, the world was etc. [thermographed]	Blue, red	VEDay	Czubay	C
4544	Let's blow them / off the map [handpainted]	Black, red	Japan	Wolf, CL	B
4545	Let's dedicate ourselves etc.	Unknown	Unk	Clark	A
4546	Let's dedicate ourselves to / "the old homestead" way of life / Swanzey etc.	Blue, red	Home	Quigley	B
4547	Let's do it again! / 4th / War Loan / [etc.] / Buy that extra bond!	Blue	Hawai	Sayama	B
4548	Let's finish / the job! / Buy extra / war bonds [envelope 6 3/4x3 3/4 in.]	Red	Bonds	Lowell	A
4549	Let's finish the job / V ···‒ / Seventh / War etc. [no picture]	Unknown	Bonds	Lowell	A
4550	Let's give / Hitler's / goose-steppers / the bird - / Here's the bird! [handpainted]	Blue, red	Eagle	Klaas	C
4551	Let's give / Red Cross	Blue, red	RedCr	Linto	B
4552	Let's give / Red Cross / 8-16-'44——Allies hold 70-mile / beach-line in etc.	Multicolored	Event	Linto	B
4553	Let's go - / It's "K.O." for Tokyo! / Ready! / Aim! / Fire..... etc. [thermographed]	Red	Axis	Crosby	B
4554	Let's go - Army / It's "K.O." / [etc.] / ...mark! mark! fire! etc. [thermographed]	Red	Axis	Crosby	B
4555	Let's go - Army / It's "K.O." for Tokyo / [etc.] / Remember Pearl Harbor, Midway, Wake etc. [thermo]	Red	Axis	Crosby	B
4556	Let's go - Army / It's "K.O." for Tokyo / [etc.] / "Remember Pearl Harbor" [thermographed]	Red	Axis	Crosby	B
4557	Let's go - Army / It's "K.O." for Tokyo! / [etc.] / Pearl Harbor [thermographed]	Red	Axis	Crosby	B
4558	Let's go - Army / It's "K.O." for Tokyo! / Ready! / Aim! / Fire.... [thermographed]	Red	Axis	Crosby	B
4559	Let's go - Marines / It's "K.O." for Tokyo! / Ready! / Aim! etc. [thermographed]	Brown/Red	Axis	Crosby	B
4559A	Let's go - Navy / It's "K.O." for Tokyo! / [etc.] / Remember Pearl Harbor, Midway, Wake etc. [thermo]	Red	Axis	Crosby	B

NO.	CACHET TEXT	COLOR	TOPIC	PUBLISHER	$
4560	Let's go . . Navy / It's "K.O." for Tokyo! / [etc.] / "Pearl Harbor" [thermographed]	Black	Axis	Crosby	B
4561	Let's go / America / Keep 'em flying [envelope 7 1/2x3 3/4 in.]	Blue, red	Air	Temple	B
4562	Let's go / America / Keep 'em flying [envelope 7 1/2x4 in.]	Unknown	Unk	Dime Store	A
4563	Let's go all the way! / for the / U.S.A.	Multicolored	Eagle	Myers	A
4564	Let's go America / "Keep 'em flying" / "We're / carrying on!" [thermographed]	Blue	Armed	Czubay	A
4565	Let's go America [diagonal] [no picture] [handpainted]	Blue, red	Home	Barwicki	B
4566	Let's go U.S.A. [envelope 7 1/2x3 7/8 in.]	Black	Eagle	Unknown	A
4567	Let's go U.S.A. keep 'em flying / Wings of the navy / Aircraft carrier /.S.S. Lexington etc.	Red	Air	Unknown	C
4568	Let's go U.S.A.! / Keep 'em sending! [handpainted]	Blue	Home	Parker	B
4569	Let's go U.S.A.! / Keep 'em sending! [handpainted] [postmarked 6/6/44]	Multicolored	Dday	Parker	D
4570	Let's go USA [envelope 7 1/2x4 in.]	Unknown	Unk	Nelson, KE	A
4571	Let's go! / for the / knock-out blow [no picture] [green envelope]	Black	Home	Temple	A
4572	Let's go! / More / production / for / Axis / destruction [no picture]	Blue, red	Home	Kosko	A
4573	Let's go! / U.S.A. / "...with liberty and / justice for all."	Blue, red	Liber	Mayo	A
4574	Let's go! / U.S.A. / Keep / 'em flying	Blue	Flag	Muridge	B
4575	Let's go! / U.S.A. / Keep / 'em flying! [handpainted]	Multicolored	Air	Adler	D
4576	Let's go! / U.S.A. / Keep 'em flying!	Blue, red	Japan	Artcraft	A
4577	Let's go! / U.S.A. / Keep 'em flying!	Blue, red	Air	Wash Stamp	A
4578	Let's go! / U.S.A. / Our liberties / keep it burning!	Blue, red	Liber	Artcraft	A
4579	Let's go! / U.S.A. / Remember Pearl Harbor!	Blue, red	Pearl	Artcraft	A
4580	Let's go! / U.S.A. / Stamp 'em out!	Blue, red	Axis	Artcraft	A
4581	Let's go! / U.S.A. / The key to victory	Blue, red	ORN	Artcraft	A
4582	Let's go! / U.S.A. Keep 'em flying! / A powerful air force / A mighty army etc.	Multicolored	Eag+	Edmunds	C
4583	Let's go! / USA / Keep / 'em flying	Red	Unk	Wash Cover	A
4584	Let's go! / USA / Keep / 'em flying	Red	Unk	Quigley	B
4585	Let's go! girls / Keep 'em happy / Uncle Sam wants girls / to be true to etc.	Black	Home	Lohr	A
4586	Let's go! U.S.A. / Be a U.S. Army / Aviation Cadet etc. [env. 10 3/8x4 1/2 in.]	Blue	Air	War Dept	D
4587	Let's go! U.S.A. / Buy bonds / and stamps	Blue, orange	EagSh	Sweet	A
4588	Let's go! U.S.A. / Keep em flying	Black, grey	Air	Millinery	B
4589	Let's go! U.S.A. / Keep 'em flying! / The Marines Hymn / Here's etc. [thermographed]	Blue, red	USMC	Crosby	B
4590	Let's go! U.S.A. / Keep 'em flying! / U.S. Army Air Base / Will Rogers Field etc.	Blue, red	Air	Edmunds	C
4591	Let's go! U.S.A. / Keep 'em flying! [text, picture above 7 vertical lines]	Blue, red	Air	Wash Stamp	A
4592	Let's go! U.S.A. / Keep 'em flying! [thermographed]	Blue	Flag	Crosby	A
4593	Let's go! U.S.A. / V / ··· – / Victory / Remember Pear Harbor!	Blue, orange	VforV	Sweet	A
4594	Let's go! U.S.A. / We did it before and / we can do it again [in quotes]	Unknown	Unk	Unk	A
4595	Let's go! U.S.A. Keep 'em flying! / [etc.] / "Our first duty, defend America"!	Multicolored	Armed	Edmunds	C
4596	Let's go! USA	Black, red	EagSh	Mission	A
4597	Let's go! USA / Keep 'em flying	Black	Unk	Pflanz	A
4598	Let's go! USA / Keep 'em flying [text in box under flag]	Unknown	Flag	Schnecken	A
4599	Let's go! USA / Keep 'em flying!	Unknown	Unk	Mission	A
4600	Let's go! USA / Keep 'em flying! [blue envelope 6x3 1/2 in.]	Unknown	Unk	Dis Am Vet	A
4601	Let's go! USA / Keep 'em flying! [env. 6 1/2x 3 5/8, 9 1/2x4 1/8 in.]	Blue	Unk	Gunter	A
4602	Let's go! USA / Keep 'em flying! [envelope 9 1/2x4 1/8 in.]	Black	Air	War Dept.	C
4603	Let's go! USA / Keep 'em flying! [on flap]	Unknown	Unk	Dis Am Vet	A
4604	Let's go, / US ["US" letters 63mm high] [handpainted]	Multicolored	Home	Adler	D
4605	Let's go.. Marines / It's "K.O." for Tokyo! / Ready! / Aim! etc. [thermographed]	Black	USMC	Crosby	B
4606	Let's go... / It's "K.O." for Tokyo! / [etc.] / "Remember Pearl Harbor" [thermographed]	Red	Axis	Crosby	B
4607	Let's go... / It's "K.O." for Tokyo! / [etc.] / mark! mark! fire! [thermo]	Red	Axis	Crosby	B
4608	Let's go——Seabees / It's "K.O." for Tokyo! / Ready! / Aim! etc. [thermographed]	Red	Axis	Crosby	B
4609	Let's have / a clean / slate—— / erase the / Axis!	Blue	Axis	Richardson	A
4610	Let's have no slips or falls - just a falling off in accidents	Black	Home	Runge	A
4611	Let's help Tojo and Hitler / learn more about / Shangri-La	Multicolored	Axis	Linto	B
4612	Let's keep / America free / I am proud to be / a nephew of the / world's etc.	Aqua, violet	Uncle	Neal	A
4613	Let's keep / the / Americas / for / Americans etc. [cachet height 69 mm]	Blue, red	Map	AMC-Bower	A
4614	Let's keep / the / Americas / for / Americans etc. [cachet height 72 mm]	Blue, red	Map	Chester	B
4615	Let's keep it / land of the / free	Multicolored	EagFl	Minkus	A
4616	Let's keep the flag flying / Gen. Douglas MacArthur etc.	Black/Blue	Mac	Bean	B
4617	Let's launch / battleships / not rumors [env. 6 1/2x3 5/8, 7 1/2x4 in.]	Blue, red	Navy	Fleetwood	B

NO.	CACHET TEXT	COLOR	TOPIC	PUBLISHER	$
4618	Let's make / him walk / the plank / Don't try / to / come back	Blue/Red	Unk	Peters	A
4619	Let's make / him walk / the plank!	Blue	Japan	Dale	A
4620	Let's make / him walk / the plank!	Red	Unk	Peters	A
4621	Let's make / him walk / the plank! / This is too good / for his ilk	Blue, red	Japan	Dale	A
4622	Let's make it a / straight / flush!	Red	Nazis	Barnes	A
4623	Let's make it a straight flush!	Red	Nazis	Barnes	A
4624	Let's not / get nosey, bud [in quotes] / never etc. [picture blue]	Blue, red	Armed	Mutual	A
4625	Let's not / get nosey, bud [in quotes] / never etc. [picture red]	Blue, red	Armed	Mutual	A
4626	Let's not forget the / horrors of Bataan! / Let's not forget the / ones who want etc.	Gold, silver	Flag	Linto	B
4627	Let's not forget this soldier / food for victory	Blue, red	Home	Baur	A
4628	Let's open up / a second etc. [label + blue "Victory" border]	Multicolored	Home	Unknown	B
4629	Let's open up / a second etc. [label + red "Victory" border]	Multicolored	Home	Unknown	B
4630	Let's open up / a second etc. [label + red "Win the War" border]	Multicolored	Home	Unknown	B
4631	Let's put 'em where / they belong. [handpainted]	Blue	Axis	Parker	B
4632	Let's put it / over the top! / the Victory Loan / October 29 - December 8, 1945	Blue, red	Bonds	Eichenlaub	A
4633	Let's put our hands / to the plow / protect America	Multicolored	Home	Minkus	A
4634	Let's quit politics! / Draft Pres. Roosevelt / for the duration	Gold, green	FDR	Linto	B
4635	Let's ring it again	Unknown	Unk	Harrington	A
4636	Let's set / the Rising Sun [thermographed]	Gold	Japan	Czubay	B
4637	Let's 'set' the / 'Rising Sun'	Blue	Japan	Dietz	A
4638	Let's 'set' the / 'Rising Sun'	Blue	Japan	Dietz	A
4639	Let's set the Rising Sun / win the / war [thermographed]	Unknown	Japan	Crosby	B
4640	Let's shorten / this war—— / because we are / Americans! / Let's all get etc.	Blue, red	Flag	Brenn	A
4641	Let's split the Atlantic Ocean with the Huns etc. [eagle, globe] [thermographed]	Red	Eagle	Crosby	B
4642	Let's split the Pacific Ocean with the etc. [text above eagle, globe] [thermographed]	Gold/Green	Eagle	Crosby	B
4643	Let's split the Pacific Ocean with the etc. [text below eagle, globe] [thermographed]	Multicolored	Eagle	Crosby	B
4644	Let's split the Pacific Ocean with the Japs etc. [map of Pacific] [thermographed]	Green	Map	Crosby	B
4645	Let's stop all waste / Start with Washington, D.C. / Too etc. [no picture]	Multicolored	Home	Linto	B
4646	Let's take / a nip / out of the / Nipponese	Red	Japan	Barnes	A
4647	Let's win / and / then grin [handpainted]	Black, red	Holid	Wolf, CL	C
4648	Let's win the war in / 44 [envelope 7 1/2x4 in.]	Unknown	Unk	Baur	A
4649	Let's win the war of / this generation before / planning for the next etc.	Multicolored	Uncle	Linto	B
4650	Let's work for victory	Blue, red	Home	Dime Store	A
4651	Letter carrier / don't miss / this address!	Black	Navy	Lupton	A
4652	Letter carrier / please don't / miss this / address!	Black	USMC	Lupton	A
4653	Lettuce / win the war [handpainted]	Black	Home	Gawne	B
4654	Leyte / "I came through and I returned" / Gen. Douglas MacArthur [thermographed]	Blue/Purple	Mac	Crosby	B
4655	Leyte [thermogrpahed]	Unknown	Phili	Crosby	B
4656	Liberation / comes / as Allies / begin / freeing of / Belgium's / homeland	Black, pink	Event	Griffith	B
4657	Liberation / from Nazi terror will come / through our victory	Blue, red	Torch	Minkus	A
4658	Liberation / of Paris / VIII.23. to 25.1944	Multicolored	ORN	Fluegel	C
4659	Liberation / of the occupied nations / Albania [artist: Staehle]	Multicolored	ORN	King's	C
4660	Liberation / of the occupied nations / Austria [artist: Staehle]	Multicolored	ORN	King's	C
4661	Liberation / of the occupied nations / Belgium [artist: Staehle]	Multicolored	ORN	King's	C
4662	Liberation / of the occupied nations / Czechoslovakia [artist: Staehle]	Multicolored	ORN	King's	C
4663	Liberation / of the occupied nations / Denmark [artist: Staehle]	Multicolored	ORN	King's	C
4664	Liberation / of the occupied nations / Estonia [artist: Staehle]	Multicolored	ORN	King's	C
4665	Liberation / of the occupied nations / France [artist: Staehle]	Multicolored	ORN	King's	C
4666	Liberation / of the occupied nations / Greece [artist: Staehle]	Multicolored	ORN	King's	C
4667	Liberation / of the occupied nations / Latvia [artist: Staehle]	Multicolored	ORN	King's	C
4668	Liberation / of the occupied nations / Lithuania [artist: Staehle]	Multicolored	ORN	King's	C
4669	Liberation / of the occupied nations / Luxembourg [artist: Staehle]	Multicolored	ORN	King's	C
4670	Liberation / of the occupied nations / Netherlands [artist: Staehle]	Multicolored	ORN	King's	C
4671	Liberation / of the occupied nations / Poland [artist: Staehle]	Multicolored	ORN	King's	C
4672	Liberation / of the occupied nations / Yugoslavia [artist: Staehle]	Multicolored	ORN	King's	C
4673	Liberation / of the occupied nations [artist: Staehle]	Multicolored	ORN	King's	C
4674	Liberation / of the occupied nations [artist: Staehle]	Multicolored	ORN	King's	C
4675	Liberation Day of the / occupied nations in Europe [frame has space for label]	Red	ORN	King's	B

NO.	CACHET TEXT	COLOR	TOPIC	PUBLISHER	$
4676	Liberation Day!! / Allied invasion forces / land in France etc. [no picture]	Brown	DDay	Robertson	B
4677	Liberation of / Nazie [sic] Europe. / V ····–	Blue, red	EagV	Baur	A
4678	Liberty	Blue, red	Flag	Risinger	A
4679	Liberty	Blue	Eagle	Krakora	A
4680	Liberty & freedom	Unknown	Unk	Baur	A
4681	Liberty / 1776 / 1944 / liberty / We will ne'er forget its message etc.	Blue, red	Bell	Clark	A
4682	Liberty / above all - for all [copyright "C" w/, w/o serifs]	Multicolored	Liber	Minkus	A
4683	Liberty / an / American / heritage [envelope 6 5/16x3 ½ in.]	Unknown	Unk	Krakora	A
4684	Liberty / and / justice / for / all	Blue, red	EagSh	Boone	A
4685	Liberty / and / justice / for / all. [mimeographed]	Black	Liber	Granite	A
4686	Liberty / and / justice / for all	Unknown	Unk	Boone	A
4687	Liberty / and / justice / for all / mankind [engraved]	Multicolored	EagSh	Durkin	B
4688	Liberty / and peace on earth	Unknown	Unk	Davis, Ral	A
4689	Liberty / Bell / 1776 / 1944 / This old bell now is silent, / hushed is etc.	Black	Bell	Clark	A
4690	Liberty / Church / School [handpainted]	Black	Hitle	Kirchhofer	C
4691	Liberty / for / all! / malice toward none	Multicolored	Flag+	Fleetwood	B
4692	Liberty / for all [handpainted]	Multicolored	Bell	Knapp	G
4693	Liberty / is still / alive! [cachet height 38 mm]	Blue/Red	Liber	Roberts	A
4694	Liberty / is still / alive! [cachet height 50 mm]	Orange/Purple	Liber	Roberts	A
4695	Liberty / is still / alive! [cachet height 55 mm]	Orange/Purple	Liber	Roberts	A
4696	Liberty / is still / alive! [cachet height 85 mm]	Orange/Purple	Liber	Roberts	A
4697	Liberty / is still alive [handpainted]	Multicolored	Liber	Knapp	G
4698	Liberty / keep / it / shining [colored envelopes]	Blue, red	Liber	Poppenger	A
4699	Liberty / lives in the hearts of men etc.	Blue	Unk	Cochran	A
4700	Liberty / long may it ring	Blue, red	Bell	Kosko	A
4701	Liberty / long may it ring [handpainted]	Blue, red	Bell	Krakora	B
4702	Liberty / must be preserved! [envelope 6 1/2x3 5/8, 7 1/2x4 in.]	Multicolored	Lib+	Amer Pat	A
4703	Liberty / now / and / forever [5 stars below picture]	Blue/Red	Liber	Cozart	A
4704	Liberty / now / and / forever [6 stars below picture]	Blue/Red	Liber	Cozart	A
4705	Liberty / now / and / forever [no stars below picture]	Bu/Gn/Red	Liber	Cozart	A
4706	Liberty / now and forever	Blue, red	Bell	Linprint	A
4707	Liberty / the American way of life	Blue, red	EagFl	Lowell	A
4708	Liberty / typifies true / Americanism / To keep this we / must pay / the etc.	Multicolored	Uncle	Linto	B
4709	Liberty / we fight for freedom! [colored envelopes]	Blue, red	Liber	Poppenger	A
4710	Liberty / worth fighting for / win the war / for / freedom	Unknown	Unk	French	A
4711	Liberty [handpainted]	Blue, red	EagSh	Krakora	C
4712	Liberty [in quotes] [envelope 6 3/4x3 3/4 in.]	Sepia tones	Liber	Belles-let	C
4713	Liberty [vertical]	Gold, green	Minut	Linto	B
4714	Liberty and / justice for all	Multicolored	Lib+	Dime Store	A
4715	Liberty and justice for all	Blue, red	Eagle	Abel	A
4716	Liberty and justice for all [in quotes] / The Victory Loan etc.	Blue, silver	Home	Eichenlaub	A
4717	Liberty and justice for all!	Blue, red	Flag+	Amer Pat	A
4718	Liberty and justice for all! [flag between Lincoln and Washington]	Blue, red	LinWa	Ander, EA	A
4719	Liberty and justice for all! [flag between two bells]	Blue, red	FlBel	Ander, EA	A
4720	Liberty and justice to all! [text 52 or 55 mm long] [colored envelopes]	Blue, red	Eag+	Poppenger	A
4721	Liberty and Union, now and for- / [etc.] / 10-19-'44——Philippines / invaded!	Multicolored	Event	Linto	B
4722	Liberty and Union, now and for- / ever, one and inseparable. / ——Daniel Webster	Gold, green	Hist	Linto	B
4723	Liberty bell	Brown	Liber	Polonus	A
4724	Liberty casts her shadow before / Freedom / [etc.] / "The Rising Sun sets in the west"	Multicolored	Liber	Edmunds	E
4725	Liberty for all / peace on earth etc.	Multicolored	Unk	Staehle	C
4726	Liberty is the right to / speak your / [etc.] / curb your own wartime liberty.	Blue, red/Bk	Torch	Runge	A
4727	Liberty marches on	Unknown	Unk	Davis, Ral	A
4728	Liberty must endure	Blue	Unk	Foster	A
4729	Liberty now / and forever	Blue, red	Liber	Card	A
4730	Liberty ship launched - 10 days	Unknown	Home	Linto	B
4731	Liberty victorious / V-J Day / Sept. 2 / 1945 / Japan etc. [artist: Knapp]	Blue, red	VJDay	Fleetwood	C
4732	Liberty, we will follow / thee, for our etc. [picture gold] [text above picture]	Multicolored	Liber	Amer Pat	A
4733	Liberty, we will follow / thee, for our etc. [picture green] [text above picture]	Multicolored	Liber	Amer Pat	A

NO.	CACHET TEXT	COLOR	TOPIC	PUBLISHER	$
4734	Liberty, we will follow / thee, for our etc. [picture orange] [text below picture]	Multicolored	Liber	Amer Pat	A
4735	Liberty, we will follow / thee, for our etc. [picture red] [text above picture]	Multicolored	Liber	Amer Pat	A
4736	Liberty, we will never / part, for our love and / devotion will shine etc.	Multicolored	Liber	Amer Pat	A
4737	Liberty, we will never part, for our / love and devotion etc. [blue Liberty]	Multicolored	Liber	Amer Pat	A
4738	Liberty, we will never part, for our / love and devotion etc. [gold Liberty, pink envelope]	Multicolored	Liber	Amer Pat	A
4739	Liberty, we will never part, for our / love and devotion etc. [gold Liberty]	Multicolored	Liber	Amer Pat	A
4740	Liberty, we will never part, for our / love and devotion etc. [green Liberty]	Multicolored	Liber	Amer Pat	A
4741	Liberty——a united America behind you [in quotes] [envelope 6 3/4x3 3/4 in.]	Sepia tones	Liber	Belles-let	C
4742	Licked on land and licked ate sea- / somebody take the jinx off me! [in quotes]	Blue	Musso	Roberts	A
4743	Lidice - we won't forget [in quotes] / in memory of / the people of etc.	Black, violet	ORN	Ioor	A
4744	Lidice / We won't forget / Czechoslovakia [thermographed]	Blue, red	ORN	Staehle	C
4745	Lidice [in quotes] / we won't forget! / Czechoslovakia / will live / and etc.	Blue, red	ORN	Cachet Cra	B
4746	Lidice will rise again [in quotes] / V pro Vitezstir etc. [handpainted label]	Blue, red	ORN	LeGallez	C
4747	Lieut. Gen. / Jonathan Wainwright. [handpainted]	Multicolored	Gener	Adler	D
4748	Lieut. Gen. / Mark W. Clark [handpainted]	Multicolored	Gener	Adler	D
4749	Lieut. Gen. Bradley / American commander	Unknown	Gener	Linto	B
4750	Lieut. Gen. Bradley / American commander / 9-15-'44——Germans force etc.	Unknown	Event	Linto	B
4751	Lieut. Gen. Hodges / U.S. 1st Army	Multicolored	Gener	Linto	B
4752	Lieut. Gen. Hodges / U.S. 1st Army / 12-16-'44——Huns kill etc.	Multicolored	Event	Linto	B
4753	Lieut. Gen. Hodges / U.S. 1st Army / 9-24-'44——Eastern half of / Gothic etc.	Multicolored	Event	Linto	B
4754	Lieut. Gen. Patch / U.S. 7th Army	Multicolored	Gener	Linto	B
4755	Lieut. Gen. Patton / U.S. 3rd Army	Unknown	Patt	Linto	B
4756	Lieut. Gen. Patton / U.S. 3rd Army / 9-17-'44——Great air-borne army etc.	Unknown	Event	Linto	B
4757	Lieut. Gen. Patton [thermographed]	Blue	Patt	Sadworth	B
4758	Lieut.-Gen. Hodges	Sepia, silver	Gener	Linto	B
4759	Lieut.-Gen. Hodges / 12-16-'44——San Jose, Mindoro, / taken by Yanks	Multicolored	Gener	Linto	B
4760	Lieut.-Gen. Patch	Brown, silver	Gener	Linto	B
4761	Lieut.-Gen. Patch / 12-17-'44——Huns kill / 100 unarmed Yanks	Sepia, silver	Event	Linto	B
4762	Lieut.-Gen. Patton	Gold, sepia	Patt	Linto	B
4763	Life liberty happiness / Defend your heritage / with a two ocean etc. [UL] [no picture]	Black	Navy	Bean	B
4764	Life that is / worth living / is worth / fighting for!	Brown, red	Minut	Boone	A
4765	Life that is / worth living / is worth / fighting for! [no picture]	Blue, red	Home	Boone	A
4766	Life, / liberty / and the / pursuit of / happiness [in quotes]	Black	EagFl	Jordan	A
4767	Life, liberty & the pursuit / [etc.] / Death, slavery and the / pursuit etc.	Blue	Hitle	Citret	A
4768	Life, liberty / and the pursuit / of happiness [in quotes] [copyright "C" varies]	Blue, red	Liber	Minkus	A
4769	Life, liberty and the / pursuit etc.	Black	Hitle	Wash Cover	A
4770	Life, liberty, and the / pursuit of happiness etc. [words red or blue] [thermographed]	Blue, red	Symb+	Czubay	A
4771	Life, liberty, happiness / defend your heritage	Multicolored	Flag	Minkus	A
4772	Lift up your hearts / freedom and peace / will follow the storm.	Blue, red	Relig	Lowell	A
4773	Light / of / liberty [handpainted]	Multicolored	VforV	Knapp	G
4774	Lighter than air	Blue	Unk	Unk	A
4775	Like / shootin / fish in a / barrel / ain't it Joe!	Black	Army	Wolf, CL	A
4776	Like it or / leave it	Multicolored	Flag	Linto	B
4777	Like the "Minute Men" etc.	Unknown	Flag	Linto	B
4778	Lincoln / and / American unity	Unknown	Unk	Linto	B
4779	Lincoln's Gettysburg Address / November 19, 1863 [env. 7 1/2x3 7/8 in.]	Red	Anniv	Fagenson	B
4780	Listen / don't be nap'in / let's get Jap'in / buy more bonds	Blue, red	Bonds	Kosko	A
4781	Listen to me if you please / for our service folks overseas etc. [no picture]	Unknown	Unk	Rowe	A
4782	Listen, mister! / Were you ever hungry, mister? etc. [no picture]	Unknown	Home	Yontz	A
4783	Listen, world! / Nazism ... must and shall be etc.	Unknown	Unk	Orr	A
4784	Little Bo Peep / Little Bo Peep buys bonds to keep / She's never cashed or etc.	Green, violet	Home	Threl+Thar	A
4785	Little White House / place of death / In memory etc.	Multicolored	FDR	Cachet Cra	E
4786	Live with the / symbol / [etc.] / Help etc. [env. 6 1/2x3 5/8, 6 3/4x3 3/4 in.]	Blue, red	Flag	Czubay	A
4787	Live with the / symbol / of liberty / in your heart	Blue, red	Liber	Sanders	A
4788	Live with the / symbol of liberty / in your home	Blue, red	Flag	Czubay	A
4789	Living cost soaring! / "Hold the line" / order affects wages only! / We etc.	Multicolored	Home	Linto	B
4790	Loan your money / to / Uncle Sam etc.	Unknown	Unk	Kosko	A
4791	London, September 1——(AP) etc. [newspaper clipping on cacheted cover; 9/3/39]	Black, green	Event	Unknown	F

NO.	CACHET TEXT	COLOR	TOPIC	PUBLISHER	$
4792	Lonesome. [handpainted]	Multicolored	Home	Cowdery	D
4793	Long distance / calls you don't / make help speed / vital war calls. [buff envelope]	Red	Home	Mich Bell	B
4794	Long may / it wave	Unknown	Flag	Phill, CR	A
4795	Long may it ring	Blue	Bell	Krakora	A
4796	Long may it wave	Blue, red	Flag	Smith, W	A
4797	Long may it wave / Flag Day / June 14th	Black	Flag	Dime Store	A
4798	Long may it wave / o'er the land of the free / and the home [in quotes] etc.	Multicolored	Flag	Thorpe	A
4799	Long may it wave / Remember Pearl Harbor etc. [flag with shadows] [thermographed]	Unknown	Flag	Crosby	B
4800	Long may it wave / Remember Pearl Harbor etc. [flag without shadows] [thermographed]	Unknown	Flag	Crosby	B
4801	Long may it wave / The Star-Spangled Banner / Oh say! can etc. [thermographed]	Blue, red	Flag	Crosby	B
4802	Long may it wave [envelope 5 1/2x3 1/8 in.]	Unknown	Flag	Dime Store	A
4803	Long may it wave [handpainted]	Multicolored	Flag	Barwicki	C
4804	Long may it wave [in quotes] [flag with three stars]	Unknown	Flag	Cox	A
4805	Long may it wave [in quotes] [UR: Buy / bonds / for / victory]	Blue, red	Flag	Herst	A
4806	Long may it wave [in quotes] [UR: eagle, shield and globe]	Blue, red	Flag	Herst	A
4807	Long may it wave [in quotes] [UR: plain]	Blue, red	Flag	Herst	A
4808	Long may it wave!	Blue, red	Flag	Mission	A
4809	Look at / the captive / young Hun / Shall our children mix with them? No!	Gold, purple	Nazis	Linto	B
4810	Look at 'em, U.S. war bonds etc.	Unknown	Bonds	Linto	B
4811	Look to the / future, guard it / "well." [handpainted]	Multicolored	Eagle	Adler	D
4812	Look to the future / guard it well [colors vary]	Multicolored	Armed	Minkus	A
4813	Look to the sky, America	Blue	Air	Foster	A
4814	Look! / He is giving / everything! / [etc.] / Victory Fleet Day etc.	Multicolored	Navy	Linto	B
4815	Look! / He is giving / everything! / What is your / privilege? / Buy bonds!	Multicolored	Bonds	Linto	B
4816	Look, Adolf! two loop-holes	Black	Unk	McCluney	A
4817	Lookin' for a / cool, shady spot! [handpainted]	Multicolored	Army	Cowdery	D
4818	Looking after / the / stars and stripes [handpainted]	Multicolored	Eagle	Adler	D
4819	Looking at this miserable world / today you can still thank God / for His etc.	Multicolored	Relig	Linto	B
4820	Lookout [colored envelopes]	Blue	Armed	Huss	A
4821	Loose / talk / can tip-off the enemy / Can it! [no picture] [multicolor varieties]	Multicolored	Home	Linto	B
4822	Loose talk costs lives.	Black	Navy	Wolf, CL	A
4823	Lord God of hosts / be with us yet / lest we forget / lest we forget	Gold, silver	Relig	Linto	B
4824	Lost nation / Germany surrenders / V-Day and liberation / Hell / Hitler! etc.	Orange, red	VEDay	Czubay	C
4825	Lost nation / Germany surrenders etc.	Unknown	VEDay	Czubay	C
4826	Loug [sic] may it wave / the star-spangled etc. [thermographed]	Unknown	Flag	Crosby	B
4827	Love / ends / war [envelope 6x3 ½ in.]	Unknown	Unk	Unknown	A
4828	Love / ends / war [no picture]	Black	Home	Johnson, C	A
4829	Love is like war / ——it depends on the proper use of arms	Black	Armed	Lupton	A
4830	Loyal Japanese / will get protection in / [etc.] / 1-4-'45——Nips lose 30 etc.	Multicolored	Event	Linto	B
4831	Loyal Japanese / will get protection in / internment camps!	Multicolored	AJA	Linto	B
4832	Loyal Japs / loyal to Japan / This is no time / for silly etc. [no picture]	Multicolored	AJA	Linto	B
4833	Loyalty / God and country / Army Training School / Springfield, Ohio	Blue, red	Eagle	Wittenberg	B
4834	Lt. Col. / Henry / Mucci / led Luzon etc.	Unknown	Army	Linto	B
4835	Lt. Gen. Alexander Patch [handpainted]	Multicolored	Gener	Knoll	D
4836	Lt. Gen. Eichelberger [handpainted]	Multicolored	Gener	Knoll	D
4837	Lt. Gen. H. [sic] Doolittle / [etc.] / Japan surrenders / today etc. [thermographed]	Blue, red	VJDay	Crosby	B
4838	Lt. Gen. H. [sic] Doolittle / [etc.] / Lt. Col. Jimmy Doolittle etc. [thermographed]	Brown, red	Dool	Crosby	B
4839	Lt. Gen. H. [sic] Doolittle / first / [etc.] / Japan surrenders to etc. [thermographed]	Blue, red	VJDay	Crosby	B
4840	Lt. Gen. Holland M. Smith, commander of the / Marine Expeditionary Force etc. [thermographed]	Red	Gener	Crosby	B
4841	Lt. Gen. Johnathan [sic] M. Wainwright [colored envelopes]	Black/Blue	Gener	Huss	A
4842	Lt. Gen. Jonathon [sic] / [etc.] / Yokohama, Japan / and etc. [thermographed]	Blue, red	VJDay	Crosby	B
4843	Lt. Gen. Jonathon [sic] M. Wainwright / The hero of Corregidor, etc. [thermographed]	Blue	Gener	Crosby	B
4844	Lt. Gen. Krueger [handpainted]	Multicolored	Gener	Knoll	D
4845	Lt. Gen. Omar Bradley	Multicolored	Gener	Knoll	D
4846	Lt. Gen. Omar Bradley [handpainted]	Multicolored	Gener	Knoll	D
4847	Lt. Gen. Patch	Unknown	Gener	Linto	B
4848	Lt. Gen. Patton [handpainted]	Multicolored	Patt	Knoll	E
4849	Lt. Gen. Simpson	Multicolored	Gener	Knoll	D

NO.	CACHET TEXT	COLOR	TOPIC	PUBLISHER	$
4850	Lt. John Mitchell / stops blast at Remagen bridge	Unknown	Hero	Linto	B
4851	Lt. John Mitchell / stops blast at Remagen bridge / 3-10-'45——Yanks after etc.	Unknown	Event	Linto	B
4852	Lt.. Gen. Courtney Hodges [handpainted]	Multicolored	Gen	Knoll	D
4853	Lt.-Col. / Henry / Mucci / [etc.] / 2-22-'45——Jap prison ship / carrying etc.	Unknown	Event	Linto	B
4854	Lt.-Col. / Henry / Mucci / led Luzon / rescue raid	Unknown	Hero	Linto	B
4855	Lt.-Gen. / Ben Lear	Green, silver	Gener	Linto	B
4856	Lt.-Gen. / Ben Lear / 1-27-'45——U.S. subs sink 21 / ships. Credit to subs etc.	Multicolored	Event	Linto	B
4857	Lt.-Gen. / Dan Sultan	Unknown	Gener	Linto	B
4858	Lt.-Gen. / Geo. C. Kenny	Unknown	Gener	Linto	B
4859	Lt.-Gen. / Herbert / Lumsden	Unknown	Gener	Linto	B
4860	Lt.-Gen. / Herbert / Lumsden / 1-10-'45——Yanks, 100,000 / strong, move for etc.	Unknown	Event	Linto	B
4861	Lt.-Gen. / Holland / M. Smith / Iwo Jima / invasion	Unknown	Gener	Linto	B
4862	Lt.-Gen. / Holland / M. Smith / Iwo Jima / invasion / 2-28-'45——Yanks 1st etc.	Unknown	Event	Linto	B
4863	Lt.-Gen. / Ira Eaker	Unknown	Gener	Linto	B
4864	Lt.-Gen. / Ira Eaker / 1-3-'45——Yanks lose / toeholds in Reich	Unknown	Event	Linto	B
4865	Lt.-Gen. / Jimmy Doolittle / first to bomb Tokyo	Unknown	Doo	Linto	B
4866	Lt.-Gen. / Jonathan M. / Wainwright / [etc.] / 1-13-'45——Yanks now 20 etc.	Multicolored	Event	Linto	B
4867	Lt.-Gen. / Jonathan M. / Wainwright / [etc.] / 8-16-'45——etc.	Multicolored	Event	Linto	B
4868	Lt.-Gen. / Jonathan M. / Wainwright / prisoner of / filthy Japs	Multicolored	Gener	Linto	B
4869	Lt.-Gen. / Jonathan M. Wainwright [Linto cover #1004]	Unknown	Gener	Linto	B
4870	Lt.-Gen. / Jonathan M. Wainwright [Linto cover #831]	Unknown	Gener	Linto	B
4871	Lt.-Gen. / L.K. / Truscott	Unknown	Gener	Linto	B
4872	Lt.-Gen. / L.K. Truscott / 12-21-'44——Huns widen / wedge in Belgian lines	Multicolored	Event	Linto	B
4873	Lt.-Gen. / Leonard Gerow	Unknown	Gener	Linto	B
4874	Lt.-Gen. / Millard Harmon etc.	Unkown	Gener	Linto	B
4875	Lt.-Gen. / Richard / Sutherland / [etc.] / 7-29-'45--Yanks sink / 30 more Jap ships	Black, green	Event	Linto	B
4876	Lt.-Gen. / Richard / Sutherland / Chief of Staff / to MacArthur	Green	Gener	Linto	B
4877	Lt.-Gen. / Simon B. Buckner	Unknown	Gener	Linto	B
4878	Lt.-Gen. / W.D. / Morgan / [etc.] / 4-30-'45——Munich / falls to Yanks	Gold, silver	Event	Linto	B
4879	Lt.-Gen. / W.D. / Morgan / of British Army / negotiated the / surrender of etc.	Gold, green	Gener	Linto	B
4880	Lt.-Gen. / Wainwright / when rescued / from the / filthy Japs	Unknown	VJDay	Linto	B
4881	Lt.-Gen. / Walter B. / Smith / signed surrender / of Germany / document etc.	Gold, silver	Gener	Linto	B
4882	Lt.-Gen. Kurt Dittmar, Huns' spokes- / [etc.] / 9-4-'44——Yanks sink and etc.	Unknown	Event	Linto	B
4883	Lt.-Gen. Kurt Dittmar, Huns' spokes- / man, Aug. 29, 1944, advised the etc.	Unknown	Event	Linto	B
4884	Lt.-Gen. Robert L. Eichelberger	Unknown	Gener	Linto	B
4885	Lt.-Gen. Robert L. Eichelberger / 2-2-'45——British forces / land on Burma islan	Unknown	Event	Linto	B
4886	Luck and strikes / won't win the war / but / hard work and bonds / will	Brown	Home	Huss	A
4887	Lucky / 7 / Buy 'till you're / busted / 7th war loan drive / May etc.	Blue, red	Bonds	Eichenlaub	A
4888	Lucky / California! [torn right edge]	Multicolored	Army	Cowdery	D
4889	Lucky 7th / Let's not / gamble / with / victory [handpainted]	Multicolored	Bonds	Adler	E
4890	Lucy Brewer might well be called etc. [thermographed]	Unknown	Unk	Baur	A
4891	Ludendorf Bridge etc. [thermographed]	Unknown	Unk	Crosby	B
4892	Luther S. Smith	Unknown	Gener	Linto	B
4893	Luxembourg	Multicolored	ORN	Runge	A
4894	Luxembourg	Br,Tan/Bu,Y	ORN	Runge	A
4895	Luxembourg / crushed / but will live / again!	Blue, red	ORN	Cachet Cra	B
4896	Luxembourg / liberated / capital of Luxembourg / September 10, 1944	Multicolored	ORN	Teixeira	D
4897	Luxembourg / liberated / capital of Luxembourg etc. [9/10/44 + 5/8/45 pmarks]	Multicolored	Event	Teixeira	F
4898	Luxembourg / The Grand Duchy of etc.	Bk/Bu/Red	ORN	Clifford	A
4899	Luxembourg / United Nations [handpainted]	Multicolored	UN	Weigand	B
4900	Luxembourg [thermographed]	Green, red	ORN	Jordan	B
4901	Luxemburg	Black	ORN	Lowry	A
4902	Luxemburg / The capital of / Luxemburg was / liberated by U.S. / troops etc.	Multicolored	ORN	Fluegel	C
4903	Luzon 1945 / Tokyo ??	Black, red	Phili	McCluney	A

4394

4407

4443

4446

4498

4528

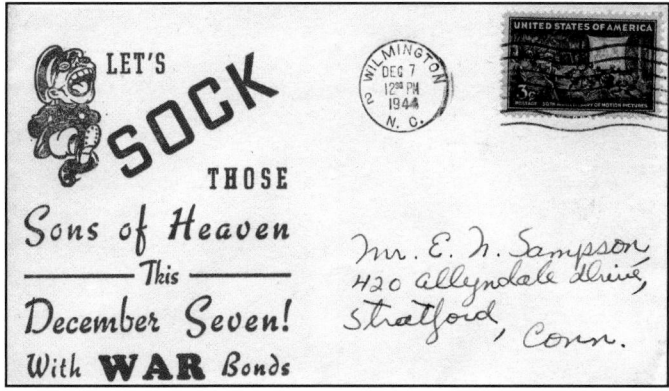

4533

4535

4547

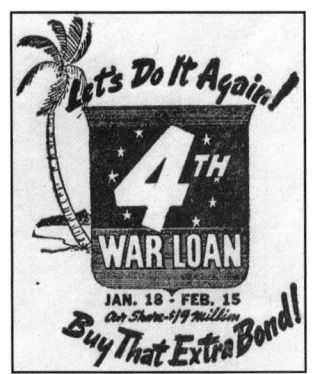

4555

4559A

4567

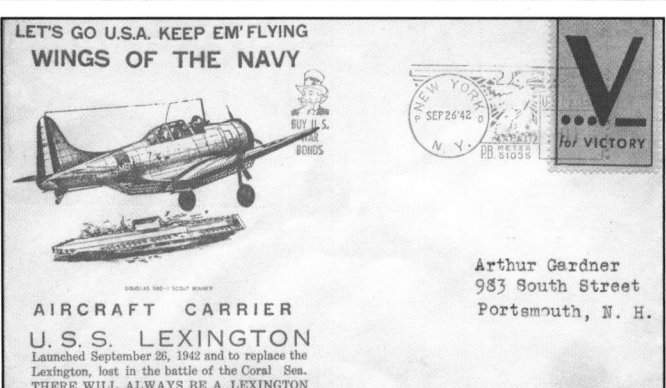

4654

4657

4676

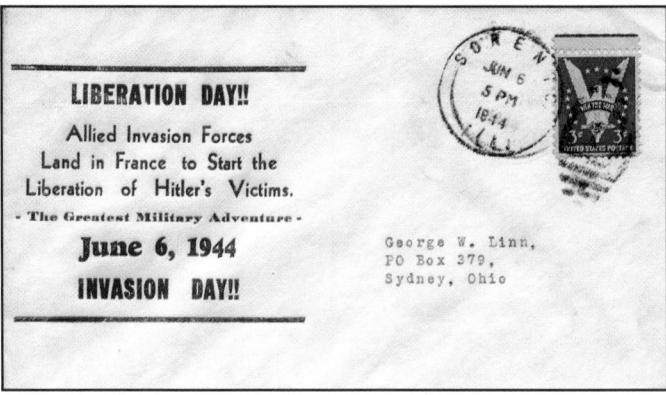

4682

4684

4691

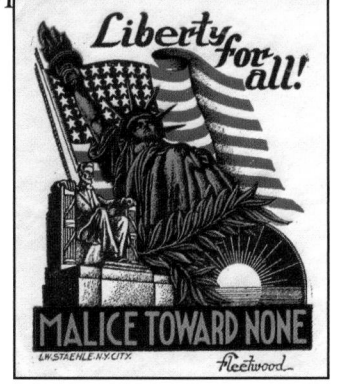

4694

4702

4706

4764

4839

4840

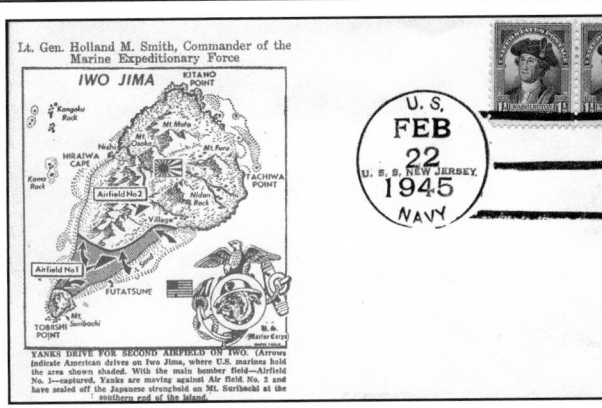

4842

4902

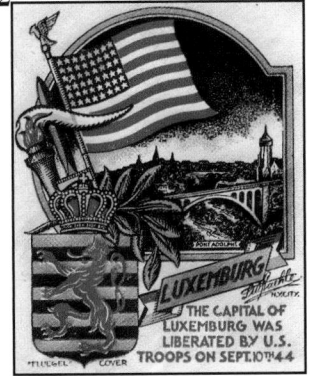

CACHET TEXT BEGINNING WITH "M"

NO.	CACHET TEXT	COLOR	TOPIC	PUBLISHER	$
4904	M.S.C. / Mission Stamp Club / Shelby, Ohio / Ever onward!	Unknown	Home	Mission	A
4905	M.S.C. / Mission Stamp Club / Shelby, Ohio / Freedom / our heritage	Unknown	Home	Mission	A
4906	M.S.C. / Mission Stamp Club / Shelby, Ohio / Let's go! U.S.A.	Unknown	Home	Mission	A
4907	M.S.C. / Mission Stamp Club / Shelby, Ohio / One / out of many	Unknown	Home	Mission	A
4908	M.S.C. / Mission Stamp Club / Shelby, Ohio / Our flag	Unknown	Flag	Mission	A
4909	M.S.C. / Mission Stamp Club / Shelby, Ohio / Strength / in unity	Unknown	Home	Mission	A
4910	Ma said / there'd be / days like this / but she didn't / say how / many!	Black	Army	Lupton	A
4911	Mac [in quotes] / the man / of the/ hour in / Pacific etc.	Unknown	Mac	Linto	B
4912	MacArthur - gives us back the / Philippines etc.	Unknown	Mac	Runge	B
4913	MacArthur - he promised - he returned	Unknown	Mac	Runge	B
4914	MacArthur / of etc. [1, 1.5, or 2 mm space between text lines] [colored envelopes]	Multicolored	Mac	Poppenger	B
4915	MacArthur / returns / U.S. forces invade / [etc.] / Leyte, October 20, 1944	Multicolored	Mac	Teixeira	D
4916	MacArthur / takes / over / Gen. Douglas MacArthur / takes over etc.	Multicolored	Mac	Teixeira	D
4917	MacArthur / the / "fightin'est" / man / Uncle Sam's etc. [env. 7 1/2x4 in.]	Blue, red	Mac	Fleetwood	C
4918	MacArthur / V ["MacArthur" across "V"] [MacArthur and Winged Victory]	Brown	MacFD	Dewitz	C
4919	MacArthur [picture over 5 stars, under eagle] [brown env. 9 1/2x6 ½½ in.]	Black	Mac	McFarland	B
4920	MacArthur and his gang / say / "Hand us" etc. [env. 6 1/2x3 5/8 or 7 1/2x4 in.]	Blue, red	Mac	Fleetwood	B
4921	MacArthur could clean up / [etc.] / Commemorating "Bill of Rights" Day etc.	Unknown	Home	Linto	B
4922	MacArthur could clean up / [etc.] / Roosevelt inaugurated Jan. 20, '41, etc.	Multicolored	FDR	Linto	B
4923	MacArthur could clean up / Washington wilderness but / we etc. [no picture]	Blue, gold	Mac	Linto	B
4924	MacArthur Day / June 13, 1942 / For victory / V / ···– / General etc. [thermographed]	Blue, red	Mac	Crosby	B
4925	MacArthur Day June 13, 1942 / General Douglas MacArthur, etc. [thermographed]	Gn/Pu/Red	Mac	Crosby	B
4926	MacArthur enters Philippines [on cut-&-pasted paper near previously printed cachet]	Black	Event	Muzzy	C
4927	MacArthur in Australia	Unknown	Mac	Linto	C
4928	MacArthur lands / Luzon / "...and I will / return"	Multicolored	Mac	Peer	B
4929	MacArthur of Bataan / "Every centavo that can be spared must be invested" etc.	Multicolored	Mac	Advertiser	B
4930	MacArthur, W. Va. / named in honor of our / "Hero of Bataan" / Douglas MacArthur / First Day etc.	Multicolored	MacFD	Linto	C
4931	MacArthur, W. Va. / New post office first day cover / in honor of General etc.	Blue, red	Mac	Alden	C
4932	MacArthur's message / to victorious troops / [etc.] / 2-6-'45——Manila / in etc.	Multicolored	Event	Linto	B
4933	MacArthur's message / to victorious troops / In requesting divine services etc.	Gold, purple	Mac	Linto	B
4934	Mad Japan / 1——A deck wet down with Yankee blood, / a proud flag sinking etc.	Multicolored	Liber	Weigand	B
4935	Mad Japan / 3——So humbly they apologize [sic] / with breath that whistles etc.	Multicolored	Liber	Weigand	B
4936	Made / in / U.S.A. [handpainted]	Black, silver	Axis	Wolf, CL	B
4937	Made a slight mistake at bayonet practice	Black	Army	Lupton	A
4938	Made in U.S.A. / for: Japan / via: B-29's / from: all of us [diagonal] [thermographed]	Red	Air	Sadworth	B
4939	Made of steel V ···– / nerves of steel [thermographed]	Blue, orange	Home	Von Los	B
4940	Mail / it / today / your service letter etc.	Orange	Home	Abel	A
4941	Mail / X'mas / packages / by Dec. 1st / to etc. [brown env. 5 1/16x3 5/8 in.]	Unknown	Holid	Altenbernd	A
4942	Mail / X'mas / packages / by Dec. 1st / to those in etc. [no picture]	Blue	Holid	Altenbernd	A
4943	Mail [soldier leaning on mailbox, dog sitting nearby] [handpainted]	Multicolored	Dog	Dannells	B
4944	Mail builds morale / Remember to write / the boys who fight!	Blue	Home	Bean	A
4945	Mail from home makes him happy	Blue	Army	Hillerich	A
4946	Mail it today! / We can stand the flies and the sand / in our eyes, / the orders etc.	Red	Home	Brenn	A
4947	Mail that letter today, / to that boy over there. [no stars]	Red	Home	Baur	A
4948	Mail that letter today, / to that boy over there. [with stars]	Red	Home	Baur	A
4949	Mail Xmas packages to those in the service etc.	Unknown	Holid	Runge	A
4950	Mailed aboard / U.S.S. Cushing Destroyer 797 / in Tokyo Bay etc. [Tokyo Bay]	Blue	VJDay	Navy ship	D
4951	Maj Gen. Wedemeyer [handpainted]	Multicolored	Gener	Knoll	D
4952	Maj. Gen. / Alfred M. / Gruenther	Gold, green	Gener	Linto	B
4953	Maj. Gen. / Alfred M. / Gruenther / 11-22-'44——Yanks drive / into Eschweiler	Gold, green	Event	Linto	B
4954	Maj. Gen. / Alfred M. / Gruenther / 11-22-'44——Yanks drive / into etc.	Unknown	Event	Linto	B
4955	Maj. Gen. / Anthony / McAuliffe / "Nuts" / [etc.] / 5-20-'45——Yanks win etc.	Green	Event	Linto	B
4956	Maj. Gen. / Anthony / McAuliffe / "Nuts" was his / answer to the etc.	Green	Gener	Linto	B
4957	Maj. Gen. / Anthony / McAuliffe / [etc.] / 5-20-'45——Yanks win etc.	Unknown	Event	Linto	B
4958	Maj. Gen. / Barney / Giles / Deputy Chief / Army Air Force	Green	Gener	Linto	B
4959	Maj. Gen. / Curtis / LeMay	Unknown	Gener	Linto	B

NO.	CACHET TEXT	COLOR	TOPIC	PUBLISHER	$
4960	Maj. Gen. / F.B. / Mallon	Gold	Gener	Linto	B
4961	Maj. Gen. / F.B. / Mallon / 6-24-'45——French and / Syrians fighting again	Sepia, silver	Event	Linto	B
4962	Maj. Gen. / Frederick / A. Irving	Gold, green	Gener	Linto	B
4963	Maj. Gen. / J.E. / Dahlquist / to whom Goering / surrendered	Sepia tones	Gener	Linto	B
4964	Maj. Gen. / Maurice / Rose / deliberately / slain while / surrendering etc.	Gold, silver	Gener	Linto	B
4965	Maj. Gen. / Maxwell D. / Taylor	Green, silver	Gener	Linto	B
4966	Maj. Gen. / W.H. / Simpson	Gold	Gener	Linto	B
4967	Maj. Gen. / Willis / H. Hale / Pacific A.F. commander / now speeding / up etc.	Black	Gener	Linto	B
4968	Maj. Gen. Parker [handpainted]	Multicolored	Gener	Knoll	D
4969	Maj.-Gen / Claire L. / Chenault / 14th Air F.	Green, purple	Gener	Linto	B
4970	Maj.-Gen / Lowell W. / Rooks	Bicolor var	Gener	Linto	B
4971	Maj.-Gen. / Alfred / Wedemeyer / [etc.] / 3-2-'45——U.S. flag / flies over etc.	Unknown	Event	Linto	B
4972	Maj.-Gen. / Alfred / Wedemeyer / Chinese / theater / of war	Unknown	Gener	Linto	B
4973	Maj.-Gen. / Alfred M. / Gruenther	Green, sepia	Gener	Linto	B
4974	Maj.-Gen. / Anthony / McAuliffe / "Nuts" was his / answer to the etc.	Multicolored	Gener	Linto	B
4975	Maj.-Gen. / Barney / Giles	Unknown	Gener	Linto	B
4976	Maj.-Gen. / Charles E. / Gross	Gold	Gener	Linto	B
4977	Maj.-Gen. / Claire L. / Chenault	Gold, red	Gener	Linto	B
4978	Maj.-Gen. / Claire L. / Chenault / 14th Air F.	Multicolored	Gener	Linto	B
4979	Maj.-Gen. / Claire L. / Chenault / 14th Air F. / 2-14-'45——U.S. subs claim etc.	Multicolored	Event	Linto	B
4980	Maj.-Gen. / Clarence R. / Heubner	Unknown	Gener	Linto	B
4981	Maj.-Gen. / Clarence R. / Huebner / 7-3-'45——Aussies take / Borneo oilfields	Unknown	Gener	Linto	B
4982	Maj.-Gen. / Clifton B. / Gates	Green/Multi	Gener	Linto	B
4983	Maj.-Gen. / Clifton B. / Gates / 2-17-'45——U.S. Paratroopers land etc.	Multicolored	Event	Linto	B
4984	Maj.-Gen. / Curtis / LeMay / well known in / Pacific theater / of war	Unknown	Gener	Linto	B
4985	Maj.-Gen. / Edwin M. / Watson / [etc.] / 2-20-'45——Stubborn battle / still etc.	Multicolored	Event	Linto	B
4986	Maj.-Gen. / Edwin M. / Watson / Aide to / Roosevelt, / died at sea etc.	Multicolored	Gener	Linto	B
4987	Maj.-Gen. / Elwood R. / Quesada / U.S. 9th / Tactical Air	Gold	Gener	Linto	B
4988	Maj.-Gen. / F.B. / Mallon	Unknown	Gener	Linto	B
4989	Maj.-Gen. / Floyd L. / Parks / 4-3-'45——Yanks cut Reich in two	Unknown	Gener	Linto	B
4990	Maj.-Gen. / Floyd L. / Parks / 6-22-'45——U.S. naval force / "camping" etc.	Multicolored	Event	Linto	B
4991	Maj.-Gen. / Floyd L. / Parks [bicolor varieties]	Black, silver	Gener	Linto	B
4992	Maj.-Gen. / Frederick A. / Irving	Unknown	Gener	Linto	B
4993	Maj.-Gen. / Frederick H. / Osborn	Gold	Gener	Linto	B
4994	Maj.-Gen. / Frederick H. / Osborne	Unknown	Gener	Linto	B
4995	Maj.-Gen. / Geoffrey / Keyes	Gold, green	Gener	Linto	B
4996	Maj.-Gen. / George / Parker	Unknown	Gener	Linto	B
4997	Maj.-Gen. / George / Parker / 8-30-'45——Miyakaskima / Japs fire etc.	Unknown	Gener	Linto	B
4998	Maj.-Gen. / George / Parker / Rescued with Wainwright	Unknown	Gener	Linto	B
4999	Maj.-Gen. / Graves B. / Erskine / [etc.] / 2-15-'45——U.S. Navy / attacks Tokyo	Multicolored	Event	Linto	B
5000	Maj.-Gen. / Graves B. / Erskine / 3rd Div.	Green	Gener	Linto	B
5001	Maj.-Gen. / H.C. / Davidson / 10th Air F.	Multi/Bk, red	Gener	Linto	B
5002	Maj.-Gen. / H.C. / Davidson / 10th Air F. / 2-21-'45——Yanks battle for 2nd etc.	Black, red	Event	Linto	B
5003	Maj.-Gen. / H.P. / Berney-Ficklin	Unknown	Gener	Linto	B
5004	Maj.-Gen. / Henry C. / Pratt	Multicolored	Gener	Linto	B
5005	Maj.-Gen. / Innis / Swift	Unknown	Gener	Linto	B
5006	Maj.-Gen. / Innis Swift / 2-12-'45——Down and out / go 24 more Jap ships	Unknown	Event	Linto	B
5007	Maj.-Gen. / Isaac / White / 2nd Armored / Div. 9th Army	Black, gold	Gener	Linto	B
5008	Maj.-Gen. / Isaac / White / 2nd Armored / Div. 9th Army	Black, gold	Gener	Linto	B
5009	Maj.-Gen. / J.E. / Dahlquist / to whom Goering / surrendered	Unknown	Gener	Linto	B
5010	Maj.-Gen. / James / Gavin	Multicolored	Gener	Linto	B
5011	Maj.-Gen. / James / Gavin / 12-25-'44——Yanks win / campaign for Leyte	Multicolored	Event	Linto	B
5012	Maj.-Gen. / Jens A. / Doe	Gold, silver	Gener	Linto	B
5013	Maj.-Gen. / Jens A. / Doe / 41st div. / Pacific	Multicolored	Gener	Linto	B
5014	Maj.-Gen. / John R. / Hodge	Unknown	Gener	Linto	B
5015	Maj.-Gen. / John W. / Leonard / 9th Armored Division	Unknown	Gener	Linto	B
5016	Maj.-Gen. / Joseph M. / Swing / Seized Aparri airfield. / May spearhead etc.	Unknown	Gener	Linto	B
5017	Maj.-Gen. / Julian C. / Smith	Unknown	Gener	Linto	B

NO.	CACHET TEXT	COLOR	TOPIC	PUBLISHER	$
5018	Maj.-Gen. / Keller E. / Rockey / 5th Div.	Multicolored	Gener	Linto	B
5019	Maj.-Gen. / Keller E. / Rockey / 5th Div. / 12-19-'44——Fierce battle / etc.	Multicolored	Event	Linto	B
5020	Maj.-Gen. / Lowell W. / Rooks	Gold, silver	Gener	Linto	B
5021	Maj.-Gen. / Lowell W. / Rooks / 7-1-'45——Aussies land / on Balikpapan	Multicolored	Event	Linto	B
5022	Maj.-Gen. / Lyman / Lemnitzer / Mediterranean / theater of war	Unknown	Gener	Linto	B
5023	Maj.-Gen. / Maurice / Rose / 3rd Army Div. / First to reach Cologne	Unknown	Gener	Linto	B
5024	Maj.-Gen. / Maurice / Rose / deliberately / slain while / surrendering etc.	Gold	Gener	Linto	B
5025	Maj.-Gen. / Maxwell D. / Taylor	Unknown	Gener	Linto	B
5026	Maj.-Gen. / Maxwell D. / Taylor / 1-6-'45——Yanks hit Nips for 95 ships etc.	Unknown	Event	Linto	B
5027	Maj.-Gen. / Nathan / Twining	Unknown	Gener	Linto	B
5028	Maj.-Gen. / Nathan / Twining / 1-4-'45——U.S. 1st Army digs into / Nazis' etc.	Unknown	Event	Linto	B
5029	Maj.-Gen. / O.W. / Griswold	Unknown	Gener	Linto	B
5030	Maj.-Gen. / O.W. / Griswold / 1-8-'45——Yanks reach / Nazi dams	Unknown	Event	Linto	B
5031	Maj.-Gen. / Patrick J. / Hurley	Unknown	Gener	Linto	B
5032	Maj.-Gen. / Patrick J. / Hurley / 2-11-'45——Allies battle / into Kleve	Unknown	Event	Linto	B
5033	Maj.-Gen. / Rapp / Brush / invaded Panay	Black, silver	Gener	Linto	B
5034	Maj.-Gen. / Rapp / Brush / invaded Panay / 4-3-'45——Yanks cut Reich in two	Silver, black	Event	Linto	B
5035	Maj.-Gen. / Raymond S. / McLain	Unknown	Gener	Linto	B
5036	Maj.-Gen. / Robert S. / Beightler / Pacific	Multicolored	Gener	Linto	B
5037	Maj.-Gen. / Robert S. / Beightler / Pacific / 2-16-'45——Yanks / capture Bataan	Multicolored	Event	Linto	B
5038	Maj.-Gen. / Terry / Allen	Gd,Vi/Multi	Gener	Linto	B
5039	Maj.-Gen. / Terry / Allen / 12-9-'44——Yanks shell and bomb etc.	Multicolored	Gener	Linto	B
5040	Maj.-Gen. / Thomas / M. Robins	Multicolored	Gener	Linto	B
5041	Maj.-Gen. / W.H. Simpson	Multicolored	Gener	Linto	B
5042	Maj.-Gen. / Wade H. / Haselip	Unknown	Gener	Linto	B
5043	Maj.-Gen. / Willis H. / Hale	Multicolored	Gener	Linto	B
5044	Maj.-Gen. / Willis H. / Hale / 3-7-'45——Nazis flee / from Yanks trap	Multicolored	Event	Linto	B
5045	Maj.-Gen. / Willis H. / Hale / Pacific A.F. / Commander / now speeding / up etc.	Multicolored	VJDay	Linto	C
5046	Maj.-Gen. / Wm. C. / Chase	Unknown	Gener	Linto	B
5047	Maj.-Gen. / Wm. C. / Chase / 7-28-'45——U.S. Senate voted	Unknown	Gener	Linto	B
5048	Maj.-Gen. / Wm. C. / Livesay	Unknown	Gener	Linto	B
5049	Maj.-Gen. / Wm. E. / Kepner	Unknown	Gener	Linto	B
5050	Maj.-Gen. / Wm. H. / Arnold	Brown , green	Gener	Linto	B
5051	Maj.-Gen. Geoffrey Keyes	Unknown	Gener	Linto	B
5052	Maj.-Gen.. / Thomas / M. Robins / 2-25-'45——Yanks now / 15 miles from etc.	Multicolored	Event	Linto	B
5053	Major / Thomas W. / Ferebee / [etc.] / 8-7-'45——Pres. Truman / home from etc.	Unknown	Event	Linto	B
5054	Major / Thomas W. Ferebee / bombardier on / "Enola Gay" / who etc. [8/7/45]	Sepia tones	Atom	Linto	D
5055	Major General, Lewis E. Brereton / left on October 25, 1941 for etc. [handpainted]	Blue, red	Event	Batura	D
5056	Make / your / dollar / count / buy more war bonds	Red	Bonds	Harrington	A
5057	Make / your / dollar / count / invest it in / war bonds	Bu,R/Bk/Red	Bonds	Harrington	A
5058	Make America / strong by making / [etc.] / 9-1-'44——Russians reach etc.	Gold, silver	Event	Linto	B
5059	Make America / strong by making / Americans / stronger [no picture]	Gd/Gd,Silver	Home	Linto	B
5060	Make 'em / "say Uncle!"	Blue	Axis	Wash Cover	A
5061	Make 'em / say Uncle	Blue	Unk	Quigley	B
5062	Make every / pay day / bond day [envelope 6x3 ½ or 7 1/2x4 in.]	Unknown	Bonds	Cleveland	A
5063	Make him / swallow / that bond. [handpainted]	Multicolored	Japan	Adler	D
5064	Make him / walk the / plank! / 5th war loan [handpainted]	Multicolored	Japan	Meyers	C
5065	Make Ickes Japs' / custodian at his / own expense [no picture]	Gd/Gd,Green	AJA	Linto	B
5066	Make it a pushover / the Victory Loan etc.	Unknown	Bonds	Eichenlaub	A
5067	Make Jap flag a / thing of the past	Bn,S/Gn,S	Japan	Linto	B
5068	Make Jap flag a / thing of the past / 3-30-'45——Reds take / Danzig and 45 etc.	Multicolored	Event	Linto	B
5069	Make much more / Keep on producing —— [handpainted]	Blue, red	Home	Martin	B
5070	Make no mistake! / England is interested / [etc.] / 5-26-'44——Cisterna and etc.	Multicolored	Event	Linto	B
5071	Make no mistake! / England is interested / [etc.] / June 6, '44——Allied etc.	Multicolored	DDay	Linto	B
5072	Make no mistake! / England is interested / only in its empire!	Multicolored	Army	Linto	B
5073	Make the / world safe for democracy.	Blue, red	Globe	McGovern	A
5074	Make this pledge / I will pay no more etc.	Blue	Home	Limoges	A
5075	Make your dreams come true etc.	Unknown	Unk	Eichenlaub	A

NO.	CACHET TEXT	COLOR	TOPIC	PUBLISHER	$
5076	Making ends meet / after Xmas! [handpainted]	Multicolored	Army	Cowdery	D
5077	Mamas' [sic] little helper. [handpainted]	Multicolored	Army	Cowdery	D
5078	Manila / anchor of / Nipponese / invasion / liberated by / Americans	Blue, pink	Event	Griffith	B
5079	Manila / and / Cavite / fall Jan. 2, 1942 [no picture]	Black	Event	Fidelity	B
5080	Manila / liberated / Freedom rings again / for the Philippines capital etc.	Multicolored	Event	Teixeira	D
5081	Manila / retaken / by / Yanks [no picture]	Red	Event	Boone	B
5082	Manila / taken / Jan. 2, 1942 / Singapore / taken etc. [handpainted label]	Black	Event	LeGallez	C
5083	Manila freed / Feb. 5th 1945 / 3,700 prisoners liberated [handpainted]	Multicolored	Battl	Smith, LH	B
5084	Manila invaded / MacArthur's Headquarters, Central Luzon: etc. [no picture]	Blue, red	Event	Fidelity	B
5085	Manila's liberation / U.S. forces enter the capital / of the etc. [thermographed]	Blue, red	Event	Smartcraft	C
5086	Man-power / registration / day / April 27, 1942 [no picture]	Blue	Event	Fidelity	B
5087	Many a Marine / is alive today / because a / corpsman / reached his side etc.	Bu/Bu, green	USMC	Burdick	A
5088	Many t'anks - / folks, for the mail, / and here's one / for etc. [env. 8 7/8x3 7/8 in.]	Multicolored	Army	Porto-serv	B
5089	Mar. 03, 1943 / 22 Jap / ships sunk [no picture]	Brown, silver	Event	Linto	B
5090	March / 07th / 1945 / Cologne falls to Allies / Doom of the etc. [handpainted]	Multicolored	Army	Smith, LH	C
5091	March 01, 1943 / "Point" rationing / Russian offensive etc. [no picture]	Brown	Event	Fidelity	B
5092	March 03, 1943 / 22 Jap / ships sunk [no picture]	Multicolored	Event	Linto	B
5093	March 05, 1945 / Yanks enter Cologne / (Germany's 4th largest city) etc.	Black, yellow	Event	Fidelity	B
5094	March 06, 1945 / United States, thru Sec. / Byrnes, told Russia etc.	Multicolored	Event	Linto	B
5095	March 06, '45 / Cologne / falls to / U.S. 1st / Army	Gold, violet	Event	Linto	B
5096	March 07, 1945 / U.S. 1st Army, / [etc.] / 3-7-'45——Bill to draft / nurses etc.	Unknown	Event	Linto	B
5097	March 07, 1945 / U.S. 1st Army, under / L.-Gen. C.H. Hodges, crossed etc.	Multicolored	Event	Linto	B
5098	March 08, 1942 / Japs captured / Rangoon [no picture]	Multicolored	Event	Linto	B
5099	March 08, 1945 / Yanks cross the Rhine	Black, red	Event	Fidelity	B
5100	March 13, 1945 / Russia / crosses / Oder / Kustrin's fall etc. [no picture]	Orange, red	Event	Fidelity	B
5101	March 17, 1942 - Gen. Douglas MacArthur arrives in Australia etc. [handpainted]	Multicolored	Mac	Smith, LH	C
5102	March 1942 / "I'll be back" / A-Day / Oct 19 etc. [no picture]	Unknown	Mac	McCluney	B
5103	March 1944 / The Red Cross asks etc.	Blue, red	RedCr	Brenn	A
5104	March 20, 1945 / Iloilo taken by Maj.-Gen / [etc.] / 3-20-'45——U.S. planes etc.	Brown, green	Event	Linto	B
5105	March 20, 1945 / Iloilo taken by Maj.-Gen / Rapp Brush's 40th Infantry etc.	Brown, green	Event	Linto	B
5106	March 25, 1945 / Four Allied armies / crossed Rhine / on a etc. [no picture]	Blue, red	Event	Fidelity	B
5107	March 26, 1945 / Patton / Berlin [handpainted]	Multicolored	Patt	Smith, LH	C
5108	March 27, 1945 / Danzig invaded / Argentina / declares / war [no picture]	Green, purple	Event	Fidelity	B
5109	March 30, 1945 / Negros, last big / Phillipine [sic] island etc. [handpainted]	Multicolored	Map	Smith, LH	C
5110	March, / 06th / 1945 / [etc.] / Cologne / "Our prize of victory"	Multicolored	Event	Staehle	C
5111	March, / 06th / 1945 / [etc.] / Cologne / "Our prize" etc. [blue color missing]	Multicolored	Event	Staehle	D
5112	Marching home? / They will. And soon, / if we buy bonds	Gd,Pu/Multi	Army	Linto	B
5113	Marching on to / victory	Bu/Gn/Pu/Re	Unk	Harrington	A
5114	Marching to victory	Unknown	Unk	Cozart	A
5115	Marine bases / [etc.] / Hawaii, key to our Pacific etc. [white or pink env.]	Multicolored	USMC	Pilgrim	D
5116	Marine bases / [etc.] / North Atlantic bastions etc. [blue or yellow envelope]	Multicolored	USMC	Pilgrim	D
5117	Marine bases / [etc.] / Panama Canal to Washington etc. [orange envelope]	Multicolored	USMC	Pilgrim	D
5118	Marine bases / [etc.] / South Pacific outpost is strategic etc. [blue envelope]	Multicolored	USMC	Pilgrim	D
5119	Marine detachment / Bermuda / [etc.] / Naval Operating Base / Bermuda [thermographed]	Green	USMC	Czubay	D
5120	Marine detachment / Portland Bight Jamaica Br. / Fleet Marine etc. [thermographed]	Green	USMC	Czubay	D
5121	Marine detachment / U.S.S. Ranger airplane carrier [thermographed]	Gold	USMC	Crosby	B
5122	Marine flyer Major BT Kelly / survived etc.	Black	USMC	Burdick	A
5123	Marine honor roll / Guam / Saipan / Tarawa / Okinawa / Iwo Jima / Guadalcanal	Bu, R/Red	USMC	Brenn	A
5124	Marine insignia	Black	USMC	Huss	A
5125	Marines / Navy / Army / Coast Guard [blue envelope 3 1/2x2 ½ in.]	Brown/Red	Armed	Baur	A
5126	Marines / Navy / Army / Coast Guard [thermographed]	Brown/Red	Armed	Baur	A
5127	Marines / The US Marine Corps, organized etc.	Black/Purple	USMC	Cliff	A
5128	Marines call on Hirohito [envelope 6 1/2x3 5/8, 6x3 1/2 in.]	Blue	USMC	Powers	A
5129	Marine's mail / rush like / h——-!	Black	USMC	Lupton	A
5130	Marines V ···· / The situation is in hand [thermographed]	Green, red	USMC	Von Los	B
5131	Marinettes / Corps / unselfish / in the service	Gold, silver	WomM	Linto	B
5132	Mark Wayne Clark etc. [thermographed]	Unknown	Gener	Crosby	B
5133	Mars —— Roman god of / war. Stamp him out!! [in quotes] [handpainted]	Multicolored	Antiq	White, TM	F

NO.	CACHET TEXT	COLOR	TOPIC	PUBLISHER	$
5134	Marshal Henri Philippe Petain / was convicted of treason etc. [no picture] [handpainted]	Black	Event	Batura	D
5135	Marshal Joseph Stalin / Union of Soviet Socialist Republics	Black	USSR	Pacific	A
5136	Marshall - his plans give us a / merry etc.	Unknown	Marsh	Runge	B
5137	Marshall Timoshenko	Unknown	USSR	Runge	A
5138	Marshalls / invaded / Feb. 4, 1944 [no picture]	Blue	Event	Fidelity	B
5139	Martial law abolished / October 24, 1944 / Territory of Hawaii military etc.	Black	Hawai	Sayama	B
5140	Mass crossing / of the Rhine / March 24, 1945 / You "punks" / cant stop us etc.	Multicolored	Event	Fluegel	C
5141	Material / conservation [label + blue "Victory" border]	Multicolored	Japan	Unknown	B
5142	Material / conservation [label + red "Victory" border]	Multicolored	Japan	Unknown	B
5143	Material / conservation [label + red "Win the War" border]	Multicolored	Japan	Unknown	B
5144	May / Day / May one [postmarked 5/1/41]	Blue, gold	Holid	Linto	B
5145	May / liberty's / torch / shine / forever! [handpainted]	Multicolored	Torch	Knapp	G
5146	May 01, 1945 / Hitler left for / parts unknown / Reported dead	Gd, S/Multi	Event	Linto	C
5147	May 01, 1945 / Is / Hitler / dead / ???? [no picture]	Brown, red	Event	Fidelity	C
5148	May 02, 1945 / Down goes / Berlin / to the Reds! / But where / is Hitler?	Multicolored	Event	Linto	B
5149	May 02, 1945 / Reds take Berlin!	Gold/Multi	Event	Linto	B
5150	May 04th / 1945 / 5th and / 7th / U.S. Army / meet on / Brenner Pass	Multicolored	Event	Fluegel	C
5151	May 05th 1945 / Amsterdam / the capital of the / Netherlands was liberated etc.	Multicolored	Event	Fluegel	C
5152	May 05th 7.59 AM / Copenhagen / the capital of / Denmark was liberated etc.	Multicolored	Event	Fluegel	C
5153	May 06, 1942 / Corregidor / surrendered / to Japs [no picture]	O, silver	Event	Linto	C
5154	May 06, 1945 / Pilsen, last Hun / arsenal, taken / by Patton	Unknown	Event	Linto	B
5155	May 07, / 1945 / Germany / surrenders / unconditionally [handpainted]	Multicolored	Ike	Smith, LH	C
5156	May 08 1945 / V-E Day / proclaimed by / Truman, Churchill etc. [handpainted]	Multicolored	Ally	Smith, LH	C
5157	May 08, 1945 / Germany surrenders / From those who etc. [postmark 5/8/45 & 9/2/45]	Blue, red	VEDay	Levering	D
5158	May 08, 1945 / Germany surrenders / From those who etc. [postmarked 5/8/45 only]	Blue, red	VEDay	Levering	B
5159	May 09, 1942 / Japs repulsed in / Coral Sea battle	Brown, green	Event	Linto	B
5160	May 10, 1945 / End of war in Europe etc.	Unknown	Event	Linto	B
5161	May 14 to June 30 / Buy bonds / for / V / o'er the rising sun / 7th War Loan [handpainted]	Multicolored	Bonds	Myers	D
5162	May 14, 1943 / Yanks battle Japs on Attu / Nazis kill 70 etc. [no picture]	Pink, silver	Event	Linto	B
5163	May 17, 1944 - Myitkyina Burma-airfield captured / by etc. [handpainted]	Multicolored	Map	Smith, LH	C
5164	May 19, 1943 / Prime Minister Churchill / addressed a joint etc. [no picture]	Brown, silver	Event	Linto	B
5165	May 25, 1945——Maj.-Gen. / Hershey announced conscientious etc. [no picture]	Gold	Home	Linto	B
5166	May 30, 1942 / R.A.F. used 1100 / planes to raid / Cologne [no picture]	Black, gold	Event	Linto	B
5167	May 30-31: First anniversary of / mass raid etc. [cut-&-pasted paper]	Black	Anniv	Temple	B
5168	May America / in her day of victory / be strong, of great etc. [no picture]	Blue, red	Home	Boone	A
5169	May Christmas foretell to / a free people etc. [no picture]	Unknown	Holid	Boone	A
5170	May God bless, / may God protect, / may God give strength / to our forces etc.	Gold, silver	DAY	Linto	C
5171	May it please God to / bless those dear souls / who have so faithfully etc.	Gold, green	Home	Linto	B
5172	May it ring / forever [spacing between words varies]	Bu, Br/Red	Bell	Agnew	A
5173	May it ring / forever [text height 6 or 9 mm]	Blue	Bell	Agnew	A
5174	May liberty's torch / shine forever! [handpainted]	Multicolored	Torch	Knapp	G
5175	May our army give us / an early victory for a / Christmas present.	Blue, gold	EagSh	Runge	A
5176	May right prevail	Unknown	Unk	Runge	A
5177	May the binding together of the / United Nations draw more tightly / and etc.	Blue	Bonds	Brenn	A
5178	May the coming / New Year / bring to you / health - - happiness / and etc. [thermogr]	Blue, red	Holid	Unknown	C
5179	May your Xmas / be happy / with victory [handpainted]	Multicolored	Holid	Wolf, RL	C
5180	Maybe you can't go across but etc.	Unknown	Bonds	Quigley	B
5181	McArthur [sic] —— gives us back the / Philippines for a Christmas gift.	Gold, red	Mac	Runge	B
5182	McArthur [sic] - He Promised - He Returned	Blue, red	Mac	Unknown	A
5183	Me / with those / "no new letter, / blues" etc. [burned edge] [handpainted]	Multicolored	Home	Cowdery	D
5184	Me worry? H... no! / I'm in the Navy now [thermographed]	Blue	Navy	Crosby	B
5185	Measure your / patriotism with / U.S. war bonds	Gold, green	Flag	Linto	B
5186	Meat a-plenty for / chair-warmers! / War workers / [etc.] / Navy Day——27-10-'43	Multicolored	Navy	Linto	B
5187	Meat a-plenty for / chair-warmers! / War workers get! / Oh, heck! [color var.]	Multicolored	Home	Linto	B
5188	Medical / technicians / needed in / [etc.] / 8-10-'44——Yanks sink 16 more etc.	Multicolored	Event	Linto	B
5189	Medical / technicians / needed in / the WAC / If you can qualify go to etc.	Multicolored	WAC	Linto	B
5190	Medical Corps / ANC / Give to / Red Cross / war fund [thermographed]	Unknown	Nurse	Czubay	B

NO.	CACHET TEXT	COLOR	TOPIC	PUBLISHER	$
5191	Medical Corps. / Give to / Red Cross / war fund [thermographed]	Red	RedCr	Czubay	B
5192	Medical Corps. / N.A.S. c/o P.M. / Pasco, Wash. / Let's go America etc. [thermogr]	Black	Medic	Czubay	B
5193	Medical Department / Careless talk / costs lives / and ships! [thermographed]	Red	Army	Unknown	B
5194	Medical services [colored envelopes]	Black/Brown	Medic	Huss	A
5195	Meet [sic] out justice / [etc.] / 2-19-'44——Yankees land on Eniwetok etc.	Multicolored	Event	Linto	B
5196	Meet [sic] out justice / swift and sure to / derelicts / traitors / and spies	Multicolored	Eagle	Linto	B
5197	Mein / Kampf / Adolf Hitler / Germany surrenders etc.	Red	VEDay	Threl+Thar	A
5198	Mein / Kampf / Adolf Hitler [thermographed]	Red	Hitle	Threl+Thar	A
5199	Mein / Kampf / Adolf Hitler [thermographed]	Red	Hitle	Threl+Thar	A
5200	Mein gott!! / Der Yanks / again! / Now commences der / end of etc. [handpainted]	Multricolored	Hitle	Parker	C
5201	Memorial / Day	Black	Holid	Peters	A
5202	Memorial / Day	Black	Holid	Brenn	B
5203	Memorial / Day	Blue, brown	Holid	Unknown	A
5204	Memorial / Day / May 30 [postmarked 5/30/40] [thermographed]	Black	Holid	Nicholson	B
5205	Memorial / Day / May thirty [postmarked 5/30/41]	Gold, silver	Holid	Linto	B
5206	Memorial Day / "May the great God, / whom I worship, grant / to my" etc.	Multicolored	Holid	Griffith	B
5207	Memorial Day / Asleep are the ranks of the dead; / under the sod etc.	Blue, red	Holid	Brenn	A
5208	Memorial Day / May 30	Unknown	Holid	Lupton	A
5209	Memorializing / our heroes of World War II etc. [thermographed]	Unknown	Hero	Unknown	A
5210	Memory / Monday / In honor of our recent / Gold Star heroes / They died etc.	Blue, gold	Holid	Brenn	B
5211	Memory Monday / in honor of / our Gold Star heroes / These sons etc. [text 21, 26, or 29 mm high]	Blue, red	Holid	Brenn	B
5212	Memory Monday / in honor of / our recent / Gold Star heroes / In etc.	Blue, gold	Holid	Brenn	B
5213	Memory Monday / in honor of our fallen service / men and women during etc.	Blue, red	Holid	Brenn	B
5214	Memory Monday / in honor of our recent Gold Star heroes / etc. [flag & star]	Blue, gold	Holid	Brenn	B
5215	Memory Monday / in honor of our recent Gold Star heroes / etc. [shields & stars]	Blue, gold	Holid	Brenn	B
5216	Memory Monday / Memory Monday does not honor / heroes of long past etc.	Blue, red	Holid	Brenn	B
5217	Memory Monday / originated in Sioux City etc. [text blue] [eagle]	Blue, red	Holid	Brenn	B
5218	Memory Monday / originated in Sioux City etc. [text blue] [flag]	Blue, red	Holid	Brenn	B
5219	Memory Monday / originated in Sioux City etc. [text red] [eagle]	Blue, red	Holid	Brenn	B
5220	Memory Monday / originated in Sioux City etc. [text red] [flag]	Blue, red	Holid	Brenn	B
5221	Men in service fight to / [etc.] / 1-28-'44——Russians take Leningrad etc.	Multicolored	Event	Linto	B
5222	Men in service fight to / secure freedom while / politicians run the war!!	Gd,Gn/Gd,S	Army	Linto	B
5223	Men of steel V ···– / in machines of steel [thermographed]	Unknown	Armed	Von Los	B
5224	Memorial Day / God bless / America / We are proud to etc. [white or pink envelope]	Bu, R/Blue	Holid	Cover News	A
5225	Merchant / Marine [thermographed]	Green	Merch	Czubay	B
5226	Merchant / vessel / [etc.] / ships for victory	Red	Merch	Wash Cover	A
5227	Merchant Marine	Brown	Merch	Czubay	A
5228	Merchant Marine / "She's in the Navy now!" [postmarked 8/8/41]	Multicolored	Merch	Unknown	C
5229	Merchant Marine / posted on the high seas / souvenir cancels etc. [thermographed]	Black	Merch	Czubay	B
5230	Merry / Christmas / don't forget the boys / over there	Unknown	Holid	Baur	A
5231	Merry / Christmas / Happy / New Year [handpainted]	Multicolored	Holid	Adler	D
5232	Merry / Christmas [below ringing bell]	Blue, red	Holid	Levering	A
5233	Merry / Christmas [handpainted]	Multicolored	Holid	Richards	B
5234	Merry / Christmas [holly, lamp, ribbon] [handpainted]	Multicolored	Holid	Adler	D
5235	Merry / Christmas [within circle with holly leaves an candle]	Black	Holid	Unknown	A
5236	Merry / Xmas / V [handpainted]	Multicolored	Holid	Adler	D
5237	Merry Christmas / at Palestine, Texas 1943 / Peace on earth	Unknown	Holid	Zunks	B
5238	Merry Christmas / Buy / more / war / bonds / Happy New Year [handpainted]	Black, red	Holid	Wolf, CL	C
5239	Merry Christmas / buy seals / stamp out the Axis etc. [no picture]	Unknown	Holid	Harmer	A
5240	Merry Christmas / to our boys and girls etc.	Unknown	Holid	Baur	A
5241	Merry Christmas / to you	Red	Holid	Unknown	A
5242	Merry Christmas / U S Navy [thermographed]	Unknown	Holid	Crosby	B
5243	Merry Christmas / U.S. Marine Corps [thermographed]	Gold	Holid	Crosby	B
5244	Merry Christmas / United States Army [thermographed]	Unknown	Holid	Crosby	B
5245	Merry Christmas / United States Navy [thermographed]	Unknown	Holid	Crosby	B
5246	Merry Christmas [music notes and flag or Santa Claus with flag]	Unknown	Holid	Runge	A
5247	Merry Mary / Mary , Mary, don't be wary / Tell us how your fortunes grow, etc.	Green, orange	Verse	Threl+Thar	A

NO.	CACHET TEXT	COLOR	TOPIC	PUBLISHER	$
5248	Merry Xmas / This is no [thermographed]	Green	Holid	Czubay	B
5249	Merry Xmas [Santa Claus in helmet across "V" made of holly] [handpainted]	Multicolored	Holid	Knoll	C
5250	Merry. / Christmas. [snow-covered cottage, pine cones] [handpainted]	Multicolored	Holid	Adler	D
5251	Mess cooking / again! / "This is the life——plenty / of chow to scoff when" etc.	Black	Navy	Lupton	A
5252	Mess Sarge / ain't lookin' pal etc. [envelope 8 1/4x3 7/8 in.]	Multicolored	Army	Porto-serv	B
5253	Message from / "Quig" / Suite 521 / Northern / Life Tower / Seattle 1	Blue	Home	Quigley	A
5254	Message to Mussolini / Muzzy you have had your day. / Your etc. [no picture]	Blue	Musso	Abel	A
5255	Message to Tojo / You sneaked up on Pearl Harbor / and you etc. [no picture]	Black	Japan	Abel	A
5256	Methods and systems / for victory [envelope 9 1/2x4 1/8 in.]	Unknown	Unk	Hadley	B
5257	Mexico / at war / with / Axis [no picture]	Red	Event	Fidelity	B
5258	Micah has uniform trouble! [thermographed] [envelope 6 1/2x4 11/16 in.]	Unknown	Unk	Cleveland	A
5259	Micah thrives / on pandemonium! [thermographed] [envelope 6 1/2x4 11/16 in.]	Unknown	Unk	Cleveland	A
5260	Mid-Pacific Security Force / Hawaiian area [thermographed]	Unknown	Navy	Crosby	B
5261	Midway / where he "lost pants" / trying to "save face" [colored envelopes]	Bu, R/Multi	Japan	Poppenger	B
5262	Might [in quotes] [envelope 6 9/16x 3 3/4 or 6 3/4x3 7/8 in.]	Sepia tones	Ord	Belles-let	C
5263	Military / cancel [artist: George Neumann]	Green	Army	Woodbury	A
5264	Military / intelligence / They don't know etc.	Black/Blue	Unk	Huss	A
5265	Military men are poor / insurance risk but are a / good risk to assure etc.	Gold, silver	Armed	Linto	B
5266	Militia / in / training / Look out / Japs [white, blue, or yellow envelope]	Black	Armed	Turley	A
5267	Miners ordered back to work	Unknown	Home	Linto	B
5268	Minnesota / produces / more / milk and butter / for / Victory [lower left corner]	Black	Home	Social Sec	A
5269	Minnesota post-war / public etc. [cream envelope 9 1/2x4 1/8 in.]	Blue	Home	Northwest	B
5270	Mir woelle bleiwe [in quotes] / [etc.] / Luxembourg [thermographed] [artist: Staehle]	Blue, red	ORN	Cachet Cra	B
5271	Miss America 1944 -- [handpainted]	Black	WAC	Clendennen	D
5272	Miss Muffet / Little Mis Muffet / bought her a tuffet / at twice what she etc.	Bu, pink	Verse	Threl+Thar	B
5273	Missing in action / France / Belgium / Germany / Are you etc. [no picture]	Green	Home	Rowe	A
5274	Mission completed! / From Pearl Harbor until etc. [8/14/45 w/fancy cancel]	Blue	VJDay	Levering	D
5275	Mission Stamp Club / Shelby, Ohio / "What so proudly / we hail!"	Unknown	Flag	Mission	A
5276	Mission Stamp Club / Shelby, Ohio / Long may it wave / we hail!"	Unknown	Flag	Mission	A
5277	Mission Stamp Club / Shelby, Ohio / Long may it wave!	Unknown	Flag	Mission	A
5278	Mitscher [handpainted]	Multicolored	Admir	Knoll	D
5279	Mmmmm! / Ahhhhh! / Home / cooking!! [handpainted]	Blue	Army	Parker	C
5280	Modern / infantry / still / the / backbone of etc. [envelope 6x3 ½ in.]	Multicolored	Army	Cozart	A
5281	Modern as today's / war planes [rose envelope]	Black	Air	Hans	A
5282	Modern Mother Goose / 1-Hey diddle, diddle, while we played etc. [handpainted]	Multicolored	Liber	Weigand	B
5283	Money in the bag and in / your pocket / [etc.] / 7-9-'45——Chinese liberate etc.	Multicolored	Event	Linto	B
5284	Money in the bag and in / your pocket if invested in / United States war bonds	Multicolored	Bonds	Linto	B
5285	Money is like some / people. Have to be urged / into action. / Put your etc.	Unknown	Bonds	Linto	B
5286	Monroe / Wis. / Day / February 29th / 1944	Black, orange	Axis	Unknown	C
5287	Montgomery fills the bases, / Patton drives them home; / Adolph and etc.	Blue, red	Patt	Boone	B
5288	Morale is spelled / m-a-i-l! / Did you write that / V-mail etc. [no picture]	Red	Home	Davis, Ray	A
5289	More busy hands / less / artificial / limbs [no picture]	Blue, red	Home	Ang	A
5290	More girls needed for / Women's Army Corps / 11-2-'44 -- Romania break [sic] etc.	Multicolored	Event	Linto	B
5291	More girls needed for / Women's Army Corps [no picture]	Pi,S/Gd,Pi	WAC	Linto	B
5292	More like / the Fourth / of July! / Merry Christmas [thermographed]	Blue	Navy	Crosby	B
5293	More tax money waste / [etc.] / 4-25-'45——United Nations etc.	Unknown	UN	Linto	B
5294	More tax money waste / 2,400,000 troughs were made in / California. etc.	Gold, silver	Flag	Linto	B
5295	Morganthau [sic] suggests / reducing / [etc.] / 9-23-'44——Halsey's men etc.	Unknown	Event	Linto	B
5296	Morganthau [sic] suggests / reducing Germany to / small farms only. / Now etc.	Gold, violet	Flag	Linto	B
5297	Mother / no fortune or fame can ever compare etc. [thermographed]	Unknown	Home	Baur	A
5298	Mother Goose / ...up to date etc. [3rd line has dot or 3 stars] [no picture]	Blue/Red	Home	Boone	A
5299	Motion pictures / [etc.] / They also serve etc.	Multicolored	Home	Fleetwood	B
5300	Mount Vernon / (The P is White House!)	Multicolored	Wash	Brenn	A
5301	Moving base / Tyndall Field, Fla.	Green	Armed	Unknown	A
5302	MP [on MP's armband]/ Trash [on trash can, with soldier hiding in can] [handpainted]	Multicolored	Army	Dannells	C
5303	Mr. Fala [in quotes] / This is- / rea-ally / my day / Wilhelmstrasse	Black	FDR	Fountaine	B
5304	Mr. Hirohito, how do you / like the sting of our Navy.	Blue, red	Japan	Baur	A

NO.	CACHET TEXT	COLOR	TOPIC	PUBLISHER	$
5305	Mr. Hitler: here we come!	Blue, red	Lib+	Powers	A
5306	Mr. Hoover, tho innocent, / was blamed for the depres- / sion but they etc.	Blue, red	Home	Linto	B
5307	Mr. Jap, you'll be sorry! / We / etc. [1st line 57, 63 mm] [Marine] [thermographed]	Blue, red	USMC	Crosby	B
5308	Mr. Jap, you'll be sorry! / We / will / avenge Pearl Harbor! [sailor] [thermographed]	Blue, red	Navy	Crosby	B
5309	Mr. Jap, you'll etc. [1st line w/, w/o serifs; 56, 64 mm long] [colored envelopes]	Bu, R/Multi	Japan	Poppenger	A
5310	Mr. Lincoln, we'll keep faith! / "Surely each man has" etc. [colored envelopes]	Blue, red	Linc	Poppenger	A
5311	Mr. Roosevelt says he / will obey / [etc.] / 7-11-'44——Reds crush Nazis' etc.	Multicolored	Event	Linto	B
5312	Mr. Roosevelt says he / will obey the will of / the sovereign people etc.	Multicolored	Home	Linto	B
5313	Mr. Roosevelt says: "Fair for one, fair for all" / Is that etc. [no picture]	Gd,Gn/Gd,S	FDR	Linto	B
5314	Mr. Roosevelt says: / "Fair for one," / [etc.] / 1-22-'44——Dem. Nat. Com. etc.	Multicolored	Home	Linto	B
5315	Mrs. Bixby of our time [in quotes] (Whistler's) etc. [env. 6 9/16x3 11/16 in.]	Sepia tones	Home	Belles-let	C
5316	Mrs. Vanderhokum, sir,——wants to / know why her son, Willie, hasn't been etc.	Black	Army	Deming	A
5317	Mud and the enemy / can't stop them / Lack of etc. [env. 6 1/2x3 5/8, 6x3 ½ in.]	Bu/Br/Red	Army	Conner	A
5318	Mud and the enemy / can't stop them / Lack of supplies might. [env. 9 3/8x4 1/4 in.]	Red	Army	Conner	B
5319	Mum's the word / if you've news etc. [no picture]	Unknown	Home	Levering	A
5320	Munda falls to U.S. / troops; Orel, Belgo- / rod etc. [no picture] [thermogr]	Red	Event	Boone	B
5321	Murderers' row [in quotes] [envelope 7x4 in.]	Sepia tones	Navy	Belles-let	C
5322	Mussolini / kicked / out / July 25, 1943	Aqua, black	Event	Fidelity	B
5323	Mussolini / shot / Mussolini shot by partisans / near Dongo while trying etc.	Multicolored	Event	Teixeira	D
5324	Mussolini / we're glad you're dead—— / you rascal you	Black, red	Musso	Boone	A
5325	Mussolini escapes! / ——so what? / September 18, 1943	Multi/Bk,Gn	Event	Fidelity	B
5326	Mussolini out / One / down / two / to go	Blue, red	Musso	Griffith	A
5327	Mussolini resigns	Unknown	Musso	Linto	B
5328	Mussolini's day is done, / Hitler is on the run, / Now Mr. etc. [no picture]	Blue	Verse	Ang	A
5329	Must / you telephone? / Well then / leave / seven-ten / for etc. [no picture]	Red	Home	Rowe	A
5330	Must Britain yield? [envelope 9 1/2x4 1/8 in.]	Unknown	Ally	Unknown	B
5331	My / "male" makes / good backing! —— / and plenty of it. [handpainted]	Multicolored	Army	Cowdery	D
5332	My / chin's / still up / so —— / it couldn't / be me!! [handpainted]	Multicolored	Home	Cowdery	D
5333	My / soldier / always makes a / hit. [burned left, torn right edge]	Multicolored	Army	Cowdery	D
5334	My / soldier [burned left edge] [handpainted]	Multicolored	Army	Cowdery	D
5335	My / Uncle / ! / Victory and peace his goal / faith and courage his strength	Blue, red	Uncle	Fleetwood	B
5336	My America [on flap] [white or brown env. 5 3/4 or 6 3/4x3 3/4, 7 1/2x 4 in.]	Multicolored	Unk	Dime	A
5337	My American freedom lets / me scratch my fleas whenever / wherever and etc.	Black	Dog	Littlefiel	A
5338	My China baby-doll! [in quotes]	Black	USMC	Lupton	A
5339	My country! 'tis of thee, sweet land of liberty etc. [thermographed]	Unknown	Unk	Baur	A
5340	My country, 'tis of thee / sweet land of liberty / of thee I sing, / land etc.	Unknown	Home	Boone	A
5341	My country, 'tis of thee, / sweet land of liberty, / of thee I sing. Land etc.	Blue, red	FlBel	Amer Pat	A
5342	My Easter greetings for '44 / "Let's do more to win this war!" [handpainted]	Multicolored	Holid	Unknown	B
5343	My flag - long may it wave / a flag etc. [thermographed]	Unknown	Flag	Unknown	A
5344	My heart is always / there / in the land of the / free	Multicolored	Flag	Amer Pat	A
5345	My heart is always there, in the land of the free	Multicolored	Flag	Amer Pat	A
5346	My heart rejoices / when I say etc. [flag draped or hanging, no stars]	Multi/Blue,	Flaf	Amer Pat	A
5347	My heart rejoices / when I say etc. [flag draped or hanging, with stars]	Multi/Bu, red	Flag	Amer Pat	A
5348	My horoscope says not to worry today [in quotes]	Multicolored	Army	Unknown	B
5349	My pledge to you: / I charge no more than top legal prices / I sell etc.	Blue, red	Home	Threl+Thar	A
5350	My prayers follow you [in quotes] etc. [envelope 6 3/4x3 7/8 in.]	Sepia tones	Unk	Cozart	A
5351	Myrtle Point, Ore. / salutes it's [sic]: "Fighting Bobcats" / in all branches etc.	Green, red	Armed	Myers	B

4920

4929

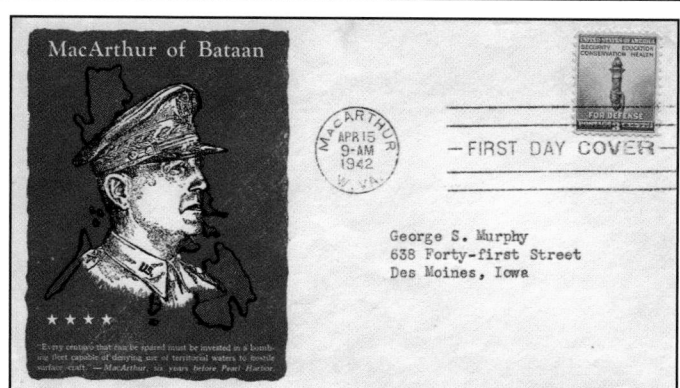

4931

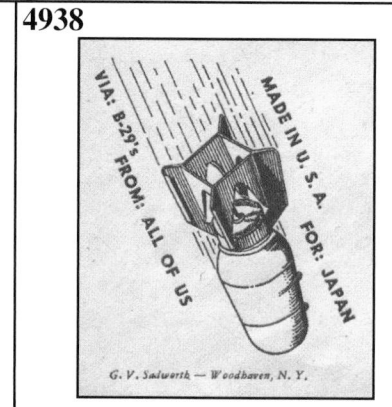

4938

5067

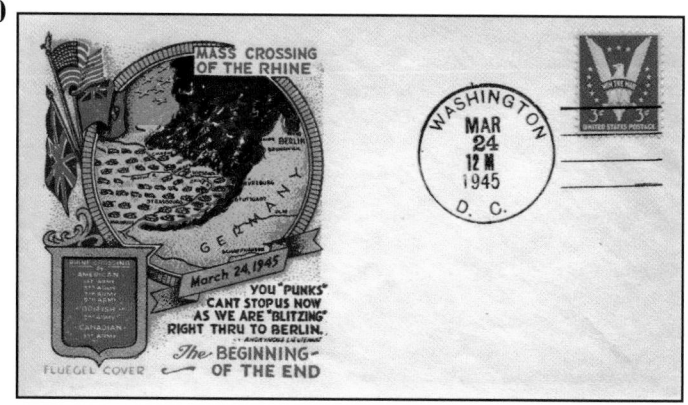

5140

5151

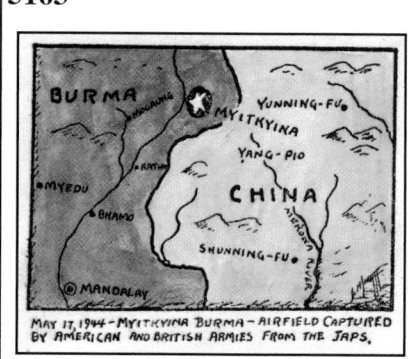

5163

5191

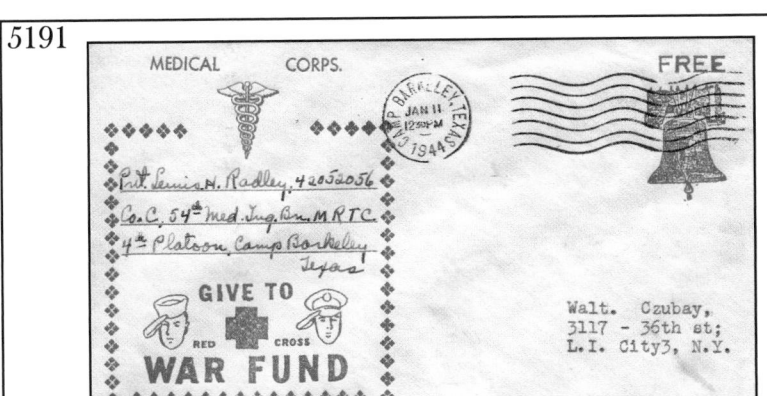

5215

5233

5262

5302

5307

5315

5323

CACHET TEXT BEGINNING WITH "N"

NO.	CACHET TEXT	COLOR	TOPIC	PUBLISHER	$
5352	Na···y / 1——A cry of revenge rings out from the sea, / from etc. [handpainted]	Multicolored	Liber	Weigand	B
5353	Nailing down the Rome end	Multicolored	Gener	Peer	B
5354	Napoleon / in / 1805 / The Yanks / in / 1945 / The historical Rhine crossing	Multicolored	Event	Fluegel	C
5355	Nation of suckers [in quotes] / Perhaps you will be interested in the etc.	Aqua	AJA	Linto	B
5356	National / defense / Make America strong!	Bk/Green/Red	Unk	Cliff	A
5357	National / defense program	Unknown	Unk	Unknown	A
5358	National Aviation Day / at Orrs Island etc.	Blue, red	Air	Cleveland	A
5359	National Aviation Day / at Victory, Kentucky / August 19th, 1941 etc.	Blue, red	Air	Zunks	C
5360	National Aviation Day / August 19th, 1944. / "On to victory" / "Keep 'em flying"	Blue, red	Air	Zunks	C
5361	National defense - through - fire defense / [etc.] / friend of the enemy.	Multicolored	Axis	Unknown	C
5362	National defense / 1940 / Millions for defense etc.	Unknown	Unk	Unknown	A
5363	National defense / Artillery / United States Army [thermographed]	Multicolored	EagSh	Von Los	B
5364	National defense / Aviation / Corps. / United States Army [thermographed]	Multicolored	EagSh	Von Los	B
5365	National defense / Cavalry / United States Army [thermographed]	Mulicolored	Army	Von Los	B
5366	National defense / Engineers / United States Army [thermographed]	Unknown	Army	Von Los	B
5367	National defense / First anniversary of the draft, October 16, 1941 [colored envelopes]	O, purple	Liber	Pilgrim	C
5368	National Defense / First line / of defense [thermographed]	Blue	Navy	Unknown	B
5369	National defense / Infantry / United States Army [thermographed]	Multicolored	Army	Von los	B
5370	National defense / Machine Gun / United States Army [thermographed]	Unknown	Army	Von Los	B
5371	National defense / Medical Corps / United States Army [thermographed]	Unknown	Medic	Von Los	B
5372	National defense / Ordnance / Department / United States Army [thermographed]	Unknown	Ordna	Von Los	B
5373	National defense / Quartermaster / United States Army [thermographed]	Unknown	Army	Von Los	B
5374	National defense / Signal Corps / United States Army [thermographed]	Unknown	Army	Von Los	B
5375	National defense / United States Army / Artillery [thermographed]	Blue, red	VforV	Von Los	B
5376	National defense / United States Army / Aviation [thermographed]	Blue, red	VforV	Von Los	B
5377	National defense / United States Army / Cavalry [thermographed]	Blue, red	VforV	Von Los	B
5378	National defense / United States Army / Infantry [thermographed]	Blue, red	VforV	Von Los	B
5379	National defense / United States Army / Machine Gun [thermographed]	Blue, red	VforV	Von Los	B
5380	National defense / United States Army / Ordnance [thermographed]	Blue, red	VforV	Von Los	B
5381	National defense / United States Army / Quartermaster [thermographed]	Blue, red	VforV	Von Los	B
5382	National defense / United States Army / Signal Corps. [thermographed]	Blue, red	VforV	Von Los	B
5383	National defense / United States Army [thermographed]	Unknown	Army	Von Los	B
5384	National defense / United States of America [printed frame for stickers]	Blue, red	Home	Goldstein	B
5385	National defense [eagle on shield] [frame 57 or 59 mm high]	Unknown	EagSh	Unknown	A
5386	National defense [text above Statue of Liberty]	Green, red	Liber	Unknown	A
5387	National defense [text above US seal in circle with flags]	Unknown	Flag	Unknown	A
5388	National defense [three servicemen with flag]	Blue, red	Flag	Cal-Craft	A
5389	National defense National defense / National defense etc. [perimeter of envelope]	Blue, red	Shiel	Sadworth	A
5390	National Draft Lottery [in quotes] / First historic / ceremony during etc.	Multicolored	Event	Hutnick	D
5391	National Opinion Research Center / [etc.] / 7-30-'44——Reported Nazi etc.	Multicolored	Event	Linto	B
5392	National Opinion Research Center / claims majority of Americans favor etc.	Aqua, silver	Home	Linto	B
5393	Nations united / fighting for the / great principles / of freedom	Gn/Gn,Yello	VforV	Staehle	C
5394	Nations united / for victory and peace [thermographed]	Unknown	UN	Farnam	A
5395	Nations united for victory	Red	UN	Unk	A
5396	Naval pursuit [handpainted]	Multicolored	Air	Price, EK	C
5397	Naval Training School / [etc.] / Harvard University etc. [env. 5 1/2x4 in.]	Blue	Navy	Hampshire	E
5398	Navigator [envelope 6 1/2x3 5/8, 6 1/8x3 5/8 in.] [colored envelopes]	Blue	Air	Huss	A
5399	Navy / Day / Oct. 27, 1943 [ship thermographed]	Blue, red	Navy	Dye	B
5400	Navy / hundred years / US Naval Academy etc.	Multicolored	Navy	Staehle	C
5401	Navy / YMCA	Blue, red	Navy	YMCA	B
5402	Navy Day / at Farragut, Idaho, October 27th, 1943. "Back the attack" etc.	Blue, red	Navy	Amer Naval	A
5403	Navy Day / at Torpedo, Pennsylvania etc. [env. 6 1/2x3 5/8, 6 5/16x3 ½ in.]	Blue, red	Navy	Amer Naval	A
5404	Navy Day / Greetings / from / Sublimity / Oregon [each word vertical]	Gold	Navy	Linto	B
5405	Navy Day / Keep 'em / flying / Wings / of / the / Navy [thermographed]	Aqua/Red	Air	Czubay	B
5406	Navy Day / Oct. 27 / True blue / USS Potomac [thermographed]	Unknown	Navy	Crosby	B
5407	Navy Day / Oct. 27, 1943 / Buy bonds	Multicolored	Bonds	Linto	B

NO.	CACHET TEXT	COLOR	TOPIC	PUBLISHER	$
5408	Navy Day / Oct. 27, 1943 / Buy bonds / [etc.] / When better navies are etc.	Multicolored	Navy	Linto	B
5409	Navy Day / Oct. 27, 1943 / Buy Bonds / 10-27-'43——U.S. planes bomb etc.	Multicolored	Event	Linto	B
5410	Navy Day / Oct. 27, 1943 / Sail to / victory / Holo ia / lanakila	Blue, red	Navy	Sayama	B
5411	Navy Day / October 27 [postmarked 10/27/41]	Multicolored	Navy	Linto	B
5412	Navy Day / October 27, 1943 / [etc.] / 10-27-'42——London——Mrs. Franklin D. etc.	Multicolored	Anniv	Linto	B
5413	Navy Day / October 27, 1943 / [etc.] / When better navies are built Uncle etc.	Multicolored	Navy	Linto	B
5414	Navy Day / October 27, 1943 / Keep on building ships / and more ships	Multicolored	Navy	Linto	B
5415	Navy Day / October 27th / "The Navy - / defender" etc. [env. 9 1/2x4 1/8 in.]	Blue	Navy	Navy Dept.	C
5416	Navy Day / Pittsburgh welcomes etc. [no picture]	Unknown	Navy	Hamilton	A
5417	Navy Day 1942 / "A really great people,...would face all the" etc. [thermographed]	Blue	Navy	Unknown	B
5418	Navy Day 1944 / For victory / buy etc. [envelope 6x3 ½ in.]	Black	Navy	Phill, CR	A
5419	Navy Day October / 27th / Wings / of / the / Navy [thermographed]	Red	Navy	Czubay	B
5420	Navy Day October 27 / [etc.] / USS Calypso [thermographed]	Unknown	Navy	Crosby	B
5421	Navy Department / [etc.] / Remember / Pearl Harbor! / December 7, etc. [thermographed]	Blue/Red	Pearl	Sadworth	B
5422	Navy Department / United States of America [cachet diameter varies] [thermographed]	Bk/Blue/Bro	Navy	Sadworth	B
5423	Navy of the United States / Let's go! U.S.A. / keep 'em etc. [thermographed]	Blue	Navy	Crosby	B
5424	Navy of the United States / U.S. Marines, "Devil Dogs," etc. [thermographed]	Red	USMC	Crosby	B
5425	Navy Yeomanette Corps / [etc.] / 1-24-'45——Halsey's men bag / 215 ships, etc.	Unknown	Event	Linto	B
5426	Navy Yeomanette Corps / on the job for Uncle Sam	Unknown	Navy	Linto	B
5427	Nazi / invincibility / a shattered myth	Black, red	Nazis	McCluney	B
5428	Nazi agents / Cads who will try to undermine / the morale of our boys in etc.	Multicolored	Nazis	Linto	B
5429	Nazi divisions! / Ha! Ha! / Russian winters too cold. / Now / too hot here.	Bk/Blue/Red	Devil	Carpenter	A
5430	Nazi werewolves [handpainted]	Multicolored	Hitle	Long	C
5431	Nazi yoke / lifted in / Italy	Multicolored	Nazis	Fluegel	C
5432	Nazi-ism / crumbles / April 25, 1945 / -Berlin- / is encircled, / capture etc.	Multicolored	Nazis	Fluegel	C
5433	Nazis 3rd offensive on Russians	Unknown	Event	Linto	B
5434	Nazis capture Tobruk	Unknown	Event	Linto	B
5435	Nazis captured Sevastopol	Unknown	Event	Linto	B
5436	Nazis face / rout in / Sicily	Black	Event	Boone	B
5437	Nazis flee / Sicily [no picture]	Black	Event	Boone	B
5438	Nazis wiped out Lidice	Unknown	Event	Linto	B
5439	Nebraska State Capitol Building [text 36 or 37 mm long]	Unknown	Unk	Unknown	A
5440	Needed meat wasted / Sheep raisers / [etc.] / 8-26-'44——Bulgaria quits etc.	Multicolored	Event	Linto	B
5441	Needed meat wasted / Sheep raisers are forced, thru / O.P.A. etc. [no picture]	Gold, green	Home	Linto	B
5442	Neither snow, nor rain, / [etc.] / safe delivery of the United States air-mail	Black	Air	Lowry	A
5443	Nest eggs won't / hatch unless you / set on them! / Hang on to your etc.	Green, yellow	Home	Kosko	A
5444	Netherlands	Unknown	ORN	Clifford	A
5445	Netherlands / fights / for freedom!	Blue, red	ORN	Cachet Cra	B
5446	Netherlands / shall / rise / again	Bk/Br/Gold	ORN	Runge	A
5447	Netherlands / Since May 10, 1939 [sic] when the forces of Nazi Germany etc.	Bk/Blue/Red	ORN	Cliff	A
5448	Netherlands shall rise again / Hague, N.Y., U.S.A., salutes / The Hague etc.	Black	ORN	Rameco	B
5449	Never again / too little / too late	Unknown	Unk	Runge	A
5450	Never again—— / too little, / too late! [envelope 9 1/2x4 1/8 in.]	Brown/Green	Unk	Lee	B
5451	Never before have so many / owed so much to so few [in quotes] etc.	Multicolored	Winst	Advertiser	B
5452	Never forget the / boys who gave etc.	Unknown	Unk	Levering	A
5453	Never in the field of human / conflict was so much owed by [in quotes] etc.	Blue, red	Winst	Unknown	B
5454	Never in the history of / this country etc.	Blue, red	Home	Brenn	A
5455	New / Caledonia / Noumea, N.C. [thermographed]	Blue, green	Air	Crosby	B
5456	New arms for / the production battle [envelope 9 1/2x4 1/8 in.]	Blue, red	Eagle	Bellows	C
5457	New emperor of Japan [postmarked 9/2/45]	Black	Mac	Unk	C
5458	New features on the map	Blue	Axis	Citret	A
5459	New Hampshire / the Granite State / always loyal, always ready. / Her etc.	Black	Home	Clark	A
5460	New Hebrides / Espirtu [sic] Santo, N.H. [thermographed]	Blue, green	Air	Crosby	B
5461	New liberty / new hope , independence / V-Day in Europe today / Hell / Hitler!	Green, red	VEDay	Czubay	C
5462	New name for a nightmare	Black	Japan	Davis, D	A
5463	New regular / 8 cent air mail / [etc.] / ..Doolittle	Black	Air	Artcraft	A
5464	New York World-Telegram / Atom bomb stuns foe etc. [headlines] [8/6/45]	Red	Atom	Unknown	D
5465	New Zealand / United Nations [handpainted]	Multicolored	UN	Weigand	B

NO.	CACHET TEXT	COLOR	TOPIC	PUBLISHER	$
5466	New Zealand troops / are fighting everywhere / for etc. [handpainted]	Multicolored	Map	Smith, LH	C
5467	New Zealand troops / are fighting on all / fronts for the etc. [handpainted]	Multicolored	Map	Smith, LH	C
5468	New's [sic] / Berlin falls to the / Russians. / Goebbels etc. [no picture]	Red	Event	Threl+Thar	B
5469	Next! / Did you buy yours / today? [handpainted]	Black, blue	Uncle	Parker	B
5470	Next! [handpainted]	Multicolored	Women	Clendennen	E
5471	Nicaragua / United Nations [handpainted]	Multicolored	UN	Weigand	B
5472	Nimitz - West Va. / First day cover / 9 - 10 - 45 / First day cover / from etc.	Black	NimFD	Trail	C
5473	Nine reasons why / we will win	Bu,R/Br,Gree	FDR	Cozart	B
5474	Nineteen [19] July 4th 40 / Liberty and union / America for Americans etc.	Blue	Holid	Unknown	A
5475	Nineteen eighteen [1918] / Yank by Yank / [etc.] / Win the / war in / 1944	Green	Armed	Ang	A
5476	Nineteen eighteen [1918] 1944 / Victory / on land, on sea, and in the air etc.	Blue, red	Flag	Byrd Stamp	A
5477	Nineteen eighteen [1918] 1944 / We done it before and / we have etc.	Blue, red	Home	Unknown	A
5478	Nineteen eighteen [1918]-1942 / "And our / dead shall not" etc. [no picture]	Blue	Holid	Fidelity	B
5479	Nineteen eighteen [1918]-1943 / 25th anniversary / Armistice Day	Black	Holid	One A Cov	B
5480	Nineteen forty-five [1945] - A glorious victory [thermographed]	Gold	Liber	Neal	A
5481	Nineteen forty-five [1945] / Generals of the Army / Eisenhower / MacArthur etc.	Multicolored	VJDay	Staehle	C
5482	Nineteen forty-five [1945] / One day nearer victory	Blue, red	Liber	Smith, W	A
5483	Nineteen forty-five [1945] / The U.S. Marines / Commemorating etc.	Multicolored	USMC	Fluegel	C
5484	Nineteen forty-five [1945] / War ends in Europe / Hitler & Goebbels die etc.	Black	VEDay	Abel	B
5485	Nineteen forty-five [1945] / war fund [handpainted]	Multicolored	RedCr	Hadley	B
5486	Nineteen forty-five [194V] [within outline of soldier's head and helmet] [handpainted]	Black	Army	Klondike	C
5487	Nineteen forty-five [handpainted]	Multicolored	Axis	Adler	D
5488	Nineteen forty-four [1944] / The fall of / Rome / Clark / of the 5th etc.	Multicolored	Event	Staehle	C
5489	Nineteen forty-four [1944] / A merry Christmas greeting / and a happy etc.	Green	Holid	Abel	A
5490	Nineteen forty-four [1944] / Athens / the capital of / Greece was etc.	Multicolored	Event	Staehle	C
5491	Nineteen forty-four [1944] / Bang / there / goes / Tokyo [handpainted]	Multicolored	Air	Borkowski	D
5492	Nineteen forty-four [1944] / Belgrade / the / capital of / Yugoslavia etc.	Multicolored	Event	Fluegel	C
5493	Nineteen forty-four [1944] / Dewey-Roosevelt / Bricker etc.	Unknown	FDR	McCluney	B
5494	Nineteen forty-four [1944] / In memory / of the heroic / defense and etc.	Multicolored	Phili	Staehle	C
5495	Nineteen forty-four [1944] / It's victory [handpainted]	Black, red	Home	Wolf, CL	B
5496	Nineteen forty-four [1944] / January / 1 / Happy / new / year / "Make" etc.	Blue, red	Holid	Zunks	B
5497	Nineteen forty-four [1944] / June 4th. / The fall of / Rome / Alexander	Multicolored	Event	Staehle	C
5498	Nineteen forty-four [1944] / June 4th. / The fall of / Rome / Pope etc.	Multicolored	Event	Staehle	C
5499	Nineteen forty-four [1944] / One day nearer victory	Blue, red	Liber	Smith, W	A
5500	Nineteen forty-four [1944] / One year nearer / victory [handpainted]	Multicolored	Bonds	Myers	C
5501	Nineteen forty-four [1944] / The / greatest blow / of all!	Black/Red	Hitle	Carpenter	A
5502	Nineteen forty-four [1944] / The / greatest blow / of all! [handpainted]	Black	Hitle	Klaas	D
5503	Nineteen forty-four [1944] / The last quarter / they're in a huddle	Black	Unk	Neal	A
5504	Nineteen forty-four [1944] ?	Black/Multi	Axis	Barnes	A
5505	Nineteen forty-four [1944] [Mary, Joseph, Jesus] [handpainted]	Multicolored	Holid	Adler	D
5506	Nineteen forty-four [1944] Drive starts in March / Give to / Red etc.	Red	RedCr	Czubay	A
5507	Nineteen forty-four [1944] Red Cross war fund etc. [envelope 8 7/8x3 7/8 in.]	Unknown	RedCr	Cleveland	B
5508	Nineteen forty-four [1944] war fund / Get busy- scratch etc. [handpainted]	Red	RedCr	Muzzy+Nich	C
5509	Nineteen forty-four [1944]. [handpainted]	Multicolored	Axis	Adler	D
5510	Nineteen forty-four [1944]-1945 / Lest we forget / "D-Day" etc. [thermographed]	Blue, red	Anniv	Boone	B
5511	Nineteen forty-one [1941] / Our first line / of defense / Don't etc. [thermographed]	Blue	Navy	Bund	B
5512	Nineteen forty-one [1941] / Our first line / of defense / Don't give up etc.	Violet	Navy	Bund	B
5513	Nineteen forty-one [1941] / They answered the call / so let's etc.	Blue	Unk	Foster	A
5514	Nineteen forty-three [1943] / V / Merry Xmas [handpainted]	Multicolored	Holid	Adler	D
5515	Nineteen forty-three [1943] [vertical] / The Cairo Meeting [artist: Staehle]	Multicolored	Heads	Smartcraft	C
5516	Nineteen forty-three [1943] [date split] / The Quebec / Conference [artist: Staehle]	Multicolored	Heads	Smartcraft	C
5517	Nineteen forty-three [1943] [same] / The Quebec / Conference / Second etc.	Multicolored	Heads	Smartcraft	C
5518	Nineteen forty-three [1943] [vertical] / The Teheran Meeting [artist: Staehle]	Multicolored	Heads	Smartcraft	C
5519	Nineteen ten [1910]-1945 / Korea / liberated / after 35 year / Jap etc.	Multicolored	ORN	Fluegel	C
5520	Ninetieth [90th] Division / Texas & Oklahoma [90th Division insignia]	Multicolored	Unit	McCluney	B
5521	Ninety-eighth [98th] Div. [under insignia] [handpainted]	Multicolored	Unit	Dannells	B
5522	Ninety-first [91st] Div [under insignia] [handpainted]	Black, green	Unit	Dannells	B
5523	Ninety-third [93rd] Division [handpainted]	Black, blue	Army	Teixeira	D

NO.	CACHET TEXT	COLOR	TOPIC	PUBLISHER	$
5524	Ninth / Troop / Carrier / Squadron [handpainted]	Black, blue	Pelic	Parker	B
5525	Ninth [IX] Corps. [under insignia] [handpainted]	Multicolored	Unit	Dannells	B
5526	Nippon / Amphibious forces / Occupation etc. [U.S.S. Goodhue] [Tokyo Bay]	Black, red	VJDay	Navy ship	D
5527	NNC [on anchor, above 3 flags] [envelope 6x3 1/2 in.]	Unknown	Navy	Amer Pat	A
5528	No blackout [in quotes] [3/4x3 7/8 in.]	Unknown	Unk	Belles-let	C
5529	No empty victory this time [in quotes]	Blue	Eagle	Neal	A
5530	No foolin' —— we are determined!	Blue	Navy	Lawrence	A
5531	No gamble / When the war is over etc. [no picture]	Unknown	Home	Carpenter	A
5532	No good / 'til I'm aboard [thermographed] [envelope 6 1/2x4 11/16 in.]	Unknown	Navy	Cleveland	A
5533	No mail today!	Black	Army	Unknown	A
5534	No man can suffer too much, and / [etc.] / 10-15-'44——Hungary now / wants etc.	Black, gold	Event	Linto	B
5535	No man can suffer too much, and no man / can fall too soon. etc. [no picture]	Black, gold	Hist	Linto	B
5536	No man is worth his salt who is not / [etc.] / 10-9-'44——Yanks cut off etc.	Multicolored	Event	Linto	B
5537	No man is worth his salt who is not / ready at all times to etc. [no picture]	Gold, silver	Hist	Linto	B
5538	No matter who wins the / election, we must win the / war!	Gold, silver	FDR	Phill, CR	B
5539	No more / a slave / France's / greatest / maritime / city / feels / Allies / remove etc.	Black, red	ORN	Griffith	A
5540	No more / a slave / France's / greatest / maritime / city / feels / Allies / remove etc.	Black, red	Event	Griffith	B
5541	No more Hitlerism —— no more supermen / Schicklgruber / That liberty etc.	Black	Hitle	Sadworth	B
5542	No nation is worthy of the name etc.	Unknown	Unk	Brenn	A
5543	No one will / get yours. [envelope 4 5/8x3 7/8 in.] [handpainted]	Multicolored	Home	Cowdery	D
5544	No power on earth can / prevent our destroying the / German etc. [no picture]	Blue, red	Heads	McCluney	A
5545	No profits / no wars!	Gold, green	Home	Linto	B
5546	No rent..no bills..nothing to worry about! [in quotes] [brown or buff envelope]	Multicolored	Army	Amer Art	A
5547	No strike bill voted	Unknown	Event	Linto	B
5548	No task too great / in calm or squalls / [etc.] / Dedicated to fallen etc.	Purple	Verse	Neal	A
5549	No task too great / in calm or squalls, / no job too tough / when duty etc.	Bu/Gn/O/Pu/	Verse	Neal	A
5550	No, Mr. President! / Press representatives etc.	Unknown	Home	Linto	B
5551	No. / 3. [handpainted]	Multicolored	Musso	Adler	E
5552	No. 1. [handpainted]	Multicolored	Hitle	Adler	E
5553	No. 2. [handpainted]	Multicolored	Japan	Adler	E
5554	Nonstop / to Tokyo [thermographed] [artist: DW Knapp]	Red	Air	Rush, JM	D
5555	Nope! no escaped German prisoner / 'round here!	Bk/Bu/Red	Army	Donaldson	A
5556	Normandy / June 1944 etc.	Unknown	DDay	McCluney	B
5557	North Africa. Sicily / Rome - Normandy [thermographed]	Unknown	Unk	Neal	A
5558	Norway	Black	ORN	Lowry	A
5559	Norway	Unknown	ORN	Clifford	A
5560	Norway / home of the / sons of the / Vikings, / who gave / their lives etc.	Multicolored	ORN	Runge	A
5561	Norway / Norway invaded / Largest naval battle vs. / Japan is raging in Pacific	Blue, red	Event	Fidelity	B
5562	Norway / Sons of the Vikings	Unknown	ORN	Runge	A
5563	Norway / The Kingdom of Norway, cruelly betrayed and over- / run by the etc.	Bk/Blue/Red	ORN	Cliff	A
5564	Norway / Vi / Vill / Vinne!	Blue, red	ORN	Cachet Cra	B
5565	Norway [thermographed]	Unknown	ORN	Jordan	B
5566	Norway will rise again [picture red or black]	Red,Bk/Bk	ORN	Huss	A
5567	Not a chance, / Adolf! / Not efen / a viggle! / Samson the / second etc.	Bk/Bu/Br/Pu	Hitle	Roberts	A
5568	Not a pretty picture / but.....a reminder!! / Defense savings stamps etc.	Blue	Pearl	Harrington	A
5569	Not a pretty picture / but.....a reminder!! / Remember Pearl Harbor!!!	Red	Pearl	Harrington	A
5570	Not a pretty picture / but.....a reminder!! / that / we will always etc.	Blue/Red	Pearl	Harrington	A
5571	Not a pretty picture / but.....a reminder!! / The Yanks / will get 'em	Bk/Blue/Red	Pearl	Harrington	A
5572	Not a pretty picture / but.....a reminder!! / The Yanks need tanks etc.	Black/Blue	Ordn	Harrington	A
5573	Not censored / This is / America! [no picture]	Unknown	Home	Boone	A
5574	Not censored! / We're in the USA	Bu, red	Home	Smith, W	A
5575	Not rabbits, / Mr. Jap! [airplanes coming out of Uncle Sam's hat] [handpainted]	Multicolored	Air	Klaas	D
5576	Not so fast, / Adolf! [in quotes] [copyright "C" w, w/o serifs]	Multicolored	Hitle	Minkus	A
5577	Note to strikers / There are 47 rules for / winning a war etc. [no picture]	Blue/Purple	Home	Boone	A
5578	Note to Tokyo: / Have you-all heard / the story of the B's / B-29's etc.	Blue, red	Air	Boone	A
5579	Note: this cartoon is drawn with / apologies to all real monkeys. [thermographed]	Brown/Green	Axis	Sadworth	B
5580	Notice / to those who hunt and / [etc.] / 9-8-'44——Yanks take Liege! Reds etc.	Multicolored	Event	Linto	B
5581	Notice / to those who hunt and / fish for pleasure! / There etc. [no picture]	Green, pink	Home	Linto	B

NO.	CACHET TEXT	COLOR	TOPIC	PUBLISHER	$
5582	Nov. 01, 1943 —— / U.S. Marines / and army troops / establish etc. [handpainted	Multicolored	Map	Smith, LH	C
5583	Nov. 01, 1944 - Jap navy crushed in / second battle etc. [handpainted]	Multicolored	Battl	Smith, LH	B
5584	Nov. 01, 1944 - Jap navy crushed in / second battle of the Philippine Sea.	Black	Battl	Smith, LH	A
5585	Nov. 02, 1944-Korea honored by the United / States for their etc. [handpainted]	Multicolored	Map	Smith, LH	C
5586	Nov. 07, 1942 - Yanks land in Algiers [handpainted]	Multicolored	Map	Smith, LH	C
5587	Nov. 13, 1942 / U.S. draft age / lowered to 18 [no picture]	Green, purple	Event	Linto	B
5588	Nov. 14, 1942 / Allied troops / invade Tunisia	Unknown	Event	Linto	B
5589	Nov. 15, 1942 / Japs lost 28 ships / in battle of / Guadalcanal [no picture]	Brown, silver	Event	Linto	B
5590	Nov. 18th / 1944 / Marshal Tito / Tirana / the / capital of Albania / was etc.	Multicolored	ORN	Fluegel	C
5591	Nov. 21, 1944 / French soldiers laying / pontoon bridge etc. [handpainted]	Multicolored	Ally	Smith, LH	C
5592	Nov. 24, 1944—— Allies / drive for the Rhine [handpainted]	Multicolored	Map	Smith, LH	C
5593	Nov. 28, 1942 / Coffee / rationing / begins / Confirmation etc. [no picture]	Blue	Event	Fidelity	B
5594	Nov. 28, 1944 - Those / Bee-29's sting again [handpainted]	Multicolored	Japan	Smith, LH	C
5595	Nov-11th / Armistice / Day [handpainted]	Multicolored	Flag	Unknown	B
5596	November 03, 1939 - The special session / of the 76th Congress etc. [typed]	Unknown	Home	Batura	E
5597	November 04, 1939 - The "President" / signed the Neutrality Bill etc. [typed]	Black	Event	Batura	E
5598	November 08, 1942 / We opened / the / second front / with a / bang!	Black, red	Event	Fidelity	B
5599	November 11, 1942 / Admiral Darlan / captured at Algiers etc. [no picture]	Green	Event	Linto	B
5600	November 11, 1943 / 25th anniversary / of the / armistice / A repeat etc.	Blue, red	Holid	Griffith	B
5601	November 20 / December 16 / "Back and" etc. [cut-&-pasted paper] [colored envelopes]	Black	Bonds	Temple	C
5602	November 22, 1943 / Roosevelt, Churchill / and Chiang Kai Shek / meet in etc.	P, silver	Event	Linto	B
5603	Now - all together	Black	Unk	Phill, CR	A
5604	Now / as then / worth / fighting / for / 1776 1944 [handpainted]	Multicolored	Bell	Klaas	C
5605	Now / D-Day / desperation / decision deliverance / Later etc. [no picture]	Blue, red	DDay	Lawrence	B
5606	Now / for / the / knockout! [thermographed]	Blue, red	Japan	Yontz	B
5607	Now / soon	Black/Red	Hitle	Davis, D	A
5608	Now as then we must fight etc.	Unknown	Unk	Risinger	A
5609	Now for a long rest if these / foolish mortals will let me. [handpainted]	Multicolored	Antiq	Clendennen	D
5610	Now he's Tokyo bound!! / War bonds etc.	Black	Bonds	Conner	A
5611	Now I know what / happened to that / missing U.S.O. / entertainer [thermographed]	Red	Navy	Crosby	B
5612	Now if I were down there in / Washington... [in quotes] That's Joe etc.	Blue, red	Liber	Brenn	A
5613	Now is the time for all good men etc. [5 or 6 lines of text]	Unknown	Unk	Levering	A
5614	Now that we have won / let "Old Glory" wave [envelope 6 1/2x3 5/8, 7 1/2x4 in.]	Bu/Br/Gn/Red	VJDay	McFarland	B
5615	Now the West is / free let's take the / [etc.] / 5-15-'45——Marines and / etc.	Multicolored	Event	Linto	B
5616	Now the West is / free let's take the / East out of its / bondage!!	Multicolored	Flag	Linto	B
5617	Now! All aboard for the / ten percent / U.S. bond drive / We must show etc.	Blue, red	Bonds	Linto	B
5618	Now! All together boys! / We'll see you all again next year / when the etc.	Blue, red	Verse	Rathkamp	B
5619	Now, more than ever, / MacArthur, Eisenhower / and Doolittle need your etc.	Unknown	Flag	Linto	B
5620	Number of persons / receiving incomes of / $100,000 increased / 43 per etc.	Gd,S/Multi	Minut	Linto	B
5621	Number of persons / receiving incomes of / [etc.] / Navy Day——Oct.27, 1943	Multicolored	Navy	Linto	B
5622	Nurse Corps U.S.N. / On sea and ashore / NNC / U.S. Naval etc. [thermographed]	Red	Nurse	Crosby	B

Cover Values (from Table 6, p. 136)

Value	*Price Range*
A	$ 3 - 6
B	$ 7 - 15
C	$ 16 - 30
D	$ 31 - 60
E	$ 61 - 125
F	$ 126 - 250
G	$ 251 - 500
H	$ 501 - 1000
I	$ >1000
X	Unpriced: Suspicious or fraudulent cover

5353

5359

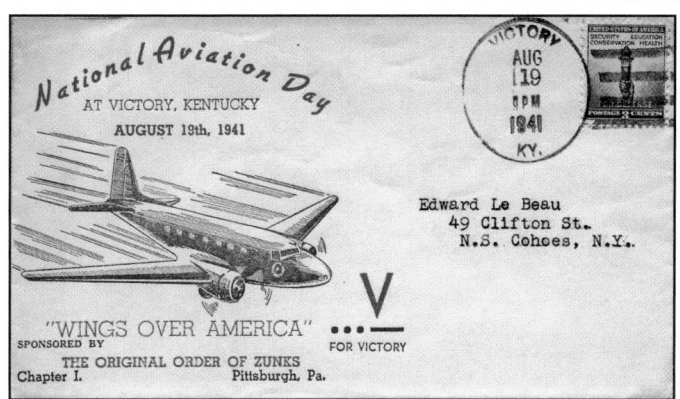

5367

5410

5413

5419

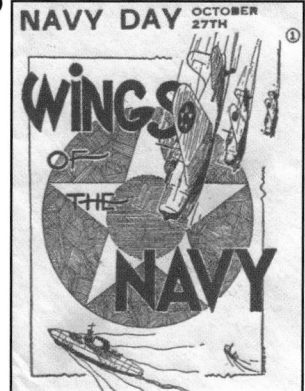

5460

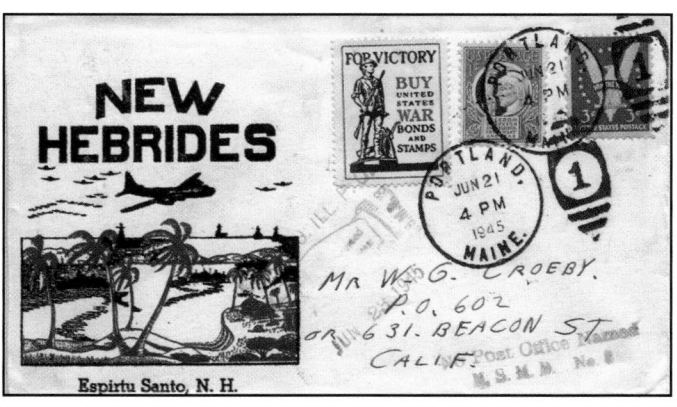

5473

5515

5516

5518

5526

5530

5541

5546

5554

5579
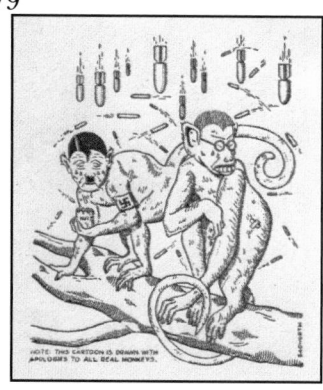

5622
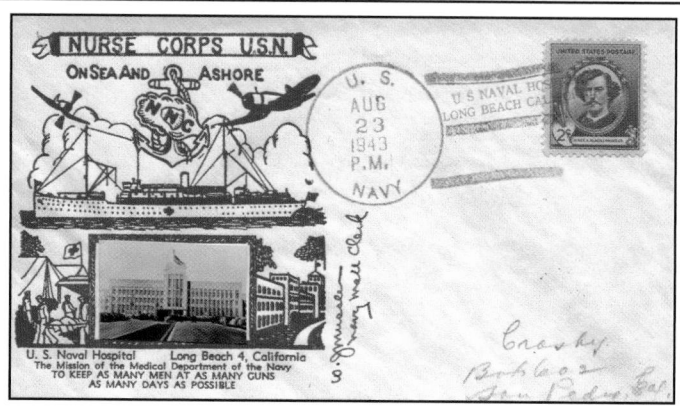

CACHET TEXT BEGINNING WITH "O"

NO.	CACHET TEXT	COLOR	TOPIC	PUBLISHER	$
5623	O' / show me the / way to / Berlin [handpainted]	Multicolored	Armed	Borkowski	D
5624	O come, desire / of nations, bind / all peoples in one / heart and mind etc.	Multicolored	Verse	Griffith	A
5625	O, yeah? / "Zeke, ah cain't see a thing. / That thar war stuff is just" etc.	Bu,red/Blue	Home	Boone	A
5626	O.K. Rembrandt... / where the hell's / our planes! [handpainted]	Multicolored	Air	Unknown	B
5627	O.P.A. continues to sanction / [etc.] / 8-6-'44——Convoy of 7 German etc.	Unknown	Event	Linto	B
5628	O.P.A. continues to sanction / commodity price increases! / Wages? Oh well, etc.	Red	Home	Linto	B
5629	O.P.A. decisions / Monday—— / [etc.] / 4-27-'44——Sewell Avery, Montgomery etc.	Unknown	Event	Linto	B
5630	O.P.A. decisions / Monday——Yes / Tuesday——No / Wednesday——Yes etc.	Unknown	Home	Linto	B
5631	O.P.A. has ruled price of / writing-paper tablets cannot / be etc. [no picture]	Gold, violet	Home	Linto	B
5632	Observe good / faith and / justice / toward all. [in quotes]	Blue, red	Wash	Brenn	A
5633	Observe the midnight / curfew / stay etc.	Unknown	Home	Kosko	A
5634	Occupation Day / Tokyo / Bay / Sept 2 / 1945 [Tokyo Bay]	Black	VJDay	Navy ship	D
5635	Occupation Force / [etc.] / Tokyo / Honshu, Japan / Aug 28, 1945 [Tokyo Bay]	Black	VJDay	Navy ship	E
5636	Occupational force —— Tokyo Bay / USS Delta [Tokyo Bay]	Multicolored	VJDay	Navy ship	D
5637	Occupied / Nations / series / V / Victory / Austria	Unknown	ORN	Unknown	A
5638	Occupied / Nations / V / Victory / Poland	Unknown	ORN	Kosko	A
5639	Occupied Nations / Honoring / 1918 Poland 1939 / Attack on Poland starts etc.	Red	ORN	Coll Surp	A
5640	Occupied Nations / Honoring / 1918 Poland 1939 / For two decades peace etc.	Red	ORN	Coll Surp	A
5641	Occupied Nations / Honoring / 1918 Poland 1939 / Formerly partitioned etc.	Red	ORN	Cleveland	A
5642	Occupied Nations / Honoring / 1918 Poland 1939 / Ignace / Jan / Paderewski	Red	ORN	Coll Surp	A
5643	Occupied Nations / Honoring / 1918 Poland 1939 / Vaulting ambitions and etc.	Red	ORN	Coll Surp	A
5644	Occupied Nations / Honoring / Belgium / Nazi intrigue befuddled weak Leopold etc.	Red	ORN	Coll Surp	A
5645	Occupied Nations / Honoring / Czechoslovakia / Czechoslovakia was etc.	Blue	ORN	Coll Surp	A
5646	Occupied Nations / Honoring / Czechoslovakia / Dr. / Thomas / G. Masaryk etc.	Blue	ORN	Coll Surp	A
5647	Occupied Nations / Honoring / Czechoslovakia / The wrath of / Lidice	Black	ORN	Coll Surp	A
5648	Occupied Nations / Honoring / Denmark / April 9 etc.	Purple	ORN	Coll Surp	A
5649	Occupied Nations / Honoring / Denmark / Hopelessly etc.	Purple	ORN	Coll Surp	A
5650	Occupied Nations / Honoring / Luxemburg etc.	Orange	ORN	Coll Surp	A
5651	Occupied Nations / Honoring / Netherlands etc.	Green	ORN	Coll Surp	A
5652	Occupied Nations / Honoring / Norway / King Haakon VII chose etc.	BlueBrown	ORN	Coll Surp	A
5653	Occupied Nations / Honoring / Norway / Proudly Norse hostages have faced etc.	Blue/Brown	ORN	Coll Surp	A
5654	Occupied Nations / Honoring / The Philippines / August etc.	Red	ORN	Coll Surp	A
5655	Occupied Nations / Honoring / The Philippines / Dr. / Jose etc.	Red	ORN	Coll Surp	A
5656	Occupied Nations / Honoring / The Philippines / On the rural / Filipino / home etc.	Red	ORN	Coll Surp	A
5657	Occupied Nations / Honoring / The Philippines / The march etc.	Red	ORN	Coll Surp	A
5658	Occupied Nations / Honoring / The Philippines / Tough etc.	Red	ORN	Coll Surp	A
5659	Occupied Nations / Honoring / Yugoslavia etc. [envelope 9 1/2x4 1/8 in.]	Green	ORN	Coll Surp	B
5660	Oct. 03, 1944 —— Siegfried line broken [handpainted]	Multicolored	Map	Smith, LH	C
5661	Oct. 13 - 1943 - Badoglio government / of Italy declares etc. [handpainted]	Multicolored	Map	Smith, LH	C
5662	Oct. 19, 1944 - "By the grace / of God Almighty —— / I" etc. [handpainted]	Multicolored	Mac	Smith, LH	C
5663	Oct. 21, 1944 / Aachen - first great German / city falls to Allies. Now the etc. [hp]	Multicolored	Hist	Smith, LH	B
5664	Oct. 25, 1943 / Hitler / worries / as / Hull, Eden, and etc. [no picture]	Blue	Event	Fidelity	B
5665	October 05, 1944 / Greece / We invade Greece	Blue	Event	Fidelity	B
5666	October 19, 1944 / Czechoslovakia / is invaded / by Russia	Green, red	Event	Fidelity	B
5667	October 20, 1944 / Philippines / MacArthur returns / Aachen also surrenders	Blue, red	Event	Fidelity	B
5668	October 25, 1943 / Dnieper bastions / fall to Russians. / Two important etc.	Multicolored	Event	Linto	B
5669	October 27, 1939 / Navy Day [thermographed]	Blue	Navy	Crosby	B
5670	Of all the thirty-six alternatives [in quotes] etc. [env. 6 9/16x3 3/4 in.]	Brown	Nazis	Belles-let	C
5671	Of courage undaunted [in quotes]	Unknown	Unk	Mayfield	A
5672	Of the people, / by the people / for the people [in quotes]	Unknown	Linc	Ioor	A
5673	Of vital importance / in defense: / Bell Telephone service etc. [allover, back] [11/41]	Black	Home	Mich Bell	C
5674	Official / checkerboard / 99th Division / slogan / Each move to victory	Blue	Unit	Army	A
5675	Official / VE / Day / yesterday - perhaps etc. [handpainted] [imprint: D.W.M.]	Multicolored	VEDay	Unknown	B
5676	Official / V-J Day / proclaimed by / [etc.] / Harry S. Truman [thermographed]	Blue, red	VJDay	Crosby	B
5677	Official / V-J Day / proclaimed by / [etc.] / Japan surrenders etc. [thermographed]	Blue, red	VJDay	Crosby	B
5678	Official / V-J Day / proclaimed by / [etc.] / Signers of Japan's etc. [thermographed]	Blue, red	VJDay	Crosby	B

NO.	CACHET TEXT	COLOR	TOPIC	PUBLISHER	$
5679	Official V-J Day / Saipan, M.I. [with previously printed cachet]	Black	VJDay	Unknown	C
5680	Oh boy! A letter from home! [colored envelopes]	Black/Blue	Army	Huss	A
5681	Oh boy, we now / have coffee! / [etc.] / 8-31-'40——Airliner crashed at etc.	Multicolored	Anniv	Linto	B
5682	Oh boy, we now / have coffee! / If we could get / some meat! [multicolor var.]	Multicolored	Flag	Linto	B
5683	Oh lookee —— let's take a ride!	Black	Chute	Ang	A
5684	Oh Mr. Hitler / A snazi Nazi once was I etc. [env. 6 1/2x3 5/8, 7 1/2x4 in.]	Red	Hitle	Abel	A
5685	Oh say! Can you see the flag / of the land / of the free / Its [sic] the etc.	Blue, red	Flag	Cliff	A
5686	Oh! How I / hate to get up in / the morning! [handpainted]	Multicolored	Army	Cowdery	D
5687	Oh! how I hate / to get up in / the morning!!! [handpainted]	Black	Army	Parker	B
5688	Oh! I must / tell Jiggs / 7th Bond sale / $25.00 value / for $18.75 [handpainted]	Multicolored	Bonds	Clendennen	C
5689	Oh! Miller, let's ride? / No, Lou, I must write a / letter to Marion.	Brown, red	Chute	Ang	A
5690	Oh, gee! / It's daddy! / He's coming / [etc.] / 10-1-'44——Canadians take etc.	Multicolored	Event	Linto	B
5691	Oh, gee! / It's daddy! / He's coming / home! / Help make / this real!	Gd,Gn/Multi	Home	Linto	B
5692	Oh, how I miss / you tonight [handpainted]	Multicolored	Hitle	Gatens	C
5693	Oh, Washington! thou hero, patriotic sage etc.	Unknown	Wash	Card	A
5694	Oh, yeah? / "Attempts to create other / fronts can no longer stop / the" etc.	Blue	Nazis	Levering	C
5695	Oh, yeah? / "Australia will be shown / the keen cutting quality / of the" etc.	Blue	Japan	Levering	C
5696	Oh, yeah? / "Dynasties created by man / may collapse, but the" etc.	Blue	Japan	Levering	C
5697	Oh, yeah? / "Even America, who prides / herself in her material" etc.	Blue	Japan	Levering	C
5698	Oh, yeah? / "Germans are pursuing / the operations in France / with firm" etc.	Black	Japan	Levering	C
5699	Oh, yeah? / "Germany will not be / overrun, neither from / within nor" etc.	Blue	Hitle	Levering	C
5700	Oh, yeah? / "Germany's new secret / weapon is probably a / weapon of" etc.	Blue	Nazis	Levering	C
5701	Oh, Yeah? / "Germany's new secret / weapon is probably" etc.	Blue	Nazis	Levering	C
5702	Oh, Yeah? / "Germany's new secret / weapon" etc. [postmark 9/2/45 + fancy cancel]	Blue	Nazis	Levering	D
5703	Oh, yeah? / "If Satan / offered himself / to me as an ally" etc.	Blue	Hitle	Levering	C
5704	Oh, yeah? / "If the rest of the world / says 'War,' I can only / say," etc.	Blue	Hitle	Levering	C
5705	Oh, yeah? / "In the bitter fighting in / various areas, the Imperial / Army" etc.	Blue	Japan	Levering	C
5706	Oh, yeah? / "In the bitter fighting in / various areas, the Imperial" etc.	Blue	Japan	Levering	C
5707	Oh, yeah? / "In the fifth year of war / there is still a rich / cultural life" etc.	Blue	Nazia	Levering	C
5708	Oh, yeah? / "Miracles! This word / sums up / what we have done / in Libya" etc.	Blue	Musso	Levering	C
5709	Oh, yeah? / "Miracles! This word" / [etc.] / same / miracles / little / son!	Blue	Musso	Levering	C
5710	Oh, yeah? / "No matter where he chooses / as the next place" etc.	Blue	Hitle	Levering	C
5711	Oh, yeah? / "No one speaks now of / the Bolshevik offensives" etc.	Blue	Hitle	Levering	C
5712	Oh, yeah? / "Not much is left of the / British empire, and what / is left" etc.	Blue	Ally	Levering	C
5713	Oh, yeah? / "Our army and our weapons / are the best guarantee / of "" etc.	Blue	Nazis	Levering	C
5714	Oh, yeah? / "Our victory over the / American navy has / delayed the" etc.	Blue	Japan	Levering	C
5715	Oh, yeah? / "Our victory over the / American" etc.	Black	Unk	Levering	C
5716	Oh, yeah? / "Professor Saichi Sakuda / prepared a program of / economic" etc.	Blue	Japan	Levering	C
5717	Oh, yeah? / "Saipan, which for 24 / years has basked in the / benevolence" etc.	Blue	Japan	Levering	C
5718	Oh, yeah? / "The Allies have not got / the shipping to make an / attempt at" etc.	Blue	Nazis	Levering	C
5719	Oh, yeah? / "The bulk of the bolshevik / army in the central sector" etc.	Blue	Ally	Levering	C
5720	Oh, yeah? / "The convoy system has ended / in complete failure / for the" etc.	Blue	Air	Levering	C
5721	Oh, yeah? / "The expansion of the / Chinese war to Shanghai / and" etc.	Blue	Japan	Levering	C
5722	Oh, yeah? / "The hour will come / when one of us will / crack——and it" etc.	Blue	Hitle	Levering	C
5723	Oh, yeah? / "The Imperial army accomplishes / its mission through the" etc.	Blue	Japan	Levering	C
5724	Oh, yeah? / "The Italian people / deserve and / will have victory" etc.	Blue	Musso	Levering	C
5725	Oh, yeah? / "The plutocratic western / world may undertake its" etc.	Blue	Hitle	Levering	C
5726	Oh, yeah? / "The Russian army / has been / destroyed" / Hitler / Oct. 3, 1942	Blue	USSR	Levering	C
5727	Oh, yeah? / "The Soviets are committing one / of their greatest errors" etc.	Blue	Hitle	Levering	C
5728	Oh, yeah? / "There is no room / for doubt / that the goal of / the three" etc.	Blue	Japan	Levering	C
5729	Oh, Yeah? / "There is no room / for doubt" etc. [9/2/45 postmark+ fancy cancel]]	Blue	VJDay	Levering	D
5730	Oh, yeah? / "There must be people in / Britain who think that / America" etc.	Blue	Uncle	Levering	C
5731	Oh, yeah? / "We will carry the war / even to Washington and / London." etc.	Blue	Japan	Levering	C
5732	Oh, yeah? / "With a leader such as / we have, a people such as / we are," etc.	Blue	Nazis	Levering	C
5733	Oh, yeah? / "With the success achieved / in the Coral Sea, the Pacific" etc.	Blue	Japan	Levering	C
5734	Oh, yeah? / Mein / Kampf / Hitler / "I believe" etc.	Black	Hitle	Levering	C
5735	Oh, yeah? /It must be considered bad / taste to publicly eat a / ham" etc.	Blue	Nazis	Levering	C
5736	Ohio / fights for / freedom [handpainted]	Blue, red	Home	Klaas	C

NO.	CACHET TEXT	COLOR	TOPIC	PUBLISHER	$
5737	Ohio's war effort / demands an efficient / state government / co-operating etc.	Blue, red	Home	Payne, AE	A
5738	O-ho, Ma-ma! / [etc.] / Roosevelt inaugurated Jan. 20, 41, / for first third term etc.	Red	Anniv	Linto	B
5739	O-ho, Ma-ma! / WMC now learns that babies / need diapers! etc. [no picture]	Multicolored	Home	Linto	B
5740	Oil is / ammunition / Use etc. [envelope 9 1/2x4 1/8 in.]	Unknown	Unk	LA Oil	B
5741	Oil is / ammunition / Use it wisely!	Black	Unk	Tidewater	B
5742	Okinawa / April 1, 1945 ["Okinawa" printed diagonally] [no picture]	Orange, red	Event	Fidelity	B
5743	Okinawa / April-1 / 1945 / We are now / looking down / the Japs' throat	Multicolored	Event	Fluegel	C
5744	Okinawa / captured / June 21, 1945 etc.	Multicolored	Event	Fluegel	C
5745	Okinawa / is ours! [thermographed]	Unknown	Event	Boone	B
5746	Okinawa / Japan / Dishonorable / Jap lose shirt [handpainted]	Multicolored	Japan	Barwicki	C
5747	Okinawa / May 25, 1945 / Today it is / secure ["Okinawa" printed diagonally]	Orange, red	Event	Fidelity	B
5748	Okinawa [thermographed]	Black	Battl	Crosby	B
5749	Old / Glory [handpainted]	Blue, red	Flag	Krakora	C
5750	Old / Glory [thermographed]	Blue, red	Flag	Krakora	B
5751	Old / Ironsides [in quotes] VJ Day [thermographed]	Multicolored	VJDay	Unknown	C
5752	Old Glory / Keep it free	Unknown	Flag	Davis, Ral	A
5753	Old Glory / Long may it wave [thermographed]	Unknown	Flag	Crosby	B
5754	Old Glory / marches on!	Black	Flag	Davis, Ral	A
5755	Old Glory / On to Tokio / Back the attack / Buy Bonds / Remember etc.	Blue, red	Flag	Fabian	A
5756	Old Glory / Pearl Harbor / 1941 / 1945 / has been avenged! / waves over Japan	Blue, red	Flag	Davis, Ral	A
5757	Old Glory / soon to fly in Berlin!	Unknown	Flag	Ander, EA	A
5758	Old Glory / the flag of the free	Blue, red	Flag	Smith, W	A
5759	Old Glory / waves over Tokyo!	Unknown	Flag	Davis, Ral	A
5760	Old Glory [in quotes] / champion for liberty [signed "W": serviced by the Weigands] [handpainted]	Multicolored	FlLib	Weigand	E
5761	Old Glory flies / over Kwajalein / as Yanks take / over [no picture]	Blue, red	Event	Boone	B
5762	Old Glory marches on	Black	Flag	Davis, Ral	A
5763	Old Glory must never trail in etc. [in quotes] [large print] [envelope 6 9/16x3 in.]	Blue, red	Flag	Belles-let	D
5764	Old Glory must never trail in etc. [in quotes] [small print] [envelope 7x4 in.]	Blue, red	Flag	Belles-let	D
5765	Old Glory over Iwo Jima [thermographed]	Unknown	Flag	Crosby	B
5766	Old Ironsides [in quotes]	Black	Navy	Lupton	A
5767	Old King Cole is a merry old soul / and a merry old soul is he / for old etc.	Green, violet	Verse	Threl+Thar	A
5768	Old Mother Hubbard / Old Mother Hubbard / went to the cupboard / to see etc.	Black, red	Verse	Threl+Thar	A
5769	On / July / 4th / we salute [handpainted]	Multicolored	Holid	Cowdery	D
5770	On / to / Tokyo! [in quotes] / and / how!	Blue, red	Uncle	Boone	A
5771	On / to / Tokyo! [in quotes] / and / how! / Japan / surrenders / to the etc.	Blue, red	VJDay	Boone	B
5772	On / to / victory / V [handpainted]	Multicolored	Air	Babcock	B
5773	On / to victory / for liberty! [copyright "C" w, w/o serifs] [colors vary]	Multicolored	Lib+	Minkus	A
5774	On a field where courage was the rule, / his [in quotes] / [etc.] / MacArthur!	Blue	Mac	Edmunds	C
5775	On again, off again, / on again! O.P.A. / always in a quandary [no picture]	Gold, pink	Home	Linto	B
5776	On Earth peace, / good will toward man. / This cover mailed on / opening etc.	Multicolored	UN	Went	C
5777	On guard / America! / A symbol / of liberty!	Blue, red	Minut	Mayo	A
5778	On guard / America! / A symbol / of liberty	Blue, red	Minut	Sweet	A
5779	On July 25, 1943 / Benito Mussolini / resigned etc. [handpainted]	Multicolored	Musso	Smith, LH	B
5780	On land and sea / and in the air / they give their best / for Uncle Sam	Blue	Eagle	Abel	A
5781	On land, on sea / and in the air / we're doing / our share etc. [thermographed]	Blue	Armed	Yontz	A
5782	On land, on sea, and in the air / he guards our freedom etc. [blue envelope]	Gold	Eagle	Myers	A
5783	On land-on sea / and in the air / may etc.	Unknown	Unk	Lowell	A
5784	On liberty / at Waikiki beach	Black/Blue	Navy	Lupton	A
5785	On Sunday Dec. 7 - 1941 / Japan made etc. [UL] [hp] [12/7/41 machine cancel]	Blue, red	Event	Batura	H
5786	On the / honor roll V...- / of the steelworkers [thermographed]	Blue, red	Army	Von Los	B
5787	On the / lookout / for [envelope 8 7/8x3 7/8, 8 11/16x3 5/8 in.]	Multicolored	Navy	Porto-Serv	B
5788	On the ammunition / party!	Black	Navy	Lupton	A
5789	On the assembly lines [in quotes] [envelope 6 9/16x3 3/4, 6 3/4x3 7/8 in.]	Unknown	Home	Belles-let	C
5790	On the day of prayer, Aug. 19, 1945, / set aside by Presidential decree, etc.	Multicolored	Event	Fluegel	C
5791	On the home front / "Rosie the Riveter"	Green	Home	Neal	A
5792	On the job delivering the goods / United States / Navy cargo ship [thermographed]	Blue	Navy	Sadworth	B
5793	On the job! / The boys need guns / Save waste etc. [label + printed border]	Multicolored	Home	Artists	B
5794	On their way to Tokyo [envelope 6 1/2x3 5/8, 7 1/2x4 in.]	Brown	Unk	Harrington	A

NO.	CACHET TEXT	COLOR	TOPIC	PUBLISHER	$
5795	On their way to Tokyo [handpainted]	Green	Armed	Borkowski	D
5796	On to / victory! [minuteman]	Unknown	Minut	Lowe	A
5797	On to / victory! [ship]	Bu,Gn/R,Y	Merch	Lowe	A
5798	On to / victory! [soldier]	Red, yellow	Army	Lowe	A
5799	On to / victory! [tank]	Bk,Y/R,Yello	Ordna	Lowe	A
5800	On to / victory! [train]	Gn,Vi/R,Pu	Home	Lowe	A
5801	On to Berlin / Bombs / bullets / brutality / nothing can stop us	Black, red	Air	McCluney	B
5802	On to Berlin / Bombs / bullets / brutality / nothing can stop us [no picture]	Unknown	Nazis	McCluney	A
5803	On to Berlin / Bombs / bullets / brutality / nothing can stop us [soldiers]	Blue, yellow	Armed	McCluney	A
5804	On to Berlin / Bombs / bullets / brutality / nothing can stop us [tank]	Blue, red	Ordn	McCluney	A
5805	On to Berlin / Bombs / bullets / brutality / nothing etc. [airplane bombing]	Blue, red	Air	McCluney	A
5806	On to Berlin / Bombs / bullets / brutality / nothing etc. [airplane, no bombs]	R,Bu/Bk,Bu	Air	McCluney	A
5807	On to Tokyo	Purple	Eagle	Neal	A
5808	On to Tokyo / Gen. MacArthur	Unknown	Mac	Runge	B
5809	On to Tokyo!	Blue, red	Mac	Davis, Ral	B
5810	On to victory	Red	EagV	Lowe	A
5811	On to victory / for liberty [colors vary]	Multicolored	Lib+	Minkus	A
5812	On to victory! / "Let / freedom ring / for all" [env.6 1/2x3 5/8, 7 1/2x4 in.]	Blue, red	Bell	Fleetwood	B
5813	On to victory! / V...- / Unite! / let's win this war!	Multicolored	FlagV	Bean	A
5814	On we go / to Tokyo [airplane dropping bombs]	Blue, red	Air	McCluney	A
5815	On we go / to Tokyo [airplane, no bombs]	Blue, red	Air	McCluney	A
5816	On we go / to Tokyo [battleship]	Blue, red	Navy	McCluney	A
5817	On we go / to Tokyo [tank]	Blue, red	Ordna	McCluney	A
5818	On with / Eisenhower / and / Doolittle etc. [no picture]	Unknown	Ike	Carpenter	B
5819	On with the march of / freedom, etc. [large Washington head, flag at left edge]	Multicolored	Wash	Amer Art	A
5820	On with the march of / freedom, etc. [large Washington head, stars vary]	Multicolored	Wash	Amer Pat	A
5821	On with the march of / freedom, etc. [small Washington head, flag left]	Multicolored	Wash	Amer Pat	A
5822	On with the march of / freedom, etc. [small Washington head, flag top]	Multicolored	Wash	Amer Pat	A
5823	Once again Tojo, / we scratch your face.	Blue, red	Japan	Baur	A
5824	Once more to peace / to butterflies etc.	Unknown	Unk	Carpenter	A
5825	Once more to peace, / to butterflies, bees and clover, / when Hitler and etc.	Blue, red	Home	Carpenter	A
5826	Once there was a Tokyo / Who's sorry now etc.	Green	Unk	Foster	A
5827	Once we were indispensable / not so any etc.	Black	Unk	Abel	A
5828	One / down	Unknown	Musso	Wolf, CL	A
5829	One / down / and / two / to / go / Springfield / Armory ...- etc. [handpainted]	Multicolored	Axis	Borkowski	D
5830	One / down / two / to go! [thermographed]	Black/Red	Axis	Crosby	B
5831	One / down- / two / to go! [thermographed]	Black/Red	Axis	Ang	B
5832	One / out of many	Blue, red	EagSh	Mission	A
5833	One / two / three! / In America, that means "yer out!" etc.	Blue, red	FDR	Unknown	B
5834	One away [in quotes]—— / yer out! / Mussolini struck out etc. [handpainted]	Multicolored	Musso	Myers	B
5835	One country / indivisible etc. [on back] [envelope 8 7/8x3 7/8 in.]	Unknown	Unk	Kent-Moore	B
5836	One day nearer victory [handpainted]	Multicolored	Home	Babcock	C
5837	One dollar [symbol+numerals] extra in war stamps from every etc.	Red	Bonds	Czubay	A
5838	One down - two to go [handpainted]	Multicolored	UncAx	Adler	C
5839	One down / and two to go [thermographed]	Red	Axis	Crosby	B
5840	One flag / one country [flag on flap] [envelope 5 3/4x3 3/4 in.]	Blue, red	Flag	Dime	A
5841	One flag / one country [shield on flap] [envelope 5 3/4x3 3/4 in.]	Blue, red	FlSh	Dime	A
5842	One flag / one country [UL, w/ eagle & shield] [env. 6 1/2x3 5/8in, + others]	Blue, red	EagSh	Dime	A
5843	One flag / one country [UL, w/ flag] [env. 6 1/2x3 5/8, 9 1/2x4 1/8 in.]	Blue, red	Flag	Dime	A
5844	One flag / one country [UL, w/ shield] [env. 5 3/8x3 3/8 in.]	Blue, red	Shiel	Dime	A
5845	One flag / one country [UL, w/ shield] [handpainted]	Blue, red	Shiel	Unknown	B
5846	One for all / all for Uncle Sam	Black/Blue	Unk	McFarland	A
5847	One for all / all for Uncle Sam	Brown	Uncle	Cozart	A
5848	One God - one country - / one flag	Blue, red	Wash	Neal	A
5849	One hundred thirtieth [130th] / anniversary / And the star spangled / banner in etc.	Multicolored	Flag	Griffith	A
5850	One hundred [100] lbs. / of / waste paper / will——make etc. [no picture]	Red	Home	Rowe	A
5851	One hundred fiftieth [150th] / anniversay / of the Bill of / Rights etc.	Blue, red	Home	Fleetwood	B
5852	One hundred fiftieth [150th] anniversary / Bill of Rights / Freedom of etc.	Blue, red	Home	Fleetwood	B

NO.	CACHET TEXT	COLOR	TOPIC	PUBLISHER	$
5853	One hundred fifty-fifth [155th] / anniversary / 1945 [handpainted label]	Multicolored	Coast	LeGallez	C
5854	One hundred fourth [104th] Div. [under insignia] [handpainted]	Multicolored	Unit	Dannells	B
5855	One hundred seventy-five thousand [175,000] + 17 Generals captured	Unknown	Event	Linto	B
5856	One hundred seventy-four [174] ships launched	Unknown	Navy	Linto	B
5857	One hundred sixty-fifth [165th] anniversary / [etc.] / of marines. [thermographed]	Red	USMC	Crosby	B
5858	One hundred sixty-fifth [165th] anniversary / [etc.] / U.S. Marines [thermographed]	Red, silver	USMC	Unknown	C
5859	One hundred thousand [100,000] / other Yanks / are ready etc. [colored envelopes]	Blue, red	Dool	Poppenger	B
5860	One hundred thousand [100,000] Yanks land on Luzon / January 10, 1945	Blue, red	Event	Fidelity	B
5861	One hundred twenty-fifth [125th] anniversary / Transportation etc.	Unknown	Home	Fleetwood	B
5862	One hundredth [100th] anniversary / ..telegraph / ... / V	Blue, red	Home	Fleetwood	B
5863	One hundredth [100th] anniversary / Restoration Day / 1843 - July 31 - etc.	Blue, red	Hawai	Sayama	B
5864	One is helping in / the war effort / the other [in quotes] etc. [handpainted]	Multicolored	Home	Knoll	C
5865	One nation, indivisible / with liberty [in quotes] etc. [env. 6 3/4x3 3/4 in.]	Unknown	Unk	Battles	A
5866	One of our freedoms	Unknown	Unk	Carpenter	A
5867	One of their last acts / July 7, 1945——Berlin / Nazis, in their brutish etc.	Gold, silver	Event	Linto	B
5868	One should never christen these ships / with Kentucky mountain dew? [in quotes]	Brown	Home	Ang	A
5869	One team / 16 air forces / 75,000 airplanes / 2,300,000 individuals / one goal	Blue	Air	Carter	A
5870	One thousand [1,000] European refugees / enjoy under protection of the etc.	Blue	Home	Wright	A
5871	Only / 36 / shopping days / for / G.I. Christmas / Deadline = / October 15 [handpaint]	Green, red	Holid	Myers	B
5872	Only 59,625 to go for the camp record! [in quotes] [yellow envelope]	Multicolored	Army	Amer Art	A
5873	Only a cross / records his part / in victory!	Blue, red	Army	Davis, Ral	B
5874	Only a heel / would drive / over thirty five!	Black	Home	Burdick	A
5875	Only dead Japs are / good Japs. Give us / more dead Japs!!	Red, silver	Japan	Linto	B
5876	Only the / beginning [handpainted] / 5th war loan etc. [cut-&-pasted paper]	Black	Japan	Wolf, RL	C
5877	Onward / to victory / Trailin' etc. [cowboys with cactus]	Green, purple	Home	White, B	B
5878	Onward / to victory / Trailin' etc. [cowboys, no cactus]	Green, purple	Home	White, B	B
5879	Onward to Berlin [envelope 6 1/2x3 5/8, 6 7/16x3 15/16 in.]	Unknown	Unk	Baur	A
5880	Onward! onward! / all hearts resolved in / victory or death [printing varies]	Red, violet	DDay	Boone	C
5881	OPA decisions / Monday——yes / Tuesday——no / [etc] / 4-27-'44——Sewell Avery etc.	Red, silver	Event	Linto	B
5882	OPA decisions / Monday——yes / Tuesday——no / Wednesday——yes / Saturday—— etc.	Red, silver	Event	Linto	B
5883	OPA established	Unknown	Event	Linto	B
5884	OPA has ruled price of / writing paper etc.	Unknown	Event	Linto	B
5885	OPA humbuggery / Roll back meat prices! / Pay packers the etc. [no picture]	Multicolored	Home	Linto	B
5886	OPA red tape / Bayonne, N.J.——Seaman James Walker, / twice etc. [no picture]	Multicolored	Home	Linto	B
5887	OPA roll back killed	Unknown	Event	Linto	B
5888	Open / season / [etc.] / Japanese hunting etc. [Japanese figure] [thermographed]	Red	Japan	Czubay	C
5889	Open / season / [etc.] / Japanese hunting etc. [Japanese head] [thermographed]	Green/Red	Japan	Czubay	C
5890	Open / season / [etc.] / Japanese hunting etc. [soldier w/ bayonet] [thermographed]	Red	Japan	Czubay	C
5891	Open / season / [etc.] / Japanese hunting license / War bonds, etc. [thermographed]	Purple	Japan	Czubay	C
5892	Opening day / 6th / war loan drive [no picture]	Black	Bonds	Dahlem	B
5893	Opening day / the / mighty / 7th / war loan / drive	Black	Bonds	Dahlem	B
5894	Opening of drive / When you buy a bond / you fight by his side / Fifth war loan	Multicolored	VforV	Griffith	B
5895	Opening of hostilities etc. [no picture] [thermographed] [postmarked 12/7/41]	Black	Pearl	Mayne	H
5896	Or [sic] the land of the free / and the home of the brave. [in quotes]	Bk/Bu/Red	FlLib	Smith, AD	A
5897	Oran, Algiers / Nov. 7 / 1942 / We pledge - "that they / shall not have died" etc.	Multicolored	Event	McCluney	C
5898	Oran, Algiers / Nov. 7 / 1942 / We pledge etc. [1st Div insignia] [postmarked 11/7/43]	Multicolored	Anniv	McCluney	B
5899	Oran, Algiers / Nov. 7 / 1942 / We pledge etc. [34th Div insignia] [postmarked 11/7/43]	Multicolored	Anniv	McCluney	B
5900	Oran, Algiers / Nov. 7 / 1942 / We pledge etc. [9th Div insignia] [postmarked 11/7/43]	Multicolored	Anniv	McCluney	B
5901	Oregon Women's Ambulance Corps / 2nd Plat., Co. G, 2nd Bn.	Black, yellow	Women	Myers	B
5901A	Original Landing ["N's" printed backwards] / V-J Day / [[etc.] / 9/2/45 / U.S.S. Missoula [Tokyo Bay]	Red	VJDay	Navy ship	D
5902	Oslo / liberated / Capital of Norway / May 8, 1945	Multicolored	Event	Teixeira	D
5903	Oslo / liberated / Capital of Norway / May 8, 1945 [2 5/8/45 postmarks; 1 blue, 1 red]	Multicolored	Event	Teixeira	F
5904	Ouch!	Green	Hitle	Peer	B
5905	Ouch! / Himmler shoots Herr Hitler / so the rumor goes / Now isn't that etc.	Green	Hitle	Abel	A
5906	Our / army / is as / good / as its / infantry	Blue, red	Army	Schirmer	A
5907	Our / best gift / Service / above self	Multicolored	Flag	Linto	B
5908	Our / Father / who art / in Heaven ... / Hallowed be thy name. Thy will / be etc.	Gold	Relig	Linto	B
5909	Our / first / duty / "Defend America," always victorious!	Multicolored	Flag+	Edmunds	D

NO.	CACHET TEXT	COLOR	TOPIC	PUBLISHER	$
5910	Our / G.I. / Joes / on the road to victory	Green	Unk	Harmer	A
5911	Our / new President / carries on	Blue	HST	Richardson	E
5912	Our / right / to liberty [8 1/2x3 3/4 in. wrapper, unfolds to 8 1/2x11 in. sheet] [meter]	Red	Uncle	Amer Loan	D
5913	Our 33rd President / "In the words of Franklin D." etc. [bell at left]	Blue/Red	HST	Brenn	B
5914	Our 33rd President / "In the words of Franklin D." etc. [flag at left]	Blue/Red	HST	Brenn	B
5915	Our aid / to / victory / 20% pay roll etc. [on back] [envelope 8 7/8x3 7/8 in.]	Blue, red	Air	Univ Engin	C
5916	Our air warden / for aid, comfort and / protection for all [thermographed]	Blue, red	Home	Sadworth	B
5917	Our armed forces / 1——"A" is for the Army / a great place to be, / "N" is etc.	Multicolored	Liber	Weigand	B
5918	Our armed forces are / in action etc.	Unknown	Armed	Kosko	A
5919	Our battle will / not be won with / the victory un- /less we destroy / the etc.	Multicolored	Minut	Linto	B
5920	Our bonds will launch a / submarine / Keep them / rolling / by / buying bonds	Blue	Bonds	Peters	A
5921	Our boys	Blue	Armed	Hillerich	A
5922	Our boys and girls / all over / the / country / are fighting for / freedom.	Blue, red	Home	Unknown	A
5923	Our boys are / ready - willing - true!! / to the cause of the- / red-white etc.	Purple/Red	Armed	Harrington	A
5924	Our boys are / ready——willing——true / to the cause of the / red——white——blue	Black/Blue	Armed	Harrington	A
5925	Our boys are every- / where fighting for / our freedom! And you? [colored varieties]	Multicolored	Globe	Linto	B
5926	Our boys girls / all over / the / country / are fighting for / freedom.	Black, green	Home	Baur	A
5927	Our boys have / the spirit. Let's / give them all / the equipments / to etc.	Multicolored	Bonds	Linto	B
5928	Our boys in / the service etc. [musicians]	Unknown	Unk	Runge	A
5929	Our boys in / the service etc. [stage coach]	Unknown	Unk	Runge	A
5930	Our boys in / the service etc. [two skaters]	Unknown	Unk	Runge	A
5931	Our boys in / the service etc. [wise men]	Gree, red	Unk	Runge	A
5932	Our boys in the / combat zones have / no middle ground	Blue, gold	Armed	Linto	B
5933	Our boys over there / give 24 hours etc.	Unknown	Unk	Brenn	A
5934	Our boys rate ace high in / fighting for peace and / liberty- etc. [thermographed]	Bk/Bu/Red	Ordna	Crosby	B
5935	Our British ally / Air Marshall Tedder [handpainted]	Multicolored	Ally	Knoll	C
5936	Our commander-in-chief / F.D.R.	Black	FDR	Brenn	B
5937	Our commander-in-chief / For the greatest good to the / greatest number	Blue, red	FDR	Hill	B
5938	Our commander-in-chief / See him through to victory	Blue	FDR	Carpenter	B
5939	Our country / our government etc. [on back] [env. 9 1/2x4 1/8 in.]	Unknown	Home	Wol-Detroi	B
5940	Our country / prayer / Lead us by thy / might great / God / our King	Blue, red	VforV	Unknown	A
5941	Our country / right / or / wrong / our country [thermographed]	Red	Shiel	Jarrett	A
5942	Our country / right / or wrong / our country	Red	Unk	Jarrett	A
5943	Our country, strong and indivisible [Uncle Sam steering: larger picture]	Blue	Uncle	Donaldson	A
5944	Our country, strong and indivisible	Blue	Home	Donaldson	A
5945	Our country, strong and indivisible / All for one, —— one for all	Blue/Brown	Home	Carpenter	A
5946	Our country, strong and indivisible [thermographed]	Blue	Home	Von Los	B
5947	Our country, strong and indivisible [Uncle Sam steering]	Blue	Uncle	Von Los	B
5948	Our country's / prayer / Lead us by Thy / might..great God etc. [thermographed]	Purple/Red	ShieV	Avy	A
5949	Our country's / prayer / Lead us by Thy / might..great God etc. [thermographed]	Bk/Bu/Br/Gn	ShieV	Avy	A
5950	Our country's defenders / Lexington / Valley Forge / Mexico / Gettysburg etc.	Blue, red	Army	Cachet Cra	A
5951	Our days of victory are in the making [in quotes] / We will win the war etc.	Black/Blue	Admir	Bean	A
5952	Our demand has been etc. [Roosevelt and Truman]	Black	Japan	Davis, Ray	A
5953	Our demand has been, / and it remains —— etc. [bayoneting the Japanese flag]	Black	Japan	Davis, Ray	A
5954	Our eagle assures us etc.	Unknown	Eagle	Phill, CR	A
5955	Our eyes can / see the glory / of victory	Unknown	Unk	Amer Pat	A
5956	Our Father, Thou hast delivered us / from our enemies. All glory to etc.	Green, silver	Relig	Linto	B
5957	Our fighting / forces need / gas and oil! / Do you?	Multicolored	Home	Linto	B
5958	Our fighting men give / valor etc.	Unknown	Unk	Brenn	A
5959	Our fighting navy [colored envelopes]	Black	Navy	Huss	A
5960	Our first / duty / buy more / war / bonds——stamps [envelope 6x3 ½ in.]	Blue, red	Bonds	Kosko	A
5961	Our first / duty, / defend / America / Freedom of the seas, land, and air! etc.	Multicolored	Eag+	Edmunds	D
5962	Our first duty / defend America [in quotes] / The Marines have landed! Situation well in hand! etc.	Multicolored	USMC	Edmunds	D
5963	Our first duty, defend America [in quotes]! [eagle, shield with planes, etc.]	Multicolored	Eag+	Edmunds	D
5964	Our first duty, defend America [in quotes]! [eagle, Washington, Lincoln, flag]	Multicolored	EagFl	Edmunds	D
5965	Our first duty, defend America! / [etc.] / Remember Pearl Harbor! Dec. 7, 1941 etc.	Multicolored	Pearl	Edmunds	D
5966	Our first duty, defend America! / United / we will / stand! / Let's go U.S.A.! etc.	Multicolored	Eagle	Edmunds	D
5967	Our first duty, defend America! [Flag, early US flags, Minute Man, etc.]	Multicolored	Flag+	Edmunds	D

NO.	CACHET TEXT	COLOR	TOPIC	PUBLISHER	$
5968	Our first line / of defense	Unknown	Unk	Baur	A
5969	Our five ocean Navy / A toast to health of / Japan's Navy / bottoms up etc.	Blue	Japan	Harrington	A
5970	Our five ocean Navy / Beware mister Jap / your suns gonna / turn black.. etc.	Black	Japan	Harrington	A
5971	Our five ocean Navy / U.S.S. Marblehead / a light cruiser, too tough etc.	Black	Navy	Harrington	A
5972	Our flag	Blue, red	Flag	Mission	A
5973	Our flag - over the Philippines again.	Aqua/Bu,gold	Flag	Runge	A
5974	Our flag -- over the Philippines again.	Aqua	Phili	Altenbernd	A
5975	Our flag - over the Philippines again. / Invest Ohio's etc.	Unknown	Flag	Runge	A
5976	Our flag - this Xmas / and all others	Blue/Green	Flag	Phill, CR	A
5977	Our flag / champion of the oppressed / Liberty forever. [thermographed]	Blue, red	Flag	Unknown	B
5978	Our flag / Hats off! Along the street there / comes a blare of bugles etc.	Blue, red	Home	Brenn	A
5979	Our flag / It's flying high over etc.	Unknown	Flag	Abel	A
5980	Our flag / Long may it wave	Unknown	Flag	Ang	A
5981	Our flag / Long may it wave / V / for victory / The Star-Spangled etc. [thermographed]	Blue, red	Flag	Crosby	B
5982	Our flag / Made by liberty etc.	Unknown	Flag	Brenn	A
5983	Our flag / To those now held in bondage etc. [no picture]	Unknown	Flag	Reynolds	A
5984	Our flag / was still / there [in quotes] / Battle- etc. [envelope 9 1/2x4 1/8 in]	Black	VJDay	Southworth	C
5985	Our flag victorious / in a thousand etc. [thermographed]	Unknown	Flag	Baur	A
5986	Our forefathers / paid the price for / liberty / We can, and will, / do it now!	Gold, silver	Liber	Linto	B
5987	Our forefathers fought for / liberty. etc. [env. 6 1/2x3 5/8, 6 1/4x3 9/16 in.]	Blue/Red	Bonds	Runge	A
5988	Our forefathers fought for / liberty. Preserve it. / Buy war bonds. [env. 9 1/2x4 1/4 in.]	Purple	Bonds	Unknown	A
5989	Our forefathers fought for / liberty. Preserve it. Buy war bonds.	Brown/Purple	Bonds	Haynes	A
5990	Our French ally / Buy war bonds / Gen. DeGaulle [handpainted]	Multicolored	Ally	Knoll	D
5991	Our glorious banner / will never etc. [thermographed]	Unknown	Flag	Baur	A
5992	Our glorious flag, long may it wave over etc.	Unknown	Flag	Reuss	A
5993	Our heritage / [etc.] / fight for it! [env. 6 1/2x3 5/8, 9 1/2x4 1/8 in.]	Multicolored	Uncle	Ever Ready	B
5994	Our hero / Gen MacArthur [handpainted]	Blue, red	Mac	Krakora	B
5995	Our heroes' [w/, w/o apostrophe] awards / Soldier's Medal	Red	Medal	Cox	A
5996	Our heroes' awards / Air Medal	Unknown	Medal	Cox	A
5997	Our heroes' awards / Congressional / Medal of Honor	Black, gold	Medal	Cox	A
5998	Our heroes' awards / Distinguished / Flying Cross	Unknown	Medal	Cox	A
5999	Our heroes' awards / Distinguished / Service Cross	Unknown	Medal	Cox	A
6000	Our heroes' awards / Distinguished / Service Medal	Unknown	Medal	Cox	A
6001	Our heroes' awards / Order of Merit	Unknown	Medal	Cox	A
6002	Our heroes' awards / Purple Heart	Unknown	Medal	Cox	A
6003	Our heroes' awards / Silver Star	Unknown	Medal	Cox	A
6004	Our heroes' awards / United States Discharge Medal	Red	Medal	Phill, CR	A
6005	Our heroic dead / No slavish bonds restrain our hand, etc. [no picture]	Bu/Green/Red	Unk	Phill+Cox	A
6006	Our job now is to / keep the peace / [etc.] / 8-25-'45——Groups of Japs etc.	Multicolored	Event	Linto	B
6007	Our job now is to / keep the peace / with God's help [no picture]	Gold, green	Relig	Linto	B
6008	Our job-keep 'em firing! [on front] / Our etc. [on back] [env. 9 1/2x4 1/8 in.]	Unknown	Home	Oldsmobile	B
6009	Our land vibrates from / freedoms / [etc.] / let freedom ring! [text on beam]	Multicolored	FlBel	Amer Pat	A
6010	Our land vibrates from / freedoms [etc.] / let freedom ring! [text above bell]	Multicolored	FlBel	Amer Pat	A
6011	Our land vibrates from / freedoms [etc.] / let freedom ring! [text under bell]	Multicolored	FlBel	Amer Pat	A
6012	Our land vibrates from / freedoms ring, / let us etc. [text on floral design]	Multicolored	FlBel	Amer Pat	A
6013	Our land vibrates from / freedoms ring, / let us etc. [text on stars]	Multicolored	FlBel	Amer Pat	A
6014	Our land vibrates from / freedoms ring, let us etc. [text under medallion]	Multicolored	Bell	Amer Pat	A
6015	Our men in the armed / forces can say etc.	Unknown	Armed	Threl+Thar	A
6016	Our mistaken friend / Tokyo / we'll bring etc.	Multicolored	Air	Amer Pat	A
6017	Our navy / first line of defense / "Freedom of the seven seas" [thermographed]	Blue/Red	Navy	Crosby	B
6018	Our navy / first line of defense / Department of the Navy / United etc. [thermogr]	Blue/Green	Navy	Sadworth	B
6019	Our navy / first line of defense / Gateway of etc. [thermographed]	Unknown	Navy	Crosby	B
6020	Our navy / first line of defense / Remember etc. [thermographed]	Unknown	Navy	Crosby	B
6021	Our navy / first line of defense / United States Navy [thermographed]	Black	Navy	Crosby	B
6022	Our navy / guardian of our shores [handpainted]	Multicolored	Navy	Knapp	G
6023	Our navy air / force gave us / most etc.	Unknown	Unk	Runge	A
6024	Our navy and marines / still tops / on the seven seas.	Blue, red	Navy	Carpenter	A
6025	Our navy leads / the way now / as always... / to victory	Unknown	Navy	Boone	A

NO.	CACHET TEXT	COLOR	TOPIC	PUBLISHER	$
6026	Our navy will / lead the way to / Tokyo!	Unknown	Navy	Boone	A
6027	Our object is, / freedom for all.	Bk/Bu/Brown	Armed	Harrington	A
6028	Our object is, / freedom for all.	Blue, red	Armed	Harrington	A
6029	Our pioneers / fought / for America	Unknown	Unk	Davis, Ral	A
6030	Our pioneers / fought for America	Unknown	Unk	Davis, Ral	A
6031	Our pledge / ....liberty and / justice for all	Multicolored	Torch	Minkus	A
6032	Our President / Franklin Delano Roosevelt / died April 12, 1945 / 31st etc.	Black	FDR	Abel	B
6033	Our Red Cross workers / [etc.] / 9-30-'44———British sink 37 / German ships	Unknown	Event	Linto	B
6034	Our Red Cross workers / go everywhere on / missions of mercy [no picture]	Gold, green	RedCr	Linto	B
6035	Our sailors are singing, / where palm trees are swinging, / If we can't etc.	Bu/Blue,Gree	Navy	Fost+Carp	A
6036	Our second wartime / Navy / Day etc.	Blue	Navy	Harrington	A
6037	Our ships ride the seas	Unknown	Navy	Runge	A
6038	Our shores are unharmed	Blue, silver	Home	Runge	A
6039	Our stepping stones / to victory / [etc.] / Nimitz / MacArthur [no picture]	Blue, red	Battl	Baur	A
6040	Our sweetheart [envelope 6x3 ½ in.]	Unknown	Unk	Powers	A
6041	Our symbol of / freedom	Blue, red	Flag	Harrington	A
6042	Our symbol of / freedom / long may it wave!!! [text blue]	Blue, red	Flag	Harrington	A
6043	Our symbol of / freedom / long may it wave!!! [text red and blue]	Blue, red	Flag	Harrington	A
6044	Our terms are unconditional surrender [in quotes]	Bk/Bu/Br/O/R	FDR	Shaw, MM	B
6045	Our thanks to O.P.A. / [etc.] / 3-4-'44———3000 Japs killed and wounded on etc.	Multicolored	Event	Linto	B
6046	Our thanks to O.P.A. / Buy lard, / melt it, / exchange / for points etc.	Multicolored	Home	Linto	B
6047	Our trees are fighting too etc. [on back] [green envelope 6x3 ½ in.]	Unknown	Home	Amer Fores	B
6048	Our troop carriers / are bringing etc.	Unknown	Unk	Parker	A
6049	Our two ocean navy / A toast etc. [ship 37 mm long]	Black	Navy	Harrington	A
6050	Our two ocean navy / A toast etc. [ship 42 mm long]	Black	Navy	Harrington	A
6051	Our two ocean navy / Beware mister Jap / your suns gonna / turn black.. etc.	Black	Japan	Harrington	A
6052	Our two ocean navy / First day / post etc.	Green	Navy	Harrington	A
6053	Our two ocean navy / Uncle Sam / shall etc.	Unknown	Navy	Harrington	A
6054	Our U.S. Navy / is second to none	Bk/Brown/Re	Navy	Harrington	A
6055	Our Uncle Sam / is at the helm / His course is straight ahead to / victory	Blue	Uncle	Harrington	A
6056	Our unsung heroes	Blue	Merch	Brenn	A
6057	Our war time President	Brown	FDR	Shaw, MM	B
6058	Our wartime President. / We will win; / so help us God! / F.D.R.	Unknown	FDR	Ander, EA	B
6059	Our wish for / the new year: / Victory / in / 1944 [+ cut-&-pasted paper] [handpainted]	Multicolored	Holid	Temple	C
6060	Ours to fight for / freedom from fear	Unknown	Unk	Rush, H	A
6061	Ours to fight for / freedom from want	Unknown	Unk	Rush, H	A
6062	Ours.... / an heroic / past etc. [colors vary]	Multicolored	Armed	Minkus	A
6063	Ous ker spiel / Vy? [thermographed]	Blue, red	Hitle	Baur	A
6064	Out here we are doing it "right". You / haven't "left" it all to us to do etc.	Blue, red	Home	Quigley	B
6065	Out of focus / Greetings / U.S.A. / U.S.A. [handpainted]	Black	Japan	Mack	D
6066	Out on a limb, are three of a kind———one a / Jap, one a sap, one etc. [thermographed]	Brown	Axis	Crosby	B
6067	Out there [in quotes] / fighting for etc. [print style varies] [colored envelopes]	Blue, red	Armed	Poppenger	A
6068	Out! / Three yellow rats	Unknown	Axis	Linto	B
6069	Over / a million / Nazis surrender in / [etc.] / May 5, 1945 [no picture]	Orange, red	Event	Fidelity	B
6070	Over 480,000 Jap / casualties result / from the 2 atomic / bombs dropped	Gold, silver	Atom	Linto	C
6071	Over half million small / firms forced out of / business etc. [no picture]	Green, silver	Home	Linto	B
6072	Over the top / to victory	Bk,R/Br,green	Ordna	Unknown	A
6073	Over th'top / 1943 style [white or blue envelope]	Black	Armed	Wolf, CL	A
6074	Overcrowded! / so please postpone your trip	Unknown	Navy	Linto	B
6075	Oysters / $1.80 a quart / and my pay is froze [no picture]	Unknown	Home	Boone	A

5625

5635

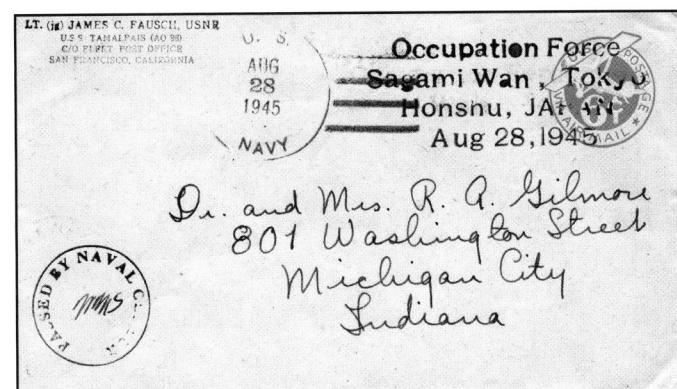

5676

5683

5684

5708

5725

5761

5764

5831

5859

5916

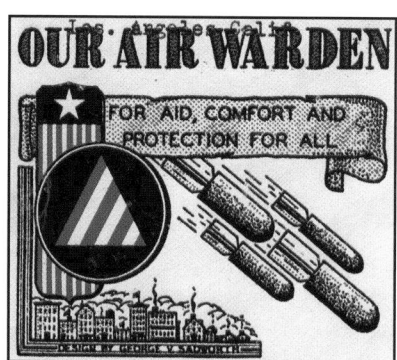

5935

5938

5962

5967

6062

6070

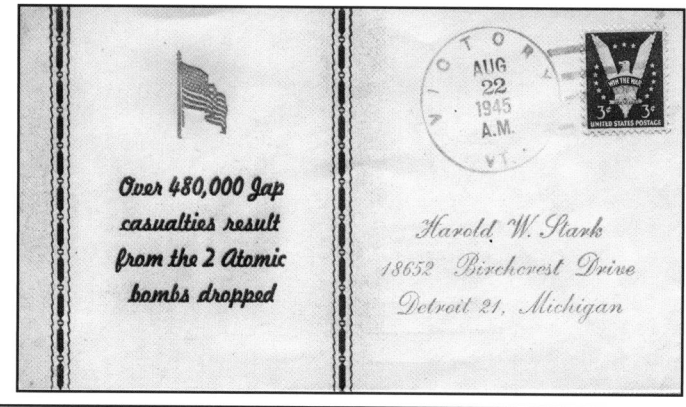

CACHET TEXT BEGINNING WITH "P"

NO.	CACHET TEXT	COLOR	TOPIC	PUBLISHER	$
6076	P.C.E.C. -278 / Season's greetings	Blue	Holid	Abel	A
6077	P.M. Winston Churchill's ridicule / of Americans and their policies, / in etc.	Unknown	Winst	Linto	B
6078	P.T. boats / deal death to "honorable" Japrats	Purple	Navy	Sadworth	B
6079	P.T. boats / deal death to "honorable" Japrats [thermographed]	Purple	Navy	Sadworth	B
6080	P.T. boats [thermographed]	Purple	Navy	Sadworth	B
6081	P.W. / camp / 3819 / V	Multicolored	VforV	Davis, JC	B
6082	P-38 scores another [colored envelopes]	Black	Air	Huss	A
6083	Pacific Fleet of 1940 / The U.S. Fleet arrived in Hawaii May 6,7 & 8, 1940 etc.	Blue	Navy	Unknown	B
6084	Pacific victory / August 14, 1945. [below newspaper headlines] [handpainted]	Black	VJDay	Unknown	C
6085	Pacific war chart / Unconditional / ——surrender / August-14- etc. [handpainted]	Black	Japan	Hadley	D
6086	Pagoda——China eternal—— [in quotes] [envelope 6 3/4x3 7/8 in.]	Sepia tones	China	Belles-let	C
6087	Pan American Union / This union is supported etc.	Unknown	Ally	Grandy	A
6088	Panama / United Nations [handpainted]	Multicolored	UN	Weigand	B
6089	Paper / packs a war / punch!	Black	Home	Linto	B
6090	Paper / packs a war / punch! / 8-23-'44——Romania quit Axis! / Yanks etc.	Unknown	Event	Linto	B
6091	Papua cleared of Japanese	Unknown	Event	Linto	B
6092	Parachute battalion [thermographed]	Unknown	Chute	Crosby	B
6093	Parachute infantry / 511	Magenta	Chute	Unknown	B
6094	Parachutist / fighting for / freedom's sake	Unknown	Chute	Cozart	A
6095	Paratroopers / the first to invade etc.	Unknown	Chute	Baur	A
6096	Paratroops / dropping / to victory [env. 6 1/2x3 5/8, 6 3/4x3 3/4 in.]	Unknown	Chute	Kosko	A
6097	Paratroops / out of the sky [thermographed]	Unknown	Chute	Von Los	B
6098	Paratroops V...- / out of the sky [thermographed]	Unknown	Chute	Von Los	B
6099	Pardon us if our ships show	Black	Navy	Davis, D	A
6100	Paris / "Liberation" [handpainted]	Multicolored	Event	Shaffer, A	E
6101	Paris / Axis / rule / is / spent [acronym spells "Paris"]	Blue, red	Event	Griffith	B
6102	Paris / Axis / rule / is / spent [postmarked 8/23/44]	Pink, black	Event	Griffith	B
6103	Paris / is free again [thermographed]	Blue, red	Event	Smartcraft	C
6104	Paris / liberated / Capital of France / August 25, 1944	Multicolored	Event	Teixeira	E
6105	Paris / liberated / Capital of France / August 25, 1944 [8/25/44 + 5/8/45 postmarks]	Multicolored	Event	Teixeira	F
6106	Paris / surrenders / to the / French patriots [gray envelope]	Unknown	Event	Baur	B
6107	Partners for victory / Farmer [thermographed] [envelope 6 1/2x4 3/4 in.]	Unknown	Home	Unknown	B
6108	Partners for victory / Machinist [thermographed] [envelope 6 1/2x4 3/4 in.]	Multicolored	Home	Unknown	B
6109	Partners for victory / Nurse [thermographed] [envelope 6 1/2x4 3/4 in.]	Unknown	Nurse	Unknown	B
6110	Pass [in hands of whistling soldier] [handpainted]	Multicolored	Army	Dannells	C
6111	Pass Hitler / the aspirin	Multicolored	Hitle	Linto	B
6112	Pass Hitler / the aspirin / Dec. 7, 1941, a date we will help / the slimy etc.	Multicolored	Pearl	Linto	B
6113	Paste the paperhanger - / with waste paper! [handpainted]	Black	Hitle	Jarrett	B
6114	Patriotism demands / [etc.] / 9-20-'44——British tanks go / into Germany	Unknown	Event	Linto	B
6115	Patriotism demands / we prevent waste! / Does that also apply to etc.	Unknown	Home	Linto	B
6116	Patriots / do your duty / Remember Pearl Harbor / [etc.] / Be prepared	Purple, red	Pearl	Unknown	B
6117	Patriots / to / patriots; / the hour is here. / We etc. [flag above text]	Blue, red	Flag	Amer Pat	A
6118	Patriots / to / patriots; / the hour is here. / We etc. [flag and eagle above text]	Multicolored	EagFl	Amer Pat	B
6119	Patriots / to / patriots; / the hour is here. / We etc. [flag left of text]	Blue, red	Flag	Amer Pat	A
6120	Patriots day / April 19, 1941 / May all Americans serve their country / as etc.	Unknown	Holid	Unk	B
6121	Patriots to patriots; / the hour is here. We etc. [Wash. head 30x25 mm]	Multicolored	Wash	Amer Pat	A
6122	Patriots to patriots; / the hour is here. We etc. [Wash. head 40x32 mm]	Multicolored	Wash	Amer Pat	A
6123	Patriots to patriots; / the hour is here. We etc. [Wash. head 43x32 mm]	Multicolored	Wash	Amer Pat	A
6124	Patrol Wing One / Wings / of / the / Navy [thermographed]	Aqua	Air	Czubay	B
6125	Patton - gave France back to etc.	Unknown	Patt	Runge	B
6126	Patton has been punished / for his offense, but Short / and Kimmel case etc.	Multicolored	Pearl	Linto	B
6127	Patton prays / for weather / ——and gets it / "Almighty and most merciful" etc.	Unknown	Patt	Linto	B
6128	Patton vs. Somerville / Ability vs. squandermania / Squandermania wins! etc.	Unknown	Patt	Linto	B
6129	Patton's Third Army [handpainted]	Black	Hitle	Clendennen	D
6130	Paul Revere then, / every American now! [distance between two lines varies]	Blue/Red	Hist	Apnew	A
6131	Pay call! [handpainted]	Multicolored	Army	Cowdery	D

NO.	CACHET TEXT	COLOR	TOPIC	PUBLISHER	$
6132	Pay Japan back for / bayoneting our wounded men / instead of conveying etc.	Red	Japan	Peters	A
6133	Pay Japan back for / hanging, beating and / decapitating our soldiers, etc.	Red	Japan	Peters	A
6134	Pay Japan back for / practicing the "fine art" / of burying alive etc.	Red	Japan	Peters	A
6135	Peace / "And he shall judge among the / nations, and shall rebuke many" etc.	Blue	Relig	Brenn	A
6136	Peace / "V-J" Day / Japan surrenders / unconditionally [artist: Knapp]	Blue	VJDay	Brenn	A
6137	Peace / [etc.] / Japan / surrenders / on U.S.S. / Missouri [thermographed]	Blue, red	VJDay	Richardson	C
6138	Peace / Germany / surrenders ...-	Multicolored	VJDay	Smartcraft	C
6139	Peace / Let us give thanks. Let us conse- / crate ourselves to the etc.	Blue, red	VEDay	Lowell	B
6140	Peace / on / Earth/ Good / will / toward / Men... [handpainted]	Blue	VJDay	Brenn	B
6141	Peace / Peace, so clearly yet so dearly won. / Ours was a battle for no etc.	Multicolored	Holid	Adler	D
6142	Peace / Sep. 2 1945 / [etc.] / V-J Day etc. [sword pierces flag] [handpainted]	Blue	VJDay	Brenn	B
6143	Peace / Sept. 2 1945 / [etc.] / V-J Day etc. [no sword] [handpainted]	Multicolored	VJDay	Knapp	I
6144	Peace / to the / world	Multicolored	VJDay	Knapp	I
6145	Peace / VJ / "The Lord will bless / his people with peace" etc. [handpainted]	Black	Relig	Abel	A
6146	Peace / V-J Day / Japan surrenders / unconditionally [artist: Knapp]	Multicolored	VJDay	Unknown	B
6147	Peace for peace; / or / steel for steel [flag next to large soldier]	Blue, red	VJDay	Fleetwood	C
6148	Peace for peace; / or / steel for steel. [flag over small soldier]	Multicolored	Flag	Amer Pat	A
6149	Peace for peace; / or / steel for steel. [shield alone or between two soldiers]	Multicolored	Flag	Amer Pat	A
6150	Peace for peace; / or / steel for steel. [soldier at each side of flag]	Multicolored	Shiel	Amer Pat	A
6151	Peace in the future and / the security etc. [envelope 7 1/2x4 in.]	Multicolored	Flag	Amer Pat	A
6152	Peace on earth / good will to men / Season's greetings! / Richard P. Boone	Unknown	Unk	Turner	A
6153	Peace on earth [in quotes] / is held in trust / until the etc. [no picture]	Blue	Holid	Boone	B
6154	Peace on earth again / We are thankful that the brutal drama of war / is etc.	Green, red	Holid	Boone	A
6155	Peace on earth good / will toward man. / Let freedom ring over / all the land.	R,Bu/Br,Gn	VJDay	Cozart	B
6156	Peace, defense, safety and good will [in quotes] / United States Army Base etc.	Green, red	Bell	Baur	A
6157	Pearl Harbor - 7 Dec 41 / V Day / via atomic / [etc.] / 2 Sep 1945 etc. [no picture] [handpainted]	Blue	Bases	Hutnick	C
6158	Pearl Harbor / "Praise / the Lord / and pass / the / ammunition"	Purple, red	VJDay	Unknown	B
6159	Pearl Harbor / 1——The rosy dawn had scarse [sic] begun. etc. [handpainted]	Black	Pearl	Coll Surp	A
6160	Pearl Harbor / Day / Dec. 7 / 1944 / in the / 6th / War / Loan [yellow envelope]	Multicolored	Liber	Weigand	B
6161	Pearl Harbor / Dec. / 7, / 1941 / Third anniversary [handpainted]	Black	Bonds	Temple	A
6162	Pearl Harbor / has been avenged! [picture: bell and warship]	Multicolored	Pearl	Maul	C
6163	Pearl Harbor / has been avenged! [picture: Gen. MacArthur]	Unknown	VJDay	Davis, Ral	B
6164	Pearl Harbor avenged / Flag raising on Iwo Jima etc. [9/2/45] [photo + stamps]	Unknown	VJDay	Davis, Ral	B
6165	Pearl Harbor Day / December 7, 1943 / The Rising Sun etc. [env. 9 5/8x4 1/4"]	Black	VJDay	Fetzer	G
6166	Pedro Leao Valloso, acting / Foreign Minister of Brazil etc. [typed][no picture]	Red	Pearl	Navy	B
6167	People advocating / easy terms for Japs / [etc.] / 1-10-'45——Allied tanks win etc.	Black	Event	Batura	C
6168	People advocating / easy terms for Japs / and Huns should be / made to etc.	Multicolored	Event	Linto	B
6169	People want Mac- / Arthur to clean up / Washington's jungle / but one good etc.	Gold, red	Flag	Linto	B
6170	People who say some / wage-earners are / [etc.] / 9-13-'40——Buckingham etc.	Aqua, gold	Mac	Linto	B
6171	People who say some / wage-earners are not / patriotic should etc. [no picture]	Multicolored	Anniv	Linto	B
6172	Perhaps / now the Japs / have quit we / may get the / truth of / Pearl Harbor!	Gold, pink	Home	Linto	B
6173	Perpetual / motion [handpainted]	Gold, purple	Flag	Linto	B
6174	PHIB Group 12 / First seaborne landing / U.S. Army Occupation etc. [Tokyo Bay]	Multicolored	Japan	Long	C
6175	Philippine / Islands [Japanese soldier shot out of a cannon] [handpainted]	Black	VJDay	Navy ship	E
6176	Philippine / Islands [thermographed]	Multicolored	Japan	Barwicki	C
6177	Philippines	Red	Phili	Crosby	B
6178	Philippines [thermographed]	Black	Phili	Lowry	A
6179	Philippines - Iwo - Okinawa / Death and destruction to Japs wherever found	Multicolored	Phili	Crosby	B
6180	Philippines / "I came through and I returned" / Gen. etc. [thermographed]	Black	Battl	Davis, Ray	A
6181	Philippines / invaded / Gen. Douglas / MacArthur / Mar. 17, 1942 etc.	Blue/Red	Phili	Crosby	B
6182	Philippines / Jap soon / to lose it's [sic] / stepping stone... [handpainted]	Gold	Event	Linto`	B
6183	Philippines / Let freedom ring	Multicolored	Japan	Borkowski	D
6184	Philippines / reconquest / begun	Multicolored	Phili	Ioor	A
6185	Philippines / The Philippine Islands have been under Japanese / control etc.	Multicolored	Phili	Griffith	A
6186	Philippines / United Nations [handpainted]	Bk/Bu/Pu/Red	Phili	Ander, CS	A
6187	Philippines / We'll be back / and this octopus etc. [thermographed] [artist: Staehle]	Multicolored	UN	Weigand	B
6188	Philippines [text under goat] [envelope 6 1/2x3 5/8, 7 1/2x4 in.]	Blue, red	Phili	Smartcraft	C
6189	Philippines, we have come, / to avenge our comrades of Bataan.	Green	Phili	Harrington	A
		Blue, red	Phili	Baur	A

NO.	CACHET TEXT	COLOR	TOPIC	PUBLISHER	$
6190	Picatinny Arsenal / Dover, N.J. [handpainted] [envelope 7 1/2x3 15/16 in.]	Multicolored	Eagle	Stawuszew	D
6191	Pick out the biggest and fire / On the night etc.	Unknown	Unk	Card	A
6192	Pin 'em back [handpainted]	Brown	Bonds	Harmer	A
6193	Pin up / your future / with / war / bonds	Bk,R/Bu/Red	Japan	Dale	A
6194	Pincer / movement	Red	Home	Christens	A
6195	Pin-up girl	Black	Women	Field	A
6196	Pin-ups boost morale etc. [woman taking off sweater]	Black	Women	Field	A
6197	Pin-ups boost morale etc. [woman with bath towel]	Black	Women	Field	A
6198	Pin-ups boost morale etc. [woman with grass skirt] [envelope size varies]	Black	Women	Field	A
6199	Pin-ups boost morale-Be a booster! [woman stepping into skirt]	Black	Women	Field	A
6200	Pin-ups boost morale-Be etc. [woman seated] [env. 6 1/2x3 5/8, 7 1/2x4 in.]	Bk,bu/Bk,red	Hero	Gustafson	A
6201	Pioneer American ace / first to break record of World War I / 27 Jap etc.	Multicolored	Event	Unknown	C
6202	Pisa / falls / to / the Allies / Sept. 2 / 1944 [handpainted]	Blue, green	VforV	Boone	A
6203	Pistol Packin' GI Joe / "We'll push you 'cross the river / and through" etc.	Blue, red	Uncle	Butzen	A
6204	Pistol packin' Uncle / Help me hold those etc. [env. 6 1/2x3 5/8, 7 1/2x4 in.]	Multicolored	Home	Carter Mrs	C
6205	Plan now / 1945 / V-garden [handpainted]	Blue	Home	Unknown	A
6206	Plan now to vist historic Chattanooga etc.	Multicolored	Event	Linto	B
6207	Plan to win the / victories first! / [etc.] / 11-28-'44——Jap planes raid etc.	Multicolored	Flag	Linto	B
6208	Plan to win the / victories first! / Peace plans / can wait!	Brown	Home	Runge	A
6209	Planes - tanks - guns / Never again- / too little, / too late!	Unknown	Unk	Eichenlaub	A
6210	Planes don't fly on water etc.	Multicolored	Bonds	Linto	B
6211	Planes——-ships——-munitions / Many more needed! / Buy bonds!!	Multicolored	Home	Linto	B
6212	Planning to win the / victory is far more / important than etc. [no picture]	Multicolored	Home	Knoll	C
6213	Plant a / victory garden [handpainted]	Black, red	Japan	Price, EK	B
6214	Planted in Japan's / black heart. / Tokyo [handpainted]	Multicolored	Flag	Knapp	G
6215	Planting time is in full swing in the Pacific [handpainted] [monarch size envelope]	Unknown	Blood	Myers	A
6216	Plasma / saves their lives / Be a donor!	Gold, silver	Blood	Linto	B
6217	Plasma / will save / lives / Please donate blood [no picture]	Multicolored	Home	Borkowski	D
6218	Play ball with Uncle / Sam / To / win / the / war / buy U.S. etc. [handpainted]	Black	Home	Ander, EA	A
6219	Play square / stamp out black market	Multicolored	Home	Davis, D	C
6220	Please -- / write often [handpainted]	Black	Home	Ohio Bell	D
6221	Please / make only / essential etc. [no picture] [manila envelope]	Black, red	Musso	Andrews	B
6222	Please cancel / lightly / Rome / July 25 / 11 p.m. / 1943 / Italy / or if etc.	Green	Unk	Crosby	B
6223	Please do not neglect / military etc. [thermographed]	Multicolored	Home	Unknown	B
6224	Please keep the / bombs [in quotes] etc. [label + blue "Victory" border]				
6225	Please keep the / bombs [in quotes] etc. [label + red "Victory" border]				
6226	Please keep the / bombs [in quotes] etc. [label + red "Victory" border]	Multicolored	Home	Unknown	B
6227	Please keep the / bombs [in quotes] etc. [label + red "Win the War" border]	Multicolored	Home	Unknown	B
6228	Please, Congress! / Clean out the bureaucrats / before it is too late!	Gold, silver	EagSh	Linto	B
6229	Please, O Lord —— / we ask Thee for his safe return. [in quotes]	Blue	Home	Hillerich	A
6230	Pleasure-seekers! / Please / keep off the trains!	Unknown	Home	Linto	B
6231	Pledge / I pledge allegiance / to the etc. [eagle 37x30 mm] [envelope size varies]	Multicolored	EagFl	Amer Pat	A
6232	Pledge / I pledge allegiance / to the etc. [eagle 50x41 mm] [envelope size varies]	Multicolored	EagFl	Amer Pat	A
6233	Pledge / I pledge allegiance / to the etc. [flag above text]	Multicolored	EagFl	Amer Pat	A
6234	Pledge / I pledge allegiance / to the etc. [flag at left, no eagle, no stars]	Multicolored	Flag	Amer Pat	A
6235	Pledge / I pledge allegiance / to the etc. [flag flying, eagle attacking]	Multicolored	EagFl	Amer Pat	A
6236	Pledge / I pledge allegiance / to the etc. [text above eagle]	Multicolored	EagFl	Amer Pat	A
6237	Pledge / I pledge allegiance / to the etc. [two rows of red stars]	Multicolored	EagFl	Amer Pat	A
6238	Pledge / I pledge allegiance / to the etc. [vertical lines in gold]	Multicolored	EagFl	Amer Pat	A
6239	Plenty of / grit! [handpainted]	Multicolored	Army	Cowdery	D
6240	Plowshares turned / into swords / Army trucks "deliver the / goods" to the etc.	Bk/Gn/Red	Ordna	Coll Surp	A
6241	Plowshares turned / into swords / Jeeps leap into action in Sicily	Bk/Gn/Red	Ordna	Coll Surp	A
6242	Plowshares turned / into swords / Landing boats aid in unloading men etc.	Bk/Gn/Red	Ordna	Coll Surp	A
6243	Plowshares turned / into swords / Light armed / infantry mops / up Jap etc.	Bk/Gn/Red	Army	Coll Surp	A
6244	Plowshares turned / into swords / Our fighter planes / rip to pieces Nazi etc.	Bk/Gn/Red	Air	Coll Surp	A
6245	Plowshares turned / into swords / U.S. artillery / blasts Axis / forces in etc.	Bk/Gn/Red	Ordna	Coll Surp	A
6246	Plowshares turned / into swords / U.S. Flying Fortresses / bomb Germany	Bk/Gn/Red	Air	Coll Surp	A
6247	Plowshares turned / into swords / U.S. tanks —— General Grants and etc.	Bk/Gn/Red	Ordna	Coll Surp	A

NO.	CACHET TEXT	COLOR	TOPIC	PUBLISHER	$
6248	Plowshares turned / into swords / U.S. warships hit / hard in the / South etc.	Bk/Gn/Red	Navy	Coll Surp	A
6249	Plowshares turned / into swords / United / States / submarines / send etc.	Bk/Green/Red	USsub	Coll Surp	A
6250	Plucked / The Jap / navy	Multicolored	Japan	Peer	B
6251	Poison / antidote / buy war bonds / now! [thermographed]	Red	Axis	Crosby	B
6252	Poland	Brown	ORN	Runge	A
6253	Poland	Black, red	ORN	Clifford	A
6254	Poland	Black	ORN	Lowry	A
6255	Poland / Commemorating Poland's / heroic etc.	Black	ORN	Unknown	A
6256	Poland / fights on!	Blue, red	EagV	Cachet Cra	A
6257	Poland / first to fight [colored envelopes]	Black/Blue	ORN	Huss	A
6258	Poland / first to fight [tattered Polish flag]	Blue, red	ORN	Jancowski	A
6259	Poland / Norway / Holland / [etc.] / Wake up America——he's not dead yet	Unknown	ORN	Mayfield	A
6260	Poland / The invasion of the republic of Poland by Germany / on September etc.	Bk/Bu/Red	ORN	Ander, CS	A
6261	Poland / United Nations [handpainted]	Multicolored	UN	Weigand	B
6262	Poland [57x80 mm] [thermographed]	Unknown	ORN	Jordan	B
6263	Poland crucified	Red	ORN	Jancowski	A
6264	Poland fights again [buff envelope]	Brown	ORN	Huss	A
6265	Poland fights on [colored envelopes]	Blue	ORN	Huss	A
6266	Poland lives again [colored envelopes]	Blue	ORN	Huss	A
6267	Poland shall be free	Unknown	ORN	Runge	A
6268	Poles wipe out / Gestapo agents / [etc.] / 2-20-'44——2000 Amer. planes etc.	Unknown	Event	Linto	B
6269	Poles wipe out / Gestapo agents / During 1943 Polish underground forces etc.	Unknown	ORN	Linto	B
6270	Polish Premier Osubka Morawski / announced national etc. [typed] [no picture]	Black	Event	Batura	C
6271	Polish underground [colored envelopes]	Black	ORN	Huss	A
6272	Politicians / stop clowning / [etc.] / 8-31-'40——Airliner crashed at etc.	Multicolored	Anniv	Linto	B
6273	Politicians / stop clowning / Get down to real war / business. Play tomorrow	Multicolored	Home	Linto	B
6274	Poor you! [handpainted]	Multicolored	Army	Cowdery	D
6275	Poorer and poorer / are der chances / for / der Fuehrer [handpainted]	Black, red	Hitle	Wolf, CL	B
6276	Poorer and poorer / are der chances / for / der Fuehrer! / Doom	Unknown	Hitle	Temple	A
6277	Porky wallowed deep in a ditch; / Hitler lay at his side; / Porky jumped etc.	Orange	Verse	Rush, H	A
6278	Port of Dunkerque, where Britain in / [etc.] / 7-8-'45——British etc.	Unknown	Event	Linto	B
6279	Port of Dunkerque, where Britain in etc.	Unknown	Event	Linto	B
6280	Porthole of enchantment	Black/Brown	Navy	Lupton	A
6281	Post-war / planning now etc. [first 2 lines blue] [no picture]	Blue, red	Unk	Boone	A
6282	Post-war / planning now! [in quotes] / "We must" etc. [first 2 lines red] [no picture]	Blue, red	Home	Boone	A
6283	Pots and pans to build new air force planes / All out for defense	Multicolored	Home	Fleetwood	B
6284	Potsdam / Conference / The new Big "3" / Truman- [etc.] / August 1, 1945	Multicolored	Event	Teixeira	D
6285	Potsdam / ultimatum! / I hereby accept terms	Bu,R/Bu/Red	VJDay	Boone	D
6286	Potsdam / ultimatum! / I hereby accept terms [postmarked 9/2/45]	Blue, red	VJDay	Boone	D
6287	Pour it on the Axis / with your waste fat	Red	Home	Davis, Ray	A
6288	Power of veto / used by Presidents from / Washington to etc. [no picture]	Multicolored	FDR	Linto	B
6289	Power of veto / used by Presidents from etc.	Unknown	Home	Linto	B
6290	Practice, don't preach / save paper [not on turned cover]	Green	Eagle	Carpenter	A
6291	Practice, don't preach / save paper [on turned cover]	Green	Eagle	Carpenter	C
6292	Prague / liberated / Capital of Czechoslovakia / May 8, 1945	Multicolored	Event	Teixeira	D
6293	Prague / liberated / Capital of Czechoslovakia etc. [two 5/8/45 postmarks; 1 violet, 1 blue]	Multicolored	Event	Teixeira	F
6294	Praise / the Lord / and pass etc.	Black	Pearl	Huss	A
6295	Praise the Lord / and / pass the ammunition	Blue	Unk	Buckalew	B
6296	Praise the Lord [in quotes] and buy 'em / ammunition so they will etc.	Blue	Bonds	Lawrence	A
6297	Pray for the safe return of all / our etc.	Unknown	Unk	Phill, CR	A
6298	Pray for the safe return of all / our fighting men this Christmas.	Green, red	Holid	Lind	A
6299	Pray for the success / [etc.] / "D" Day etc. [cut-&-pasted paper] [colored envelopes]	Bk,R/Black	DDay	Temple	B
6300	Prayer for men in service / God bless our lads / "God bless our" etc. [flag]	Blue/Green	Relig	Brenn	A
6301	Prayer for men in service / God bless our lads / "God bless our" etc. [flame]	Bk/Bu/Red	Relig	Brenn	A
6302	Prepared for anything! [colored envelopes]	Blue	Army	Huss	A
6303	Pres. Roosevelt says: / "Fair for one, fair for all" / That's etc. [no picture]	Multicolored	FDR	Linto	B
6304	Pres. Truman / announces / Japan's acceptance / of etc. [no picture] [handpainted]	Black	VJDay	Batura	D
6305	Presenting the United Nations / Charter to the etc. [typewritten] [no picture]	Black	Event	Batura	C

NO.	CACHET TEXT	COLOR	TOPIC	PUBLISHER	$
6306	Preserve / liberty / buy V...-bonds	Unknown	Bonds	Risinger	A
6307	Preserve / our democracy! / [etc.] / Jan. 1, 1941——Neutral Eire / bombed etc.	Multicolored	Anniv	Linto	B
6308	Preserve / our democracy! / Stamp out / bureaucracy! [no picture]	Blue, silver	Home	Linto	B
6309	Preserve a free nation	Brown	Wash	Runge	A
6310	Preserve a free nation / with etc. [brown envelope 7 1/2x4 in.]	Unknown	Unk	Runge	A
6311	Preserve our / American way / of life —— / Buy war bonds [colored envelopes]	Black/Brown	Home	Huss	A
6312	Preserve the freedom and liberties / that brought our forefathers / to America. etc.	Blue	Hist	Hill	A
6313	President / Franklin D. Roosevelt / [etc.] / thy / servant sleeping....	Multicolored	FDR	Fluegel	E
6314	President / Franklin D. Roosevelt / Jan 20, 1941 / Inauguration [sic] etc.	Orange	FDR	Mello+Stan	E
6315	President [in quotes] Harry / Hopkins said: / "We are too dumb to / know" etc.	Gold	Home	Linto	B
6316	President F.D. Roosevelt / signed / an appropriation measure / adding etc. [hp]	Multicolored	Event	Batura	E
6317	President Franklin D. Roosevelt / announced that he etc. [handpainted] [12/3/41]	Unknown	Event	Batura	E
6318	President Harry S. Truman / announced to the U.S. / that etc. [handpainted] [no pict]	Blue	Event	Batura	D
6319	President Harry S. Truman / United States of America	Black	HST	Pacific	B
6320	President Roosevelt's visit to [in quotes] etc. [2 men] [env. 6 9/16x3 5/8 in.]	Sepia tones	Ally	Belles-let	C
6321	President Roosevelt's visit to [in quotes] etc. [5 men] [env. 6 9/16x3 5/8 in.]	Sepia tones	Ally	Belles-let	C
6322	President Truman / announced that hostilities / had ceased. etc. [handpainted] [no pict]	Blue	VJDay	Batura	D
6323	President Truman / proclaims / V-E Day! [no picture]	Black	VEDay	Butzen	B
6324	President Truman / was selected Chairman / of the "Big" etc. [typed] [no picture]	Black	Event	Batura	C
6325	President Truman announced at 7 p.m. etc. [beside Gen. Eisenhower cachet]	Black	VJDay	Southworth	B
6326	President Truman announced at 7 p.m. etc. [beside Gen. MacArthur cachet]	Black	VJDay	Southworth	B
6327	President Truman announces / the unconditional sur- / render etc. [tan envelope]	Red	VJDay	Unknown	B
6328	President Truman arrived / in Antwerp and toured the etc. [typed] [no picture]	Black	Event	Batura	C
6329	President Truman grasping / the reins as presiding etc. [typed] [no picture]	Black	Event	Batura	C
6330	President Truman issued / a new surrender ultimatum / to etc. [handpainted] [no pict]	Blue	Event	Batura	C
6331	President Truman reviewed / the famed / "Hell on Wheels" etc. [typed] [no pict]	Black	Event	Batura	C
6332	President Truman speaking / at a symbolic flag-raising etc. [typed] [no pict]	Black	Event	Batura	C
6333	Prime Minister / Clement Richard Attlee / took office etc. [typed] [no picture]	Black	Event	Batura	C
6334	Prime Minister Churchill / and his Conservative etc. [typed] [no picture]	Black	Event	Batura	C
6335	Prime Minister Churchill / has sent a message / of etc. [typed] [no picture]	Black	Event	Batura	C
6336	Proclaim liberty throughout all	Unknown	Unk	Ioor	A
6337	Proclaim liberty throughout all the land / unto all the etc. [in quotes]	Multicolored	Liber	Dime	A
6338	Proclamation / by the President of the United States / Hon. Harry S. etc.	Red	VEDay	Unknown	B
6339	Proclamation of the President / [etc.] / "Now, therefore I" etc. [thermography]	Blue	FDR	Unknown	B
6340	Produce / and / conserve / Share / and / play square / Food / fights etc. [handpainted]	Multicolored	Home	Unknown	B
6341	Produce to win the race	Bk,R/Bu,gold	Flag	Runge	A
6342	Produce what we need or / you won't have needs	Unknown	Unk	Quigley	B
6343	Producing for / victory [envelope 8 7/8x3 7/8, 9 1/2x4 1/8 in.]	Unknown	Home	AC Spark	B
6344	Production / backbone of / defense [art: Knapp] [env. 7 1/2x4, 8 5/8x4 1/4 in.]	Blue, red	Home	Fleetwood	C
6345	Progress of a paperhanger! / 1939=Tomorrow the world! / 1943= etc. [no picture]	Red	Hitle	Davis, Ray	A
6346	Protect / the heritage of our / children / Buy U.S. war bonds now [yellow envelope]	Blue	Bonds	Huss	A
6347	Protect / this / country / from / "isms"	Gold, silver	Flag	Linto	B
6348	Protect / us / by Thy / might	Blue, red	Eagle	McCluney	A
6349	Protect / your / liberty / with / war / bonds	Multicolored	Liber	Boone	A
6350	Protect freedom of speech / Win the war	Blue,red	Home	Speede	A
6351	Protect our / rights and liberties	Blue, red	Home	Card	A
6352	Protect our country / from saboteurs! / Intern all Japs and / Germans!	Multicolored	Home	Linto	B
6353	Protect the Panama Canal / cross roads etc. [thermographed]	Unknown	Unk	Crosby	B
6354	Protect your independence with / war bonds	Blue, red	FlLib	Boone	A
6355	Protecting health / for victory [envelope 9 1/2x4 1/8 in.]	Blue, red	Eagle	Smith-Lee	B
6356	Protecting the U.S.A.	Bu/Br/Gn/Red	Map	Auge	B
6357	Proud / to be an / American	Blue	Eagle	Krakora	A
6358	Proud / to be an / American [two shields above text] [handpainted]	Blue, red	Shiel	Krakora	A
6359	Proud to be an American [eagle flying to right]	Bu,R/Multi	Eagle	Krakora	A
6360	Proud to be an American [sitting eagle facing left]	Blue, red	Eagle	Krakora	A
6361	Psychoneurotics or / bureaucratic / [etc.] / 3-17-'44——Just released——etc.	Unknown	Event	Linto	B
6362	Psychoneurotics or / bureaucratic slackers? / Army rejects? / Most of them etc.	Unknown	Home	Linto	B
6363	PT 10 [on bow of PT boat] [colored envelopes]	Blue	Navy	Huss	A

NO.	CACHET TEXT	COLOR	TOPIC	PUBLISHER	$
6364	PT-10 in action [colored envelopes]	Black	Navy	Huss	A
6365	PT-10 in action [thermographed] [colored envelopes]	Black	Navy	Huss	B
6366	Puget Sound / Navy Yard / Bremerton, Wash. / U.S.C.S. / John Paul Jones etc.	Blue/Green	Home	Wash Cover	A
6367	Purchases / of U.S. / Defense / Bonds / will win / this war / V ...-	Unknown	Bonds	Linto	B
6368	Purple Heart medal description etc. [thermographed]	Purple, red	Medal	Crosby	B
6369	Put a bond away / for that rainy day	Brown/Purple	Bonds	Ryscovers	A
6370	Put forth thine hand / and take it by the tail / [etc.] / Bible [handpainted]	Multicolored	Japan	Steinhardt	C
6371	Put more / pep into / your / patriotism! / Buy more war bonds [green envelope]	Gold, pink	Bonds	Linto	B
6372	Put them on the scrap heap! -- where they belong. [handpainted]	Multicolored	Axis	Parker	C
6373	Put this / 5th war loan / [etc.] / 6-12-'44——German 14th army, in / Italy etc.		Event	Linto	B
6374	Put this / 5th war loan / over now to make / sure of putting / Axis down under!	Multicolored	Bonds	Linto	B
6375	Put your / in America / or get your / out of it	Unknown	Unk	Boone	A
6376	Put your cash on the line / Get the Nazi etc.	Blue	Unk	Carpenter	A
6377	Put your trust / in / America	Blue, red	Home	Krakora	A

Cover Values (from Table 6, p. 136)

Value	*Price Range*
A	$ 3 - 6
B	$ 7 - 15
C	$ 16 - 30
D	$ 31 - 60
E	$ 61 - 125
F	$126 - 250
G	$251 - 500
H	$501 - 1000
I	$ >1000
X	**Unpriced: Suspicious or fraudulent cover**

6078

DEAL DEATH TO "HONORABLE" JAPRATS

6119

PATRIOTS
TO
PATRIOTS;
The hour is here.
We will never let
our spirits die, for
OLD GLORY
is our
ALLY.

6123

PATRIOTS to PATRIOTS;
The hour is here. We will
never let our spirits die, for
OLD GLORY is our ALLY.

6137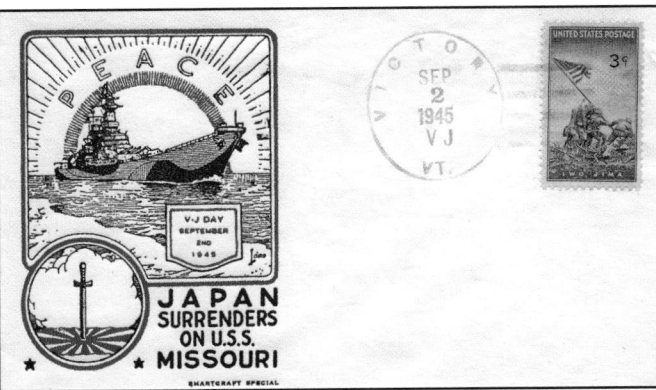

PEACE

V-J DAY
SEPTEMBER
2ND
1945

JAPAN
SURRENDERS
ON U.S.S.
MISSOURI

6147

PEACE FOR PEACE;
OR
STEEL FOR STEEL

6161

PEARL HARBOR

DEC. 7, 1941

I WON'T FORGET IT

THIRD ANNIVERSARY

ARTHUR KNOLL
660 EMERSON AVE.
HAMILTON, OHIO.

6167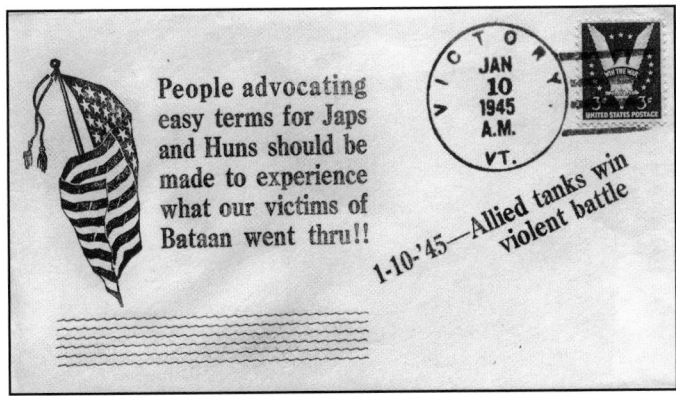

People advocating
easy terms for Japs
and Huns should be
made to experience
what our victims of
Bataan went thru!!

1-10-'45—Allied tanks win
violent battle

6175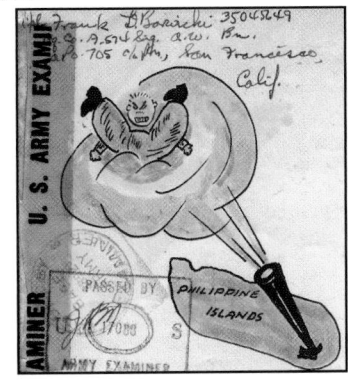

6192

PIN'EM BACK

6213

6214

6251

6266

6299

6320

6364

CACHET TEXT BEGINNING WITH "Q"

NO.	CACHET TEXT	COLOR	TOPIC	PUBLISHER	$
6378	Quantum mutatus ab illo	Black/Green	Musso	McCluney	B
6379	Quartermaster / for freedom's sake	Unknown	Army	Cozart	A
6380	Quartermaster Corps [colored envelopes]	Blue/Brown	Army	Huss	A
6381	Quiet! / O.P.A. has another / knotty problem! / Shall we or shall / we not?	Multicolored	Home	Linto	B
6382	Quit cluttering up my / floor with your junk. [handpainted]	Multicolored	Japan	Adler	D

CACHET TEXT BEGINNING WITH "R"

NO.	CACHET TEXT	COLOR	TOPIC	PUBLISHER	$
6383	R.A.F. / A.A.F. / Constellations that Hitler's / horoscope failed to etc.	Bk, orange	Air	Andrews	B
6384	R.A.F. / pilot [colored envelopes]	Bk/Bu/Br	Air	Huss	A
6385	R.-Adm. / Gerald F. / Bogan	Unknown	Admir	Linto	B
6386	R.-Adm. / Jesse D. / Jewell	Blue, sepia	Admir	Linto	B
6387	R.-Adm. / Jesse D. / Jewell / 12-20-'44——Monschau / falls to Yanks	Unknown	Event	Linto	B
6388	R.-Adm. / Joseph J. / Clark	Gold, sepia	Admir	Linto	B
6389	R.-Adm. / Theodore E. / Chandler / [etc.] / 2-7-'45——Yanks enter / Reich etc.	Multicolored	Event	Linto	B
6390	R.-Adm. / Theodore E. / Chandler / killed in / action / Luzon	Sepia, silver	Admir	Linto	B
6391	R.-Adm. / W.H.P. / Blandy / Pacific	Multi/Gd,R	Admir	Linto	B
6392	R.-Adm. / W.H.P. / Blandy / Pacific / 2-18-'45——Yank Marines land on Iwo Jima	Multicolored	Event	Linto	B
6393	R.-Adm. Frederick C. Sherman	Red, sepia	Admir	Linto	B
6394	R.-Adm. Frederick C. Sherman / 2-1-'45——Eighth army / lands south of Manila	Multicolored	Event	Linto	B
6395	R.F.D.——faithful link between / fighting farm boys and home	Blue, red	Home	Davis, D	A
6396	Radio / technician	Black/Brown	Army	Huss	A
6397	Radio Tokio say —— "Today Japanese / navy sink entire American fleet." etc.	Red	Japan	Conner	A
6398	Radio Tokio say —— / " —— Today Japanese / navy" etc.	Purple	Japan	Conner	A
6399	Radio Tokio say —— / "Emperor Hirohito inspect / today our most glorious" etc.	Red	Japan	Conner	A
6400	Radio Tokio say —— / "His Majesty today summoned hon. / Privy Council" etc.	Purple	Japan	Conner	A
6401	Radio Tokio say —— / "Hon. Japanese aircraft / industry now preparing" etc.	Purple	Japan	Conner	A
6402	Radio Tokio say —— / "Japanese fleet soon to / baffle pitiful Allied" etc.	Purple	Japan	Conner	A
6403	Radio Tokio say —— / "Japanese scientists developing / new secret weapon" etc.	Brown/Red	Japan	Conner	A
6404	Radio Tokio say —— / "Many people now leaving town / because of warm" etc.	Red	Japan	Conner	A
6405	Radio Tokio say —— / "Next program" etc.	Red	Japan	Conner	A
6406	Radio Tokio say —— / "The High command" etc.	Purple	Japan	Conner	A
6407	Radio Tokio say —— / "The Japanese government are very / proud to" etc.	Green	Japan	Conner	B
6408	Radio Tokio say —— / "The Japanese government has de- / cided to hold" etc.	Purple	Japan	Cozart	A
6409	Radio Tokio say —— / "The Japanese government have decided / to dictate" etc.	Green	Japan	Conner	A
6410	Radio Tokio say —— / "Today his majesty" etc.	Green	Japan	Conner	A
6411	Radio Tokio say —— / "Today Japanese navy sink entire / American fleet." etc.	Red	Japan	Conner	A
6412	Radio Tokio say —— / "Today Japanese navy sink entire Ameri- / can" etc.	Green	Japan	Conner	A
6413	Radio Tokio say —— / "Today Japanese navy sink entire Yan- / kee fleet." etc.	Red	Japan	Conner	A
6414	Radio Tokio say —— / "Upstart Admiral Halsey / shall ride no white horse" etc.	Red	Japan	Conner	A
6415	RAF raids Cologne	Unknown	Event	Linto	B
6416	Rain or shine, hot or cold, war or peace - / - the U.S. mail etc. [thermographed]	Blue	Home	Lind	A
6417	Raising / U.S. Flag / Iwo Jima / 2-23-'45 / Conquest / cost / 19,938 etc.	Multicolored	USMC	Linto	B
6418	Rally to the / 7th U.S. / war bond / drive / it's up to us! [no picture]	Multicolored	Bonds	Linto	B
6419	Rangoon / the capital of / ——Burma—— / was liberated by British troops etc.	Multicolored	Event	Fluegel	C
6420	Rathkamp Memorial Society / [etc.] / Why shouldn't we be having fun? etc.	Red	Home	Rathkamp	A
6421	Rathkamp Memorial Society / [etc.] / With a magic V and the ···– jive, etc.	Blue	Home	Rathkamp	A
6422	Rats / fight fiercest when / "cornered" [handpainted]	Multicolored	Axis	Adler	D

NO.	CACHET TEXT	COLOR	TOPIC	PUBLISHER	$
6423	Rattlesnakes are rattlesnakes / regardless of place of birth. / This hold true etc.	Gold	Japan	Linto	B
6424	Read / "What is planned for you" / by Ralph Robey in / April, 1945, etc.	Multicolored	Home	Linto	B
6425	Ready [all-over cachet] [handpainted]	Blue, red	UncEa	Krakora	C
6426	Ready aim fire.... / Up and at 'em / Let's go! / Help win this war etc. [thermographed]	Black/Red	Axis	Crosby	B
6427	Ready to defend	Blue, red	EagSh	Steeg	A
6428	Ready to defend / America [envelope 6 3/4x3 3/4 in.]	Unknown	Unk	Steag	A
6429	Ready! / Aim! / Fire / Remember Pearl Harbor [envelope 5 1/2x 3 1/8 in.]	Unknown	Pearl	Unknown	A
6430	Really true blue	Unknown	Home	Linto	B
6431	Rear Adm. W.H. Munroe	Unknown	Admir	Linto	B
6432	Rear Adm. W.H. Munroe / 12-14-'44——Yanks blast / on close to Roer	Unknown	Event	Linto	B
6433	Rear Adml Joseph J. Clark [handpainted]	Multicolored	Admir	Knoll	D
6434	Rear Adml. Frederick C. Sherman [handpainted]	Multicolored	Admir	Knoll	D
6435	Rear-Adm. / Arthur D. / Struble	Gd,Gy/Sp,Vi	Admir	Linto	B
6436	Rear-Adm. / Arthur D. / Struble / 12——31-'44——Sovietized gov. etc.	Multicolored	Event	Linto	B
6437	Rear-Adm. / R.S. Berkey	Multicolored	Admir	Linto	B
6438	Rear-Adm. / R.S. Berkey / 12-30-'44——Gen. Patton has / strong hold etc.	Multicolored	Event	Linto	B
6439	Rear-Adm. Frederick C. / Sherman	Unknown	Admir	Linto	B
6440	Rear-Adm. Gerald F. / Bogan	Unknown	Admir	Linto	B
6441	Rear-Adm. Jesse D. Jewell	Unknown	Admir	Linto	B
6442	Rear-Adm. Jesse D. Jewell / 12-20-'44——Monschau / falls to Yanks	Unknown	Event	Linto	B
6443	Rear-Adm. Joseph J. / Clark	Unknown	Admir	Linto	B
6444	Rear-Adm. Theodore E. / Chandler	Unknown	Admir	Linto	B
6445	Rear-Adm. W.H. Blandy	Unknown	Admir	Linto	B
6446	Recognize our heroes / Official etc.	Unknown	Unk	Garfield	A
6447	Recognize the good work of the / Volunteer Canteen Corps	Multicolored	Flag	Linto	B
6448	Recordio-gram / A personally / recorded message / for you [env. 63/4x6 3/4 in.]	Blue, red	Armed	USO	C
6449	Recruit Depot 21st Tng. / [etc.] / the title of / United States Marine. [thermographed]	Red	USMC	Crosby	B
6450	Red / Cross / You can help by giving in 1945 [nurse with Red Cross flag]	Blue, red	RedCr	McFarland	A
6451	Red / Cross / You can help by giving in 1945 [nurse and Uncle Sam]	Blue, red	RedCr	McFarland	A
6452	Red / Cross / You can help by giving in 1945 [nurse saluting]	Blue, red	RedCr	McFarland	A
6453	Red / Cross / You can help by giving in 1945 [nurse, red cross, eagle]	Blue, red	RedCr	MacFarland	A
6454	Red / Cross / You can help by giving in 1945 [woman knitting]	Blue, red	RedCr	McFarland	A
6455	Red bomber [in quotes] / "The old sock, that turned the tide"	Black	Hitle	Donaldson	A
6456	Red Cross - blood plasma / In honor of etc.	Unknown	RedCr	Ander, EA	A
6457	Red Cross / blood plasma / Give etc.	Unknown	RedCr	Unknown	A
6458	Red Cross / for / our service / men essential	Multicolored	RedCr	Linto	B
6459	Red Cross / for / our service / men / essential / 3-1-'45——U.S. 9th take etc.	Multicolored	Event	Linto	B
6460	Red Cross / S.O.S. call / Please answer etc.	Unknown	RedCr	Linto	B
6461	Red Cross arts and skills / [etc.] / 12-23'44——Hun robot bombs hit / U.S. etc.	Unknown	Event	Linto	B
6462	Red Cross arts and skills / corps need [sic] more recruits	Unknown	RedCr	Linto	B
6463	Red Cross blood plasma / [etc.] / Blood transfusion in the etc. [thermographed]	Blue	RedCr	Crosby	B
6464	Red Cross blood plasma / [etc.] / U.S. naval hospital ship etc. [thermographed]	Blue, red	Navy	Crosby	C
6465	Red Cross blood plasma / [etc.] / U.S.N. Convalescent etc. [thermographed]	Purple	RedCr	Crosby	B
6466	Red Cross Gray Ladies / perform noble service	Gray, green	RedCr	Linto	B
6467	Red Cross war fund / goal for 1944 etc.	Red	RedCr	Boone	A
6468	Red Cross worker	Unknown	RedCr	Linto	B
6469	Red Diamond Division / far away from the USA / serving our country night and day	Black, red	Unit	McCluney	A
6470	Red for the valor of patriots true / White etc. [env. 6 1/2x3 5/8, 7 1/2x4 in.]	Unknown	Unk	Louisville	A
6471	Red tape leads / to strikes! / Cut red tape for / harmony's sake! [no picture]	Blue, silver	Home	Linto	B
6472	Red vulture / of the Pacific	Red	Japan	Neal	A
6473	Redeployment [in quotes]	Green	Army	Foster	A
6474	Reds capture Kiev	Unknown	Event	Linto	B
6475	Refugees from 19 European nations etc.	Blue	Home	Wright	A
6476	Regardless of all the known / [etc.] / January 18 is the day! / Everybody etc.	Multicolored	Bonds	Linto	B
6477	Regardless of all the known / bureaucratic blunderings we / still have etc.	Multicolored	Uncle	Linto	B
6478	Register now / for the / Red Cross / motor corps	Multicolored	RedCr	Linto	B
6479	Reinforcements needed / to guard the rear!	Black	Army	Lupton	A
6480	Relax later etc.	Unknown	Home	Linto	B

NO.	CACHET TEXT	COLOR	TOPIC	PUBLISHER	$
6481	Religion / press / speech / fear / freedom	Unknown	Unk	Baur	A
6482	Remagen bridge / crossing of the Rhine	Blue, red	Event	Cachet Cra	B
6483	Remagen Bridge / In honor / of the / U.S. Army	Blue, red	Battl	Smartcraft	B
6484	Re'mber "Pearl" / Harbor? [handpainted]	Multicolored	Pearl	Adler	D
6485	Rember [sic] "Pearl" / Harbor. [handpainted]	Multicolored	Pearl	Adler	D
6486	Remember —— / loneliness cuts down on morale, / but mail cuts etc. [no picture]	Green	Home	Davis, D	A
6487	Remember / 3——For the men the Japs / [etc.] / 4——So, remember the men etc. [handpaint]	Multicolored	Verse	Weigand	B
6488	Remember / blackout / of homes / lifted after / 879 / [etc.] / Pearl Harbor	Multicolored	Hawai	Sayama	D
6489	Remember / Dec. 7 1944 / Remember / Pearl Harbor / Pearl Harbor	Multicolored	Pearl	Sayama	C
6490	Remember—— / God will secure / the victory! / Your victory etc. [no picture]	Red, silver	Home	Linto	B
6491	Remember / it depends on who you are etc.	Blue	Unk	Lawrence	A
6492	Remember—— / Japs multiply like rats! / [etc.] / 9-5-'44——Aachen and etc.	Multicolored	Event	Linto	B
6493	Remember—— / Japs multiply like rats! / Curb this menace! / Remember—— etc.	Gold, green	AJA	Linto	B
6494	Remember / July / 4 / 1945 / Pearl Harbor	Multicolored	Holid	Sayama	D
6495	Remember / July 4, 1944 / V ···– / Pearl Harbor	Multicolored	Holid	Sayama	D
6496	Remember / Lei Day / May 1 / 1944 / Pearl Harbor	Multicolored	Hawai	Sayama	D
6497	Remember / Let's go! U.S.A. / Keep 'em etc. [thermographed]	Blue, red	Unk	Crosby	B
6498	Remember / Pearl / Harbor / ···– [words across blue "V"]	Multi/R,Blue	Pearl	Boone	A
6499	Remember / Pearl / Harbor / Buy / defense bonds [no picture]	Unknown	Pearl	Shaw, MM	A
6500	Remember / Pearl / Harbor / Buy U.S. war bonds [air mail or buff envelope]	Bu/Bu, red	Pearl	Foster	A
6501	Remember / Pearl / Harbor / Dec. 7th 1941 [flag left of text]	Blue, red	Pearl	Boone	A
6502	Remember / Pearl / Harbor / December 7th , 1941	Blue, red	Pearl	Boone	A
6503	Remember / Pearl / Harbor / December 7th, 1941 / Win the War	Blue, red	Pearl	Boone	A
6504	Remember / Pearl / Harbor / Japan / Tokyo [bomb hitting sign saying "Tokyo"]	Multicolored	Pearl	Borkowski	C
6505	Remember / Pearl / Harbor / Smash the Japs	Blue	Pearl	Gillespie	A
6506	Remember / Pearl / Harbor / V [blue, red "V"]	Multicolored	Pearl	Boone	A
6507	Remember / Pearl / Harbor [bomb below "Remember"] [handpainted]	Multicolored	Pearl	Unknown	B
6508	Remember / Pearl / Harbor [bomb dropping, fire below] [colored envelopes]	Multicolored	Pearl	Poppenger	A
6509	Remember / Pearl / Harbor [bomb dropping] [upper left]	Blue, red	Pearl	Aylward	A
6510	Remember / Pearl / Harbor [colors vary] [handpainted]	Multicolored	Pearl	Adler	D
6511	Remember / Pearl / Harbor [dagger]	Blue/Red	Pearl	Richardson	A
6512	Remember / Pearl / Harbor [first word around blue circle with white stars]	Blue, red	Pearl	Boone	A
6513	Remember / Pearl / Harbor [flag draped in ring in claws of eagle, left of text]	Unknown	Pearl	Boone	A
6514	Remember / Pearl / Harbor [green words on "V" made of red, blue lines or stars]	Multicolored	Pearl	Boone	A
6515	Remember / Pearl / Harbor [red words on blue "V" or blue words on red "V"]	Blue, red	Pearl	Boone	A
6516	Remember / Pearl / Harbor [text above picture][handpainted]	Blue, red	Pearl	Krakora	B
6517	Remember / Pearl / Harbor [text runs diagonally] [ship exploding]	Blue/Red	Pearl	Boone	A
6518	Remember / Pearl / Harbor! / Work for victory [w, w/o copyright "C"]	Blue, red	Pearl	Cachet Cra	A
6519	Remember / Pearl / Harbor! [text on hand with fingers giving "V" sign]	Unknown	Pearl	Boone	A
6520	Remember / Pearl / V / Harbor / December 7th, 1941	Blue, red	Pearl	Ander, EA	A
6521	Remember / Pearl Harbor	Green	Pearl	Price, EK	A
6522	Remember / Pearl Harbor - [the Spirit of '75]	Black	Pearl	Runge	A
6523	Remember / Pearl Harbor / ···– [red text on blue "V" or blue on red "V"]	Blue, red	Pearl	Boone	A
6524	Remember / Pearl Harbor / ···– [silver text on "V" made of red & blue stars]	Multicolored	Pearl	Boone	A
6525	Remember / Pearl Harbor / Buy war bonds [eagle and shield]	Blue, orange	Pearl	Runge	A
6526	Remember / Pearl Harbor / December 7th, 1941 ["Remember" curved, R or Bu]	Blue, red	Pearl	Boone	A
6527	Remember / Pearl Harbor / December 7th, 1941 [flag above text; blue "Remember"]	Blue, red	Pearl	Boone	A
6528	Remember / Pearl Harbor / December 7th, 1941 [flag above text; red "Remember"]	Blue, red	Pearl	Boone	A
6529	Remember / Pearl Harbor / For victory / buy / United etc. [first word vertical]	Blue, red	Pearl	Boone	A
6530	Remember / Pearl Harbor / Give 'em 'ell [env. 6 1/2x3 5/8, 9 1/2x 4 1/8 in.]	Blue, red	Pearl	Runge	A
6531	Remember / Pearl Harbor / Japan	Black/Brown	Pearl	Harrington	A
6532	Remember / Pearl Harbor / On / active / service	Blue/Brown	Pearl	Wash Cover	A
6533	Remember / Pearl Harbor / On / active / service / John Paul Jones chapter etc.	Blue/Brown	Pearl	Muridge	B
6534	Remember / Pearl Harbor / On Sunday morning, December 7, 1941, / the etc.	Multicolored	Pearl	Advertiser	B
6535	Remember / Pearl Harbor / Second anniversary etc. [handp+ cut-&-pasted]	Multicolored	Pearl	Temple	C
6536	Remember / Pearl Harbor / Smash the Japs	Blue/Red	Pearl	Unknown	A
6537	Remember / Pearl Harbor / Sunday, December 7th, 1941 / The Axis is axed!	Multicolored	VJDay	Boone	B
6538	Remember / Pearl Harbor / Sunday, December 7th, 1941 [eagle + shield]	Blue, red	Pearl	Boone	A

NO.	CACHET TEXT	COLOR	TOPIC	PUBLISHER	$
6539	Remember / Pearl Harbor [battleship burning] [handpainted]	Multicolored	Pearl	Knapp	H
6540	Remember / Pearl Harbor [clock at upper left]	Unknown	Pearl	Garfield	A
6541	Remember / Pearl Harbor [eagle and flag]	Unknown	Pearl	Boone	A
6542	Remember / Pearl Harbor [first word arches over flag and two stars]	Blue, red	Pearl	Boone	A
6543	Remember / Pearl Harbor [first word vertical] [no star before or after text]	Blue, red	Pearl	Boone	A
6544	Remember / Pearl Harbor [first word vertical] [star after text]	Blue, red	Pearl	Boone	A
6545	Remember / Pearl Harbor [first word vertical] [star before text]	Blue, red	Pearl	Boone	A
6546	Remember / Pearl Harbor [first word vertical] [with Minute Man]	Blue, red	Pearl	Boone	A
6547	Remember / Pearl Harbor [in quotes] / "Give 'em 'ell"	Blue, red	Pearl	Runge	A
6548	Remember / Pearl Harbor [in quotes] / "Give 'em 'ell" [EK Price corner card]	Unknown	Pearl	Price, EK	A
6549	Remember / Pearl Harbor [in quotes] / "Give 'em 'ell" [envelope 9 1/2x4 1/8 in.]	Black, red	Pearl	Runge	B
6550	Remember / Pearl Harbor [in quotes] [Minute man]	Brown	Pearl	Runge	A
6551	Remember / Pearl Harbor [Japanese officer with bloody knife and globe]	Green	Pearl	Fagenson	A
6552	Remember / Pearl Harbor [large eagle, small planes] [handpainted]	Multicolored	Pearl	Unknown	C
6553	Remember / Pearl Harbor [seaplane above flag]	Unknown	Pearl	Dime	A
6554	Remember / Pearl Harbor [text in panel across legs of soldier]	Blue, red	Pearl	Boone	A
6555	Remember / Pearl Harbor [Uncle Sam pointing] [env. 6 9/16x3 3/4, 7x4 in.]	Blue, red	Pearl	Belles-let	D
6556	Remember / Pearl Harbor [Uncle Sam rolling up sleeves]	Unknown	Pearl	Ang	A
6557	Remember / Pearl Harbor and Bataan [first word vertical]	Blue, red	Pearl	Boone	A
6558	Remember / Pearl Harbor! / America / will win [frame of stars] [thermographed]	Blue	Pearl	Crosby	B
6559	Remember / Pearl Harbor! / America / will win [no frame] [thermographed]	Blue	Pearl	Crosby	B
6560	Remember / Pearl Harbor! [diving plane, UL; text, R; ship, LR] [env. 8 7/8x4 in.]	Blue, red	Pearl	Navy Dept.	D
6561	Remember / Pearl Harbor! [under flag and airplane]	Blue, red	Pearl	Unknown	A
6562	Remember / Remember Pearl Harbor of peace etc. [no picture]	Unknown	Pearl	Weigand	B
6563	Remember / Shangri-la! [thermogrpahed]	Unknown	Unk	Rush, JM	B
6564	Remember / the Lexington, Wasp, etc.	Unknown	Navy	Myers	A
6565	Remember / Wake Island and Guam	Black	Unk	Runge	A
6566	Remember Bataan / and the / "March of Death" [no picture]	Br, green	Phili	Linto	B
6567	Remember me... / Any mail for [envelope 8 7/8x3 7/8 in.]	Multicolored	Navy	Porto-serv	B
6568	Remember me? I' G.I. Joe --/ Fo't in World War II you know [handpainted]	Red	Army	Shaw, TC	B
6569	Remember our boys over there / Give to the Red Cross [handpainted]	Red	RedCr	Barwicki	B
6570	Remember Pearl Harbor	Unknown	Pearl	Linto	B
6571	Remember Pearl Harbor	Black	Pearl	Rush, JM	A
6572	Remember Pearl Harbor	Red	Pearl	Price, EK	A
6573	Remember Pearl Harbor .. December 7, 1941 / Farewell to the U.S.S. etc.	Black	Pearl	Oregon St	A
6574	Remember Pearl Harbor / [etc.] / Buy war stamps and bonds [thermographed]	Unknown	Pearl	Crosby	B
6575	Remember Pearl Harbor / 3——If needed or if asked of us, each man etc. [handpainted]	Multicolored	Pearl	Weigand	B
6576	Remember Pearl Harbor / 4——Pacific or Atlantic——- / The fleet will not be etc.	Multicolored	Pearl	Weigand	B
6577	Remember Pearl Harbor / and Manila too; / [etc.] / business to do. [in quotes]	Blue, red	Pearl	Horowitz	A
6578	Remember Pearl Harbor / Buy bonds / so long as etc. [env. 6 3/4x3 3/4 in.]	Black	Pearl	Fabian	A
6579	Remember Pearl Harbor / Buy defense etc. [thermographed]	Unknown	Pearl	Crosby	B
6580	Remember Pearl Harbor / Buy war bonds	Unknown	Pearl	Runge	A
6581	Remember Pearl Harbor / Buy war bonds [envelope 6 5/16x3 1/2 in.]	Unknown	Pearl	Price, EK	A
6582	Remember Pearl Harbor / Buy war stamps and bonds / Let's go! etc. [thermographed]	Bu,R/Bu,Gd	Pearl	Crosby	B
6583	Remember Pearl Harbor / Dec. the 7th! 1941 / Navy etc. [env. 8 7/8x3 7/8 in.]	Blue	Pearl	Navy Yard	C
6584	Remember Pearl Harbor / Dec. the 7th! 1941 / Navy etc. [env. 8 7/8x3 7/8 in.]	Blue	Eagle	Navy	B
6585	Remember Pearl Harbor / Dec. the 7th! 1942 / Navy Yard / [etc.] / First etc.	Plue, purple	Pearl	Navy Yard	B
6586	Remember Pearl Harbor / Dec. the 7th! 1942 / Navy Yard Pearl Harbor	Purple	Pearl	Navy Yard	B
6587	Remember Pearl Harbor / December 7, 1941 / "...A date which" etc. [no picture]	Black	Pearl	Unknown	A
6588	Remember Pearl Harbor / December 7, 1941 [env. 6 1/2x3 5/8, 6 3/4x3 3/4 in.]	Unknown	Pearl	Davis, Ral	A
6589	Remember Pearl Harbor / December 7, 1941 etc. [no picture]	Unknown	Pearl	Bean	A
6590	Remember Pearl Harbor / For defense / buy etc. [thermographed]	Unknown	Pearl	Crosby	B
6591	Remember Pearl Harbor / For national defense etc. [thermographed]	Unknown	Pearl	Crosby	B
6592	Remember Pearl Harbor / Help put / 'em etc. [sailor speaking] [thermographed]	Unknown	Pearl	Crosby	B
6593	Remember Pearl Harbor / Keep 'em dying	Bk/Bu/Gd/Gn	Pearl	McCluney	A
6594	Remember Pearl Harbor / Keep 'em flying etc.	Unknown	Pearl	Bean	A
6595	Remember Pearl Harbor / Let's / [etc.] / and do not / forget etc. [thermographed]	Unknown	Pearl	Crosby	B
6596	Remember Pearl Harbor / Let's / [etc.] / Buy war etc. [thermographed]	Unknown	Pearl	Crosby	B

NO.	CACHET TEXT	COLOR	TOPIC	PUBLISHER	$
6597	Remember Pearl Harbor / Let's / [etc.] / do not / forget Wake etc. [thermographed]	Unknown	Pearl	Crosby	B
6598	Remember Pearl Harbor / Let's / [etc.] / U.S. Marines etc. [thermographed]	Unknown	Pearl	Crosby	B
6599	Remember Pearl Harbor / Old Glory / Back the etc.	Blue, red	Pearl	Fabian	A
6600	Remember Pearl Harbor / Old Glory / Remember etc.	Blue, red	Pearl	Fabian	A
6601	Remember Pearl Harbor / Old Glory / The Star- etc. [envelope 6 3/4x3 3/4 in.]	Blue, red	Pearl	Fabian	A
6602	Remember Pearl Harbor / Remember Japanese etc. [envelope 6 3/4x3 3/4 in.]	Unknown	Pearl	Fabian	A
6603	Remember Pearl Harbor / Stand by / your President [thermographed]	Black	FDR	Osborn	C
6604	Remember Pearl Harbor / The Star- Spangled Banner / Oh!—— etc. [permit imprint]	Black	Pearl	Russell	C
6605	Remember Pearl Harbor / The Star-Spangled Banner etc. [env. 6 3/4x3 3/4 in.]	Unknown	Pearl	Fabian	A
6606	Remember Pearl Harbor / United States Army / in the etc. [thermographed]	Unknown	Pearl	Crosby	B
6607	Remember Pearl Harbor / United States Coast Guard etc. [thermographed]	Unknown	Pearl	Crosby	B
6608	Remember Pearl Harbor / We must win / Buy etc. [thermographed]	Unknown	Pearl	Lind	B
6609	Remember Pearl Harbor [eagle and shield]	Brown	Pearl	Runge	A
6610	Remember Pearl Harbor [flag UL, plane diving at ship LL]	Unknown	Pearl	Dime	A
6611	Remember Pearl Harbor [in quotes] / American Indian scout is etc. [thermographed]	Red	Pearl	Crosby	B
6612	Remember Pearl Harbor [in quotes] / Ace of Spades of Marine etc. [thermographed]	Black	USMC	Crosby	B
6613	Remember Pearl Harbor [in quotes] / and do not / forget Wake etc. [thermographed]	Red	Pearl	Crosby	B
6614	Remember Pearl Harbor [in quotes] / and do not etc. [thermographed]	Gray	Pearl	Crosby	B
6615	Remember Pearl Harbor [in quotes] / Buy war stamps and bonds [thermographed]	Brown	Axis	Crosby	B
6616	Remember Pearl Harbor [in quotes] / For national defense / A etc. [thermographed]	Green	Pearl	Sadworth	B
6617	Remember Pearl Harbor [in quotes] / Sarge, will you / sell me etc. [thermographed]	Brown	Pearl	Crosby	B
6618	Remember Pearl Harbor [in quotes] / See etc. [top line 63 or 44 mm] [thermographed]	Red	Army	Crosby	B
6619	Remember Pearl Harbor [in quotes] / Torpedo / them / sky etc. [thermographed]	Black	Air	Crosby	B
6620	Remember Pearl Harbor [in quotes] / United States Army etc. [Alaska church]	Blue	Pearl	Crosby	B
6621	Remember Pearl Harbor [in quotes] [eagle and soldier] [handpainted]	Black	Pearl	Unknown	C
6622	Remember Pearl Harbor [in quotes] [eagle]	Brown/Red	Pearl	Runge	A
6623	Remember Pearl Harbor [in quotes] [env. 6 1/2x3 5/8, 6 3/4x3 3/4 in.]	Red	Pearl	Haynes	A
6624	Remember Pearl Harbor [in quotes] [UL, below flag]	Blue, red	Pearl	Unknown	A
6625	Remember Pearl Harbor [printed 4 times, once along each border] [12/20/41]	Blue, red	Pearl	Unknown	F
6626	Remember Pearl Harbor [rubber stamp]	Violet	Pearl	Rio Grande	B
6627	Remember Pearl Harbor [soldier with rifle at attention]	Black	Pearl	Unknown	C
6628	Remember Pearl Harbor! / Keep / 'em / flying [envelope 9 1/2x4 1/8 in.]	Unknown	Pearl	Garfield	A
6629	Remember Pearl Harbor! [airplane gunner, 13 stars in semi-circle]	Blue, red	Pearl	Powers	A
6630	Remember Pearl Harbor! [flag UL; text printed red, UR]	Blue, red	Flag	Linprint	A
6631	Remember Pearl Harbor! [text printed black, UR; flag, left, handpainted]	Multicolored	Flag	Van Alsbur	C
6632	Remember Pearl Harbor!!! [in quotes] [no picture]	Red	Pearl	Unknown	C
6633	Remember Pearl Harbor, Midway / [etc.] / Keep 'em frying / Buy etc. [thermographed]	Red	Axis	Crosby	B
6634	Remember Pearl Harbor, Midway / [etc.] / Keep 'em frying [thermographed]	Red	Axis	Crosby	B
6634A	Remember Pearl Harbor, Midway / [etc.] / "Keep 'em on the run" etc. [double cachet] [thermographed]	Red	Axis	Crosby	D
6635	Remember Pearl Harbor, Midway, Wake, etc. [map, South Pacific] [thermographed]	Blue	Map	Crosby	C
6636	Remember Pearl Harbor/ Help put / 'em etc. [soldier speaking] [thermographed]	Unknown	Pearl	Crosby	B
6637	Remember Red Cross / and / Pearl Harbor	Bk/Br/Red	RedCr	McFarland	A
6638	Remember Red Cross / and / Pearl Harbor [envelope 9 1/2x4 1/8 in.]	Blue/Brown	RedCr	Cozart	A
6639	Remember the / Pearl Harbor sneak attack / Finish the fight	Blue, red	Pearl	Morri, PC	A
6640	Remember the / U.S.S. Panay? / bombed by Japs etc. [thermographed]	Unknown	Navy	Crosby	B
6641	Remember the boys "over there" / and buy more war bonds	Unknown	Bonds	Runge	A
6642	Remember the dollars you gave / to the Red Cross last March? etc. [no picture]	Blue, red	RedCr	Brenn	A
6643	Remember the Panay! Remember Manila! / Maintain American traditions! etc.	Multicolored	Flag	Edmunds	D
6644	Remember the Philippines [in quotes] / Buy war bonds	Blue, red	Eagle	Runge	A
6645	Remember to / buy / that / Victory / bond / to-day! [handpainted]	Multicolored	Bonds	Borkowski	D
6646	Remember Wake Is. and Guam	Blue, red	Eagle	Runge	A
6647	Remember! / Our boys, / roaming the seven seas, etc. [no picture] [color varieties]	Multicolored	Bonds	Linto	B
6648	Remember! The Lexington, the / Yorktown etc.	Unknown	Navy	Brenn	A
6649	Remembering Pearl Harbor / Coral Sea / Midway / [etc.] / Dec. 7th / 1941-1943	Blue, red	Pearl	Sayama	B
6650	Remember-Pearl / Harbor	Black	Pearl	Unknown	A
6651	Remember-Pearl / Harbor	Black	Pearl	Unknown	A
6652	Remember——when / spending for / [etc.] / 9-13-'40——Buckingham Palace etc.	Multicolored	Anniv	Linto	B
6653	Remember——when / spending for / pleasure bonds / come first! [no picture]	Multicolored	Bonds	Linto	B

NO.	CACHET TEXT	COLOR	TOPIC	PUBLISHER	$
6655	Rememer [sic] / Pearl Harbor / Give 'em 'ell	Unknown	Pearl	Price, EK	A
6656	Remind Jap sympathizers / the Nips / [etc.] / 6-3-'45——"Wildcat" Halsey etc.	Multicolored	Event	Linto	B
6657	Remind Jap sympathizers / the Nips started this war. / We're going to etc.	Multicolored	Flag	Linto	B
6658	Rendezvous for another "Big Three"	Multicolored	Nazis	Peer	B
6659	Rep. Adolph J. Sabath, Dem., / Illinois, wants to know why / 30,000 officers etc.	Gold, silver	Armed	Linto	B
6660	Rescued Allied prisoners / reveal Nazi bestial treat- / ment equal to the etc.	Multicolored	Flag	Linto	B
6661	Resolve now to free our / [etc.] / 7-4-'44——St. Jores, Normandy / captured etc.	Multicolored	Event	Linto	B
6662	Resolve now to free our / country from the clutches / of the bureaucrats!	Blue, gold	Bell	Linto	B
6663	Resolved—— / We will, we must, / save more waste / paper in 1945!!	Blue	Flag	Davis, D	A
6664	Restoration Day / March 10, 1943 / Territory of Hawaii, U. S. A. etc.	Blue	Hawai	Sayama	C
6665	Return our / government / to its status of / a republic / Nov. 7, 1944	Gold, orange	Home	Linto	B
6666	Review of 1943 [artist: Staehle]	Multicolored	Ally	Smartcraft	C
6667	Rickenbacker's / crew believed / in etc.	Unknown	Unk	McGovern	A
6668	Riding for a downfall, / on a dying horse. [handpainted]	Multicolored	Hitle	Parker	B
6669	Right / in der / Fuhrer's ["u" with umlaut] / face [in quotes]	Blue/Red	Hitle	Mutual	A
6670	Right / Might [text diagonal] / Both on our side	Blue	Amed	Griffith	A
6671	Right / Might [text diagonal] / Both on our side / as the invasion starts	Blue	Armed	Griffith	A
6672	Right in der Fuehrer's face etc. [envelope 8 11/16x3 5/8 in.]	Unknown	Hitle	ITE Circui	B
6673	Right in der Fuehrer's face!	Bu,br/Bu,R	Hitle	Boone	A
6674	Right in the Fuerhrer's [sic] face / Perhaps you etc. [no fancy cancel]	Green	Hitle	Buckalew	B
6675	Right in the Fuerhrer's [sic] face / Perhaps you haven't etc. [with fancy cancel]	Green	Hitle	Buckalew	C
6676	Right in ther [sic] Fuehrers face! / This is a salute / to etc. [handpainted]	Multicolored	Hitle	Borkowski	D
6677	Right in Tojo's face!	Blue, red	Ordna	Boone	A
6678	Right thinking is all / important and our / faith in God will / bring the etc.	Unknown	Flag	Linto	B
6679	Right where the Rising Sun sets [text below picture] [cachet colors vary]	Multicolored	Japan	Peer	B
6680	Right where the Rising Sun sets! [text above picture] [cachet colors vary]	Multicolored	Japan	Peer	B
6681	Right where the Rising Sun sets! [text below picture] [cachet colors vary]	Multicolored	Japan	Peer	B
6682	Ring it for the world in '45	Brown	Unk	Harrington	A
6683	Road to / victory [on back] [envelope 7 1/2x4 in.]	Unknown	Unk	Johnson, D	A
6684	Roads to / Berlin / Friday, August 18, 1944 etc. [no picture]	Unknown	Event	Boone	B
6685	Roads to / Berlin / Saturday August 5th, 1944 etc. [no picture]	Red	Event	Boone	B
6686	Rock-a-bye baby, sleep like a top / You're very safe, for your mom and etc.	Blue, red	Verse	Threl+Thar	A
6687	Romania / joins Allies [no picture]	Red	Event	Boone	A
6688	Romania / joins Allies [thermographed]	Unknown	Event	Boone	B
6689	Romania, / [etc.] / at / war / with U.S.A. / Dec. 13, 1941 [no picture] [card]	Red	Event	Fidelity	D
6690	Rome / + / Berlin / + / Tokyo = [handpainted]	Multicolored	Japan	Long	C
6691	Rome / bombed / July 19 / 1943	Black, red	Event	Fidelity	B
6692	Rome / falls to / Allies [no picture]	Green	Event	Boone	B
6693	Rome falls! / Axis world crumbles / When falls the Colisuem, / Rome shall fall etc.	Violet	Battl	Griffith	A
6694	Rommel the——— / In Normandy, once more they meet, Montgomery again etc.	Blue, red	Romm	Carpenter	A
6695	Roosevelt / and / MacArthur / in Hawaii / F.D.R. visits etc. [no picture]	Blue, red	Event	Fidelity	B
6696	Roosevelt / Churchill / Kai-shek / confer at / Cairo [no picture]	Black, red	Event	Fidelity	B
6697	Roosevelt [flags of Big 4 nations surround FDR]	Blue, gold	FDR	Runge	B
6698	Roosevelt makes / startling discovery! / Maturity, efficiency / are necessary!	Blue, gold	FDR	Linto	B
6699	Roosevelt memorial	Unknown	FDR	Staehle	C
6700	Roosevelt memorial / Franklin D. Roosevelt etc.	Purple	FDR	Farnam	B
6701	Roosevelt slept here / [etc.] / Le Chateau / Frontenac in etc. [handpainted]	Multicolored	FDR	Larocque	D
6702	Roosevelt with the Chinese 'Royal Family' [envelope 6 9/16x3 3/4 in.]	Unknown	FDR	Belles-let	C
6703	Roosevelt's / patriotic stamps / "Did I ever show you my stamps Winnie?" etc.	Black	FDR	Linprint	B
6704	Rough / and / ready	Unknown	Unk	Schirmer	A
6705	Round three! / Invasion bond drive / [etc.] / Dec. 7, 1941, a date we will etc.	Multicolored	Pearl	Linto	B
6706	Round three! / Invasion bond drive / Let's show Uncle / we etc. [no picture]	Multicolored	Bonds	Linto	B
6707	RU / waiting or working / for victory?	Unknown	Unk	McCluney	A
6708	Rub-a-dub-dub, most any day, now / [etc.] / Hon. / Jap fleet [handpainted]	Black	Japan	Sturgill	E
6709	Ruin / Holding back the guillotine [handpainted]	Multicolored	Hitle	Adler	D
6710	Rumors [in quotes] [handpainted]	Blue	Army	Wolf, CL	C
6711	Run, damn you, / run! You ask / for it. You're / going to / get it!	Unknown	Japan	Linto	B
6712	Run, run, as fast as you can, / but where to my little man?	Blue/Red	Hitle	Ang	A

NO.	CACHET TEXT	COLOR	TOPIC	PUBLISHER	$
6714	Running to beat hell / War bonds will speed his return	Black	Japan	Donaldson	A
6715	Running to buy a war bond / Have you bought yours today?	Black	Bonds	Unknown	A
6716	Run-Tojo-run / We're gonna set / your rising sun / war / bonds	Purple	Japan	Yontz	A
6717	Run-Tojo-run / We're gonna set / your rising sun [thermographed]	Purple/Red	Japan	Yontz	B
6718	Run-Tojo-run / We're gonna set / your rising sun [with map of Pacific islands]	Red	Japan	Yontz	A
6719	Russan [sic] brake [sic] / pact with / Japan [handpainted]	Multicolored	Japan	Monty	C
6720	Russia / at war with / Japan / Russia declares war / on Japan / August 8, 1945	Multicolored	Event	Teixeira	D
6721	Russia / declares / war / with / Japan [thermographed]	Unknown	Event	Boone	B
6722	Russia / United Nations [handpainted]	Multicolored	UN	Weigand	B
6723	Russia declares / war on Japan / On Aug. 8th / Japan's / worst fears etc.	Multicolored	Event	Fluegel	C
6724	Russia declares war on Japan	Multicolored	Event	Smartcraft	C
6725	Russia for Russians / Hell for Japs and Huns / America for Americans	Multicolored	Flag	Linto	B
6726	Russia is fighting! / Why worry about / what they may do?	Multicolored	Eagle	Linto	B
6727	Russian / marines / capture naval etc. [thermographed]	Unknown	Event	Boone	B
6728	Russian army / enters Germany	Unknown	Event	Thr+Bu+T	B
6729	Russian drive / Dismember the German etc.	Unknown	USSR	Runge	A
6730	Russians / capture / Odessa [no picture]	Blue, red	Event	Boone	B
6731	Russians / enter / Bulgaria / Americans etc. [no picture] [thermographed]	Black	Event	Boone	B
6732	Russians / siege / Sevastapol / 24 days and take it / It had etc. [no picture]	Black, red	Event	Fidelity	B
6733	Russians are / helping the / [etc.] / America awakened by Japs / December etc.	Multicolored	Pearl	Linto	B
6734	Russians are / helping the / [etc.] / Commemorating "Bill of Rights" Day etc.	Aqua, gold	Home	Linto	B
6735	Russians are / helping the / Germans to / get home by / Christmas! [no picture]	Green, red	Holid	Linto	B
6736	Russians blitz Smolensk	Unknown	Event	Linto	B
6737	Russians capture / Potsdam / - Yanks etc. [no picture] [thermographed]	Unknown	Event	Boone	B
6738	Russians capture Anapa	Unknown	Event	Linto	B
6739	Russians capture Kharkov	Unknown	Event	Linto	B
6740	Russians capture Rostov	Unknown	Event	Linto	B
6741	Russians recapture Orel	Unknown	Event	Linto	B
6742	Russians regain Novorossisk	Unknown	Event	Linto	B
6743	Russians stop Nazi attack	Unknown	Event	Linto	B
6744	Russians take Dnieper	Unknown	Event	Linto	B
6745	Russia's cancellation / of Jap treaty / [etc.] / Does your cigarette taste etc.	Black	Japan	Krakora	B

Cover Values (from Table 6, p. 136)

Value	*Price Range*
A	$ 3 - 6
B	$ 7 - 15
C	$ 16 - 30
D	$ 31 - 60
E	$ 61 - 125
F	$ 126 - 250
G	$ 251 - 500
H	$ 501 - 1000
I	$ >1000
X	Unpriced: Suspicious or fraudulent cover

6383

6419

6454

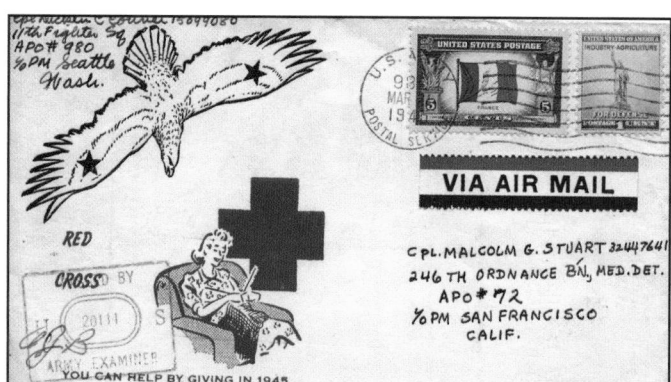

6472

6488

6508

6518

6539

6584

6631

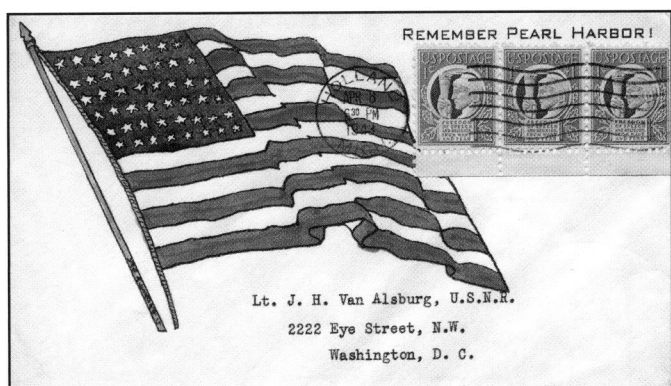

6634A

6680

6691

6701

6720

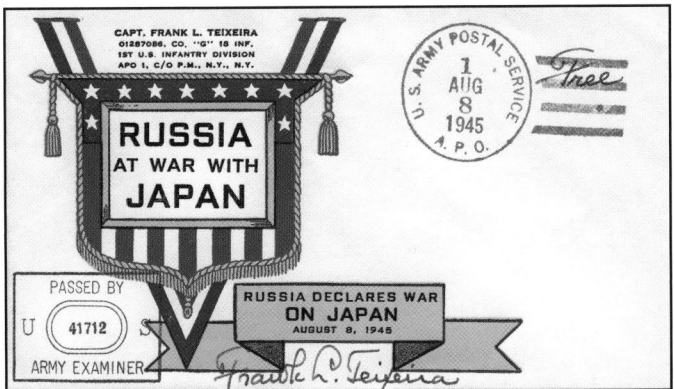

6724

CACHET TEXT BEGINNING WITH "S"

NO.	CACHET TEXT	COLOR	TOPIC	PUBLISHER	$
6746	S.O.S. to / Abe Lincoln! / Please come and help! / Washington, D.C. etc.	Gold, silver	Linc	Linto	B
6747	Sabotage by Poles / [etc.] / 2-22-'44——Russians run Huns out of / Krivoi etc.	Unknown	Event	Linto	B
6748	Sabotage by Poles / during 1943 / Blowing up 3 ammunition / trains and etc.	Unknown	ORN	Linto	B
6749	Sabotage! / Beware of / black markets! [no picture]	Multicolored	Home	Linto	B
6750	Saburo Kurusu, special / Japanese envoy / [etc.] / Nov. 15, 1941. [handpainted]	Black, gold	Event	Batura	E
6751	Sacred [in quotes] / German / soil / Russia	Gold, green	USSR	Peer	B
6752	Sacred soil? / Today on Germany's etc.	Red	Unk	Abel	A
6753	Sacrifice / "but not our" / freedom [handpainted]	Multicolored	Flag	Adler	D
6754	Sacrifice / the privilege of free men / Find your etc. [label + printed border]	Multicolored	Army	Artists	B
6755	Sacrifice with a grin, and help the Allies reach Berlin	Multicolored	Home	Runge	A
6756	Sacrifice with a grin, and help the Allies reach Berlin	Blue/Gold/Re	Home	Runge	A
6757	Sad Sack in Normandy. [handpainted]	Black	Army	Schirmer	B
6758	Sad words of '43 / 16 / Butter / points per pound [handpainted]	Black	Home	Wolf, CL	B
6759	Sad words of '43 / Closed / for the / duration [handpainted]	Black	Home	Wolf, CL	B
6760	Sad words of '43 / No / beer / today [handpainted]	Black	Home	Wolf, CL	B
6761	Sad words of '43 / Only one / to a / customer [handpainted]	Black	Home	Wolf, CL	B
6762	Sad words of '43 / Pay / as you / go [handpainted]	Black	Home	Wolf, CL	B
6763	Safe and sure / your war bond / dollars	Brown	Bonds	Phill, CR	A
6764	Safe and sure / your war bond / dollars [no picture]	Brown	Bonds	Phill, CR	A
6765	Safe and sure / your war bond / dollars [thermographed]	Unknown	Bonds	Phill, CR	A
6766	Safeguard our / American ideals	Multicolored	Uncle	Linto	B
6767	Safely guard our / sacred birthright	Blue, red	Flag	Carpenter	A
6768	Saidor / Tokyo - you're doomed! [32nd Infantry Division insignia]	Multicolored	Japan	McCluney	B
6769	Sail to / victory / Holo ia / lanakila	Blue, red	Hawai	Sayama	B
6770	Sailing for / victory [sailing ship]	Unknown	Unk	Card	A
6771	Sailing for / victory [steamship]	Unknown	Unk	Card	A
6772	Sailing for victory	Unknown	Unk	Kosko	A
6773	Sailing for victory [border: ship and anchor]	Unknown	Unk	Kosko	A
6774	Saipan / Aleutians / Casablanca / Rabaul / [etc.] / shall / not have / died in vain. [hp]	Multicolored	Battl	Griffith	B
6775	Saipan / Tinian / Guam	Red	Armed	Christens	A
6776	Salute / Marine / Corps / Women's / Reserves	Gold, pink	USMC	Linto	B
6777	Salute the / U.S. military / [etc.] / 10-25-'44——U.S. carrier / etc.	Multicolored	Event	Linto	B
6778	Salute the / U.S. military / medical staff / little heard of / but doing much!	Multicolored	Medic	Linto	B
6779	Salute to / Czechoslovakia / Tyranny / cannot crush / a noble spirit	Blue, red	ORN	Fleetwood	B
6780	Salute to / Denmark / Bid / freedom / arise / o'er Danish skies	Blue, red	ORN	Fleetwood	B
6781	Salute to / Luxembourg / A nation small / will risk its all / for liberty	Blue, red	ORN	Fleetwood	B
6782	Salute to / Moss Hart's / Winged Victory etc. [envelope 9 1/2x4 1/4 in.]	Red	Home	Amer Canc	B
6783	Salute to / Netherlands / "The triumph of justice / will turn the wheels" etc.	Blue, red	ORN	Fleetwood	B
6784	Salute to / you / Pvt. Ray! [burned left, torn right edge] [handpainted]	Multicolored	Army	Cowdery	D
6785	Salute to / Yugoslavia / A valiant spirit / is unconquerable	Blue, red	ORN	Fleetwood	B
6786	Salute to Albania / The / eagle of freedom / wields the sword / of justice	Blue, red	ORN	Fleetwood	B
6787	Salute to Austria / The / light of freedom / will shine / out of the darkness	Blue, red	ORN	Fleetwood	B
6788	Salute to Belgium / The lion of Belgium / still roars defiance	Blue, red	ORN	Fleetwood	B
6789	Salute to France / "To arms, to arms, / ye brave! / The avenging sword" etc.	Blue, red	ORN	Fleetwood	B
6790	Salute to Free Poland / from Warsaw, N.Y. / on day of liberation	Black	ORN	Rameco	A
6791	Salute to Greece / The ages / will applaud a nation's / heroic struggle	Blue, red	ORN	Fleetwood	B
6792	Salute to Korea / That all people may be free from bondage	Blue, red	ORN	Fleetwood	B
6793	Salute to Norway / The / Viking spirit / will not submit / to the oppressor	Blue, red	ORN	Fleetwood	B
6794	Salute to Philippines / I shall etc.	Blue, red	ORN	Fleetwood	B
6795	Salute to Poland / The hearts of / people once free / cannot be enslaved	Blue, red	ORN	Fleetwood	B
6796	Salute to the / Women's / Air Force	Black, gold	WAF	Linto	B
6797	Salute to the / Women's / Air Force / 1-21-'45——Jesse Jones out, / H. etc.	Unknown	Event	Linto	B
6798	Salute, gladly! / You are looking at / [etc.] / 7-4-'44——Jap ships sunk etc.	Unknown	Event	Linto	B
6799	Salute, gladly! / You are looking at the best / flag God ever made!	Unknown	Flag	Linto	B
6800	Salutes to our boys / 1——Salute our boys and make them feel etc. [handpainted]	Multicolored	Liber	Weigand	B
6801	Saluting the / U.S. / Merchant / Marines	Multicolored	FlLib	Linto	B

NO.	CACHET TEXT	COLOR	TOPIC	PUBLISHER	$
6802	Saluting the / U.S. / Merchant / Marines / 11-5-'44——Robot bombs continue etc.	Multicolored	Event	Linto	B
6803	Salvage / all waste fats / It will help / save / some etc. [no picture]	Green	Home	Rowe	A
6804	Salvage / for Victory [wrapper] [folded: 6x3 1/8 in.; unfolded: 9 3/8x6 in.]	Black	Home	War Prod 1	D
6805	Salvage [in quotes]	Blue	Axis	Lawrence	A
6806	Salvage for / victory / committees / vital to the war / effort but little etc.	Multicolored	Flag	Linto	B
6807	Sample of "Der / Master Race" / National Zoo [handpainted]	Multicolored	Hitle	Parker	C
6808	San Francisco / No >> 80108 / U.S. Army / American Base / Forces A.P.O. 914	Blue	Army	Czubay	C
6809	San Francisco / No >> 80118 / U.S. Army / American Base / Forces A.P.O. 915	Blue	Army	Czubay	C
6810	San Francisco / No >> 80240 / U.S. Army / Postal Service / A.P.O. 502	Blue	Army	Czubay	C
6811	San Francisco Conference / Concentration etc.	Red	UN	Coll Surp	A
6812	San Francisco Conference / In any country etc.	Red	UN	Coll Surp	A
6813	San Francisco Conference / Prisoners etc.	Red	UN	Coll Surp	A
6814	San Francisco Conference / United etc.	Red	UN	Coll Surp	A
6815	San Francisco Conference / We had thought etc.	Red	UN	Coll Surp	A
6816	Sandstorm Division [in quotes] / Attack / attack / "Let us keep faith" etc.	Multicolored	Unit	Goede	B
6817	Sandstorm Division [in quotes] / Attack / attack [34th Infantry Division insignia]	Black, red	Unit	Unknown	B
6818	Sandstorm Division [in quotes] / We pledge -'that they / have not died in vain'	Black, red	Unit	Goede	B
6819	Santa / Maria [in quotes] [handpainted]	Multicolored	Hist	Shaffer, A	C
6820	Santa asks us all to give war / bonds & stamps as gifts / this Christmas.	Bu/Gn/Red	Holid	Phill, CR	B
6821	Santa says / "This Christmas / give war bonds" etc.	Unknown	Holid	Lowell	B
6822	Santa says: Give bonds and etc. [thermographed] [env. 4 9/16x4 5/8 in.]	Unknown	Holid	Phill, CR	B
6823	Santa says: Give only gifts that etc. [thermographed] [env. 5 3/4x4 3/4 in.]	Unknown	Holid	Phill, CR	B
6824	Santa says: We're buying etc. [thermographed] [env. 5 7/8x4 7/8 in.]	Unknown	Holid	Phill, CR	B
6825	Sarge, will you / sell me about / [etc.] / Buy defense stamps etc. [thermographed]	Brown	Army	Crosby	B
6826	Sarge, will you / sell me about / [etc.] / Remember Pearl etc. [thermographed]	Brown	Army	Crosby	B
6827	Sarge, will you / sell me about 60 / feet of barbed / wire? etc. [thermographed]	Brown	Army	Crosby	B
6828	Sarge, will you / sell me etc. [w/, w/o "Greetings from", UL] [thermographed]	Unknown	Army	Crosby	B
6829	Savagery / at its worst - / from now on! [handpainted]	Multicolored	Axis	Knapp	G
6830	Save / for the future / by / buying etc.	Unknown	Bonds	Kosko	A
6831	Save / newspapers / Back the attack! / Turn in your scrap!	Black, red	Home	Speede	A
6832	Save / waste / paper / Help fight / the paper / hanger with / it	Green	Home	Rowe	A
6833	Save /a / bundle / of / waste paper / a / week / The waste etc. [no picture]	Green	Home	Unknown	B
6834	Save a / life / Your blood is needed etc.	Unknown	Blood	Kosko	A
6835	Save all / brown paper and / brown paper board / for victory etc. [color varieties]	Multicolored	Flag	Linto	B
6836	Save and / prepare / all cans / and / help etc. [no picture]	Unknown	Home	Rowe	A
6837	Save every drop / of fat / It will / help etc. [no picture]	Unknown	Home	Rowe	A
6838	Save fats! / America's bullets are fired etc.	Bu/Gn/Purple	Unk	Lowe	A
6839	Save for / victory / V / The Savings Banks / of New York State	Black	VforV	Lohr	A
6840	Save for / war bonds / and / victory	Green	Bonds	Hillerich	A
6841	Save freedom of speech / Buy war bonds	Unknown	Bonds	Rush, H	A
6842	Save freedom of worship / Buy war bonds	Unknown	Bonds	Rush, H	A
6843	Save manpower for warpower / "So sorry accident keep / you from making" etc.	Brown	Japan	Burdick	A
6844	Save manpower for warpower / Any cigarette will / cause irritation—— / if etc.	Black	Home	Burdick	A
6845	Save manpower for warpower / Steady production / will keep him / on top!	Bk/Bu/Brown	Army	Burdick	A
6846	Save paper, all paper is valuable etc.	Unknown	Home	Brenn	A
6847	Save rubber / Check your tires now	Blue, red	Flag	Rush, H	A
6848	Save waste fats / to bomb Axis rats	Black/Red	Axis	Smith, AD	A
6849	Save waste fats for explosives etc.	Unknown	Home	Rush, H	A
6850	Save your cans / Help pass etc.	Unknown	Home	Rush, H	A
6851	Save! / your old papers / call the / Salvation Army	Blue, red	Uncle	Unk	A
6852	Saving "face" [thermographed]	Blue, red	Japan	Von Los	B
6853	Saving / face [thermographed]	Blue, red	Japan	Von Los	B
6854	Saving just a small percent etc.	Blue	Unk	Temple	A
6855	Say it with / 1944 / V / bombers [handpainted]	Blue, red	Air	Klaas	C
6856	Say, bud! How about / investing in a little / freedom today? [handpainted]	Black	Bonds	Parker	B
6857	Scales to / weigh the / anchor, sir! [thermographed] [envelope 6 1/2x4 11/16 in.]	Unknown	Navy	Cleveland	A
6858	Schicklegruber / blues: / "O Lord , if you / can't help me; / for" etc.	Brown, red	USSR	Boone	A
6859	Schicklgruber	Black	Hitle	Sadworth	A

NO.	CACHET TEXT	COLOR	TOPIC	PUBLISHER	$
6860	Schicklgruber / That liberty / shall not / perish from etc. [thermographed]	Black/Multi	Hitle	Sadworth	B
6861	Schnicklegrubber / has big / ears for / gossip. / So keep your mouth etc. [handpainted]	Blue	Hitle	Parker	B
6862	Schubert / didn't / finish his / symphony——— / damned if / I don't etc. [handpainted]	Multicolored	Uncle	Steinhardt	C
6863	Scores of these planes over Germany soaring / are a pain in the neck etc.	Blue	Air	Carter	A
6864	Scouting squadron [border for horizontal label] [thermographed]	Blue	Air	Lind	A
6865	Scouting squadron [border for horizontal or vertical label] [thermographed]	Brown	Air	Lind	A
6866	Scram / the one word they'll never forget!	Blue	Axis	Lawrence	A
6867	Scraping the bottom of the barrel	Multicolored	Nazis	Peer	B
6868	Scratch / one flat top [in quotes]	Black	Air	Coll Surp	A
6869	Scrubanwashclos! [in quotes]	Black	Navy	Lupton	A
6870	Seabees / are a most / [etc.] / 10-31-'44———Allies win the battle / of Antwerp	Unknown	Event	Linto	B
6871	Seabees / are a most / important link / for victory	Unknown	Navy	Linto	B
6872	Seabees / If the army or the navy, / ever gaze on heaven's scenes, / they etc.	Blue/Yellow	Navy	McCluney	B
6873	Seabees / U.S. Naval Construction Training Center	Blue	Navy	Navy Dept.	C
6874	Seabees / U.S. Navy	Blue	Navy	Navy	A
6875	Seabees / United States / Naval Construction Battalions	Unknown	Navy	McCluney	A
6876	Seabees / United States Navy [envelope 7 1/2x4 in.]	Blue	Navy	Navy	B
6877	Seabees etc.	Unknown	Navy	Linto	B
6878	Sealed lips / will save / our ships	Blue, red	Navy	Roberts	A
6879	Season's / greetings [coat of arms]	Unknown	Holid	Runge	B
6880	Season's / greetings [eagle above flag]	Unknown	Holid	Runge	B
6881	Season's / greetings [poinsettia] [handpainted]	Multicolored	Holid	Adler	C
6882	Season's / greetings [postmarked 12/25/41]	Multicolored	Holid	Linto	B
6883	Seasons greetings / Merry Christmas etc. [thermographed]	Unknown	Holid	Czubay	B
6884	Season's greetings, 1944 [Uncle Sam]	Green, red	Holid	Carpenter	B
6885	Sec. Morgenthau says he / [etc.] / 1-26-'44———Germans surrender / Cassino etc.	Multicolored	Event	Linto	B
6886	Sec. Morgenthau says he / hasn't time to milk his / pedigreed etc. [no picture]	Gd,Vi/Gn,S	Home	Linto	B
6887	Sec. Stimson calls for / draft of labor! / [etc.] / 2-2-'40———Finland asks etc.	Unknown	Anniv	Linto	B
6888	Sec. Stimson calls for / draft of labor! / Has anyone ever heard / any of etc.	Unknown	Home	Linto	B
6889	Second / anniversary / of Pearl Harbor / Dec. 7, 1941 Dec. 7, 1943 [no picture]	Unknown	Pearl	Morri, EW	A
6890	Second [2d] Battalion F.A.S. Detachment / Fort Sill / Oklahoma [coat of arms]	Black, purple	Unit	Ashley	A
6891	Second [2nd] strike - coal miners	Unknown	Home	Linto	B
6892	Second [2nd] war bond day / May 1, 1943 / Lei Day / Hawaii / 1943 etc.	Blue, red	Hawai	Sayama	B
6893	Second Army [manuscript lettering under numeral insignia] [handpainted]	Black, red	Unit	Dannells	B
6894	Second Army [typed under numeral insignia] [handpainted]	Black, red	Unit	Dannells	B
6895	Second front / France / June 6, 1944 / "Under the command / of" etc. [no picture]	Blue, red	Event	Fidelity	B
6896	Second to none / U.S. Army	Blue, red	Army	Boone	A
6897	Secure your / victory vacation / [etc.] / 10-5-'44———Yank subs sink 11 etc.	Multicolored	Event	Linto	B
6898	Secure your / victory vacation / with / victory bonds [no picture]	Gold, silver	Bonds	Linto	B
6899	Security / war bonds / 7th war loan drive / May 14 - June 30, 1945	Gold, purple	Bonds	Eichenlaub	B
6900	See / here / before / all else / buy war bonds	Unknown	Bonds	Kosko	A
6901	See what I mean / Captain? From the / air it looks like etc. [thermographed]	Red	Army	Crosby	B
6902	Seeing stars——— / and stripes	Red	Japan	Neal	A
6903	Seeking a bird's perspective [in quotes] [env. 6 9/16x3 3/4, 6 3/4x 3 7/8 in.]	Multicolored	Globe	Belles-let	D
6904	Semper Fidelis	Black	USMC	Lupton	A
6905	Semper Fidelis / "Wake Island" - "Guadalcanal" / "Tarawa" - "Saipan"	Red	USMC	Neal	A
6906	Semper Fidelis / Fly high, sky high/ with / United States Air Force [thermographed]	Gold	Air	Crosby	B
6907	Semper Fidelis / If the army / [etc.] / Corps Base San Diego etc. [thermographed]	Black, orange	USMC	Crosby	B
6908	Semper Fidelis / If the army / [etc.] / Holland M. Smith etc. [thermographed]	Unknown	USMC	Crosby	B
6909	Semper Fidelis / If the army / [etc.] / Rifle range, Marine Corps etc. [thermographed]	Red	USMC	Crosby	B
6910	Semper Fidelis / If the army / [etc.] / U.S.S. Saratoga [thermographed]	Black, orange	USMC	Crosby	B
6911	Semper Fidelis / If the army and the navy etc. [3 bullseye symbols] [thermographed]	Red	USMC	Crosby	B
6912	Semper Fidelis / If the army and the navy etc. [artillery] [scroll 40 mm] [thermographed]	Red/Silver	USMC	Crosby	B
6913	Semper Fidelis / If the army and the navy etc. [artillery] [scroll 50 mm] [thermographed]	Bk, O/R/S	USMC	Crosby	B
6914	Semper Fidelis / If the army and the navy etc. [beach landing] [thermographed]	Silver	USMC	Crosby	B
6915	Semper Fidelis / U.S. Marines	Unknown	USMC	Boone	A
6916	Semper Fidelis / U.S. Marines [thermographed]	Unknown	USMC	Baur	A
6917	Semper Fidelis / United States / [etc.] / On land and sea / and etc. [thermographed]	Blue, red	USMC	Sadworth	B

NO.	CACHET TEXT	COLOR	TOPIC	PUBLISHER	$
6918	Semper Fidelis [envelope 5 5/8x4 3/8 in.]	Multicolored	USMC	Teich	A
6919	Semper Fidelis [in quotes] / [etc.] / On land and sea / and in the air [thermographed]	Blue, red	USMC	Crosby	B
6920	Semper Fidelis [in quotes] / United States / [etc.] / On land and etc. [thermographed]	Blue, red	USMC	Sadworth	B
6921	Semper fidelis [small USMC symbol, upper left]	Blue	USMC	Unknown	A
6922	Send another line today	Green	Unk	Foster	A
6923	Send him down / anytime! [in quotes] / Buy war bonds [handpainted]	Multicolored	Devil	Knoll	C
6924	Send Hitler back his out- / [etc.] / 12-27-39——Earthquake in Turkey. etc.	Multicolored	NeuNa	Linto	B
6925	Send Hitler back his out- / casts to refill his very fast etc. [no picture]	Gold, red	Hitle	Linto	B
6926	Send letters / to those in the service / by / air mail	Bk,Gn/Gn,Re	Armed	Swartz	A
6927	Send us some / more Japs! [in quotes] / Wake / Island	Black	Armed	Coll Surp	A
6928	Send your wastepaper to war! / etc.]] / 6-19-'45——Yank subs have etc.	Unknown	Event	Linto	B
6929	Send your wastepaper to war! It's vital!	Gold, silver	Home	Linto	B
6930	Sep. 8th / 1943 / Via Sicily / to Italy / and —— "Italy's / surrender" [Ike]	Multicolored	Event	Staehle	C
6931	September 01, 1945 / we are committed / [etc.] / 9-1-'45——This is a etc.	Multicolored	VJDay	Linto	B
6932	Sept 02 1945 [printed vertically] / China / The Chinese / are free - after etc.	Multicolored	China	Fluegel	C
6933	Sept. / Labor Day / one [postmarked 9/1/41]	Multicolored	Holid	Linto	B
6934	Sept. 01, 1944 / (The news is good and getting) etc. [no picture]	Unknown	Unk	McCluney	A
6935	Sept. 02nd V-J Day 1945 / Victory! / "Peace on earth again"	Multicolored	VJDay	Fluegel	C
6936	Sept. 03, 1939 - Britain declares war on Germany [handpainted]	Multicolored	Map	Smith, LH	C
6937	Sept. 03, 1943 - Allied invasion / forces land on the toe of Italy [handpainted]	Multicolored	Map	Smith, LH	C
6938	Sept. 03, 1943 / Allies / invade / Italy [no picture]	Brown, silver	Event	Linto	B
6939	Sept. 05, 1944 - The crumbling fortress [handpainted]	Multicolored	ORN	Smith, LH	C
6940	Sept. 08, 1943——The / Casablanca ultimatum / receives its etc. [handpainted]	Multicolored	Map	Smith, LH	C
6941	Sept. 12, 1944 - Yanks / penetrate the Reich [handpainted]	Multicolored	Map	Smith, LH	C
6942	Sept. 18, 1943 - Important Jap base of Lae falls to / Allies [handpainted]	Multicolored	Map	Smith, LH	C
6943	Sept. 21, 1943——Group of Mediterranean islands / occupied etc. [handpainted]	Multicolored	Map	Smith, LH	C
6944	Sept. 27, 1944 - Phillipines [sic] honored / by the United States etc. [handpainted]	Multicolored	Map	Smith, LH	B
6945	Sept. 28, 1943 - Russians / 100 miles from Polish frontier [handpainted]	Multicolored	Map	Smith, LH	B
6946	September 01, 1945 / Eisenhower MacArthur / Japan signs peace / Truman etc.	Blue, red	VJDay	Fidelity	B
6947	September 01, 1945 / Japan signs peace etc.	Unknown	VJDay	Linto	B
6948	September 01, 1945 / We are committed / [etc.] / 9-1-'45——This is a victory etc	Multicolored	VJDay	Linto	B
6949	September 01, 1945 / We are committed by the Potsdam declaration...to etc.	Gd,S/Multi	VJDay	Linto	B
6950	September 01, 1945 / We shall not forget Pearl Harbor. The etc. [no picture]	Multicolored	VJDay	Linto	B
6951	September 04, 1944 / Belgium / World War II enters its 6th / year as we etc.	Blue, yellow	Event	Fidelity	B
6952	September 05, 1944 / Netherlands / We invade Holland; / Finland quits; etc.	Blue, red	Event	Fidelity	B
6953	September 06, 1944 / Yugoslavia / Soviets invade Yugoslavia; / official etc.	Blue, red	Event	Fidelity	B
6954	September 08, 1943 / Italy accepts / unconditional / surrender etc. [no picture]	S,Gn/S,Purple	Event	Linto	B
6955	September 09, 1944 / Luxembourg / We invade Luxemburg [sic] / We fight etc.	Blue, red	Event	Fidelity	B
6956	September 21, 1939 / A special session of the 76th Congress etc. [typed]	Unknown	Event	Batura	E
6957	September 27, 1944 / We invade Albania	Black, red	Event	Fidelity	B
6958	Serve in silence [V ···– before and after text]	Blue, red	VforV	Dime	A
6959	Service / Commission / National Lutheran Council [Cross and shield] [UL]	Blue, red	Relig	Nat Luther	A
6960	Service man's / wish for 1944 / A WAAC in every shack / a WAVE in every etc.	Blue, red	Armed	Griffith	A
6961	Service men's / Division / National Lutheran Council [Cross and shield] [UL]	Blue, red	Relig	Nat Luther	A
6962	Services at sea	Sepia tones	VJDay	Southworth	B
6963	Serving in etc. [thermographed]	Unknown	Unk	Crosby	B
6964	Sesqui-cuarto centennial / 1492 - 1942 / Columbus etc. [no picture] [thermographed]	Black	Holid	Crosby	B
6965	Set 'em / on their / Axis	Unknown	Axis	East Texas	A
6966	Set 'em / on their / Axis!	Unknown	Axis	Wichita	A
6967	Set your course Buy war bonds [colored envelopes]	Black/Blue	Bonds	Huss	A
6968	Seven [7] .7 / The Japs / started it / on the 7th etc. [no picture]	Unknown	Japan	Ang	A
6969	Seventeen / March / Seventeen / March [postmarked 3/17/41]	Gold, silver	Holid	Linto	B
6970	Seventeen [17]-year-olds / join the Army / specialized / reserves	Multicolored	FlLib	Linto	B
6971	Seventeen ninety [1790]——August 4—/ [etc.] / 8-4-'45——U.S. 11th A.A.F. etc.	Multicolored	Event	Linto	B
6972	Seventeen ninety [1790]——August 4——1945 / 155th birthday of a / little etc.	Green, silver	Coast	Linto	B
6973	Seventeen ninety-three [1793] - 1943--Anniversary of laying of etc. [thermographed]	Violet	Hist	Crosby	B
6974	Seventeen seventy-six [1776]-1812-1845-1865 / 1898-1917 and now etc.	Blue, red	Flag	Unknown	A
6975	Seventh [7th.] [under insignia] [handpainted]	Black, red	Unit	Dannells	B

NO.	CACHET TEXT	COLOR	TOPIC	PUBLISHER	$
6976	Seventh [7th] / war / loan / drive / opens / today / Dig! [no picture]	Red	Bonds	Boone	A
6977	Seventh [7th] / war / loan [no picture] [thermographed]	Red	Bonds	Phillips	B
6978	Seventh [7th] / war / loan [thermographed]	Red	Bonds	Unknown	B
6979	Seventh [7th] war loan / Buy war bonds / Help plant etc. [handpainted]	Multicolored	Bonds	Knoll	C
6980	Seventh Marines / First Marine Division / Fleet Marine Force / First Day etc.	Black	USMC	Czubay	B
6981	Seventy sixth [76th] Squadron / 23rd Fighter [at right] [env. 6 1/4x3 3/16 in.]	Red	Air	Air Force	D
6982	Seventy-fifth [75th] anniversary / of transcontinental / railroads etc.	Black/Purple	Home	Cliff	A
6983	Seventy-fifth [75th] anniversary of the / U.S. railroad etc. [thermographed]	Unknown	Home	Crosby	B
6984	Seventy-fifth anniversary / first / transcontinental / [etc.] / sinews of war	Blue, red	Home	Fleetwood	B
6985	Seventy-second [72nd] Bombardmet [sic] Squadron [under insignia] [handpainted]	Black	Unit	Dannells	B
6986	Seventy-sixth Div. [under insignia] [handpainted]	Multicolored	Unit	Dannells	B
6987	Sez der Fuerher [sic]: / "We are fewer and fewer, since / Italy took to" etc.	Blue, red	Axis	Brenn	A
6988	Sez der Furor [sic] - Ach! / dos tanks wit Yanks! / War bond's [sic] etc.	Bk/Br/Purple	Hitle	Harrington	A
6989	Sgt. / Theodore / Richardson / [etc.] / 2-23-'45———U.S. flag / flies over etc.	Multicolored	Event	Linto	B
6990	Sgt. / Theodore / Richardson / one of 3 / liberators of / Cabanabuan etc.	Green, silver	Hero	Linto	B
6991	Sgt. Joe Louis says / "We're" etc. [env. 6 9/16x3 3/4, 6 3/4x 3 7/8, 7x4 in.]	Unknown	Army	Belles-let	C
6992	Shake off the / shackles of a / "dole" / government [no picture]	Gold, green	Home	Linto	B
6993	Shake off the / shackles of a / [etc.] / 8-28-'44———Huns flee up Rhone! etc.	Multicolored	Event	Linto	B
6994	Shall Hirohito / Hitler supplement King Neptune etc. [thermographed]	Multicolored	Axis	Crosby	B
6995	Shall the Axis replace King Neptune? / Let's set the "Rising" etc. [thermographed]	Multicolored	Axis	Crosby	B
6996	Shall wave / "in honor" / again. [handpainted]	Blue, red	ORN	Adler	D
6997	Shall we fail / those on the / battle fronts? / No! / We will / buy U.S. etc.	Multicolored	Bonds	Linto	B
6998	Shall we go / Pattonslappingly / [etc.] / Commemorating "Bill of Rights" etc.	Multicolored	Anniv	Linto	B
6999	Shall we go / Pattonslappingly / [etc.] / Jan. 1, 1941———Neutral Eire etc.	Multicolored	Nazis	Linto	B
7000	Shall we go / Pattonslappingly / along, and just / penalize privates? etc.	Multicolored	Patt	Linto	B
7001	Shangri-la ? [name on bow of aircraft carrier, question mark at lower right]	Black	Navy	Swartz	A
7002	Share your rides! [handpainted]	Black	Home	Nichols	C
7003	Sharpen the eagles claws! / Buy plenty of war bonds! [handpainted]	Black	Eagle	Klondike	D
7004	Shattered swastika / (Ah love! could you) etc. [env. 6 9/16x3 3/4, 7x4 in.]	Blue, red	Nazis	Belles-let	C
7005	Shattered swastika / (The worldly hope men) etc. [env. 6 9/16x3 3/4, 7x4 in.]	Blue, red	Nazis	Belles-let	C
7006	She gives without stint, always has, always will, love etc.	Blue, red	Women	Brenn	A
7007	She loves me, / she loves me not—— [in quotes]	Multicolored	Air	Amer Art	A
7008	She serves her country / well and true / What more could / any woman do.	Green	WAC	Abel	A
7009	She was a lady to the end [in quotes] / USS / Lexington (CV-2) etc.	Black/Blue	Navy	Christens	A
7010	Shell the Axis / Shell out for more / bonds - for victory	Blue, red	Ordna	Risinger	A
7011	Shell the Axis / Shell out for more / war bonds etc.	Blue, red	Ordna	Risinger	A
7012	Shell the Axis / Shell out for war bonds	Blue, red	Ordna	Risinger	A
7013	She's ready, too etc. [label + blue "Victory" border]	Multicolored	Bonds	Unknown	B
7014	She's ready, too etc. [label + red "Victory" border]	Multicolored	Bonds	Unknown	B
7015	She's ready, too etc. [label + red "Win the War" border]	Multicolored	Bonds	Unknown	B
7016	Ship repair unit [handpainted]	Multicolored	Navy	Steinhardt	C
7017	Ships for / victory [envelope 9 1/2x4 1/8in.]	Unknown	Navy	Propeller	B
7018	Ships for victory	Unknown	Navy	Boone	A
7019	Ships for victory / Allies / invade / Japan	Unknown	VJDay	Boone	B
7020	Ships for victory / Allies take etc. [thermographed]	Unknown	Unk	Boone	A
7021	Ships for victory / Churchill / defeated etc. [thermographed]	Unknown	Winst	Boone	B
7022	Ships for victory / Cruiser St. Paul etc. [thermographed]	Unknown	Navy	Boone	A
7023	Ships for victory / Gen. Wainwright etc. [thermographed]	Unknown	Gener	Boone	A
7024	Ships for victory / Japan / surrenders / to etc.	Unknown	VJDay	Boone	B
7025	Ships for victory / Laval the traitor etc. [thermographed]	Unknown	ORN	Boone	B
7026	Ships for victory / Yanks / move into / Berlin [thermographed]	Unknown	Event	Boone	B
7027	Ships for victory [UL] [border of blue stars around envelope]	Blue, red	Eagle	Unknown	A
7028	Ships vital to victory / Buy more U.S. bonds now	Gold	Bonds	Linto	B
7029	Shoot some / ink this way—— / for [envelope 8 13/16x3 7/8 in.]	Multicolored	Army	Porto-serv	B
7030	Shoot the / pants / off the / Japanazi	Black	Axis	Unknown	A
7031	Shore Patrol [in quotes] [w/, w/o 4 stars upper & lower right] [blue envelope]	Multicolored	Navy	Amer Art	A
7032	Should you champion the / cause of small business be / careful, lest the etc.	Gold	FDR	Linto	B
7033	Show me the / way to / Berlin [handpainted]	Multicolored	Army	Borkowski	D

NO.	CACHET TEXT	COLOR	TOPIC	PUBLISHER	$
7034	Show that you / [etc.] / United War Fund [on back] [envelope 6 3/4x3 3/4 in.]	Unknown	Home	Boston Ed	B
7035	Showing mercy to / Nazis is like / [etc.] / 6-18-'45——Lt.-Gen. Simon etc.	Multicolored	Event	Linto	B
7036	Showing mercy to / Nazis is like asking / for a kick in the / face!	Multicolored	Flag	Linto	B
7037	Shtop / those / bombs!! / Ve / giff / up! [handpainted]	Multicolored	Axis	Parker	C
7038	Shtop / those bombs!!/ Ve / giff / up! [handpainted]	Black, blue	Axis	Parker	B
7039	Shtop!! / Ve vas only fooling!! / Stamp 'em out!! / Buy war stamps etc. [handpainted]	Multicolored	Axis	Parker	C
7040	Sicily / encircled / August 17, 1943	Green, red	Event	Fidelity	B
7041	Sick old bird / "Too much Sicily" [first line same width as tree branch]	Black	Nazis	Neal	A
7042	Sick old bird / "Too much Sicily" [first line wider than tree branch]	Blue	Nazis	Neal	A
7043	Sighted sub, sank same / This phrase etc.	Unknown	Unk	Card	A
7044	Signing of / Declaration of Independence / July 4, 1776 [thermographed]	Blue, red	Flag	Baur	A
7045	Silence / Don't you love / me any more ? / ? / ? [burned edge] [handpainted]	Multicolored	Army	Cowdery	D
7046	Silence demanded / of those returning / [etc.] / 1-28-'44--Russians take Leningrad etc.	Black	Event	Linto	B
7047	Silence demanded / of those returning / from Bataan! / Why? [no picture]	Multicolored	Battl	Linto	B
7048	Silence is golden / especially in matters / [etc.] / Our privilege to give etc.	Multicolored	Home	Linto	B
7049	Silence is golden / especially in matters / [etc.] / Pearl Harbor was etc.	Multicolored	Pearl	Linto	B
7050	Silence is golden / especially in matters / concerning any and all etc.	Multicolored	Army	Linto	B
7051	Silence might have prevented this	Magenta	Home	Davis, Ray	A
7052	Since D Day we have set a stride / unheard of in any other war. / We fight etc.	Black/Red	EagFl	Abel	A
7053	Since Harold Ickes has expressed / himself on what our attitude etc. [no picture]	Multi/Gd,S	Home	Linto	B
7054	Singapore / surrenders / Feb. 15, 1942 [no picture]	Black	Event	Fidelity	B
7055	Singapore surrendered to Japs	Unknown	Event	Linto	B
7056	Sinking of the Rising Sun [handpainted]	Black, red	Japan	Smith, LH	B
7057	Sir / Bernard / Montgomery / one of the / greatest / soldiers / of all times	Green, red	Gener	Linto	B
7058	Sitka Alaska (An old Russian city [sic] / Madonna and Child, an almost etc.	Gold	Alask	Crosby	B
7059	Sittin' pretty	Blue	Navy	Lawrence	A
7060	Six [6] Jap / war ships / sunk / including 45,000 / ton etc. [no picture]	Black, red	Event	Fidelity	B
7061	Sixth [6th] / war / loan [bomb falling on Japanese flag] [handpainted]	Blue, red	Bonds	Klaas	D
7062	Sixth [6th] / war / loan [bomb falling on Japanese flag] [thermographed]	Red	Bonds	Burdick	A
7063	Sixth [6th] / war / loan [bomb falling on Nazi flag] [handpainted]	Multicolored	Bonds	Klaas	D
7064	Sixth [6th] / war / loan [Minute Man] [handpainted]	Multicolored	Bonds	Klaas	D
7065	Sixth [6th] / war / loan drive / opens etc. [thermographed] [no picture]	Unknown	Bonds	Boone	A
7066	Sixth [6th] / war loan / Nov. 20 - Dec. 16, 1944	Red	Uncle	Sayama	B
7067	Sixth [6th] / war loan / Nov. 20 - Dec. 16, 1944 / Dec. 7 / 1944 / etc.	Red/Violet	Uncle	Sayama	D
7068	Sixth [6th] war loan / drive / Nov.20 Dec.16 44 / Buy an extra bond	Purple	Bonds	Kosko	A
7069	Sixth [6th] war loan / Help push / em over / buy / war / bonds	Blue, red	Bonds	Burdick	B
7070	Sixth Army [under insignia]	Red	Unit	Dannells	B
7071	Sixth war loan / Nov. 20 to Dec. 16 / Let's make it etc. [handpainted]	Multicolored	Dog	Myers	B
7072	Sixth war loan / something for / [etc.] / 11-20-'44——Saar invaded! / etc.	Multicolored	Event	Linto	B
7073	Sixth war loan / something for / you / to gladly / work for [no picture]	Multicolored	Bonds	Linto	B
7074	Sixty-sixth [66th] Calvary [sic] Division [under insignia] [handpainted]	Multicolored	Unit	Dannells	B
7075	Sizz - (I) - lization [Hitler and globe] [env. 6 9/16x3 3/4, 6 3/4x3 7/8 in.]	Blue, red	Hitle	Belles-let	C
7076	Ski troops [colored envelopes]	Blue	Army	Huss	A
7077	Skulduddery [in quotes] / "He who laughs last, laughs best."	Black	Axis	Donaldson	A
7078	Slant eye / 1——Oh slanty eyed imperial son / of the Rising Sun or moon, etc.	Multicolored	Liber	Weigand	B
7079	Slap a Jap / with a / defense bond [rubber stamp] [12/20/41] [yellow envelope]	Black	Bonds	New Mexico	C
7080	Slap the Jap / with / scrap [envelope 9 1/2x4 1/8 in.]	Black	Japan	Cover News	C
7081	Slap the Jap / with scrap / To insure a win / save more etc. [handpainted]	Multicolored	Japan	Myers	B
7082	Slap the Jap / with scrap [handpainted]	Multicolored	Japan	Myers	B
7083	Slap the Jap with a war stamp [no picture]	Unknown	Bonds	Kosko	A
7084	Slap the Jap with a war stamp!	Blue, red	Bonds	Ander, EA	A
7085	Slave / world / or / free / world / Keep the etc. [label + printed border]	Multicolored	Nazis	Artists	B
7086	Slave / world / or free / world / Fight today for etc. [label + printed border]	Multicolored	Home	Artists	B
7087	Slave world / or free / world / Fight for the etc. [label + printed border]	Multicolored	Torch	Artists	B
7088	Slave world / or free world? Concentrate on etc. [label + printed border]	Multicolor	Conc	Artists	B
7089	Slave world——or free world? / Fight for the four etc. [label + printed border]	Multicolored	Liber	Artists	B
7090	Slay 'em in the aisles - / Your bonds help [thermographed]	Black/Blue	Japan	Crosby	B
7091	Sleeping wont win the war/ wake up——keep the etc. [thermographed]	Blue, red	Home	Baur	A

NO.	CACHET TEXT	COLOR	TOPIC	PUBLISHER	$
7092	Sleight-of-hand charity? / Wealthy corporations / [etc.] / 3-6-'44——Allies etc.	Blue, gold	Event	Linto	B
7093	Sleight-of-hand charity? / Wealthy corporations evade war etc. [no picture]	Multicolored	Home	Linto	B
7094	Sling, sling the lumber, Washington / can help shelter the world	Unknown	Unk	Quigley	B
7095	Slogans help / but actions win	Unknown	Army	Runge	A
7096	Sluggards / always complain / There's no place for a sluggard / in America etc.	Green	Home	Unknown	A
7097	Smash / the Axis / buy / war bonds [brown envelope]	Red	Uncle	Ohio Bell	D
7098	Smash that Jap / Buy more bonds [cannon firing to right]	Red	Flag	Yontz	A
7099	Smash that Jap / Buy more bonds [cannon left] [env. 6 1/2x3 5/8, 7 1/2x4 in.]	Red	Japan	Yontz	A
7100	Smash that Jap / Buy war bonds [cannon firing to right] [envelope 7 1/2x4 in.]	Black	Flag	Yontz	A
7101	Smile with Uncle Sam [in quotes] / Give your / country / 100% etc.	Multicolored	Uncle	Linto	B
7102	Smitten by war, ——the wise men of the west / gathered etc. [no picture]	Unknown	VJDay	Clark	B
7103	Smoke in der / Fuehrer's eyes / Feb. 3-13 1945 / The Big 3 etc. [handpainted]	Multicolored	Event	Smith, LH	C
7104	SMTWTFS / 1234567 / Each day brings US etc. [no picture]	Unknown	Unk	Stefun	A
7105	Snake / in your grass / It's going to cost billions to / defang etc. [artist: Dr. Seuss]	Black/Green	Japan	Yontz	D
7106	Snake in the gas / There was a crooked man and he / lived in crooked style etc.	Black, red	Home	Threl+Thar	A
7107	So long Shangri-la [colored envelopes]	Black	Dool	Wolf, ID	B
7108	So long, / big sho [sic]	Red	Axis	Barnes	A
7109	So solly pliss! / "What did Uncle Sam do, Tojo?" / "He made a dummy "" etc.	Brown/Red	Japan	Eichenlaub	A
7110	So solly! / Now you poor / devils hari kari. / V.J. Day. [handpainted]	Multicolored	VJDay	Unknown	C
7111	So solly! Me fliend!! No wany fight! / Don't believe it! / Knock out etc. [handpainted]	Multicolored	Japan	Parker	B
7112	So solly!! [thermographed]	Blue	Japan	Sadworth	B
7113	So sorry / If you wonder why we're unhappy, / if you wonder why we're etc.	Green/Red	Axis	Abel	A
7114	So sorry accident keep / you from making guns / for honorable [in quotes] etc.	Blue	Japan	Quigley	B
7115	So sorry, now —— I thought / it was only an eaglet. [in quotes]	Blue	Japan	Lawrence	A
7116	So that / "Peace on Earth" etc.	Red	Unk	Harmer	A
7117	So that the free people / of this earth / shall [in quotes] etc. [thermographed]	Green	Navy	Sadworth	B
7118	So when we reach the / Isle of Japan etc. [no picture]	Unk	Unk	Baur	A
7119	So when we reach the Isle of Japan / with etc. [no picture]	Unknown	Unk	Davis, Ray	A
7120	Soap [on box] [soldier sitting on box, peeling potatoes] [handpainted]	Multicolored	Army	Dannells	C
7121	Soap [soldier sitting on soap box, writing letter to sweetheart] [handpainted]	Multicolored	Army	Dannells	C
7122	Society of Philatelic / Americans / V [colored envelopes]	Black	Armed	Soc Philat	A
7123	Softies or Bunds? / Washington, D.C.-6-11-'45 / By a vote of 5 to 4 the etc.	Gold, violet	Flag	Linto	B
7124	Soldier's flower order [no picture]	Unknown	Unk	Florists	A
7125	Soldier's mail / "Somewhere in the U.S.A." [envelope 7 1/2x3 7/8 in.]	Blue	Army	Dime	A
7126	Solomon Islands—— / "We hit them high wide and handsome"	Black	Navy	Coll Surp	A
7127	Solomon Islands [handpainted]	Multicolored	Map	Smith, LH	C
7128	Solomon Islands attacked	Unknown	Event	Linto	B
7129	Solomon Islands campaign [postmarked 1943 or later]	Purple	Eagle	Christens	A
_7130_	Solomon Islands campaign [postmarked December 1942 or earlier]	Purple	Eagle	Christens	C
7131	Some fresh officer tried to pick me up / today——How can a second "louie" etc.	Black	Women	Deming	A
7132	Some ideas of technocracy / are being / [etc.] / Pearl Harbor was attacked etc.	Multicolored	Pearl	Linto	B
7133	Some ideas of technocracy / are being applied to etc. [no picture] [color varieties]	Multicolored	Home	Linto	B
7134	Some more Nips / gone to roast with / there [sic] honorable etc. [handpainted]	Multicolored	Air	Parker	B
7135	Some non-rationed / humor [envelope 6 3/4x3 3/4 in.]	Unknown	Home	Quigley	B
7136	Some people say: / "Don't change horses in / the middle of" etc. [no picture]	Multicolored	Home	Linto	B
7137	Somebody smell something burning?	Multicolored	Hitle	Peer	B
7138	Someday / "they'll" let me / mail it! / ??? / I hope! [burned edge] [handpainted]	Multicolored	Army	Cowdery	D
7139	Someone / talked! / Ship talk can be sabotalk! [label + printed border]	Multicolored	Home	Artists	B
7140	Someone knew the sailing time	Black	Unk	Davis, Ray	A
7141	Someone talked [floating cap]	Blue	Navy	Leonard	A
7142	Someone talked! [listing ship]	Blue	Navy	Roberts	A
7143	Someone talked! / ... and many died! Think before etc. [label + printed border]	Multicolored	Home	Artists	B
7144	Someone talked! / Talk is not cheap! Be careful! [label + printed border]	Multicolored	Navy	Artists	B
7145	Something / smells bad! / Why not! Look / what is loose!	Unknown	Hitle	Linto	B
7146	Something else to remember / Russia declares / war etc. [handpainted]	Black	Event	Sturgill	E
7147	Something to smile / about!!! [handpainted]	Black	Japan	Parker	B
7148	Somewhere [in quotes] / with the / U.S. naval / forces	Bu/Green/Red	Navy	Muridge	B
7149	Somewhere [in quotes] / with the / U.S. naval / forces [thermographed]	Blue, gold	Eagle	Bartley	B

NO.	CACHET TEXT	COLOR	TOPIC	PUBLISHER	$
7150	Song of a Jeep / (Part one) / A Jeep can swim over the ocean, / a Jeep etc.	Blue, red	Verse	Brenn	A
7151	Song of a Jeep / (Part two) / One Jeep lost its driver in battle, / kept etc.	Blue, red	Verse	Brenn	A
7152	Soon any ship will be safe on any sea / see	Unknown	Unk	Quigley	B
7153	Soon it may wave / over Berlin and Tokyo.	Black	Flag	Unknown	A
7154	Sooo...solly pleese [handpainted]	Multicolored	Japan	McBarrar	C
7155	Sorry / you're still being / held "incommunicado" [burned edges] [handpainted]	Multicolored	Army	Cowdery	D
7156	South Africa / United Nations [handpainted]	Multicolored	UN	Weigand	B
7157	Southern coast of / France / invaded etc. [no picture]	Blue, red	Event	Boone	B
7158	Southern Cross / Philippines [bombers in shape of cross] [handpainted]	Multicolored	Phili	Adler	D
7159	Soviets / reach / Polish / border! / January 4, 1944 [no picture]	Red	Event	Fidelity	B
7160	SPARS / always ready [thermographed]	Unknown	SPARS	Baur	A
7161	SPARS / second / anniversary / Nov.23 / Serving their / country	Green, violet	SPARS	Dale	A
7162	SPARS / second / anniversay / Nov. 23 / Serving their country	Green, purple	SPARS	Dale	A
7163	Speak nothing but good / of the dead. / [etc.] / 6-2-'45——Russia deadlocks etc.	Multicolored	Event	Linto	B
7164	Speak nothing but good / of the dead. / If Hitler is dead? Good.	Multicolored	Hitle	Linto	B
7165	Speaker of the U.S. House of Representatives / Samuel Rayburn etc. [handpainted]	Black	Event	Batura	E
7166	Speakin' of track an' field events, / you folks who are givin' etc. [thermogr]	Blue/Red	Axis	Czubay	B
7167	Spearheading for victory / U.S. naval / amphibious / forces [thermographed]	Gold, red	Navy	Czubay	B
7168	Speed / all-out / production / with etc.	Unknown	Unk	Kosko	A
7169	Speed / the way / to / V-J Day / Buy / United States / war etc. [no picture]	Blue	Bonds	Unknown	B
7170	Speed / your / mail / Use your / zone / numbers [no picture]	Black	Home	Unknown	B
7171	Speed the attack. / Gain the victory. / Hurry the homecoming.	Blue, red	EagSh	Buxton	A
7172	Speed them back / WAC's [handpainted]	Multicolored	WAC	Adler	D
7173	Spend sucker, spend! etc. [lower border "s" on or below line] [no picture]	Red/Blue, red	Home	Boone	A
7174	Spend sucker, spend... etc. [last line solid or double-line caps] [no picture]	Blue	Home	Boone	A
7175	Spies / have big / ears	Bu/Br/Red	Devil	Richardson	A
7176	Spirit / of '76 / U.S. Marines / raise U.S. / Flag on / Mt. Suribachi etc.	Multicolored	Event	Linto	B
7177	Spirit of '41 / Oh, Mr. Adolf Hitler, this is your un- etc. [no picture]	Blue, red	Verse	Nelson, L	A
7178	Spirit of '44 [in quotes] / "It's a different war, gran- / pappy; the" etc.	Bu,red/Black	Home	Boone	A
7179	Spirit of '45 [in quotes] / Iwo Jima.	Blue, red	Battl	Grandy	A
7180	Spirit of '76 - spirit of '41 etc. [lines narrowly spaced]	Blue/Red	Unk	Apnew	A
7181	Spirit of '76 - spirit of '41 etc. [lines widely spaced]	Blue/Red	Unk	Apnew	A
7182	Spirit of '76 / will guide our boys to victory [thermographed]	Unknown	Unk	Baur	A
7183	Spirit of Bataan [in quotes] / Dedication / July 18——1943 / Albuquerque etc.	Black	Air	Unknown	A
7184	Spots before / his eyes. [handpainted]	Black	Hitle	Wolf, CL	B
7185	Spreading false / rumors is / sabotage	Blue, red	Home	Kosko	A
7186	Spreading false / rumors is / sabotage / -Stop those rumors- [colored envelopes]	Blue/Brown	Home	Huss	A
7187	Squadrons / fleet / flagships / United Sytatesd / Navy / Marine Corps etc.	Green	Navy	Bean	A
7188	St. Patrick drove the snakes out of etc.	Green	Unk	Brenn	A
7189	St. Patrick's Day / March 17, 1942 / Gen. Douglas / MacArthur arrived / in etc.	Green, silver	Event	Linto	C
7190	St. Patrick's Day / March 17, 1942 / Gen. Douglas etc.	Unknown	Mac	Linto	B
7191	Stalin	Red, silver	USSR	Runge	A
7192	Stalin dissolves the Comintern	Unknown	Event	Linto	B
7193	Stalin looks out for Russia, / Churchill for England, too; etc. [no picture]	Gold, silver	FDR	Schaefer	B
7194	Stamp 'em out! [copy of Minkus cachet w/ color, picture variations] [handpainted]	Multicolored	Axis	Nielsen	D
7195	Stamp 'em out! [copyright "C" w/, w/o serifs]	Multicolored	Axis	Minkus	A
7196	Stamp out aggression / Win the war	Blue, red	Armed	Cachet Cra	A
7197	Stand by for / Japanese / acceptance etc.	Red	Japan	Boone	A
7198	Stand by for / the world's / largest etc. [no picture]	Unknown	Unk	Boone	A
7199	Stand by for / V / victory / over Germany [no picture]	Unknown	Unk	Boone	A
7200	Stand by for / victory / over Germany! [no picture]	Multicolored	VforV	Boone	A
7201	Stand by your colors and / your etc. [thermographed]	Unknown	Unk	Baur	A
7202	Stand fast!!! / America / Armistice Day / November 11 / 1940	Blue	Holid	Alden	C
7203	Stand firm, people of the / Philippines, your day is coming. [in quotes] etc.	Blue, red	Phili	Brenn	A
7204	Stand up and fight for your Uncle Sam, / or you will be doomed like etc.	Blue, red	Uncle	Amer Pat	A
7205	Stand your ground. Don't fire unless / [etc.] / 10-14-'44——British and etc.	Gold, pink	Event	Linto	B
7206	Stand your ground. Don't fire unless / fired upon, but if they mean to etc.	Gold	Hist	Linto	B
7207	Star of glory / In the windows of Hamburg etc	Unknown	Unk	Baur	A

NO.	CACHET TEXT	COLOR	TOPIC	PUBLISHER	$
7208	Stars and Stripes / "G.I. like it"	Blue	Army	Huss	A
7209	Stars and stripes around the world	Red	Globe	Hillerich	A
7210	Stars and stripes fearlessly floating for / humanity and democracy [thermogr]	Blue, red	Flag	Unknown	B
7211	Start a / victory / garden / today / [etc.] / in / your own back yard	Blue, red	VforV	Lowell	A
7212	Start a / victory / garden / today / [etc.] / You owe one / to the world	Green, red	VforV	Lowell	B
7213	Start an architect on / a postwar etc. [envelope 9 1/2x4 1/8 in.]	Black	Home	Detroit St	B
7214	Start saving now for the mighty 7th war loan	Multicolored	Uncle	Linto	B
7215	Start to worry, every Jap / We are getting in our scrap / iron steel rags etc.	Black, red	Japan	Makomb	A
7216	Starting to-day all cars 35 miles p.h. / A slip / of the lip etc. [handpainted]	Unknown	Axis	Unknown	C
7217	Starts November 20th / Sixth / war / loan etc. [thermographed]	Unknoown	Bonds	Boone	A
7218	State and federal / employees total / 6,337,000 / still etc. [no picture]	Pink, silver	Home	Linto	B
7219	State and federal / employess total / [etc.] / Dec. 7, 1941, a date we etc.	Multicolored	Pearl	Linto	B
7220	Station Force ABD Camp Thomas / Davisville, Rhode Island [4 small cachets] [hp]	Aqua	Armed	Cozart	A
7221	Statue of Liberty [vertical] / It is the 155 foot high, bronze statue etc.	Red, sepia	Liber	Smith, AD	A
7222	Statue of Liberty [in quotes] [envelope 6 9/16x3 3/4, 6 3/4x3 7/8 in.]	Sepia tones	Liber	Belles-let	C
7223	Steel / at war V···‒ / guns of steel [thermographed]	Unknown	Unk	Von Los	B
7224	Steel / goes to war V ···‒ / walls of steel	Unknown	Unk	Von Los	B
7225	Steel / men V ···‒ / in ships of steel [thermographed]	Unknown	Unk	Von Los	B
7226	Steeled / for / victory / buy / U.S. / war bonds [on back of 9 1/2x4 1/8 in. envelope]	Green	Bonds	Pittsburgh	B
7227	Step on it / Save tin cans	Blue	Home	Amer Legio	A
7228	Step on it Uncle [in quotes] [handpainted]	Multicolored	Japan	Van Alsbur	C
7229	Step up / your / bond / buying / Fifth war / loan etc. [no picture]	Green, violet	Bonds	Threl+Thar	A
7230	Step up ship production / Buy more bonds!	Gold	Bonds	Linto	B
7231	Stick it out! / Finish the job by sticking to yours! [on 8 1/2x5 1/2 in. penalty wrapper]	Black	Home	War Prod 2	D
7232	Still - / the laugh's on / me - 'cause I don't / know nothin'!! [handpainted]	Multicolored	Home	Cowdery	D
7233	Still puffing away [handpainted]	Multicolored	USSR	Newton FN	C
7234	Still waving / as the "Son" goes down	Blue, red	Flag	Carpenter	A
7235	Stock / in / United States of America / Today's best seller /	Green/Purple	Bonds	Christens	A
7236	Stop / look / listen / This is / April first [postmarked 4/1/41]	Multicolored	Holid	Linto	B
7237	Stop / thinking about it / Do it now etc.	Unknown	Unk	Kosko	A
7238	Stop Hitler now!	Black/Green	Uncle	Roberts	A
7239	Stop inflation! / Start that savings account / today! Buy a bond!	Blue, red	Bonds	Speede	A
7240	Stop squawking, / you yellow rat. / [etc.] / 6-9-'45——U.S. 13th / Air etc.	Multicolored	Event	Linto	B
7241	Stop squawking, / you yellow rat. / You ask for it, now take it!	Gold, silver	Japan	Linto	B
7242	Stop throwing away / waste paper / Start etc. [no picture]	Unknown	Home	McCluney	A
7243	Stop waste! [envelope 6x3 1/2 in.]	Unknown	Home	Powers	A
7244	Stop! / and think! / Are you really / [etc.] / Navy Day——Oct.27, 1943	Multicolored	Navy	Linto	B
7245	Stop! / and think! / Are you really / doing all you / can to etc. [color varieties]	Multicolored	Home	Linto	B
7246	Stop! / Don't / cash / that bond!	Blue, red	Bonds	Eichenlaub	A
7247	Stop! / Don't get hurt / Our enemies / will use / the minutes we lose.	Bk/Bu/R/Vi	Axis	Kosko	A
7248	Stop! / Listen! Those in the / service / [etc.] / Navy Day——Oct. 27, 1943	Multicolored	Navy	Linto	B
7249	Stop! / Listen! Those in the / service rightfully expect etc. [color varieties]	Multicolored	Home	Linto	B
7250	Stormy petrel - lone wandering etc. [envelope 6 9/16x3 3/4 in.]	Unknown	Unk	Belles-let	C
7251	Strength / in unity	Blue	EagSh	Mission	A
7252	Strength / in unity [thermographed]	Blue	EagSh	Mission	A
7253	Strike a blow / for victory / Buy etc.	Unknown	Unk	Kosko	A
7254	Strike! [bowling ball] [handpainted]	Blue	Axis	Parker	B
7255	Strip ship / first step / toward / ready for action [postmarked 4/11/41]	Unknown	Navy	Unknown	A
7256	Sub / smasher / Perrin Field / helps make this / possible [handpainted]	Multicolored	Air	Knapp	G
7257	Submarine / force / U.S. / fleet [picture 38 or 52 mm high] [thermographed]	Blue	USsub	Sadworth	B
7258	Submarine chaser PC-46P / decommissioned etc.	Unknown	Event	Linto	B
7259	Subscribe to the / national war fund / [etc.] / 10-20-'44——Aachen and etc.	Multicolored	Event	Linto	B
7260	Subscribe to the / national war fund / for our own——for our allies	Gold, silver	Eagle	Linto	B
7261	Subsidy plan permits selling / [etc.] / 7-8-'44——British and Nazis in etc.	Unknown	Event	Linto	B
7262	Subsidy plan permits selling / surplus millions of / eggs 5c etc. [no picture]	Gold, green	Home	Linto	B
7263	Sue / Carolina / Sue / sweetheart / Sue etc. [w/ w/o stars UR&LR] [blue envelope]	Multicolored	Navy	Amer Art	A
7264	Sugar / registration / day / May 4, 1942 [no picture]	Gold	Event	Fidelity	B
7265	Sugar report!! [handpainted]	Black	Army	Parker	B

NO.	CACHET TEXT	COLOR	TOPIC	PUBLISHER	$
7266	Sunday through Saturday / Each day brings US etc. [no picture]	Unknown	Unk	Stefun	A
7267	Sunk by / steel V ··· – / and men of steel [thermographed]	Unknown	Unk	Von Los	B
7268	Sunrise. / December 7, 1941 / V-J / day! / Sunset. etc. [no picture]	Black	VJDay	Rankin	B
7269	Sunset and shadows	Multicolored	Japan	Sayama	B
7270	Superman?? [handpainted]	Black	Hitle	Nichols	C
7271	Supply Det., Section I / Camp Sibert / Alabama [handpainted]	Multicolored	EagSh	Stawuszew	C
7272	Supreme Court curfew for Japanese	Unknown	Event	Linto	B
7273	Sure, / I run away / but / he catch me / ! / Jap Navy [cachet colors vary]	Multicolored	Japan	Peer	B
7274	Sure, I like to drive my Buick / Nope, not paying an election bet / Yeah, etc.	Brown, green	Home	Eichenlaub	A
7275	Sure, we'll / work, fight, give! make / democracy live! etc. [no picture]	Pink, silver	Home	Linto	B
7276	Surely each man has / as strong a motive now [in quotes] etc. [4 stars, R & L]	Blue, red	Linc	Brenn	A
7277	Surely each man has / as strong a motive now [in quotes] etc. [colored envelopes]	Multicolored	Linc	Poppenger	A
7278	Surrender - Tokyo Bay, 2 September 1945 [U.S.S. Wallace L. Lind] [Tokyo Bay]	Black	VJDay	Navy Ship	D
7279	Surrender Day / World War II ends! etc. [in black on Minkus cover] [8/14/45]	Black	VJDay	Ellis	C
7280	Swabbo! / "We have just / begun to fight!"	Black	USMC	Lupton	A
7281	Swastika / defeated Hitler is missing / Germany / [etc.] / Hell / Hitler! etc.	Red	VEDay	Czubay	B
7282	Sweden is offended because / we requested them to stop etc. [color varieties]	Multicolored	Minut	Linto	B
7283	Symbol / of / freedom	Blue	Liber	Krakora	A
7284	Symbol / of / freedom [handpainted]	Blue, red	Liber	Krakora	C
7285	Symbol / of / liberty [Statue of Liberty in front of 5-pointed star] [handpainted]	Blue, red	Liber	Krakora	B
7286	Symbol of / invasion / emblem of / Eisenhower / [vertical text] / Flaming sword	Multicolored	Ike	Griffith	B
7287	Symbol of freedom	Blue, red	Liber	Unknown	A
7288	Symbols / of / liberty [first line 20 or 22 mm long] [colored envelopes]	Blue, red	Eagle	Poppenger	A
7289	Symbols of / God bless / America / liberty	Unknown	Unk	Ander, EA	A

Cover Values (from Table 6, p. 136)

Value	*Price Range*
A	$ 3 - 6
B	$ 7 - 15
C	$ 16 - 30
D	$ 31 - 60
E	$ 61 - 125
F	$ 126 - 250
G	$ 251 - 500
H	$ 501 - 1000
I	$ >1000
X	Unpriced: Suspicious or fraudulent cover

6754

6769

6804

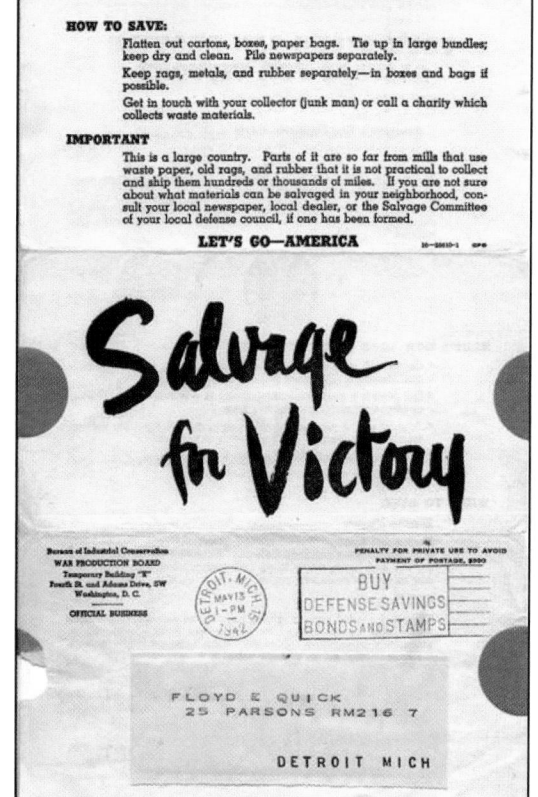

6903

6923

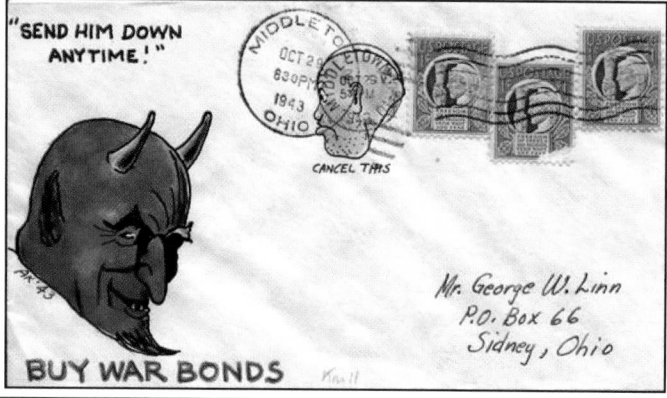

6952

6967

6977

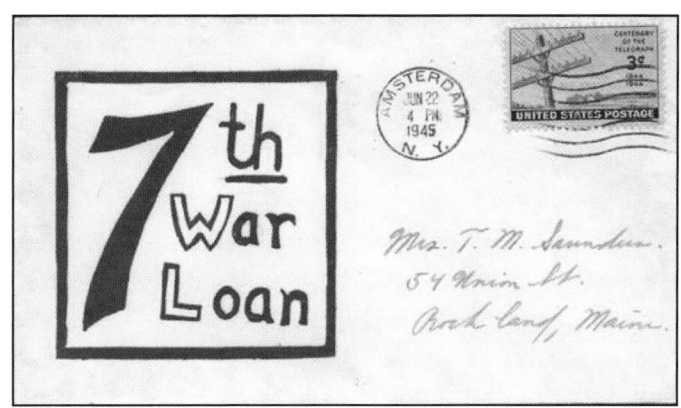

7029

7031

7051

7062

7063

7069

7130

7178

7195

7259

7263

7269

7273

7288

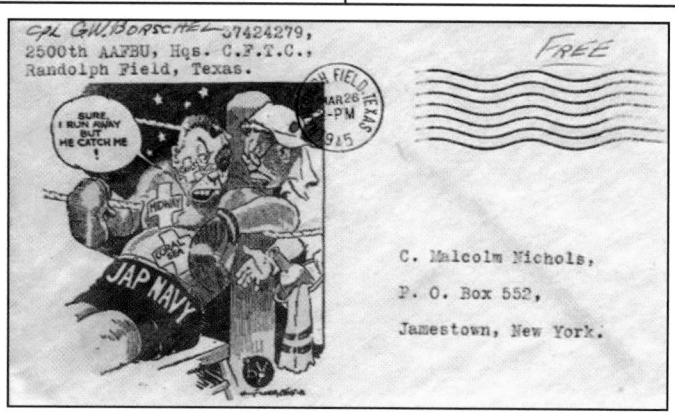

CACHET TEXT BEGINNING WITH "T"

NO.	CACHET TEXT	COLOR	TOPIC	PUBLISHER	$
7290	T kio / Biak / Mariannas [sic] / Truk [handpainted]	Multicolored	Japan	Adler	D
7291	T.G. Masaryk	Black	Hero	Huss	A
7292	T.N.T. / today not tomorrow	Multicolored	EagSh	Unknown	B
7293	Ta tata ta ta	Blue	Unk	Scott+Conn	A
7294	Take a / Red Cross / home / nursing / course / Learn to guard the home front	Sepia tones	RedCr	Linto	B
7295	Take a smear of red from the early / morning sky, / a handful of white etc.	Blue, red	Flag	Brenn	A
7296	Take profits out of war to / eliminate unpleasant sights!	Black, silver	Home	Linto	B
7297	Take the axe / to the Axis	Blue/Red	Hitle	Richardson	B
7298	Take the lead away from the quill, / or with any kind of a pen, let us etc.	Unknown	Unk	Quigley	B
7299	Takes more than slaps / to lick the Japs -- / ···- Buy war stamps & bonds ···-	Black	Bonds	Runge	A
7300	Takes more than slaps / to lick the Japs -- / ···- Buy war stamps etc. [with blue stars]	Blue, red	Bonds	Runge	A
7301	Tank destroyer insignia [colored envelopes]	Black	Unit	Huss	A
7302	Tank I go home! [handpainted] [torn stamp]	Multicolored	Ordna	Cowdery	D
7303	Tanks - a million! [envelope 6x3 1/2 in.]	Blue, red	Ordna	Powers	A
7304	Tanks guns shells ships food oil planes etc. [colored envelopes]	Unknown	Ordna	Poppenger	A
7305	Tarawa - Saipan - Iwo Jima etc.	Purple	Battl	Harvey	A
7306	Tarawa-Guam-Saipan / Iwo Jima etc.	Green	Battl	Neal+Harv	A
7307	Task / Force / 58 / war [handpainted]	Multicolored	Navy	Adler	D
7308	Teheran / meeting / "Big Three" meet / at Teheran / Persia - November 26, 1943	Multicolored	Heads	Teixeira	D
7309	Teheran conference	Unknown	Event	Linto	C
7310	Teheran conference - Iran [3 or 12 men] [envelope 6 9/16x3 3/4 in.]	Unknown	Heads	Belles-let	C
7311	Teheran meeting / Roosevelt, Stalin and Churchill / the "big three" meet etc.	Multicolored	Heads	Teixeira	D
7312	Telephone / lines are needed / for the war effort / make etc. [brown envelope]	Brown	Home	Ohio Bell	D
7313	Tell 'em you're / gonna write [handpainted]	Multicolored	Home	Cowdery	D
7314	Tell it to the / US Marines / From the halls etc. [thermographed]	Red	USMC	Czubay	A
7315	Tell it to the Marines! / From the halls of Montezuma / to the etc. [thermographed]	Blue, red	USMC	Cliff	A
7316	Tell mother I / did my duty! [in quotes] [no stars]	Multicolored	Navy	Amer Art	A
7317	Tell mother I / did my duty! [in quotes] [with 4 stars upper & lower right]	Multicolored	Navy	Amer Art	A
7318	Tell President Quezon and Gen- / eral MacArthur I will do my [in quotes] etc.	Blue, red	Phili	Brenn	A
7319	Tell your / Congressman / V / stands for / victory / not / votes etc. [handpainted]	Multicolored	VforV	Unknown	B
7320	Temporary hold / Disaster [handpainted]	Multicolored	Hitle	Sturgill	E
7321	Tempus fugit / Japan	Blue	Japan	Puls	A
7322	Ten [10] % or better by March 1, 1943 [envelope 6 1/2x3 5/8 in.]	Unknown	Bonds	ITE Circui	B
7323	Ten [10] Jap ships sunk	Unknown	Event	Linto	B
7324	Ten cents / a day / will keep / Hitler away / 130,000,000 stamps etc. [typed]	Black	Bonds	Shaffer, A	A
7325	Ten thousand [10,000] mil [sic] / to Buster [ink] [handpainted]	Multicolored	USMC	Graves	C
7326	Ten thousand [10,000] miles / to / Fremont [civilian with baggage] [ink] [handpainted]	Black	USMC	Graves	C
7327	Ten thousand [10,000] miles / to / Fremont [Marine PFC with baggage] [ink] [handp]	Black	USMC	Graves	C
7328	Ten thousand [10,000] miles / to Freemont [sic] [airplane pulling marine] [ink] [hp]	Multicolored	Air	Graves	C
7329	Tendin' / strictly to / my / knittin' [handpainted]	Multicolored	Home	Cowdery	D
7330	Tennessee / the Volunteer State upholds tradition. / All out for victory!!	Blue, red	Flag	Ross	A
7331	Ten-shun / forward / march	Unknown	Unk	Threl+Thar	A
7332	Tenshun / Jun 15 1944 / First observance / Infantry / Day / To take and to hold	Blue, red	Army	Griffith	B
7333	Terrific / Nazi / counter / assault	Black, blue	Event	Fidelity	B
7334	Testing and experimenting / saves lives	Black	Unk	Durnbaugh	A
7335	Texas State Guard / 27th Battalion / Fort Worth, Texas [Unit insignia]	Multicolored	Unit	McCluney	B
7336	Text of Japanese order / "Kill Americans cruelly. Do / not kill with one" etc.	Gold/Gn,S	Japan	Linto	B
7337	Text of Japanese order / "Kill" / [etc.] / 3-27-'45——Yanks / land on Cebu etc.	Green, silver	Event	Linto	B
7338	Thank God- / we are Americans	Blue	Home	Hunt	A
7339	Thank God- / we are Americans / U.S.A. / "Let's protect it"	Blue, red	Map	Hunt	A
7340	Thank God you / are on the home / front willing to / help etc. [no picture]	Gold, silver	Home	Linto	B
7341	Thank you, Mr. Ickes / for securing a truce in / the coal etc. [no picture]	Multicolored	Home	Linto	B
7342	Thank your / lucky stars / for America / and our / fighting boys	Gold	Armed	Linto	B
7343	Thanks / Uncle [cachet upper right] [envelope 6x3 1/2 in.]	Unknown	Unk	Unknown	A
7344	Thanks for making our / enemy surrender so / daddy can come home. [in quotes]	Bk/Bu/Green	VJDay	Cozart	B
7345	Thanks for those bombs / they perfected our ato-mizer!	Blue	Atom	Harrington	C

NO.	CACHET TEXT	COLOR	TOPIC	PUBLISHER	$
7346	Thanksgiving / "The Marines have landed, / and have the situation well in" etc.	Bk/Blue/Red	USMC	Shaw, MM	B
7347	Thanksgiving / Day. 1944. [handpainted]	Multicolored	Holid	Adler	D
7348	Thanksgiving / for some. For millions / [etc.] / Germans should thank etc.	Multicolored	Nazis	Linto	B
7349	Thanksgiving / for some. For millions / just another Thursday. etc. [no pict]	Multicolored	Holid	Linto	B
7350	Thanksgiving Day / at Cranberry Isles, Me. / November 27th, 1941. / Defend etc.	Black, red	Holid	Zunks	B
7351	Thanksgiving Day / at Turkey, Arkansas. / [etc.] / "America offers thanks"	Blue, red	Holid	Zunks	B
7352	That extra bond / will put him / over the top / to victory	Green, red	VforV	Myers	A
7353	That first night / on / the desert! [handpainted]	Multicolored	Army	Cowdery	D
7354	That government of / the people by the / [etc.] / Sun / Yat Sen / China etc.	Blue, red	China	Cowdery	B
7355	That government of the people, / by the people, for the etc. [handpainted]	Multicolored	Linc	Cachet Cra	B
7356	That government..by the people shall not perish etc. [newspaper mailing tube]	Black	Ordna	Knapp	H
7357	That hurt! / 26 / Jap / ships sunk-damaged / off Philippines: etc. [thermographed]	Blue	Japan	Unknown	C
7358	That Jap flag will have to change a bit, / for when Uncle Sam is through, etc.	Blue	Flag	Boone	A
7359	That ocean-guarded flag of light / forever etc.	Unknown	Unk	Carpenter	A
7360	That same Liberty March / no goose-step here.	Blue, red	Hist	Card	A
7361	That the govern- / ment of the people, by / the people [in quotes] etc. [handp]	Multicolored	Linc	Carpenter	A
7362	That these dead shall not have / died in vain.... [in quotes] Lincoln etc.	Gray	Pearl	LeGallez	C
7363	That this nation, under God / shall have etc.	Unknown	Unk	Bean	B
7364	That this nation, under God, / [etc.] / 10-11-'44——Allies now / blasting etc.	Gold, red	Event	Card	A
7365	That this nation, under God, shall have a / new birth of etc. [no picture]	Gold	Linc	Linto	B
7366	That we may have / a just peace that / will endure forever etc. [no picture]	Blue, red	Home	Linto	B
7367	That's a / regulation hair- / cut - Some / trimming I / took - no tips for etc.	Black	Navy	Poppenger	A
7368	That's America! / To keep her free / we must win the war	Blue, red	Flag	Lupton	A
7369	That's my letter / buddy! [handpainted]	Multicolored	Army	French	D
7370	That's the point- / Get in the scrap!	Brown,	Home	Cowdery	A
7371	That's what he said: "I'll be back.!" That's what he did: etc. [frame varies]	Blue, red	Mac	Eichenlaub	B
7372	That's what they said! / On November 11, 1918, people in the etc. [no picture]	Red	Bonds	Brenn	A
7373	That's what this war is being fought for... / all us little etc. [handpainted]	Multicolored	Women	Price, R	C
7374	The "Aryan" duet. The song is / ended but the memories will / linger on.	Black/Brown	Axis	Hadley	A
7375	The "Big T" was there! [U.S.S. Ticonderoga] [Tokyo Bay]	Blue	VJDay	Lawrence	E
7376	The "four freedoms," to end war, / is teaching man, to etc. [brown envelope]	Blue, red	Eagle	Navy ship	A
7377	The "mighty" Schickelgruber fans out	Multicolored	Hitle	Shaw, TC	B
7378	The "missing" link / (moved?) [handpainted]	Multicolored	Hitle	Peer	B
7379	The "point" of a / Victory garden this / summer -- / "point free" / meals etc. [no pict]	Gn/O/Pu/Red	Home	Davis, D	A
7380	The "point" of a / Victory garden this summer—— etc. [no picture]	Green	Home	Phill, CR	A
7381	The "Prairie Division" [33rd Infantry Division insignia]	Black, gold	Unit	Phill, CR	B
7382	The "super race" / and monkey race / should learn much / from the super-plan	Gold, silver	Axis	McCluney	B
7383	The "super" race / and monkey race / [etc.] / 6-10-'44——Japs lost et 39 etc.	Multicolored	Event	Linto	B
7384	The "super" race / and monkey race / should learn much / from the etc.	Gold, silver	Army	Linto	B
7385	The "super" race / and monkey race / should learn much / from the super-plan!	Gold, silver	Army	Linto	B
7386	The $100 haircut	Purple	Navy	Linto	A
7387	The $64 question / which is worse? / A rat or a Jap etc. [env. 9 1/2x4 1/8 in.]	Black	Japan	Christens	B
7388	The / 3rd / war loan / All / of US [handpainted]	Multicolored	Hitle	Unknown	D
7389	The / 4 freedoms / Freedom of speech / of religion / from want / from fear etc.	Blue, red	Torch	Borkowski	C
7390	The / America's -- / Gaurdian! [sic] [handpainted]	Black	Globe	Staehle	C
7391	The / anchor / watch [thermographed]	Blue	Navy	Klondike	B
7392	The / big / V / means / we [handpainted]	Multicolored	VforV	Crosby	D
7393	The / bombing / of / Tokyo / March 10, 1945 / The blaze that will etc.	Multicolored	Event	Adler	C
7394	The / Casablanca / Conference / 1943 [vertical] [artist: Staehle]	Multicolored	Event	Fluegel	C
7395	The / dream still / lives! [burned left edge] [handpainted]	Multicolored	Home	Smartcraft	D
7396	The / end / is / near [handpainted]	Black	Hitle	Cowdery	B
7397	The / flag / of the / free / Let's / keep / it that / way etc. [postmarked 5/8/45 & 9/2/45] [thermographed]	Multicolored	VJ	Wolf, CL	E
7398	The / hundreth / time! [burned top left, torn right edge] [handpainted]	Multicolored	Home	Von Los	D
7399	The / Japan / Italy / Germany / is up!	Green	Axis	Cowdery	B
7400	The / Japan / Italy / Germany / is up! Italy / surrenders etc. [thermographed]	Green, red	Event	Boone	B
7401	The / Japan / Italy / Germany / is up! / Who's next?	Bu,R/Gn,Rd	Axis	Boone	B
7402	The / Japan / Italy / Germany / is up! Who's next?	Green	Axis	Boone	B
7403	The / Japan / Italy / Germany / is up! Who's next? [last line type varies]	Bicolor var	Axis	Boone	B

NO.	CACHET TEXT	COLOR	TOPIC	PUBLISHER	$
7404	The / lights / go on / again in / England / Sept. 17, 1944 [no picture]	Gold/Red	Ally	Threl+Thar	A
7404A	The / meeting / of / ...- / Franklin D. Roosevelt / [etc.] / Flagship / *Augusta* / August 9, 1941 etc.	Blue, red	Heads	Unknown	G
7405	The / mighty / 7th / war bond drive etc.	Multicolored	Bonds	Smith, LH	C
7406	The / mighty / 7th / war loan	Unknown	Bonds	Ang	A
7407	The / mighty / 7th / war loan / May 14-June etc.	Unknown	Bonds	Ang	A
7408	The / mighty / 7th / war loan / That did it / [etc.] / Today is / V-J Day	Multicolored	VJDay	Cox+Price	B
7409	The / nation's / first line of defense	Bu/Br/Green	Navy	Ander, CS	A
7410	The / Pacific	Multicolored	Japan	Peer	B
7411	The / Pacific Ocean / If he discovered / it today...what / would he name it?	Multicolored	Hist	Andrews	B
7412	The / Philippines / "I will be back" [artist: Staehle]	Blue, red	Mac	Cachet Cra	B
7413	The / Pledge to the / Flag / I pledge allegiance to the flag / of the etc.	Unknown	Flag	Boone	A
7414	The / Pledge to the / Flag / I pledge allegiance to the flag etc. [thermographed]	Blue, red	Flag	Amer Pat	A
7415	The / post I'm / tied to! [handpainted] [envelope 5 11/16x3 13/16 in.]	Multicolored	Home	Cowdery	D
7416	The / Quartermaster / Corps / the unsung heroes / of the war. etc. [no picture]	Red	Army	Rowe	A
7417	The / reason / the / eighth / annual / banquet / of / Fort Hamilton etc.	Black	Hitle	Fort Hamil	A
7418	The / Sad / Sack / G.I. Joe - experience? [handpainted]	Multicolored	Army	Maul	C
7419	The / seabees of the U.S. / Navy	Multicolored	Navy	Staehle	C
7420	The / Service / mail-kit / United States / Army [env. 10 1/2x7 9/16 in.]	Blue, red	FlagV	Unknown	D
7421	The / sun never sets / on the / fighting / Seabees	Blue/Red	Navy	Unknown	A
7422	The / U.S.A. / is gunning for / these Axis boys!	Blue, red	Axis	Boone	A
7423	The / U.S.A. / will knock the / Germ out / of / Germany etc. [no picture]	Blue, red	Axis	Boone	A
7423A	The / U.S. Marine Corps / Reserve! / honors / John Philip Sousa / "The President's Own" etc.	Multicolored	USMC	USMC	D
7424	The / U.S.S.--L.S.T. / 541	Blue	Navy	Card	A
7425	The / United / Nations / Nations united for victory [thermographed]	Unknown	UN	Crosby	B
7426	The / world / counts on / America / to win the war / and etc. [no picture]	Blue, red	Home	Meylan	A
7427	The 1943 Prince Charming / has / new use for his / charms! [handpainted]	Multicolored	Army	Cowdery	D
7428	The 1945 / March of Dimes / is on! / [etc.] / 1-15-'45———National "dimout" etc.	Gold, silver	Home	Linto	B
7429	The 1945 / March of Dimes / is on! / Get in line! [no picture]	Gold/Gd,S	Home	Linto	B
7430	The A.N.C.S / Argonauts salute the / heroic men who died etc. [thermographed]	Black	Navy	Amer Naval	B
7431	The administration / suggests a stiff tax / [etc.] / Dec. 7, 1941, a date etc.	Multicolored	Anniv	Linto	B
7432	The administration / suggests a stiff tax / [etc.] / Navy Day———Oct. 27, 1943	Multicolored	Navy	Linto	B
7433	The administration / suggests a stiff tax / [etc.] / Pearl Harbor was etc.	Multicolored	Pearl	Linto	B
7434	The administration / suggests a stiff tax / increase to etc. [no picture]	Multicolored	Home	Linto	B
7435	The air road / is the victory road etc. [thermographed]	Unknown	Unk	McCluney	A
7436	The Air Transport Command / United States Army Air Forces	Multicolored	Globe	Unknown	A
7437	The all nations society / St. Petersburg, Fla. etc. [artist: Staehle]	Blue, red	UN	Chamber	C
7438	The Allies crossed Volturno / Axis found retreat was / [etc.] / October 1943	Blue, red	Event	Griffith	B
7439	The American / eagle's / protection makes / merry Xmas / possible / in 1943	Green, red	Holid	Runge	B
7440	The American / neutrality / humanity	Blue, red	RedCr	Brenn	A
7441	The American creed [in quotes] / I believe in the United States of etc.	Unknown	Unk	Schnecken	A
7442	The American eagle protects her own / war bonds help	Unknown	Eagle	Runge	A
7443	The American eagle, / rules over Tokyo!	Bk/Bu/Br/Gn/R	EagFl	Harrington	A
7444	The American eagle, / rules over Tokyo!	Blue, red	EagFl	Harrington	A
7445	The American Eagle, / rules over Tokyo! [postmarked 8/27/45]	Blue, red	EagFl	Harrington	D
7446	The American Red Cross / organized Aug. 22 etc.	Unknown	RedCr	Brenn	A
7447	The American Red Cross / organized Aug. 22, 1881 / Let this banner down etc.	Blue, red	RedCr	Brenn	A
7448	The American Red Cross / wherever he is etc.	Unknown	RedCr	Brenn	A
7449	The American soldier speaks / When we come home again / forget the band! etc.	Bu,R/Multi	Verse	Carpenter	B
7450	The American soldier speaks / When we come home again / forget the band. etc.	Blue, red	Verse	Carpenter	B
7451	The American way / Roosevelt wins, God bless etc. [no picture]	Unknown	FDR	Abel	B
7452	The American way / Roosevelt wins, God bless him, / more fishin trips etc.	Red	FDR	Abel	B
7453	The American's creed / I believe in etc.	Unknown	Unk	Schnecken	A
7454	The America's Guardian! [handpainted]	Black	Globe	Klondike	C
7455	The Anglo-American armies / under the command of [in quotes] etc. [no picture]	Brown, red	Event	Fidelity	B
7456	The answer to 'isms / "Keep / 'em / flying" / "Our first duty, defend America"!	Multicolored	Flag+	Edmunds	D
7457	The arrogance of / Roosevelt / [etc.] / 1-23-'45———Reds reach / Oder river	Multicolored	Event	Linto	B
7458	The arrogance of / Roosevelt indicates / he wants to head / a monarchy!	Multicolored	FDR	Linto	B
7459	The Atlantic——— / "Sighted sub; / sank same"	Black	Air	Coll Surp	A

NO.	CACHET TEXT	COLOR	TOPIC	PUBLISHER	$
7460	The atomic bomb / The most powerful weapon of war ever devised by etc. [postmarked 8/6/45]	Multicolored	Atom	Fluegel	D
7461	The Axis / on its last "leg" now [handpainted]	Multicolored	Map	Babcock	B
7462	The Axis enemy / "We shall hit him and hit him / again-wherever we find him"--FDR	Bk/Bu/Brown	FDR	Harrington	B
7463	The Axis enemy / We shall hit him and hit him again / wherever we may etc.	Br/Blue,Red	FDR	Harrington	B
7464	The Axis gets together [handpainted]	Handpainted	Axis	Parker	C
7465	The Axis nations . May they go swiftly down to etc. [env. 9 1/2x4 1/8 in.]	Blue	Axis	Unknown	A
7466	The Axis powers shall learn / what etc.	Unknown	Axis	Carpenter	A
7467	The B-29's are buzzin' over Tokyo!	Blue, red	Air	Boone	A
7468	The banner of freedom / shall never fail!	Blue, red	Flag	Ander, EA	A
7469	The banner of freedom / shall never fail!	Blue, red	Flag	Ander, EA	A
7470	The battle of the / Carolinas / The Red Army etc.	Unknown	Unk	Unknown	A
7471	The battle of the bulges	Multicolored	Nazis	Peer	B
7472	The battle-cry of freedom! / Keep 'em flying! [last line 41 mm long]	Bicolor var	Air	Poppenger	A
7473	The battle-cry of freedom! / Keep 'em flying! [last line 46 mm long]	Bicolor var	Air	Poppenger	A
7474	The battle-cry of freedom! / Keep 'em flying! [last line 54 mm long]	Bicolor var	Air	Poppenger	A
7475	The best defense is a strong offense / VJ	Blue, purple	VJDay	Unknown	C
7476	The big / strike / Berlin / Feb. 5, 1945 / 4000 Allied etc. [handpainted]	Multicolored	Nazis	Smith, LH	C
7477	The Big Four powers agreed / to accept Japan's surrender etc. [handpainted] [no picture]	Blue	Event	Batura	D
7478	The big push / continues [envelope 6 3/4x3 3/4 in.]	Unknown	Unk	Quigley	B
7479	The big push is on! / for victory! / Buy war bonds	Blue, red	Ordna	Ander, EA	A
7480	The big push is on: / for victory! / Buy war bonds	Blue, red	Ordna	Ander, EA	A
7481	The Big Three announced that / Germany will be stripped etc. [typed] [no picture]	Black	Event	Unknown	B
7482	The Big Three announced that / Germany will be stripped of etc. [hp] [no picture]	Blue	Event	Batura	D
7483	The Bill of Rights / The Bill of Rights, proclaimed on Dec. etc. [no picture]	Blue	Home	Unknown	A
7484	The bonds you buy today will pave your way to a better tomorrow etc.	Blue	Bonds	Lawrence	A
7485	The book of / free men / will survive etc.	Unknown	Unk	Card	A
7486	The booming roar of a .44 / spelled death to badmen / in etc. [handpainted]	Black	Hitle	Unknown	B
7487	The boys are coming / home, take care of them [imprint: LSS]	Unknown	Unk	Unk	A
7488	The bridge to victory / U.S. war etc. [brown mailing tube 7 3/8x4 1/8 in.]	Black	Bonds	Klaus Dept	C
7489	The bridge to victory / U.S. war etc. [on back] [envelope 9 1/2x4 1/8 in.]	Blue	Unk	Detr Fuel	B
7490	The British Lion, The Russian Bear, The American boys, all of them there etc.	Blue, pink	Ally	Griffith	B
7491	The broken talisman / "Schicklegruber, you're next"	Black	Axis	Donaldson	A
7492	The B's are / buzzin' over / Tokyo	Blue, red	Air	Boone	A
7493	The B's are / buzzin' over / Tokyo! / 1500 planes hit Tokyo	Blue, red	Air	Boone	A
7494	The Bureau of Labor Statistics / [etc.] / 2-26-'44——Yankee carriers etc.	Multicolored	Event	Linto	B
7495	The Bureau of Labor Statistics, in its under estimate, claims etc. [no picture]	Gold, silver	Home	Linto	B
7496	The Cairo meeting [artist: Staehle]	Multicolored	Ally	Staehle	C
7497	The Call / Hurry, Marshal Kesselring / make it etc. [no picture] [thermographed]	Red	Verse	Baur	A
7498	The Cathedral of St. Basil—Moscow [in quotes] [envelope 6 3/4x3 7/8 in.]	Sepia tones	Relig	Belles-let	C
7499	The cheerful cherub / The human race is / all at war / and thinks of etc.	Black	Verse	Morris	A
7500	The chief says: / heap big bonds will / heap big bombs etc. [env. 6x3 ½ in.]	Silver	Bonds	Phill, CR	A
7501	The chief says: / heap big bonds will / heap big bombs etc. [env. 6x3 ½ in.]	Gn/Pu/Red	Bonds	Cox	A
7502	The cycle of war / War begets poverty / poverty——peace: / Peace begets etc.	R,Br/Bu,Br	Verse	Boone	A
7503	The dawn of peace / May the divine promise of / "peace on earth" / renew etc.	Blue, red	VJDay	Lowell	B
7504	The day of victory / when we march etc.	Black	Unk	Rameco	A
7505	The democratic / way is the real / [etc.] / 7-30-'44——Reds enter / East Prussia	Unknown	Event	Linto	B
7506	The democratic / way is the real / American way!	Unknown	Uncle	Linto	B
7507	The Detroit Free Press / [etc.] / Momentous news of the week / Sun. Aug. 5--etc.	Black, red	VJDay	Layne	C
7508	The Devil's companion now	Black	Hitle	Sadworth	A
7509	The dragon / of Fu Hi / The U.S. / eagle / China United U.S. / in / the etc.	Unknown	China	Goldsten	B
7510	The eagle / fights back	Blue, red	Eagle	Knapp	C
7511	The eagle / will get the rattlesnake [colored envelopes]	Blue, red	Axis	Poppenger	A
7512	The eagle has talons / Keep America free in the air	Blue, red	Air	Minkus	A
7513	The Eagle readies his / brood for Tokyo! [eagle + 5 planes] [handpainted]	Brown	Eagle	Klondike	D
7514	The eagle screams / the lion roars / The Russian bear / rolls on and on etc.	Green	Eagle	Abel	A
7515	The end / of all rats!	Black	Hitle	Unknown	A
7516	The end is near! [envelope 6 1/2x3 5/8, 7 1/2x3 7/8 or 4 in.]	Blue	Navy	Fertig	B
7517	The end of / a swell day [burned left edge] [handpainted]	Multicolored	Army	Cowdery	D

NO.	CACHET TEXT	COLOR	TOPIC	PUBLISHER	$
7518	The end of your / rope——Tojo!	Blue	Japan	Peters	A
7519	The end of your / rope——Tojo! / Be careful! / the end / is near	Red	Japan	Peters	A
7520	The end of your / rope——Tojo! / So solly!	Blue, red	Japan	Dale	A
7521	The enemies' humor is the fumer / who etc.	Unknown	Unk	Brenn	A
7522	The enemy is listening	Black	Hitle	Peters	A
7523	The enemy is listening / Idle chatter can be etc. [label + printed border]	Multicolored	Hitle	Artists	B
7524	The enemy must be hit and hit hard from / so many [in quotes] etc. [thermographed]	Black	Axis	Sadworth	B
7525	The Evening Star / [etc.] / June 18,1945 / Triumphant homecoming of General etc.	Blue, red	Ike	Layne	B
7526	The Evening Star / [etc.] / This is the best we could / do, General... etc.	Blue, red	Ike	Unknown	B
7527	The evils and false / isms rampant in etc. [env. 6 1/2x3 5/8, 9 1/2x4 1/8 in.]	Blue	Liber	Buxton, D	A
7528	The eyes of Christendom are upon us etc.	Unknown	Unk	Murrman	A
7529	The eyes of Texas / shine with pride / Her etc.	Unknown	Unk	McCluney	A
7530	The fairest flag that fearless floats / fair in war and peace	Blue, red	Flag	Amer Pat	A
7531	The fall of the / Reichs capital / Berlin etc. [thermographed] [artist: Staehle]	Black, red	Event	Smartcraft	C
7532	The fate of Germany / in future generations was / made etc. [typed] [no picture]	Black	Event	Batura	C
7533	The Fighting Irish [in quotes] / "Captain Colin Kelly" etc. [env. 7x3 3/4 in.]	Multicolored	Air	Belles-let	D
7534	The fighting Marines / afloat, ashore and in etc.	Blue/Red	USMC	Bean	A
7535	The first / V-E-V-J / Thanksgiving etc.	Unknown	Unk	Amer Pat	A
7536	The first American - / A tribute to the Indian, / fighting with our armed etc.	Red	Home	Neal	A
7537	The first American soldier to kill a Jap was / Mike Murphy / The first etc.	Gn,S/Multi	Hero	Linto	B
7538	The flag of the free there is comfort in thee	Multicolored	Flag	Amer Pat	A
7539	The flag still floats unblotted / by defeat! / But ah! the blood that etc.	Blue, red	Flag	Brenn	A
7540	The flag that / shows you mercy etc. [envelope 71/2x4 in.]	Multicolored	Flag	Amer Pat	A
7541	The flag that has been / tried / and victory never denied.	Blue, red	Flag	Amer Pat	A
7542	The flag that shows / you mercy will etc. [1 star below text] [color varieties]	Multicolored	Flag	Amer Pat	A
7543	The flag that shows / you mercy will etc. [stars border text] [color varieties]	Multicolored	Flag	Amer Pat	A
7544	The fortress of the Axis / is crumbling in decay / first Italy etc.	Blue, red	Axis	Griffith	A
7545	The four freedoms, are up to you,—— / Be you Protestant, Catholic, or etc.	Blue, red	Eagle	Shaw, TC	A
7546	The freedom way / Buy war bonds / today! [colored envelopes]	Black/Blue	Eagle	Huss	A
7547	The future / He's meeting the extra / dollar for each 3 that / he etc.	Green	Home	Phill, CR	A
7548	The future / He's meeting the extra etc.	Gray/Gold	Unk	Phill+Cox	A
7549	The future belongs to those / who prepare etc.	Unknown	Unk	Quigley	B
7550	The future is not in the hands etc.	Blue	Unk	Carter	A
7551	The G.I. home front / by Russel Kay / (Part one) / If you etc. [no picture]	Blue, red	Verse	Brenn	A
7552	The G.I. home front / by Russel Kay / (Part three) / etc.	Blue, red	Verse	Brenn	A
7553	The G.I. home front / by Russel Kay / (Part two) / etc.	Blue, red	Verse	Brenn	A
7554	The garbage can / has Muzzy and Hitler / Hirohito is next [thermographed]	Black	Axis	Sadworth	B
7555	The Garfield-Perry Stamp Club, Inc. / [etc.] / Buy defense stamps too!	Blue, red	Flag	Garfield	B
7556	The Garfield-Perry Stamp Club, Inc. / [etc.] / Remember Pearl Harbor!	Blue, red	Flag	Garfield	B
7557	The Garfield-Perry Stamp Club, Inc. / Hollenden Hotel etc. [10 flags form "V"]	Blue, red	Flag	Garfield	B
7558	The Garfield-Perry Stamp Club, Inc. / Hollenden Hotel etc. [row of 12 flags]	Blue, red	Flag	Garfield	B
7559	The Garfield-Perry Stamp Club, Inc. / Hollenden Hotel etc. [Uncle Sam + flag]	Blue, red	Uncle	Garfield	B
7560	The gem / of the oceans [thermographed] [buff envelope]	Unknown	Unk	Baur	A
7561	The gift of life is / yours / to / give. / Donate your pint of blood now.	Multicolored	Blood	Swave+Mill	A
7562	The gift of life is / yours / to / give. / Donate your pint of etc. [thermographed]	Gold, Red	Blood	Swave+Mill	B
7563	The goal - victory / The place - Europe etc.	Blue	Unk	Ander, EA	A
7564	The goal - victory! / the place - Europe. / The year - 1944!	Blue	Army	Ander, EA	A
7565	The God who gave us / life gave us / [etc.] / 9-3-'44——Yanks liberate etc.	Gold	Event	Linto	B
7566	The God who gave us / life gave us liberty at / the same time. / ——Thomas etc.	Bk,Gold/Bro	Flag	Linto	B
7567	The God who gave us life gave / [etc.] / 10-17-'44——Formosa gets / third etc.	Multicolored	Event	Linto	B
7568	The God who gave us life gave / us liberty at the same time. etc. [no picture]	Gold, silver	Hist	Linto	B
7569	The golden date / of humanity / April 25, 1945 / United Nations etc. [no picture]	Gold	UN	Amer Pat	A
7570	The golden date / of humanity / April 25, 1945 etc. [in blue irregular border]	Blue, gold	UN	Amer Pat	A
7571	The golden date / of humanity / April 25, 1945 etc. [on calendar or over eagle]	Gold, red	UN	Amer Pat	A
7572	The golden date / of humanity / April etc. [over eagle] [env. 7 1/2x3 7/8 in.]	Blue, gold	UN	Amer Pat	A
7573	The golden date / of humanity/ April 25, 1945 etc. [no border, no picture]	Gold, green	UN	Amer Pat	A
7574	The golden date. / The golden state / The golden gate etc.	Gold	UN	Amer Pat	A
7575	The government is safe [in quotes] / Pres. Truman says: "When a speech" etc.	Multicolored	HST	Linto	B

NO.	CACHET TEXT	COLOR	TOPIC	PUBLISHER	$
7576	The grandest / thing in this / world is a / clear conscious [sic] [handpainted]	Multicolored	Uncle	Adler	D
7577	The graves which America decor- / ates today are more than a mem- / ory, etc.	Blue, red	Liber	Brenn	A
7578	The greatest Mother / in the world etc.	Unknown	Unk	Unknown	A
7579	The guy who paid for my rifle - / took it back ! / Buy war bonds—— etc. [handpainted]	Black	Army	Martin	C
7580	The hand of / opportunity / is rapping for you / Buy war bonds!	Black, red	Bonds	Speede	A
7581	The handwriting on the wall	Black	Unk	McCluney	A
7582	The hard assignment / is to win the war; / who keeps us from / winning the etc.	Blue	Home	Shaw, TC	A
7583	The heroes of Bastogne! / There is a new etc. [all text below flag]	Unknown	Unk	Levering	A
7584	The heroes of Bastogne! / There is a new etc. [first line above flag]	Unknown	Unk	Levering	A
7585	The historical Rhine crossing	Multicolored	Event	Fluegel	C
7586	The home front / We are promised "The Four Freedoms," etc. [colored envelopes]	Blue, red	Flag	Shaw, TC	A
7587	The home front, / answers the call.	Blue, green	Home	Baur	A
7588	The hope and pride / of America [colored envelopes]	Bk, R/Bu,Red	Armed	Poppenger	A
7589	The House of Representatives by a vote / of 224 to 161 etc. [handpainted] [11/28/41]	Black	Event	Batura	E
7590	The Huns finally / surrendered to Allies! / Paper were [sic] etc. [no picture]	Green, silver	VEDay	Linto	B
7591	The immortal Fifth [5th Infantry Division insignia]	Multicolored	Unit	McCluney	B
7592	The infantry / Who travels the last hundred yards to victory? [thermographed]	Brown, red	Army	Unknown	A
7593	The infantry, the infantry, with / dirt behind their ears. Are doing etc.	Blue, red	Army	Baur	A
7594	The International Red Cross / organized Aug. 22, 1864 / The American Red etc.	Blue, red	RedCr	Brenn	A
7595	The International Red Cross / organized etc.	Unknown	RedCr	Brenn	A
7596	The invasion / is on! / Eisenhower hurls troops / against etc. [no picture]	Red	Event	Boone	B
7597	The invasion / is on! / Eisenhower hurls troops etc. [no picture] [thermographed]	Red	Event	Boone	B
7598	The issue is still in doubt / After 15 days etc.	Unknown	Unk	Card	A
7599	The It is out of Italy / The Germ in Germany next / Then / the Allies will etc.	Multicolored	Axis	Boone	B
7600	The Japanese believe their / country resulted when a pair etc. [handpainted]	Blue	Japan	Unknown	B
7601	The Japanese can't / pronounce L, but / L day taught them / what etc. [4/1/45]	Black	Event	Malaney	D
7602	The Japs / are next	Unknown	Unk	Ang	A
7603	The Japs / started it / on the 7th / Let's / finish them / with etc. [thermographed]	Black/green	Bonds	Ang	B
7604	The Japs / started it / on the 7th / Let's / finish them / with the 7th	Black/Green	Bonds	Ang	A
7605	The Jap's turn will come	Multicolored	Axis	Peer	B
7606	The Japs will pay / for the atrocities / on American boys!	Blue, red	Japan	Boone	A
7607	The job in Germany is done! / Before us etc. (postmarked 5/8/45 only)	Blue, red	VEDay	Levering	B
7608	The job in Germany is done! / Before us etc. [postmarked 5/8/45 plus 9/2/45]	Blue, red	VEDay	Levering	D
7609	The knock-out / war loan [arm in shape of a "7"] [postmarked 6/29/45] [handpainted]	Multicolored	Japan	Adler	D
7610	The land of the free / Let's keep it that way! [w/, w/o 2 red stars] [thermographed]	R,Bk/R,blue	Flag	Von Los	B
7611	The last hour / of the last war etc. [no picture]	Unknown	Holid	Davis, Ray	B
7612	The last quarter / They're in a huddle	Black	Axis	Neal	A
7613	The last round / up. [handpainted]	Multicolored	Japan	Adler	D
7614	The leading ace / of the / AAF / Maj. Richard I. Bong / Poplar, Wis. etc.	Black	Hero	Garland	A
7615	The letter / somebody didn't write / It ain't etc.	Unknown	Unk	Brenn	A
7616	The Lexington sails on / 1——They say the Lexington / [etc.] / 2——The etc. [handpainted]	Multicolored	Liber	Weigand	B
7617	The Lexington sails on / 3——When the big / [etc.] / 4——Then came the etc. [handpainted]	Multicolored	Liber	Weigand	B
7618	The Lexington sails on / 6——But the old "Lex" / [etc.] / 7——As you etc. [handpainted]	Multicolored	Liber	Weigand	B
7619	The liberty of America / originates etc.	Blue	Unk	Neal	A
7620	The light / of liberty / will not be / extinguished / by etc. [red envelope]	Multicolored	Liber	Linto	B
7621	The light of hope!	Blue, red	Liber	Mission	A
7622	The light of liberty / will always burn! [13 blue stars at top]	Blue, red	Liber	Davis, Ral	A
7623	The light of liberty / will always burn! [13 red stars at top]	Blue, red	Liber	Davis, Ral	A
7624	The light of liberty / will always burn! [no stars at top]	Blue, red	Liber	Davis, Ral	A
7625	The light of victory / shines from / Statue of Liberty / eagerly / awaiting / the return / of our / boys	Black, blue	Liber	Unknown	B
7626	The light within / When evening comes etc. [on back] [envelope 6 3/4x3 3/4 in.]	Unknown	Unk	Boston Ed	B
7627	The little boy who got just / what he asked for. [handpainted]	Multicolored	Nazis	Sturgill	E
7628	The majesty of defense [small square or tall caps] [envelope 6 3/4x3 7/8 in.]	Unknown	Unk	Belles-let	C
7629	The majesty of defense [envelope 6 9/16x3 3/4 in.]	Unknown	Unk	Belles-let	C
7630	The man behind the hoe / The man behind the hoe backs up the man behind etc.	Bk/Bu/Green	Home	Smith, AD	A
7631	The man of / the hour—— [handpainted]	Black	USSR	Clendennen	C
7632	The man of the hour / A small West Virginia mining town / is etc. [artist: Knapp]	Blue, red	MacFD	Fleetwood	B
7633	The man with the 'bear' behind	Bk/Bu/Bk,R	USSR	Burdick	A

NO.	CACHET TEXT	COLOR	TOPIC	PUBLISHER	$
7634	The Marines / have landed / and have the / [etc.] / Japan / surrenders etc.	Red, purple	VJDay	Boone	B
7635	The Marines / have landed / and have the / situation / well in hand!	Blue, red	Japan	Boone	A
7636	The Marines / have landed / and have the / situation / well in hand! [all caps]	Blue, red	Japan	Boone	A
7637	The Marines / have landed! - / and have the / situation well / in hand -	Black	USMC	Lupton	A
7638	The Marines have landed / The situation is well in hand [thermographed]	Red	USMC	Crosby	B
7639	The Marines' Hymn / From the halls of Montezuma, / to the shores etc. [thermographed]	Red	USMC	Crosby	B
7640	The master-ed race——the embrace of [in quotes] etc. [env. 6 9/16x3 3/4 in.]	Brown	Nazis	Belles-let	C
7641	The men behind the gun [in quotes] [envelope 6 3/4x3 3/4 in.]	Sepia tones	Army	Belles-let	C
7642	The men behind the gun [in quotes] [envelope 6 9/16x3 3/4 in.]	Sepia tones	Army	Belles-let	C
7643	The mighty 7th / 7 [thermographed]	Unknown	Bonds	Baur	A
7644	The mighty 7th / war loan drive / Smash etc. [thermographed]	Unknown	Bonds	Yontz	B
7645	The military / forces have / confidence in / your support! etc. [color var.]	Multicolored	Bonds	Linto	B
7646	The more / bonds you buy—— / the more / planes will fly [colored envelopes]	Bk/Bu/Brown	Air	Huss	A
7647	The more bonds / you buy / the more etc.	Unknown	Bonds	Vollhardt	A
7648	The more bonds and stamps you buy etc.	Unknown	Bonds	Lowe	A
7649	The more U.S. bonds and stamps / you sell etc. [no picture]	Unknown	Bonds	Lowe	A
7650	The more war bonds / you buy etc. [1 airplane]	Blue, red	Air	Ander, EA	A
7651	The more war bonds / you buy etc. [2 airplanes]	Blue, red	Air	Ander, EA	A
7652	The more women at work / the sooner we win [upper right]	Red	Women	Unknown	A
7653	The more you write / the better he'll etc. [text height 27 mm] [thermographed]	Unknown	Armed	Yontz	B
7654	The more you write / the better he'll etc. [text height 29 mm] [thermographed]	Unknown	Armed	Yontz	B
7655	The most important question to be settled	Black	Ally	Smith, DH	A
7656	The nation mourns / 1882-1945 [handpainted label with photo of FDR]	Black	FDR	LeGallez	F
7657	The nation will carry on! etc. [line 6: "immortality"] [no picture]	Unknown	Unk	Levering	A
7658	The nation will carry on! etc. [line 6: "imortality"] [no picture]	Unknown	Unk	Levering	A
7659	The national security / American Base Forces / A.P.O. No [sic] 809 Br.	Blue	Bases	Unknown	C
7660	The nation's first line of defense / A navy second to none! For the etc.	Blue, red	Navy	Boone	A
7661	The nations pride / United States Navy [front imprint: ES]	Bu/Br/Green	Navy	Unknown	B
7662	The Nazi departure / from Russia / is going according / to plan. / In etc.	Blue	USSR	James	A
7663	The Nazi read only what / Goebbels wants them to [in quotes] etc. [handpainted]	Multicolored	Nazis	Knoll	C
7664	The Nazis surrender! [printed diagonally] [no picture]	Black	VEDay	Butzen	B
7665	The Netherlands	Black	ORN	Lowry	A
7666	The newest art work / [etc.] / World War Two etc.	Black	Unk	Doughboy	A
7667	The news of the war, good / [etc.] / Feb. 11, '44——British cargo convoy etc.	Unknown	Event	Linto	B
7668	The news of the war, good / or bad, belongs to the peo- / ple. Quit etc.	Unknown	Flag	Linto	B
7669	The Nip's [sic] wanted / all of Asia- / We'll give etc. [text position varies]	Green, red	Devil	Runge	A
7670	The oath in our naturalization laws / [etc.] / 8-31-'44——Russians liberate etc.	Gold, green	Event	Linto	B
7671	The oath in our naturalization laws / demand [sic] allegiance to etc. [no picture]	Gold, green	Home	Linto	B
7672	The officers and men / of the / United etc. [thermographed]	Unknown	Unk	Sadworth	B
7673	The old gray / mare, she / aint what she / used to be!	Green	Musso	Roberts	A
7674	The old trail / Argonne / 1917 / Soissons etc.	Unknown	Hist	Baur	A
7675	The ole boy's got / a lot on the ball	Blue, red	Globe	Andrews	A
7676	The one regret / Our greatest leader of all / could not share the Allies etc.	Black	FDR	Carpenter	A
7677	The one word they'll never forget!	Blue	Unk	Lawrence	A
7678	The original "Purple Heart" / The original "Purple Heart" etc. [thermographed]	Purple	Medal	Crosby	B
7679	The Pacific Ocean has / been divided into etc.	Black	Unk	Runge	A
7680	The Pacific problem is / vital! Send more sup- / plies etc. [no picture]	Brown, green	Mac	Linto	B
7681	The paws that depresses	Black/Bk, red	USSR	Andrews	A
7682	The peace / We hope United States / representatives, who will / help draw etc.	Multicolored	Minut	Linto	B
7683	The pen is mightier / than the sword / you've often heard them say / The etc.	Blue, red	Home	Griffith	A
7684	The people are / on the march! / Work! / Fight! etc. [label + printed border]	Multicolored	Home	Artists	B
7685	The people are / on the march/ United Nations etc. [label + printed border]	Multicolored	UN	Artists	B
7686	The Philippines / "I will be back" [artist: Staehle]	Blue, red	Mac	Cachet Cra	B
7687	The Philippines / Victim of Japs' early drive in World / War II - etc.	Black	Phili	Howe	A
7688	The pin up boys / They used to be / the pin up boys / in their native etc.	Black	Axis	Abel	A
7689	The pirate ship / beware / we are ready for etc. [thermographed] [yellow envelope]	Blue	Navy	Czubay	B
7690	The Pledge to the Flag / "I pledge allegiance to the flag" etc. [colored envelopes]	Blue, red	Flag	Poppenger	A
7691	The Pledge to the Flag / I pledge allegiance etc. [envelope 7 1/2x4 in.]	Unknown	Flag	Amer Phila	A

NO.	CACHET TEXT	COLOR	TOPIC	PUBLISHER	$
7692	The Pledge to the Flag / I pledge etc.	Multicolored	Flag	Poppenger	A
7693	The President of the / United States of / America etc. [handpainted] [9/20/41]	Multicolored	Event	Batura	E
7694	The President of the / United States ordered / me [in quotes] etc. [no picture]	Blue, red	MacFD	Fidelity	C
7695	The President's ship "The Hoosier" / USS Indianapolis [blue envelope]	Black	Navy	Lupton	A
7696	The price of liberty is the same yesterday, [in quotes] etc. [no picture]	Multicolored	Home	Hunt	A
7697	The Purple Heart / "for military merit" [thermographed]	Purple	Armed	Crosby	B
7698	The quickest, surest way / you can help win this / war... / V / Buy etc.	Black	UncV	Unknown	A
7699	The rail splitters [84th Infantry Division insignia]	Black, red	Unit	McCluney	B
7700	The Rainbow Division [42nd Infantry Division insignia]	Multicolored	Unit	McCluney	B
7701	The ramparts we watch	Multicolored	Home	Minkus	A
7702	The rays of the Rising Sun / are getting shorter [thermographed]	Unknown	Japan	Baur	A
7703	The real "400" / ...the Wake Island Marines / Glory! Glory! / The gilded etc.	Blue, red	USMC	Boone	A
7704	The real "Rising Sun" / and the "fade-out"! / Buy war bonds and etc. [thermographed]	Red	Japan	Unknown	B
7705	The reason / the eleventh / anniversary / banquet / of the / Fort etc.	Brown, red	Hitle	Fort Hamil	A
7706	The Red Bomber [in quotes] [handpainted]	Multicolored	USSR	Knoll	C
7707	The Red Cross / Volunteer Nurses' / [etc.] / 10-29-'44——Russia refuses to etc.	Unknown	Event	Linto	B
7708	The Red Cross / Volunteer Nurses' / Aide Corps bring / sunshine to our etc.	Unknown	RedCr	Linto	B
7709	The Red Cross needs your / aid [handpainted]	Multicolored	RedCr	Clendennen	C
7710	The Red Cross organization / needs etc.	Unknown	RedCr	Smith, W	A
7711	The Red Cross organization / stands back of our fighting men / doing a big job!	Blue, red	RedCr	Smith, W	A
7712	The rehabilitation / program for those / [etc.] / 9-11-'44——Yanks etc.	Multicolored	Event	Linto	B
7713	The rehabilitation / program for those / [etc.] / 9-12-'44——Yankee columns etc.	Multicolored	Event	Linto	B
7714	The rehabilitation / program for those / returning from / service must be etc.	Multicolored	Flag	Linto	B
7715	The rehabilitation program for / those etc.	Unknown	Unk	Baur	A
7716	The resurrection	Blue	Unk	Citret	B
7717	The return shall be triumphant; / the departure avenged.	Blue	Mac	Davis, Ray	A
7718	The right name / "Black Market" doesn't etc.	Unknown	Unk	Threl+Thar	A
7719	The right side of the fence / The Victory etc.	Unknown	Unk	Eichenlaub	A
7720	The rising / sun has set / Japan surrenders etc.	Red	VJDay	Czubay	D
7721	The rising scum / is setting! / ——and how! [2nd and 3rd word print varieties]	Blue, red	Japan	Boone	A
7722	The rising sun / [etc.] / "Japan surrenders" etc. [postmarked 8/14 & 9/2/45]	Brown	VJDay	Czubay	D
7723	The rising sun / has set / Victory V-J Day	Brown/Multi	VJDay	Czubay	D
7724	The rising sun / has set / Victory V-J day [thermographed]	Brown	VJDay	Czubay	D
7725	The rising sun began / to set Dec. 7, 1941	Blue, red	Army	Boone	A
7726	The road / to Rome [handpainted]	Multicolored	Army	Borkowski	D
7727	The road back [cachet colors vary]	Multicolored	Nazis	Peer	B
7728	The road to liberty cannot / be reached with armchair / chatter. Action, etc.	Gd,S/Multi	Bell	Linto	B
7729	The Roman / candle [handpainted]	Multicolored	Nazis	Smith, LH	C
7730	The rose of no mans land / the American nurse [thermographed]	Unknown	Nurse	Baur	A
7731	The Russians are coming! [in quotes]	Multicolored	Nazis	Peer	B
7732	The safest investment in / the world today / U.S. war bonds / $4 back for etc.	Blue, red	Bonds	Ang	A
7733	The safest investment in the world!	Red, sepia	Bonds	Boone	A
7734	The scourge of Europe. [handpainted]	Blue	Hitle	Clendennen	C
7735	The seal of security	Green	Navy	Ander, CS	A
7736	The second / world war / is over [no picture] [handpainted]	Blue	VJDay	Batura	D
7737	The seventh of December / 1——'Twas the seventh of December / in the year etc.	Multicolored	Verse	Weigand	B
7738	The Sgt. / is a jerk	Unknown	Unk	Threl+Thar	A
7739	The sign of the / V / won't win / Let's produce [no picture]	Unknown	Unk	Threl+Thar	A
7740	The snow cruiser / reaches the / South Pole / Defense plans halted / Byrd etc.	Bk/Black, red	Event	Fidelity	C
7741	The soldier's dream [handpainted]	Multicolored	Home	Shaffer, A	C
7742	The son / Peace on earth / [etc.] / Christmas 1944 / The sunrise / Year 1945	Green	Holid	Hyde	B
7743	The souvenir hound	Blue	Army	Burdick	A
7744	The souvenir I'm taking home / is not a German gat; / it's not a German etc.	Gn/Red, blue	Verse	Carpenter	A
7745	The spider to the flies says: / "I / will prevent / inflation!" etc. [no picture]	Unknown	Home	Linto	B
7746	The spider to the flies says: / [etc.] / 6-2-'44——Yankee shuttle bombers etc.	Unknown	Event	Linto	B
7747	The spirit / of 1775 / carries on	Red	Hist	Carpenter	A
7748	The spirit of '43 / the same as in '76	Blue, red	Bell	Boone	A
7749	The spirit of '76	Br/Red, blue	Hist	Runge	A

NO.	CACHET TEXT	COLOR	TOPIC	PUBLISHER	$
7750	The spirit of '76 / carries onward!	Blue, red	Bell	Boone	A
7751	The spirit of '76 / Our forefathers fought etc.	Purple	Hist	Runge	A
7752	The spirit of '76 carries on!	Blue, red	Minut	Cachet Cra	A
7753	The staggering profits made / in this / [etc.] / 6-15-'45——British capture etc.	Unknown	Event	Linto	B
7754	The staggering profits made / in this war etc.	Unknown	Home	Linto	B
7755	The Star Spangled Banner / Long may it wave [thermographed]	Unknown	Unk	Yontz	B
7756	The Star Spangled Banner / of America / One flag / one people / one etc.	Blue, red	Flag	Linprint	A
7757	The Star Spangled Banner, / long may / it wave, / o'er the / land of etc.	Blue, red	Flag	Linprint	A
7758	The Stars and Stripes / "G.I. like it" [2nd line 36 mm] [colored envelopes]	Black/Blue	Army	Huss	A
7759	The Stars and Stripes / "G.I. like it" [2nd line 44 mm] [colored envelopes]	Black/Blue	Army	Huss	A
7760	The Stars and Stripes forever [in quotes] / for victory	Blue, red	Flag	Grandy	A
7761	The Stars and Stripes forever [in quotes] / National defense	Blue, red	Flag	Grandy	A
7762	The sublimity of defense [in quotes] [envelope 6 3/4x3 7/8, 6 9/16x3 3/4 in.]	Sepia tones	Air	Belles-let	C
7763	The summer soldier and the sun- / shine patriot etc.	Unknown	Unk	Boone	A
7764	The tail-ender	Multicolored	Japan	Peer	B
7765	The tanks / are coming [handpainted]	Black, blue	Ordna	Parker	B
7766	The Teheran meeting [artist: Staehle]	Multicolored	Heads	Smartcraft	C
7767	The three stars / Two seemed to etc. [green envelope 5 3/8x3 3/8 in.]	Unknown	Unk	Baur	A
7768	The three who would rule the world! / Yeah...the other world! / The Devil etc.	Blue, red	Axis	Boone	A
7769	The tin can / empty it / clean it / flatten it etc. [no picture]	Unknown	Home	Rowe	A
7770	The torch of liberty	Blue, red	Torch	Risinger	A
7771	The torch of liberty / He who is shirking / at feeding the flame, / will etc.	Bk/Blue, red	Liber	Reynolds	A
7772	The torch of liberty / Keep it burning	Blue, red	Torch	Linprint	A
7773	The torch of liberty. / The hope of the world.	Blue, red	Liber	Card	A
7774	The U.S. Army / has landed	Unknown	Army	Crosby	B
7775	The U.S. Army / has landed / The United States Army infantry [thermographed]	Blue	Army	Crosby	B
7776	The U.S. Army / has landed / The United States Army Medical Corps [thermographed]	Unknown	Army	Crosby	B
7777	The U.S. Army / has landed / U.S. Army Air Corps [thermographed]	Silver	Air	Crosby	B
7778	The U.S. Army / has landed / U.S. Army Chemical Warfare [thermographed]	Blue	Army	Crosby	B
7779	The U.S. Army / has landed / U.S. Army Coast Artillery [thermographed]	Red	Ordna	Crosby	B
7780	The U.S. Army / has landed / U.S. Army Communications [thermographed]	Green	Army	Crosby	B
7781	The U.S. Army / has landed / U.S. Army Engineers [thermographed]	Green/Red	Army	Crosby	B
7782	The U.S. Army / has landed / U.S. Army Field Artillery [thermographed]	Red	Ordna	Crosby	B
7783	The U.S. Army / has landed / U.S. Army Infantry [thermographed]	Green	Army	Crosby	B
7784	The U.S. Army / has landed / U.S. Army Medical Corps——"Service" etc. [thermographed]	Purple	Chute	Crosby	B
7785	The U.S. Army / has landed / U.S. Army Ordnance Dept. [thermographed]	Unknown	Army	Crosby	B
7786	The U.S. Army / has landed / U.S. Army Ordnance Dept. [thermographed]	Unknown	Army	Crosby	B
7787	The U.S. Army / has landed / U.S. Army Parachute Troopers [thermographed]	Green	Chute	Crosby	B
7788	The U.S. Army / has landed / U.S. Army Parachutist [thermographed]	Unknown	Chute	Crosby	B
7789	The U.S. Army / has landed / U.S. Army Quartermaster Corps [thermographed]	Brown	Army	Crosby	B
7790	The U.S. Army / has landed / U.S. Army Signal Corps [thermographed]	Orange	Army	Crosby	B
7791	The U.S. eagle / fights back [artist: Knapp]	Blue, red	Eagle	Fleetwood	C
7792	The U.S. Marines / are tops [no picture]	Unknown	USMC	Ang	A
7793	The U.S. Marines / can and do / fight [thermographed]	Mulricolored	USMC	Ang	A
7794	The U.S. Marines, the / Navy and Air Force / are giving etc. [in parentheses]	Green, red	Japan	Boone	A
7795	The U.S.A. / Land of the Free [all-over cachet] [handpainted]	Blue, red	Map	Krakora	B
7796	The ugly / duckling!	Blue/Red	Hitle	Boone	A
7797	The United / Nation [sic] / invasion egg [handpainted]	Multicolored	Hitle	Borkowski	D
7798	The United Nations / fight for one brotherhood / of / free men / get in etc.	Blue, red	UN	Boone	A
7799	The United Nations / freedom from want and etc. [thermographed]	Unknown	UN	Crosby	B
7800	The United Nations fight for freedom [env.6 9/16x3 3/4, 6 1/2x3 11/16 in.]	Multicolored	Liber	Belles-let	D
7801	The United Nations fighting for / liberty and peace on earth [artist: Staehle]	Unknown	UN	Jordan	C
7802	The United States / declares war / on Japan etc. [no picture] [thermo] [12/8/41]	Black	Event	Mayne	F
7803	The United States / honors the / countries of the Asiatic etc. [thermographed]	Red	Eagle	Crosby	B
7804	The United States / made a formal declaration etc. [hp] [no picture] [12/8/41]	Blue	Event	Batura	E
7805	The United States and Great Britain / recognized the etc. [typed] [no picture]	Black	Event	Batura	C
7806	The United States and Mexico have / reached a friendly etc. [handpainted] [11/19/41]	Black	Event	Batura	D
7807	The United States Fleet / enters etc. [typed above printed cachet] [postmark 8/26/45]	Red	VJDay	Leach	D

NO.	CACHET TEXT	COLOR	TOPIC	PUBLISHER	$
7808	The United States honors the / [etc.] / The whole world etc. [thermographed]	Unknown	Unk	Crosby	B
7809	The United States honors the / [etc.] / United States etc. [thermographed]	Unknown	Unk	Crosby	B
7810	The United States honors the / countries / [etc.] / Fights on! [thermographed]	Blue, red	Uncle	Crosby	B
7811	The United States honors the / countries / [etc.] / On the Axis! [thermographed]	Blue, red	Uncle	Crosby	B
7812	The United States honors the / countries of the Asiatic etc. [thermographed]	Blue	Eagle	Crosby	B
7813	The United States honors the / countries of the Asiatic etc. [thermographed]	Blue, red	Japan	Crosby	B
7814	The United States honors the nations / [etc.] / Albania's King etc. [thermographed]	Unknown	ORN	Crosby	B
7815	The United States honors the nations / [etc.] / Albania's Queen etc. [thermographed]	Unknown	ORN	Crosby	B
7816	The United States honors the nations / [etc.] / Austria etc. [thermographed]	Unknown	ORN	Crosby	B
7817	The United States honors the nations / [etc.] / Belgium etc. [thermographed]	Unknown	ORN	Crosby	B
7818	The United States honors the nations / [etc.] / Czechoslovakia etc. [thermographed]	Unknown	ORN	Crosby	B
7819	The United States honors the nations / [etc.] / Denmark etc. [thermographed]	Unknown	ORN	Crosby	B
7820	The United States honors the nations / [etc.] / France etc. [thermographed]	Unknown	ORN	Crosby	B
7821	The United States honors the nations / [etc.] / Greece etc. [thermographed]	Unknown	ORN	Crosby	B
7822	The United States honors the nations / [etc.] / Luxemburg etc. [thermographed]	Blue	ORN	Crosby	B
7823	The United States honors the nations / [etc.] / Norway etc. [thermographed]	Unknown	ORN	Crosby	B
7824	The United States honors the nations / [etc.] / Poland etc. [thermographed]	Red	ORN	Crosby	B
7825	The United States honors the nations / [etc.] / The Netherlands etc. [thermographed]	Unknown	ORN	Crosby	B
7826	The United States honors the nations / [etc.] / Yugoslavia etc. [thermographed]	Unknown	ORN	Crosby	B
7827	The United States Marines / "Corpsman" / Navy medical corpsmen...serving etc.	Brown	USMC	Burdick	A
7828	The unknown soldier in No / Man's etc.	Unknown	Unk	Symbols	B
7829	The ups and downs of / army life !! [handpainted]	Multicolored	Army	Cowdery	D
7830	The very essence of free government con- / sists in considering etc.	Black	Uncle	Ryscovers	A
7831	The victory girl [handpainted]	Multicolored	Women	Clendennen	D
7832	The vision of today, / the reality of the future. / One world, etc.	Green, red	Map	Schust	A
7833	The WAC / She serves her country well etc.	Green	WAC	Abel	A
7834	The WACS and WAVES / are deserving of praise, / and so are the Marines etc.	Blue	Women	Spauld, RY	A
7835	The Waikiki conference [in quotes] / July 27, 28, 29, 1944 / Honolulu, Hawaii	Blue	Event	Sayama	B
7836	The Wallop Poll [handpainted]	Multicolored	Axis	Adler	D
7837	The war ends today Peace is here / Remember / Pearl / Harbor / Dec. 7th, 1941	Blue, red	VJDay	Boone	B
7838	The war ends today Peace is here / Once more to peace, / to butterflies, etc.	Black, red	VJDAy	Carpenter	B
7839	The war time commander-in-chief	Black	FDR	Phill, CR	B
7840	The war will not all be / [etc.] / 6-3-'44——Student operator erroneously etc.	Multicolored	Event	Linto	B
7841	The war will not all be / won over there unless / we do our part on our etc.	Multicolored	Home	Linto	B
7842	The WASPS / have earned our / [etc.] / 11-4-'44——British and Greeks rout etc.	Multicolored	Event	Linto	B
7843	The WASPS / have earned our / united thanks	Multicolored	FlLib	Linto	B
7844	The watch on the Rhine——zero hour [color var.] [env. 7 1/2x4, 6 1/2x3 5/8 in.]	Multicolored	Hitle	Peer	B
7845	The weaker sex / WACS WAVES / SPARS Marines / [etc.] / If this is the etc.	Green	Women	Davis, Ray	A
7846	The weapons of our warfare are mighty / through God to the etc. [handpainted]	Multicolored	Relig	Steinhardt	C
7847	The welfare of our children will / [etc.] / 6-2-'44——Pope pleads that Rome etc.	Multicolored	Event	Linto	B
7848	The welfare of our children will / be as good as your effort to / secure etc.	Gold, silver	Home	Linto	B
7849	The White House / The cornerstone of etc.	Unknown	Hist	Unknown	A
7850	The White House announced / that an "atomic bomb" etc. [handpainted] [no picture]	Blue	Atom	Unknown	D
7851	The wind from over / the sea etc.	Black/Brown	Unk	Lupton	A
7852	The windmills of Holland will turn again [in quotes] [env. 6 11/16x3 7/8 in.]	Sepia tones	ORN	Belles-let	C
7853	The winning of / this war is as- / sured..Are you / doing your part / The etc.	Unknown	Eagle	Linto	B
7854	The wise guy / will buy / war bonds / to supply bombs / for the A.A.F. [handpainted]	Black, yellow	Owl	Myers	C
7855	The wolf pack / Someone / talked	Unknown	Uboat	Baur	A
7856	The women behind the men / behind the guns	Unknown	Women	Cozart	A
7857	The world has more / land, food and resources / than humanity can use. etc.	Blue, red	Dove	Symbols	B
7858	The world of the past is / slavery etc.	Red	Unk	Harrington	A
7859	The world's "pain in the neck" / Buy war bonds [handpainted]	Black, red	Hitle	Knoll	C
7860	The world's / largest / unfilled order / victory [no picture]	Unknown	Unk	Boone	A
7861	The world's most peaceful border / The United / States & / Dominion / of Canada etc.	Blue	Globe	Jackson, C	A
7862	The world's public / enemy / Hitler / number 1	Blue, red	Hitle	Boone	A
7863	The world's public / enemy / Tojo / number 2	Blue, red	Japan	Boone	A
7864	The wrapper got here all right but the / package didn't quite [in quotes] etc.	Red	Army	Burdick	A
7865	The Yalta conference [thermographed]	Blue, red	Ally	Unknown	C

NO.	CACHET TEXT	COLOR	TOPIC	PUBLISHER	$
7866	The Yanks / are coming / Hirohito!!	Black	Home	Runge	A
7867	The Yanks / are marching on / to victory!	Unknown	Unk	Davis, Ral	A
7868	The Yanks are / comin'!! / "Iki, waki, konki, sookekki"	Brown	Japan	Lawrence	A
7869	The Yanks are / on the march! / Are you doing your part?	Unknown	Unk	Boone	A
7870	The Yanks are coming [in quotes] [env. 6 3/4x3 7/8, 6 9/16x3 3/4 in.]	Sepia tones	Armed	Belles-let	C
7871	The Yanks land in Algiers	Black	Army	Coll Surp	A
7872	The young dead soldiers do not speak / Nevertheless they are heard in the etc.	Bk,Bu/Bk,Gn	Verse	Smith, AD	A
7873	The young dead soldiers do not speak / Nevertheless they are heard in the etc.	Bu,R/Gn,Red	Verse	Smith, AD	A
7874	The young dead soldiers do not speak / Nevertheless they are heard in the etc.	Black/Blue	Verse	Smith, AD	A
7875	The young dead soldiers do not speak / Nevertheless they are heard in the etc.	Bk,R/Bu,Gn	Verse	Smith, AD	A
7876	Their "mother" / over there / the Red Cross etc.	Unknown	RedCr	Phill, CR	A
7877	Their home-coming depends on / your purchases of U.S. bonds!!!	Gold	Army	Linto	B
7878	Their one objective / victory / in etc. [picture: MacArthur, Halsey, Truman]	Black, red	Armed	Knoll	B
7879	Their one objective / victory / in the Pacific [picture: Nimitz, Spruance]	Black, red	Armed	Knoll	B
7880	Their one objective / V-J Day by etc. [Halsey, Nimitz, Spruance] [handpainted]	Multicolored	VJDay	Knoll	C
7881	Their one objective / V-J Day by proclamation / in the Pacific [handpainted]	Multicolored	VJDay	Knoll	C
7882	Then / 1850 / Missionary ship / 1945 now [U.S.S. St. Mary's] [Tokyo Bay]	Black	VJDay	Navy ship	E
7883	Then / rolling for victory / now [envelope 7 1/2x4 in.]	Green,	Home	Kosko	B
7884	Then and now / The Kaiser went to Holland / when World War I was thru. etc.	Blue	Hitle	Abel	A
7885	Then and now··· / sailing for victory [copyright "C" w/, w/o serifs]	Multicolored	Navy	Minkus	A
7886	Then conquer we must, when our cause it is just, / and this be etc. [thermographed]	Blue, red	Flag	Yontz	B
7887	Then conquer we must, when our etc.	Unknown	Unk	Thorpe	A
7888	There are many roads / to Tokyo; we will neg- /lect none of them. [in quotes] etc.	Blue, red	FDR	Unknown	B
7889	There are many roads to Tokyo; / we will neglect none of them [in quotes] etc.	Blue, red	EagFl	Boone	A
7890	There are no blue notes in the song / of these birds so etc. [handpainted]	Multicolored	Axis	Martin	C
7891	There are some things / worth fighting for! [handpainted]	Multicolored	Home	Stoll	B
7892	There is a need for the OPA / as nearly all etc.	Blue	Home	Ryscovers	A
7893	There is an interesting / [etc.] / 11-19-'44——Circling of Metz / now complete	Unknown	Event	Linto	B
7894	There is an interesting / career for you in the / U.S. Maritime Service	Unknown	Merch	Linto	B
7895	There is no / indispensable / [in quotes] / [etc.] / 7-26-'44——Yanks etc.	Unknown	Event	Linto	B
7896	There is no / indispensable man [in quotes] / From F.D.R.'s New York etc.	Black, silver	FDR	Linto	B
7897	There is no North, there is no South etc. [text blue] [eagle in cloud]	Blue, red	Eagle	Boone	A
7898	There is no North, there is no South etc. [text blue} [eagle with flag]	Blue, red	Eagle	Boone	A
7899	There is no North, there is no South etc. [text red] [eagle with flag]	Blue, red	EagFl	Boone	A
7900	There is no North, there is no South etc. [text red] [eagle in cloud]	Blue, red	Eagle	Boone	A
7901	There is no time / like the present / to make a first- / class and sound etc.	Blue, red	Uncle	Linto	B
7902	There never was a / time when / liberty / meant so much to so / many etc.	Multicolored	Liber	Linto	B
7903	There never was a / time when / Liberty / meant so much to so / many etc.	Multicolored	Liber	Linto	B
7904	There she stands, a monument more / lasting than steel, more [in quotes] etc.	Blue	Liber	Brenn	A
7905	There will be no / pleasure for you / if Hitler wins / Buy bonds today	Unknown	Bonds	Linto	B
7906	There'll / be two tomorrow / Pvt. Ray! [handpainted]	Multicolored	Army	Cowdery	D
7907	There'll always / be / an England / "This blessed plot, this earth," etc.	Multicolored	Ally	Advertiser	B
7908	There'll always be an England	Blue, red	Ally	Unknown	A
7909	There'll always be an England! / [etc.] / 9-22-'44——The 8th Army in etc.	Multicolored	Event	Linto	B
7910	There'll always be an England! / England shall be free / if England means etc.	Gd,Gray/Mul	Ally	Linto	B
7911	There'll be a / red / hot time in Berlin / pretty soon!	Blue, red	USSR	Boone	A
7912	There's / nothing / in front / of the etc.	Unknown	Unk	Schirmer	A
7913	There's a / happy Jap / for every gap etc. [envelope 6x3 ½ in]	Blue, red	Home	Kosko	A
7914	There's a blue star in our window, / shining on a field of white. / It's etc.	Blue, red	Verse	Carpenter	A
7915	There's a gap in the line etc. [label + blue "Victory" border]	Multicolored	Army	Unknown	B
7916	There's a gap in the line etc. [label + red "Victory" border]	Multicolored	Army	Unknown	B
7917	There's a gap in the line etc. [label + red "Win the War" border]	Multicolored	Army	Unknown	B
7918	There's a kid Marine 'over there" etc.	Unknown	USMC	Brenn	A
7919	There's a lot to be done yet! / Buy another war bond... / and another... etc.	Blue, red	Flag	Lowell	A
7920	There's a new star / in glory [in quotes] / 2nd Div. U.S.M.C. / Tarawa	Multicolored	USMC	McCluney	B
7921	There's a special art in writing / to the etc.	Unknown	Unk	Dailey	A
7922	There's always / somethin' nice / about a soldier! [handpainted] [stamp missing]	Multicolored	Army	Cowdery	D
7923	There's an "L" of a difference / between the etc. [no picture]	Unkown	Unk	Carpenter	A

NO.	CACHET TEXT	COLOR	TOPIC	PUBLISHER	$
7924	There's Micah! [thermographed] [envelope 6 1/2x4 11/16 in.]	Unknown	Unk	Cleveland	A
7925	There's nothing hits / the spot like snacks / from home! [handpainted]	Black	Army	Parker	B
7926	There's only / one soldier / like my / Pvt. [burned left edge] [handpainted]	Multicolored	Army	Cowdery	D
7927	There's something - / about a soldier. [in quotes] [handpainted]	Black	Army	Wolf, CL	B
7928	There's something rotten in Denmark [in quotes] [envelope 6 3/4x3 7/8 in.]	Blue	Nazis	Belles-let	C
7929	Ther's one / thing about this / army I'm crazy about! [handpainted]	Multicolored	Home	Cowdery	D
7930	These / three / Axis / boys can dish it out / but...can they / take it!	Blue, red	Axis	Boone	A
7931	These / two rats / [etc.] / dead	Black, red	Axis	Carter	A
7932	These Japs are pretty / good ball players, but / they won't steal any more etc.	Blue, red	Japan	Carpenter	A
7933	These shells don't / get any lighter etc.	Black	Unk	Lupton	A
7934	They / came from / "Shangri-la"	Black	Air	Coll Surp	A
7935	They / gave it / Let's / protect it / The Victory etc.	Unknown	Unk	Eichenlaub	A
7936	They / need / your / loyalty / [etc.] / 6-19-'44——Reds capture Finn rail etc.	Unknown	Event	Linto	B
7937	They / need / your / loyalty / and / your / prayers	Unknown	Army	Linto	B
7938	They / offer / their / lives! / [etc.] / 2-5-'45——Yank 3rd flanks etc.	Unknown	Event	Linto	B
7939	They / offer / their / lives! / Can you / spare / some / blood?	Unknown	Blood	Linto	B
7940	They / started / it! / We'll finish it! [colored envelopes]	Blue, red	Army	Poppenger	A
7941	They [in quotes] got the Navys goat. / And the war ended	Blue	Japan	Harrington	A
7942	They are dying! / Are you buying? / bonds / Fourth etc. [no picture]	Unknown	Bonds	Threl+Thar	A
7943	They are giving their lives etc.	Unknown	Unk	Levering	A
7944	They are on the way / Keep them going! Buy war bonds	Bk/Bu/Gn/R	Bonds	Conner	A
7945	They are on the way / Keep them going! Buy war bonds	Black, red	Bonds	Conners	A
7946	They asked for it / Give it to 'em / Remember Pearl Harbor etc. [thermographed]	Blue, red	Japan	Crosby	B
7947	They asked for it / You can answer them / Buy war bonds-now!	Blue, red	Flag	Card	A
7948	They asked for it / You can answer them / Buy war bonds-now! / Freedom of etc.	Red	Flag	Cozart	A
7949	They asked for it and they are going etc. [in quotes] [env. 9 5/8x4 1/8 in.]	Multicolored	Air	Ever Ready	B
7950	They asked for it! / [etc.] / "Buddies" [handpainted]	Multicolored	Army	Parker	C
7951	They asked for it! [envelope 6 1/2x3 5/8, 6x3 ½ in.]	Blue, red	Navy	Powers	A
7952	They asked for it. F.D.R. [buff envelope]	Bu/Blue, red	FDR	Foster	B
7953	They asked for it... etc. [label + blue "Victory" border]	Multicolored	Air	Unknown	B
7954	They asked for it... etc. [label + red "Victory" border]	Multicolored	Air	Unknown	B
7955	They asked for it... etc. [label + red "Win the War" border]	Multicolored	Air	Unknown	B
7956	They both agree it's / the world's best Navy / Our next etc. [handpainted]	Multicolored	FDR	Knoll	C
7957	They buy bonds / Can we do less?	Unknown	Bonds	McCluney	A
7958	They can't be beat	Brown/Red	Unk	McFarland	A
7959	They can't be beat	Black/Green	Unk	Cozart	A
7960	They died together so we could live together.	Black/Brown	Hero	Davis, Ray	A
7961	They don't know anything / so don't tell them anything etc. [colored envelopes]	Black	Japan	Poppenger	A
7962	They 'dood' it —— the / invasion / begins / Strike hard at etc. [no picture]	Red	DDay	Boone	B
7963	They 'dood' it——the / "D" / Day / arrives [no picture]	Bu,R/Blue	DDay	Boone	B
7964	They fight / you write	Blue, red	Armed	Yontz	A
7965	They fought to make us free; / we fight to make all men free.	Multicolored	FlMin	Grandy	A
7966	They give their all / How much do you give?	Blue	Armed	Harrington	A
7967	They give their lives / for freedom's cause!	Blue, red	Armed	Davis, Ral	A
7968	They give their lives / You lend etc. [2 red & 3 white stars, lower border]	Blue, red	Bonds	Ander, EA	A
7969	They give their lives / You lend etc. [4 white stars in blue squares]	Blue, red	Bonds	Ander, EA	A
7970	They give their lives / You lend etc. [4 white stars in red squares]	Blue, red	Bonds	Ander, EA	A
7971	They give their lives / You lend etc. [5 flags, lower border]	Brown/Red	Bonds	Ander, EA	A
7972	They give their lives / You lend etc. [no flags or stars, lower border]	Brown/Red	Bonds	Ander, EA	A
7973	They grow / war bonds / 7th war loan drive / May 14 - June 30 - 1945	Brown, green	Bonds	Eichenlaub	A
7974	They have come from all four etc.	Unknown	Unk	Brenn	A
7975	They have not / died in vain etc.	Brown	Unk	Runge	A
7976	They have not / died in vain etc. [EK Price corner card]	Brown	Unk	Price, EK	A
7977	They issue everything that you need etc. [thermographed]	U&nknown	Unk	Baur	A
7978	They made America free / Let's keep it free	Unknown	Unk	Mayfield	A
7979	They made America free / Let's keep it free!	Unknown	Unk	Mayfield	A
7980	They made America free / Let's keep it that way	Multicolored	Hist	Unknown	A
7981	They may be singing / "The watch on the Rhine", / but Uncle Sam has put etc.	Red	Uncle	Carpenter	A

NO.	CACHET TEXT	COLOR	TOPIC	PUBLISHER	$
7982	They raise the / flag again on / Corregidor [handpainted]	Multicolored	Flag	Sturgill	E
7983	They said they'd punish me / if I was over leave but I / didn't believe them!	Black	Army	Lupton	A
7984	They shall be / avenged	black, red	Phili	Unknown	A
7985	They shall be free / Poland / Norway / Holland / Belgium / Greece etc.	Blue, red	ORN	Mayfield	A
7986	They shall not pass	Blue, red	Liber	Linprint	A
7987	They shall not pass [in quotes] / National defense [1st line 38 or 40 mm long]	Blue, red	Bell	Grandy	A
7988	They tell us margarine / is / [etc.] / 12-2-'44——Yanks enter / Saarlautern	Gold, silver	Event	Linto	B
7989	They tell us margarine / is equal to butter! / If this be true-?-Why / not etc.	Gold, silver	Flag	Linto	B
7990	They will always / live in our / hearts. [handpainted]	Multicolored	LinWa	Borkowski	D
7991	They will be free again / Occupied nations	Multicolored	ORN	Staehle	B
7992	They won in '65 / we win in '45	Blue	Unk	Hillerich	A
7993	They're / rolling / Buy U.S. war bonds / now! [back of envelope] [env. 8 5/8x3 3/4 in.]	Black	Bonds	Pittsburgh	B
7994	They're closer / than you think! [label + blue "Victory" border]	Multicolored	Axis	Unknown	B
7995	They're closer / than you think! [label + red "Victory" border]	Multicolored	Axis	Unknown	B
7996	They're closer / than you think! [label + red "Win the War" border]	Multicolored	Axis	Unknown	B
7997	They're fighting fools! / ...We must give them backing! [colored envelopes]	Blue, red	Army	Poppenger	A
7998	They're in a / huddle on / best / [etc.] / 6-10-'45——More U.S. / bombs etc.	Unknown	Event	Linto	B
7999	They're in a / huddle on / best buys? / Answer—— / U.S. / bonds	Unknown	Bonds	Linto	B
8000	They're protecting us / on every etc.	Unknown	Unk	Garfield	A
8001	Think it over! / This is a funny world, / its wonders never cease; all etc.	Multicolored	Ordna	Linto	B
8002	Think of the barbarian / instincts / [etc.] / Leif Erikson Day / first to etc.	Multicolored	Home	Linto	B
8003	Think of the barbarian / instincts of the Japs to / realize etc. [no picture]	Gold, silver	Japan	Linto	B
8004	Think what you like / [etc.] / 11-29-'44——Jap convoy of 13 / ships reach etc.	Multicolored	Event	Linto	B
8005	Think what you like / but don't let it / interfere with the etc. [no picture]	Gold, violet	Home	Linto	B
8006	Think, act and / live the / American way / 8-2-'44——Turks off with Nazis! etc.	Multicolored	Event	Linto	B
8007	Think, act and / live the / American way [no picture]	Pi,Si/Multi	Home	Linto	B
8008	Third / Amphibious Force etc. [70 mm tall] [U.S.S. Pamina] [Tokyo Bay]	Blue	VJDay	Navy ship	E
8009	Third / Amphibious Force etc. [74 mm tall] [U.S.S. Medea] [Tokyo Bay]	Blue	VJDay	Navy ship	E
8010	Third / Amphibious Force etc. [74 mm tall] [U.S.S. Mt. Olympus] [Tokyo Bay]	Blue	VJDay	Navy ship	E
8011	Third [3rd] / war loan / Dig!	Gold, silver	Bonds	Linto	B
8012	Third [3rd] / war loan / dig! / 10-27-'41——Pres. Roosevelt said: etc.	Multicolored	Hist	Linto	B
8013	Third [3rd] / war loan / dig! / Dec. 7, 1941, a date we will help etc.	Multicolored	Pearl	Linto	B
8014	Third [3rd] / war loan / Speed the / [etc.] / Dec. 7, 1941, a date we etc.	Multicolored	Pearl	Linto	B
8015	Third [3rd] / war loan / Speed the / invasion / and victory!	Multicolored	Bonds	Linto	B
8016	Third [3rd] Div. [under insignia] [handpainted]	Black, blue	Unit	Dannells	B
8017	Third [III] Corps [under insignia] [handpainted]	Black, blue	Unit	Dannells	B
8018	Third anniversary / congratulations / WAVES / 1942 1945 / Keep etc. [thermographed]	Black	WAVE	Boone	A
8019	Third Fleet USS Missouri / Surrender cachet [card] [Tokyo Bay]	Black	VJDay	Navy ship	F
8020	Third victory war loan / Back the attack / Monument grounds unit / A.P.O. etc.	Blue, red	Bonds	Czubay	C
8021	Third war loan drive / September 9 - 30, 1943 / [etc.] / Kuai no lanakila	Blue, red	Bonds	Sayama	B
8022	Thirteenth [13th] / Battalion / [etc.] / Marine Corps Reserve etc. [thermo]	Red	USMC	Unknown	B
8023	Thirty-five [35] miles per hour, / until victory.	Blue, red	Home	Baur	A
8024	Thirty-second [32nd] Div. [under insignia] [handpainted]	Black, red	Unit	Dannells	B
8025	Thirty-seventh [37th] Div. [under insignia] [handpainted]	Black, red	Unit	Dannells	B
8026	Thirty-sixh [36th] General Hospital / "Service above self" [thermographed]	Purple	Medic	Crosby	B
8027	This / is / inflation! / Take etc. [+ German stamp within printed black border]	Black	Bonds	Ang	A
8028	This / is / the / enemy	Black	Hitle	Wolf, CL	A
8029	This / is the / enemy / Serve in silence	Black	Hitle	McCluney	B
8030	This / is the enemy / Extinguish this menace to etc. [label + printed border]	Multicolored	Hitle	Artists	B
8031	This America! / Worth a bond each payday? [handpainted] [blue envelope]	Blue, red	Bonds	Buxton, D	B
8032	This American and / his followers / [etc.] / 2-22-'42——India conference etc.	Multicolored	Event	Linto	B
8033	This American and / his followers fought / for and established / a democracy	Multicolored	Wash	Linto	B
8034	This Axis yap / has been shut! / Who's next? [last line all caps]	Bu,gn/Bu,red	Axis	Boone	B
8035	This Axis yap / has been shut! / Who's next? [last line in script]	Blue, red	Axis	Boone	B
8036	This big letter / will tell you / all about [env. 9 5/8x6 1/4 in.]	Blue, red	USMC	Earnshaw	D
8037	This bird has yet / to fail us / For etc. [env. 6 1/2x3 5/8, 7 1/2x4 in.]	Gn/Pu/Red	Eagle	Phill, CR	A
8038	This blood I give today / will save the life / of some guys over there.	Multicolored	Blood	Borkowski	C
8039	This cover / made in / America	Black	EagSh	Phill, CR	A

NO.	CACHET TEXT	COLOR	TOPIC	PUBLISHER	$
8040	This cover / made in / America	Black	EagSh	Phill, CR	A
8041	This cover commemorates the appoint- / ment of General Douglas MacArthur etc.	Red	Mac	Unknown	B
8042	This cover commemorates the creation of / the Post Office named in honor etc.	Red	MacFD	Unknown	B
8043	This cover commemorates the noble / birth of Adolf Hitler (born Adolf) etc.	Red	Hitle	Unknown	X
8044	This cover commemorates the second anniver- / sary of Japan's treacherous etc.	Purple/Red	Pearl	Unknown	A
8045	This cover is one of a series of 20 / [etc.] / Adm. Callaghan was killed etc.	Blue	Admir	Unknown	A
8046	This cover is one of a series of 20 / [etc.] / Adm. Halsey led squadron etc.	Blue	Admir	Unknown	A
8047	This cover is one of a series of 20 / [etc.] / Barney Ross saved wounded etc.	Orange	Hero	Unknown	A
8048	This cover is one of a series of 20 / [etc.] / Capt. Joe Foss is champion etc.	Orange	Hero	Unknown	A
8049	This cover is one of a series of 20 / [etc.] / Capt. Seligman commanded etc.	Blue	Hero	Unknown	A
8050	This cover is one of a series of 20 / [etc.] / Capt. Wheless outmaneuvered etc.	Orange	Hero	Unknown	A
8051	This cover is one of a series of 20 / [etc.] / Gen. Clare Chenault etc.	Orange	Gener	Unknown	A
8052	This cover is one of a series of 20 / [etc.] / Gen. Clark prepared the etc.	Orange	Gener	Unknown	A
8053	This cover is one of a series of 20 / [etc.] / Gen. Eichelberger captured etc.	Blue	Gener	Unknown	A
8054	This cover is one of a series of 20 / [etc.] / Gen. Patton led tank etc.	Orange	Patt	Unknown	B
8055	This cover is one of a series of 20 / [etc.] / Gen. Wainwright withstood etc.	Blue	Gener	Unknown	A
8056	This cover is one of a series of 20 / [etc.] / John Bulkley, PT hero at etc.	Orange	Hero	Unknown	A
8057	This cover is one of a series of 20 / [etc.] / Maj. Demarest and Lt. etc.	Blue	Hero	Unknown	A
8058	This cover is one of a series of 20 / [etc.] / Maj. John Roosevelt led etc.	Blue	Hero	Unknown	A
8059	This cover is one of a series of 20 / [etc.] / Meyer Levin was Kelly's etc.	Orange	Hero	Unknown	A
8060	This cover is one of a series of 20 / [etc.] / Pvt. Albert Schmidt killed etc.	Blue	Hero	Unknown	A
8061	This cover mailed aboard the / ship SS Arauca etc. [typed] [12/28/39]	Black	Nazis	Unknown	D
8062	This day we humbly thank our etc.	Unknown	Unk	Linto	B
8063	This envelope contains / one Japanese hunting license / Let's go etc. [thermographed]]	Black/Red	USMC	Crosby	B
8064	This envelope contains / one Japanese hunting license / Sarge, etc. [thermographed]	Brown	Army	Crosby	B
8065	This envelope contains / Uncle Sam's peace terms / One down etc. [thermographed]	Red	Axis	Sweet	C
8066	This envelope contains Adolf Hitler's / last will and testament etc. [thermographed]	Red	Axis	Sweet	C
8067	This fellow, / as always, / takes 2nd / place with / Japs!	Multicolored	Devil	Linto	B
8068	This is / a cal. .50 / machine gun! / Tyndall Field	Bk/Bu/Gn/Re	Unit	Auge	B
8069	This is / V-J / Day / The Axis is axed! [no picture]	Multicolored	VJDay	Boone	B
8070	This is / V-J / Day [no picture]	Red, yellow	VJDay	Boone	B
8071	This is / V-J / Day [text is within a blue circle]	Blue, red	VJDay	Boone	B
8072	This is / V-J / Day [text over Japanese man]	Unknown	VJDay	Boone	B
8073	This is a "tail" that's going around——— / "Be a good scottie, little" etc.	Bk/Blue, red	Dog	Quigley	B
8074	This is a safe Jap [in quotes]	Black	Skull	Yontz	A
8075	This is a safe Nazi [in quotes]	Black	Skull	Yontz	A
8076	This is a true story / (AP) During the liberation etc.	Purple	Unk	Cox	A
8077	This is her day——no / bands, no medals, / no parades. Only the / deepest etc.	Blue, red	Women	Brenn	A
8078	This is no / bum steer! / It will / be over / quicker / if etc. [handpainted]	Multicolored	Bonds	Martin	B
8079	This is our 1943 model in petunia pink! [in quotes] [no stars UR & LR]	Multicolored	Navy	Amer Art	A
8080	This is our 1943 model in petunia pink! [in quotes] [with 4 stars UR & LR]	Multicolored	Navy	Amer Art	A
8081	This is our war! / Join the WAACS [handpainted]	Multicolored	WAC	Knapp	G
8082	This is our zone of / national defense / No trespassing	Blue, red	Map	Linprint	A
8083	This is the / enemy / Fight for your right to etc. [label + printed border]	Multicolored	Relig	Artists	B
8084	This is the / enemy / Just another atrocity story, eh? [label + printed border]	Multicolored	Axis	Artists	B
8085	This is the / enemy / Loose lips = lost lives! [label + printed border]	Multicolored	Uboat	Artists	B
8086	This is the / enemy / Only a numbskull would slacken! [label + printed border]	Multicolored	Nazis	Artists	B
8087	This is the best we could / do, general etc.	Unknown	Unk	Wash Star	A
8088	This is the big day- / when Uncle Sam takes / care of his nephews!- / Navy etc.	Black	Navy	Lupton	A
8089	This is the enemy	Unknown	Unk	McCluney	A
8090	This is the enemy	Red	Japan	Knoll	B
8091	This is the enemy / An eye for an eye——the swine etc. [label + printed border]	Multicolored	Nazis	Artists	B
8092	This is the enemy / Praise the Lord and pass the etc. [label + printed border]	Multicolored	Relig	Artists	B
8093	This is the enemy / Rid them of the specter of etc. [label + printed border]	Multicolored	Nazis	Artists	B
8094	This is the enemy / Wipe this slime and crime etc. [label + printed border]	Multicolored	Japan	Artists	B
8095	This is the enemy [envelope 6 9/16x3 3/4 in.]	Unknown	Unk	Belles-let	C
8096	This is the goal / for which we strive / Freedom for all / in 1945	Multicolored	Holid	Griffith	B
8097	This is the 'Purple Heart'——that / kid next door may have earned / while etc.	Purple	Medal	Lawrence	A

NO.	CACHET TEXT	COLOR	TOPIC	PUBLISHER	$
8098	This is the year! / 194V / if we buy bonds! [colored envelopes]	Black	VforV	Temple	A
8099	This is too good / for his ilk	Blue, red	Hitle	Dale	A
8100	This is too good / for his ilk [Japanese officer on plank over ocean]	Blue, red	Japan	Dale	A
8101	This is why I'm buying / war bonds! [label with printed border]	Multicolored	Bonds	Foster	B
8102	This is worth fighting for [colors vary]	Multicolored	Home	Minkus	A
8103	This isn't hurting us!	Blue	UncJa	Lawrence	A
8104	This kind of equip- / ment is defeating / the Axis gang!! [print varieties]	Black, green	Ordna	Phill, CR	A
8105	This land I love / Part of a poem / [etc.] / 8-25-'45——Winston Churchill etc.	Multicolored	Event	Linto	B
8106	This land I love / ——Part of a poem by Philip Jackson / This nation of the etc.	Green, red	Unk	Linto	B
8107	This land we love is free etc. [poinsettia]	Unknown	Home	Runge	A
8108	This land we love is free etc. [winter scene]	Unknown	Home	Runge	A
8109	This letter is for [thermographed]	Blue	Navy	Sadworth	A
8110	This Memorial Day let / us pause in / [etc.] / 5-30-'44——Allies bomb Axis.	Unknown	Event	Linto	B
8111	This Memorial Day let / us pause in reverence / to those who etc. [no picture]	Gold	Holid	Linto	B
8112	This one should do it!! / 7th / war / loan / Buy your war bonds / now!	Black, red	Hitle	McCluney	A
8113	This punk hasn't long to live, / he's up against the wall—— / He couldn't etc.	Green, red	Axis	Boone	A
8114	This slap-happy / Jappy - / took a Marine / for a sappy - etc. [handpainted]	Black	Japan	Martin	C
8115	This Thanksgiving / they ask us / for etc.	Brown/Purple	Holid	Phill, CR	A
8116	This umbrella the / folks sent me sure / makes this mid / watch etc. [thermographed]	Blue	Navy	Lupton	A
8117	This victory / sign means / nothing if you / fail to do / your part!	Multicolored	VforV	Linto	B
8118	This war / isnt [sic] won [handpainted]	Multicolored	Japan	Adler	D
8119	This war, for us, means / self / [etc.] / 5-18-'44——Allies now occupy etc.	Unknown	Event	Linto	B
8120	This war, for us, means / self preservation! etc.	Unknown	Home	Linto	B
8121	This we missed in '44 / but our '45 is loaded!	Blue	Axis	Lawrence	A
8122	This will / help some / He's / high / strung / all / right / but / not etc.	Black	Hitle	Andrews	A
8123	This world cannot exist half / slave and half free. [in quotes]	Green, violet	Linc	Threl+Thar	B
8124	Those dear souls who are planning / for the rehabilitation of Europe—— / etc.	Multicolored	Uncle	Linto	B
8125	Those enjoying / liberty know its / [etc.] / 7-4-'44——Yankees captured etc.	Multicolored	Event	Linto	B
8126	Those enjoying / liberty know its / value etc.	Silver, tan	Home	Linto	B
8127	Those on the / fighting fronts / [etc.] / 7-6-'44——Japs retreat 30 miles etc.	Multicolored	Event	Linto	B
8128	Those on the / fighting fronts / have to stay at / their posts! / Let's etc.	Gold, red	Home	Linto	B
8129	Those physically fit / for / [etc.] / 1-17-'45——Russians / liberate Warsaw	Multicolored	Event	Linto	B
8130	Those physically fit / for sports are / [etc.] / 1-3-'45——Yank air force etc.	Multicolored	Event	Linto	B
8131	Those physically fit / for sports are / physically fit for / the Service!	Gd,Gn/Multi	Flag	Linto	B
8132	Those who expect to reap the / blessings of freedom must, [in quotes] etc.	Bk/Bu/Brown	EagFl	Harrington	A
8133	Three / of a / kind [colored envelopes]	Black	Axis	Wolf, CL	B
8134	Three / war / bond / cheers / [etc.] / 10-24-'44——3000 Japs killed / on etc.	Multicolored	Event	Linto	B
8135	Three / war / bond / cheers / for / the / red, / white / and etc. [no picture]	Multicolored	Bonds	Linto	B
8136	Three [3] / cheers / Three of them!—— / count 'em—— / and count on 'em!	Blue, red	EagFl	Stanard	A
8137	Three [3] cents [symbol] / First day / local mail / An extra cent etc.	Green, red	Home	Sayama	B
8138	Three [3] years ago / "Wonder where" [etc.] / And / today etc. [handpainted]	Multicolored	Axis	Knapp	G
8139	Three letters in / Demo program / [etc.] / 10-19-'44——Huns driven back etc.	Multicolored	FDR	Linto	B
8140	Three letters in / Demo program / [etc.] / 7-17-'44——Yanks capture St. Lo! etc.	Green, olive	Event	Linto	B
8141	Three letters in / Demo program / F-D-R / mean waste [no picture]	Green, olive	FDR	Linto	B
8142	Three of a kind [thermographed]	Green/Purple	Axis	Crosby	B
8143	Three of a kind from / Rome - Berlin - Tokyo / There would be etc. [thermographed]	Red	Axis	Crosby	B
8144	Three standards / Drafting men / [etc.] / 1-24-'41——Brit. Amb. Viscount etc.	Multicolored	Anniv	Linto	B
8145	Three standards / Drafting men for military / service etc. [multicolor varieties]	Multicolored	Home	Linto	B
8146	Three tyrants sought to rule the world	Unknown	Axis	Linto	B
8147	Three yellow rats	Unknown	Axis	Linto	B
8148	Three yellow rats / out!	Unknown	Axis	Linto	B
8149	Throughout long days and nights steamed the / convoys, always etc. [thermographed]	Silver	Navy	Neal	B
8150	Thumbs / up! [picture: Uncle Sam]	Blue, red	VEDay	Unknown	B
8151	Thunder on! Stride on, democracy! Strike with vengeful stroke! [in quotes] etc.	Black	VforV	Bean	A
8152	Thursday, November 23, 1944 / It's more etc. [cut-&-pasted paper] [colored envelopes]	Black	Holid	Temple	C
8153	Tick-tock, tick-tock / tempus fugit etc. [buff envelope]	Unknown	Unk	Stefun	A
8154	Till we meet again / Buy war bonds [label + blue "Victory" border]	Multicolored	Bonds	Unknown	B
8155	Till we meet again / Buy war bonds [label + red "Victory" border]	Multicolored	Bonds	Unknown	B

NO.	CACHET TEXT	COLOR	TOPIC	PUBLISHER	$
8156	Till we meet again / Buy war bonds [label + red "Win the War" border]	Multicolored	Bonds	Unknown	B
8157	Time / for us / to / clean / up! / The Axis is axed!	Blue, red	Uncle	Boone	A
8158	Time / for us / to / clean / up! / V-J Day	Multicolored	VJDay	Boone	A
8159	Time / for us / to / clean / up! [Uncle Sam, Axis leaders, globe of world]	Blue, red	Uncle	Cachet Cra	A
8160	Time someone was / tossin' a line	Purple	Unk	Foster	A
8161	Time to change flags, Adolf [in quotes]	Red	Hitle	Ang	A
8162	Time to start / to work / for/ victory [handpainted]	Blue, red	Home	Lemponen	B
8163	Tirana / liberated / Capital of Albania / November 18, 1944	Multicolored	ORN	Teixeira	D
8164	Tirana / liberated / Capital of Albania etc. [11/18/44 + 5/8/45 postmark]	Multicolored	Event	Teixeira	F
8165	Tis ['Tis] the Star Spangled Banner / O long may it etc. [1 row of stars]	Unknown	Flag	Boone	A
8166	Tis ['Tis] the Star Spangled Banner / O long may it etc. [2 rows of stars]	Unknown	Flag	Boone	A
8167	Title of military governor relinquished / July 21, 1944 / Territory of etc.	Black	Hawai	Sayama	B
8168	TNT / today not tomorrow [color varieties]	Unknown	Unk	Runge	A
8169	To / airmen and seamen and ground etc.	Blue	Unk	Carpenter	A
8170	To / day / fresh / fish / Save / wrapping / paper··· [handpainted]	Multicolored	Home	Borkowski	D
8171	To / Tokio / let this be / America's answer [colored envelopes]	Unknown	Unk	Poppenger	A
8172	To a sweet fellow / in the Coast Guard / Bet this etc. [env. 9 1/2x4 1/8 in.]	Unknown	Coast	Meryle	B
8173	To Adolf + Tojo / Roses are red / an' some are pink / We'll etc. [handpainted]	Black, silver	Home	Wolf, CL	B
8174	To arms / America!	Multicolored	EagSh	Advertiser	B
8175	To be prepared for war is one etc.	Unknown	Unk	Lowe	A
8176	To be prepared for war is one of / [etc.] / 10-16-'44——Allies take Fort etc.	Multicolored	Event	Linto	B
8177	To be prepared for war is one of / [etc.] / 1-25-'45——Elliott Roosevelt etc.	Multicolored	Event	Linto	B
8178	To be prepared for war is one of / the most effective means etc. [no picture]	Gd,Pi/Gd,Vi	Wash	Linto	B
8179	To beat the Axis / ···– buy war stamps etc.	Blue	Unk	Haynes	A
8180	To beat the Axis / buy war bonds	Blue, red	EagSh	Runge	A
8181	To Berlin and / to Tokyo, the Yanks go / marching on	Blue, yellow	Army	Carpenter	A
8182	To date / destroyer Fletcher / skippered by etc. [no picture]	Unknown	Navy	Cox	A
8183	To G.I. Joe / When this war is over, / and hostilities cease; both etc.	Black	Home	Shaw, TC	A
8184	To guard their safety / the Victory loan etc.	Unknown	Bonds	Eichenlaub	A
8185	To have and to hold / the Victory loan	Unknown	Bonds	Eichenlaub	A
8186	To have walked with you a while, dear lad, / was better far etc. [no picture]	Blue, gold	Verse	Carpenter	A
8187	To hell with defense!! / I'm on the offense!!	Black/Red	Minut	Shaw, TC	B
8188	To his daddy / over there!	R,Bk/Bk/Red	Home	Harrington	A
8189	To honor our airmen	Multicolored	Air	Runge	A
8190	To Italy / Remember that hymn, / "There's a stranger / at the gate!" / Can etc.	Gd,Gn/Multi	Minut	Linto	B
8191	To Italy / Remember that hymn, / [etc.] / 12-27-'39——Earthquake in Turkey. etc.	Multicolored	Anniv	Linto	B
8192	To Italy / Remember that hymn, / [etc.] / Pearl Harbor was etc.	Multicolored	Pearl	Linto	B
8193	To keep 'em droppin' / buy more bonds / and let 'em hatch, brother, etc.	Blue, red	Bonds	Boone	A
8194	To keep 'em droppin' / buy more bonds [vertical] / Back the attack...now!	Blue, red	Bonds	Boone	A
8195	To keep 'em flying / Buy more bonds	Blue, red	Air	Boone	A
8196	To keep the torch of liberty / burning bright / work or fight with all etc.	Gold, red	Torch	Myers	A
8197	To make him squeal / buy more bonds / back the attack...now!	Unknown	Unk	Kosko	A
8198	To market——to market / Ration / point / range [handpainted]	Multicolored	Home	Knapp	H
8199	To our boys in the services / Season's etc.	Unknown	Holid	Runge	B
8200	To our fighting / Irish heroes. [handpainted] [envelope 6 7/8x3 15/16 in.]	Multicolored	Home	Carpenter	C
8201	To our fighting forces / welcome home [colored envelopes]	Blue	Armed	Huss	A
8202	To our unsung / heroes / LCT boys	Unknown	Navy	Baur	A
8203	To protect the / nation we must etc.	Unknown	Unk	Symbols	B
8204	To strikers! / When the ack-ack sounds like thunder / and etc. [no picture]	Blue	Verse	Boone	A
8205	To the American people: / Your sons, husbands and brothers etc. [thermo]	Blue	Bonds	Unknown	A
8206	To the last man [13th Infantry]	Black	Army	Unit	A
8207	To the last man [13th Infantry] [thermographed]	Black	Army	Unit	A
8208	To the memory of / Franklin Delano Roosevelt / President and philatelist	Black	FDR	Butzen	E
8209	To the rear - march! [in quotes] [handpainted]	Multicolored	Army	Dannells	C
8210	To the rear——ma... [cartoon figures]	Brown	Army	Unknown	A
8211	To Tokyo / we go [handpainted]	Multicolored	Army	Adler	D
8212	To unconditional surrender [vertical] / When success / goes to the head etc.	Multicolored	Axis	Andrews	B
8213	To victory	Black	Unk	Nichols	B

NO.	CACHET TEXT	COLOR	TOPIC	PUBLISHER	$
8214	To you, brave comrades, / there is nothing impossible	Br/Blue,Red	Army	Neal	A
8215	To: / Rush!	Black	Navy	Lupton	A
8216	To: / USN	Black	Navy	Lupton	A
8217	Today .. more than ever / And that government of etc. [w/, w/o copyright "C"]	Multicolored	Linc	Minkus	A
8218	Today / Germany / surrenders [printed diagonally] [no picture]	Blue	VEDay	Rollins	B
8219	Today / Japan / surrenders [printed diagonally] [no picture]	Red	VJDay	Rollins	B
8220	Today / now they tell us / their end is in sight	Red	Axis	Abel	A
8221	Today / the war was half-ended! / Germany / Japan / Get busy! / Finish the etc.	Black, red	VEDay	Shaffer, A	C
8222	Today is "B" Day! / Buy a batch of bonds / to / back a bunch of boys etc. [typed]	Black, red	Bonds	Myers	A
8223	Today is / V-J / Day / [flag+V, Minute men, Japanese flag] [thermographed]	Blue, red	VJDay	Boone	B
8224	Today is / V-J / Day / V [thermographed]	Blue, red	VJDay	Boone	C
8225	Today is / V-J / Day [text above Japanese flag or in circle] [thermographed]	Blue, red	VJDay	Boone	C
8226	Today is the 'morrow U thot of yesterday etc.	Black	Unk	Stefun	A
8227	Today June 6, 1944 / Allied troops invaded / France etc.	Red	DDay	Phill, CR	B
8228	Today, as / always ———— / I / love / you [handpainted]	Multicolored	Home	Cowdery	D
8229	Today, July 25th, 1943, Benito / Mussolini, the dictator of Italy, leader etc.	Black	Event	Unknown	B
8230	Today, May 8, 1945, at 9.00 A.M., the Pres- / ident of the United States, etc.	Blue	VEDay	Unknown	B
8231	Today, President Franklin / Delano Roosevelt and Prime / Ministyer Winston etc.	Blue	FDR	Unknown	B
8232	Today, Sept. 3, 1943, on the fourth / anniversary of the Declaration / [etc.] / England invaded Italy etc.	Red	Event	Unknown	C
8233	Today, we went into / Tokyo Bay etc. [thermo] [U.S.S. Niobrara] [Tokyo Bay] *	Green, red	VJDay	Navy ship	X
8234	Today's bad news for the Axis / Russia / denounces etc. [no picture]	Unknown	Event	Threl+Thar	B
8235	Today's headache for the Japs / Russia / declares etc. [no picture]	Unknown	Event	Threl+Thar	B
8236	Today's headache for the Japs / Yanks / land / in / Japan [no picture]	Unknown	Event	Threl+Thar	B
8237	Together to victory [in quotes] [handpainted]	Blue	Uncle	Howe	B
8238	Tojo / out / Saipan [handpainted]	Black	Japan	Wolf, CL	B
8239	Tojo is a bum / Hitler is a heel / God bless America / Buy war bonds / and etc.	Unknown	Axis	Ander, EA	A
8240	Tojo say to Hirohito, / "Boss, look like we defeato." etc. [no picture]	Blue	Verse	Shaw, CF	A
8241	Tojo: / we have 40 / more stars / coming your way!	Blue, red	Japan	Boone	A
8242	Tojo: look! / Uncle Sam's boys / are going to / work on you!	Blue, red	Japan	Boone	A
8243	Tokens for—— / Tokyo / Berlin / Rome / Buy war bonds / to send 'em 'home' etc.	Black, red	Bonds	Boone	A
8244	Tokio / so sorry [envelope 6 3/4x3 7/8 in.]	Purple	Japan	Foster	A
8245	Tokio and four other / industrial centres of Japan / bombed etc. [posted 4/19/42]	Black, blue	Event	First Day	E
8246	Tokio kid say -- etc. [label + blue "Victory" border]	Multicolored	Japan	Unknown	B
8247	Tokio kid say -- etc. [label + red "Victory" border]	Multicolored	Japan	Unknown	B
8248	Tokio kid say -- etc. [label + red "Win the War" border]	Multicolored	Japan	Unknown	B
8249	Tokio! / here we come!	Multicolored	Air	Amer Pat	A
8250	Tokio; / we will be there etc.	Unknown	Unk	Amer Pat	A
8251	Tokyo - Japan / Aug 30 1945 / USS Grimes [UL] [[postmark 8/30/45] [Tokyo Bay]	Black	VJDay	Navy ship	E
8252	Tokyo - our destination [on letter sheet]	Blue	USMC	Neal	B
8253	Tokyo / 9-2-45 / U.S.S. Quincy [Tokyo Bay]	Unknown	VJDay	Navy ship	E
8254	Tokyo / Bay [8/30/45] [Tokyo Bay]	Black	VJDay	Navy ship	F
8255	Tokyo / bombed / so sorry! [on cacheted cover]	Red	Event	Boone	D
8256	Tokyo / for everlasting glory / we will come! [battleship colors vary]	Multicolored	Shiel	Amer Pat	A
8257	Tokyo / here we come for the / betterment of man!	Multicolored	Navy	Amer Pat	A
8258	Tokyo / here we come! [3 diving North American P-51 "Mustangs"+ flag]	Multicolored	Air	Amer Pat	A
8259	Tokyo / here we come! [diving Lockheed P-38 + flag 65 mm long] [colors vary]	Multicolored	Air	Amer Pat	A
8260	Tokyo / here we come! [diving Lockheed P-38 + flag 74 mm long] [colors vary]	Multicolored	Air	Amer Pat	A
8261	Tokyo / here we come! [diving North American P-51 "Mustang" + flag]	Multicolored	Air	Amer Pat	A
8262	Tokyo / here we come! [shield rim gold; "Tokyo" gold or green]	Multicolored	EagSh	Amer Pat	A
8263	Tokyo / here we come! [shield rim silver; "Tokyo" gold or green]	Multicolored	EagSh	Amer Pat	A
8264	Tokyo / here we come! [shield rim silver; battleships orange or gold]	Multicolored	Navy	Amer Pat	A
8265	Tokyo / here we come! [shield rim yellow; battleships orange or gold]	Multicolored	Navy	Amer Pat	A
8266	Tokyo / LSD 17 / Japan [inside circle] [no picture] [8/31/45] [Tokyo Bay]	Black	VJDay	Navy ship	F
8267	Tokyo / our floating irons / has [sic] weight, etc. [shield rim gold]	Multicolored	Navy	Amer Pat	A
8268	Tokyo / our floating irons / has [sic] weight, etc. [shield rim silver]	Multicolored	Navy	Amer Pat	A
8269	Tokyo / our mistaken friend / [etc.] / dividends	Unknown	Unk	Amer Pat	A
8270	Tokyo / our mistaken friend, we / come for the final end.	Multicolored	EagSh	Amer Pat	A
8271	Tokyo / so sorry	Red/Purple	Japan	Foster	A

NO.	CACHET TEXT	COLOR	TOPIC	PUBLISHER	$
8272	Tokyo / triumphantly we will come!	Multicolored	EagSh	Amer Pat	A
8273	Tokyo / we / have / come / V-J-Day-is-here [handpainted]	Multicolored	VJDay	Borkowski	E
8274	Tokyo / we are coming for / the betterment of man. [shield rim gold]	Multicolored	Navy	Amer Pat	A
8275	Tokyo / we are coming for the betterment of man. [shield rim silver]	Multicolored	Navy	Amer Pat	A
8276	Tokyo / we are returning / your gratitude! [3 diving P-51 "Mustangs" above text]	Multicolored	Air	Amer Pat	A
8277	Tokyo / we are returning / your gratitude! [3 diving P-51 "Mustangs" below text]	Multicolored	Air	Amer Pat	A
8278	Tokyo / we are returning / your gratitude! [diving Lockheed P-38]	Multicolored	Air	Amer Pat	A
8279	Tokyo [Japanese mouth] Italy [Mussolini's mouth] [3 Axis heads] [handpainted]	Multicolored	Wash	Borkowski	D
8280	Tokyo and four other / industrial centres of Japan etc. [typed] [postmarked 4/19/42]	Black, blue	Event	First Day	E
8281	Tokyo Bay / Sept 2 1945 / USS Mt. Olympus [circular postmark] [Tokyo Bay]	Black, blue	Event	First Day	E
8282	Tokyo Bay / USS / Whiteside [Tokyo Bay]	Black	VJDay	Navy ship	E
8283	Tokyo Bay [lower left] [U.S.S. Gardiners Bay] [Tokyo Bay]	Black	VJDay	Navy ship	E
8283A	Tokyo Bay [obscured text ends with " bomb helped too!"] [U.S.S. Botetourt] [Tokyo Bay]	Red	VJDay	Navy ship	E
8284	Tokyo Bay [U.S.S. Detroit] [Tokyo Bay]	Magenta	VJDay	Navy ship	E
8285	Tokyo Bay! / Japan! [handpainted, lower right] [U.S.S. St. Paul] [Tokyo Bay]	Blue	VJDay	Navy ship	E
8286	Tokyo bombed - Doolittle	Unknown	Hero	Linto	D
8287	Tokyo bound / Once there was a Tokyo / who's sorry now 'tis no mo!	Green	Air	Unknown	A
8288	Tokyo bound / rubber / out	Blue	Unk	Foster	A
8289	Tokyo bound [on letter sheet]	Black	Navy	Neal	B
8290	Tokyo bound. [handpainted]	Multicolored	Armed	Adler	D
8291	Tokyo express arrives [Tokyo Bay]	Black	VJDay	Navy ship	D
8292	Tokyo radio report:——"We are pleased to announce / the destruction of an" etc.	Blue	Air	Carter	B
8293	Tokyo; / for everlasting glory / we will come! [battleship colors vary]	Multicolored	Navy	Amer Pat	A
8294	Tokyo; / great men never die etc.	Unknown	Unk	Amer Pat	A
8295	Tokyo; / great men never die, for / their spirits live on for / greater etc.	Multicolored	Unk	Amer Pat	A
8296	Tokyo; / here we come!	Multicolored	Air	Amer Pat	A
8297	Tokyo; / here we come! [5 diving North American P-51 "Mustangs"; no flag]	Multicolored	Air	Amer Pat	A
8298	Tokyo; / here we come! [5 diving North American P-51 "Mustangs"; with flag]	Multicolored	Air	Amer Pat	A
8299	Tokyo; / here we come! [5 diving North American P-51 "Mustangs"]	Multicolored	Air	Amer Pat	A
8300	Tokyo; / here we come! [battleship colors vary]	Multicolored	Shiel	Amer Pat	A
8301	Tokyo; / here we come! [diving gold & yellow or blue & yellow Lockheed P-38]	Multicolored	Air	Amer Pat	A
8302	Tokyo; / here we come! [eagle with spread wings; shield at top]	Multicolored	EagSh	Amer Pat	A
8303	Tokyo; / here we come! [one diving Lockheed P-38; flag at left edge]	Multicolored	Air	Amer Pat	A
8304	Tokyo; / here we come! [one diving P-51"Mustang"; w/ flag]	Multicolored	Air	Amer Pat	A
8305	Tokyo; / our floating irons / has [sic] weight, they can / speak for etc.	Multicolored	Navy	Amer Pat	A
8306	Tokyo; / our mistaken friend, we / come for the final end.	Multicolored	EagSh	Amer Pat	A
8307	Tokyo; / triumphantly we will come! [1 diving P-51; flag at left edge]	Multicolored	Air	Amer Pat	A
8308	Tokyo; / triumphantly we will come! [3 diving P-51s; flag at left edge]	Multicolored	Air	Amer Pat	A
8309	Tokyo; / we are coming for the / betterment etc. [red stars in 2 vertical rows]	Multicolored	Navy	Amer Pat	A
8310	Tokyo; / we are coming for the / betterment of man [shield rim color varies]	Multicolored	Navy	Amer Pat	A
8311	Tokyo; / we are coming for the / betterment of man.	Multicolored	Navy	Amer Pat	A
8312	Tokyo; / your rent is due / We'll come etc.	Unknown	Unk	Amer Pat	A
8313	Tokyo; here we come! / From the boys in the / U.S.A. [battleship colors vary]	Multicolored	Navy	Amer Pat	A
8314	Tokyo; here we come! / from the boys in the / USA	Multicolored	Navy	Amer Pat	A
8315	Tokyo; here we come! From the boys in the / U.S.A. [shield rim gold]	Multicolored	Air	Amer Pat	A
8316	Tokyo; here we come! From the boys in the / U.S.A. [shield rim silver]	Multicolored	Air	Amer Pat	A
8317	Tokyo; our mistaken friend, we / come for the final end.	Multicolored	EagSh	Amer Pat	A
8318	Tommy's idea / of his dad's / homecoming [yellow envelope]	Multicolored	Home	Amer Art	A
8319	Tomorrow comes on wings! / Jap saboteurs! / [etc.] / 1791-December 15- etc.	Blue, red	Home	Edmunds	B
8320	Too little? / too late? / No / More than enough? etc. [no picture]	Unknown	Unk	Sedgwick	A
8321	Too much / bureaucracy / for a / democracy! [no picture]	Gold, green	Home	Linto	B
8322	Torch of / freedom [text vertical] / Keep it / burning [handpainted]	Multicolored	Torch	Babcock	B
8323	Toro [in quotes] Jr. [under baby with red bow in hair] [ink] [handpainted]	Black, red	Home	Graves	C
8324	Torpedo Squadron [printed border has space for label] [thermographed]	Unknown	Air	Lind	B
8325	Total / victory / VJ Day 1945 / The battleship "Missouri" [front imprint: HF.]	Blue	VJDay	Farnam	B
8326	Total / victory / VJ Day 1945 / The battleship "Missouri" [imprint: HF]	Blue	VJDay	Farnam	B
8327	Total blackout? Never! [handpainted]	Multicolored	Liber	Knapp	G
8328	Total destruction of German / and Jap war / [etc.] / 5-16-'44——Hitler' etc.	Multicolored	Event	Linto	B

NO.	CACHET TEXT	COLOR	TOPIC	PUBLISHER	$
8329	Total destruction of German / and Jap war machines and / industries must etc.	Multicolored	Air	Linto	B
8330	Total disaster / Japan / total war [handpainted]	Multicolored	Japan	Long	C
8331	Totin' / to / Tokyo	Unknown	Unk	McCluney	A
8332	Tough hombre's [sic] [in quotes] / Texas / Oklahoma / "The Fighting Ninetieth" etc.	Red	Unit	Schirmer	A
8333	Toughy sez:- / "One way to help / your buddy over there / is to guard [handpainted]	Multicolored	Home	Myers	C
8334	Toward a / better / world / In memory etc.	Black/Green	Unk	Abel	A
8335	Toward a / better / world / United Nations / Conference etc. [env. 7 1/2x4 in.]	Green	UN	Abel	A
8336	Toward United Nations	Multicolored	UN	Griffith	A
8337	Toward United Nations / Franklin D. Roosevelt	Black, purple	Event	Fidelity	B
8338	Toward United Nations [handpainted]	Multicolored	Eagle	Stawuszew	C
8339	Traitor's / ["Black" crossed out] / market	Black	Home	Threl+Thar	B
8340	Tramp tramp tramp / our boys are marching / Africa / Italy etc. [chevron with 1 stripe]	Blue, orange	Army	Threl+Thar	A
8341	Tramp tramp tramp / our boys are marching / Africa / Italy etc. [chevron with 5 stripes]	Blue, orange	Army	Threl+Thar	A
8342	Transfer Fifth U.S. Infantry / from Portland, Maine to / Panama Canal Zone etc. [10/30/39]	Black	Event	Unknown	E
8343	Transport	Blue, red	Navy	Kosko	A
8344	Trash [MP looking for soldier hiding in trash can] [handpainted]	Multicolored	Army	Dannells	C
8345	Treat a Jap like a / Jap! It will make / him velly happy!! / Buy bonds	Unknown	AJA	Linto	B
8346	Triumph over tyranny! / Buy war bonds	Blue/Red	Bonds	Smith, AD	A
8347	Triumph over tyranny! / Buy war bonds / The more women at work etc.	Blue, red	Women	Smith, AD	A
8348	Troop / carriers / assure / victory / and / liberty	Blue	Unk	Parker	A
8349	Troop carriers assure / victory and liberty	Blue	Unk	Parker	A
8350	Trouble - interned Japs	Unknown	AJA	Linto	B
8351	Trouble for the Axis!	Blue, red	Air	Ander, EA	A
8352	True Americans / will not put their / [etc.] / 6-1-'44———3,657,000 Yanks etc.	Multicolored	Event	Linto	B
8353	True Americans / will not put their profits / above the lives of / those etc.	Gold, silver	Liber	Linto	B
8354	True or false / 2 down and 1 to go! etc. [no picture]	Unknown	Axis	Levering	A
8355	Truk / attacked / Feb. 18, 1944 [no picture]	Blue, red	Event	Fidelity	B
8356	Truth is / stranger / than fiction / "We are invincible and the gods" etc.	Multicolored	Japan	Lowell	A
8357	Try the / telephone / [etc.] / wires for war [no picture] [brown envelope]	Unknown	Home	Ohio Bell	D
8358	Tulips will bloom again, / for etc. [w/background] [colors, env. size vary]	Multicolored	ORN	Amer Pat	A
8359	Tulips will bloom again, / for etc. [without background] [print size varies]	Multicolored	ORN	Amer Pat	A
8360	Turkey declares / war on Germany [thermographed]	Unknown	Event	Boone	B
8361	Turn on the juice with / more war bonds [thermographed]	Red	Axis	Crosby	B
8362	Turn on the juice with more war bonds [thermographed]	Red	Axis	Crosby	B
8363	TVA area / wins its wings / [etc.] / Bird o'er paradise [env. 9 1/2x4 1/8 in.]	Multicolored	Eagle	Andrews	C
8364	TVA area / wins its wings / [etc.] / Chattanooga, Tennessee / dynamo for etc.	Multicolored	Eagle	Andrews	A
8365	TVA area / wins its wings / What triumphs of destiny shaped / this region etc.	Bk/Bu/Bk,Blue	Eagle	Andrews	A
8366	Twas ['Twas] ever thus / Man is being put to test etc. [no picture]	Unknown	Unk	Abel	A
8367	Twelve [12] steps to / Tokyo / Gilberts etc.	Unknown	Unk	Boone	A
8368	Twenty-eighth [28th] Div. [under insignia] [handpainted]	Black, red	Unit	Dannells	B
8369	Twenty-fifth [25th] / Armistice Day / 1918-Nov 11-1943 etc.	Red	Holid	Lawrence	A
8370	Twenty-fifth [25th] anniversary / November 11th 1943 / Liberty bonds etc.	Blue	Holid	Beck	A
8371	Twenty-fifth [25th] annual / national convention / American / Legion / Sept. etc.	Blue	Home	Unknown	A
8372	Twenty-first [Roman numerals] / annuale / Quantum mutatus ab illo	Black	Musso	McCluney	A
8373	Twenty-five [25] dollars for $18.75 / Where else can you get etc. [no picture]	Multicolored	Bonds	Linto	B
8374	Twenty-five thousand [25,000] and 6 generals captured	Unknown	Event	Linto	B
8375	Twenty-four [24]-hour day / co-operation / to win / the war / Payne etc.	Blue, red	Home	Payne, AE	A
8376	Twenty-ninth [29th] Div. [under insignia] [handpainted]	Black, blue	Unit	Dannells	B
8377	Twenty-second [XXII] Corps [under insignia] [handpainted]	Black, blue	Unit	Dannells	B
8378	Twenty-sixth [26th.] [under insignia] [handpainted]	Multicolored	Unit	Dannells	B
8379	Twenty-sixth [26th] / annual / convention / Department of New York / American etc.	Blue, red	Home	Yontz	A
8380	Twenty-two [22] Jap ships sunk	Unknown	Event	Linto	B
8381	Two / to / go [handpainted]	Blue, red	Axis	Wolf, CL	B
8382	Two [2] [numeral insignia of 2nd Army] [handpainted]	Black, red	Unit	Dannells	B
8383	Two [2] down / 2 strikes and / 1 to go etc. [envelope 7 1/2x4 in.]	Unknown	Unk	Levering	A
8384	Two [2] down, 1 to go [envelope 6 1/2x3 5/8, 7 1/2x4 in.]	Brown	Unk	Harrington	A
8385	Two [2] down, 1 to go. [handpainted]	Multicolored	Axis	Borkowski	D
8386	Two bad eggs / Tojo / Adolph / Help smash 'em ——— / by [sic] war bonds	Blue, red	Axis	Smith, W	A

NO.	CACHET TEXT	COLOR	TOPIC	PUBLISHER	$
8387	Two down- / one to / go! [thermographed]	Green	Japan	Ang	B
8388	Two down and one to go / Wanted / dead or / alive / Target-Tokio [handpainted]	Multicolored	UncJa	Hadley	C
8389	Two hundred eighty-seven [287] Refrig. / Quartermaster Company / A.P.O. 181 etc.	Red	Eagle	Czubay	B
8390	Two hundred eighty-seven [287] Refrig. / Quartermaster Company / A.P.O. 181 etc.	Red	EagFl	Roth	A
8391	Two hundred tenth [210th] birthday anniversary / of George Washington etc.	Blue	Wash	Unknown	A
8392	Two more to / go folks! / Up / and at 'em! / Make / with etc. [handpainted]	Black	Axis	Unknown	B
8393	Two outstanding things in my life - etc. [burned right edge] [handpainted]	Multicolored	Home	Cowdery	D
8394	Two worn out heels [in quotes] / Buy / war bonds [handpainted]	Black, tan	Axis	Knoll	C
8395	Two years ago Adm. Yamamoto, / who since has gone to join his [in quotes] etc.	Multicolored	Japan	Knoll	C
8396	Tyndall Field, Fla.	Brown/Green	Unit	Auge	B
8397	Tyndall Field, Fla. / "The skeet range"	Br/O/Red	Unit	Auge	B
8398	Tyndall Field, Fla. / Moving base	Green	Unit	Auge	B
8399	Tyndall Field, Fla. / Zing	Blue/Red	Unit	Auge	B

*U.S.S. *Niobrara* Tokyo Bay cancel on cachet 8233 is listed as a fake in Kent, David A. (Ed.). *Catalog of United States Naval Postmarks* (New Britain, CT: Universal Ship Cancellation Society, Fifth Edition, 1997), p. N8.

Cover Values (from Table 6, p. 136)

Value	*Price Range*
A	$ 3 - 6
B	$ 7 - 15
C	$ 16 - 30
D	$ 31 - 60
E	$ 61 - 125
F	$ 126 - 250
G	$ 251 - 500
H	$ 501 - 1000
I	$ >1000
X	Unpriced: Suspicious or fraudulent cover

7311

7350

7373

7397

7404A

7421

7423A

7460

7514

THE EAGLE SCREAMS
THE LION ROARS
THE RUSSIAN BEAR
ROLLS ON AND ON
DEFEAT FOR HITLER
NOW IS SURE
BEFORE THE END
OF '44.

G. H. A.

7515

THE END
OF ALL RATS!

7526

7531

7562

7632

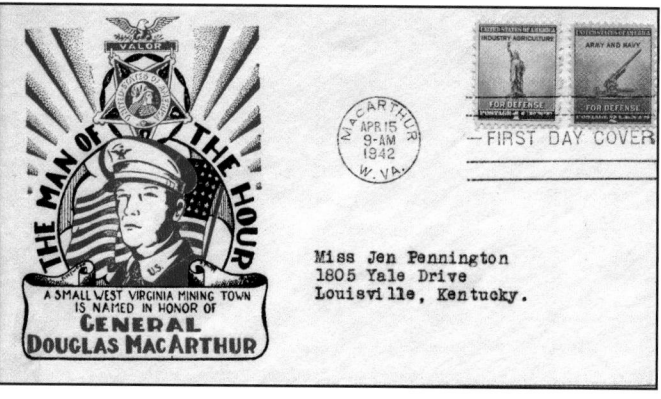

7637

7656

7661

7673

7696

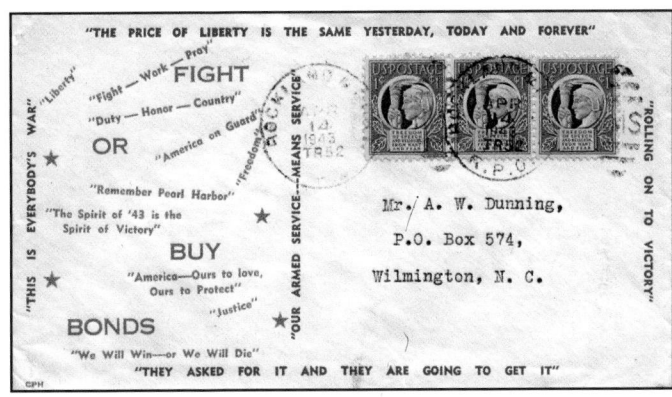

7724

7726

7740

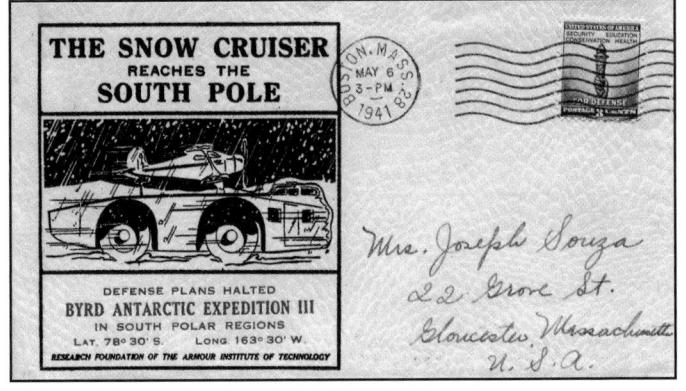

7741

7797

7859

7878

7907

7940

7946

8009

8091

8094

8150

8187

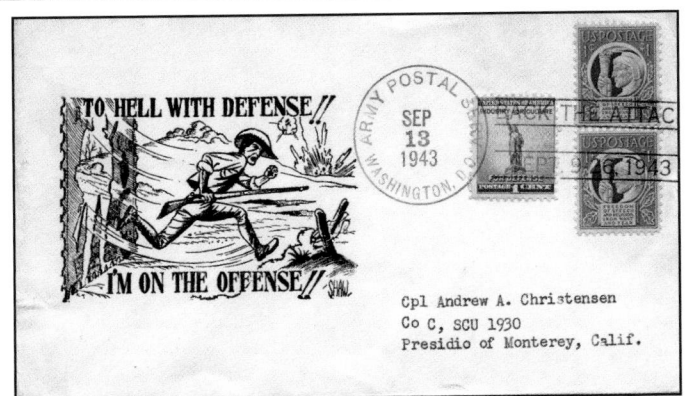

8242

8260

8282

8283A

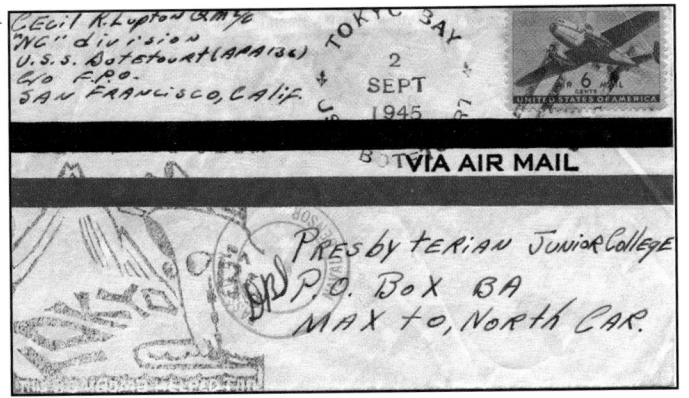

8363

CACHET TEXT BEGINNING WITH "U"

NO.	CACHET TEXT	COLOR	TOPIC	PUBLISHER	$
8400	U / S / Army [envelope 5 5/8x4 3/8 in.]	Unknown	Army	Curt-Teich	A
8401	U Army S / Aberdeen Proving / Ground / No. 201	Blue, red	Unit	Osborn	A
8402	U Army S / Alabama ordnance / works	Unknown	Army	Richardson	A
8403	U Army S / Alabama Ordnance / Works / No. 203	Blue, red	Unit	Osborn	B
8404	U Army S / American forces / Newfoundland	Unknown	Bases	Richardson	C
8404A	U Army S / Arlington Cantonment / No. 209	Blue, red	Unit	Osborn	B
8405	U Army S / Army A.C. Tr. Sta. / Goodfellow Field / No. 2	Blue, red	Unit	Osborn	B
8406	U Army S / Barksdale Field / No. 3	Blue, red	Unit	Osborn	B
8407	U Army S / Biggs Field / No 7	Blue, red	Unit	Osborn	B
8408	U Army S / Boeing Field / No. 8	Blue, red	Unit	Osborn	B
8409	U Army S / Headquarters / Ninth Army Corps Area / No. 206	Blue, red	Unit	Osborn	B
8410	U.N.C. / United Nations' Conference / April etc.	Unknown	UN	Linto	B
8411	U.S. - Jap naval battle / The Rising Sun etc.	Unknown	Navy	Abel	A
8412	U.S. / air power [envelope 6 1/2x3 5/8, 7 1/2x4 in.]	Multicolored	Japan	Peer	B
8413	U.S. / Army / defenders / of / our life, / liberty / and etc. [thermographed]	Blue, red	Army	Sadworth	B
8414	U.S. / Army / defenders / of / our life, / liberty / and etc. [thermographed]	Bu,Red/Blue	Army	Sadworth	B
8415	U.S. / Army / U.S. / Army	Multicolored	Army	Cowdery	D
8416	U.S. / Chief-of- / Staff / Marshall / arrives in / London etc. [no picture]	Red	Event	Fidelity	B
8417	U.S. / honors the / occupied / nations etc.	Unknown	ORN	Staehle	B
8418	U.S. / Marine Corps / Semper Fidelis / U.S. Marines, "Devil Dogs," etc. [therm]	Red	USMC	Crosby	B
8419	U.S. / Marine Corps / Semper Fidelis [thermographed]	Red	USMC	Crosby	B
8420	U.S. / Naval / Air / Station / Pasco / [etc.] / Fly high with U.S. Navy [thermographed]	Red	Unit	Unknown	A
8421	U.S. / Navy	Bk/Bu/Gn/O/P	Navy	Erwin	A
8422	U.S. / Navy	Red	Navy	Erwin	A
8423	U.S. / pilot [colored envelopes]	Black	Air	Huss	A
8424	U.S. / war / bond	Aquamarine	Uncle	Davis, D	A
8425	U.S. [envelope 5 5/8x4 3/8 in.]	Unknown	Unk	Curt-Teich	A
8426	U.S. [handpainted]	Multicolored	Flag	Adler	C
8427	U.S. [on helmet]	Brown	Armed	Harrington	A
8428	U.S. [on piggy bank, 3 war bonds and 1 flag above bank]	Blue	Bonds	Carpenter	A
8429	U.S. Air Corps V ⋯ – / "Greetings for the Nips"	Red	Air	Von Los	A
8430	U.S. Air Corps V ⋯ – / "The robot"	Blue, red	Air	Von Los	A
8431	U.S. Air Force / Mission accomplished [thermographed]	Unknown	Air	Von Los	A
8432	U.S. Air Forces / full speed ahead / to victory! [thermographed]	Blue	Eagle	Sadworth	B
8433	U.S. Air Forces [above picture] [thermographed]	Red	Axis	Crosby	B
8434	U.S. air mail / six / [etc.] / armed forces of the etc.	Unknown	Unk	Grandy	A
8435	U.S. and Great Britain / took control of 12 of Berlin's etc. [typed] [no picture]	Black	Event	Batura	C
8436	U.S. Army / Air Base	Red	Air	Army	B
8437	U.S. Army / Air Force / Day / Aug. 1, 1907——Wright Bros. etc. [handpainted]	Multicolored	Air	Smith, LH	C
8438	U.S. Army / an army whose / gallantry remains / unchallenged [thermographed]	Multicolored	Army	Czubay	B
8439	U.S. Army / Engineers	Unknown	Army	Von Los	A
8440	U.S. Army / Follow me	Blue, red	Army	Army	B
8441	U.S. Army / Hey, Mr. Postman, take this etc. [envelope 7 1/2x4 in.]	Unknown	Army	Fertig	B
8442	U.S. Army / In tribute to / our etc. [thermographed]	Unknown	Army	Smartcraft	B
8443	U.S. Army / Military Police [thermographed]	Unknown	Army	Crosby	B
8444	U.S. Army / The U.S. Army, backbone of national etc.	Black/Purple	Army	Cliff	A
8445	U.S. Army / Who says the army / is mechanized? [colored envelopes 7 1/2x3 7/8 in.]	Blue	Army	Unknown	A
8446	U.S. Army [13 stars in wreath above eagle, shield] [handpainted]	Multicolored	EagSh	Adler	C
8447	U.S. Army [colored envelopes]	Brown	Army	Huss	A
8448	U.S. Army [in ribbon held in eagle's beak] [handpainted]	Multicolored	EagSh	Adler	D
8449	U.S. Army [thermographed]	Unknown	Army	Czubay	B
8450	U.S. Army Air Corps / Let's go! U.S.A. / Keep 'em flying! / Sheppard Field, Texas	Blue, red	Air	Edmunds	C
8451	U.S. Army Air Force / Let's go! U.S.A. / Keep 'em flying! / Ellington Field, Texas	Blue, red	Air	Edmunds	C
8452	U.S. Army Air Force / Let's go! U.S.A. / Keep 'em flying! / Will Rogers Field etc.	Blue, red	Air	Edmunds	C
8453	U.S. Army Air Forces / "Bombs away"	Blue	Air	Air Force	A
8454	U.S. Army Air Forces / "Keep 'em flying" [first line 49 mm long]	Blue	Air	Ross	B

NO.	CACHET TEXT	COLOR	TOPIC	PUBLISHER	$
8455	U.S. Army Air Forces / "Keep 'em flying" [first line 52 mm long]	Blue	Air	Ross	B
8456	U.S. Army Air Forces / "Keep 'em flying" [with star in circle]	Blue	Air	Ross	A
8457	U.S. Army Air Forces [insignia 24 mm high, UL]	Blue	Air	Unknown	A
8458	U.S. Army Medical Corps / Service above self [thermographed]	Unknown	Medic	Crosby	B
8459	U.S. Army Nurse Corps	Unknown	Nurse	Linto	B
8460	U.S. Army Nurse Corps	Unknown	Nurse	Linto	B
8461	U.S. Army occupy / Dakar / Dec. 23, 1942	Unknown	Event	Linto	B
8462	U.S. Army Postal Service / APO c/o Postmaster [frame varies] [thermographed]	Bk/Bu/Red	Army	Czubay	B
8463	U.S. Army Postal Service [thermographed]	Unknown	Army	Czubay	B
8464	U.S. Coast Guard	Unknown	Coast	Amer Pat	A
8465	U.S. Coast Guard / Revenue cutter's etc.	Green	Coast	Coll Surp	A
8466	U.S. Coast Guards / live up to their / [etc.] / 10-23-'44——U.S. subs Golet etc.	Multicolored	Event	Linto	B
8467	U.S. Coast Guards / live up to their / long-standing / tradition [no picture]	Gold, silver	Coast	Linto	B
8468	U.S. declaration of / war / December 8, 1941 [postmarked 12/8/41]	Blue, red	Event	Newton	D
8469	U.S. Fleet / Aloha Hawaii	Green	Hawai	Lupton	A
8470	U.S. Fleet / in / Tokyo Bay / on / Victory Day [U.S.S. Briscoe] [Tokyo Bay]	Black	VJDay	Navy ship	D
8471	U.S. Fleet Hawaiian cruise	Black/Green	Navy	Lupton	A
8472	U.S. forces occupy Okinawa / June 21, 1945. [typed] [no picture]	Black	Event	Batura	C
8473	U.S. landings / To Tokyo / we go [handpainted]	Multicolored	Armed	Adler	D
8474	U.S. lands in Northern Ireland	Unknown	Event	Linto	B
8475	U.S. lands on Woodlark Islands	Unknown	Event	Linto	B
8476	U.S. Marine Corps / 1945 / "Semper fidelis" / Iwo / Jima	Black	USMC	Staehle	B
8477	U.S. Marine Corps / Gen. Alexander Vandegrift [handpainted]	Multicolored	USMC	Knoll	C
8478	U.S. Marine Corps / U.S. Marines, "Devil Dogs," etc. [1st line 70 mm] [thermographed]	Red	USMC	Crosby	B
8479	U.S. Marine Corps / U.S. Marines, "Devil Dogs," etc. [1st line 80 mm] [thermographed]	Red	USMC	Crosby	B
8480	U.S. Marines / "Devil Dogs" / ashore, afloat / and in the air etc. [thermographed]	Red	USMC	Crosby	B
8481	U.S. Marines / Iwo Jima [handpainted]	Multicolored	USMC	LeGallez	C
8481A	U.S. Marines / land on / Iwo Jima and / put the / squeeze on / the Japs [handpainted]	Multicolored	USMC	Knapp	H
8482	U.S. Marines / Old Glory raised on Mt. Suribachi, Iwo Jima	Blue, red	USMC	Smartcraft	B
8483	U.S. Marines land / on Iwo Jima [thermographed]	Blue, red	Event	Boone	D
8484	U.S. Marines proudly / maintain the tradition / of their etc. [no picture]	Gold, Gray	USMC	Linto	B
8485	U.S. Marines, "Devil Dogs", ashore, afloat and in the air / U.S. etc. [thermographed]	Red	USMC	Crosby	B
8486	U.S. Marines, "Devil Dogs," ashore, afloat and in the air [parachutes] [thermographed]	Red	USMC	Crosby	B
8487	U.S. Maritime Service / Hoffman Island, N.Y. [thermographed]	Silver	Merch	Crosby	B
8488	U.S. Maritime Service / Santa Catalina Island, California etc. [thermographed]	Blue	Merch	Crosby	B
8489	U.S. Merchant Marine / In honor of our brave etc. [thermographed]	Unknown	Merch	Crosby	B
8490	U.S. Merchant Marine [thermographed]	Unknown	Merch	Crosby	B
8491	U.S. naval amphibious / training base / Coronado, Calif. [thermographed]	Blue	Navy	Crosby	B
8492	U.S. naval amphibious force [thermographed]	Red, yellow	Navy	Crosby	C
8493	U.S. Naval Hospital, Long Beach, California [thermographed]	Red	Medic	Crosby	B
8494	U.S. Navy (Navy Day, Oct. 27, 1940) [postmarked 10/27/40]	Blue, red	Navy	Alden	C
8495	U.S. Navy / A lonesome gob writing to [envelope 7 1/2x4 in.]	Unknown	Navy	Fertig	B
8496	U.S. Navy / commissions / Tenth / Naval District / San Juan, P.R. / etc.	Blue	Navy	Unknown	A
8497	U.S. Navy / Crush the / Japanese etc. [under 3 targets] [thermographed]	Blue	Navy	Crosby	B
8498	U.S. Navy / Crush the / Japanese etc. [under flags] [thermographed]	Blue	Navy	Crosby	B
8499	U.S. Navy / Floating fire power [thermographed]	Unknown	Navy	Von Los	B
8500	U.S. Navy / For strength of victory / we have it	Unknown	Navy	Amer Pat	A
8501	U.S. Navy / Hey, Mr. Postman, take this etc. [envelope 7 1/2x4 in.]	Unknown	Navy	Fertig	B
8502	U.S. Navy / Nurse Corps / [etc.] / 10-22-'44——Yanks rushing / toward Saar Basin	Unknown	Event	Linto	B
8503	U.S. Navy / Nurse Corps / is calling for girls / ages 22 to 40 / who can etc.	Unknown	Nurse	Linto	B
8504	U.S. Navy / our first line of defense / [etc.] / Join the / U.S. Navy etc. [double cachet] [thermographed]	Blue-1 & 2	Navy	Crosby	D
8505	U.S. Navy / our first line of defense / guardians of the seven seas [thermographed]	Red	Navy	Crosby	B
8506	U.S. Navy / second to none [thermographed]	Blue	Navy	Crosby	B
8507	U.S. Navy / Since the earliest days of our nation the navy has stood as etc.	Blue	Navy	Ander, CS	A
8508	U.S. Navy / The Axis rats / don't like our sting [thermographed]	Bk/Bu/Red	Navy	Sadworth	B
8509	U.S. Navy / The Axis rats / don't like our sting [thermographed]	Blue	Navy	Sadworth	B
8510	U.S. Navy / Type Z / for the duration	Red	Navy	Quigley	B
8511	U.S. Navy / Type Z / for the duration	Blue	Navy	Muridge	B

NO.	CACHET TEXT	COLOR	TOPIC	PUBLISHER	$
8512	U.S. Navy / U.S.S. / Vincennes / part of a strong navy / second etc. [thermographed]	Blue	Navy	Sadworth	B
8513	U.S. Navy / WAVES / Remember / Pearl Harbor [thermographed]	Black	WAVES	Czubay	B
8514	U.S. Navy / We / will win! [thermographed]	Red	Navy	Sadworth	B
8515	U.S. Navy / Welcome to Seattle / John Paul Jones Chapter / U.S.C.S.	Black	Navy	Bartley	A
8516	U.S. Navy [in hat on standing sailor]	Blue, red	Navy	Krakora	A
8517	U.S. Navy [passenger ship]	Red	Navy	Czubay	A
8518	U.S. Navy [sailor in life buoy + eagle & shield] [colored envelopes]	Blue, red	Navy	Unknown	A
8519	U.S. Navy [sailor in life buoy]	Black	Navy	Lupton	A
8520	U.S. Navy [shield above battleship]	Unknown	Navy	Amer Pat	A
8521	U.S. Navy [text under Navy insignia] [envelope 7 1/2x4 in.]	Unknown	Navy	Unknown	A
8522	U.S. Navy [warship]	Red	Navy	Czubay	A
8523	U.S. Navy announces / Jap suicide plane blasted / U.S. etc. [typed] [no picture]	Black	Event	Batura	C
8524	U.S. Navy Construction Battalion / Keep etc. [thermographed]	Unknown	Navy	Crosby	B
8525	U.S. Navy forever / Watchdogs of the deep [thermographed]	Unknown	Navy	Crosby	B
8526	U.S. Navy forges victory / Buy war bonds	Blue	Bonds	Leonard	A
8527	U.S. Navy Nurse Corps / is calling for girls / ages 22 to 40 etc. [no picture]	Gold, silver	Nurse	Linto	B
8528	U.S. Navy V ···– / Floating fire power [thermographed]	Unknown	Navy	Von Los	B
8529	U.S. Navy V ···– / Somewhere, somebody talked [thermographed]	Unknown	Navy	Von Los	B
8530	U.S. Nurses' Cadet Corps / calling for recruits [no picture]	Gold, green	Nurse	Linto	B
8531	U.S. occupation of Japan / V	Red	VJDay	Abel	B
8532	U.S. occupy Dakar	Unknown	Event	Linto	B
8533	U.S. occupy Iceland	Unknown	Event	Linto	C
8534	U.S. pilot [colored envelopes]	Blue	Air	Huss	A
8535	U.S. planes raid Wake island	Unknown	Event	Linto	B
8536	U.S. planes sink 7 Jap ships	Unknown	Event	Linto	B
8537	U.S. President Harry S. Truman / sailed for the / Big etc. [typed] [no picture]	Black	Event	Batura	C
8538	U.S. runs the railroads / Offensive reaches New Britain etc. [no picture]	Black, red	Event	Fidelity	B
8539	U.S. safe after / air bombing / Roosevelt etc. [no picture]	Unknown	Event	Abel	B
8540	U.S. Senate / considers / Moscow pact / and we take over etc. [no picture]	Black, red	Event	Fidelity	B
8541	U.S. Senate / Foreign Relations Committee / approved the etc. [typed] [no picture]	Black	Event	Batura	C
8542	U.S. Senate / Foreign Relations Committee / begins etc. [typed] [no picture]	Black	Event	Batura	C
8543	U.S. Senate votes to arm ships. / Lifts ban on entree into war ports. etc.	Unknown	Event	Batura	E
8544	U.S. slogan: / "Back the attack." / Jap slogan: / "Attack the back."	Black	Uncle	Carpenter	A
8545	U.S. Submarine / Bream / 243 / On to victory / "Remember Pearl Harbor" [thermographed]	Orange	USsub	Czubay	B
8546	U.S. submarines [cachet 60x42 mm] [UL] [thermographed]	Blue	USsub	Czubay	B
8547	U.S. submarines [cachet 82x57 mm.] [thermographed]	Blue	USsub	Czubay	B
8548	U.S. subs sink 10 Jap ships	Unknown	Event	Linto	B
8549	U.S. subs sink 12 Jap ships	Unknown	Event	Linto	B
8550	U.S. troops invade Manila, Feb. 4, 1945 [thermographed]	Multicolored	Event	Smartcraft	C
8551	U.S. troops occupy Surinam, / (Dutch Guiana) Nov. 24, 1941. etc. [handpainted]	Unknown	Event	Batura	E
8552	U.S. war bonds / mean / the American way of life / Buy them hold them	Blue, red	Liber	Card	A
8553	U.S. war bonds / mean / the American way of life / Buy them hold them etc.	Blue	Liber	Cozart	A
8554	U.S. war cost / is now / $300,000,000 / a day! / 2-18-'44——Pres. Roosevelt etc.	Multicolored	Event	Linto	B
8555	U.S. war cost / is now / $300,000,000 / a day! [no picture]	Gold, silver	Home	Linto	B
8556	U.S. war cost / is now / [etc.] / 2-18-'44——Pres. Roosevelt vetoes etc.	Unknown	Event	Linto	B
8557	U.S.A. / is U.N.O. / headquarters / Big 3's / foreign / ministers / confer / at / Moscow etc. [no picture]	Unknown	UN	Fidelity	B
8558	U.S.A. / Keep 'em flying	Unknown	Unk	Jordan	B
8559	U.S.A. / Liberty	Blue, red	Bell	Krakora	B
8560	U.S.A. / National defense / Army Navy / be ready to defend	Blue, red	Home	Staehle	C
8561	U.S.A. / national defense / Army Navy / be ready to defend [thermographed]	Bk,R/Bu,Red	Armed	Czubay	B
8562	U.S.A. / national defense / Army Navy / be ready to defend [thermographed]	Green, red	Armed	Czubay	B
8563	U.S.A. / On to / victory	Unknown	Unk	Kosko	A
8564	U.S.A. / Remember / Pearl / Harbor!	Blue, red	Pearl	Boone	A
8565	U.S.A. / Wings over America [handpainted]	Blue, red	Air	Krakora	C
8566	U.S.A. [above ship steering wheel]	Blue	Navy	Krakora	A
8567	U.S.A. [above star and 2 chevrons] [handpainted]	Blue	Armed	Unknown	A
8568	U.S.A. [across chest of strong man] [handpainted]	Multicolored	Hitle	Adler	D
8569	U.S.A. [across outline map of U.S. states, letters 5mm high + bell]	Blue, red	Bell	Krakora	A

NO.	CACHET TEXT	COLOR	TOPIC	PUBLISHER	$
8570	U.S.A. [across outline map of US, letters 10mm high + shield]	Blue, red	Shiel	Krakora	A
8571	U.S.A. [across top of shield, below eagle] [handpainted]	Multicolored	EagSh	Adler	D
8572	U.S.A. [on shield, under eagle] [handpainted]	Multicolored	EagSh	Adler	D
8573	U.S.A. [under anchor and chevrons]	Blue/Red	Navy	Krakora	A
8574	U.S.A. [under anchor and two stars]	Red	Navy	Krakora	A
8575	U.S.A. [under eagle, shield, and 2 chevrons] [handpainted]	Multicolored	EagSh	Buxton, D	B
8576	U.S.A. [under eagle, shield, flags] [handpainted]	Multicolored	EagSh	Adler	C
8577	U.S.A. [under star and wings]	Blue/Red	Armed	Krakora	A
8578	U.S.A. [under star, wing, and propellor] [handpainted]	Blue	Armed	Krakora	A
8579	U.S.-Jap naval battle / The rising sun of Japan has set / upon the ocean's etc.	Green, red	Japan	Abel	A
8580	U.S.M.C. / "To the Marine Corps fell the / signal honor of" etc. [thermographed]	Blue, red	USMC	Sadworth	B
8581	U.S.M.C. / United States devil dogs [thermographed]	Gold	USMC	Crosby	B
8582	U.S.N. / A merry Christmas	Red	Holid	Unknown	B
8583	U.S.N. / Saluting the U.S. Marines / 2nd Marine Airc'ft Group etc. [no picture]	Blue	USMC	Unknown	A
8584	U.S.S. / 2 / Sep / 1945 / Proteus [cancel used as cachet] [Tokyo Bay]	Black	VJDay	Navy ship	D
8585	U.S.S. / Navy [at left, in form of navy cancel 40 mm high, 76 mm wide]	Purple/Red	Navy	Erwin	A
8586	U.S.S. / Navy [at left, in form of navy cancel 40 mm high, 76 mm wide]	Bk/Bu/Gn/O	Navy	Erwin	A
8587	U.S.S. / San Francisco / the / "one ship navy" / sunk a battleship etc. [thermographed]	Black	Anniv	McCluney	C
8588	U.S.S. Alabama / off Tokyo Japan [Tokyo Bay]	Unknown	VJDay	Navy ship	D
8589	U.S.S. Bennington [in quotes] / VJ-Day [Tokyo Bay]	Bk, magenta	VJDay	Navy ship	D
8590	U.S.S. Boise / Pick out the / biggest one etc. [no picture]	Unknown	Navy	McCluney	A
8591	U.S.S. Boston [Tokyo Bay]	Black	VJDay	Navy ship	D
8592	U.S.S. Braxton APA-138 / the first naval transport etc. [8/30/45] Tokyo Bay]	Black	VJDay	Navy ship	F
8593	U.S.S. Gasconade / Tokyo Bay [Tokyo Bay]	Black	VJDay	Navy ship	D
8594	U.S.S. Hancock CV 19 / Fighting Squadron Six [upper left] [Tokyo Bay]	Black	VJDay	Navy ship	D
8595	U.S.S. Hope (AH-7) / [etc.] / U.S. Naval hospital ship [thermographed]	Red	Navy	Crosby	C
8596	U.S.S. Marvin H. McIntyre / [etc.] / V-J Day, September 2, 1945 [Tokyo Bay]	Blue/Red	VJDay	Navy ship	D
8597	U.S.S. Missouri / battleship / [etc.] / V-J Day / Japan signs surrender etc.	Multicolored	VJDay	Werve	C
8598	U.S.S. New Mexico foreshadows / Fujiyama, Sagami Bay, etc. [Tokyo Bay]	Black	VJDay	Navy ship	D
8599	U.S.S. New York / the grand old etc.	Blue	Navy	Abel	A
8600	U.S.S. Pasadena [Tokyo Bay]	Black	VJDay	Navy ship	E
8601	U.S.S. Piedmont / participating in the / occupation etc. [8/28/45] [Tokyo Bay]	Unknown	VJDay	Navy ship	F
8602	U.S.S. Saint Paul CA73 / Third Fleet / Tokyo Bay / September 2, 1945 [Tokyo Bay]	Black	VJDay	Navy ship	E
8603	U.S.S. Shangri-La / launched / Dec. 7, 1943 / [etc.] / Tokio we are on / our way. etc.	Red	Navy	Czubay	B
8604	U.S.S. Springfield CL-66 / Tokyo Bay / occupation force etc. [Tokyo Bay]	Black	VJDay	Navy ship	E
8605	U.S.S. West Virginia (BB48) / [etc.] / Empire occupation forces - Japan [Tokyo Bay]	Black	VJDay	Navy ship	E
8606	U.S.S. Wilkes-Barre / Tokyo Bay [with cancelled Japanese stamp] [Tokyo Bay]	Unknown	VJDay	Navy ship	D
8607	U-Boat shoots down Navy blimp K-74	Unknown	Event	Linto	B
8608	Uncle / Sam / declares / war / on / Japan / Dec. 8, 1941 [no picture] [card]	Blue, red	Event	Fidelity	C
8609	Uncle / Sam / is the / man / we should always etc.	Unknown	Uncle	Czubay	A
8610	Uncle / Sam / says: / Cut red tape / and / win the war	Gold	Uncle	Linto	B
8611	Uncle / Sam / says: / We / must / mail / GI Joe / his 'Santa Claus etc.	Red	Uncle	Boone	A
8612	Uncle / Sam / says: / We have no time for / red tape fooling. / Let's win etc.	Unknown	Uncle	Linto	B
8613	Uncle / Sam [in quotes, on tag on bird's leg] / Sept. 30, 1942 [handpainted]	Black	Hitle	White, TM	C
8614	Uncle / Sam [in quotes] / Sept. 30, 1942 [handpainted]	Multicolored	Hitle	White, TM	E
8615	Uncle / Sam sez / "The more war / bonds" etc.	Unknown	Bonds	Linto	B
8616	Uncle / Sam sez / "The more war" / [etc.] / 7-23-'45——Yanks take 80,000 etc.	Unknown	Event	Linto	B
8617	Uncle / Sam sez / fill a tin / and turn it / [etc.] / 7-6-'45——Fred Vinson etc.	Unknown	Event	Linto	B
8618	Uncle / Sam sez / fill a tin / and turn it / in etc.	Unknown	Home	Linto	B
8619	Uncle / Sam sez / get extra / red points / [etc.] / 8-5-'45——Yanks wreck etc.	Unknown	Event	Linto	B
8620	Uncle / Sam sez / get extra / red points etc.	Unknown	Home	Linto	B
8621	Uncle / stepping / from Berlin / to Tokyo / and how!	Unknown	Unk	Linto	B
8622	Uncle / stepping / from Berlin / to Tokyo / and how! / 5-27-'45——Chinese etc.	Unknown	Event	Linto	B
8623	Uncle / Surrender terms [handpainted]	Multicolor	Japan	Long	C
8624	Uncle Sam / can't wait / Rush / Buy a bond today!	Blue, red	Uncle	Burdick	A
8625	Uncle Sam / needs nurses / Compare your etc.	Red	Nurse	Boone	A
8626	Uncle Sam / needs your / fighting / dollars now / Buy war bonds	Orange	Bonds	Sadworth	A
8627	Uncle Sam / needs your help / Supplies are playing / a big part / in etc.	Gree, red	Uncle	Lowell	A

NO.	CACHET TEXT	COLOR	TOPIC	PUBLISHER	$
8628	Uncle Sam / says / Remember / Pearl / Harbor	Pink	Pearl	Albrecht	A
8629	Uncle Sam / says- / Remember Pearl Harbor [lower left]	Red	Uncle	Unknown	A
8630	Uncle Sam / says,- / You do your part etc. [env. 7 3/8x3 7/8, 7 1/2x4 in.]	Blue, red	Uncle	Fleetwood	C
8631	Uncle Sam / shall always / sail the high seas!	Blue/Red	Unk	Harrington	A
8632	Uncle Sam calling! / Third / war bond / drive etc. [no picture]	Unknown	Bonds	Boone	A
8633	Uncle Sam clears his throat [env. 6 9/16x3 3/4, 6 3/4x3 3/4 in.] [in quotes]	Sepia tones	Ordna	Belles-let	C
8634	Uncle Sam depends on us	Unknown	Home	Linto	B
8635	Uncle Sam has a very / attractive buy / [etc.] / 6-26-'45——United Nations etc.	Unknown	UN	Linto	B
8636	Uncle Sam has a very / attractive buy for etc.	Unknown	Unk	Linto	B
8637	Uncle Sam has helped you / Now it is / up to you / to help / Uncle / Sam / now!	Multicolored	Uncle	Linto	B
8638	Uncle Sam has spoken / "I'll / take / Manila!" [thermographed]	Red	Uncle	Crosby	B
8639	Uncle Sam is in a scrap / Help him etc. [no picture]	Unknown	Unk	Shaw, MM	A
8640	Uncle Sam is not going to relax / so be sure etc.	Unknown	Home	Linto	B
8641	Uncle Sam says / Buy / war bonds [no picture]	Unknown	Bonds	Ang	A
8642	Uncle Sam says / Conserve / gas and coal [no picture]	Green, red	Home	Ang	A
8643	Uncle Sam says / Donate / a pint of blood [no picture]	Unknown	Blood	Ang	A
8644	Uncle Sam says / Don't / gossip [no picture]	Unknown	Home	Ang	A
8645	Uncle Sam says / Grow more / for victory [no picture]	Unknown	Home	Ang	A
8646	Uncle Sam says / Knit / for the Red Cross [no picture]	Unknown	RedCr	Ang	A
8647	Uncle Sam says / Obey / ration laws [no picture]	Unknown	Home	Ang	A
8648	Uncle Sam says / Save / all tin cans [no picture]	Unknown	Home	Ang	A
8649	Uncle Sam says / Save / waste paper [no picture]	Unknown	Home	Ang	A
8650	Uncle Sam says / You must / work or fight [no picture]	Gree, red	Home	Linto	B
8651	Uncle Sam says.... / "If we cease the war effort / when Germany falls" / Supplies etc.	Gy,Vi/Bk,Red	Uncle	Lowell	A
8652	Uncle Sam says: "Work or fight" / With him we all agree / Us little fellows do etc.	Blue	Flag	Abel	A
8653	Uncle Sam says: / Forestall inflation / buy war bonds	Blue, red	Uncle	Ander, EA	A
8654	Uncle Sam shall always / sail the high seas	Pink	Uncle	Harrington	A
8655	Uncle Sam shall ever / sail the seven etc.	Blue/Green	Unk	Harrington	A
8656	Uncle Sam will ever / sail the etc. [1 line above picture] [73 mm high]	Black/Blue	Uncle	Harrington	A
8657	Uncle Sam will ever / sail the etc. [1 line above picture] [78 mm high]	Black/Blue	Uncle	Harrington	A
8658	Uncle Sam will ever / sail the etc. [2 lines above picture]	Bk/Bu/Gn	Uncle	Harrington	A
8659	Uncle Sam will show 'em! [in quotes] [handpainted] [envelope 5 3/4x3 13/16 in.]	Multicolored	Uncle	White, TM	F
8660	Uncle Sam would / appreciate your / study of this / thoughtful verse etc.	Gold, silver	Uncle	Linto	B
8661	Uncle Sam, / shall always / sail the high seas! / defending for us / our etc.	Blue	Navy	Harrington	A
8662	Uncle Sam, / shall always: / sail the high seas!	Blue, red	Uncle	Harrington	A
8663	Uncle Sam, don't worry / I'll protect you !! etc.	Black/Blue	Uncle	Harrington	A
8664	Uncle Sammy [in quotes] / says / "Let's all do our / share to insure etc. [handpainted]	Multicolored	Uncle	Unknown	B
8665	Uncle Sam's / golden opportunity / for you to share in the etc. [no picture]	Multicolored	Bonds	Linto	B
8666	Uncle Sam's / victory / smile	Unknown	Uncle	Kosko	A
8667	Uncle Sam's / victory / smile	Unknown	Uncle	Boone	A
8668	Uncle Sam's boys / will pay him back / Put your money to work and / back etc.	Blue, red	Bonds	Boone	A
8669	Uncle Sam's golden opportunity / [etc.] / 1-22-'44——Allies make surprise etc.	Multicolored	Event	Linto	B
8670	Uncle Sam's peace terms. [handpainted]	Black	UncAx	Clendennen	E
8671	Uncle says: / Buy another bond	Red	Bonds	Burdick	A
8672	Uncle's boys will / knock the "P" / out of the Japs [no picture]	Multicolored	Japan	Linto	B
8673	Unconditional / surrender	Blue	Unk	Foster	A
8674	Unconditional / Surrender / 2:40 A.M. May 7th / V-E / [etc.] / V-J. Day [VE+VJ postmarks]	Black	VJDay	Unknown	E
8675	Unconditional / surrender / Nazi armies crushed by Allied might, / Germany etc.	Purple	VEDay	Unknown	B
8676	Unconditional / surrender / of / Germany / announced by etc. [no picture]	Red	VEDay	Harmer	B
8677	Unconditional / surrender [army, marines, navy symbols] [handpainted]	Multicolored	VEDay	LeGallez	E
8678	Unconditional / surrender [handpainted]	Multicolored	Ally	Adler	D
8679	Unconditional / Surrender [in quotes] / August 14th/45 [date typed] [pmk 8/14/45]	Multicolored	VJDay	Unknown	C
8680	Unconditional surrender	Copper, green	Unk	Peer	B
8681	Unconditional surrender / of Japan. / Sept. 2 - 1945 [no picture] [handpainted, pen & ink]	Blue	VJDay	Batura	D
8682	Unconditional surrender of the Axis. [in quotes] / V / "Freedom" etc. [thermographed]	Blue, red	UncV	Bean	A
8683	Unconditional surrender or annihilation	Green	Unk	Foster	A
8684	Underground [determined man with lamp and rifle] [handpainted]	Multicolored	ORN	Adler	D
8685	Union Pacific Railroad / on the job for Uncle Sam [all-over cachet, back of envelope]	Blue, red	Home	Union Pac	B

NO.	CACHET TEXT	COLOR	TOPIC	PUBLISHER	$
8686	Unite for America	Black	Eagle	Unknown	A
8687	United / for / victory	Blue, red	Armed	Baur	A
8688	United / for / victory / Buy etc. [envelope 7 1/2x4 in/]	Unknown	Unk	Atkins	A
8689	United / for defense / Health / Education / [etc.] / United States of America	Blue, red	Flag	Staehle	B
8690	United / for victory	Blue	Unk	Nixon	A
8691	United / hemisphere defense / commemorating / [etc.] / Antigua, B.W.I. etc.	Black	Bases	Unknown	D
8692	United / hemisphere defense / commemorating / [etc.] / British Guiana, S.A.	Black	Bases	Unknown	D
8693	United / hemisphere defense / commemorating / [etc.] / Greenland	Black	Bases	Unknown	D
8694	United / hemisphere defense / commemorating / [etc.] / in Bermuda etc.	Black	Bases	Unknown	D
8695	United / hemisphere defense / commemorating / [etc.] / Jamaica B.W.I.	Black	Bases	Unknown	D
8696	United / hemisphere defense / commemorating / [etc.] / Newfoundland	Black	Bases	Unknown	D
8697	United / hemisphere defense / commemorating / [etc.] / St. Lucia, Windward etc.	Black	Bases	Unknown	D
8698	United / hemisphere defense / commemorating / [etc.] / Trinidad	Black	Bases	Unknown	D
8699	United / in one course to / bring home victory etc. [artist: Staehle]	Multicolored	Globe	Fleetwood	C
8700	United / Nations	Bk/Bu/Gn/R/Y	UN	Jarrett	A
8701	United / Nations	Blue, red	Globe	Unknown	A
8702	United / Nations / "The enemy must be hit and hit hard from / so" etc. [thermograph]	Black	Axis	Sadworth	B
8703	United / Nations / conference / for a / lasting etc.	Unknown	UN	Fleetwood	B
8704	United / Nations / conference / San Francisco etc.	Unknown	UN	Ioor	A
8705	United / Nations / on to victory [w/, w/o return address] [env. 6x3 ½ in.]	Unknown	UN	Dime	A
8706	United / Nations / the / hope / of all / humanity [colored envelopes]	Blue, red	Globe	Poppenger	A
8707	United / Nations / The United States of America, / The United Kingdoms of etc.	Blue/Red	UN	Brenn	A
8708	United / Nations / They came from etc.	Unknown	UN	Brenn	A
8709	United / Nations / united for / victory	Blue, red	UN	Cachet Cra	A
8710	United / Nations / united for / victory [3 red stars]	Blue, red	UN	Ioor	A
8711	United / Nations / united for / victory [3 white stars]	Blue, red	UN	Ioor	A
8712	United / Nations / United Nations Peace Conference / "We are all agreed that" etc.	Red	UN	Brenn	A
8713	United / Nations / United we will win	Blue	UN	McFarland	A
8714	United / Nations united	Blue, red	FlLib	Goldstein	B
8715	United / to stamp out the Axis [belt & arm; eagle & New Zealand stamp]	Bk,R/Br/Red	Axis	Runge	A
8716	United / to stamp out the Axis [belt & arm]	Bk,R/Br/Red	Axis	Runge	A
8717	United / to stamp out the Axis [eagle & New Zealand stamp, no belt]	Bk,R/Br/Red	Axis	Runge	A
8718	United / we / stand	Blue	EagSh	Krakora	A
8719	United / we / stand	Blue, red	Uncle	Krakora	A
8720	United / we / stand / divided / we / fall	Green	Home	Christens	A
8721	United / we / stand, / divided / we fall	Green/Red	Home	Christens	A
8722	United / we are strong / 32 united nations fight etc. [env. 6 9/16x3 3/4 in.]	Multicolored	UN	Belles-let	D
8723	United / we are strong / United / [etc.] / 6-19-'44———Allies started Huns etc.	Gray, purple	Event	Linto	B
8724	United / we are strong / United we will win	Gray	UN	Linto	B
8725	United / we fight [handpainted]	Multicolored	Armed	Adler	D
8726	United / we stand	Blue	Unk	Harvey	A
8727	United at Cassino [envelope 7 1/2x4 in.]	Unknown	Unk	Runge	A
8728	United for / post-war co-operation [handpainted]	Blue, red	UN	Klaas	C
8729	United for / victory / ··· – [envelope 6 1/2x3 5/8, 9 1/2x4 1/8 in.]	Multicolored	VforV	Ever Ready	A
8730	United for freedom and equality [copyright "C" w/, w/o serifs, or no "C"]	Multicolored	Eagle	Minkus	A
8731	United for victory	Blue, red	Wash	Abel	A
8732	United for victory [copyright "C" w/, w/o serifs]	Multicolored	VforV	Minkus	A
8733	United for victory [on flap] [envelope 7 1/2x4 in.]	Unknown	Unk	Abbott	B
8734	United for war / united in peace [handpainted]	Multicolored	EagSh	Stoll	B
8735	United in defense / of freedom	Multicolored	Globe	Minkus	A
8736	United in democracy	Blue, red	Flag	McGovern	A
8737	United in war / united in peace / united in the hearts of their countrymen	Multi;Bu,Red	Ally	Schust	A
8738	United Nations / against the Axis / United States etc. [thermographed] [nations T&B]	Blue	Eagle	Sadworth	B
8739	United Nations / against the Axis / United States etc. [thermographed] [no list T&B]	Blue	Eagle	Sadworth	B
8740	United Nations / conference / Representatives etc.	Unknown	UN	Czubay	A
8741	United Nations / conference / World peace etc.	Unknown	UN	Grimsland	A
8742	United Nations / Free France fights on	Bk,R/Bu,Red	UN	Runge	A
8743	United Nations / on to victory	Unknown	UN	Baur	A

NO.	CACHET TEXT	COLOR	TOPIC	PUBLISHER	$
8744	United Nations / peace conference etc.	Blue	UN	Ander, EA	A
8745	United Nations / united / for victory [engraved]	Blue	UN	Grimsland	B
8746	United Nations / United Nations peace etc.	Red	UN	Brenn	A
8747	United Nations / V··· – / V··· – [no picture]	Unknown	UN	Dime	A
8748	United Nations conference	Blue, red	UN	Fidelity	B
8749	United Nations conference / on international etc.	Unknown	UN	Smartcraft	B
8750	United Nations conference / Representatives of the / United Nations etc.	Blue, red	UN	Sanders	A
8751	United Nations conference / San Francisco etc.	Purple	UN	Sharon	A
8752	United Nations Conference / San Francisco etc.	Unknown	UN	Linto	B
8753	United Nations conference of international	Unknown	UN	Staehle	B
8754	United Nations determination / American production	Bk/Bu/Red	Hitle	Donaldson	A
8755	United Nations News / Italy / surrenders / unconditionally etc. [artist: Knapp]	Blue, red	Event	Fleetwood	C
8756	United Nations peace conference / "The world is one world," "All na-" etc.	Red	EagSh	Brenn	A
8757	United Nations peace conference / You have created etc.	Red	UN	Brenn	A
8758	United States / amphibious force etc. [thermographed]	Unknown	Unk	Crosby	B
8759	United States / armed forces / U.S. Army Air Corps	Aquamarine	Chute	Crosby	B
8760	United States / armed forces / U.S. Army Coast Artillery [thermographed]	Unknown	Army	Crosby	B
8761	United States / armed forces / U.S. Army Engineers [thermographed]	Unknown	Army	Crosby	B
8762	United States / armed forces / U.S. Army Field Artillery [thermographed]	Unknown	Army	Crosby	B
8763	United States / armed forces / U.S. Army parachutist [thermographed]	Unknown	Chute	Crosby	B
8764	United States / Army	Black	Army	Allen	A
8765	United States / Army [circle UL] [env. 6x3 ½ in.]	Unknown	Army	Unknown	A
8766	United States / Army [envelope 5 3/4x3 5/8 in.]	Unknown	Army	Unknown	A
8767	United States / Army Air Corps [circle UL] [env. 6x3 ½, 5 3/4x3 5/8 in.]	Unknown	Air	Unknown	A
8768	United States / Artillery [envelope 5 1/8x4 1/8 in.]	Unknown	Ordna	Unknown	A
8769	United States / declares war on / Germany and Italy / Dec. 11 etc. [no picture]	Blue, red	Event	Unknown	C
8770	United States / destroyer mail [thermographed]	Bu/Gy/Green	Navy	Sadworth	B
8771	United States / Greenland / England / [etc.] / The sun never sets on Old Glory.	Blue, red	Flag	Unknown	A
8772	United States / honors the / occupied / nations / in Europe [artist: Staehle]	Multicolored	ORN	King's	B
8773	United States / Infantry [envelope 5 1/8x4 1/8 in.]	Unknown	Army	Unknown	A
8774	United States / Marine base / Antigua	Multicolored	Bases	Unknown	B
8775	United States / Marine base / St. Lucia	Multicolored	Bases	Unknown	B
8776	United States / Marine base / Trinidad, B.W.I.	Multicolored	Bases	Unknown	B
8777	United States / Marine Corps / Christmas greetings [thermographed]	Unknown	USMC	Sadworth	B
8778	United States / Marine Corps / Honor Roll / Never forget / [etc.] / Solomon Islands [thermograph]	Unknown	USMC	Sadworth	B
8779	United States / Marine Corps / Honor Roll / Never forget our dead / at Palau etc. [thermographed]	Unknown	USMC	Sadworth	B
8780	United States / Marine Corps / Honor Roll / Never forget our dead / at Tulagi etc. [thermographed]	Gray	USMC	Sadworth	B
8781	United States / Marine Corps / Honor Roll / Never forget our dead / at Wake Island [thermograph]	Green	USMC	Sadworth	B
8782	United States / Marine Corps / On land and sea / and in the air [thermographed]	Blue, red	USMC	Crosby	B
8783	United States / Marine Corps / United States / Army / [etc.] / V / J / Day	Black	VJDay	Unknown	B
8784	United States / Marine mail [thermographed]	Green	USMC	Sadworth	B
8785	United States / Marines / proudly etc.	Unknown	USMC	Unknown	A
8786	United States / Marines [circle UL] [envelope 6x3 ½ in.]	Unknown	USMC	Unknown	A
8787	United States / Marines [envelope 5 1/8x4 1/8 in.]	Unknown	USMC	Unknown	A
8788	United States / Maritime service / U.S. etc. [thermographed]	Unknown	Merch	Crosby	B
8789	United States / Naval Hospital / Quantico, Va.	Red	Medic	Farnsworth	B
8790	United States / Naval Training Station / [etc.] / Recruits drilling [thermographed]	Black	Navy	Crosby	B
8791	United States / Navy	Purple/Red	Navy	Erwin	A
8792	United States / Navy	Bk/Bu/Br/Gn/O	Navy	Erwin	A
8793	United States / Navy / Naval shore stations / The U.S. Navy-the first line etc.	Green	Navy	Unknown	A
8794	United States / Navy [circle UL] [envelope 6x3 ½ in.]	Unknown	Navy	Unknown	A
8795	United States / Navy [envelope 5 3/4x3 5/8, 5 1/8x4 1/8 in.]	Unknown	Navy	Unknown	A
8796	United States / Navy Air Corps [envelope 5 1/8x4 1/8 in.]	Unknown	Navy	Unknown	A
8797	United States / Navy cargo ship [thermographed]	Unknown	Navy	Sadworth	B
8798	United States / Nurses Corp [sic] [logo] [UL] [env. 6 1/2x3 5/8, 6x3 ½ in.]	Multicolored	Nurse	Army	B
8799	United States / of / America / National defense etc. [engraved]	Unknown	Home	Grimsland	A
8800	United States / of / America / The flag / we love [engraved]	Blue, red	Flag	Grimsland	B
8801	United States / our first line of defense / Navy vessel [thermographed]	Blue, red	Navy	Sadworth	B

NO.	CACHET TEXT	COLOR	TOPIC	PUBLISHER	$
8802	United States / Post Office / Neither rain nor sleet / nor snow nor hail etc.	Blue, red	Home	Unknown	A
8803	United States / submarine mail	Blue	USsub	Sadworth	B
8804	United States / submarine mail [77 or 57 mm high] [thermographed]	Br/Gn/Pu/Red	USsub	Sadworth	B
8805	United States / Tank Corps [envelope 5 3/4x3 5/8, 5 1/8x4 1/8 in.]	Unknown	Ordna	Unknown	A
8806	United States / WAAC [envelope 5 3/4x3 5/8 in.]	Unknown	WAC	Unknown	A
8807	United States / Waves [envelope 5 1/8x4 1/8 in.]	Unknown	WAVES	Unknown	A
8808	United States 1776 / United Nations 1942	Unknown	Unk	Runge	A
8809	United States Air / [etc.] / "Pearl Harbor" [2nd line below picture] [thermographed]	Red	Axis	Crosby	B
8810	United States Air / [etc.] / "Pearl Harbor" [both lines above picture] [thermographed]	Red	Axis	Crosby	B
8811	United States Air Corps [under insignia, UL]	Blue	Air	Unknown	A
8812	United States Air Forces / Remember etc. [1st line above picture] [thermographed]	Blue	Air	Crosby	B
8813	United States Air Forces / Remember etc. [both lines above picture] [thermographed]	Blue	Air	Crosby	B
8814	United States Air Forces [thermographed]	Red	Axis	Crosby	B
8815	United States armed forces / Keep on writing etc.	Unknown	Unk	Jordan	A
8816	United States Army - Navy - Coast / Guard - Seabees - Marines etc. [thermographed]	Blue	Armed	Crosby	B
8817	United States Army / Amphibious Force / Army landing [thermographed]	Blue, gold	Army	Crosby	B
8818	United States Army / Anti-tank Corps [thermographed]	Blue	Army	Crosby	B
8819	United States Army / Attacked by planes etc. [ribbon on eagle] [thermographed]	Unknown	Army	Crosby	B
8820	United States Army / Buy war stamps and bonds [ribbon on eagle] [thermographed]	Unknown	Bonds	Crosby	B
8821	United States Army / Defend Alaska / [etc.] / Old Russian Church, etc. [thermograph]	Blue	Alask	Crosby	B
8822	United States Army / Defend Alaska / Baby etc. [ribbon on eagle] [thermographed]	Unknown	Alask	Crosby	B
8823	United States Army / Defend Alaska / Brenda etc. [ribbon on eagle] [thermographed]	Blue	Alask	Crosby	B
8824	United States Army / Defend Alaska! / ADF / Brenda, a balancing etc. [thermograph]	Blue	Alask	Crosby	B
8825	United States Army / First Day Post Office dedication etc. [4 stars] [thermographed]	Gold	MacFD	Crosby	C
8826	United States Army / First Day Post Office dedication etc. [two flags] [thermographed]	Red	MacFD	Crosby	C
8827	United States Army / General Douglas MacArthur etc. [2 flags, 8 stars] [thermograph]	Blue, red	MacFD	Crosby	C
8828	United States Army / Jeep acts as telephone car etc. [ribbon on eagle] [thermograph]	Unknown	Army	Crosby	B
8829	United States Army / Jeep towing a 37-MM etc. [ribbon on eagle] [thermograph]	Unknown	Army	Crosby	B
8830	United States Army / Keep the home fires etc. [ribbon on eagle] [thermographed]	Unknown	Army	Crosby	B
8831	United States Army / Parachute battalion [ribbon on eagle] [thermographed]	Red/Silver	Chute	Crosby	B
8832	United States Army / The United Nations etc. [thermographed]	Unknown	UN	Crosby	B
8833	United States Army / The United Nations fight etc. [ribbon on eagle] [thermographed]	Unknown	UN	Crosby	B
8834	United States Army / U.S. Army infantry tank corps [thermographed]	Aquamarine	Ordna	Crosby	B
8835	United States Army [blue text] [space for vertical label]	Blue, red	Army	Sadworth	B
8836	United States Army [red text] [space for horizontal label]	Blue, red	Army	Sadworth	B
8837	United States Army [under insignia, UL]	Blue	Army	Unknown	A
8838	United States Army Air Forces / Keep 'em flying	Blue	Air	Unknown	A
8839	United States Army Air Forces [under emblem 12 mm high, UL]	Blue	Air	Unknown	A
8840	United States Army Air Forces [under emblem 8 mm high, UL]	Blue	Air	Unknown	A
8841	United States Capitol / Washington, D.C.	Unknown	Unk	Grandy	A
8842	United States Coast Guard / 1790	Blue/Brown	Coast	Fagenson	A
8843	United States Coast Guard / 1790 [envelope 6x3 ½ in.]	Unknown	Coast	Amer Pat	A
8844	United States Coast Guard / Always ready! [thermographed]	Unknown	Coast	Crosby	B
8845	United States Coast Guard / Let's go! etc. [thermographed]	Unknown	Coast	Crosby	B
8846	United States Coast Guard [thermographed]	Blue	Coast	Crosby	B
8847	United States Coast Guard 1790 [wording around shield]	Unknown	Coast	Linto	B
8848	United States discharge medal	Unknown	VJDay	Lupkin	B
8849	United States Fleet / [etc.] / Hawaiian cruise	Unknown	Navy	Lupton	A
8850	United States Fleet / Battle force [thermographed]	Blue, red	Navy	Crosby	B
8851	United States Fleet [aircraft carrier] [blue picture width 102 mm]	Blue, orange	Navy	Lupton	A
8852	United States Fleet [aircraft carrier] [blue picture width 65 mm]	Blue, orange	Navy	Lupton	A
8853	United States Fleet [aircraft carrier] [blue picture width 77 mm]	Blue, orange	Navy	Lupton	A
8854	United States Fleet [aircraft carrier] [blue picture width 98 mm]	Blue, orange	Navy	Lupton	A
8855	United States Fleet [battleship] [blue picture width 82 mm]	Blue, red	Navy	Lupton	A
8856	United States Fleet [battleship] [blue picture width 94 mm]	Blue, red	Navy	Lupton	A
8857	United States Fleet [battleship] [blue picture width 97 mm]	Blue, red	Navy	Lupton	A
8858	United States Fleet [battleship] [blue picture width 98 mm]	Blue, red	Navy	Lupton	A
8859	United States Fleet [battleship] [blue picture width 99 mm]	Blue, red	Navy	Lupton	A

NO.	CACHET TEXT	COLOR	TOPIC	PUBLISHER	$
8860	United States Fleet [named warship varies]	Blue, red	Navy	Lupton	A
8861	United States Fleet [Old Ironsides]	Blue, red	Navy	Lupton	A
8862	United States Great Britain / V-J Day / and the end of the / greatest war etc.	Aqua, red	VJDay	Brown, G	C
8863	United States Greenland England Iceland etc. [gray envelope]	Unknown	Unk	Baur	A
8864	United States honors the / occupied nations in Europe [env. 8 1/4x5 ½ in.]	Multicolored	ORN	Staehle	D
8865	United States Marine Corps / "Keep the home fires burning" etc. [thermographed]	Red	USMC	Crosby	B
8866	United States Marine Corps / "Remember Pearl Harbor" / and do not etc. [thermographed]	Gold/Red	USMC	Crosby	B
8867	United States Marine Corps / [etc.] / Color guard [thermographed]	Red	USMC	Crosby	B
8868	United States Marine Corps / [etc.] / Color guard, U.S. Marine etc. [thermographed]	Red	USMC	Crosby	B
8869	United States Marine Corps / [etc.] / U.S.S. Mississippi etc. [thermographed]	Gold	USMC	Crosby	B
8870	United States Marine Corps / Americans remember / Pearl etc. [thermographed]	Unknown	USMC	Crosby	B
8871	United States Marine Corps / Fly high with the U.S.M.C. / U.S. etc. [thermographed]	Red	USMC	Crosby	B
8872	United States Marine Corps / Marine detachment / U.S. Marines etc. [thermographed]	Red	USMC	Crosby	B
8873	United States Marine Corps / Ready to defend America	Blue	USMC	Lindhardt	A
8874	United States Marine Corps / Second Marine Division / Camp Elliott etc. [thermograph]	Red	USMC	Crosby	B
8875	United States Marine Corps / Semper fidelis [Marine symbol + 2 flags] [thermographed]	Red	USMC	Crosby	B
8876	United States Marine Corps / Semper fidelis [USMC symbol 20 mm high] [thermograph]	Red	USMC	Crosby	B
8877	United States Marine Corps / U.S. Marines etc. [symbol 25 mm high] [thermographed]	Gold/Red	USMC	Crosby	B
8878	United States Marine Corps / U.S. Marines etc. [symbol 29 mm high] [thermographed]	Red	USMC	Crosby	B
8879	United States Marine Corps [USMC symbol 25 mm high] [thermographed]	Red	USMC	Crosby	B
8880	United States Marine Corps. / From the halls of Montezuma, / to the shores etc.	Blue	USMC	Lindhardt	A
8881	United States Marine Corps. / Here's health to you and to our corps, which etc.	Blue	USMC	Lindhardt	A
8882	United States Marines / First Day Postal Service / First Marines / First etc.	Bu/Brown/Red	USMC	Hutnick	B
8883	United States Marines / First Day postal service / First Marines etc. [thermographed]	Blue	USMC	Hutnick	B
8884	United States Marines / First Day postal service / Second Marine etc.	Violet	USMC	Hutnick	B
8885	United States Marines / First Day postal service / Sixth Defense Batta. etc.	Gold	USMC	Hutnick	B
8886	United States Marines / Let's go! / [etc.] / "Fighting Marines" [thermographed]	Red	USMC	Crosby	B
8887	United States Marines / Let's go! / [etc.] / afloat and in the air [thermographed]	Red	USMC	Crosby	B
8888	United States Marines / Let's go! / [etc.] / Dogs of the deep—— / etc. [thermographed]	Red	USMC	Crosby	B
8889	United States Marines / U.S. Marines raising the / American flag on Iwo Jima	Green, red	USMC	Fidelity	B
8890	United States naval / postmarks / first day postal service / official etc.	Black/Blue	Bases	Czubay	D
8891	United States naval / postmarks / first day postal service etc. [thermographed]	Black/Green	Bases	Czubay	D
8892	United States Navy	Red	Navy	Amer Naval	A
8893	United States Navy "second to none" [thermographed] [+ U.S.S. Dewey label]	Multicolored	Navy	Sharon	C
8894	United States Navy "second to none" [thermographed] [+ U.S.S. Los Angeles label]	Multicolored	Navy	Sharon	C
8895	United States Navy "second to none" [thermographed] [+ U.S.S. Pennsylvania label]	Multicolored	Navy	Sharon	C
8896	United States Navy "second to none" [thermographed] [+ U.S.S. Ranger label]	Multicolored	Navy	Sharon	C
8897	United States Navy / [name of ship] / First day postal service / Neutrality patrol fleet / recommissioned	Blue, red	Navy	Hutnick	B
8898	United States Navy / Amphibious Force / Navy landing [thermographed]	Gold, red	Navy	Crosby	B
8899	United States Navy / Atlantic / Amphibious Force / Branch / etc. [thermographed]	Black	Navy	Hutnick	B
8900	United States Navy / avengers / Remember Pearl Harbor	Black, green	Navy	Eichenlaub	A
8901	United States Navy / Don't give up the ship / You may fire when ready, etc.	Blue, red	Navy	Cachet Cra	A
8902	United States Navy / exterminators / Jap rats our specialty	Brown, gold	Navy	Eichenlaub	A
8903	United States Navy / first day / [etc.] / Bermuda etc. [thermographed] [no picture]	Gold	Bases	Hutnick	B
8904	United States Navy / first day cancellation / Miami, Florida etc. [postmarked 4/01/41]	Blue	Bases	Hutnick	B
8905	United States Navy / First Day postal service / First Marine / Aircraft etc.	Multicolored	USMC	Hutnick	B
8906	United States Navy / guardians etc.	Unknown	Navy	Eichenlaub	A
8907	United States Navy / harbingers etc.	Blue, green	Navy	Eichenlaub	A
8908	United States Navy / last day cancellation / New York City etc. [postmarked 3/31/41]	Blue	Bases	Hutnick	B
8909	United States Navy / Let's go etc. [1st line print style varies] [thermographed]	Unknown	Navy	Crosby	B
8910	United States Navy / protectors etc.	Blue, green	Navy	Eichenlaub	A
8911	United States Navy / second to none [circling Navy seal, diam 19 mm] [thermograph]	Blue	Navy	Crosby	B
8912	United States Navy / the nation's / life buoy	Blue, red	Navy	Ioor	A
8913	United States Navy [above fish emblem]	Unknown	Navy	Amer Pat	A
8914	United States Navy [above insignia]	Blue	Navy	Unknown	A
8915	United States Navy [blue lines on both sides of insignia]	Blue	Navy	Unknown	A
8916	United States Navy [head of sailor in life buoy] [buff envelope]	Black/Brown	Navy	Huss	A
8917	United States Navy [under blue insignia, lines and stars UL]	Blue, red	Navy	Unknown	A

NO.	CACHET TEXT	COLOR	TOPIC	PUBLISHER	$
8918	United States Navy [under red insignia UL] [env. 6 1/2x3 5/8, 6x3 ½ in.]	Blue, red	Navy	Unknown	A
8919	United States Neutrality Patrol [postmarked 1939 or 1940]	Green	Uncle	Christens	D
8920	United States Nurses Corps [nurse with ambulance in background] [UL]	Multicolored	Nurse	Army	B
8921	United States of / America [in quotes] / Symbol of democracy. United to preserve etc.	Blue, red	Home	Harmer	A
8922	United States of America	Blue, red	EagFl	Staehle	C
8923	United States of America / honoring the / [etc.] / Belgium [engraved]	Unknown	ORN	Grimsland	B
8924	United States of America / honoring the / [etc.] / Czechoslovakia [engraved]	Blue, red	ORN	Grimsland	B
8925	United States of America / honoring the / [etc.] / Luxembourg [engraved]	Multicolored	ORN	Grimsland	B
8926	United States of America / honoring the / [etc.] / Netherlands [engraved]	Blue, red	ORN	Grimsland	B
8927	United States of America / honoring the / [etc.] / Philippines [engraved]	Unknown	ORN	Grimsland	B
8928	United States of America / honoring the / [etc.] / Yugoslavia [engraved]	Multicolored	ORN	Grimsland	B
8929	United States of America / honoring the oppressed nation / Albania [engraved]	Multicolored	ORN	Grimsland	B
8930	United States of America / honoring the oppressed nation / Austria [engraved]	Blue, red	ORN	Grimsland	B
8931	United States of America / honoring the oppressed nation / Belgium [engraved]	Multicolored	ORN	Grimsland	B
8932	United States of America / honoring the oppressed nation / Denmark [engraved]	Blue, red	ORN	Grimsland	B
8933	United States of America / honoring the oppressed nation / France [engraved]	Unknown	ORN	Grimsland	B
8934	United States of America / honoring the oppressed nation / Greece [engraved]	Multicolored	ORN	Grimsland	B
8935	United States of America / honoring the oppressed nation / Norway [engraved]	Blue, red	ORN	Grimsland	B
8936	United States of America / honoring the oppressed nation / Poland [engraved]	Blue, red	ORN	Grimsland	B
8937	United States of America / The flag we love	Unknown	Flag	Grimsland	A
8938	United States of America / win the war	Purple	Eagle	Grimsland	A
8939	United States of America [in quotes] / First day cancellation etc. [thermographed]	Gold	MacFD	Hutnick	C
8940	United States Pacific Fleet / U.S. Naval Air Forces / Carrier etc. [thermographed]	Black	Navy	Crosby	B
8941	United States paratroops	Blue	Chute	Army	B
8942	United States Presidents / In God we trust etc.	Black	Unk	Allen	A
8943	United States saving bond	Black	Bonds	Burdick	A
8944	United States Savings Bond [photo of $100 bond]	Sepia tones	Bonds	Burdick	A
8945	United States Ship Brent / Uncle Sam / shall etc.	Blue	Navy	Harrington	A
8946	United States Ship Juneau / [etc.] / Sullivan brothers / who lost etc. [thermographed]	Blue	Navy	Crosby	B
8947	United we stand	Black/Purple	Flag	Davis, Ray	A
8948	United we stand	Black/Purple	Flag	McFarland	A
8949	United we stand ... victory for liberty! / V ···–	Blue, red	VforV	Boone	A
8950	United we stand / for victory	Blue, red	VforV	Krakora	A
8951	United we stand / for victory!	Unknown	Unk	Ander, EA	A
8952	United we stand [artist: Staehle]	Multicolored	FlMin	Fleetwood	C
8953	United we stand [colored envelopes]	Bk/Bu/Gn/Red	Globe	Huss	A
8954	United we stand [letters form an arc]	Blue, red	Eagle	Krakora	A
8955	United we stand [text red, under flag]	Blue, red	Flag	Unknown	A
8956	United we stand! [in quotes] / Conquer we must etc. [copyright position varies]	Multicolored	Armed	Minkus	A
8957	United we stand! or divided we fall!	Multicolored	UN	Schust	A
8958	United we will win / Liberty for all [handpainted]	Multicolored	Globe	Babcock	C
8959	United... / ...we fight [handpainted]	Multicolored	Armed	Adler	D
8960	United States of America / allied with / China / in the etc.	Blue	Ally	Grimsland	A
8961	Unity / here / V / victory / over / there! [no picture]	Unknown	VforV	Carpenter	A
8962	Unity / here / victory / over / there	Aqua, orange	Liber	Carpenter	A
8963	Unity / V / victory ["V" 64 mm high] [handpainted]	Multicolored	VforV	Adler	D
8964	Unity of all races and / creeds will bring about / world's peace and etc.	Blue, red	Wash	Symbols	B
8965	Unsung heroes / of the / service	Blue	Air	Carter	A
8966	Unwept, unhonored and unsung	Multicolored	Hitle	Peer	B
8967	Up and at 'em! / Thomas Dewey, New York's / Governor, really told the etc.	Multicolored	Home	Linto	B
8968	Up and atom! / Japan's last round	Black, red	Atom	Griffith	C
8969	Upton Close / fearless commentator / [etc.] / 2-20-'44———German planes bomb etc.	Multicolored	Event	Linto	B
8970	Upton Close / fearless commentator / puts all cards on the table / White etc.	Multicolored	Home	Linto	B
8971	US / on guard [soldier on globe] [5 stars or no stars at top]	Bu/Br/Gn/Red	Globe	Cozart	A
8972	US [on helmet]	Black	Unk	Harrington	A
8973	US [ribbon runs through upper part of "US"]	Multicolored	Home	Adler	D
8974	US Army / 1775 1776 / 1777 1781 / [etc.] / "The spirit of '76" [colored envelopes]	Blue, red	Hist	Alden	B
8975	US Army [soldier shooting at plane] [handpainted]	Multicolored	Army	Borkowski	D

NO.	CACHET TEXT	COLOR	TOPIC	PUBLISHER	$
8976	US Fleet / famous / 'round the world / Navy / Day	Blue/Red	Navy	Unknown	A
8977	US Navy / First day cancellation / U.S. / [etc.] / Newfoundland [5/21/41] [thermographed]	Gold/Silver	Navy	Hutnick	C
8978	US Navy / First day postal service / U.S. Naval-Air-Station / Antigua, B.W.I. [7/30/41] [thermographed]	Silver	Bases	Hutnick	C
8979	US Navy / type Z / for the duration	Blue	Liber	Muridge	A
8980	USA / On to Victory	Blue, red	EagSh	Kosko	A
8981	USA [7 stars inside "S"] [no picture] [handpainted]	Multicolored	Home	Adler	D
8982	USA [above eagle] [handpainted]	Multicolored	EagSh	Richards	C
8983	USA [below eagle, on shield]	Multicolored	EagSh	Adler	D
8984	USA [below eagle, shield, and ribbons] [handpainted]	Multicolored	EagSh	Adler	D
8985	USA [diagonal, letters 42mm high] [handpainted]	Multicolored	Home	Adler	D
8986	USA [on bell] [handpainted]	Multicolored	Bell	Klaas	D
8987	U-S-Army	Green	Army	Abel	A
8988	Use it up - wear it out / make it do - etc.	Unknown	Home	Bean	A
8989	Use the zone / number / [etc.] / and help speed / the mails	Blue	Home	Lowe	A
8990	Use V mail / ... V - / and conserve / shipping space [upper left]	Blue	VforV	Rowe	A
8991	Use V mail / V ···– / and conserve / shipping space	Blue	VforV	Rowe	A
8992	USMC [on blanket of marine daydreaming of red-haired woman] [ink] [handpainted]	Black, red	USMC	Graves	C
8993	USMC land in Sol Is [rubber stamp] [with cachet 2163] [postmarked Aug. 7, 1942]	Violet	Event	Unknown	B
8994	USN / United States Sea-bees / fighting construction battalion / We'll go etc.	Br/Gn/Red	Navy	Cozart	B
8995	USN / USN	Bu/Br/Gy/Pu/R	Navy	Weigand	A
8996	USNAS USN / Cape May, N.J. / Remember / Pearl Harbor	Blue	Eagle	Czubay	A
8997	USO / United Service Organizations	Black/Blue	Home	USO	B
8998	USS / Marblehead (CL-12) / the ship that was bombed / to hell / "We'll be" etc.	Red	Navy	Christens	A
8999	USS / Northampton / "The Fighting Nora" etc. [no picture] [blue envelope]	Unknown	Navy	McCluney	A
9000	USS / San Francisco / the / one ship etc. [thermographed]	Unknown	Navy	McCluney	B
9001	USS [vertical] / The seal of the State of Washington 1889	Blue	Ship	Quigley	A
9002	USS Augusta - Flagship / Western Task Force / June 6 1944 etc. [mimeographed & typed]	Black	DDay	Navy ship	E
9003	USS Boise / "Pick out the / biggest one / and fire" / Commodore Moran	Red	Navy	McCluney	A
9004	USS Boise / "Pick out the / biggest one / and fire" / Commodore Moran [no picture]	Red	Navy	McCluney	A
9005	USS Cecil (APA 96) [Tokyo Bay]	Magenta	VJDay	Navy ship	D
9006	USS Colorado - / in Japan [handpainted] [Tokyo Bay]	Black	VJDay	Navy ship	E
9007	USS Delta / Occupational force——Tokyo Bay [postmarked 8/31/45] [Tokyo Bay]	Multicolored	VJDay	Navy ship	F
9008	USS Helena sunk	Unknown	Navy	Linto	B
9009	USS Missouri / Chester W. Nimitz / [etc.] / New post office, Nimitz, etc.	Multicolored	NimFD	Fluegel	C
9010	USS Missouri / Com 3rd Fleet [Tokyo Bay]	Black	VJDay	Navy ship	H
9011	USS Oklahoma / sunk at / Pearl Harbor / Dec. 7, 1941 / Up again / Feb. 12, etc.	Blue	Pearl	Navy ship	B
9012	USS Quincy / Tokio / 9-2-45 [Tokyo Bay]	Gray	VJDay	Navy ship	D
9013	USS San Francisco / [etc.] / In memoriam / "Uncle Dan" / Still cancelling Japs	Blue	Japan	Christens	A
9014	USS Taussig (DD476) / off Tokyo / V-J Day [Tokyo Bay]	Black	VJDay	Navy ship	D
9015	USS Teton / Initial occupation / Tokyo [postmarked 9/1/45] [Tokyo Bay]	Black, purple	VJDay	Navy ship	E
9016	USS Teton / Sept 2 1945 / Japanese / surrender [Tokyo Bay]	Black	VJDay	Navy ship	E

Cover Values (from Table 6, p. 136)

Value	*Price Range*
A	$ 3 - 6
B	$ 7 - 15
C	$ 16 - 30
D	$ 31 - 60
E	$ 61 - 125
F	$ 126 - 250
G	$ 251 - 500
H	$ 501 - 1000
I	$ >1000
X	Unpriced: Suspicious or fraudulent cover

8430

"The Robot"

8504

8602

8608

8659

8670

8699

8722

8730

8735

8738

8759

8769

8770

8780

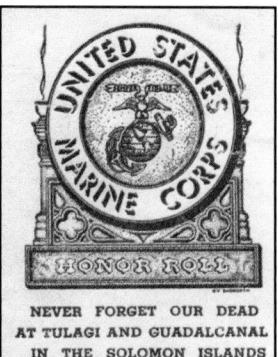

8824

8897

8919

8946

8952

8963

8964

8975

8978

8984

9009

9010

9011

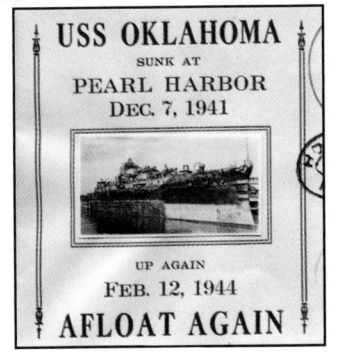

CACHET TEXT BEGINNING WITH "V"

NO.	CACHET TEXT	COLOR	TOPIC	PUBLISHER	$
9017	V [upper 2/3 of "V" starts at lower edge] [torch and plane] [handpainted]	Blue, red	VforV	Krakora	C
9018	V -- for / Victory [2 V's form part of screws closing on Hitler] [handpainted]	Blue	Hitle	Parker	B
9019	V ··· ·· - / Victory in 1944 ["···-" and "44" printed backwards]	Red	VforV	Buxton Mrs	A
9020	V ···· / "Tokio, here we come!"	Blue, red	VforV	Grandy	A
9021	V ···· / Extract from a service man's / letter etc.	Blue, red	VforV	Swartz	A
9022	V ···· / for / freedom / of speech / religion / from etc. [handpainted label]	Multicolored	Flag	LeGallez	C
9023	V ···· / for victory [handpainted]	Multicolored	VforV	Adler	D
9024	V ···· / for Victory [handpainted]	Multicolored	Hitle	Parker	B
9025	V ···· / God save America / Remember Holland's fate / V ···-	Violet	VforV	Unknown	A
9026	V ···· / ictory / in 1945	Blue	VforV	Harrington	A
9027	V ···· / ictory / Sap a Jap etc. [5 or 8 small flags]	Black	VforV	Harrington	A
9028	V ···· / Liberation of Nazie [sic] Europe.	Multicolored	VEDay	Baur	B
9029	V ···· / On land on sea / and in the air / May etc. [env. 6 3/4x3 3/4 in.]	Unknown	Unk	Lowell	A
9030	V ···· / The United Nations fight etc. [envelope 6 9/16x3 3/4 in.]	Multicolored	UN	Belles-let	D
9031	V ···· / V ···- / for / Victoire	Unknown	VforV	Shaffer,A	A
9032	V ···· / V for victory—— / V for valor / Back our valorous / boys with etc.	Blue, red	VforV	Price, R	A
9033	V ···- / Victory / and liberation / day / Peace / on etc. [artist: Staehle]	Multicolored	VEDay	Smartcraft	C
9034	V ···- / Victory / Help set Japan's Rising Sun etc. [env. 5 3/4x 3 3/4 in.]	Unknown	Unk	Umbarger	A
9035	V ···- / Victory / It can't happen here! etc.	Blue	VforV	Nixon	A
9036	V ···- / Victory / It can't happen here! etc.	Blue	VforV	Peters	A
9037	V ···- / Victory / It can't happen here! etc.	Blue	VforV	Buxton	A
9038	V ···- / Victory / It can't happen here! etc.	Blue	VforV	Robertson	A
9039	V ···- / Victory / means / security / for / democracy / ···-	Multicolored	VforV	Linto	B
9040	V ···· / Victory / Merry Xmas	Unknown	Holid	Kosko	B
9041	V ···· / Victory / Start a / victory / garden etc.	Bu,R/Gn, red	VforV	Lowell	A
9042	V ···· / Victory / They asked for it etc.	Blue	VforV	Buxton	A
9043	V ···· / Victory / They asked for it etc.	Blue	VforV	Robertson	A
9044	V ···· / Victory / Victory	Unknown	VforV	Kosko	A
9045	V ···· / Victory / We are in a / fight / to win! / We / can help by / buying U.S. etc.	Blue	VforV	Robertson	A
9046	V ···· / Victory / We are in a / fight / to win! / We / can help by etc.	Blue	VforV	Buxton	A
9047	V ···· / Victory / Yours and mine	Blue	VforV	Buxton	A
9048	V ···· / Victory! ["···-" across "V"]	Blue, red	VforV	Davis, Ral	A
9049	V ···· / Win the war / "On to victory"	Multicolored	EagSh	Staehle	B
9050	V ···· ["···-" printed diagonally across "V"] [envelope 5 5/8x3 11/16 in.]	Violet	VforV	Unknown	A
9051	V ···· ["V' 55 mm tall] ["···-" across "V"] [handpainted] [envelope 9 1/2x4 1/8 in.]	Black, red	VforV	Knoll	C
9052	V ···· ["V" comes between "..." and "-"] [handpainted]	Multicolored	VforV	Parker	B
9053	V ···· [31x15 mm] [no border, no picture]	Red	VforV	Unknown	A
9054	V ···· [above planes attacking two tanks]	Black	Air	Barwicki	B
9055	V ···· [eagle standing on rock, thin-line frame, 3 stars above frame]]	Blue, red	EagV	Bartz	A
9056	V ···· [envelope 7 1/2x4 in.]	Unknown	VforV	Ang	A
9057	V ···· [inside outline of shield] [handpainted] [postmarked 5/8/45]	Multicolored	VforV	Adler	E
9058	V ···· E Day / Victory in Europe / etc. [on "Let Freedom Ring" cachet]	Black + Multi	VEDay	Curtiss, H	C
9059	V ···· Victory / U.S. war bonds / mean / the American way etc. [colored envelopes]	Blue	VforV	Peters	A
9060	V / -- for victory [handpainted]	Multicolored	VforV	Adler	D
9061	V / - Dedicated to U.S. heroes on all fronts -	Blue, red	VforV	Neal+Harv	B
9062	V / -- for / Victory / ···- [reddish pink cross] [handpainted]	Multicolored	VforV	Adler	D
9063	V / -- for / Victory / ···- [yellow cross] [handpainted]	Multicolored	VforV	Adler	D
9064	V / "Remember / Peal Harbor"	Blue	UncV	Dietz	A
9065	V / "United we stand"	Blue, red	EagV	Grandy	A
9066	V / "V-E" Day / Germany surrenders / May 8, 1945 / Allied victory etc. [handpainted]	Multicolored	VEDay	Knapp	I
9067	V / "We've just begun / to fight" / ——John Paul Jones.	Multicolored	Navy	Unknown	A
9068	V / ···- / ···- / Victory [handpainted]	Multicolored	VforV	Adler	D
9069	V / ···- / 5th / war / loan [handpainted]	Multicolored	VforV	Unknown	B
9070	V / ···- / B 29's bomb / Japan / today, June 15	Unknown	Event	Boone	B
9071	V / ···- / British acdept [sic] the / surrender etc. [thermographed]	Unknown	Event	Boone	B
9072	V / ···- / Confederate Memorial Day etc.	Unknown	VforV	Boone	A

NO.	CACHET TEXT	COLOR	TOPIC	PUBLISHER	$
9073	V / ··· / for victory	Green/Red	VforV	Cozart	A
9074	V / ··· / for victory! / Buy etc. [line above "V"]	Unknown	Unk	Ander, EA	A
9075	V / ··· / for victory! / Buy etc. [no line above "V"]	Bk/Gn/Red	VforV	McFarland	A
9076	V / ··· / for-victory	Purple, red	Bonds	Kosko	A
9077	V / ··· / Give 'em both / barrels etc.	Blue, red	VJDay	Boone	B
9078	V / ··· / Japan / surrenders / to etc. [red shield]	Blue, red	Liber	Sanders	A
9079	V / ··· / Live with the / symbol / of liberty / in your heart	Blue, red	Liber	Sanders	B
9080	V / ··· / Live with the / symbol of / liberty / in your heart [thermographed]	Unknown	Unk	Boone	A
9081	V / ··· / Pistol packin' GI Joe / We'll push you etc.	Blue, red	Uncle	Boone	A
9082	V / ··· / Put your in America!	Blue, red	Air	Grandy	A
9083	V / ··· / Tokio, here we come!	Unknown	Army	Flesch	A
9084	V / ··· / U.S. Army / Follow me	Blue, red	UN	Bendix	A
9085	V / ··· / United Nations / V / ···	Red	VforV	Schaefer	A
9086	V / ··· / V / ··· / for / victoire zwyciestwo / sejr / [etc.] / victory	Bk/Bu/Gn/R	Uncle	Cozart	A
9087	V / ··· / V / ··· / My Uncle	Unknown	Unk	Ander, EA	A
9088	V / ··· / V / ··· / Slap the Jap with etc. [envelope 6 3/4x3 3/4 in.]	Blue	VforV	Unknown	B
9089	V / ··· / V / ··· / V / ··· / V [continues on back]	Blue, red	VforV	Ander, EA	A
9090	V / ··· / V / ··· / Zip your lip. Save a ship	Unknown	VforV	Ander, EA	A
9091	V / ··· / V / V / ··· / Day / date	Blue, red	VforV	Homestead	A
9092	V / ··· / victory	Multicolored	VforV	Linto	B
9093	V / ··· / Victory / means / security / for / democracy / ··· - ["V" 64 mm high]	Multicolored	VforV	Adler	D
9094	V / ··· / Victory ["··· -" and "Victory" across "V"] [handpainted]	Unknown	VforV	Card	A
9095	V / ··· / Victory [square with flags at corners]	Black	VforV	Davis, Ral	A
9096	V / ··· / Victory!	Unknown	Event	Boone	B
9097	V / ··· / Yanks / enter / Germany [thermographed]	Purple	UncV	Unknown	A
9098	V / ··· ["V" and "··· -" at open edge of circle] [Uncle Sam inside circle]	Blue, red	VforV	Roberts	A
9099	V / ··· ["V" 45 or 50 mm high]	Blue, red	VforV	Boone	A
9100	V / ··· ["V" made of blue stars and red stars, "··· -" and Minute Man blue]	Blue, red	VforV	Boone	A
9101	V / ··· ["V" made of blue stars, "··· -" and Minute Man red]]	Black	VforV	Unknown	A
9102	V / ··· [above see-hear-speak no evil monkeys]	Black	VforV	Unknown	A
9103	V / ··· [at bottom left] [V 14 mm tall]	Blue, red	Flag	Runge	A
9104	V / ··· [below flag, adjacent to "Spirit of '76"]	Unknown	VforV	Huss	A
9105	V / ··· [below plane and flag] [yellow envelope]	Blue, red	EagV	Risinger	A
9106	V / ··· [below three red stars and eagle on rock]	Blue, red	UncV	Risinger	A
9107	V / ··· - [blue or red "V" across red Uncle Sam]	Blue, red	VforV	Boone	A
9108	V / ··· [blue, 31x11 mm] [repeated red "··· -" and blue "··· -" on env. border]	Blue, red	EagV	Boone	A
9109	V / ··· [blue, 31x11 mm] [repeated red "··· -" and blue "··· -" on env. border] [eagle, flag]	Blue, red	VforV	Boone	A
9110	V / ··· [blue] [2 red bars across envelope]	Blue, red	VJDay	Field	B
9111	V / ··· [border of stars]	Brown	EagV	Harrington	A
9112	V / ··· [eagle inside "V" outline]	Multicolored	VforV	Price, R	B
9113	V / ··· [handpainted]	Red	VforV	Morse	A
9114	V / ··· [in single-line frame] ["V" 72 mm high]	Unknown	VforV	Clarke+W	A
9115	V / ··· [LL]	Multicolored	VforV	Shaffer	C
9116	V / ··· [on red and blue star] [handpainted]	Blue, red	VforV	Boone	A
9117	V / ··· [red, 31x11 mm] [red line and blue line form envelope border]	Blue, red	VforV	Linprint	A
9118	V / ··· [red, in blue frame of four lines]	Unknown	VforV	Dime	A
9119	V / ··· [repeated in vertical band] [violet envelope 6x3 ½ in.]	Unknown	VforV	Czubay	A
9120	V / ··· [UL]	Blue, red	VforV	Parker	B
9121	V / ··· [with 3 small airplanes] [handpainted]	Red	VforV	Boone	A
9122	V / ··· - [withing line frame] ["V" 51 mm tall]	Multicolored	EagV	Knapp	G
9123	V / ··· for victory [handpainted]	Unknown	VforV	Carpenter	A
9124	V / 1944 / for / victory	Unknown	Bonds	Baur	A
9125	V / 5th loan / Back the / invasion [brown envelope]	Unknown	Bonds	McCluney	A
9126	V / 5th war loan / ··· / Be glad you're alive etc.	Unknown	VforV	Grandy	A
9127	V / All out for victory!	Unknown	Unk	Boone	B
9128	V / Allied chiefs proclaim full / victory / as all etc.	Unknown	Event	Boone	B
9129	V / Americans / capture / Leipzig	Multicolored	VforV	Linto	B
9130	V / America's only object / in this Hitler-made war / is: to secure a etc.				

NO.	CACHET TEXT	COLOR	TOPIC	PUBLISHER	$
9131	V / Bulgaria / calls etc. ["V" height of envelope] [thermographed]	Red	Event	Boone	B
9132	V / Buy / war / bonds	Unknown	Bonds	Fort Morg	A
9133	V / Buy bonds / ···–	Unknown	Bonds	Boone	A
9134	V / Cavite / Naval Base etc. ["V" height of envelope] [thermographed]	Gn,R/Red	Event	Boone	B
9135	V / Day [+ soldier or sailor label] [crayon]	Blue, red	VEDay	Unknown	B
9136	V / Day / Date	Red, silver	VEDay	Unknown	B
9137	V / Day / Date 5-8-45 [2 smaller "V / ···–" flank first "V"]	Bu,R/R,Si/Re	VEDay	Ander, EA	B
9138	V / Day / ———Flash special——— / War ends in Pacific / Tokio falls, / Japan etc.	Red	VJDay	Abel	B
9139	V / Day / On to Tokyo!	Bk/Bu/Gn/P/	VEDay	Ander, CS	B
9140	V / Day / On to Tokyo!	Bk/Bu/Pu/Red	VEDay	Cliff	B
9141	V / Day / V-Day for Manila / MacArthur etc.	Black	Phili	Abel	B
9142	V / Day / Victory!	Red	VEDay	Czubay	C
9143	V / day / Victory! / ———Flash special——— / War ends in Pacific / Tokio etc.	Red	VJDay	Abel	B
9144	V / Day [in shield below eagle] [handpainted]	Multicolored	VJDay	Glase	C
9145	V / Day [Minute Man]	Unknown	Unk	Boone	B
9146	V / Day [on diagonal stripes in shield below eagle] [handpainted]	Multicolored	VJDay	Glase	C
9147	V / Day [on vertical stripes in shield below eagle] [handpainted]	Multicolored	VJDay	Glase	C
9148	V / Dedicated to U.S. heroes on all fronts	Blue, red	Symb+	Neal+Harv	B
9149	V / -E / Day / May 8, 1945	Blue, red	VEDay	Fidelity	B
9149A	V / E / Day / Unconditional Surrender [Eisenhower pictured] [handpainted label]	Multicolored	VEDay	LeGallez	E
9150	V / E / Germany surrenders! ["V" 58 mm high] [handpainted]	Black	VEDay	Unknown	C
9151	V / E / Germany surrenders! [handpainted]	Multicolored	VEDay	Klondike	D
9152	V / Fight! / for victory [handpainted]	Multicolored	Armed	Knapp	G
9153	V / Finland / quits war with / Russia etc. ["V" height of envelope] [thermographed]	Red	Event	Boone	B
9154	V / Finland breaks etc. ["V" height of envelope] [thermographed]	Bu,R/Red	Event	Boone	B
9155	V / First victory then peace forever [thermographed]	Unknown	Unk	Huss	A
9156	V / for / victory	Black	VforV	Kosko	A
9157	V / for / victory / ···–	Unknown	VforV	Dime	A
9158	V / for / Victory / ···– [on unprocessed V-Mail] [fancy flag cancel]	Black	VforV	Payne	C
9159	V / for / victory / in / 1944 / Work / and etc.	Unknown	VforV	Nelson, KE	A
9160	V / for / victory! ["V" height of envelope]	Blue, red	VEDay	Runge	B
9161	V / for victory / ···–	Blue, red	VforV	Unknown	A
9162	V / for victory / Buy United etc.	Unknown	Bonds	Boone	A
9163	V / for victory / is just half of / W etc.	Unknown	VforV	Sedgwick	A
9164	V / for victory [engraved]	Blue	VforV	Unknown	A
9165	V / for victory [envelope 9 1/2x4 1/8 in.]	Unknown	VforV	Klaus	B
9166	V / for victory [handpainted]	Multicolored	ShieV	Adler	D
9167	V / for victory [shield in V]	Unknown	ShieV	Dime	A
9168	V / for victory [thermographed]	Unknown	VforV	Huss	A
9169	V / for victory [with planes, ships, tanks] [cachet 38x34 mm] [bottom left]	Blue, red	VforV	Unknown	A
9170	V / for victory! / Slap the Jap with a war stamp!	Blue, red	FlBel	Ander, EA	A
9171	V / for Victory! [cross above "V"] [handpainted]	Blue	VforV	Parker	B
9172	V / Gen. MacArthur / [etc.] / J Day	Black	VJDay	Knoll	B
9173	V / God save America / Remember Holland's fate / ...V_ [rubber stamps]	Purple	ORN	Unknown	B
9174	V / I / c / t / o / r / y [in shape of "V"]	Black	VforV	Littlefiel	A
9175	V / I have / returned etc. ["V" height of envelope] [thermographed]	Red	Event	Boone	B
9176	V / ictory / ···–	Unknown	VforV	Boone	A
9177	V / ictory / It won't be / long now! [red or blue "V"]	Blue, red	VforV	Boone	A
9178	V / ictory [red "V", blue "ictory"] [25 mm from lower edge]	Blue, red	VforV	Boone	A
9179	V / ictory [red "V", blue "ictory"] [at lower edge]	Blue, red	VforV	Boone	A
9180	V / ictory [red"V", red "ictory"] [25 mm from lower edge]	Red	VforV	Boone	A
9181	V / ictory! [red "Victory" surrounded by 11 blue stars]	Blue, red	VforV	Puls	A
9182	V / ictory. / Hats of to our armed forces. [typed text after "V"] [handpainted]	Black, red	VEDay	Sharon	C
9183	V / It's over / over / there / J	Aquamarine	VJDay	Unknown	B
9184	V / J / Day [in shield below eagle] [handpainted]	Multicolored	VJDay	Glase	C
9185	V / J / Day [on vertical stripes in shield below eagle] [handpainted]	Multicolored	VJDay	Glase	C
9185A	V / J / Surrenders to Allies [inside "J"] [handpainted label]	Multicolored	VJDay	LeGallez	E
9186	V / Keep 'em flying / Keep on etc.	Unknown	UncV	Risinger	A

NO.	CACHET TEXT	COLOR	TOPIC	PUBLISHER	$
9187	V / Keep 'em flying / Remember Pearl Harbor / Keep 'em rolling	Blue	UncV	Risinger	A
9188	V / La Roche / falls to / U.S. ["V" height of envelope] [thermographed]	Blue	Event	Boone	B
9189	V / Let's produce to win	Unknown	Unk	Threl+Thar	A
9190	V / MacArthur	Black	Mac	Dewitz	B
9191	V / Make 1943 the victory etc. [blue envelope 8 13/16x3 7/8 in.]	Unknown	VforV	McClung	B
9192	V / May 8th / 1945 / -E Day / Oslo / the capital of / Norway was liberated etc.	Multicolored	VEDay	Fluegel	C
9193	V / Mussolini resigns etc. ["V" height of envelope] [thermographed]	Red	Event	Boone	B
9194	V / My uncle	Blue, green	UncV	Cozart	A
9195	V / Old Glory flies / over Kwajalein / as Yanks take / over [no picture]	Blue, red	Event	Boone	B
9196	V / On to victory	Blue/Red	VforV	Masten	A
9197	V / Philippine Timetable / Oct. 20--Americans land on Leyte etc. ["V" height of env.]	Blue, red	Event	Boone	B
9198	V / Reds / capture / Kielce ["V" height of envelope] [thermographed]	Blue, red	Event	Boone	B
9199	V / Reds / enter / Germany ["V" height of envelope] [thermographed]	Unknown	Event	Boone	B
9200	V / Reds / smash etc. ["V" height of envelope] [thermographed]	Red	Event	Boone	B
9201	V / Remember / Pearl / Harbor	Unknown	VforV	Elgin Café	A
9202	V / Return in five etc. [45 mm long]	Blue, red	VforV	Dime	A
9203	V / Return in five etc. [46 mm long]	Blue, red	VforV	Dime	A
9204	V / Return in five etc. [54 mm long]	Blue, red	VforV	Dime	A
9205	V / Russians / enter / Germany ["v" height of envelope] [thermographed]	Blue, red	Event	Boone	B
9206	V / Russians capture / Warsaw ["V" height of envelope] [thermographed]	Blue, red	Event	Boone	C
9207	V / Save for / victory	Black	Home	Lohr	A
9208	V / Speed up for victory / keep on buying / bonds for victory	Blue, red	EagFl	Bartz	A
9209	V / The / home / front / United for / victory	Blue, red	Home	Cachet Cra	A
9210	V / The life of the land / is perpetuated etc.	Unknown	Hawai	Sayama	B
9211	V / The Spirit of '76	Unknown	Hist	Runge	A
9212	V / The Spirit of '76 / ···–	Unknown	Hist	Runge	B
9213	V / There's no time / to loose! [sic] / Only time to win!	Multicolored	VforV	Griffith	A
9214	V / They asked for / and they got it	Unknown	Unk	Ang	A
9215	V / They who deny freedom to / others etc.	Unknown	Unk	Threl+Thar	B
9216	V / To Adolf / ···– / You know you're doomed	Black, blue	Hitle	Baur	A
9217	V / To Adolf / ···– / You know you're doomed	Black, red	Hitle	Roberts	A
9218	V / to Adolf: / ···– / You know you're doomed	Black, red	VforV	Unknown	A
9219	V / Tokyo blasted / by heaviest etc. ["V" height of envelope]	Blue, red	Event	Boone	B
9220	V / Triumvirate / for victory [all caps]	Blue	Heads	Yontz	B
9221	V / Triumvirate for victory [all caps]	Black	Heads	Yontz	B
9222	V / Triumvirate for victory [caps and lower case]	Black	Heads	Yontz	B
9223	V / U.S. invades Rendova Island	Unknown	Event	Boone	B
9224	V / U.S. pilots / down 204 / Jap planes ["V" height of envelope]	Blue, red	Event	Boone	B
9225	V / United we stand - victory etc.	Unknown	Unk	Boone	A
9226	V / V / ···– / Victory / insures / freedom [handpainted]	Multicolored	VforV	Adler	D
9227	V / V / V [eagle and fanciful animals]	Multicolored	VforV	Stoll	B
9228	V / V [above U.S. arms] [envelope 9 1/2x4 1/8 in.]	Silver	VforV	Runge	B
9229	V / V is for victory, / to win we must work, / our role in the triumph etc.	Blue, red	VforV	Boone	A
9230	V / V is for victory, to win we must work, / our etc. [first "V" thermographed]	Blue, red	VforV	Boone	B
9231	V / V···– / V ···– / Day / Date [no stars above text]	Red	VforV	Unknown	B
9232	V / V···– / V ···– / Day / Date [with 4 stars above text]	Red	VforV	Unknown	B
9233	V / Victory	Blue	EagSh	Levering	A
9234	V / Victory / ···– ···– [thermographed]	Red	VforV	Cleveland	A
9235	V / Victory / ···– [in circle]	Unknown	VforV	Davis, Ral	A
9236	V / Victory / First / then a etc. [thermographed]	Unknown	Unk	Huss	A
9237	V / Victory / is / ours / "War is hell". / Sherman / Let us make sure etc.	Blue, red	VEDay	Threl+Thar	B
9238	V / Victory / The President announces etc. [thermograpged]	Unknown	Unk	Unknown	A
9239	V / Victory / V-E Day ["V" 68 mm high]	Multicolored	VEDay	Boone	B
9240	V / Victory ["V" 68 mm high]	Red	VEDay	Boone	B
9241	V / Victory ["V" 74 mm high, in star] [handpainted]	Black, red	VEDay	Sharon	C
9242	V / Victory [cachet 28x30 mm] [engraved]	Blue, red	Air	Unknown	B
9243	V / Victory [flags outside "V"] [thermographed]	Unknown	FlagV	Huss	A
9244	V / Victory [heads of FDR, Churchill, "Monty," "Ike," Stalin, DeGaulle]	Blue	Ally	Knoll	B

NO.	CACHET TEXT	COLOR	TOPIC	PUBLISHER	$
9245	V / Victory [red "V" 68 mm high] [silver stars along borders]	Red, silver	VforV	Boone	A
9246	V / Victory [thermographed]	Unknown	Unk	Huss	A
9247	V / Victory [UL, "V" made of 2 stars, 6 stripes] [all caps]	Blue	VforV	Dime	A
9248	V / Victory [UL, "V" made of 2 stars, 6 stripes] [caps and lower case]	Blue	VforV	Dime	A
9249	V / Victory and peace [thermographed]	Multicolored	VJDay	Smartcraft	C
9250	V / Victory for liberty [under Statue of Liberty] [thermographed]	Unknown	Liber	Huss	A
9251	V / Victory with our navy	Blue	Navy	Neal	A
9252	V / Von Mackensen / captured by / Americans ["V" height of envelope] [thermographed]	Blue	Event	Boone	B
9253	V / voor victorie / Invaded / but not / conquered [handpainted label 61x45 mm]	Multicolored	ORN	LeGallez	C
9254	V / voor victorie / Invaded / but not / conquered [handpainted label 69x53 mm]	Multicolored	ORN	LeGallez	C
9255	V / War won't wait / Uncle Sam needs etc. [envelope 9 1/2x4 1/8 in.]	Unknown	VforV	Downs	B
9256	V / We'll win, / America... / Let's go!	Blue, red	VforV	Sosland	A
9257	V / Wings / for / victory [handpainted]	Multicolored	Air	Knapp	G
9258	V / Wings / to / win! / V-E Day May 8, 1945 [artist: Knapp]	Vi/R,Vi/Vi,Y	VEDay	Richardson	C
9259	V / Wings / to / win! / V-E Day May 8, 1945 [artist: Knapp]	Bu,V/Gn,V	VEDay	Richardson	C
9260	V / Yanks / assault / Truk / War Dept. announces etc. ["V" height of envelope]	Red	Event	Boone	B
9261	V / Yanks / capture etc. ["V" height of envelope] [thermographed]	Red	Event	Boone	B
9262	V / Yanks / head for / Manila	Blue, red	Event	Boone	B
9263	V / Yanks enter etc. ["V" height of envelope] [thermographed]	Red	Event	Boone	B
9264	V / Yours and mine [on back]	Black	VforV	Mueller, B	A
9265	V /···– / America's position is / now definite! / We must defeat / Hitler etc.	Multicolored	Hitle	Linto	B
9266	V ["V" 75 mm tall] [soldier saluting] [handpainted]	Multicolored	Army	Adler	D
9267	V ["V" 92 mm high]	Unknown	VforV	Runge	A
9268	V [2 stars before, 2 after "V"] [blue eagle and ribbon across red "V"] [UL]	Blue, red	EagV	Unknown	A
9269	V [4 red stars before and after flying blue eagle, red "V" below eagle]	Blue, red	EagV	Muzzy	B
9270	V [4 stars at top of "V", dove with olive branch across "V"]	Brown/Green	VJDay	Jarrett	B
9271	V [5 stars before, 5 after 5 mm high "V"] [below plane dropping paratroopers]	Blue, red	Chute	Unknown	A
9272	V [63 mm high] / France / Freedom / of Nazie [sic] / rule / Jugoslavia etc.	Blue, red	VEDay	Baur	B
9273	V [75 mm tall] [left arm of "V": white stars; right arm: blue field, red & white stripes] [hp]	Multicolored	Air	Adler	C
9274	V [across Uncle Sam, who is pointing at viewer] [thermographed]	Red	UncV	Grover	A
9275	V [across Uncle Sam]	Red	UncV	Boone	A
9276	V [across Uncle Sam]	Blue	UncV	Risinger	A
9277	V [behind 2 servicemen]	Blue	VforV	Richardson	A
9278	V [below cross] [handpainted]	Multicolored	Relig	Shaffer	C
9279	V [below eagle and stars]	Blue, red	EagV	Nichols	B
9280	V [below saluting soldier] [handpainted]	Multicolored	Army	Adler	D
9281	V [blue "V" below red eagle] [UL]	Blue, red	EagV	Unknown	A
9282	V [blue eagle and ribbon across red "V"] [UL]	Blue, red	EagV	Unknown	A
9283	V [blue, across Uncle Sam] / V [red, centered between stars, below larger "V"]	Blue, red	UncV	Risinger	A
9284	V [bust of Lincoln inside "V"]	Black	Linc	Threl+Thar	A
9285	V [cannon and ship] [colored envelopes]	Black	VforV	Soc Philat	A
9286	V [centered between 10 blue stars, under airplane]	Blue, red	Air	Risinger	A
9287	V [centered between 10 blue stars, under jeep]	Blue, red	Army	Risinger	A
9288	V [centered between 10 blue stars, under landing craft]	Blue, red	Navy	Risinger	A
9289	V [centered between 10 blue stars, under Minute Man]	Blue, red	Minut	Risinger	A
9290	V [centered between 10 blue stars, under plane and parachute]	Blue, red	Chute	Risinger	A
9291	V [centered between 10 blue stars, under soldiers and machine gun]	Blue, red	Army	Risinger	A
9292	V [centered between 10 blue stars, under speedboat]	Blue, red	Navy	Risinger	A
9293	V [centered between 10 blue stars, under tank]	Blue, red	Ordna	Risinger	A
9294	V [centered between 10 blue stars, under truck]	Blue, red	Army	Risinger	A
9295	V [centered between 10 red stars, under antiaircraft gun]	Blue, red	Army	Risinger	A
9296	V [centered between 10 red stars, under balloon]	Blue, red	Air	Risinger	A
9297	V [centered between 10 red stars, under bomb]	Blue, red	Air	Risinger	A
9298	V [centered between 10 red stars, under civilian and soldier]	Blue, red	Home	Risinger	A
9299	V [centered between 10 red stars, under eagle and flag]	Blue, red	EagFl	Risinger	A
9300	V [centered between 10 red stars, under listening device]	Blue, red	Army	Risinger	A
9301	V [centered between 10 red stars, under searchlight]	Blue, red	Army	Risinger	A
9302	V [centered between 10 red stars, under soldier on motorcycle]	Blue, red	Army	Risinger	A

NO.	CACHET TEXT	COLOR	TOPIC	PUBLISHER	$
9303	V [eagle across "V", flying left]	Blue	EagV	Lohr	A
9304	V [eagle across "V", flying right]	Bu/Gn/Red	EagV	Weston	A
9305	V [eagle between arms of "V"; row of stars above & below "V"]	Unknown	EagV	Risinger	A
9306	V [eagle in front of outlined "V"] [upper left] [colored envelopes]	Red	EagV	Payne, ER	A
9307	V [eagle inside "V" outline]	Blue	EagV	Kosko	A
9308	V [eagle inside "V" outline]	Blue	EagV	Harri	A
9309	V [eagle inside "V" outline]	Blue	EagV	Dusold	A
9310	V [eagle inside "V" outline]	Blue	EagV	Harmer	A
9311	V [eagle inside "V" outline]	Bk/Bu/Pi/Red	EagV	Harrington	A
9312	V [eagle with lowered wings, standing on "V"] [handpainted]	Multicolored	EagV	Myers	C
9313	V [eagle with wings superimposed on "V"] [handpainted]	Multicolored	EagV	Myers	B
9314	V [head of Lincoln] [envelope 6 1/2x3 5/8, 7 1/2x4 in.]	Black/Purple	Linc	Threl+Thar	A
9315	V [height of envelope]	Black	VforV	Unknown	A
9316	V [height of envelope] [center of envelope] [handpainted] [torn envelope face]	Multicolored	VforV	Cowdery	D
9317	V [held by Uncle Sam]	Unknown	UncV	Hoerth	A
9318	V [in quotes] for / Victory Put the / screws /on him [handpainted]	Blue	Hitle	Parker	B
9319	V [in quotes] for victory	Unknown	VforV	Advertiser	B
9320	V [in quotes] for victory [5 symbols in V formation extending above and below text]	Blue, red	Flag+	Unknown	A
9321	V [massed flags]	Blue	VforV	Boone	A
9322	V [Minute Man] [envelope 8 13/16x3 7/8 in.]	Unknown	Minut	Unknown	B
9323	V [red "V" height of envelope] [blue & red arrow contains "Via Air Mail" arrow sticker]	Blue, red	VforV	Boone	A
9324	V [red "V" UL, small blue eagle with snake in claws, no stars]	Blue, red	EagV	Dime	A
9325	V [red "V" UL, small blue eagle with snake in claws, red & blue stars at sides]	Blue, red	EagV	Dime	A
9326	V [red stars and blue stars in "V", 82 mm high]	Blue, red	VforV	Boone	A
9327	V [red, across blue Uncle Sam]	Blue, red	UncV	Roberts	A
9328	V [ribbon across "V"] [brown envelope 7 1/2x4 in.][env. 5 3/4x3 3/4 in.]	Unknown	VforV	Dime	A
9329	V [ribbon through "V"] [UL] [colored envelopes 5 9/16x3 13/16 in.]	Blue, red	VforV	Unknown	A
9330	V [Santa Claus in helmet across "V" made of holly] [handpainted]	Multicolored	Holid	Knoll	C
9331	V [Santa Claus in helmet across red "V" with holly] [handpainted]	Multicolored	Holid	Knoll	C
9332	V [stars in "V"] [eagle and shield] [thermographed]	Blue	EagSh	Grover	A
9333	V [UL]	Unknown	VforV	Salem Vic	A
9334	V [Uncle Sam pointing finger] [thermographed]	Red	Uncle	Grover	A
9335	V [Uncle Sam superimposed on "V"]	Multicolored	UncV	Unknown	B
9336	V [Uncle Sam]	Brown	UncV	Shenton	A
9337	V [white stars, blue stripes under red eagle]	Blue, red	VforV	Dime	A
9338	V [yellow "V" behind blue and red star-spangled hat] [handainted]	Multicolored	VforV	Klaas	C
9339	V Day [6 war leaders: FDR, Churchill, " Monty," " Ike," Stalin, De Gaulle]	Black, red	VJDay	Knoll	B
9340	V E Day / Gen. Dwight D. Eisenhower / Supreme Allied commander	Brown	VEDay	Czubay	C
9341	V for ···/ Victory! [5 planes] [handpainted]	Multicolored	VforV	Parker	C
9342	V for sejer / For / freedom / and peace [handpainted label]	Multicolored	ORN	LeGallez	C
9343	V for victory	Unknown	VforV	Ander, EA	A
9344	V for victory ["V" 87 mm high] [handpainted]	Multicolored	EagV	Knapp	G
9345	V for victory. / ···– / Thumbs / up! [envelope 9 1/2x4 1/8 in.]	Multicolored	VforV	Fleetwood	C
9346	V gates - hell - / Just make it V. [handpainted]	Multicolored	Uncle	Steinhardt	C
9347	V J Day / Buy / war / bonds	Multicolored	VJDay	Baur	B
9348	V pour la victoire / Occupied / but not / conquered [handpainted label]	Multicolored	ORN	LeGallez	C
9349	V Znamie Turjciestua / Occupied / but not / conquered [handpainted label]	Multicolored	ORN	LeGallez	C
9350	V··· – [two warships, two planes] [handpainted]	Blue	Navy	Klondike	D
9351	V.-Adm. / Daniel E. / Barbey	Unknown	Admir	Linto	B
9352	V.-Adm. / Daniel E. / Barbey / 1-26-'45——Yankees route / Nazis on Moder river	Unknown	Event	Linto	B
9353	V.-Adm. / J.H. / Towers	Black, sepia	Admir	Linto	B
9354	V.-Adm. / J.H. / Towers / 6-21-'45——Gen. Stillwell / will command U.S. 10th	Black, sepia	Event	Linto	B
9355	V.-Adm. / Marc / Mitscher	Unknown	Admir	Linto	B
9356	V.-Adm. / Marc / Mitscher / 11-9-'44——G. Patton forges / pincers around Metz	Unknown	Event	Linto	B
9357	V.-Adm. / T.C. / Kinkaid	Sepia, silver	Admir	Linto	B
9358	V.-Adm. / T.C. / Kinkaid / 12-8-'44——Yanks win back / Pideura, Italy	Sepia, silver	Event	Linto	B
9359	V.-Adm. Sir / Henry H.B. / Rawlings / British / Pacific / Fleet	Multicolored	Admir	Linto	B
9360	V.E. Day. / [etc.] / May 8, 1945 [handpainted on printed cachet]	Black, red	VEDay	Shaw, TC	B

NO.	CACHET TEXT	COLOR	TOPIC	PUBLISHER	$
9361	V.G. Masaryk [colored envelopes]	Black	Ally	Huss	A
9362	V.J. / Day / Japan signs surrender / terms this day, / marking etc. [no picture]	Red	VJDay	Unknown	B
9363	V.J. / Day / Japan signs surrender / terms this day, / marking the end of etc.	Red	VJDay	Unknown	B
9364	V.J. Day / Sunday morning, September 2, 1945 / On board the etc. [gray envelope]	Black	VJDay	Harmer	B
9365	V.V / Win the war / Win the war	Unknown	Unk	McCluney	A
9366	V.Victory	Unknown	Unk	Levering	A
9367	VAdm Daniel E. Barbey	Unknown	Admir	Linto	B
9368	VAdm Daniel E. Barbey / 1-26-'45——Yankees route [sic] / Nazis etc.	Unknown	Event	Linto	B
9369	VAdm H.L. Vickery	Unknown	Admir	Linto	B
9370	VAdm J.H. Ingram	Unknown	Admir	Linto	B
9371	VAdm J.H. Ingram / 12-13-'44——B-29s put Nagoya etc.	Unknown	Event	Linto	B
9372	VAdm Jesse B. Oldendorf	Unknown	Admir	Linto	B
9373	VAdm Marc Mitscher	Unknown	Admir	Linto	B
9374	VAdm Sir Henry H.B. Rawlins etc.	Unknown	Admir	Linto	B
9375	V-Adm T.C. Kinkaid	Unknown	Admir	Linto	B
9376	V-Adm T.C. Kinkaid / 12-8-'44——Yanks win back etc.	Unknown	Event	Linto	B
9377	Valentine / Day / Feb. / 14 [yellow envelope]	Brown, silver	Holid	Linto	B
9378	Vas ist los? [in quotes]	Black	Hitle	Lawrence	A
9379	V-Day / Japan surrenders	Unknown	VJDay	Price, R	B
9380	V-Day in Europe / Battle for air supremacy / Franklin / Delano / Roosevelt etc.	Purple/Red	VEDay	Coll Surp	C
9381	V-Day in Europe / Guerrilla cooperation / [etc.] / Gen. / Charles / De Gaulle etc.	Purple/Red	VEDay	Coll Surp	C
9382	V-Day in Europe / Immediately after the Japanese perfidy of etc. [no picture]	Purple/Red	VEDay	Coll Surp	C
9383	V-Day in Europe / Marshal / Joseph Stalin, [etc.] / Battle of / Stalingrad	Purple/Red	VEDay	Coll Surp	C
9384	V-Day in Europe / Winston / Churchill——Prime / [etc.] [env. 9 1/2x4 1/8 in.]	Purple	VEDay	Coll Surp	C
9385	V-Day in Europe / Winston / Churchill——Prime / [etc.] / The / desert etc.	Purple/Red	VEDay	Coll Surp	C
9387	V-E / Day	Gold, purple	VEDay	Unknown	B
9388	V-E / Day / May 8, 1945	Unknown	VEDay	Detroit Ph	C
9389	VE / Day / May 8, 1945 ["V" 47 mm high] [handpainted]	Multicolored	VEDay	Unknown	C
9390	VE / Day / May 8th	Blue	VEDay	Unknown	B
9391	VE / Day / United Nations / conference / international organization etc.	Orange	VEDay	Unknown	B
9392	V-E / Day / Victory in Europe / Germany surrenders / May 8, 1945	Multicolored	VEDay	Teixeira	E
9393	V-E / Day [below alighting eagle] [envelope 7 1/2x3 15/16 in.]	Purple	VEDay	Detroit Ed	C
9394	VE / -Day- [blue "VE" 73 mm high] [handpainted]	Blue, red	VEDay	Davis, D	B
9395	VE / V-E-Day / Victory in Europe / May 8, 1945 ["VE" across map of Europe]	Violet	VEDay	Unknown	B
9396	V-E [in quotes] Day / Allied victory in Europe / V / May 8, 1945 [words in ribbons] [VforV]	Multicolored	VEDay	Knapp	I
9397	V-E [in quotes] Day / Allied victory in Europe / May 8, 1945 [eagle, boot, swastika, flags] [VforV]	Multicolored	VEDay	Knapp	I
9398	VE Day / Charles de Gaulle	Multicolored	VEDay	Runge	B
9399	VE Day / Churchill	Multicolored	VEDay	Runge	B
9400	VE Day / Field Marshall Montgomery	Multicolored	VEDay	Runge	B
9401	VE Day / Gen. Dwight D. etc. [thermographed]	Unknown	VEDay	Czubay	C
9402	VE Day / Gen. Eisenhower	Multicolored	VEDay	Runge	B
9403	VE Day / Gen. Marshall	Multicolored	VEDay	Runge	B
9404	V-E Day / Let us redouble our efforts / and speed final victory.	Blue, red	VEDay	Nat Soc St	B
9405	V-E Day / May 8th 1945. / Prague / the capital / of Czechoslovakia / was etc.	Multicolored	VEDay	Fluegel	C
9406	VE Day / on the .... / Legurian Sea [thermographed]	Black	VEDay	Navy ship	C
9407	VE day / Roosevelt	Multicolored	VEDay	Runge	B
9408	VE Day / Stalin	Multicolored	VEDay	Runge	B
9409	V-E Day / United Nations News / Germany / surrenders etc. [artist: Knapp]	Blue, red	VEDay	Fleetwood	C
9410	V-E Day / Victory / Germany surren- / ders to the Allies [border of stars]	Multicolored	VEDay	Boone	B
9411	V-E Day / Victory / Germany surren- / ders to the Allies [no border of stars]	Multicolored	VEDay	Boone	B
9412	V-E Day / Victory / War / ends / in / Europe	Multicolored	VEDay	Boone	B
9413	V-E Day / Victory in Europe [envelope 7 1/2x4 in.]	Unknown	VEDay	Nat Motor	B
9414	V-E Day ["Day" vertical] / Proclamation by / President Harry etc.	Blue, red	VEDay	Unknown	C
9415	V-E Day [above globe of world] [thermographed]	Gray/R,Yello	VEDay	Czubay	C
9416	V-E Day [on "Capt. Arthur W. Wermuth" cachet] [colored envelopes]	Black	VEDay	Huss	B
9417	V-E Day cover [in quotes] [on "General Eisenhower" cachet] [colored envelopes]	Blue	VEDay	Huss	B
9418	VE-Day / May 8, 1945 / Feather your etc. [yellow envelope]	Unknown	VEDay	Huss	B
9419	VE-Day / May 8, 1945 / Feather your nest with / war bonds [yellow envelope]	Blue, red	VEDay	Dailey	B

NO.	CACHET TEXT	COLOR	TOPIC	PUBLISHER	$
9420	VE-Day / Victory in Europe / First Day Cover / Via etc. [embossed] [env. 7 1/2x4 in.]	Black	VEDay	Nat Motor	D
9421	V-E-Day [rubber stamp above other cachets]	Purple	VEDay	Unknown	B
9422	Ventilation / for / victory [on back] [envelope 9 1/2x4 1/8 in.]	Unknown	Home	ILG Electr	B
9423	Very simple, Tojo	Black	Japan	Smith, DH	A
9424	V——for / victory / ⋯ [handpainted]	Multicolored	Relig	Adler	D
9425	Via - air mail [handpainted]	Multicolored	Pelic	Parker	B
9426	Via B 29s / From: all of us / made etc. [thermographed]	Unknown	Unk	Sadworth	A
9427	Via Sicily / to Italy / and - / "Italy's / surrender" [Gen. Bernard Montgomery]	Multicolored	Gener	Staehle	C
9428	Via Sicily / to Italy / and - / "Italy's / surrender" [Gen. Dwight Eisenhower]	Multicolored	Ike	Staehle	C
9429	Via Sicily / to Italy / and - / "Italy's / surrender" [Gen. George Patton]	Multicolored	Patt	Staehle	C
9430	Via Sicily / to Italy / and - / "Italy's / surrender" [Gen. Mark Clark]	Multicolored	Gener	Staehle	C
9431	Vice Adm. D.W. Bagley	Sepia, silver	Admir	Linto	B
9432	Vice Adm. D.W. Bagley / 12-12-'44——First Army / near Duren	Sepia, silver	Event	Linto	B
9433	Vice Adm. Marc A. Mitscher / Task Force 58 [handpainted]	Multicolored	Admir	Knoll	C
9434	Vice Adm. T.C. Kinkaid	Unknown	Admir	Linto	B
9435	Vice Adml. John S. McCain [handpainted]	Multicolored	Admir	Knoll	D
9436	Vice-Adm. / Jesse B. Oldendorf	Gold, purple	Admir	Linto	B
9437	Vice-Adm. / Jesse B. Oldendorf / 1-23-'45——Halsey's Jan., 1945, record 345 etc.	Multicolored	Event	Linto	B
9438	Vice-Adm. J.H. Ingram	Sepia, silver	Admir	Linto	B
9439	Vice-Adm. J.H. Ingram / 12-13-'44——B-29s put Nagoya, / Honshu Is., in flames	Multicolored	Admir	Linto	B
9440	Vichy relations severed	Unknown	Event	Linto	B
9441	Victoria [large V] [⋯- above "ictoria"] [Puerto Rican flag]	Blue, red	VforV	Unknown	B
9442	Victories that are / easy are cheap - / those only are worth / having etc.	Multicolored	Battl	Griffith	B
9443	Victorious American lead flew / in the Argonne Forest in 1918 / Victorious etc.	Blue, red	Flag	Hill	A
9444	Victory	Red	Unk	Harriman	A
9445	Victory	Brown	Unk	Lawrence	A
9446	Victory - buy U.S. defense bonds - stamps [no picture]	Unknown	Bonds	Efengee	A
9447	Victory - then peace / A decisive victory / in this war means etc.	Green, red	Eagle	Neal	A
9448	Victory ⋯-	Unknown	Unk	Muzzy	B
9449	Victory ⋯- ["..." made of 3 stars] [below eagle]	Blue	Eagle	Nichols	B
9450	Victory ⋯- [below eagle, shield, flag, & globe] [colored envelopes]	Blue, red	Eag+	Poppenger	A
9451	Victory / - if / we work and fight / defeat / - if / we shirk and strike [no picture]	Red	Home	Schaefer	A
9452	Victory / ⋯- / V / E ["Victory" on ribbon across "V"] [handpainted]	Blue, red	VEDay	Unknown	C
9453	Victory / ⋯- / Victory / ⋯-	Blue, red	VforV	Roberts	A
9454	Victory / ⋯- [handpainted, ink]	Blue	Torch	Unknown	B
9455	Victory / 1944 [below 3 stars] [handpainted]	Multicolored	Home	Shaffer, A	C
9456	Victory / 1944 [below 5 stars] [handpainted]	Blue, red	Home	Shaffer, A	C
9457	Victory / 75th anniversary / [etc.] / railroad	Blue	Home	Neal	A
9458	Victory / And over the ghostly etc. [thermographed] [green envelope]	Silver	VJDay	Neal	B
9458A	Victory / Aug. 14, 1945 - Surrender Day / Japan agrees to surrender [handpainted].	Multicolored	VJDay	Knapp	I
9459	Victory / British seize Ham / burg etc.	Unknown	Event	Boone	B
9460	Victory / Day / Peace on earth——good will toward men	Multicolored	VEDay	Fluegel	C
9461	Victory / Day / The liberation / of Europe	Black	VEDay	Wash Star	B
9462	Victory / D-Day today is V-Day / Germany surrenders / Hell / Hitler! etc.	Unknown	VEDay	Czubay	C
9463	Victory / first / then plan / for the / peace! / V	Multicolored	VforV	Linto	B
9464	Victory / first / then plan / for the / peace! / V / Navy Day——Oct.27, 1943	Multicolored	Navy	Linto	B
9465	Victory / first / V / then a just peace / inspired by genuine etc. [engraved]	Blue, red	ShieV	Huss	B
9466	Victory / first! / Then plan your amusement [no picture]	Multicolored	Home	Linto	B
9467	Victory / for freedom	Unknown	Unk	Davis, Ral	A
9468	Victory / for liberty	Blue, red	Bell	Davis, Ral	A
9469	Victory / for peace!	Unknown	Unk	Davis, Ral	A
9470	Victory / German armies in / Italy etc. [thermographed]	Unknown	Event	Boone	B
9471	Victory / God was / on / [etc.] / Allies [thermographed]	Unknown	Event	Boone	B
9472	Victory / -if / we work and fight / Defeat / -if / we shirk etc. [no picture]	Black	Home	Shaffer, A	A
9473	Victory / in '44 [allover]	Aquamarine	VforV	Gielarow	B
9474	Victory / in Europe. [postmarked 5/8/45]	Blue, red.	VEDay	Baur	B
9475	Victory / In honor of the / boys in service / United effort / Seventh etc.	Multicolored	Eag+	Fort Hamil	A
9476	Victory / in Manila / on to Tokyo!	Unknown	Event	Myers	B
9477	Victory / in the air / on land / V / on sea / To win the fight——fight etc.	Red	VforV	Burdick	A

NO.	CACHET TEXT	COLOR	TOPIC	PUBLISHER	$
9478	Victory / is / coming / to / our / rugged / Yanks [no picture]	Blue	Armed	Davis, Ray	A
9479	Victory / is / worth / any sacrifice etc.	Blue	Unk	Lawrence	A
9480	Victory / is all our / business! / Buy etc.	Unknown	Bonds	Kosko	A
9481	Victory / is in the air / Work or etc.	Unknown	Unk	Myers	A
9482	Victory / is worth / any sacrifice / since Valley Forge / to Tokyo!	Blue	VforV	Kirchner	A
9483	Victory / It won't be / long now! [red "V" height of envelope]	Blue, red	VforV	Boone	A
9484	Victory / Land of liberty	Blue	Eagle	Buxton, D	A
9485	Victory / Land of liberty [colored envelopes]	Blue	EagV	Buxton, D	A
9486	Victory / Let's all work / to end the war soon! / The golden opportunity etc.	Black/Purple	EagFl	Burdick	B
9487	Victory / sap a Jap & Hitler / Invest in U.S.A. / Buy bonds often	Red	Bonds	Harrington	A
9488	Victory / starts / here! Stay on your job to the etc. [label + printed border]	Multicolored	Air	Artists	B
9489	Victory / starts here	Black	Unk	Lohr	A
9490	Victory / starts here / Lives depend on your job! [label + printed border]	Multicolored	Home	Artists	B
9491	Victory / starts here / Victory is in your hands! [label + printed border]	Multicolored	Home	Artists	B
9492	Victory / Sweetest word in the etc.	Blue	Unk	Lawrence	A
9493	Victory / The Star-Spangled Banner etc.	Black	Unk	Fabian	A
9494	Victory / The V-E Day / we've waited for! / Hitler and his gang have etc.	Bk/Br/Pu/Red	VEDay	Rinker	B
9495	Victory / through / unity [stencilled] [no picture]	Blue, red	Home	Wolf, CL	A
9496	Victory / V	Unknown	Unk	Davis, Ral	A
9497	Victory / V / ··· – / Victory / for freedom	Blue, red	VforV	Davis, Ral	A
9498	Victory / V / Liberty [cachet 31x30 mm] [engraved]	Blue, red	Lib+	Huss	B
9499	Victory / V / Liberty [engraved]	Blue, red	VJDay	Huss	C
9500	Victory / V / The President announces the / unconditional etc. [thermographed]	Blue, red	VEDay	Unknown	B
9501	Victory / V / There's no time / to loose [sic]! / Only time to win!	Multicolored	Home	Griffith	A
9502	Victory / V / V..J Day	Blue, red	VJDay	James	B
9503	Victory / V / Victory! / for freedom	Blue, red	VforV	Davis, Ral	A
9504	Victory / V [eagle and shield on "V"]	Blue, red	VJDay	Lowell	B
9505	Victory / V is for virtue / I is for intellect / C is for etc. [no picture]	Gold, silver	Home	Linto	B
9506	Victory / V za pobeda [handpainted label]	Multicolored	ORN	LeGallez	C
9507	Victory / V-Day today is V-Day / Germany surrenders / Heil / Hitler! etc.	Blue, red	VEDay	Czubay	C
9508	Victory / Victory / God was / on / our side!	Multicolored	VJDay	Boone	B
9509	Victory / Victory / God was / on / our side! / Two atom bombs / set the etc.	Multicolored	VJDay	Boone	C
9510	Victory / Victory / God was / on / our side! / Two atom etc. [thermographed]	Multicolored	VJDay	Boone	C
9511	Victory / Victory / God was / on / our side! / V ["V" 32 mm high]	Multicolored	VJDay	Boone	B
9512	Victory / Victory / Japan / surrenders / to the / Allies [thermographed]	Multicolored	VJDay	Boone	B
9513	Victory / Victory / Remember / Pearl Harbor / Victory	Multicolored	VJDay	Boone	B
9514	Victory / Victory / Remember / This V-J Day / Pearl Harbor / Victory	Multicolored	VJDay	Boone	B
9515	Victory / Victory / Russia / declares war on / Japan [thermographed]	Multicolored	Event	Boone	B
9516	Victory / Victory / Today Sept. 2 etc.	Unknown	VJDay	Boone	B
9517	Victory / Victory / Today, Sept. 2, 1945 / is official / V-J / Day	Multicolored	VJDay	Boone	B
9518	Victory / Victory / Two atom bombs / set the rising sun	Blue, red	VJDay	Boone	B
9519	Victory / Victory / V-J / Day	Multicolored	VJDay	Boone	B
9520	Victory ["ictory" at lower edge or 25 mm above edge] [thermographed]	Unknown	VforV	Boone	A
9521	Victory [above eagle and shield] [handpainted]	Multicolored	EagSh	Stawuszew	D
9522	Victory [above eagle and sun] [handpainted]	Multicolored	Eagle	Klaas	C
9523	Victory [above eagle and V]	Blue	EagV	Levering	A
9524	Victory [below eagle and stars] [handpainted]	Blue, red	Eagle	Klaas	C
9525	Victory [below eagle]	Blue, red	Eagle	Nichols	B
9526	Victory [between arms of "V", above eagle and two flags] [embossed]	Multicolored	VforV	Puls	B
9527	Victory [black letters across red "V," inside 5-pointed star] [handpainted]	Black, red	VEDay	Sharon	C
9528	Victory [circle of blue stars] [env. 6 1/2x3 5/8, 7 1/2x4 in.]	Blue, red	VforV	Puls	A
9529	Victory [circle of red stars] [envelope 6 5/16x3 ½ in.]	Blue, red	VforV	Puls	A
9530	Victory [diagonal across shield] [eagle standing on shield] [handpainted]	Multicolored	EagSh	Dannells	C
9531	Victory [eagle alighting onto "Victory," 7 stars about wings]] [handpainted]	Blue, red	Eagle	Klaas	D
9532	Victory [eagle emblem, seven wing emblems]	Unknown	Eagle	Dime	A
9533	Victory [eagle flying under "Victory," "V" touching right wing] [handpainted]	Blue, red	Eagle	Klaas	D
9534	Victory [eagle flying under "Victory," in front of sun and rays] [handpainted]	Multicolored	Eagle	Klaas	D
9534A	Victory [flags of U.S. and Albania in front of sun, rays, parting clouds] [handpainted]	Multicolored	VEDay	Knapp	I

NO.	CACHET TEXT	COLOR	TOPIC	PUBLISHER	$
9534B	Victory [flags of U.S. and Austria in front of sun, rays, parting clouds] [handpainted]	Multicolored	VEDay	Knapp	I
9534C	Victory [flags of U.S. and Belgium in front of sun, rays, parting clouds] [handpainted]	Multicolored	VEDay	Knapp	I
9534D	Victory [flags of U.S. and Czechoslovakia in front of sun, rays, parting clouds] [handpainted]	Multicolored	VEDay	Knapp	I
9534E	Victory [flags of U.S. and Denmark in front of sun, rays, parting clouds] [handpainted]	Multicolored	VEDay	Knapp	I
9534F	Victory [flags of U.S. and France in front of sun, rays, parting clouds] [handpainted]	Multicolored	VEDay	Knapp	I
9534G	Victory [flags of U.S. and Greece in front of sun, rays, parting clouds] [handpainted]	Multicolored	VEDay	Knapp	I
9534H	Victory [flags of U.S. and Luxembourg in front of sun, rays, parting clouds] [handpainted]	Multicolored	VEDay	Knapp	I
9534I	Victory [flags of U.S. and Netherlands in front of sun, rays, parting clouds] [handpainted]	Multicolored	VEDay	Knapp	I
9534J	Victory [flags of U.S. and Norway in front of sun, rays, parting clouds] [handpainted]	Multicolored	VEDay	Knapp	I
9534K	Victory [flags of U.S. and Poland in front of sun, rays, parting clouds] [handpainted]	Multicolored	VEDay	Knapp	I
9534L	Victory [flags of U.S. and Yugoslavia in front of sun, rays, parting clouds] [handpainted]	Multicolored	VEDay	Knapp	I
9535	Victory [heads of servicemen on "V"] [colored envelopes]	Blue	VforV	Huss	A
9536	Victory [in quotes]	Blue	Hist	Belles-let	B
9537	Victory [in quotes] —— courtesy Chicago Park District	Sepia tones	Army	Belles-let	B
9538	Victory [in quotes] [below flag]	Blue, red	Flag	Smith, W	A
9539	Victory [letters 34 mm high] [no picture] [postmarked 5/8/45]	Multicolored	VEDay	Boone	B
9540	Victory [letters 34 mm high] [no picture] [postmarked 9/2/45]	Multicolored	VJDay	Boone	B
9541	Victory [letters arranged in V formation pointing down, flag between "V" and "Y"]	Black	Flag	Littlefiel	A
9542	Victory [letters placed in "V" shape below soldier at attention with rifle]	Black	Army	Littlefiel	A
9543	Victory [Navy emblem]	Blue	Navy	Dime	A
9544	Victory [on rag flying from bayonet through German helmet] [handpainted]	Black	VforV	Muzzy	B
9545	Victory [on shield, diagonally, shield in claws of eagle] [handpainted]	Multicolored	EagSh	Dannells	C
9546	Victory [red "V" 49 mm high, blue "ictory" 3 mm high] [2 rows blue flags]	Blue, red	VforV	Harrington	A
9547	Victory [red "V" height of envelope, blue "ictory" 20 mm high]	Blue, red	VforV	Boone	A
9548	Victory [script, "V" 87 mm high] [handpainted]	Blue, red	VEDay	Sharon	C
9549	Victory [text 78, 83, or 97 mm wide] [on flap]	Unknown	Unk	Unk	A
9550	Victory [two rows of blue flags]	Unknown	Flag	Harrington	A
9551	Victory [under blue eagle]	Blue, red	Eagle	Davis, Ral	A
9552	Victory [under red eagle]	Blue, red	Eagle	Davis, Ral	A
9553	Victory [vertical] / Hitler Germany / brought to its / knees! / Now to etc.	Multicolored	VEDay	Linto	B
9554	Victory [wings of eagle form first letter] [thermographed]	Black	Eagle	Grover	A
9555	Victory [word shaped as V]	Black	VforV	Unknown	A
9556	Victory [word shaped as V] ["···–" above "Victory"]	Black	VforV	Unknown	A
9557	Victory [word shaped as V] [flag above "Victory"]	Black	Flag	Unknown	A
9558	Victory [word shaped as V] [man above "Victory," pointing with pride at his medal]	Black	VforV	Unknown	A
9559	Victory [word shaped as V] [star above "Victory"]	Black	Vforv	Unknown	A
9560	Victory ahead - / Guam! Saipan! / Italy! Normandy! / Southern etc. [VforV]	Blue	Bonds	Klondike	D
9561	Victory ahead! / Seek out the enemy / and destroy him! / Fight for freedom	Multicolored	Home	Ever Ready	A
9562	Victory cover / Allies / capture / Cassino	Unknown	Event	Boone	B
9563	Victory cover / Caen / falls to / Allies etc. [no picture]	Unknown	Event	Boone	B
9564	Victory cover / Paris / falls to / Allies / Victory cover [no picture]	Orange	Event	Boone	B
9565	Victory cover / The noose tightens / Florence / falls to the etc. [no picture]	Blue	Event	Boone	B
9566	Victory cover / Yanks take / Naples etc. [no picture]	Unknown	Event	Boone	B
9567	Victory curving diagonally] [eagle alighting on "V"] [upper left]	Gold	Eagle	Myers	A
9568	Victory Day in Europe / 8-5-45 / V. day / Posted on V-Day / In India [ink ms.]	Red	VEDay	Unknown	C
9569	Victory Fleet Day / [etc.] / 9-27-'40——Japs sign up with Axis / 9-27-'39 etc.	Multicolored	Anniv	Linto	B
9570	Victory Fleet Day / [etc.] / 9-27-'40——U.S. Senate ratified / the Havana etc.	Multicolored	Anniv	Linto	B
9571	Victory Fleet Day / September 27, 1943 / [etc.] / 9-27-'40--Japs sign up with Axis etc.	Multicolored	Event	Linto	B
9572	Victory Fleet Day / September 27, 1943 / and a good time to etc. [color varieties]	Multicolored	Bonds	Linto	B
9573	Victory for / liberty [cachet 40x20 mm] [engraved]	Blue, red	Liber	Unknown	B
9574	Victory for the Allies! [colored envelopes]	Blue	Air	Huss	A
9575	Victory in / Europe [battleground, olive branch] [handpainted] [2 envelope sizes]	Multicolored	VEDay	McKelvey	C
9576	Victory in / Europe [homeland, planes, olive branch] [handpainted]	Multicolored	VEDay	McKelvey	C
9577	Victory in / Europe [stars in "V"] [partial globe shows Europe]	Black	VEDay	Peters	B
9578	Victory in 1944	Black	Unk	McFarland	A
9579	Victory in 1945 / Yes / if you / [etc.] / Buy only what you need [no picture]	Aqua, red	Home	Limoges	A
9580	Victory in 1945 / Yes / If you / [etc.] / Can your family's food [no picture]	Unknown	Home	Limoges	A
9581	Victory in 1945 / Yes / If you / [etc.] / Conserve coal etc. [no picture]	Unknown	Home	Limoges	A

NO.	CACHET TEXT	COLOR	TOPIC	PUBLISHER	$
9582	Victory in 1945 / Yes / If you / [etc.] / Give 5 pints of blood [no picture]	Red	Home	Limoges	A
9583	Victory in 1945 / Yes / If you / [etc.] / Grow your etc. [no picture]	Unknown	Home	Limoges	A
9584	Victory in 1945 / Yes / If you / [etc.] / Obey all ration laws [no picture]	Unknown	Home	Limoges	A
9585	Victory in 1945 / Yes / If you / [etc.] / Save all waste paper [no picture]	Unknown	Home	Limoges	A
9586	Victory in 1945 / Yes / If you / [etc.] / Save waste kitchen fats [no picture]	Unknown	Home	Limoges	A
9587	Victory in 1945 / Yes / If you / [etc.] / Share your etc. [no picture]	Unknown	Home	Limoges	A
9588	Victory in '43 [in quotes] [text in blue diamond]	Blue, gold	Home	Boone	A
9589	Victory in '43 [in quotes] [text in red circle]	Blue, red	Uncle	Boone	A
9590	Victory in '44	Blue, red	ShieV	Smith, W	A
9591	Victory in '44 [in quotes]	Blue, red	Uncle	Boone	A
9592	Victory in '44 [in quotes] / ···–	Blue, red	Uncle	Boone	A
9593	Victory in '44 [in quotes] [machine gunner]	Unknown	Army	Boone	A
9594	Victory in '44 [in quotes] [soldier with rifle] [all caps]	Unknown	Army	Boone	A
9595	Victory in '44 [in quotes] [soldier with rifle] [caps and lower case]	Unknown	Army	Boone	A
9596	Victory in Europe / VE-Day May 8th, 1945. / V-E / "Our victory is but half won" etc.	Blue, red	VEDay	Zunks	D
9597	Victory in Japan / VJ-Day Peace at last! / V-J / "They that have lived by" etc.	Blue, red	VJDay	Zunks	D
9598	Victory in the / West assured! / [etc.] / 5-17-'45——British / and Japs clash	Multicolored	Event	Linto	B
9599	Victory in the / West assured! / Now for the / East victory!	Blue, gold	Flag	Linto	B
9600	Victory is around / the corner still / depending on / you!	Multicolored	Flag	Linto	B
9601	Victory is in the air [in quotes] [envelope 6 9/16x3 3/4, 6 3/4x3 3/4 in.]	Sepia tones	Air	Belles-let	B
9602	Victory is won / by action, not / by wishing! / Buy U.S. war / bonds today	Multicolored	Bonds	Linto	B
9603	Victory Japan / Frist [sic] Day / Cover [in form of navy cancel] [rubber stamp]	Purple	VJDay	Unknown	B
9604	Victory leaders [thermographed]	Blue, red	Heads	Crosby	B
9605	Victory means security for democracy	Unknown	Home	Linto	B
9606	Victory over Hitlerism / in Nineteen and forty-four / ···–	Blue, red	Minut	Boone	A
9607	Victory over Japan / Admiral Chester W. Nimitz / Commander of U.S. forces etc.	Blue	VJDay	Huss	B
9608	Victory over Japan / V / for victory [engraved]	Blue	VJDay	Huss	C
9609	Victory over Japan / V / victory [over fighter plane] [engraved]	Blue, red	VJDay	Huss	C
9610	Victory over Japan / V / Victory for / liberty [engraved]	Blue, red	VJDay	Huss	C
9611	Victory over Japan / WACS are soldiers, too	Blue	VJDay	Huss	B
9612	Victory over Japan [above 4-engine patrol bomber] [engraved]	Blue	VJDay	Huss	C
9613	Victory over Japan [above eagle with flag] [engraved]	Blue	VJDay	Huss	C
9614	Victory over Japan [above helmeted cartoon figure making "V" sign] [engraved]	Multicolored	VJDay	Huss	C
9615	Victory peace / tolerance 1944 freedom etc.	Unknown	Unk	Baur	A
9616	Victory starts here / As we sow, so shall we reap! [label + printed border]	Multicolored	Home	Artists	B
9617	Victory through unity / We! are united [engraved]	Black	Heads	Artcraft	A
9618	Victory V / ···– ["Victory" across "V"] [3 stars at top]	Blue, red	VforV	Clifford	A
9619	Victory valentine [map of U.S.] [handpainted]	Multicolored	Map	Shaffer, A	C
9620	Victory valentine [with heart] [handpainted]	Multicolored	Home	Shaffer, A	C
9621	Victory! / ···– / In a radio broadcast from London January 14, 1941, etc.	Multicolored	VforV	Advertiser	B
9622	Victory! / and peace! / Official / VJ Day [dove in circle]	Multicolored	VJDay	Davis, Ral	B
9623	Victory! / Let / freedom / ring / from / [etc.] / cessation of hostilities etc.	Multicolored	VJDay	Wentz	C
9624	Victory! / Official / V-J Day / and peace!	Unknown	VJDay	Davis, Ral	B
9625	Victory! / Our part in the fight for right. [handpainted]	Red	Home	Klondike	C
9626	Victory! / Tokio falls, / Japan defeated / Islands in flames and ruins.	Green	VJDay	Abel	B
9627	Victory! [below eagle]	Blue	EagV	Davis, Ral	A
9628	Victory! [hand in "V" sign]	Unknown	VforV	Boone	A
9629	Victory! And non-stop / work etc. [label + blue "Victory" border]	Multicolored	VforV	Unknown	B
9630	Victory! And non-stop / work etc. [label + red "Victory" border]	Multicolored	VforV	Unknown	B
9631	Victory! And non-stop / work etc. [label + red "Win the War" border]	Multicolored	VforV	Unknown	B
9632	Victory!! / Germany / surrenders / May 8, 1945 / Two gone one to go	Multicolored	VEDay	Lowell	C
9633	Victory!! / Italy / surrenders / Sept etc.	Unknown	Event	Lowell	B
9634	Victory, for the boys "over there" / needs etc.	Unknown	Unk	Haynes	A
9635	Victory. / Hats off to our armed forces. [handpainted]	Black, red	VEDay	Adler	E
9636	Victory-America's only objective etc.	Unknown	Home	Linto	B
9637	Victory-winning / eagles flying / with purchases / of war bonds / and stamps	Unknown	Eagle	Linto	B
9638	Vienna / liberated / Capital of Austria / April 10, 1945	Multicolored	Event	Teixeira	D
9639	Vienna / liberated / Capital of Austria / April 10, 1945 [4/10/45 + 5/8/45 postmarks]	Multicolored	Event	Teixeira	F

NO.	CACHET TEXT	COLOR	TOPIC	PUBLISHER	$
9640	Vienna taken / by Russians	Unknown	Event	Boone	B
9641	Vinegar / Joe [handpainted]	Multicolored	Gener	Barwicki	B
9642	Visions / of / victory [colored envelopes]	Blue, red	Home	Poppenger	A
9643	VJ / August 14 / 1945 / Up / and / atom	Black	VJDay	Unknown	B
9644	V-J / Day / Mark the date on the calendar / as a reminder to any / more etc.	Green	VJDay	Rinker	B
9645	V-J / Day / Total victory over / Japan today! [stars at 2 corners of picture]	Multicolored	VJDay	Ander, EA	B
9646	V-J / Day / Total victory over / Japan today.	Blue, red	VJDay	Ander, EA	B
9647	V-J / Day / Total victory over / Japan today. / Proclaimed by / President etc.	Blue, red	VJDay	Ander, EA	B
9648	V-J / Day / Total victory over / Japan today. [no picture]	Aquamarine	VJDay	Unknown	B
9649	V-J / Day / Victory in Japan / End of World War II / September 2, 1945	Multicolored	VJDay	Teixeira	E
9650	V-J / Day / Victory over Japan	Black	VJDay	Southworth	B
9651	VJ / Day / Victory over Japan / Peace at last / "Remember" etc. [on cacheted cover]	Black	VJDay	Yudkin	C
9652	VJ / Day / Victory over Japan / Peace at last / Japan etc. [on cacheted cover]	Black	VJDay	Yudkin	C
9653	V-J / Day / Well done	Multicolored	VJDay	Amer Pat	B
9654	V-J / Day [framed, below eagle; corner stars] [env. 6 1/2x3 5/8, 6x 3 ½ in.]	Blue	VJDay	Brenn	B
9655	V-J / Day [outline map of Japan]	Violet	VJDay	Blumen	B
9656	VJ / Japan's flag is white / We knocked the spots off [postmarked 8/15/45]	Blue, red	VJDay	Griffith	B
9657	V-J / U.S.S. New Mexico U.S.S. Mississippi U.S.S. Idaho etc. [Tokyo Bay]	Black/Blue	VJDay	Navy ship	D
9658	VJ / We have avenged / Pearl Harbor	Blue, red	VJDay	Threl+Thar	B
9659	V-J / well done ["V-J" horizontal, "well done" vertical]	Blue	VJDay	Unknown	B
9660	V-J [black X through "V-J"]	Black, red	VJDay	Unknown	B
9660A	VJ ["V" 61 mm high, "J"56 mm high, letters intertwined] [handpainted]	Blue, red	VJDay	Unknown	C
9661	V-J Day	Blue/Red	VJDay	Cliff	B
9662	V-J Day —— / Japan surrender / unconditionally [+ pasted picture] [handpainted]	Red	VJDay	Holton	C
9663	V-J Day / 7 p.m., Tuesday, August 14, 1945 / "Toward United Nations——" [no picture]	Black	VJDay	Unknown	B
9664	V-J Day / A new sun is rising over Tokyo	Multicolored	VJDay	Harrington	B
9665	V-J Day / Gen. / Douglas / MacArthur / redeems his / pledge, "I shall" etc.	Black	VJDay	Coll Surp	B
9666	V-J Day / Japan / surrenders / to the / Allies	Gd,Blue/Multi	VJDay	Boone	B
9667	V-J Day / Japs sign surrender papers / on U.S.S. Missouri	Black	VJDay	Coll Surp	B
9668	V-J Day / Smashing the Jap fleet in the 2nd Battle of the Philippine Sea.	Black	VJDay	Coll Surp	B
9669	V-J Day / The atomic / bomb on Hiroshima	Black	VJDay	Coll Surp	C
9670	V-J Day / The dishonesty, the trickery, the sheer treachery / of an etc.	Black	VJDay	Coll Surp	C
9671	V-J Day / U.S.S. Marvin H. McIntyre (APA129) / off Wake Island etc. [Tokyo Bay]	Blue/Red	VJDay	Navy ship	D
9672	V-J Day / Unconditional surrender instrument / signed etc. [picture engraved]	Blue, red	VJDay	Heckman	C
9673	V-J Day [above eagle holding arrows and olive branch] [handpainted]	Multicolored	VJDay	Stawuszew	E
9674	V-J Day [above flying eagle clutching 3 arrows] [handpainted]	Multicolored	VJDay	Stawuszew	D
9675	V-J Day [above globe of world] [thermographed]	Gray/Gn, Y	VJDay	Czubay	C
9676	V-J Day [below eagle tearing Japanese flag]	Bk/Bu/Gn/P/	VJDay	Ander, CS	B
9677	V-J Day [below Statue of Liberty] [env. 6 1/2x3 5/8, 6x3 ½ in.]	Blue	VJDay	Brenn	B
9678	V-J Day [diagonally across Remember / Pearl / Harbor! cachet]	Unknown	VJDay	Boone	B
9679	V-J Day [heads of MacArthur, Halsey, Truman superimposed on "V"]	Black, red	VJDay	Knoll	C
9680	V-J Day [on shield with stars, below eagle] [env. 6 1/2x3 5/8, 6x3 ½ in.]	Blue	VJDay	Brenn	B
9681	V-J Day [over picture of Earth in sky shining on landscape below] [thermographed]	Green, yellow	VJDay	Unknown	C
9682	V-J Day [Sad Sack]	Multicolored	VJDay	Lind	B
9683	VJ Day [w/ portrait of Gen. MacArthur] [printed over cachet by same publisher]	Blue, red	VJDay	Runge	B
9684	V-J Day cover [in quotes] [overprinted on cachets by Huss] [colored envelopes]	Blue/Red	VJDay	Huss	B
9685	V-J Day! [no picture] [postmarked 9/1/45] [handpainted]	Multicolored	VJDay	Dannells	C
9686	V-J Day! [typed] / ···– [below dove] / Japan signs etc. [env. 7 7/16x3 7/8 in.]	Multicolored	VJDay	Oka	G
9687	V-J Day. Empire of / Japan surrenders [rubber stamp]	Red	VJDay	Teaneck	B
9688	VJDay / Buy / war / bonds	Multicolored	VJDay	Unknown	B
9689	VJ-Day / Sunday / September 2, 1945. [postmarked 9/2/45]	Blue, red	VJDay	Unknown	C
9690	V-J-Day [6 asterisks before/after text] [typed] [from USS Wharton] [8/15/45]	Black	VJDay	Isham	C
9691	V-J-Day [Marine standing on Japanese flag, raising U.S. flag] [artist: Crocker]	Green	VJDay	Unknown	B
9692	V-mail / gets its man! / and pleases etc.	Unknown	Unk	Myers	A
9693	Vocational training for victory ["···–" beside each "V"] [env. 9 1/2x4 1/8 in.]	Blue	VforV	Arizona	D
9694	Volturno / Itri / Cape Bon etc.	Unknown	Unk	McCluney	B
9695	Von Arnim captured	Unknown	Event	Linto	B
9696	Von by Von [in quotes] / we got the Germans... / "Nip by Nip" / we will etc.	Blue, red	Axis	Boone	A

NO.	CACHET TEXT	COLOR	TOPIC	PUBLISHER	$
9697	Von Runstedt's return [in quotes] [handpainted]	Multicolored	Gener	Hadley	C
9698	Vot - next? [handpainted]	Multicolored	Uboat	Borkowski	D
9699	Vote for / who you damn pleeze / I'm etc. [no picture]	Unknown	Home	McCluney	A
9700	Vote for an / American / [etc.] / 9-14-'44——Halsey's men again / blast 84 etc.	Gold, violet	Event	Linto	B
9701	Vote for an / American / government / Nov. 7, 1944	Gold	Flag	Linto	B

Cover Values (from Table 6, p. 136)

Value	Price Range
A	$ 3 - 6
B	$ 7 - 15
C	$ 16 - 30
D	$ 31 - 60
E	$ 61 - 125
F	$ 126 - 250
G	$ 251 - 500
H	$ 501 - 1000
I	$ >1000
X	Unpriced: Suspicious or fraudulent cover

9033

9068

9107

9116

9138

9149A

9205

9242

9254

9260

9279

9345

9378

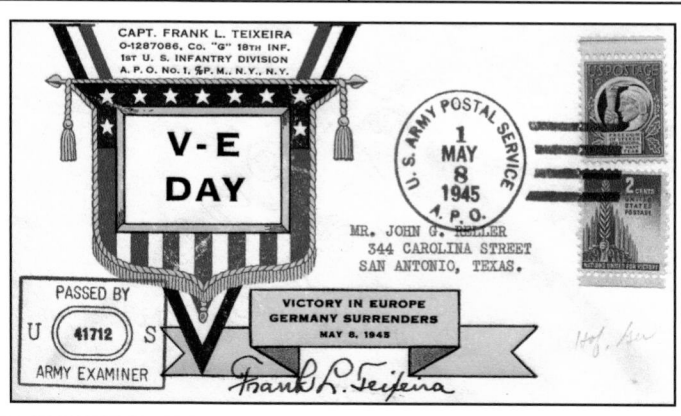

9392

9396

9420

9429

9460

9521

9575

9576

9616

9686

9689

CACHET TEXT BEGINNING WITH "W"

NO.	CACHET TEXT	COLOR	TOPIC	PUBLISHER	$
9702	W.R.A. / Hunt, Idaho [thermographed]	Green	AJA	Unknown	E
9703	WAAC [on flap, with symbol of corps]	Blue, black	WAC	Unknown	B
9704	W-A-A-C [with symbol of corps] [env. 6 3/4x3 3/4, 7 1/2x3 5/16, 7 1/2x4 in.]	Unknown	WAC	Unknown	A
9705	WAC / A salute to / American / women etc.	Unknown	WAC	Card	A
9706	WAC [WAC saluting]	Blue	WAC	Unknown	A
9707	WAC/ Women's Army Corps / V V / made part of the Army etc. [WAC symbol thermographed]	Multicolored	WAC	Andrews	C
9708	WACS / Col. Wetray Boyce	Multicolored	WAC	Knoll	D
9709	WACS are soldiers, too	Blue	WAC	Huss	A
9710	Wait 'til you see the ending!	Black	Japan	Davis, D	A
9711	Waitin' for / a green-eyed / soldier. [handpainted] [envelope 4 5/8x3 7/8 in.]	Multicolored	Army	Cowdery	D
9712	Waitin' for / you- soldier! [burned left edge] [handpainted]	Multicolored	Home	Cowdery	D
9713	Wake / up / Get ready for the / 6th war / loan [handpainted]	Unknown	Bonds	Wolf, RL	B
9714	Wake [handpainted]	Multicolored	Map	Smith, LH	B
9715	Wake is / seized by / U.S. forces [no picture]	Unknown	Event	Boone	B
9716	Wake Island - Guadalcanal etc. [thermographed]	Unknown	Battl	Neal	A
9717	Wake Island / Seized by the Japs Dec. 24, 1942 [handpainted]	Multicolored	Map	Smith, LH	B
9718	Wake up / America! / We have a war / to win! [3 print varieties] [colored envelopes]	Blue, red	Eagle	Poppenger	A
9719	Wake up / America! / We have a war to win! [colored envelopes]	Unknown	Unk	Poppenger	A
9720	Wake up / those lazy dollars! / Forestall etc.	Unknown	Unk	Ander, EA	A
9721	Wake up America! / Tomorrow will be too late! [2 print var.] [colored envelopes]	Blue, red	Eagle	Poppenger	A
9722	Wake up America! / We have a war to win! [2 print var.] [colored envelopes]	Unknown	Unk	Poppenger	A
9723	Wake up! / Back the attack with / your waste paper	Blue, red	Home	Speede	A
9724	Wake up, Kojo - I got eight / buddies and a stone wall / I want you to meet!	Red	Japan	Neal	A
9725	Wallace sent to China / [etc.] / 8-30-'44--Yanks sink 17 Jap / ships. Total down 723	Gold, silver	Event	Linto	B
9726	Wallace sent to China / Nelson sent to China / Strange acts of "sovereign" etc.	Gold, silver	China	Linto	B
9727	Walter Winchell / broadcasting / [etc.] / 12-28-'42——Rationing of canned etc.	Multicolored	Anniv	Linto	B
9728	Walter Winchell / broadcasting / Blah! / blah! / blah! [no picture]	Multicolored	Home	Linto	B
9729	Want a business for yourself? etc. [yellow envelope]	Blue	Unk	Temple	A
9730	Want action? / Join / U.S. Marine Corps! [official USMC tan env. 8 7/8x3 7/8 in.]	Black	USMC	USMC	D
9731	Want me for your pin-up girl? [no picture; space for photo above text]	Black	Women	Carpenter	A
9732	Want me for your pin-up girl? [photo of young woman pasted above text]	Black	Women	Carpenter	A
9733	Want that fighter home soon? Buy war bonds	Blue, red	Bonds	Burdick	A
9734	Want to whip the Axis? / Take them for a ride? / Put your pay etc. [no picture]	Green	Bonds	Shaw, CF	A
9735	Wanted / 1 dead Jap or / [etc.] / The State Department revealed this day etc.	Black	VJDay	Southworth	B
9736	Wanted / 1 dead Jap or / [etc.] / They did it again / This is V-J Day etc.	Black, red	VJDay	Southworth	B
9737	Wanted / 1 dead Jap or / 1 pound of used / cooking fat / Reward: 2 red etc.	Black	Japan	Southworth	B
9738	Wanted / dead or alive! / Public etc.	Unknown	Unk	Boone	A
9739	Wanted: / dead or / alive! / These / three / Axis / murderers! [busts of 3]	Blue, red	Axis	Boone	A
9740	Wanted: / dead or / alive! / These / three / Axis / murderers! [full body of 3]	Blue, red	Axis	Boone	A
9741	Wanted: / dead or alive! / Public enemies 1 & 2 / must be brought to etc.	Blue, red	Axis	Boone	A
9742	Wanted: dead or alive / These three / "Axis boys!"	Blue, red	Axis	Boone	A
9743	Wanton / post-surrender / attack on Rotterdam.	Black	ORN	Coll Surp	B
9744	War	Bk/Bu/Br/Pu/	Globe	Harrington	A
9745	War	Blue, red	Globe	Harrington	A
9746	War - offense and defense [envelope 9 1/2x4 1/8 in.]	Red	Unk	Ohio State	D
9747	War / bond / war / bond / war / bond / U.S.	Blue	Bonds	Carpenter	A
9748	War / bonds / keep it / flying / buying [flag, war bonds pennant] [handpainted]	Multicolored	Flag	Adler	D
9749	War / bonds / speed / victory [handpainted]	Black, yellow	Liber	Unknown	C
9750	War / bonds / speed/ victory [handpainted]	Black, yellow	Liber	Klaas	C
9751	War / U.S. declares war / Dec. 11, 1941 / on Germany and Italy [handpainted]	Multicolored	Event	Knapp	I
9752	War 1 War 2 / I died in vain. I wonder? etc. [thermographed]	Unknown	Unk	Baur	A
9753	War birds' nest [envelope 6 9/16x3 3/4, 6 3/4x3 3/4 in.]	Unknown	Unk	Belles-let	C
9754	War board set up	Unknown	Event	Linto	B
9755	War bonds will / prevent bonds of / slavery [no picture]	Multicolored	Bonds	Linto	B
9756	War bonds / 1/4 / off / See your local / bank or post-office etc. [no picture]	Red/Blue, red	Bonds	Harrington	A
9757	War bonds / Buy them more often, / to fill Hitlers coffin.	Blue, red	Bell	Harrington	A

NO.	CACHET TEXT	COLOR	TOPIC	PUBLISHER	$
9758	War bonds / mean more than a etc.	Black	Bonds	Card	A
9759	War bonds and stamps will / insure etc. [candle and holly]	Unknown	Bonds	Runge	A
9760	War bonds and stamps will / insure etc. [carolers]	Unknown	Bonds	Runge	A
9761	War bonds and stamps will / insure etc. [church window]	Unknown	Bonds	Runge	A
9762	War bonds and stamps will / insure etc. [fireplace]	Unknown	Bonds	Runge	A
9763	War bonds bring peace [colored envelopes]	Black	Dove	Huss	A
9764	War bonds feed both men and guns. / Through them victory will be won.	Brown, green	Bonds	Hunt	A
9765	War bonds help to win the war etc. [orange envelope]	Blue	Bonds	Temple	A
9766	War bonds today / Security tomorrow! [envelope 6 3/4x3 3/4 in.]	Unknown	Unk	Ander, EA	A
9767	War bonds today / to bomb / Tokyo / Security tomorrow! [72 mm high]	Blue, red	Bonds	Ander, EA	A
9768	War bonds today / to bomb / Tokyo / Security tomorrow! [74 mm high]	Blue, red	Bonds	Ander, EA	A
9769	War bonds will / win the war / For defense / buy / United States / Savings etc.	Blue/Red	Bonds	Bible	D
9770	War bonds will preserve the / liberty etc. [thermographed]	Unknown	Bonds	Phill, CR	A
9771	War bonds! / Buy them / or / wear them [no picture]	Unknown	Bonds	Norton	A
9772	War bonds! / Buy them / or / wear them [thermographed]	Blue	Bonds	Norton	A
9773	War bonds! / The / kick-off / to / victory	Blue, red	Bonds	Eichenlaub	A
9774	War calls / must / come first! [no picture]	Unknown	Home	NY Tel Co	B
9775	War Cover Associates ——	Blue, red	Home	Kosko	A
9776	War declared / against Japan / in retaliation for the / unwarranted etc. [thermographed]	Black, red	Event	Unknown	C
9777	War declared / Japs attack Hawaii / while talks etc. [postmarked 12/08/41]	Red	Pearl	Unknown	D
9778	War declared / June 28, 1944 / Republican party etc.	Red	Home	Abel	B
9779	War declared / on Germany / Dec. 11, 1941 / Britain and United etc. [thermographed]	Red	Event	Crosby	D
9780	War declared! / Japs attack Hawaii / Dec. 7, 1941 - etc. [postmarked 12/8/41]	Blue, red	Event	Unknown	C
9781	War dog [colored envelopes]	Black/Blue	Dog	Huss	A
9782	War ends / Germany surrenders / President etc. [env. 6 1/2x3 5/8, 7 1/2x4 in.]	Black, red	VEDay	Werve	B
9783	War ends / Japan surrenders / President Truman proclaims / Sunday, etc.	Black	VJDay	Werve	B
9784	War games - / Learning to shoot [stamp missing] [handpainted]	Multicolored	Army	Cowdery	D
9785	War games - / nightly gas attack!! [torn at right] [stamp missing] [handpainted]	Multicolored	Army	Cowdery	D
9786	War in Europe ends / "Krieg in Europa" / [etc.] / "Hitler ist kaput." [4 lines]	Green/Red	VEDay	Abel	B
9787	War in Europe ends / "Krieg in Europa" / [etc.] / "Hitler e finito" [8 lines]	Red	VEDay	Abel	B
9788	War loan / 7th / Buy War Bonds / A salute to the Army [handpainted]	Blue, red	Bonds	Card	C
9789	War loan / I don't give, I invest / V [postmarked 5/14/45, bond drive 1st day]	Multicolored	Bonds	Griffith	C
9790	War loan / VI / Buy bonds and make it / Victory [handpainted] [1st day postmark 11/20/44]	Multicolored	Bonds	Griffith	C
9791	War mobilizer James F. Byrnes, / in his Congress report, revealed / that etc.	Gold, green	Bell	Linto	B
9792	War needs the wires! / Don't etc. [no picture]	Unknown	Home	Ill Bell	B
9793	War outbreak. [typed on "F.R.S. Normandie" cacheted cover; postmarked 9/1/39]	Multicolored	Event	Batura	H
9794	War phrases that / will live / All Japanese etc. [thermographed]	Unknown	Unk	Baur	A
9795	War phrases that / will live / Congratulations to etc. [thermographed]	Unknown	Unk	Baur	A
9796	War phrases that / will live / I have returned etc. [thermographed]	Unknown	Mac	Baur	B
9797	War phrases that / will live / I hope they etc. [thermographed]	Unknown	Unk	Baur	A
9798	War phrases that / will live / I shall return etc. [thermographed]	Unknown	Mac	Baur	B
9799	War phrases that / will live / If Japan persists etc. [thermographed]	Unknown	Japan	Baur	A
9800	War phrases that / will live / Kill Japs. Kill etc. [thermographed]	Unknown	Japan	Baur	A
9801	War phrases that / will live / Perhaps we will etc. [thermographed]	Unknown	Unk	Baur	A
9802	War phrases that / will live / Remember Pearl Harbor etc. [thermographed]	Unknown	Pearl	Baur	A
9803	War phrases that / will live / Retiring at high speed etc. [thermographed]	Unknown	Unk	Baur	A
9804	War phrases that / will live / The Jap is a helluva etc. [thermographed]	Unknown	Japan	Baur	A
9805	War phrases that / will live / There are no atheists etc. [thermographed]	Unknown	Unk	Baur	A
9806	War phrases that / will live / There are no limits etc. [thermographed]	Unknown	Unk	Baur	A
9807	War phrases that / will live / Wars are won etc. [thermographed]	Unknown	Unk	Baur	A
9808	War phrases that / will live / We must employ etc. [thermographed]	Unknown	Unk	Baur	A
9809	War phrases that / will live / We will gain etc. [thermographed]	Unknown	FDR	Baur	B
9810	War phrases that / will live / We'll make them etc. [thermographed]	Unknown	Unk	Baur	A
9811	War Production Board established	Unknown	Home	Linto	B
9812	War! / "On the land, on the sea, in the air, / we must prepare, / we" etc.	Blue, red	Ordn	Swartz	A
9813	Warner & Swasey / for victory / ...-	Unknown	VforV	Warner+Sw	B
9814	Warning! / Walls have ears etc. [label + blue "Victory" border]	Multicolored	Hitle	Unknown	B
9815	Warning! / Walls have ears etc. [label + red "Victory" border]	Multicolored	Hitle	Unknown	B

NO.	CACHET TEXT	COLOR	TOPIC	PUBLISHER	$
9816	Warning! / Walls have ears etc. [label + red "Win the War" border]	Multicolored	Hitle	Unknown	B
9817	Warrior then—— / and now——always alert!	Blue, red	Home	Brenn	A
9818	Warsaw / again / returns / saved from / Acxis/ wantonness [postmarked 01/18/45]	Pink, black	Event	Brenn	A
_9819_	Warsaw / is free again / Out of the ashes of destruction etc. [artist: Staehle]	Multicolored	Event	Staehle	C
9820	Warsaw / liberated / Capital of Poland / January 17, 1945	Multicolored	ORN	Teixeira	D
9821	Warsaw / liberated / Capital of Poland / January 17, 1945 [1/17/45 + 5/8/45 postmarks]	Multicolored	Event	Teixeira	F
9822	Warsaw falls / to the etc.	Unknown	Event	Thr+Bu+T	B
9823	War-time / Christmas / Anno Domini 1942 [envelope 7 1/2x4 in.]	Unknown	Holid	Unknown	B
9824	Was is / loose? / Com- / ing / inva- / sion / Buy / that etc. [handpainted]	Multicolored	Hitle	Borkowski	D
9825	Washington / Monument / symbol of liberty	Blue	Home	Battles	A
_9826_	Washington crossing the Delaware [in quotes] [envelope 6 3/4x3 3/4 in.]	Sepia tones	Wash	Belles-let	C
9827	Washington fought for the liberty / we must preserve. / Buy war bonds.	Blue	Wash	Haynes	A
9828	Washington fought for the liberty / we must preserve. / Buy war bonds.	Blue	Wash	Price, EK	A
9829	Washington helped give us liberty—— / We must preserve it for the future.	Bk,Bu/Bu,Red	Wash	Runge	A
9830	Washington helped give us liberty—— / We must preserve it for the future.	Black	Wash	Price, EK	A
9831	Washington helped give us liberty—— / We must preserve it for the future.	Bk/Bu/Bu,Y	Wash	Runge	A
9832	Washington mathema- / ticians have odd ways / [etc.] / Navy Day——Oct. 27, 1943	Multicolored	Navy	Linto	B
9833	Washington mathema- / ticians have odd ways / in figuring etc. [no picture]	Multicolored	Home	Linto	B
9834	Washington officials say: "People have / more money now than" etc. [no picture]	Gold	Home	Linto	B
9835	Washington officials say: "People" / [etc.] / 5-29-'44——Brewster Aero. etc.	Unknown	Event	Linto	B
9836	Washington, D.C. / Six German / spies sentenced / to death etc. [no picture]	Blue	Event	Fidelity	B
9837	Washington: the very / definition of a patriot [thermographed]	Unknown	Wash	Phill, CR	A
9838	Waste / paper / saved / today / means / American / lives etc. [no picture]	Green	Home	Unknown	B
9839	Waste fats / make / ammunition	Black, green	Home	Speede	A
9840	Waste paper / is used to make / [etc.] / 9-10-'44——Huns use surrender etc.	Multicolored	Event	Linto	B
9841	Waste paper / is used to make parachutes to / drop food to our jungle etc.	Blue, gold	Chute	Linto	B
9842	Waste paper is a / vital weapon etc.	Unknown	Unk	Brenn	A
9843	Wastepaper / fights / for / freedom / Save / a bundle etc. [handpainted]	Blue, red	Home	Klaas	C
9844	Watch out, Tojo: / 1——Many brave hearts asleep in the deep etc. [no picture] [thermographed]	Black	Japan	Weigand	B
9845	Watch the yellowman / yell-ow! / when we get to Tokyo	Blue, red	Japan	Schust	A
9846	Watch this neat 3-point landing! [in quotes] [brown or buff envelope]	Multicolored	Army	Amer Art	A
9847	Watch your talk / Conversation etc.	Unknown	Unk	Kosko	A
_9848_	Watchful eyes / The Coast Guard	Multicolored	Coast	Amer Pat	A
9849	WAVE / The women behind the men / behind the guns.	Multicolored	WAVES	Cozart	A
9850	WAVE chief [VJ Day cancel]	Black	WAVES	Southworth	B
9851	Wave high, O glorious banner / Thy stars and stripes unfurled etc.	Blue, red	Flag	Boone	A
9852	WAVES / "We're behind the men behind the guns" / Since the birth of our etc.	Blue	WAVES	Lawrence	A
9853	WAVES / always faithful [thermographed]	Unknown	WAVES	Baur	A
_9853A_	WAVES / Second anniversary / July 30, 1944 [handpainted]	Multicolored	WAVES	Knoll	D
9854	WAVES [envelope 6x3 ½ in.]	Blue, green	WAVES	Unknown	A
9855	WAVES second / anniversary [cut-and-pasted paper on WAVES small envelope]	Black	WAVES	Schultze	B
9856	We "keep 'em / flying" [envelope 9 1/2x4 1/8 in.]	Unknown	Unk	Mechanical	B
9857	We / "must" / do all we / "can" [handpainted]	Multicolored	Uncle	Adler	D
9858	We / "must" / do all we / "can" [handpainted]	Multicolored	Uncle	Adler	D
9859	We / are in a / fight / to win! / We / can help by / buying U.S. war bonds	Blue, red	Uncle	Card	A
9860	We / are in a / fight / to win! / We can help by / buying U.S. war bonds	Blue, red	Bonds	Dime	A
9861	We / are in a / fight / to win! / We can help by / buying U.S. war bonds	Black	Bonds	Clendennen	B
9862	We / are in a / fight / to win! etc. [lower left corner] [cream envelope]	Black	Bonds	Harrington	A
9863	We / are in a / fight / to win! etc. [text below shield]	Unknown	Shiel	Lowell	A
9864	We / are in a / fight / to win! etc. [text between rows of flags]	Unknown	Flag	Card	A
9865	We / invade / southern / France [no picture]	Blue, red	Event	Fidelity	B
9866	We / mop up / Guadalcanal / Berlin / funeral marches / over etc. [no picture]	Red	Event	Fidelity	B
9867	We / occupy / Bizerte and Tunis / in Africa / and Russel Isles etc. [no picture]	Black, red	Event	Fidelity	B
9868	We / shall / see / you / through [handpainted]	Multicolored	Army	Adler	D
9869	We / shall / win / or / we / shall / die / MacArthur [handpainted] [imprint: CAN]	Blue, red	Maced.	Unknown	C
9870	We / stick 'em / with / bayonets / You etc. [no picture]	Unknown	Unk	Shafer, A	A
9871	We / welcome / democracy, too. / V ...- / world / wide. [handpainted]	Black, red	Ally	Shaw, TC	D
9872	We / welcome / democracy. / V ...- / worldwide. [handpainted]	Black, red	VforV	Shaw, TC	C

NO.	CACHET TEXT	COLOR	TOPIC	PUBLISHER	$
9873	We / will / win ["We" red, 'Win" blue] [handpainted] [no picture]	Multicolored	Home	Hanna	B
9874	We admire the fighting / spirit / [etc.] / Commemorating "Bill of Rights" etc.	Multicolored	Home	Linto	B
9875	We admire the fighting / spirit of the Russians and / their etc. [no picture]	Gd,Pi/Si,Pi	USSR	Linto	B
9876	We aim - to deliver	Blue, red	Eagle	Crosby	B
9877	We all have an "Axis to grind"! [colored envelopes]	Blue, red	UncAx	Poppenger	A
9878	We all make mistakes, / of course; / but we don't have to / respond to etc.	Green, red	Bonds	Jarrett	A
9879	We are "sawing wood" over here. / Only pikers "bark" when asked to / pull etc.	Blue, red	Home	Quigley	B
9880	We are "sawing wood" over here. / Only pikers "bark" when asked to / pull etc.	Blue, red	Home	Quigley	B
9881	We are a free people / wishing all-world peace	Blue, red	Flag	Linto	B
9882	We are all "conscientious" / [etc.] / Armistice day / November 11, 1943	Multicolored	Holid	Linto	B
9883	We are all "conscientious" / objectors but thank God the etc. [no picture]	Gd,Pi/Gn,Pi	Home	Linto	B
9884	We are all / free / Americans / from the north tip of Alaska to the south etc.	Multicolored	Holid	Runge	B
9885	We are all / free / Americans / Merry Christmas	Multicolored	Holid	Runge	A
9886	We are constantly warned not to / pay over ceiling prices! / Ceiling prices etc.	Unknown	Home	Linto	B
9887	We are doing a big day's work now, / are you driving or just watching?	Blue, red	Home	Quigley	B
9888	We are doing a good job! / Are you etc.	Unknown	Unk	Lemponen	A
9889	We are fighting for / "Freedom of Religion" / Swell! Let us recognize etc.	Unknown	Home	Linto	B
9890	We are fighting for / [etc.] / 8-25-'44——Paris free! / Huns mutilate Paris	Unknown	Event	Linto	B
9891	We are going places and / doing things / are you?	Unknown	Unk	Quigley	B
9892	We are in a / fight / to win etc. [on back] [envelope 8 11/16x3 5/8 in.]	Unknown	Unk	Kimball	B
9893	We are in a / fight / to win! / We / can help by / buying U.S. war bonds etc.	Black/Green	Uncle	Cozart	A
9894	We are in a / fight / to win! We etc. [envelope 9 1/2x4 1/8 in.]	Brown	Unk	Coleman	B
9895	We are proud / to be Americans	Unknown	Unk	Norona	A
9896	We are ready / Uncle Sam	Blue, red	Army	Linprint	A
9897	We are ready / Uncle Sam / The United States today declares war on Japan [12/8/41]	Multicolored	Event	Linprint	E
9898	We are telling the world / Peace and etc.	Unknown	Unk	Coryell	A
9899	We arrived / at Japan... / U.S. Army [U.S.S. New Jersey, 8/28/45] [Tokyo Bay]	Unknown	VJDay	Crosby	E
9900	We believe we speak for millions etc.	Unknown	Unk	McGovern	A
9901	We buy, sell , swap / latest rumors / Closed for duration etc. [3 print varieties]	Blue, red	Home	Boone	A
9902	We can / speed up / the home- / coming of / our boys	Green, red	Army	Linto	B
9903	We can / we must / we will	Unknown	Unk	Runge	A
9904	We can / we must / we will	Unknown	Unk	Price	A
9905	We can—— / we must—— / we will	Unknown	Home	Runge	A
9906	We can / we will / we must / eliminate / these Axis brutes / Finis	Green, red	UncAx	Boone	A
9907	We can / we will / we must eliminate etc.	Unknown	Unk	Boone	A
9908	We can [in quotes] "We will" "We must" / Remember "Pearl Harbor" / 1st etc.	Blue/Red	Pearl	Thurman	B
9909	We can all / work for / victory	Bk/Bu/Br/Red	Home	Louisville	A
9910	We can all / work for / victory	Green	Home	Murrman	A
9911	We can all / work for / victory	Green/Purple	Home	Louisville	A
9912	We can and.. / ...we will! [colored envelopes]	Blue, red	Home	Poppenger	A
9913	We can gain / [etc.] / Lt. Col. Clay Tice etc. [thermographed]	Unknown	Unk	Boone	A
9914	We can gain no lasting peace / if we approach / [etc.] / This is / V-J / day	Blue, red	VJDay	Boone	B
9915	We can gain no lasting peace / if we approach it with suspicion / and etc.	Blue, red	Flag	Boone	A
9916	We can have / victory / in 1945 / if we buy more bonds [no picture]	Red/Blue, red	Bonds	Harrington	A
9917	We can!... We will!... We must!! / For defense / buy / United etc. [thermographed]	Blue	Minut	Crosby	B
9918	We can!... We will!... We must!! Win the war [thermographed]	Red	Armed	Crosby	B
9919	We can!-we will!-we must!! / for defense etc. [thermographed]	Unknown	Unk	Crosby	B
9920	We can.. We will.. We must.. win / For defense / buy / United etc. [thermographed]	Blue	Bonds	Unknown	A
9921	We cannot afford to be / swayed with pleas / [etc.] / 6-1-'45——B-29 forts etc.	Multicolored	Event	Linto	B
9922	We cannot afford to be / swayed with pleas for / easy peace etc. [no picture]	Gold	Japan	Linto	B
9923	We cannot and will not / let the Red Cross down	Multicolored	RedCr	Linto	B
9924	We can-we will-we must-win / for defense etc. [thermographed]	Unknown	Unk	Crosby	B
9925	We capture Cassino / We warn Finland / We forge ahead in So. etc. [no picture]	Green	Event	Fidelity	B
9926	We deserve liberty / only so long etc.	Unknown	Unk	Boone	A
9927	We deserve liberty only / so long as we are [in quotes] etc. [colored envelopes]	Black/Blue	Hist	Huss	A
9928	We did it / before / and / we can / do it / again	Unknown	Unk	Baur	A
9929	We did it / before / and we can / do it again [lavender envelope 6x4 in.]	Unknown	Unk	Baur	A
9930	We did it before —— / we can do it again [env. 7 1/2x4 in.]	Blue	Navy	Navy Dept.	B

NO.	CACHET TEXT	COLOR	TOPIC	PUBLISHER	$
9931	We did it before / and / we can do it again	Unknown	Unk	Baur	A
9932	We did it before / Let's do it again!	Blue, red	Japan	Dime	A
9933	We did it before / Tokyo / Let's do it again!	Blue, red	Air	Dime	A
9934	We did it before, / we will do it again / On to victory [w/ publisher imprint]	Multicolored	EagV	Jordan	B
9935	We did it before, / we will do it again / On to victory [w/o publisher imprint]	Multicolored	EagV	Staehle	C
9936	We did it before, we can do it again. / We put the kibosh on the Kaiser etc.	Blue, green	Armed	Carpenter	A
9937	We didn't stab you in the back / Remember Pearl Harbor?	R/Bu, red	Japan	Borkowski	A
9938	We do not allow treacher- / ous snakes or wild animals / to etc. [no picture]	Gold, pink	AJA	Linto	B
9939	We done it before / We can do it again!!!	Red	Army	Harrington	A
9940	We don't mean perhaps, / this one's for the Japs! etc. [cut-&-pasted paper]	Black	Bonds	Temple	C
9941	We don't want war / Neither do we want / "conscientious" ob- / jectors. etc.	Multicolored	Minut	Linto	B
9942	We drive / Nazis / out of Naples——go / on to Rome / U-boats etc. [no picture]	Bu,R/Bu,Blac	Event	Fidelity	B
9943	We fight / to defend it / Let's attend it [env. 6 1/2x3 5/8, 6x3 1/2in.]	Gn/Blue, red	Relig	McGovern	A
9944	We fight / to defend it / Let's attend it [thermographed]	Unknown	Relig	McGovern	A
9945	We fight for four freedoms / [rose sticker with text] / Freedom from fear	Red	Eagle	Runge	A
9946	We fight for four freedoms / Freedom / of speech	Blue, gold	Eagle	Runge	A
9947	We fight for four freedoms / Freedom / of speech	Black/Blue	Home	Runge	A
9948	We fight for four freedoms / Freedom / of speech etc. [env. 6 3/4x3 3/4 in.]	Unknown	Unk	Price, EK	A
9949	We fight for four freedoms / Freedom from fear	Bk/Bu/Red	Unk	Runge	A
9950	We fight for four freedoms / Freedom from fear	Red	Home	Price, EK	A
9951	We fight for four freedoms / Freedom from want	Unknown	Unk	Price, EK	A
9952	We fight for four freedoms / Freedom from want	Br/Blue, red	Eagle	Runge	A
9953	We fight for four freedoms / Freedom of religion	Gold	Unk	Price, EK	A
9954	We fight for four freedoms / Freedom of religion	Bu/Gd/Pu/Re	Unk	Runge	A
9955	We fight for four freedoms / Freedom of speech	Unknown	Unk	Runge	A
9956	We fight for four freedoms / Freedom of speech	Unknown	Unk	Price, EK	A
9957	We fight for it / we die for it etc.	Unknown	Unk	Unk	A
9958	We fight on-We will win / The "Sleipner" / Norway	Blue, red	ORN	Staehle	B
9959	We gave England 50 / destroyers for the / privilege of etc. [no picture]	Brown, purple	Ally	Linto	B
9960	We got the Nazis / with the 6th / Let's set the rising sun with the / 7th etc.	Blue, red	Bonds	Boone	B
9961	We had to die; we were hurt too bad, but there is many an [in quotes] etc.	Blue, red	Nurse	Brenn	A
9962	We have / never / lost a / war [handpainted label]	Multicolored	EagSh	LeGallez	C
9962A	We have a war / to win [picture similar to cachet 4086] [handpainted]	Multicolored	Uncle	Adler	D
9963	We have government / now by Hague, Kelly, / Hannegann, Hillman / and etc.	Unknown	Home	Linto	B
9964	We have met the enemy and they are ours / Don't give up the ship / United etc.	Blue, red	Navy	Cachet Cra	A
9965	We have not yet begun to fight / John Paul Jones	Unknown	Hist	Wash Cover	A
9966	We have set the "Rising Sun" / Japan V ...- / surrenders / V-J Day Sept. 2 etc.	Multicolored	VJDay	Card	B
9967	We have set the "Rising Sun" / Japan V ...- surrenders / And the star- etc.	Blue, red	VJDay	Card	B
9968	We have turned the tide... / but not the corner / [etc.] / Buy etc. [thermographed]	Blue	Air	Boothroyd	A
9969	We have won the war / Now, let us build a world / of peace and liberty etc.	Red	VJDay	Harrington	A
9970	We honor / our serving sons and etc.	Unknown	Unk	Unknown	A
9971	We hope it will / please God to / [etc.] / 1-1-'44——Russians within 20 etc.	Gold, silver	Event	Linto	B
9972	We hope it will / please God to grant / us the victory etc. [no picture]	Brown, silver	Relig	Linto	B
9973	We insist on the / last word..... / ....in the only etc. [colored envelopes]	Blue, red	Ordna	Poppenger	A
9974	We keep them fit to fight / Pearl Harbor Navy Yard	Blue	Pearl	Navy Yard	B
9975	We know you're / all wet / but don't worry, / Uncle Sam / will etc.	Blue/Red	Axis	Barnes	A
9976	We may not like the / political maneuvering [sic] / but, thank God, we etc.	Gold	Liber	Linto	B
9977	We must all / fight for etc. [text below picture]	Unknown	Unk	Brenn	A
9978	We must all / fight for victory! / Buy war bonds [1st line 2 print varieties]	Blue, red	Wash	Ander, EA	A
9979	We must avenge Bataan [thermographed]	Multicolored	EagSh	Sadworth	B
9980	We must do all we can!	Multicolored	Bonds	Minkus	A
9981	We must win! / Buy / war / bonds / & stamps [thermographed]	Bu/Gn/Red	Uncle	Lind	B
9982	We must win! / Buy / more / war / bonds——stamps [no picture]	Unknown	Bonds	Kosko	A
9983	We must work, / fight, and die / to preserve our / liberty.	Black	Bell	Phillips	A
9984	We must work, / fight, and die / to preserve our / liberty. [thermographed]	Bk/Bu/Gn/Re	Bell	Phillips	A
9985	We must work, / fight, and die / to preserve our etc. [green text]	Green, red	Bell	Cox	A
9986	We must work, / fight, and die / to preserve our etc. [red text]	Green, red	Bell	Cox	A
9987	We mutually pledge to each other / our lives, our fortunes and etc. [engraved]	Blue, red	Flag	Huss	B

NO.	CACHET TEXT	COLOR	TOPIC	PUBLISHER	$
9988	We need a few men like / Abraham Lincoln / in Washington now!	Gold, silver	Linc	Linto	B
9989	We need airplanes, battle wagons etc.	Unknown	Unk	Dye	A
9990	We need American / leadership with / [etc.] / 2-14-'42——Japs in possession etc.	Multicolored	Anniv	Linto	B
9991	We need American / leadership with / American interest [no picture]	Multicolored	Home	Linto	B
9992	We need used / fats / to cook their / goose [handpainted]	Multicolored	Axis	Adler	D
9993	We now learn from Dillon S. / Myer, of W.R.A., that Japs / can be etc.	Multicolored	AJA	Linto	B
9994	We pinned 'em back / Mr. Jap —— [2 varieties, caricature of face] [handpainted]	Multicolored	Japan	Price, EK	B
9995	We play the game / March Java 1942 etc.	Unknown	Unk	McCluney	B
9996	We pledge to / each other / our lives, / our [in quotes] etc. [no picture]	Multicolored	Home	Linto	B
9997	We pledge to each other / our lives, our fortunes and / our etc. [no picture]	Gold, silver	Home	Linto	B
9998	We praise God for the birth / of the Stars and Stripes, let etc. [1 flag]	Blue, red	Flag	Amer Pat	A
9999	We praise God for the birth / of the Stars and Stripes, let etc. [3 flags]	Blue, red	Flag	Amer Pat	A
10000	We praise the land for the rights of men [draped flag at left]	Multicolored	Flag	Amer Pat	A
10001	We praise the land for the rights of men [flag on staff]	Multicolored	Flag	Amer Pat	A
10002	We praised the land for the rights of man [eagle and flag]	Multicolored	FlEag	Amer Pat	A
10003	We pray for God's / blessing on all true / mothers today and / every day	Multicolored	Women	Linto	B
10004	We pray Thee bless the silences that / fall with healing breath / where late the etc.	Blue	Verse	Neal	A
10005	We prize / our liberties / and our / rights We / will maintain / the etc.	Multicolored	Home	Edmunds	D
10006	We reach out to meet the gangsters of the sea etc. [thermographed]	Red	Map	Crosby	B
10007	We regret to inform you [in quotes], the telegram said etc. [no picture]	Unknown	Unk	Ang	A
10008	We salute our / fighting "hams" / The radio "shacks" of the etc. [no picture]	Green	Home	Davis, D	A
10009	We salute our armies / First etc.	Black	Unk	McCluney	A
10010	We salute our war nurses [2 print varieties] [colored envelopes]	Blue, red	Nurse	Poppenger	B
10011	We see you're right / behind us, folks! / 4th war / loan etc. [handpainted]	Red	Armed	Klondike	D
10012	We shall "win the war" / "That government / of the people, by / the" etc.	Black	Linc	Allen	A
10013	We shall be free again / Belgium	Multicolored	ORN	Staehle	C
10014	We shall fight for / victory / That government etc. [w/, w/o copyright "C"]	Blue, red	Army	Cachet Cra	A
10015	We shall not flag or fail. / We shall go on to the end.	Blue	Winst	Unknown	B
10016	We supply the forms on which victory etc. [envelope 8 7/8x3 7/8 in.]	Unknown	Unk	Lehman	B
10017	We thank God / for the victory He / has given us. / We pray etc. [no picture]	Gold	VEDay	Linto	B
10018	We thank thee	Blue, silver	Home	Linto	B
10019	We the people.... [in quotes] / arm for defense	Blue, red	Eagle	Wash Stamp	A
10020	We too must do something / Back the etc. [envelope 9 1/2x4 1/8 in.]	Red	Unk	Czubay	B
10021	We who died our land to save, who sleep within a white crossed [in quotes] etc.	Blue, red	RedCr	Brenn	A
10022	We will / keep the / Liberty / torch / burning in / spite of etc. [red envelope]	Multicolored	Torch	Linto	B
10023	We will / make it do- / make it last- / to win this war. [cobbler]	Black	Home	Runge	A
10024	We will / make it do- / make it last- / to win this war. [early auto]	Black	Home	Runge	A
10025	We will / make it do- / make it last- / to win this war. [man in ragged suit]	Black	Home	Runge	A
10026	We will accept no compromise / no etc.	Unknown	Unk	Phill, CR	A
10027	We will accept no compromise etc. "I came" etc. [double cachet] [thermographed]	Gn-1, Pur-2	Mac	Crosby	D
10028	We will accept no compromise, no alternative, / but [in quotes] / [etc.] / MacArthur [thermographed]	Green	Map	Crosby	B
10029	We will accept no compromise, no alternative, / but [in quotes] etc. [thermographed]	Brown	Eagle	Crosby	B
10030	We will be / free again / Greece [thermographed] [artist: Staehle]	Blue, red	ORN	Cachet Cra	B
10031	We will defend [envelope 9 1/2x4 7/8 in.]	Unknown	Home	Panama	B
10032	We will gain the / inevitable triumph [w/, w/o copyright "C"]	Blue, red	Antiq	Minkus	A
10033	We will keep 'em flying	Unknown	Air	Linto	B
10034	We will make it do- / make it last- / to win this war. [cobbler]	Black	Home	Price, EK	A
10035	We will make it do- / make it last- / to win this war. [cobbler]	Black	Home	Runge	A
10036	We will make it do- / make it last- / to win this war. [early automobile]	Black	Home	Runge	A
10037	We will make it do- / make it last- / to win this war. [flag + cobbler]	Unknown	Flag	Runge	A
10038	We will make it do- / make it last- / to win this war. [flag + early auto]	Blue, red	Flag	Runge	A
10039	We will make it do- / make it last- / to win this war. [man in ragged suit]	Unknown	Home	Runge	A
10040	We will make it do- / make it last- / to win this war. [winged "V" + auto]	Unknown	VforV	Runge	A
10041	We will make it do- / make it last- / to win this war. [winged "V" + cobbler]	Blk/Blue,Red	VforV	Runge	A
10042	We will not compete / with barbarism but / we will destroy it.	Gold	Flag	Linto	B
10043	We will not give up! / Yugoslavia [thermographed] [artist: Staehle]	Blue, red	ORN	Smart Cra	B
10044	We will sacrifice anything but our freedom [in quotes] [cachet hgt 64 or 66 mm]	Multicolored	Uncle	Minkus	A
10045	We will win / "So help us God" / Franklin D. Roosevelt [artist: Staehle]	Blue, red	Eag+	Fleetwood	C

NO.	CACHET TEXT	COLOR	TOPIC	PUBLISHER	$
10046	We will win [in quotes]	Blue, red	Eagle	Harmer	A
10047	We will win the / war, not thru / Roosevelt, but by / the etc. [no picture]	Gold, purple	FDR	Linto	B
10048	We wonder, how the / "Rising Sun" / [etc.] / 1-28-'42——21 Amer. Republics etc.	Unknown	Anniv	Linto	B
10049	We wonder, how the / "Rising Sun" looks / to the Japs now?	Unknown	Japan	Linto	B
10050	We won't forget / Guam —— Philippines —— etc. [env. 6 1/2x3 5/8, 6x3 ½ in.]	Blue, red	Eagle	Runge	A
10051	We won't forget / Guam / Philippines / Wake Is.	Brown	Eagle	Runge	A
10052	We won't forget / Guam / Philippines / Wake Is.	Brown	Unk	Price, EK	A
10053	We won't forget / Lidice / Keep America free! [colored envelopes]	Blue, red	ORN	Poppenger	A
10054	We won't give up / till they give in! [colored envelopes]	Blue, red	Eagle	Poppenger	A
10055	We won't let the three heels / forget Dec. 7th, 1941 / Buy etc. [handpainted]	Multicolored	Bonds	Knoll	C
10056	We work for victory [top center-right]	Unknown	EagSh	Gilbert	B
10057	We wuz robbed——P-o-l-I-c-e! [in quotes] [etc.] [env. 6 9/16x3 3/4 in.]	Brown	Axis	Belles-let	C
10085	We, the people [in quotes] [within outline of USA]	Multicolored	Home	Shafer, A	B
10059	We, the people.... [in quotes] / united for victory	Brown/Red	Eagle	Neal	A
10060	We, too, are fighting for / liberty and / [etc.] [typed] / Heart Mt., Wyo.	Multicolored	AJA	Oka	F
10061	We, too, must do something / [etc.] / Marshal and strengthen unity etc. [thermographed]	Red/Silver	Navy	Unit	C
10062	Weapons or no weapons / we dig 'em out	Multicolored	USMC	Unknown	A
10063	Wear / it / out / Use / it / up / Make / it do / or do without etc. [handpainted]	Black, green	Home	Martin	B
10064	Wear one of these / or "do a war job" [handpainted]	Multicolored	Women	Adler	D
10065	Welcome / General of the Army / Dwight David Eisenhower [thermographed]	Gold, green	Ike	Unknown	B
10066	Welcome / home / "Ike" / Gen. Eisenhower etc. [no picture]	Unknown	Ike	Davis, D	B
10067	Welcome / home from Europes [sic] battlefields / for a brief and well etc.	Purple	Armed	Abel	A
10068	Welcome [handpainted]	Unknown	Hitle	Shaw, TC	B
10069	Welcome home [in quotes] / to the victorious supreme- / commander etc. [thermographed]	Black, red	Ike	Smartcraft	B
10070	Welcome home fighting forces [thermographed]	Blue, red	Liber	Huss	A
10071	Welcome home, buddy! / from / Los Angeles Examiner / War wounded fund	Blue, red	Flag	LA Examine	C
10072	We'll / show / 'em!	Blue, red	Ordna	McCluney	A
10073	We'll / show / 'em! [handpainted]	Blue, red	Ordna	Krakora	B
10074	We'll be there [small circular logo with tiger head] [handpainted]	Multicolored	Unit	Conner	C
10075	We'll be there [unit insignia, 11th Fighter Squadron] [handpainted]	Multicolored	Unit	Conner	C
10076	We'll be there by / the tune of the / Yankee Doodle [bust 38 mm, above 3 stars]	Multicolored	Wash	Amer Pat	A
10077	We'll be there by / the tune of the / Yankee Doodle [bust 38 mm, below 3 stars]	Multicolored	Wash	Amer Pat	A
10078	We'll be there by / the tune of the / Yankee Doodle [bust 42 mm, above 3 stars]	Multicolored	Wash	Amer Pat	A
10079	We'll be there by / the tune of the / Yankee Doodle [bust 42 mm, below 3 stars]	Multicolored	Wash	Amer Pat	A
10080	We'll be there by / the tune of the / Yankee Doodle [bust 52 mm high, 3 stars]	Multicolored	Wash	Amer Pat	A
10081	We'll be there by / the tune of the / Yankee Doodle [bust 52 mm high, flag]	Multicolored	Wash	Amer Pat	A
10082	We'll be there by / the tune of the / Yankee Doodle [bust 52 mm high, no stars]	Multicolored	Wash	Amer Pat	A
10083	We'll bring you / victory / You keep America / American for us	Blue, red	Armed	Yontz	B
10084	We'll compose our music to / honor peace with victory	Black/Red	Home	Runge	A
__10085__	We'll crush the enemy / wherever and whenever / we find it / U.S. Navy [thermographed]	Blue, red	Navy	Sadworth	C
10086	Well done / V-J / Day [3 airplanes]	Multicolored	VJDay	Amer Pat1	C
10087	Well done / V-J / Day [3 diving P-51 Mustangs]	Multi var	VJDay	Amer Pat	C
10088	Well done / V-J / Day [sailor]	Multi var	VJDay	Amer Pat	C
10089	Well done / V-J / Day [tank]	Multicolored	VJDay	Amer Pat	C
10090	We'll keep "Nip" and "Nazi" hauling / their headache wagon if you furnish etc.	Unknown	Axis	Quigley	B
10091	We'll make him jump to / "Yankee Doodle Dandy" [handpainted]	Multicolored	Japan	Parker	B
10092	We'll patch the patches. / And keep bonds till they hatch! / To help etc. [handpainted]	Multicolored	Women	Myers	C
10093	We'll put 'em all / in hock	Red	Axis	Barnes	A
10094	We'll put em all in / hock!	Blue	Axis	Barnes	A
10095	We'll rally 'round the flag / and etc. [thermographed]	Unknown	Unk	Baur	A
__10096__	We'll set this / rising sun! [colored envelopes]	Blue, red	UncJa	Poppenger	A
10097	We'll win, / America... / Let's go! [w/, w/o copyright "C" at bottom]	Blue, red	VforV	Sosland	A
10098	Well, boys / here's the rabbit etc.	Unknown	Unk	Eichenlaub	A
10099	Well, Captain Yokohama, did you locate etc. [3rd line 36 mm] [thermographed]	Red	Japan	Yontz	B
10100	Well, Captain Yokohama, did you locate etc. [3rd line 50 mm] [thermographed]	Red	Japan	Yontz	B
10101	Well, captain, did you / locate enemy? / He sure did, and etc. [thermographed]	Red	Japan	Yontz	B
10102	We're / all behind / you! [handpainted]	Multicolored	Eagle	Adler	D
10103	We're / carrying on! [in quotes] [thermographed]	Black/Blue	Armed	Crosby	B

NO.	CACHET TEXT	COLOR	TOPIC	PUBLISHER	$
10104	We're / prepared / to deliver / the goods [thermographed]	Blue	Ordna	Unknown	A
10105	We're a little / old-maidish / ...when we invest / our etc. [handpainted]	Multicolored	Bonds	Myers	B
10106	We're as doggone / proud of our / soldier! [burned left edge] [handpainted]	Multicolored	Dog	Cowdery	D
10107	We're buying / bonds / and war etc.	Unknown	Bonds	Kosko	A
10108	We're doing / our share / how about you? [thermographed]	Blue	Unk	Yontz	A
10109	We're getting to the / bacon / We're etc.	Unknown	Unk	Eichenlaub	A
10110	We're in it / Let's win it	Unknown	Unk	Meylan	A
10111	We're in it——— / Let's win it! [top star has 1 or 2 points up] [colored envelopes]	Blue, red	VforV	Poppenger	A
10112	We're in the Army now!!	Green	Army	Christens	A
10113	We're on the road / to Berlin.... / Lookout / Manila, P.I. / U.S. Army [thermographed]	Blue, red	Japan	Crosby	B
10114	We're on the road / to Berlin.... / Lookout / Tokyo.... / U.S. Army [thermographed]	Blue, red	Japan	Crosby	B
10115	We're on the road / to Berlin.... / Lookout / Tokyo.... / U.S. Navy [thermographed]	Blue, red	Japan	Crosby	B
10116	We're on the road / to Berlin.... / Lookout / Tokyo.... [thermographed]	Blue, red	Japan	Crosby	B
10117	We're on the road / to Berlin.... / Lookout / Tokyo...... / U.S. Navy [thermographed]	Blue, red	Japan	Crosby	B
10118	We're promised, "The Four Freedoms," etc. [env. 6 1/2x3 5/8, 6 5/16x 3 ½ in.]	Blue	Verse	Shaw, TC	A
10119	We're riding the crest of the wave / but...don't relax!	Blue	Navy	Lawrence	A
10120	We're the fighting troops of / Bataan etc.	Unknown	Unk	Brenn	A
10121	We've just begun / to fight [in quotes] etc. [2 print varieties]	Blue, red	Navy	Boone	A
10122	We-want / Hiro-hi-to! [handpainted]	Multicolored	VJDay	Borkowski	E
10123	W-extra W-extra / Germany surrenders, / to the Allies. [manila envelope]	Black, red	VEDay	Baur	B
10124	Wham / boom / Buy more / U.S. war bonds / to shower / the Axis with bombs.	Multicolored	Air	Borkowski	C
10125	What / Hitler / prays / for!	Blue, red	Hitle	Boone	A
10126	What / keeps a / fighting / heart alive? / You're right / mister!!! etc.	Bu/Br/Red	Blood	Cozart	A
10127	What a difference! / 1st battleship in U.S. Navy / a modern battleship etc.	Unknown	Navy	Linto	B
10128	What a jar he / is in for! / Benito	Blue, red	Musso	Boone	A
10129	What a stew about / [etc.] / 1-11-'45———U.S.S. Dest. Hull, Monaghan etc.	Gold, silver	Event	Linto	B
10130	What a stew about / manpower yet there / are thousands on / bureaucratic etc.	Gold, silver	Flag	Linto	B
10131	What a swell job our / [etc.] / 9-2-'44———Yank forces roll / into Belgium	Multicolored	Event	Linto	B
10132	What a swell job our / boys on the fighting / fronts are etc. [no picture]	Gold, silver	Home	Linto	B
10133	What are we / fighting for? / [etc.] / Dec. 7, 1941, a date we will help etc.	Multicolored	Pearl	Linto	B
10134	What are we / fighting for? / Some Japs are being released / and are etc.	Multicolored	AJA	Linto	B
10135	What are you / doing to protect etc.	Unknown	Unk	Levering	A
10136	What are you doing / for etc. [3 mm between first 2 lines]	Unknown	Unk	Levering	A
10137	What are you doing / for etc. [9 mm between first 2 lines]	Unknown	Unk	Levering	A
10138	What are you kicking about? / No one is shooting at / you.	Green, red	Army	McCluney	B
10139	What constitutes free rights? / [etc.] / 9-4-'44———British capture Antwerp etc.	Unknown	Event	Linto	B
10140	What constitutes free rights? / Federal employees dunned / for etc.	Unknown	Home	Linto	B
10141	What did / you / do today for / freedom	Blue, red	Flag	Nichols	B
10142	What do you / mean / you / won't / buy / bonds [handpainted]	Black	Bonds	Muzzy	B
10143	What do you mean - / you won't buy bonds? [handpainted]	Unknown	Army	Wolf, CL	B
10144	What does / Roosevelt mean / by "inflation"? / What is it we etc. [no picture]	Multicolored	FDR	Linto	B
10145	What does / victory / mean to you? / Yes sir! Certainly you'll help!	Multicolored	Ordna	Linto	B
10146	What d'ya mean———you ain't gonna buy bonds!	Bu,Gd/Gd,S	Bonds	Linto	B
10147	What d'ya mean———you ain't gonna fight for me!	Green, violet	Home	Linto	B
10148	What d'ya mean———you ain't gonna fight for me! / Navy Day———27-10-'43	Multicolored	Navy	Linto	B
10149	What flavor? [in quotes] / I'll take / Manila! [handpainted]	Unknown	UncJa	Rayl	C
10150	What flower is this that greets the morn etc.	Unknown	Unk	Card	B
10151	What I think of Hitler and his pals! [env. 6 1/2x3 5/8, 7 1/2x4 in.]	Blue	Hitle	Fertig	A
10152	What is a key-man / Does business / stop when / key-men quit? [no picture]	Multicolored	Home	Linto	B
10153	What is a key-man? / Does business / stop when / key-men quit? [no picture]	Multicolored	Home	Linto	B
10154	What is the / truth about / Bataan? / [etc.] / 1-1-'44———U.S. 8th Air Force etc.	Multicolored	Event	Linto	B
10155	What is the / truth about / Bataan? / Who's covering / up who? [no picture]	Gd,Vi/Multi	Home	Linto	B
10156	What is the difference / [etc.] / 6-30-'44———U.S. severs relations / with etc.	Unknown	Event	Linto	B
10157	What is the difference / between a depression / and etc. [no picture]	Gold, green	Liber	Linto	B
10158	What she worte [sic] is under cover etc. [envelope 6 3/4x3 3/4 in.]	Unknown	Unk	Quigley	A
10159	What so proudly / we hail!	Blue, red	Flag	Mission	A
10160	What they fought for / let us preserve [thermographed]	Unknown	Unk	Baur	A
10161	What, no sedatives?	Black	Nazis	Smith, DH	A

NO.	CACHET TEXT	COLOR	TOPIC	PUBLISHER	$
10162	What's / so funny? [envelope 7 1/2x4 in.]	Unknown	Unk	Fertig	B
10163	Whats a cookin Ernest? [addressed to Ernest J. Muzzy] [cannibal, large pot] [hp]	Black	Home	Unknown	B
10164	What-where-when / 2nd front [handpainted]	Black	Hitle	Wolf, CL	B
10165	When a part of the / U.S. fleet paid visit / to Australia etc. [typed] [4/9/41]	Black	Navy	Unknown	C
10166	When a part of the / U.S. fleet paid visit / to Australia to let / Japan etc. [UL, typed]	Black	Event	Unknown	C
10167	When asked what flavor / he liked best / Gen. MacArthur etc. [no picture]	Red	Mac	Shaw, TC	B
10168	When better / bonds are sold / Uncle Sam / will sell them!	Gold	Eagle	Linto	B
10169	When bonds buy ships / to nab the Nips, / that "ten percent" etc. [no picture]	Red	Bonds	Shaw, CF	A
10170	When day is done! [handpainted]	Multicolored	Hitle	Nichols	C
10171	When dreams / are so nice / I'm / just too tired / to think etc. [handpainted]	Multicolored	Home	Cowdery	D
10172	When heel meets "heel". [in quotes] / United / Nations / Hitler [handpainted]	Unknown	UncAx	Doemick	C
10173	When in doubt - lights / out! [label + blue "Victory" border]	Multicolored	Merch	Unknown	B
10174	When in doubt - lights / out! [label + red "Victory" border]	Multicolored	Merch	Unknown	B
10175	When in doubt - lights / out! [label + red "Win the War" border]	Multicolored	Merch	Unknown	B
10176	When is / O happy day! [picture of Hitler between "when" and "is"]	Black, red	Hitle	Boone	A
10177	When it comes to war / or love, leave it to a / Marine [text above stars]	Multicolored	USMC	Amer Pat	A
10178	When it comes to war / or love, leave it to a / Marine [text on stars]	Multicolored	USMC	Amer Pat	A
10179	When Johnnie Doughboy / comes etc.	Unknown	Unk	Baur	A
10180	When our big-hearted / politicians make plans / to take care etc. [no picture]	Gold, silver	Home	Linto	B
10181	When peace is won on Europe's fields etc. [no picture]	Unknown	Unk	Carpenter	A
10182	When success / goes to the head / defeat goes / to "de-feet"	Multicolored	Musso	Andrews	A
10183	When the administra- / tion ask for new or extended / legislation Congress etc.	Gold, silver	Liber	Linto	B
10184	When the administration / ask [sic] for new or extended / legislation etc.	Gold, green	Liber	Linto	B
10185	When the administration / ask [sic] for new or extended etc. [no picture]	Multicolored	Home	Linto	B
10186	When the bells of victory / toll / will you be on the honor etc. [no picture]	Multicolored	Bonds	Linto	B
10187	When the boys / come marching / home / ——Welcome—— / home from etc.	Blue/Purple	Home	Abel	A
10188	When the Russo-Jap / treaty / [etc.] / 4-23-'45——Rebellion / starts in Berlin	Brown, silver	Event	Linto	B
10189	When the Russo-Jap / treaty was broken / a Jap general said: / 'Vodka we' etc.	Brown, silver	Flag	Linto	B
10190	When the shoe is on the other foot [cachet colors vary]	Multicolored	USSR	Peer	B
10191	When the Yanks march / through etc. [pink envelope]	Unknown	Unk	Baur	A
10192	When the Yanks squeeze / it'll be Jap-on-knees	Blue	EagFl	Foster	A
10193	When they build bigger / and better navies etc.	Unknown	Unk	Baur	A
10194	When this war is over, I do not etc.	Unknown	Unk	Brenn	A
10195	When Tojo was talking to / his honorable ancestors / did he etc. [no picture]	Gold, silver	Japan	Linto	B
10196	When visiting me in camp, stop over in / beautiful Chattanooga	Blue	Home	Unknown	A
10197	When we march / thru the / streets of / Berlin [envelope 9 1/2x4 1/8 in.]	Unknown	Unk	Rameco	B
10198	When we reach the "Isle of / Japan" / with our caps at a jaunty tilt, etc.	Blue, red	Verse	Brenn	A
10199	When will the bell / ring him out?	Red	Hitle	Roberts	A
10200	When will the war end? Look! etc. [no picture]	Unknown	Unk	Boone	A
10201	When you find / American-Japs we will / be near to utopia!	Multicolored	AJA	Linto	B
10202	When you find / American-Japs we will / be near to Utopia!	Gold, silver	AJA	Linto	B
10203	When you or your folks, found refuge here - / this was God's etc. [no picture] handpainted]	Blue, red	Bonds	Myers	B
10204	When you think of / taking etc. [3 soldiers attacking] [thermographed]	Unknown	Army	Baur	A
10205	When you think of / taking etc. [Marine] [thermographed]	Unknown	USMC	Baur	A
10206	Where / is the government / of the people / by the people etc. [no picture]	Multicolored	Home	Linto	B
10207	Where else could / you enjoy the liberty / and happiness you / do in the etc.	Blue, red	Uncle	Levering	A
10208	Where ever our boys / and girls may be / Is at there [sic] side. [Red Cross symbol]	Blu, red	RedCr	Baur	A
10209	Where is our democracy? / Congress votes / [etc.] / What a price was paid etc.	Multicolored	Anniv	Linto	B
10210	Where is our democracy? / Congress votes / [etc.] / What price the 1918 etc.	Multicolored	Anniv	Linto	B
10211	Where is our democracy? / Congress votes down OPA / subsidy etc. [no picture]	Multicolored	Home	Linto	B
10212	Where is the fleet? / (continued) / 2--Oh, wouldn't they / give a lot to know, etc.	Black, blue	Liber	Weigand	A
10213	Where is the fleet? / 3--Where is the fleet? / Just wait / and you'll hear of it--- / Its etc.	Black, blue	Liber	Weigand	A
10214	Where is the fleet? / 4--Oh, wouldn't they / give a lot to know / in Tokyo, in Tokyo etc.	Black, blue	Liber	Weigand	A
10215	Where our flag waves / the U.S. Marines, / shall be on hand to guard it	Blue	USMC	Harrington	A
10216	Where our flag waves / United States Marines / shall etc.	Bu/Br/Gn/Pin	USMC	Harrington	A
10217	Where there / is life / there is a will / to win [1 diving P-38, 75mm long]	Multicolored	Air	Amer Pat	A
10218	Where there / is life / there is a will / to win. [1 diving P-38, 50 mm long]	Multicolored	Air	Amer Pat	A
10219	Where there / is life / there is a will / to win. [2 diving P-38s]	Multicolored	Air	Amer Pat	A

NO.	CACHET TEXT	COLOR	TOPIC	PUBLISHER	$
10220	Where there's smoke / there must / [etc.] / Armistice Day / November 11, 1943	Multicolored	Holid	Linto	B
10221	Where there's smoke / there must be fire! / Read the report of Comptroller etc.	Multicolored	Flag	Linto	B
10222	Where there's smoke there should be some fire! [handpainted]	Multicolored	Japan	Newton FN	C
10223	Where's / the / garbage / can?	Blue/Red	Axis	Barnes	A
10224	Where's the aid for / under-privileged? / [etc.] / 2-16-'42——Russian etc.	Multicolored	Anniv	Linto	B
10225	Where's the aid for / under-privileged? / [etc.] / 3-22-'44——Pervomaisk etc.	Multicolored	Event	Linto	B
10226	Where's the aid for / under-privileged? / The etc. [no picture] [color varieties]	Multicolored	Home	Linto	B
10227	Wherever he is / your Red Cross / is at his side	Black	RedCr	Peters	A
10228	Wherever they go-they go together etc. [envelope 9 1/2x4 1/8 in.]	Unknown	RedCr	Amer Red	C
10229	Which flag / are we / entitled / to wave when / the boys come / home? [handpainted]	Multicolored	Uncle	Steinhardt	C
10230	While "Britannia ruled the waves" / still "Columbia is gem of the ocean"	Green	Navy	Carpenter	A
10231	While Japs are viciously / mutilating our boys Ickes / wants to shelter Japs etc.	Gold, silver	AJA	Linto	B
10232	While Washington / indulges in political / squabbles, the etc. [no picture]	Multicolored	Home	Linto	B
10233	While you strike / at home, /our boys strike / at the enemy. [handpainted]	Multicolored	Army	Borkowski	D
10234	White collar workers——take note / [etc.] / 12-23-'44——Yank 1st Army and etc.	Multicolored	Event	Linto	B
10235	White collar workers——take note / Congress has a bill to etc. [no picture]	Multicolored	Home	Linto	B
10236	Who caused a / "Feuhrer" / in a hurry? etc. [burned left edge] [handpainted]	Multicolored	Axis	Cowdery	D
10237	Who ever saw / a real / American-Jap? / Buy bonds! [no picture]	Multicolored	AJA	Linto	B
10238	Who gave / us / V / victory / Let's etc.	Unknown	Unk	Levering	A
10239	Who in the / wants a Jap?	Unknown	Devil	Linto	B
10240	Who is financing the / "Peace Now" / [etc.] / Feb. 11, '41——Italy notified etc.	Multicolored	Event	Linto	B
10241	Who is financing the / "Peace Now" movement? / Why are these Hitlerites etc.	Gold, silver	Uncle	Linto	B
10242	Who is financing the / "Peach" now	Unknown	Home	Linto	B
10243	Who is short. [in quotes] [handpainted]	Multicolored	Axis	Bates	C
10244	Who says we can't?	Multicolored	Uncle	Von Los	A
10245	Who says we can't? / Defeat / the so called / super race / in 1944	Black, orange	Nazis	Carpenter	A
10246	Who says we can't? [thermographed]	Blue	Uncle	Von Los	B
10247	Who? Me? / There was a little dope with / a fat pay envelope / and she etc.	Green, violet	Verse	Threl+Thar	A
10248	Whoopee! Running water / and showers! [handpainted]	Multicolored	Army	Cowdery	D
10249	Who's next? / One / down- / two / to go! [thermographed]	Black/Red	Axis	Ang	A
10250	Whose [sic] afraid of the big / "bad wolf"? [handpainted]	Multicolored	Japan	Parker	B
10251	Why / bonuses for war / workers? / [etc.] / 12-27-'44——Yanks retake / six etc.	Multicolored	Event	Linto	B
10252	Why / bonuses for war / workers? / For what? / What about those in service?	Multicolored	Flag	Linto	B
10253	Why / compulsory / military / [etc.] / 12-4-'44——Army rules / in Greece	Multicolored	Event	Linto	B
10254	Why / compulsory / military / training? / We thought this was a / war to etc.	Multicolored	Home	Linto	B
10255	Why are all those attacks / made against Henry J. / Kaiser? etc. [no picture]	Multicolored	Home	Linto	B
10256	Why are the Japs permitted / to store their farm etc. [no picture]	Unknown	AJA	Linto	B
10257	Why does Russia / block Allies' China / campaign?	Red, silver	USSR	Linto	B
10258	Why don't you get a war job? [in quotes] [handpainted]	Black	Women	Clendennen	D
10259	Why Jap sympathy? / Have some Americans / forgot Pearl Harbor / and etc.	Multicolored	AJA	Linto	B
10260	Why not have men in / Washington like / General MacArthur? [no picture]	Brown, silver	Mac	Linto	B
10261	Why shouldn't we be having fun? etc.	Red	Unk	Rathkamp	A
10262	Why the delay in / bringing Kimmel / [etc.] / Jan. 1, 1942——United Nations etc.	Multicolored	Anniv	Linto	B
10263	Why the delay in / bringing Kimmel / and Short to trial? etc. [no picture]	Green, violet	Pearl	Linto	B
10264	Why the postwar bug-a-boo? / Stop political maneuvering! / Concentrate on war!	Multicolored	EagSh	Linto	B
10265	Why was General / De Witt relieved / [etc.] / 10-27-'41——Pres. Roosevelt etc.	Multicolored	Anniv	Linto	B
10266	Why was General / De Witt relieved / [etc.] / Dec. 7, 1941, a date we will etc.	Multicolored	Pearl	Linto	B
10267	Why was General / De Witt relieved of / the Pacific Coast etc. [no picture]	Blue, gold	AJA	Linto	B
10268	Why waste good ammunition? / Japs are eagerly waiting for it!	Silver	Armed	Linto	B
10269	Will / Berlin / be / next? [handpainted]	Black	Hitle	Wolf, CL	B
10270	Will Congress please / check / [etc.] / 9-13-'40——Buckingham Palace etc.	Multicolored	Anniv	Linto	B
10271	Will Congress please / check government / mismanagement / and etc. [no picture]	O, violet	Home	Linto	B
10272	Will Rogers would say: / "For victory! Buy / defense bonds." Commemorating etc.	Blue	Bonds	Bailey	B
10273	Will the administration / study / [etc.] / 1-26-'44——Argentina breaks etc.	Multicoilored	Event	Linto	B
10274	Will the administration / study Benjamin Franklin / and etc. [color varieties]	Multicolored	Hist	Linto	B
10275	Will the Truman Inves- / tigating / [etc.] / 8-31-'40——Airliner crashed at etc.	Multicolored	Anniv	Linto	B
10276	Will the Truman Inves- / tigating Committee's / report on etc. [no picture]	O, silver	Home	Linto	B
10277	Will we get a real / freedom / [etc.] / 5-29-'44——Japs gain 7 miles in etc.	Multicolored	Event	Linto	B

NO.	CACHET TEXT	COLOR	TOPIC	PUBLISHER	$
10278	Will we get a real / freedom after the / victory or a new etc. [no picture]	Gold, silver	Home	Linto	B
10279	Will we win the war? / Yes! / but we must etc.	Unknown	Home	Linto	B
10280	Will you be / able to say / "present" / [etc.] / Leif Erikson Day / First etc.	Multicolored	Anniv	Linto	B
10281	Will you be / able to say / "present" when / the Honor Roll etc. [color varieties]	Multicolored	Bonds	Linto	B
10282	William Penn / founder of Pennsylvania / [etc.] / "We must give the liberty we" etc.	Black	Hist	Griffith	A
10283	Wilmington has / air raid / alarm / Sunday morning / June 6th, etc. [thermographed]	Red	Home	Boone	A
10284	Win / the / war / in / '44	Blue, red	Globe	Leonard	A
10285	Win / the / war / in / '44	Blue, red	Globe	Harrington	A
10286	Win / the / war!	Bu/Gn/O/Pu/R	EagV	Cliff	A
10287	Win the / peace [eagle's head pink] [handpainted]	Multicolored	EagFl	Adler	E
10288	Win the / peace [eagle's head white] [handpainted]	Multicolored	EagFl	Adler	E
10289	Win the / peace [handpainted]	Multicolored	EagFl	Adler	E
10290	Win the / war / "We will accept no compromise, no alternative," etc. [thermographed]	Brown/Orange	Mac	Crosby	B
10291	Win the / war / in '44	Unknown	Unk	Harrington	A
10292	Win the / war / Let's split the Pacific Ocean with the Japs etc. [thermographed]	Blue	Eagle	Crosby	B
10293	Win the peace / V / victory / buy now etc.	Blue, brown	Unk	Hamilton	A
10294	Win the war - buy defense stamps and bonds [thermographed]	Blue	Bonds	Crosby	B
10295	Win the war / "On to victory" [orange eagle]	Multicolored	Eagle	Staehle	B
10296	Win the war / "On to victory" [white eagle]	Multicolored	Eagle	Jordan	B
10297	Win the war / "We will win / or / we will die" / MacArthur	Blue, red	Mac	Stanard	B
10298	Win the war / and the peace too!	Black	VforV	Artcraft	A
10299	Win the war / Be a man / of the / minute etc.	Brown	Unk	Petrasek	A
10300	Win the war / for victory-liberty-and etc.	Blue/Red	Unk	Petrasek	A
10301	Win the war / in 'forty four / The bridge to victory / U.S. war etc.	Blue/Red	Bonds	Schaefer	D
10302	Win the war / Liberty must endure / Independence Day etc. [artist: Knapp]	Blue, red	Eag+	Fleetwood	B
10303	Win the war / Marines Army Navy / Coast Guard and / Merchant Marine [thermographed]	Blue, red	Eagle	Unknown	A
10304	Win the war / Our / right / to liberty / "Fight! Work! and Save!" / Buy war bonds etc.	Brown/Red	Bonds	McFarland	A
10305	Win the war / Our / right / to liberty / Fight, work and save.	Red	Uncle	McFarland	A
10306	Win the war / The U.S. eagle / is in it to win it [artist: Knapp]	Blue, red	Eag+	Fleetwood	B
10307	Win the war / V	Blue	VforV	Gielarow	A
10308	Win the war / We will win / or / we etc.	Unknown	Unk	Hunt	A
10309	Win the War [4 rows of stars behind eagle] [unsigned] [handpainted]	Multicolored	Eagle	Knapp	G
10310	Win the war [in quotes]	Blue, red	Eagle	Ioor	A
10311	Win the war [in quotes] / Victory in '43	Blue, red	Home	Ioor	A
10312	Win the war in / '44 / Buy war bonds [handpainted]	Multicolored	Bonds	Barnes	C
10313	Win the war in / '44 [thermographed]	Gray	Axis	Unknown	B
10314	Win the war in / '44 [upper left]	Red	Axis	Peters	A
10315	Win the war in 1944 / The Star-Spangled etc.	Unknown	Unk	Fabian	A
10316	Win the war with prayer [envelope 6x3 ½ in.]	Unknown	Unk	Dime	A
10317	Win the war! / The Spirit of 1776 / Gettysburg / Pearl Harbor	Blue, red	Hist	Unknown	A
10318	Win we must / Berlin or bust	Unknown	Unk	McCluney	B
10319	Winged / victory [handpainted]	Multicolored	Air	Knapp	G
10320	Wings / for / victory [handpainted]	Multicolored	ShieV	Knapp	G
10321	Wings / for victory [airplane rising from piano]	Black	Air	Steinway	E
10322	Wings / of / victory	Multicolored	Air	Amer Pat	A
10323	Wings / to / win [artist: Knapp]	Blue, red	Air	Fleetwood	C
10324	Wings / to / win! / V [artist: Knapp]	Bu/Gn/Pu/R/Y	EagV	Richardson	C
10325	Wings / to / win! / V-E Day May 8, 1945	Blue, yellow	VEDay	Richardson	C
10326	Wings across the Pacific Keep 'em flying! / [etc.] / Remember Pearl Harbor! etc.	Multicolored	Pearl	Edmunds	D
10327	Wings for / victory [four-engine plane]	Blue, red	Air	Card	A
10328	Wings for / victory [single-engine plane]	Blue, red	Air	Card	A
10329	Wings for victory [handpainted]	Multicolored	Air	Knapp	G
10330	Wings of the Navy / Keep 'em flying / U.S.S. Essex / aircraft etc. [thermographed]	Red	Navy	Unknown	A
10331	Wings over / America	Blue, red	Air	Krakora	A
10332	Wings over America / will keep America etc. [env. 6 1/2x3 5/8, 7 1/2x3 7/8 in.]	Blue, red	Air	Richardson	A
10333	Wings over America / will keep America etc. [envelope 7 1/2x4 in.]	Blue, red	Air	Richardson	A
10334	Wings over America [under eagle and airplane] [all-over cachet]	Blue, red	Air	Krakora	B
10335	Wings over America [under eagle and shield]	Blue, red	EagSh	Krakora	A
10336	Wings to win	Red	Unk	Richardson	A

NO.	CACHET TEXT	COLOR	TOPIC	PUBLISHER	$
10337	Winston / Churchill / British / Prime / Minister / arrives [no picture] [card]	Black, red	Event	Fidelity	C
10338	Winston Churchill / former Prime Minister of British Empire	Black	Winst	Pacific	A
10339	Winston Churchill [thermographed]	Unknown	Winst	Unknown	A
10340	Wipe / out / aggression - greed / and intolerance [handpainted]	Multicolored	Globe	Stoll	B
10341	Wipe that grin off! / Buy / more / bonds [label + printed border]	Multicolored	Japan	Foster	B
10342	Wish I / could come / with it, Pvt. Ray! [handpainted]	Multicolored	Home	Cowdery	D
10343	Wish I could / bring it! [stamp missing] [handpainted]	Multicolored	Home	Cowdery	D
10344	Wishing you and yours / unrationed etc.	Unknown	Home	Bean	A
10345	Witch'll / it be? / Bonds? / or bondage? [handpainted]	Black	Holid	Martin	C
10346	With 4th Army to victory / Quartermaster / Corps. [4th Army insignia]	Red	Unit	Unknown	A
10347	With a magic V and the etc.	Blue	Unk	Rathkamp	A
10348	With a sense of duty met / and well done / WAVES [thermographed]	Blue	WAVES	Sadworth	B
10349	With all / their / goose / steps / three / dead / ducks!	Black, red	Axis	Boone	A
10350	With all their / goose steps... / Tojo Adolf Benito / 'Three dead ducks	Green, red	Axis	Boone	A
10351	With both feet / American / Army / British / Army	Multicolored	Ally	Adler	D
10352	With confidence in our armed forces / [etc.] / The war is over! / Again etc.	Black, red	VJDay	Puls	B
10353	With confidence in our armed forces- / with the etc. [diagonal] [no picture]	Blue	FDR	Bartley	B
10354	With confidence in our armed forces——with / the etc. [Liberty bell] [buff envelope]	Black	FDR	Puls	B
10355	With confidence in our armed forces——with / the unbounding etc. [flag] [UL]	Black	FDR	Puls	B
10356	With deep humility, a / greatful [sic] nation pauses / in tribute and etc. [no picture]	Red	VJDay	Levering	C
10357	With God in our / hearts we cannot / lose the victory!	Gold, silver	Relig	Linto	B
10358	With liberty / the breath of / life is easier	Multicolored	Liber	Amer Pat	A
10359	With malice toward none / and charity for all. A. Lincoln etc. [thermographed]	Black	Linc	Crosby	B
10360	With malice toward none [in quotes] / Lincoln's birthday [cut-&-pasted paper]	Black	Linc	Temple	C
10361	With the ___ Division / in etc. [thermographed]	Unknown	Unk	Crosby	B
10362	With the Army Air Forces in Florida [on flap] [envelope 5 5/8x4 3/8 in.]	Unknown	Air	Unknown	A
10363	With you! [stamp missing] [torn at right] [handpainted]	Multicolored	Home	Cowdery	D
10364	Without freedom / liberty dies	Multicolored	FlLib	Minkus	A
10365	Woe is me / unconditional / surrender / loss of / empire [handpainted]	Unknown	Japan	Wolf, CL	C
10366	Women's / Army / Corps (WACS) [envelope 6x3 ½ in.]	Unknown	WAC	Unknown	A
10367	Women's Signal Corps / loyal to our cause	Gold, silver	WAC	Linto	B
10368	Wood pulp for / victory [envelope 6 1/2x3 5/8, 9 1/2x4 1/8 in.]	Black	Home	Olson	B
10369	Work / for / victory ["Work" red, "Victory" blue] [handpainted] [no picture]	Multicolored	Home	Hanna	B
10370	Work / for victory / in '44 [no picture]	Unknown	Unk	Davis, D	A
10371	Work / to keep free / A "sound" policy for victory! [label + printed border]	Multicolored	Home	Artists	B
10372	Work / to keep free / Your hands can shape victory! [label + printed border]	Multicolored	Home	Artists	B
10373	Work for / victory / Hawaii / victory worker / Hana / Hana no / lanakila	Blue, red	Home	Sayama	B
10374	Work for / victory [w/, w/o copyright "C"]	Blue, red	Home	Cachet Cra	A
10375	Work for victory / with the / fighting / spirit / of the / Wake Island Marines	Blue, red	USMC	Cachet Cra	A
10376	Work or fight / for Uncle Sam	Multicolored	Flag	Ang	A
10377	Work to keep free / Idle hands work for the enemy! [label + printed border]	Multicolored	Eagle	Artists	B
10378	Work to win / or / work for him	Black, red	Hitle	McCluney	B
10379	Work to win / or you'll work for him [label + blue "Victory" border]	Multicolored	Hitle	Unknown	B
10380	Work to win / or you'll work for him [label + red "Victory" border]	Multicolored	Hitle	Unknown	B
10381	Work to win / or you'll work for him [label + red "Win the War" border]	Multicolored	Hitle	Unknown	B
10382	Work together, win together! [handpainted]	Multicolored	Navy	Unknown	C
10383	Work will win the war! / Franklin Delano Roosevelt / World War II etc. [thermograph]	Blue	FDR	Crosby	B
10384	Work, fight and pray / for victory	Blue, red	EagSh	Lowell	A
10385	Work, fight and pray / for victory [cross above and below text]	Blu	Ordna	Ander, EA	A
10386	Work, fight and pray / for victory! [2 stars above text]	Red	Ordna	Ander, EA	A
10387	Work, fight and pray / for victory! [2 stars below text]	Blue, red	Ordna	Ander, EA	A
10388	Work, fight and pray / for victory! [4 stars above text]	Blue, red	Ordna	Ander, EA	A
10389	Work, fight and pray / for victory! [4 stars below text]	Blue, red	Ordna	Ander, EA	A
10390	Work, fight and pray / for victory! [no stars]	Br/Blue, red	Ordna	Ander, EA	A
10391	Work.. / for victory / in '44 [".." precedes "Work"] [no picture]	Aqua, red	VforV	Davis, D	A
10392	Work-fight / to give them a / better world [w/, w/o copyright "C"]	Blue, red	Uncle	Cachet Cra	A
10393	Working / together / means / victory	Multicolored	Flag	Linto	B
10394	Working / together / means / victory / 8-18-'44——Allies now / [etc.] / Paris	Multicolored	Event	Linto	B

NO.	CACHET TEXT	COLOR	TOPIC	PUBLISHER	$
10395	Working for / victory / V	Multicolored	Home	Minkus	A
10396	Working on the / spud pile! [in quotes]	Black	Army	Lupton	A
10397	Working with / Uncle Sam!	Multicolored	Uncle	Dime	A
10398	Work-work-work / Don't be absent etc.	Blue, red	Home	Kosko	A
10399	World conquest—— / "Time's fool" / "Heutegehort" etc. [envelope 6 1/2x3 11/16 in.]	Black	Hitle	Unknown	B
10400	World events / 1500 Navy planes etc.	Black, red	Event	Ang	B
10401	World events / Allies invade / southern France	Black, red	Event	Ang	B
10402	World events / Berlin falls etc.	Black, red	Event	Ang	B
10403	World events / British troops etc.	Black, red	Event	Ang	B
10404	World Events / Brussels taken / by Allied forces	Black, red	Event	Ang	B
10405	World events / Carrier planes etc.	Black, red	Event	Ang	B
10406	World events / Denmark, Holland set free / as Nazis there surrender	Black, red	Event	Ang	B
10407	World events / French patriots / liberate Paris	Black, red	Event	Ang	B
10408	World events / Germans / surrender	Blue, red	VEDay	Ang	B
10409	World events / Hitler escapes / assassination / plot by Generals	Black, red	Event	Ang	B
10410	World events / Jap home island / Okinawa invaded	Black, red	Event	Ang	B
10411	World events / Japs / quit	Blue, red	VJDay	Ang	B
10412	World events / Manchuria blasted / U.S.. Fights in Saar	Black, red	Event	Ang	B
10413	World events / Nazis fall back / Yanks enter Paris	Black, red	Event	Ang	B
10414	World events / Patton's men storm etc.	Black, red	Event	Ang	B
10415	World events / Port of Le Havre / falls to British	Black, red	Event	Ang	B
10416	World events / Red Army enters etc.	Black, red	Event	Ang	B
10417	World events / Reds battle Nazis / on streets of Berlin	Black, red	Event	Ang	B
10418	World events / Reds enter Posen etc.	Black, red	Event	Ang	B
10419	World events / Romania quits etc.	Black, red	Event	Ang	B
10420	World events / Roosevelt / dies etc. [postmarked 4/12/45]	Black, red	FDR	Ang	E
10421	World events / Russia denounces Jap treaty / and Koiso cabinet resigns etc.	Black, red	Event	Ang	B
10422	World events / Russians battle / way into Germany	Black, red	Event	Ang	B
10423	World events / Russians drive etc.	Black, red	Event	Ang	B
10424	World events / U.S. armies racing for Rhine	Black, red	Event	Ang	B
10425	World events / U.S. bombs Tokyo etc.	Black, red	Event	Ang	B
10426	World events / U.S. First Army / invades Germany	Black, orange	Event	Ang	B
10427	World events / U.S. invades Luzon / head for Manila	Black, red	Event	Ang	B
10428	World events / U.S. invades Luzon / head for Manila [headline thermographed]	Black, red	Event	Ang	B
10429	World events / U.S. Sixth invades / the Philippines	Black, red	Event	Ang	B
10430	World events / Vienna falls etc.	Black, red	Event	Ang	B
10431	World events / Warsaw / liberated	Black, red	Event	Ang	B
10432	World events / Yanks 3rd enters etc.	Black, red	Event	Ang	B
10433	World events / Yanks cross Rhine etc.	Black, red	Event	Ang	B
10434	World events / Yanks enter Belgium / Verdun, St. Mihiel fall	Black, red	Event	Ang	B
10435	World events / Yanks in / Manila	Black, red	Event	Ang	B
10436	World events / Yanks meet Reds	Black, red	Event	Ang	B
10437	World events / Yanks seize etc.	Black, red	Event	Ang	B
10438	World hails peace / Jap / [etc.] / The Axis is axed!	Multicolored	VJDay	Boone	B
10439	World hails peace / Jap Cabinet quits / Gas rationing ends [8/15/45]	Multicolored	VJDay	Boone	B
10440	World hails peace: / Jap cabinet quits / Gas rationing ends	Blue, red	VJDay	Boone	B
10441	World peace? / Yes! When all / people have God / in their hearts!	Gold, silver	Flag	Linto	B
10442	World situation / 1——Adolph's got a headache / [etc.] / 2——Franko's etc. [handpainted]	Multicolored	Liber	Weigand	B
10443	World War II / Chinese armies retake Kweilin / former American base	Black, blue	Event	Yudkin	B
10444	World War II / Eight hundred [800] B-29's blast the enemy / with 6000 tons etc.	Black, red	Air	Yudkin	C
10445	World War II / General Spatz [sic] is appointed Com- / ander of the Strategic etc.	Black, red	Air	Yudkin	C
10446	World War II / Historic Potsdam Conference / ("Terminal") opens; Churchill, Attlee etc.	Black, blue	Event	Yudkin	C
10447	World War II / Japanese Emperor Hirohito / issues Imperial Rescript etc.	Blue, red	Event	Yudkin	C
10448	World War II / Japan's Emperor Hirohito / broadcasts to the Japanese / people etc.	Black, blue	VJDay	Yudkin	D
10449	World War II / The B-29 Enola Gay dropped the / first wartime atomic bomb etc. [postmarked 8/6/45]	Black, red	Atom	Yudkin	E
10450	World War II / The State Department / revelled [sic] today that etc.	Red	Event	Yudkin	C
10451	World War II / United Nations Conference / held by delegates etc.	Black, blue	Event	Yudkin	B
10452	World War II / VE-Day / President Harry S. Truman / announces the surrender / of Germany.	Black, red	VEDay	Yudkin	C

NO.	CACHET TEXT	COLOR	TOPIC	PUBLISHER	$
10453	World-events / Hitler dead / Nazi radio report	Green, red	Event	Ang	C
10454	World-events / Hitler dead / Nazi radio report	Black, red	Event	Ang	B
10455	World-events / Nazis cross Rhine / gain many points	Black, red	Event	Ang	B
10456	Worlds greatest navy / U.S.S. Arizona etc.	Purple	Navy	Harrington	A
10457	Worlds greatest navy / Uncle Sam , shall ever, / sail the high seas. etc.	Black, red	Navy	Harrington	A
10458	World's greatest navy / Uncle Sam etc.	Unknown	Unk	Harrington	A
10459	World's greatest navy / United States ship Luzon / river gunboat No.7 etc.	Brown	Navy	Harrington	A
10460	World's peace is / very essential to / the welfare of / all beings	Blue, red	Liber	Symbols	B
10461	Worries [in quotes] [handpainted]	Multicolored	Hitle	Adler	E
10462	Worth / fighting / for [handpainted]	Blue, red	Bell	Klaas	C
10463	Worth / repeating! / Buy / bonds / Buy / bonds [handpainted]	Multicolored	Bonds	Stoll	C
10464	Worth fighting for [envelope 6 9/16x3 3/4 in.]	Unknown	Unk	Belles-let	C
10465	Wot-cha-got? / L-S-M-F-T / No longer etc. [no picture]	Unknown	Unk	Harrington	A
10466	Would prefer to retire / F.D.R.	Blue	FDR	McFarland	A
10467	Would you / like to be sent / to war not sure / we had enough equipments? etc.	Multicolored	Bonds	Linto	B
10468	Would you rather / buy bonds / or / be bombed	Unknown	Unk	Butzen	B
10469	Would you rather / buy bonds / or etc.	Unknown	Unk	Powell	A
10470	Would you save a / serviceman's life. / ? / Then give / your blood.	Blue, red	Blood	Baur	A
10471	Wow! The Marines did it! [thermographed]	Purple	USMC	Crosby	B
10472	Write a protest to your / Congressman and [etc.] / Labor Day——Sept. 6, 1943	Multicolored	Holid	Linto	B
10473	Write a protest to your / Congressman and Senator / about the etc. [no picture]	Blue, gold	Home	Linto	B
10474	Write him often	Unknown	Unk	Hillerich	A
10475	Write often / to / the boy / in service	Unknown	Unk	Davis, Ral	A
10476	Write regularly / via / V / mail [colored envelopes]	Black	VforV	Temple	A
10477	Writin' may be quite a task- / somethin' awful hard to do, / but think of etc.	Green, purple	Home	Eichenlaub	A
10477A	Wrought y the hand of Providence / Victory / 1944	Multicolored	Home	White, TM	E
10478	W-W-What do we do—— / salute or whistle? [2 print varieties]	Brown/Red	Army	Yontz	A

Cover Values (from Table 6, p. 136)

Value	*Price Range*
A	$ 3 - 6
B	$ 7 - 15
C	$ 16 - 30
D	$ 31 - 60
E	$ 61 - 125
F	$ 126 - 250
G	$ 251 - 500
H	$ 501 - 1000
I	$ >1000
X	**Unpriced: Suspicious or fraudulent cover**

9730

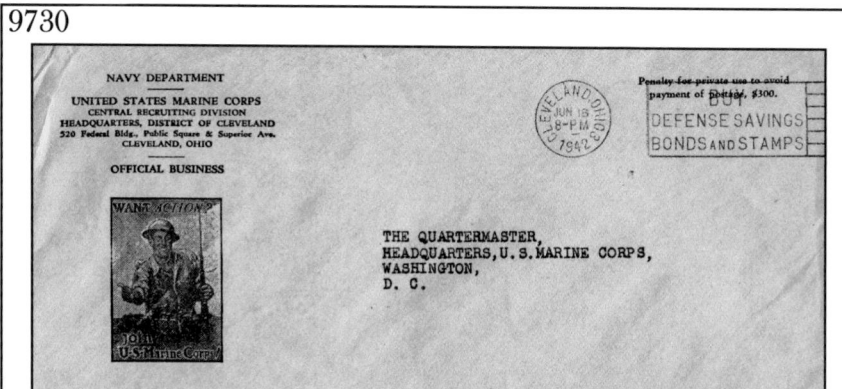

9756

9766

9819

9826

9848

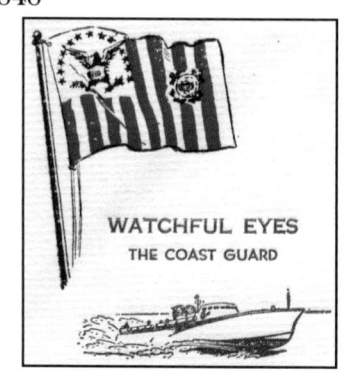

9853A

9935

10028

10085

10096

10122

10217

10267
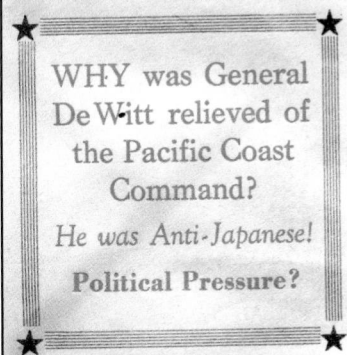

10306

10321

10323

10373

10406

10408

Paul J. Miller
46 W. Sixth St.
Pottstown, Pa.

10446

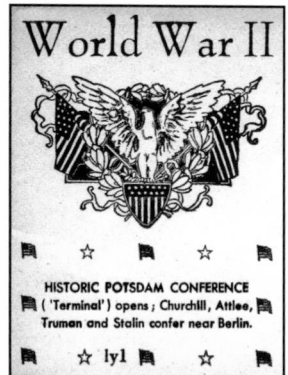

10449

10452

10453

10477A

10478

CACHET TEXT BEGINNING WITH "X"

NO.	CACHET TEXT	COLOR	TOPIC	PUBLISHER	$
10479	Xquire / What the well dressed etc.	Black/Blue	Unk	Christens	A
10480	Xtry! ['Xtry] 'Xtry! / "The White House" / "That man's here again!" Again, etc.	Unknown	FDR	Linto	B
10481	XXI / annuale / quantum mutatus ab illo	Black	Musso	McCluney	B

CACHET TEXT BEGINNING WITH "Y"

NO.	CACHET TEXT	COLOR	TOPIC	PUBLISHER	$
10482	Ya! then / I'll be a / guerrilla / fighter etc. [envelope 6 1/2x3 5/8, 7 1/2x4 in.]	Copper, green	Axis	Peer	B
10483	Yaaa who voodt / belief it. [thermographed]	Red	Hitle	Baur	A
10484	Yah sah / rain or snow / buy these bonds. [thermographed]	Black, blue	Home	Baur	A
10485	Yalta / Conference / Churchill, Roosevelt and / Stalin meet at Yalta etc.	Multicolored	Heads	Teixeira	D
10486	Yank / troops / enter / Germany / Sept. 3, 1944 [thermographed]	Unknown	Event	Threl+Thar	B
10487	Yank air boys bag 77 Jap planes etc.	Unknown	Event	Linto	B
10488	Yank paratroops / land on / Corregidor [no picture]	Unknown	Event	Boone	B
10489	Yanks / enter / Paris / V	Unknown	Event	Threl+Thar	B
10490	Yanks / reconquer / Luzon Is. [thermographed]	Unknown	Event	Boone	B
10491	Yanks / seize / Clark / Field [thermographed]	Unknown	Event	Boone	B
10492	Yanks /assault / Truk / War Dept. announces 1,000 / U.S. etc. [no picture]	Blue, red	Event	Boone	B
10493	Yanks are 50 miles / past the Rhine. / "Ach! Vot a war" / Allies [handpainted]	Multicolored	Hitle	Maul	C
10494	Yanks battle Japs on Attu	Unknown	Event	Linto	C
10495	Yanks land on Kiska	Unknown	Event	Linto	C
10496	Yanks on Bougainville	Unknown	Event	Linto	B
10497	Yanks take / Attu / Only the beginning for the "scum" etc. [thermographed]	Unknown	Event	Boone	B
10498	Yanks take Lae	Unknown	Event	Linto	B
10499	Yeah - this is / me darning / my own socks!	Black	Navy	Lupton	A
10500	Yeah!! I'd rather be home!! [envelope 6 1/2x3 5/8, 7 1/2x4 in.]	Brown/Red	Army	Harrington	A
10501	Yellow - belly	Bk/Gn/Yello	Japan	McCluney	A
10502	Yellow-eyed canary [in quotes] etc.	Brown	Japan	Belles-let	C
10503	Yellow-eyed envy [in quotes]	Brown	Japan	Belles-let	C
10504	Yes Adolf / we / are coming	Unknown	Hitle	Baur	A
10505	Yes Adolph, / we're / coming! [colored envelopes]	Blue, red	Uncle	Poppenger	A
10506	Yes indeed / If U think an / Allied second front / is not etc. [handpainted]	Multicolored	Home	Unknown	C
10507	Yes siree——— / The Yanks again / in gay Paree	Blue, red	ORN	Carpenter	A
10508	Yes sirree / the Yanks again etc. [girl dancing]	Unknown	Unk	Carpenter	A
10509	Yes sirree / the Yanks again etc. [girl seated]	Unknown	Unk	Carpenter	A
10510	Yes Tojo, when ya gotta go / ——ya gotta go!!	Blue	Japan	Lawrence	A
10511	Yes! Adolph! / Invasion Day! / D [postmarked 06/06/1944] [handpainted]	Blue, red	DDay	Robertson	C
10512	Yes, / its his / war. / But its / your war / too. [handpainted]	Multicolored	Army	Klondike	C
10513	Yes, Adolf... / "The British, Yanks, Rus- / sians, Aussies," etc. [no picture]	Blue, red	Hitle	Boone	A
10514	Yes, Huns and Japs, we'll toss / [etc.] / 3-22-'44——Yank bombers batter etc.	Multicolored	Event	Linto	B
10515	Yes, Huns and Japs, we'll toss the coin, but / it still etc. [no picture]	Multicolored	Axis	Linto	B
10516	Yes, indeed, he wants to know etc.	Blue	Unk	Carpenter	A
10517	Yesterday / Once they were happy / but now they are sad / Things are etc.	Blue	Axis	Abel	A
10518	Yippee! A six hour pass and / there's my etc. [cut-&-pasted cartoon + handpainted]	Multicolored	Army	Hadley	B
10519	Yokosuka occupation etc. [8-30-45] [Tokyo Bay] [envelope 8 7/8x3 7/8 in.]	Black	VJDay	Navy ship	E
10520	Yoo hoo! / Foreward, march	Multicolor	Golf	Linprint	A
10521	You / build the bombs / we'll etc.	Unknown	Unk	Eichenlaub	A
10522	You / can / save / lives / Donate some of your blood [no pict] [green envelope]	Multicolored	Blood	Linto	B
10523	You / give us the tools / we'll take the hit out of Hitler	Blue, brown	Air	Eichenlaub	A
10524	You / Tojo —— and your leaders / will pay / for your wanton conduct etc.	Black, red	Japan	Carpenter	A
10525	You ain't seen / nothing yet! / And we trust what you do get / is going etc.	Green, red	Japan	Boone	A
10526	You and me in '44 / Our President, right or etc.	Blue	Home	Abel	A
10527	You and your knowledge of camou- / flage——nuts!	Black	Army	Stead	A
10528	You answered the call to the colors, / you proved you were loyal and etc. [thermographed]	Blue, red	Flag	Unknown	A

NO.	CACHET TEXT	COLOR	TOPIC	PUBLISHER	$
10529	You are next - Adolf [caps with or without serifs]	Blue, red	Chute	Mayfield	A
10530	You are paying us homage with flags at half-mast; / our supreme etc.	Blue, red	RedCr	Brenn	A
10531	You asked for / my picture - so / here it is!	Black	Army	Lupton	A
10532	You asked for / my picture - so / here it is! [in quotes]	Black	Army	Lupton	A
10533	You asked for it [in quotes] [envelope 6 9/16x3 3/4, 6 3/4x3 3/4 in.]	Blue, red	Axis	Belles-let	C
10534	You asked for my / picture - so here / it is! [in quotes]	Black	Navy	Lupton	A
10535	You asked for my / picture so here / it is!	Black	USMC	Lupton	A
10536	You bet they're happy! / [etc.] / Victory Fleet Day / September 27, 1943	Unknown	Home	Linto	B
10537	You bet they're happy! They / know you'll not let them down!	Multicolored	Armed	Linto	B
10538	You bet! We'll save / waste paper, and we / hope the etc. [no picture]	Gold, pink	Home	Linto	B
10539	You birds / follow / me [handpainted]	Multicolored	Eagle	Adler	D
10540	You can / help / those who / [etc.] / 11-26-'44——Yanks / capture Weisweiler	Multicolored	Event	Linto	B
10541	You can / help / those who / protect us! / 'Nuf zed!	Multicolored	Flag	Linto	B
10542	You can help / build / the Shangri-La	Multicolored	Navy	Linto	B
10543	You can help / speed war calls / Don't make / unnecessary calls / Be brief	Brown	Home	Ohio Bell	D
10544	You can share in the / invasion! [ms., black ink] + flag [handpainted]	Multicolored	Flag	Adler	C
10545	You can't give your all as they are / doing but you can back 'em up etc.	Blue	Bonds	Lawrence	A
10546	You can't keep a / good man down etc. [env. 6 1/2x3 5/8, 6 5/16x3 1/2 in.]	Red	Uncle	Christens	A
10547	You can't let-up / and keep-up! / Stay on the job / until / victory / is ours	Bu/Gn/O/Pu	Dog	Jarrett	A
10548	You can't let-up / and keep-up! / Stay on the job / until / victory / is ours	Red/Violet	Dog	Jarrett	A
10549	You can't make those lines too long / and you can't be too long etc.	Unknown	Unk	Quigley	A
10550	You can't sneak out now Adolph! [in quotes] [handpainted]	Black	Hitle	Clendennen	D
10551	You carry our greetings, best wishes and love, by ship or by train, or etc.	Blue, red	Eagle	Carpenter	A
10552	You don't have to be crazy / but it helps!	Red	Army	Christens	A
10553	You give me aid and comfort / every time you cash a war bond! [in quotes]	Blue/Red	Japan	Schust	B
10554	You have a date / with / the boys at the front / [etc.] / Fifth war loan drive etc.	Black, blue	Bonds	Dale	B
10555	You have a special privilege. / Helping to make tomorrow's / freedom etc.	Unknown	Eagle	Linto	B
10556	You help someone you know etc.	Unknown	Unk	Rush, H	A
10557	You know what is going / [etc.] / 6-17-'44——Yanks land on Saipan——sink etc.	Unknown	Event	Linto	B
10558	You know what is going / to happen to Germany! / Avoid etc. [no picture]	Gold	Home	Linto	B
10559	You lick 'em there, soldier / and if it's only with letters etc. [handpainted]	Multicolored	Home	Cowdery	D
10560	You never know what / to expect from this gang! / "Reconnaissance" [handpainted]	Multicolored	Army	Cowdery	D
10561	You ought to cross the River Styx etc. [env. 6 1/2x3 5/8, 6 3/4x3 3/4 in.]	Unknown	Unk	Quigley	A
10562	You raise your bond quotas and we'll / raise Ned with their Axis "timber"	Blue, red	Home	Quigley	B
10563	You really put / "yourself" / into your letters [handpainted]	Multicolored	Army	Cowdery	D
10564	You shall / have work / when you / return / Uncle [handpainted]	Multicolored	Uncle	Adler	D
10565	You supply / the money! / Uncle / will apply / the heat!	Multicolored	Uncle	Linto	B
10566	You Tojo's friend / if you don't buy / war bonds [handpainted]	Multicolored	Japan	Adler	D
10567	You too, Fala / no 4th term	Black	FDR	McCluney	B
10568	You! / You can buy a minute off / this war... / You can buy a life that etc.	Blue, red	Bonds	Buxton, D	A
10569	You'd be / so nice to / come home to	Bk/Bu/Red	Home	Christens	A
10570	You'd better go, Mabel, / they put the lights / out at 9.30!	Black	Army	Lupton	A
10571	You'll be behind the ball / if you let these boys down / Buy etc. [thermographed]	Blue, black	Bonds	Baur	A
10572	You'll be saying "Uncle" / soon, too!	Blue	Axis	Lawrence	A
10573	You'll be sorry / if you don't buy that bond [thermographed]	Unknown	Bonds	Baur	A
10574	You'll soon be out of the picture, Adolph! [in quotes] [handpainted]	Black	Hitle	Clendennen	D
10575	Young majors and colonels / do minor / [etc.] / 1-18-'45——Reds slice etc.	Multicolored	Event	Linto	B
10576	Young majors and colonels / do minor clerical work in / Washington etc.	Silver, gold	Flag	Linto	B
10577	Your / blood can / save their / lives!	Blue, red	Blood	Cachet Cra	A
10578	Your / picture if we / lose the war etc. [last 3 lines upside down]	Blue, red	Home	Boone	A
10579	Your / war bonds / are etc. [on back] [envelope 9 1/2x4 1/8 in.]	Unknown	Bonds	Denver Dry	B
10580	You'r [sic] a sap, mister Jap- / We / will / avenge Pearl Harbor!	Blue, red	USMC	Poppenger	A
10581	Your Axis partner gone—— / Where to now, / Schickelgruber? [colored envelopes]	Green/Red	Hitle	Temple	B
10582	Your belt your blouse your GI tie etc. [thermographed]	Unknown	Unk	Baur	A
10583	Your bond buying bonded / this rat	Unknown	Japan	Calhoun	C
10584	Your bonds and stamps / will aid the Yanks	Red	Bonds	Ryscovers	A
10585	Your bonds at work	Unknown	Bonds	Carter	A
10586	Your bonds will keep him flying.	Black/Silver	Air	Ang	A

NO.	CACHET TEXT	COLOR	TOPIC	PUBLISHER	$
10587	Your boy needs fighting dollars / Buy more war bonds now	Unknown	Bonds	Lemponen	A
10588	Your Capitol / insures / your liberty [env. 6 1/2x3 5/8, 9 1/2x4 1/8 in.]	Multicolored	Bonds	Ever Ready	A
10589	Your country / is still at / war / Are you? / Stick to your war job etc.	Blue, orange	Air	Lowell	A
10590	Your donation of / blood / will / [etc.] / 12-27-'39——Earthquake in Turkey etc.	Multicolored	Hist	Linto	B
10591	Your donation of / blood / will be the best gift / for those etc. [no picture]	Gold, silver	Blood	Linto	B
10592	Your empty tubes / will furnish tin / to can the Axis [first line blue]	Blue, red	Axis	Richardson	A
10593	Your empty tubes / will furnish tin / to can the Axis [first line red]	Blue, red	Axis	Richardson	A
10594	Your flag / keep it flying / Buy / United States war bonds / today	Blue, red	Flag	Ang	A
10595	Your flag and my flag! [9 lines of text]	Unknown	Flag	Card	A
10596	Your flag and my flag! etc. [4 lines of text]	Unknown	Flag	Baur	A
10597	Your hon. servant is 28 yrs. old-Request that next / birthday I be 30——- etc.	Black	Japan	Curtiss, D	B
10598	Your idle money / helps the Axis—— / But, your money in / war bonds etc.	Blue, red	Bonds	Brenn	A
10599	Your letter / wuza life-saver—— / sweetheart—— so etc. [env. 8 7/8x3 7/8 in.]	Multicolored	Navy	Porto-serv	B
10600	Your metal fights the Japs... / Keep it coming!	Blue, red	Flag	Rush, H	A
10601	Your metal is on the attack etc.	Unknown	Unk	Rush, H	A
10602	Your name on one / more bond / will mean / one / less / name on etc. [handp]	Multicolored	Bonds	Unknown	C
10603	Your navy will drop the / hook in Puget Sound / ere long	Unknown	Navy	Quigley	A
10604	Your part in / war is small compared to his!	Multicolored	Navy	Linto	B
10605	Your part in / war is small compared to his!	Multicolored	Army	Linto	B
10606	Your patriotic duty / Fight / infantile / paralysis [handpainted]	Multicolored	Home	Price	B
10607	Your picture / if we lose! / ...Ax the Axis... [no picture]	Red	Axis	Boone	A
10608	Your picture / if we lose! etc. [last 2 lines upside down] [bearded face]	Blue, red	Home	Boone	A
10609	Your picture / if we lose! etc. [last 2 lines upside down] [clean-shaven face]	Blue, red	Home	Boone	A
10610	Your radio pal [in quotes] / Jimmy Miller / Buy etc. [env. 9 1/2x4 1/8 in.]	Blue, red	Home	Miller	C
10611	Your Red Cross / is at his side	Unknown	RedCr	Lowell	A
10612	Your Red Cross / must carry on. / Give!	Blue, red	RedCr	Mayo	A
10613	Your Red Cross is at his side / Keep it etc.	Black	RedCr	Peters	A
10614	Your sacrifice / now / will prevent this etc. [label + printed border]	Multicolored	ORN	Artists	B
10615	Your turn / comes / next [handpainted]	Black	Japan	Wolf, CL	B
10616	Your war bond / investment is / your investment in / America	Blue, red	Bonds	Dale	A
10617	Your war bonds / buy bombers!	Blue	Bonds	Ander, EA	A
10618	Your war efforts / are necessary to ——— / black-out / the rising sun	Blue, red	Uncle	Dale	A
10619	Your war efforts will / spring etc.	Unknown	Unk	Dale	A
10620	Your war efforts will / spring the trap on / this rat!	Blue, red	Hitle	Dale	A
10621	Your waste fat will / cook the Axis' goose	Brown	Home	Davis, Ray	A
10622	You're in the Army, bud	Unknown	Army	Ang	A
10623	You're needed / in the army [handpainted]	Multicolored	WAC	Adler	C
10624	Yours / for / ··· – / Victory	Black	VforV	Phill, CR	A
10625	Yours / to choose / bonds / or / bondage [no picture]	Unknown	Bonds	Norton	A
10626	You've / really got / something / there soldier! [handpainted]	Multicolored	Army	Cowdery	D
10627	Yowsah, folks this is me / in my new issue—— / looking very military! etc.	Black	Army	Lupton	A
10628	Yugoslavia	Black	ORN	Lowry	A
10629	Yugoslavia	Blue, red	ORN	Clifford	A
10630	Yugoslavia / fights / for / liberation [artist: Staehle]	Blue, red	ORN	Cachet Cra	B
10631	Yugoslavia / The kingdom of Yugoslavia was over-run by the Nazis etc.	Bk/Bu/Red	ORN	Cliff	A
10632	Yugoslavia / United Nations [handpainted]	Multicolored	ORN	Weigand	B
10633	Yugoslavia [thermographed]	Unknown	ORN	Jordan	B
10634	Yuletide / greetings [postmarked 12/25/40]	Multicolored	Holid	Linto	B

CACHET TEXT BEGINNING WITH "Z"

NO.	CACHET TEXT	COLOR	TOPIC	PUBLISHER	$
10635	Zip your lip / Save a ship!	Blue, red	Navy	Lowe	A
10636	Zip your lip Save a ship	Bu,Red/Blue	Eagle	Ander, EA	A
10637	Zip your lip.... / to save a ship. [handpainted]	Multicolored	Navy	Borkowski	D

10485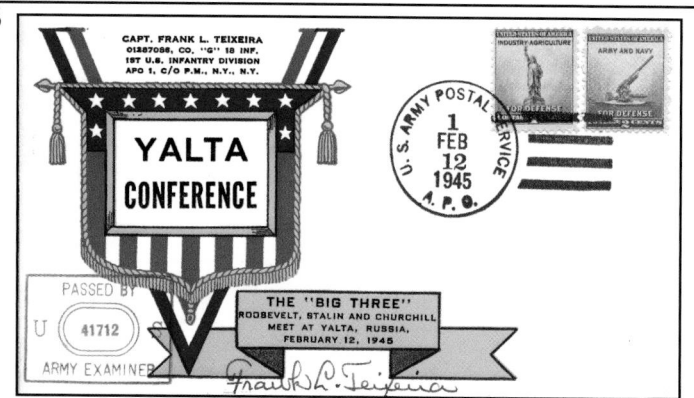

10505

10531

10533

10534

10535

10543

10546

10566

10580

10588

10593

10599

10617

10630

10636

10637

CACHETS WITH ILLUSTRATION ONLY

NO.	DESCRIPTION OF CACHET ILLUSTRATION (NO TEXT)	COLOR	TOPIC	PUBLISHER	$
10638	^^Aircraft carrier with 5 planes in air [colored envelopes]	Blue	Navy	Huss	A
10639	^^Airplane (seaplane) flying left above waves; army insignia above	Blue, orange	Air	Lupton	A
10640	^^Airplane (seaplane) flying left above waves; navy insignia above	Blue, orange	Air	Lupton	A
10641	^^Airplane and parachute, 9 stars in row above, 10 stars with V in center below	Blue, red	Air	Risinger	A
10642	^^Airplane flying left oblique, clouds below; army insignia above	Blue, orange	Air	Lupton	A
10643	^^Airplane flying left oblique, clouds below; navy insignia above	Blue, orange	Air	Lupton	A
10644	^^Airplane flying right oblique, lines for whirling props; army insignia above	Blue, orange	Air	Lupton	A
10645	^^Airplane flying right oblique, lines for whirling props; navy insignia above	Blue, orange	Air	Lupton	A
10646	^^Airplane flying right, above winged Columbia and partial globe [insignia: "Pavois"]	Blue, red	Air	Butzen	B
10647	^^Airplane flying right, behind 3 ducks; one quacking at plane [near top of envelope]	Multicolored	Air	Unknown	A
10648	^^Airplane flying right, one star with stripes above, 4 below [thermographed]	Blue	Air	Grover	A
10649	^^Airplane flying right; birds above, lines below tail; army insignia above	Blue, orange	Air	Lupton	A
10650	^^Airplane flying right; birds above, lines below tail; navy insignia above	Blue, orange	Air	Lupton	A
10651	^^Airplane in cloud, 9 stars in row above, 10 stars with V in center below	Blue, red	Air	Risinger	A
10652	^^Airplane in steep dive; bronze colors	Multicolored	Air	Amer Pat	A
10653	^^Airplane on ground, silhouetted against sky [handpainted]	Black	Air	Barwicki	C
10654	^^Airplane pilot adjusting helmet	Blue	Air	Murrman	A
10655	^^Airplane with pointed nose (P-40) flying right; army insignia above	Blue, orange	Air	Lupton	A
10656	^^Airplane with pointed nose (P-40) flying right; navy insignia above	Blue, orange	Air	Lupton	A
10657	^^Airplane with stub nose (P-47 Thunderbolt) flying right; army insignia above	Blue, orange	Air	Lupton	A
10658	^^Airplane with stub nose (P-47 Thunderbolt) flying right; navy insignia above	Blue, orange	Air	Lupton	A
10659	^^Airplane with twin tails (B-25 Mitchell) flying right; army insignia above	Blue, orange	Air	Lupton	A
10660	^^Airplane with twin tails (B-25 Mitchell) flying right; navy insignia above	Blue, orange	Air	Lupton	A
10661	^^Airplane with twin tails [B-25 Mitchell] flying left [handpainted]	Black	Air	Barwicki	B
10662	^^Airplane, B-17 Flying Fortress, flying right; army insignia above	Blue, orange	Air	Lupton	A
10663	^^Airplane, B-17 Flying Fortress, flying right; navy insignia above	Blue, orange	Air	Lupton	A
10664	^^Airplane, B-17 Flying Fortress, U.S. flag, clouds behind it [colored envelopes]	Black	Air	Huss	A
10665	^^Airplane, bomber, with flag [handpainted]	Multicolored	Air	Adler	C
10666	^^Airplane, twin-bodied (P-38), flying left; army insignia above	Blue, orange	Air	Lupton	A
10667	^^Airplane, twin-bodied (P-38), flying left; navy insignia above	Blue, orange	Air	Lupton	A
10668	^^Airplane, twin-bodied, fanciful, shooting at trucks and industrial plant on ground [hp]	Multicolored	Air	Barwicki	B
10669	^^Airplanes, 3 PBY Catalina flying boats, over bridge [env. 5 5/8x4 7/16 in.]	Multicolored	Air	Curt-Teich	A
10670	^^Airplanes, 3, B-25 Mitchells, flying right; large bomb falling [handpainted]	Multicolored	Air	Borkowski	D
10671	^^Airplanes, 3, B-25 Mitchells, flying upward from USAAF star [handpainted]	Multicolored	Air	Barwicki	B
10672	^^Airplanes, 3, lower edge; eagle above large plane; stars circle eagle	Black	Air	Lowry	B
10673	^^Airplanes, 3, taking off from carrier, flying right [handpainted]	Blue, black	Air	Barwicki	C
10674	^^Airplanes, B-17 Flying Fortresses, bombing dock facility [right 2/3 of cover]	Black	Air	Unknown	B
10675	^^Anchor and propeller symbol [UL]	Blue	Navy	Unknown	A
10676	^^Anchor and two stars	Blue	Navy	Krakora	A
10677	^^Anchor with bat-like mascot [UL]	Blue	Navy	Unknown	A
10678	^^Anchor with CG initials	Black	Coast	Unknown	A
10679	^^Angel standing between two large Christmas candles [handpainted]	Multicolored	Holid	Adler	C
10680	^^Anti-aircraft gun	Blue, red	Air	Risinger	A
10681	^^Army bugler playing reveille, sun rubbing eyes in background [env. 5 1/2x3 5/8 in.]	Blue, red	Army	Dime	A
10682	^^Army officer slides on soap as enlisted man washes floor [env. 5 1/2x3 5/8 in.]	Blue, red	Army	Unknown	A
10683	^^Army wings at top, Navy wings at bottom [frame for label]	Blue	Air	Garrison	A
10684	^^Baby in diapers wearing top hat and bow tie, carrying baton [handpainted]	Multicolored	Holid	Adler	D
10685	^^Bathing beach beauties, 2, waving, ocean background [env. 5 5/8x4 3/8 in.]	Multicolored	Home	Curt-Teich	A
10686	^^Battleship [colored envelopes]	Bk/Bu/Green	Navy	Huss	A
10687	^^Battleship firing broadside; anchors in border	Brown	Navy	Klotzbach	A
10688	^^Battleship firing broadside; border of small squares, stars, vertical lines	Blue, red	Navy	Klotzbach	A
10689	^^Battleship firing broadside; stars in border	Blue	Navy	Klotzbach	A
10690	^^Battleship sailing left	Brown	Navy	Dye	A
10691	^^Battleship sailing right [green envelope]	Black	Navy	Dailey	A
10692	^^Battleship sailing toward viewer	Black/Brown	Navy	Yontz	A
10693	^^Battleship with bow to right, at lower edge	Blue/Red	Navy	Lupton	A

NO.	DESCRIPTION OF CACHET ILLUSTRATION (NO TEXT)	COLOR	TOPIC	PUBLISHER	$
10694	^^Battleships [3], black, steaming toward viewer, colored shield above them	Multicolored	Navy	Amer Pat	A
10695	^^Battleships, 2, sailing left	Unknown	Navy	Klotzbach	A
10696	^^Bear as clown, with balloons, dancing, blowing horn at New Year's [handpainted]	Multicolored	Holid	Adler	D
10697	^^Bird with mistletoe [handpainted]	Multicolored	Holid	Cowdery	D
10698	^^Black boy wearing cap, selling newspapers [no text on newspaper] [handpainted]	Multicolored	VEDay	Adler	E
10699	^^Blue star, white background, red border, hanging flag [UL] [family member in service]	Blue, red	Home	Unknown	A
10700	^^Bomb falling	Blue, red	Air	Risinger	A
10701	^^Bomber flying in front of flag [handpainted]	Multicolored	Flag	Adler	D
10702	^^Bombs, 3, falling from black airplane, large yellow sun in background [handpainted]	Multicolored	Air	Unknown	C
10703	^^Border of stars	Blue	Home	Boone	A
10704	^^Boy, girl w/ fireworks; U.S. Flag background [7/4/41 postmark] [handpainted]	Multicolored	Holid	Swartz	B
10705	^^Cannons, 2, at lower left, one star to left, 2 with stripes to right [thermographed]	Red	Ordna	Grover	A
10706	^^Civilian and soldier heads, both with cap	Blue, red	Home	Risinger	A
10707	^^Columbia with wings, on globe	Unknown	Globe	Butzen	A
10708	^^Confederate veteran with fife, WWI vet with billowing U.S. flag	Blue, red	Flag	Ioor	A
10709	^^Crown above crossed anchors	Blue	Navy	Abel	A
10710	^^DeGaulle, Charles, facing right, Cross of Lorraine behind head [handpainted]	Multicolored	Ally	Knoll	C
10711	^^Destroyer sailing to right, 3 small birds above [colored envelopes]	Bk/Bu/Green	Navy	Huss	A
10712	^^Doctor injecting soldier, 2nd soldier faints, supported by 3rd [env. 7 1/2x3 7/8 in.]	Black	Army	Unknown	A
10713	^^Dog wearing high hat and bow tie, clock near midnight, confetti, toy horn [handpainted]	Multicolored	Holid	Adler	D
10714	^^Duck, cartoon picture, with mop and bucket	Black	Navy	Lupton	A
10715	^^Dutch girl in seventeenth century costume, wearing wooden shoes, holding flowers	Multicolored	Women	Amer Pat	A
10716	^^Eagle (wingspan 88 mm) and shield	Brown/Red	EagSh	Carpenter	A
10717	^^Eagle (wingspan 88 mm) and shield [envelope 7 1/2x4 in.]	Brown	Eagle	Carpenter	B
10718	^^Eagle above shield above U.S. Capitol [insignia: "Pavois"]	Bu, red/Blue	Shiel	Butzen	A
10719	^^Eagle above shield and between two flags	Unknown	Eag+	Hunt	A
10720	^^Eagle alighting, dimensions 73x65 mm, stars above and below	Red	Eagle	Nichols	A
10721	^^Eagle alighting, dimensions 77x60 mm, wings high as in "V" [thermographed]	Blue	Eagle	Grover	A
10722	^^Eagle at top; 3 stars and shield along side panels [frame for label]	Blue	Eagle	Goldstein	A
10723	^^Eagle at top; 3 stars, vertical, at top of side panels [frame for label]	Blue	Eagle	Linprint	A
10724	^^Eagle clutching flag in talons [handpainted]	Multicolored	EagFl	Dannells	B
10725	^^Eagle clutching Japanese soldier in talons, lifting him in air	Blue	Eagle	Carpenter	B
10726	^^Eagle flying to right, flag in claws [engraved]	Blue, red	EagFl	Huss	B
10727	^^Eagle flying to right, star on each wing	Blue	Eagle	Carpenter	A
10728	^^Eagle flying, blank scroll between wings and in front of shield [handpainted]	Multicolored	EagSh	Adler	C
10729	^^Eagle flying, holding blank scroll in beak [handpainted]	Multicolored	Eagle	Adler	C
10730	^^Eagle flying, upper left; ribbons top and left	Blue, red	Eagle	Boothroyd	A
10731	^^Eagle holding blank scroll in its talons [handpainted]	Handpainted	Eagle	Adler	C
10732	^^Eagle in fighting pose, circle of stars, ribbon	Red	Eagle	Muzzy	B
10733	^^Eagle in small medallion, one star	Black	Eagle	Conner Mrs	A
10734	^^Eagle on branch [wingspan 98 mm]	Bk,Bu,Gn,O,	Eagle	Carpenter	A
10735	^^Eagle on branch [wingspan 98 mm] [thermographed]	Red	Eagle	Carpenter	B
10736	^^Eagle on shield [small eagle, large shield] [handpainted]	Multicolored	EagSh	Adler	D
10737	^^Eagle on shield, head facing left, body in profile [envelope 9 1/2x4 1/8 in.]	Black	EagSh	Langford	A
10738	^^Eagle on shield, head facing right [eagle color: brown] [handpainted]	Multicolored	EagSh	Borkowski	D
10739	^^Eagle on shield, protecting globe, screaming [buff env. 7 5/16x5 1/2 in.]	Green	Eag+	Neal	A
10740	^^Eagle over shield [eagle black, shield blue, red] [handpainted]	Multicolored	EagSh	Unknown	C
10741	^^Eagle perched on wreath	Blue	Eagle	Krakora	A
10742	^^Eagle standing on flag, Liberty Bell in background	Blue, red	EagFl	Unknown	A
10743	^^Eagle standing on flag, looking bellicose, clouds in background [handpainted]	Multicolored	EagFl	Dannells	C
10744	^^Eagle standing on shield, head facing right [blue eagle, red and blue shield]	Blue, red	EagSh	Krakora	A
10745	^^Eagle standing on shield, head facing right, 7 stars in semi-circle above	Blue, red	EagSh	Unknown	A
10746	^^Eagle standing on shield, head facing right; border of stars, squares, lines	Blue, red	EagSh	Klotzbach	A
10747	^^Eagle standing on shield, surrounded by insignias of armed forces	Blue, red	EagSh	Cozart	A
10748	^^Eagle standing with wings raised, two epaulets left and right	Blue, red	Eagle	Krakora	A
10749	^^Eagle with flag at left edge	Multicolored	EagFl	Amer Pat	A
10750	^^Eagle with head to right, on flat shield	Blue, red	EagSh	Klotzbach	A
10751	^^Eagle with head to right, on flat shield; small picture, upper left	Blue, red	EagSh	Curtiss, D	A

NO.	DESCRIPTION OF CACHET ILLUSTRATION (NO TEXT)	COLOR	TOPIC	PUBLISHER	$
10752	^^Eagle with head to right, on flat shield; stars in border	Blue, red	EagSh	Klotzbach	A
10753	^^Eagle with olive branch, arrows [below soldier-publisher's Ccard] [handpainted]	Multicolored	EagSh	Stawuszew	C
10754	^^Eagle with shield for body, below 13 stars; upper left	Unknown	EagSh	Unknown	A
10755	^^Eagle with star on each wing, flying left	Blue	Eagle	Unknown	A
10756	^^Eagle with stylized feathers perched above star	Blue, red	Eagle	Krakora	A
10757	^^Eagle with wings in shape of "V", flag in claws	Blue, red	EagV	Risinger	A
10758	^^Eagle with wings spread, alighting [handpainted]	Multicolored	Eagle	Adler	D
10759	^^Eagle with wings spread, holding shield, 7 stars above head	Multicolored	EagSh	Dime	A
10760	^^Eagle with wings spread, map with symbols of Tennessee industrial might on wings	Red/Multi	Eagle	Andrews	A
10761	^^Eagle with wings spread, on leaves; dog chasing man	Black	Eagle	Kosko	A
10762	^^Eagle with wings spread, on leaves; no dog or man	Black	Eagle	Kosko	A
10763	^^Eagle, blue, with red and blue shield across chest [wingspan 57 mm]	Blue, red	EagSh	Local 50	B
10764	^^Eagle, head and neck in profile, outline, [90 mm high, 112 mm wide] [handpainted]	Black	Eagle	Shaffer, A	C
10765	^^Eagle, large, with shield for body, 68 mm by 65 mm	Unknown	EagSh	Unknown	A
10766	^^Eagle, red, and shield, brown	Brown, red	EagSh	Runge	A
10767	^^Eagle, shield, as in Great Seal of the United States	Blue	EagSh	Unknown	A
10768	^^Eagle, similar to Win-the-War stamp, framed by 3 stars [handpainted]	Blue/Red	Eagle	Schaefer	C
10769	^^Eisenhower, Gen. Dwight D., and MacArthur, Gen. Douglas [colored envelopes]	Black	Gener	Castellano	A
10770	^Field Artillery insignia [crossed cannons] [UL] [envelope 5 1/8x4 1/8 in.]	Multicolored	Ordna	Dime	A
10771	^^Flag in front of Liberty Bell [single line inked border] [cachet pasted on cover]	Multicolored	FlBel	LeGallez	C
10772	^^Flag, U.S., billowing, with 2 tassels	Blue, red	Flag	Smith, W	A
10773	^^Flag, U.S., being raised, three soldiers [74 or 89 mm high]	Unknown	Flag	Glenn-Corn	A
10774	^^Flag, U.S., being raised; 1 figure raising flag, 2 saluting; 87x30 mm	Multicolored	Flag	Ioor	A
10775	^^Flag, U.S., billowing in front of "Spirit of 76"	Unknown	Flag	Ioor	A
10776	^^Flag, U.S., billowing in front of staff	Blue/Red	Flag	Ioor	A
10777	^^Flag, U.S., covering entire back of envelope [publisher imprint on front]	Blue, red	Flag	Pictorial	C
10778	^^Flag, U.S., covering entire front of envelope [publisher imprint on back]	Blue, red	Flag	Stendel	C
10779	^^Flag, U.S., covering most of back of env.; complete white edge left, right	Blue, red	Flag	Pictorial	B
10780	^^Flag, U.S., draped at left edge [colors vary]	Multicolored	Flag	Amer Pat	A
10781	^^Flag, U.S., draped in ring in claws of eagle, 50 mm high overall [upper left]	Blue, red	EagFl	Risinger	A
10782	^^Flag, U.S., draped in small ring in claws of eagle with spread wings	Multicolored	EagFl	Davis, R	A
10783	^^Flag, U.S., eagle on left and right, star above and below [flag 12x12 mm]	Red	Flag	Unknown	A
10784	^^Flag, U.S., flying from halyard [colors vary]	Multicolored	Flag	Amer Pat	A
10785	^^Flag, U.S., hanging from top edge	Multicolored	Flag	Amer Pat	A
10786	^^Flag, U.S., hanging from yellow window frame [Flag Day, 6/14/41][handpainted]	Multicolored	Flag	Swartz	B
10787	^^Flag, U.S., held by eagle [colors vary]	Multicolored	EagFl	Amer Pat	A
10788	^^Flag, U.S., in circle with 10 stars, on long staff [52 mm high] [env. 5 5/8x4 3/8 in.]	Multicolored	Flag	Dime	A
10789	^^Flag, U.S., on staff with cords and tassels [green envelope]	Blue, red	Flag	Battles	A
10790	^^Flag, U.S., on staff with round ball tip; two halyards on flag [upper left]	Blue, red	Flag	Linprint	A
10791	^^Flag, U.S., one eagle left, one right, one star above, one below [flag 13x13mm]	Red	EagFl	Unknown	A
10792	^^Flag, U.S., partly covering vignette of $1 Chinese stamp with Chinese & U.S. flags	Blue, red	Flag	Unknown	A
10793	^^Flag, U.S., red, in frame 43x75 mm, blue airplane in lower right corner	Blue, red	Flag	Risinger	A
10794	^^Flag, U.S., shadowy, above plane in clouds [colored envelopes]	Bk/Blue/Bro	Flag	Huss	A
10795	^^Flag, U.S., small, blue [pink envelope]	Blue, red	Flag	Glenn-Corn	A
10796	^^Flag, U.S., UL, on mourning cover [postmarked 04/14/1945, FDR's interment]	Multicolored	Flag	Unknown	B
10797	^^Flag, U.S., UL, with two cords and tassels	Red	Flag	Unknown	A
10798	^^Flag, U.S., with 3 stars	Red	Flag	Boland	A
10799	^^Flag, U.S., with staff having spear at top, 37x34 mm	Unknown	Flag	Unknown	A
10800	^^Flag, U.S.: 10 small blue flags between two red, white, and blue flags	Blue, red	Flag	Garfield	A
10801	^^Flag, U.S.: 10 small Liberty Bells between two red, white, and blue flags	Blue, red	Flag	Garfield	A
10802	^^Flag, U.S.: 3 flags together, unfurled	Multicolored	Flag	Amer Pat	A
10803	^^Flag, U.S.: 9 small blue flags in a V; red, white, and blue flag below them	Blue, red	Flag	Garfield	A
10804	^^Flag, U.S.: Betsy Ross seated, sewing 13-star flag	Multicolored	Flag	Ioor	A
10805	^^Flag, U.S.: four crossed flags forming V	Unknown	Flag	Ioor	A
10806	^^Flag, U.S.: staff height 12 mm, flag height 10 mm [airmail envelope]	Unknown	Flag	White, B	A
10807	^^Flag, U.S.: staff height 21 mm, flag height 18 mm [lower left]	Unknown	Flag	BPOE	A
10808	^^Flag, U.S.: staff height 21 mm, flag height 20 mm [lower left]	Unknown	Flag	Dime	A
10809	^^Flag, U.S.: staff height 22 mm [upper left]	Blue, red	Flag	Risinger	A

NO.	DESCRIPTION OF CACHET ILLUSTRATION (NO TEXT)	COLOR	TOPIC	PUBLISHER	$
10810	^^Flag, U.S.: staff height 25 mm, flag height 22 mm; dome of Capitol under flag	Blue, red	Flag	Risinger	A
10811	^^Flag, U.S.: staff height 33 mm, flag height 30 mm [above Capitol dome]	Unknown	Flag	Bartz	A
10812	^^Flag, U.S.: staff height 35 mm, flag height 33 mm; liberty cap, top of staff	Multicolored	Flag	Dime	A
10813	^^Flag, U.S.: staff height 37 mm, flag height 30 mm	Unknown	Flag	Bath	A
10814	^^Flag, U.S.: staff height 37 mm, flag height 30 mm [env. has red star border]	Unknown	Flag	Boone	A
10815	^^Flag, U.S.: staff height 37 mm, flag height 36 mm; spear at top of staff	Unknown	Flag	Hise	A
10816	^^Flag, U.S.: staff height 49 mm [upper left]	Blue, red	Flag	Unknown	A
10817	^^Flag, U.S.: staff height 52 mm, flag height 41 mm; liberty cap, top of staff	Unknown	Flag	Phill, CR	A
10818	^^Flag, U.S.: staff height 52 mm, flag height 43 mm; ribbons at top of staff	Multicolored	Flag	Dime	A
10819	^^Flag, U.S.: staff height 54 mm, flag height 43mm; flag with spear tip	Multicolored	Flag	Amer Pat	A
10820	^^Flag, U.S.: staff height 59 mm, flag height 53 mm	Unknown	Flag	Holmes	A
10821	^^Flag, U.S.: staff height 89 mm [height of env.], flag height 59 mm [thermographed]	Blue, red	Flag	Unknown	A
10822	^^Flag, U.S.: three flags on staffs, wreath in circle in foreground	Blue, red	Flag	Amer Pat	A
10823	^^Flag, U.S.: two flags in heart-shaped wreath	Multicolored	Flag	Amer Pat	A
10824	^^Flags of U.S. and Cuba on separate flagpoles	Multicolored	Ally	LeGallez	B
10825	^^Flags of U.S. and Netherlands on separate flagpoles	Multicolored	ORN	LeGallez	B
10826	^^Flags of USSR, Great Britain, U.S., and China	Br/Br,Red	UN	Runge	A
10827	^^Flags, massed, 1 dozen; hand giving "V" sign; border of stars	Blue, red	FlagV	Boone	A
10828	^^Flags, U.S. and Red Cross, crossed, star between them	Blue, red	RedCr	McGovern	A
10829	^^Flamethrower scorching backside of Japanese, who is leaping [handpainted]	Multicolored	Japan	Unknown	C
10830	^^Fork spearing Mussolini, Tojo, Hitler	Blue	Axis	Price, R	A
10831	^^General MacArthur saluting	Blue	Mac	Krajora	B
10832	^^Globe of world flanked by ship and train, quill and document above	Blue, red	Globe	Mueller, B	A
10833	^^Globe of world within long, curling stylized U.S. flag, 7 stars nearby	Red	Globe	Murrman	A
10834	^^Hand giving "V" sign; border of stars	Blue, red	VforV	Boone	A
10835	^^Head of soldier looking up toward left [handpainted]	Multicolored	Army	Dannells	B
10836	^^Head of soldier, below U.S. seal	Green	Army	Unknown	A
10837	^^Hirohito caricature [without "No. 2."] [handpainted]	Multicolored	Japan	Adler	E
10838	^^Hitler as Humpty Dumpty sitting on a crumbling wall	Blue/Black	Hitle	Davis, D	A
10839	^^Hitler behind 8-ball [upper left] [handpainted]	Multicolored	Hitle	Orlando	B
10840	^^Hitler caricature [without "No. 1."] [handpainted]	Multicolored	Hitle	Adler	E
10841	^^Hitler talking into microphone, left hand raised, upper left	Red	Hitle	Unknown	A
10842	^^Hitler, head caught in mousetrap, left hand reaching for cheese bait	Red	Hitle	Unknown	A
10843	^^Humpty Dumpty on a wall	Black/Blue	Axis	Price, EK	A
10844	^^Insignia, Air Force, upper left	Black	Air	Air Force	A
10845	^^Insignia, Army Artillery, lower left	Black	Army	Army	A
10846	^^Insignia, Army, 12x12 mm	Black	Army	Bean	A
10847	^^Insignia, Army, upper left	Black	Army	Army	A
10848	^^Insignia, Coast Guard, 12x12 mm	Black	Coast	Bean	A
10849	^^Insignia, Marine Corps, 12x12 mm	Black	USMC	Bean	A
10850	^^Insignia, Marine Corps, 32x32 mm	Black	USMC	Lupton	A
10851	^^Insignia, Marine Corps, above head of Marine	Black	USMC	Lupton	A
10852	^^Insignia, Marine Corps, upper left	Black	USMC	USMC	A
10853	^^Insignia, Navy, 12 mm tall, upper left	Black	Navy	Navy	A
10854	^^Insignia, Navy, 12x12 mm	Black	Navy	Bean	A
10855	^^Insignia, Navy, 18 cm tall, upper left	Black	Navy	Navy	A
10856	^^Insignia, Signal Corps, upper left	Black	Army	Army	A
10857	^^Insignia, unknown unit, 2 squares on end, 1 blue, 1 white, brown background [hp]	Multicolored	Unit	Unknown	B
10858	^^Insignia, Womens Auxiliary Army Corps, lower left	Black	WAC	WAC	A
10859	^^Japanese being carried off by eagle	Bu/Green/Red	Japan	Carpenter	A
10860	^^Jeep crashing into traffic pole, soldier's head hitting pole [envelope 5 1/2x3 5/8 in.]	Blue, red	Army	Dime	A
10861	^^Jeep, 9 stars in row above, 10 stars with V in center below	Blue, red	Army	Risinger	A
10862	^^John Paul Jones wearing cocked hat [cachet covers left half of envelope]	Black/Blue	Hist	Wash Cover	A
10863	^^Jones, John Paul [head and shoulders]	Blue	Hist	Wash Cover	A
10864	^^Jones, John Paul, with cocked hat [cachet covers left half of envelope]	Black/Blue	Hist	Wash Cover	A
10865	^^Landing barge, 9 stars in row above, 10 stars with V in center below	Blue, red	Navy	Risinger	A
10866	^^Liberty Bell	Bu/Br/R/Vi	Bell	Harrington	A
10867	^^Liberty Bell flanked by flag draped in ring in claws of small eagle [upper left]	Blue, red	Bell	Risinger	A

NO.	DESCRIPTION OF CACHET ILLUSTRATION (NO TEXT)	COLOR	TOPIC	PUBLISHER	$
10868	^^Liberty Bell, large	Bk/Bu/Pi/Red	Bell	Harrington	A
10869	^^Liberty Bell, small	Blue	Bell	Pflanz	A
10870	^^Liberty Bell, small blue [UL], envelope has 18 red "····–" symbols around border	Blue, red	Liber	Unknown	A
10871	^^Liberty Bell, smaller	Red	Bell	Boland	A
10872	^^Liberty Bell, smaller	Brown	Bell	Phill, CR	A
10873	^^Liberty Bell, upper left, between two hanging U.S. flags	Unknown	FlBel	Risinger	A
10874	^^Lincoln, Abraham	Blue	Linc	Carpenter	A
10875	^^Lines, 2, one red, one blue, around edge of envelope, white space between	Blue, red	Home	Boone	A
10876	^^Lion of Luxembourg	Black, red	ORN	Runge	A
10877	^^Listening device	Blue, red	Armed	Risinger	A
10878	^^MacArthur, Gen. Douglas and Eisenhower, Gen. Dwight D., 4 stars above	Black	Gener	Castellano	A
10879	^^MacArthur, General Douglas, full face, eagle and flags behind him [handpainted]	Multicolored	MacFD	Unknown	D
10880	^^MacArthur, head and shoulders, surrounded by 4 large stars	Green, silver	Mac	Unknown	A
10881	^^Map of Italy and Sicily, figure of Hope	Unknown	Map	Haynes	A
10882	^^Map, shadow of American flag, plane in foreground [colored envelopes]	Black/Blue	Map	Huss	A
10883	^^Marine Corps insignia [upper left corner]	Black	USMC	Lupton	A
10884	^^Marine Corps insignia [upper left], bust of Marine with cap [lower left]	Black	USMC	Lupton	A
10885	^^Minute Man [picture is height of envelope]	Brown/Red	Minut	Boone	A
10886	^^Minute Man standing before flag	Blue	Minut	Krakora	A
10887	^^Minute Man with gun and plow, 9 stars above, 10 stars with V in center below	Blue, red	Minut	Risinger	A
10888	^^Minute Man, 21 mm tall, lower left	Black	Minut	Mueller, B	A
10889	^^Minute Man, blue; red and black lines around edge of envelope	Multicolored	Minut	Boone	A
10890	^^Minute Man, blue; red and blue lines around edge of envelope	Blue, red	Minut	Boone	A
10891	^^Minute Man, hatless, rifle on left shoulder, marching to right	Multicolored	Minut	Ioor	A
10892	^^Minute Man, UL; border of red stars	Blue, red	Minut	Boone	A
10893	^^Mussolini caricature [without "No. / 3."] [handpainted]	Multicolored	Musso	Adler	E
10894	^^Mussolini, Hitler, Hirohito looking at skull, question mark over each head	Multicolored	Axis	Knoll	B
10895	^^Navy symbol [eagle, shield, anchors], eagle in frame above, stars in rest of frame	Blue	Navy	Unknown	A
10896	^^Nurses Corps insignia [upper left] [envelope 5 1/8x4 1/8 in.]	Multicolored	Nurse	Dime	A
10897	^^Octopus	Brown	Axis	Runge	A
10898	^^Palm trees against sky [to Pvt. Ray R. Cowdery] [handpainted] [stamp missing]	Multicolored	Army	Cowdery	D
10899	^^Paratrooper falling, reading manual, chute yet to open [env. 5 1/2x3 5/8 in.]	Blue, red	Chute	Dime	A
10900	^^Pigeon flying to right ["Pigeon Section," Ft. Monmouth]	Blue	Pigeo	Army	D
10901	^^Pigeon standing , head nearly profile ["Pigeon Section," Ft. George Meade]	Black	Pigeo	Army	D
10902	^^Pigeon standing, head oblique to right ["Pigeon Lofts," Signal Corps]	Black	Pigeo	Army	D
10903	^^Pilgrim man with musket and Bible walking with Pilgrim woman	Black	Holid	Muzzy	A
10904	^^Propeller over wing	Blue/Red	Air	Krakora	A
10905	^^Pumpkin, carved face [handpainted] [orange envelope]	Black, green	Holid	Shaffer, A	C
10906	^^Red Cross flag in front of globe	Blue, red	RedCr	McGovern	A
10907	^^Religious symbols, middle east scenes, cattle, and owl [circular border]	Blue	Relig	Unit	B
10908	^^Rifles crossed under shield	Blue, red	Shiel	Krakora	A
10909	^^Sailboat and tropical island with one tree [handpainted]	Multicolored	Hawai	Adler	C
10910	^^Sailboat and tropical island with two trees [handpainted]	Multicolored	Hawai	Adler	D
10911	^^Sailing ship, border of anchors	Black, blue	Navy	Klotzbach	A
10912	^^Sailor and girl entering tunnel of love	Blue	Navy	Harrington	A
10913	^^Sailor astride warship gun in turret, holding paint brush and bucket	Black	Navy	Lupton	A
10914	^^Sailor blowing bugle on ship, sailors saluting flag on pole, planes overhead [thermographed]	Blue	Navy	Crosby	B
10915	^^Sailor on guard, warship in background	Blue	Navy	Harrington	A
10916	^^Sailor pushing mop on deck of ship	Black	Navy	Lupton	A
10917	^^Sailor smiling, standing near palm, sun behind him [handpainted] [[APO 503, 1/45]	Multicolored	Navy	Ander, HJ	E
10918	^^Sailor under palm tree [lower left]	Black/Blue	Navy	Lupton	A
10919	^^Sailor with signal flags [lower left]	Black	Navy	Lupton	A
10920	^^Sailor with white cap beside battleship [lower left]	Black	Navy	Lupton	A
10921	^^Sailor, outline of heart above head, girl in heart	Black	Navy	Lupton	A
10922	^^Sailor, outline of heart at right of head	Black	Navy	Lupton	A
10923	^^Sandman in sky sprinkling sand on army tents below [handpainted] [torn stamp]	Multicolored	Army	Cowdery	D
10924	^^Santa Claus face [handpainted]	Multicolored	Holid	Adler	C
10925	^^Santa Claus face as clown, laughing [handpainted]	Multicolored	Holid	Adler	C

NO.	DESCRIPTION OF CACHET ILLUSTRATION (NO TEXT)	COLOR	TOPIC	PUBLISHER	$
10926	^^Santa Claus face with phone [handpainted]	Multicolored	Holid	Adler	C
10927	^^Searchlight on rubber tires	Blue, red	Home	Risinger	A
10928	^^Sergeant [drawn large] chewing out soldier [drawn small]	Brown	Army	Unknown	A
10929	^^Sergeant yelling at soldier who has hat in hand [handpainted]	Multicolored	Army	Dannells	C
10930	^^Shepherd, flock, and Christmas Star [handpainted]	Multicolored	Holid	Adler	C
10931	^^Shield and anchor [handpainted]	Multicolored	Shiel	Adler	C
10932	^^Shield at upper left	Multicolored	Shiel	Amer Pat	A
10933	^^Shield at upper left, with 11 stars, spray of leaves at each side	Unknown	Shiel	Smith, W	A
10934	^^Shield at upper left, with 2 stars at each side	Blue, red	Shiel	Dime	A
10935	^^Shield, 30x25 mm, at center left	Multicolored	FlSh	Amer Pat	A
10936	^^Shield, 30x27 mm, at center left, one star at each side	Red	Shiel	Krakora	A
10937	^^Shield, 64 mm tall, 48 stars, eagle on top	Unknown	Shiel	Unknown	A
10938	^^Shield, 76 mm tall, 3 stars, U.S. seal in center	Unknown	Shiel	Unknown	A
10939	^^Shield, center left, with flag at left edge	Multicolored	FlSh	Amer Pat	A
10940	^^Shield, large, with 13 stars	Multicolored	Shiel	Ioor	A
10941	^^Shield, small	Unknown	Shiel	Hoerr	A
10942	^^Shield, small, upper left; 2-star service flag, lower left	Blue, red	Shiel	Trent	A
10943	^^Shield, tall, 52 mm high, blue and red; Spirit of '76, gray, in background	Multicolored	Sp'76	Premier	B
10944	^^Shield, tall, with 11 stars, draped in ribbon	Multicolored	Shiel	Ioor	A
10945	^^Small eagle at top of double frame, army insignia [label frame] [yellow envelope]	Blue	Eagle	Foster	A
10946	^^Small eagle at top of double frame, navy insignia [label frame] [yellow envelope]	Red	Eagle	Foster	A
10947	^^Snowman, helmeted, wearing star-spangled tie, making "V" w/left hand	Multicolored	VforV	Unknown	A
10948	^^Soldier (Pvt. Ray R. Cowdery) running toward Christmas tree [handpainted]	Multicolored	Army	Cowdery	D
10949	^^Soldier (Pvt. Ray R. Cowdery) sitting on G.I. soap box [handpainted]	Multicolored	Army	Cowdery	D
10950	^^Soldier [PFC] cutting in on Sergeant on dance floor	Brown	Army	Unknown	A
10951	^^Soldier [Pvt. Ray R. Cowdery] flanked by two sergeants, mail envs. above	Multicolored	Army	Cowdery	D
10952	^^Soldier admiring a woman sitting on ground [handpainted]	Multicolored	Army	Dannells	C
10953	^^Soldier being yanked off feet by rearing horse [env. 5 1/2x3 5/8 in.]	Blue, red	Army	Dime	A
10954	^^Soldier flying out of cannon, saluting, as Hitler reacts with alarm	Black	Hitle	Trapani	C
10955	^^Soldier in fatigues, leaning on mop, daydreaming of a woman [handpainted]	Multicolored	Army	Dannells	C
10956	^^Soldier kissing woman, head and shoulders view [handpainted]	Multicolored	Army	Dannells	C
10957	^^Soldier leaning on sign that says "home," waiting for auto to come by	Black, gray	Army	Unknown	A
10958	^^Soldier on firing range flying back from unexpected "kick" of rifle	Brown	Army	Unknown	A
10959	^^Soldier on motorcycle	Blue, red	Army	Risinger	A
10960	^^Soldier on phone, back to viewer, thinking of wife and baby [handpainted]	Multicolored	Army	Adler	C
10961	^^Soldier poised to throw brick at window to get attention of nearby woman M.P.	Black	Army	Deming	A
10962	^^Soldier reading love letter, head turned toward viewer, dog behind him [handpainted]	Multicolored	Army	Dannells	C
10963	^^Soldier running left, holding pie, cleaver flying toward head [handpainted]	Multicolored	Army	Dannells	C
10964	^^Soldier saluting [handpainted]	Black	Army	Parker	B
10965	^^Soldier saluting, flag in background, in oval	Multicolored	Army	Ioor	A
10966	^^Soldier sitting on top of moving tank, waving [env. 5 1/2x3 3/8 in.]	Red	Army	Dime	A
10967	^^Soldier sleeping in tent, snoring, feet sticking out toward viewer [handpainted]	Multicolored	Army	Dannells	C
10968	^^Soldier smiling, face and helmet shadowed [handpainted]	Multicolored	Army	Adler	C
10969	^^Soldier smiling, standing with right thumb up, left hand open [handpainted]	Multicolored	Army	Dannells	C
10970	^^Soldier standing guard, rabbit sitting nearby greeting him [envelope 9 1/2x4 1/8]	Multicolored	Army	Barg	A
10971	^^Soldier standing on barrel, surprised by cook as he's attempting to steal a pie	Multicolored	Army	Dannells	C
10972	^^Soldier standing with letter in hands, 2 hearts indicating love [handpainted]	Multicolored	Army	Dannells	C
10973	^^Soldier walking with money in hand, hidden soldier ready to attack him [handpaint]	Multicolored	Army	Dannells	C
10974	^^Soldier with axe in left hand eyeing fallen tree that's crushed his tent [handpainted]	Multicolored	Army	Dannells	C
10975	^^Soldier with fingers in ears, artillery piece firing behind him	Red	Ordna	Unknown	A
10976	^^Soldier with full pack, helmet, and rifle, sweaty and tired [handpainted]	Multicolored	Army	Dannells	C
10977	^^Soldier with helmet and rifle, 69x54 mm	Black/Blue	Army	Croy	A
10978	^^Soldier with helmet and rifle, halftone picture	Black/Blue	Army	Croy	A
10979	^^Soldier with helmet and rifle, running from a dog chasing him [handpainted]	Multicolored	Army	Dannells	C
10980	^^Soldier with helmet, head tilted up slightly [handpainted]	Multicolored	Army	Adler	C
10981	^^Soldier with mop, ready to wash floor, looking unhappy [envelope 7 1/2x4 in.]	Black, gray	Army	Unknown	A
10982	^^Soldier with new crewcut haircut looking in mirror, appearing agitated	Brown	Army	Unknown	A
10983	^^Soldier with pen in right hand, letter in left	Blue	Army	Unknown	A

NO.	DESCRIPTION OF CACHET ILLUSTRATION (NO TEXT)	COLOR	TOPIC	PUBLISHER	$
10984	^^Soldier with rifle inside ship steering wheel, anchor [handpainted]	Multicolored	Armed	Adler	C
10985	^^Soldier writing letter home dreaming of beautiful girl to whom he's writing	Brown	Army	Unknown	A
10986	^^Soldier writing lettr, thinking, small stars around him [env. 5 1/2x3 3/8 in.]	Blue	Army	Dime	A
10987	^^Soldier, driving Jeep, waving hat in right hand [handpainted]	Multicolored	Army	Dannells	C
10988	^^Soldier, hat flying off head, running toward midair envelope [handpainted]	Multicolored	Army	Dannells	C
10989	^^Soldier, head and shoulders, looking slightly to right [colored envelopes]	Black	Army	Huss	A
10990	^^Soldier, sitting, right index finger next to head, thinking of woman	Multicolored	Army	Temple	A
10991	^^Soldier, standing, looking at picture of woman in left hand [handpainted]	Multicolored	Army	Dannells	C
10992	^^Soldiers in troop train	Brown	Army	Nixon	A
10993	^^Soldiers leaping from truck to use gun	Black	Army	Rosenberg	A
10994	^^Soldiers, 3, and machine gun, 9 stars above, 10 stars with V in center below	Blue, red	Army	Risinger	A
10995	^^Speed boat, 9 stars in row above, 10 stars with V in center below	Blue, red	Navy	Risinger	A
10996	^^Spirit of '76 picture below U.S. flag	Multicolored	Sp'76	Garfield	A
10997	^^Spirit of '76, lower left, shaded red line runs left to right, wings with "V"	Multicolored	Sp'76	Runge	A
10998	^^Spirit of '76, picture 62 mm high	Multicolored	Sp'76	Ioor	A
10999	^^Spirit of '76, picture 74 mm high	Unknown	Sp'76	Unknown	A
11000	^^Star, circle at center, smaller stars + vertical stripes in circle	Blue, red	Shiel	Krakora	A
11001	^^Stars and stripes banner circling globe	Red	Globe	Murrman	A
11002	^^Statue of Liberty [Statue blue, rectangular frame of many small flags, red]	Blue, red	FlLib	Card	A
11003	^^Statue of Liberty [arm and torch] with airplane flying behind it	Blue/Red	Liber	Krakora	A
11004	^^Statue of Liberty [rectangular frame of stars and connecting lines]	Blue, red	Liber	Card	A
11005	^^Statue of Liberty [upper portion of statue] [handpainted]	Multicolored	Liber	Krakora	C
11006	^^Statue of Liberty [upper portion of statue] [statue gold, torch red]	Gold, red	Liber	Amer Pat	A
11007	^^Statue of Liberty encircled by red,white, blue ribbon [handpainted]	Multicolored	Liber	Adler	D
11008	^^Statue of Liberty in tall oval surrounded by small stars, above flag	Multicolored	FlLib	Ioor	A
11009	^^Statue of Liberty in tall oval, yellow flame from torch, yellow stars [handpainted]	Multicolored	Liber	Cowdery	D
11010	^^Statue of Liberty with rays from torch	Multicolored	Liber	Dime	A
11011	^^Statue of Liberty, airplane at right, star above torch	Blue, red	Lib+	Risinger	A
11012	^^Statue of Liberty, viewed from ground, 3 birds [buff envelope 7 5/8x5 1/2 in.]	Blue	Liber	Yontz	B
11013	^^Submarine surfacing [colored envelopes]	Bk/Blue/Gree	USsub	Huss	A
11014	^^Submarine surfacing, distant sub at left [signed by Olsen] [colored envelopes]	Bk/Bu/Green	USsub	Huss	A
11015	^^Tank [signed by Diana] [colored envelopes]	Brown	Ordna	Huss	A
11016	^^Tank at lower left, one star to left, 2 with stripes to right [thermographed]	Black/Brown	Ordna	Grover	A
11017	^^Tank at lower left, one star to left, one with stripes to right [thermographed]	Black	Ordna	Grover	A
11018	^^Tank, soldier with flag, 3 airplanes overhead	Blue, red	Army	Krakora	A
11019	^^Tank, upper left, with soldier peering from turret	Multicolored	Ordna	Dime	A
11020	^^Tanks, 2, under 2 airplanes	Brown	Ordna	Ander, EA	A
11021	^^Tanks, 3, lower left	Multicolored	Ordna	Amer Pat	A
11022	^^Tanks, 3, under 6 airplanes	Blue	Ordna	Ander, EA	A
11023	^^Tanks, 5, shield with circle of stars	Black	Ordna	Allen	A
11024	^^Trains emerging from shield, 5 stars at top of shield	Red	Shiel	Nixon	A
11025	^^Trains, 5, in yard, with tanks on flat cars	Black	Ordna	Nixon	A
11026	^^Truck, 9 stars in row above, 10 stars with V in center below	Blue, red	Army	Risinger	A
11027	^^Uncle Sam and civilian in front of flag	Blue, red	Uncle	Garfield	A
11028	^^Uncle Sam pointing at viewer	Brown	Uncle	Phill, CR	A
11029	^^Uncle Sam rolling up his sleeves [handpainted]	Multicolored	Uncle	Unknown	B
11030	^^Uncle Sam standing before a cannon	Blue, red	Uncle	Krakora	B
11031	^^Uncle Sam with outline of "V", 9 stars above, 10 stars with V in center below	Blue, red	UncV	Risinger	A
11032	^^Uncle Sam with outline of "V", no stars	Blue	UncV	Risinger	A
11033	^^Uncle Sam, head and shoulders, wearing big hat and wing-collar	Multicolored	Uncle	Ioor	A
11034	^^Uncle Sam, left hand on hip, holding rifle in right hand	Red	Uncle	Carpenter	A
11035	^^Uncle Sam, standing on map of U.S., holding card	Unknown	Uncle	Dime	A
11036	^^Uncle Sam, with hand of Uncle crushing a swastika [at left]	Blue	Uncle	Wash Cover	A
11037	^^Uncle Sam, with hand of uncle crushing a swastika [closer to center]	Black	Uncle	Quigley	A
11038	^^Uncle Sam, with hand pointing to enemy heads [at left]	Blue	Uncle	Wash Cover	A
11039	^^Uncle Sam, with hand pointing to enemy heads [closer to center]	Black	Uncle	Quigley	A
11040	^^Uncle Sam, with Uncle pointing to heads of Hitler, Mussolini, and a Japanese	Blue	Uncle	Wolf, CL	A
11041	^^V for Victory hand sign	Red	VforV	Boone	A

NO.	DESCRIPTION OF CACHET ILLUSTRATION (NO TEXT)	COLOR	TOPIC	PUBLISHER	$
11042	^^V for Victory hand sign before shield	Gn/O/Pu/Red	VforV	Boone	A
11043	^^Victory standing on sphere, left hand raised [colored envelopes]	Blue/Brown	Antiq	Huss	A
11044	^^Virgin and Child with Joseph [handpainted] [postmarked 12/25/44]	Multicolored	Holid	Adler	D
11045	^^WAC head and shoulders in profile [handpainted]	Multicolor	WAC	Dannells	C
11046	^^WAC PFC whistling at blushing PFC soldier	Brown	WAC	Unknown	A
11047	^^Warship at lower left, steaming right	Red	Navy	Unknown	B
11048	^^Warship, "US" on prow; hills+cloud in background [LCI(L)Gp33, 5/8/45] [handp]	Black	VEDay	Dye	C
11049	^^Warships at lower left, tall shield with wreath	Unknown	Navy	Allen	A
11050	^^Warships, two at left, one at right. Shield and wreath above ships at left	Black	Navy	Lowry	A
11051	^^Washington, George	Red	Wash	Phill, CR	A
11052	^^Washington, George [left half of envelope]	Purple	Wash	Carpenter	A
11053	^^Washington, George, in medallion	Blue	Wash	Abel	A
11054	^^Washington, George, in oval	Unknown	Wash	Bartz	A
11055	^^Washington, George, in oval, stars at bottom, 2 flags and 2 stars in circle	Blue, red	Wash	Risinger	A
11056	^^Wolf, human, trying to sit beside girl	Red	Women	Christens	A
11057	^^Woman holding letter and envelope against her cheek [handpainted]	Multicolored	Home	Cowdery	D
11058	^^Woman laying wreath on grave, in oval	Multicolored	Women	Ioor	A
11059	^^Woman Marine, head	Green	WomM	Unknown	A
11060	^^Womens Army Corps insignia [upper left] [envelope 5 1/8x4 1/8 in.]	Multicolored	WAC	Dime	A

Cover Values (from Table 6, p. 136)

Value	Price Range
A	$ 3 - 6
B	$ 7 - 15
C	$ 16 - 30
D	$ 31 - 60
E	$ 61 - 125
F	$ 126 - 250
G	$ 251 - 500
H	$ 501 - 1000
I	$ >1000
X	Unpriced: Suspicious or fraudulent cover

10638

10664

10670

10704

10710

10721

10744

10768

10772

10778

10829

10838

10891

10894

10960

11014

8

Publishers Catalogue

IN THE Cachet Catalogue appearing in the previous chapter, the "Publisher" column listed people, companies, or government agencies responsible for production and distribution of more than 11,060 patriotic envelopes. Room for 10 characters and spaces was allotted in the column to identify each of the 661 publishers uniquely. The last or significant name, together with first name or initials where needed, sufficed for this.

The Publishers Catalogue appearing here extends this information to include the full names of publishers, their identifying imprints, and their city and state of residence. This new catalogue lists all 661 publishers of United States patriotic covers of World War II known to me and briefly records details about them. The column headings of the catalogue are:

* Number assigned to each publisher (sequenced by alphabetic order of last name, company name, or government agency or office)
* Publisher (same as Publisher in the Cachet Catalogue)
* Imprint (or signature or logo)
* Site on envelope of imprint
* Full name of publisher
* City and State of domicile of each publisher.

Let us look at these properties of the Publishers catalogue:

NUMBER

The publishers are arranged alphabetically and numbered consecutively. Thus publisher "Abbott" (full name: Abbott Laboratories) is tabulated No. 1,

"Abel" (full name: George H. Abel) is No. 2, and "Zunks" (full name The Original Order of Zunks) is No. 661.

PUBLISHER

The Publisher Catalogue is linked to the Cachet Catalogue by the names that appear in the "Publisher" column of the latter catalogue. After locating a given cachet in the Cachet Catalogue and finding the full or fragmentary name of the publisher of that cachet, interested readers can turn to the Publishers Catalogue for more information.

IMPRINT and SITE

Some publishers placed an imprint (initials or last name or full name, sometimes with an accompanying number) on their envelopes. Only occasionally serving a copyright function, the imprint became a welcome identifying mark for collectors then and now. Some publishers regularly identified themselves in this way (Gladys Adler, Leonard Borkowski, William S. Linto, Jacques Minkus), some irregularly (Herman F. Fluegel, Matthew Huss, Dorothy W. Knapp, Etsuo Sayama).

Envelope placement of imprints—the "Site" listed in the catalogue—reflected individual publisher taste. And quite individual their tastes were. There may have been 661 cachet makers, but it sometimes seems there were 662 ways to place an imprint on an envelope.

Most publishers placed their imprints in the lower left front of the envelope ("Front" or "Fr"). Sometimes imprints took the form of the publisher's return address, or corner card ("Ccard"), at the upper left of the envelope (Teixeira, other armed forces cachet makers, and most corporate and governmental cachet makers). Sometimes they were placed at the upper right ("UR"), usually hidden by the postage stamp (Linprint). There were still other creative placements. A few imprints could be found at the front lower right of the envelope, as was the case with unit patriotics produced for American forces in Australia. Some cachet makers (Gladys Adler, Ralph E. Davis, Firstday Covers) placed their imprint on the envelope flap ("Flap" or "Fl"). Others elected to place their imprint on the back ("Back" or "B"), either below the flap along with further information (Linto and Sayama) or along the lower right border of the envelope as a copyright notice (Minkus). And of course many cachet makers simply left their designs unsigned: the wartime generation of collectors knew many of the designers and publishers, but later generations have had to search the philatelic literature to put design and designer together.

FULL NAME OF PUBLISHER, CITY and STATE

The Publishers Catalogue fleshes out the limited information given in the "Publisher" column of the Cachet Catalogue. The full name of each cachet maker and, where known, the city and state of each are listed. For publishers in the armed forces, no fixed address was possible; instead, the branch of service is designated in the "City" column and the "State" column is left blank.

PUBLISHERS CATALOGUE

NO.	PUBLISHER	IMPRINT	SITE	FULL NAME OF PUBLISHER	CITY	STATE
P 1	Abbott	Abbott Laboratories, etc.	Ccard	Abbott Laboratories	Chicago	IL
P 2	Abel	Abel; G.H.A.; GHA	Front	George H. Abel	Tribes Hill	NY
P 3	AC Spark	AC Spark Plug Division	Ccard	AC Spark Plug Division	Unknown	Unk
P 4	Acme Fast	Acme Fast Freight, etc.	Ccard	Acme Fast Freight	Unknown	Unk
P 5	Adler	Gladys Adler [handstamp]	Flap	Gladys Adler	Bellaire	TX
P 6	Advertiser	Victory Envelopes, etc.	Back	The Advertisers Press (Capitol Stamp Co.)	Des Moines	IA
P 7	Air Force		Front	U.S. Army Air Force	USAAF	
P 8	Albrecht			H.E. Albrecht	Philadelphia	PA
P 9	Alden	John Alden	Front	John Alden (see Pilgrim)	Bergenfield	NJ
P 10	All Nation	TANS	Front	The All Nations Society	Unknown	Unk
P 11	Allen			Harry C. Allen, Jr.	Cleveland	OH
P 12	Alpert			William Alpert	New York	NY
P 13	Altenbernd	AA. [+ No.]	Front	Adolf Altenbernd	Cleveland	OH
P 14	AMC-Bowers	AMC; AMC-Bowers	Fr;B	AMC-Bowers Envelope & Lithograph Co.	Indianapolis	IN
P 15	Amer Art	American Art Service etc.	Front	American Art Service	Chicago	IL
P 16	Amer Canc	American Cancer Society	Ccard	American Cancer Society	New York	NY
P 17	Amer Fores			American Forestry Association	Unknown	Unk
P 18	Amer Legio	American Legion Salvage	Ccard	American Legion Salvage Committee	Norwich	NY
P 19	Amer Loan			American Loan and Realty Company	Lebanon	OH
P 20	Amer Naval	American Naval, etc.	Front	American Naval Cancellation Society	Pittsburgh	PA
P 21	Amer Pat	American Patriotic Press	Back	American Patriotic Press (Harry E. Curtiss)	San Francisco	CA
P 22	Amer Phila			American Philatelic Society	Denver	CO
P 23	Amer Red			American Red Cross (Los Angeles)	Los Angeles	CA
P 24	Amer War M	TAWM	Front	The American War Mothers	Unknown	Unk
P 25	Amer Women			American Women Voluntary Services	Unknown	Unk
P 26	Ander, CS	C. Stephen Anderson	Front	C. Stephen Anderson	W. Orange	NJ
P 27	Ander, EA	Elmer Anderson	Back	Elmer A. Anderson (Pontiac Press)	Pontiac	RI
P 28	Ander, HJ	Sgt. H.J. Anderson	Ccard	Sgt. H.J. Anderson	U.S. Army	
P 29	Andrews	Andrews Ptg. Co.	Front	Andrews Printing Co.	Chattanooga	TN
P 30	Ang	Ang [+No.]; Mutual, etc	Front	Clinton E. Ang (Mutual Covers)	Louisville	KY
P 31	Anti-Pacif	The Anti-Pacifist, etc.	Ccard	The Anti-Pacifist Propaganda Committee	Denver	CO
P 32	Apnew			Apnew Sales Agency	Brooklyn	NY

NO.	PUBLISHER	IMPRINT	SITE	FULL NAME OF PUBLISHER	CITY	STATE
P 33	Arizona	State of Arizona Dept.	Ccard	State of Arizona Dept. of Vocational Ed.	Phoenix	AZ
P 34	Army			U.S. Army base, unit, or geographic theater	U.S. Army	
P 35	Arnold			E.G. Arnold	Brooklyn	NY
P 36	Artcraft	Artcraft	Front	Washington Stamp Exchange	Newark	NJ
P 37	Artists	Artists for Victory	Front	Artists for Victory	New York	NY
P 38	Ashley			E.O. Ashley	Chicago	IL
P 39	Atkins	E.C. Atkins & Co. etc.	Ccard	E.C. Atkins & Co.	Unknown	Unk
P 40	Atwell	Atwell	Front	(? first name) Atwell	Unknown	Unk
P 41	Auge	Auge	Front	Sgt. Kenneth G. Auge	USAAF	
P 42	Aunt Jenny	Aunt Jenny's Garden Club	Ccard	Aunt Jenny's Garden Club	Los Angeles	CA
P 43	Avy	A; S. Avy Jr	Front	Samuel Avy, Jr.	Piqua	OH
P 44	Aylward	Mrs. Rita Aylward	Ccard	Mrs. Rita Aylward	W. Swanzey	NH
P 45	Babcock			Russell Babcock	Adrian	MI
P 46	Bailey	Harry Bailey	Front	Harry Bailey	Santa Monica	CA
P 47	Barg			W.H. Barg	Unknown	Unk
P 48	Barnes	A.L. Barnes, etc.	Back	A.L. Barnes	Bartlesville	OK
P 49	Bartley	Deane C. Bartley	Ccard	Deane C. Bartley (Washington Cover Club)	Seattle	WA
P 50	Bartz	Ray Bartz	Front	Ray Bartz	Detroit	MI
P 51	Barwicki	P.F.C. Joseph Barwicki	Ccard	PFC Joseph Barwicki	U.S. Army	
P 52	Bates	Warner Bates	Front	Warner Bates	Unknown	Unk
P 53	Bath			Bath #3 Club	Albany	NY
P 54	Battles	D. Blake Battles	Ccard	D. Blake Battles	Wooster	OH
P 55	Batura			William J. Batura	Brooklyn	NY
P 56	Baur			Robert C. Baur	Buffalo	NY
P 57	Bayliss			P.H. Bayliss	Wilmington	NC
P 58	Bean	L.D. Bean, etc.	Back	Louis D. Bean	Washington	DC
P 59	Bechtold			Jane Bechtold	Little Ferry	NJ
P 60	Beck			Morris W. Beck	Menasha	WI
P 61	Bell	CEB	Front	Clarence E. Bell	Wellsville	OH
P 62	Belles-let	Belles-lettres, etc.	Back	Belles-lettres (A.F. Grymes/Thos. Kirksey)	Chicago	IL
P 63	Bellows	The Bellows Co., Senacon	Ccard	The Bellows Co., Senacon Division	Akron	OH
P 64	Bendig			A.W. Bendig	Etna	PA
P 65	Bendix	F. Bendix	Front	F. Bendix	Unknown	Unk
P 66	Bible Med	Bible Meditiation League	Ccard	The Bible Meditation League	Columbus	OH
P 67	Bible Sch	Bible School Park		Bible School Park	Johnson City	NY
P 68	Bickford			E.M. Bickford	U.S. Army	
P 69	Bison			Bison Philatelic Soc. (Marvin H. Garfinkel)	Buffalo	NY
P 70	Black			Stephen D. Black	Three Rivers	MI
P 71	Blumen	Sgt. Arthur Blumenschine	Ccard	Sgt. Arthur E. Blumenschine	U.S. Army	
P 72	Board			Board of Commerce	Sheridan	MI
P 73	Bohemian	Bohemian Benedictine etc.	Front	Bohemian Benedictine Order (Benabbey Guild)	Lisle	IL
P 74	Boland			Walter S. Boland	Audubon	NJ
P 75	Boll	Sgt. Ken Boll	Front	Sgt. Ken Boll	U.S. Army	
P 76	Boone	Boone	Front	Richard P. Boone	Wilmington	NC
P 77	Boothroyd	G.O.B.	Front	Gordon O. Boothroyd	Syracuse	NY
P 78	Borkowski	Leonard Borkowski	Front	Leonard Borkowski	Milwaukee	WI
P 79	Boston Ed	Boston Edison Co., etc.	Ccard	Boston Edison Company	Boston	MA
P 80	BPOE	Benevolent Protective etc	Ccard	Benevolent Protective Order of Elks	Bradford	PA
P 81	Brenn	B- [+ # or ltr]; Bee logo	Front	Elmer A. Brenn	Sioux City	IA
P 82	Brown, G	Gilbert Brown	Front	Gilbert Brown	Johnstown	PA
P 83	Brown, LN			Lester Norton Brown	Brooklyn	NY
P 84	Bruno			Della Bruno	Sacramento	CA
P 85	Buchwald			R Buchwald	Unknown	Unk
P 86	Bucka+Abel			Charles H. Buckalew & George H. Abel	Wilmington	DE
P 87	Buckalew	C.H.B.; Chas. H. Buckalew	Fr;Fl	Charles H. Buckalew	Wilmington	DE
P 88	Bund	J. Robert Bund	Back	J. Robert Bund (RCD #302)	Manhattan Beach	CA
P 89	Burdick	PB; Burdick; Liberty Cov	Front	Philip O. Burdick (Liberty Covers)	Louisville	KY
P 90	Burke			(? first name) Burke	Charlotte	NC

NO.	PUBLISHER	IMPRINT	SITE	FULL NAME OF PUBLISHER	CITY	STATE
P 91	Burkholder			Ralph L. Burkholder	Long Beach	CA
P 92	Burpee	W. Atlee Burpee Co.	Ccard	W. Atlee Burpee Co.	Philadelphia	PA
P 93	Burris	Gene A. Burris	Front	Cpl. Gene A. Burris	U.S. Army	
P 94	Butler			(? first name) Butler	Massapequa	NY
P 95	Butzen	Pavois	Front	Albert C. Butzen (Pavois)	Detroit	MI
P 96	Buxton Mrs			Mrs. Donald Buxton (Mildred Buxton)	Dubuque	IA
P 97	Buxton, D	DB; DEB; Don Buxton	Front	Donald Buxton	Dubuque	IA
P 98	Byrd Stamp	Admiral Byrd Stamp and Coin Club	Front	Admiral Byrd Stamp and Coin Club	Reading	PA
P 99	Cabot			George D. Cabot	Weehawken	NJ
P 100	Cachet Cra	CachetCraft	Front	Cachet Craft Cover Svc (Frederick B. Fitts)	Framingham	MA
P 101	Cadillac			Cadillac Motor Car Division	Detroit	MI
P 102	Cal-Craft	Cal-Craft	Front	Cal-Craft	Unknown	Unk
P 103	Calhoun			A.B. Calhoun	Windham	AK
P 104	Card	Card; Empire; Homestead	Front	Hallock Card (see Homestead Press)	Hostelic	NY
P 105	Carpenter	Carpenter, etc.	Front	N. LeRoy Carpenter	Holliston	MA
P 106	Carter	E.C. [+ No.]; JAC	Front	Earl L. Carter	U.S. Army	
P 107	Carter Mrs	J.C.	Front	Mrs. Earl Carter	Knightstown	IN
P 108	Castellano	JRC [+ No.]	Front	Jasper R. Castellano	Chicago	IL
P 109	Catholic	Catholic Order Foresters	Ccard	Catholic Order Foresters	Unk	Unk
P 110	Chamber			Chamber of Commerce	St. Petersburg	FL
P 111	Chapman			Robert L. Chapman	Canton	OH
P 112	Cherry			Cherry River Paper Co.	Unknown	Unk
P 113	Chester	C-AMC; A.M. Chester	Fr;B	A.M. Chester (see AMCùBower)	Seattle	WA
P 114	Christens	A.A. Christensen, etc.	Back	Sgt. Arthur A. Christensen	U.S. Army	
P 115	Citret	Ray in the [K.C.] Star	Front	Harry Citret	New York	NY
P 116	Clark	R.H.C.	Front	Ralph H. Clark	Keene	NH
P 117	Clarke+Woo	Clarke & Wood, etc.	Ccard	(? first name) Clarke + (? first name) Wood	Unknown	Unk
P 118	Clendennen	C; Wm. Clendennen, etc.	Fr;Fl	William Clendennen	Port Jervis	NY
P 119	Cleveland	Cleveland Cover Club	Front	Cleveland Cover Club (Gordon H. Hamilton;	Cleveland	OH
P 120	Cliff	AWC	Front	Athol W. Cliff (artist: C.S. Anderson)	Millburn	NJ
P 121	Clifford	J.W.C.; J.W. Clifford	Front	J.W. Clifford	New York	NY
P 122	Cochran	F.J.C. [+No.]	Front	Frederick J. Cochran	Detroit	MI
P 123	Coleman	Coleman & Co. etc.	Ccard	Coleman & Co.	Unknown	Unk
P 124	Coll Soc	TCS	Front	The Collectors Society	Unknown	Unk
P 125	Coll Surp	PentArts	Front	Collectors Surplus (Pent Arts)	Kansas City	MO
P 126	Commercial	Commercial Products, etc.	Ccard	Commercial Products Company	Unknown	Unk
P 127	Conn Light			Connecticut Light and Power Co.	Unknown	CT
P 128	Conner	DCC	Front	Dicken C. Conner (printer: Wilford Brown)	U.S. Army	
P 129	Conner Mrs			Mrs. Dicken C. Conner	Frankfort	IN
P 130	Consolidat			Consolidated Book Publishing Co.	Unknown	Unk
P 131	Cornell	Lee H [or H.] Cornell	Front	Lee H. Cornell (artist: Jean Craig)	Wichita	KS
P 132	Coryell			Harold R. Coryell	Mt. Vernon	IL
P 133	County			County Clerk, Cook County	Chicago	IL
P 134	Cover News			Cover News	Council Bluffs	IA
P 135	Coward-McC			Coward-McCann	Unknown	Unk
P 136	Cowdery			Cecile Cowdery	Long Prairie	MN
P 137	Cox	Delma Cox, etc.	Ccard	Delma Cox	Connersville	IN
P 138	Cox+Price	Cox & Price WCA	Front	Delma Cox and Robert Price	Connersville	IN
P 139	Cozart	Coz-Art Covers; R.C.	Front	Russell Cozart	Louisville	KY
P 140	Crockett	Gib Crockett	Front	Gib Crockett	Unknown	Unk
P 141	Crosby	W.G.C.; R.E.S.; Arundell	Front	Walter G. Crosby	San Pedro	CA
P 142	Croy			P.A. Croy	Roanoke	VA
P 143	Curtiss, D			David E. Curtiss	Ashaway	RI
P 144	Curtiss, H	American Patriotic Press	Back	Harry E. Curtiss (see Amer Pat)	San Francisco	CA
P 145	Curt-Teich		Back	Curt-Teich & Co.	Chicago	IL
P 146	Czubay	Czubay; Zoo-Bay; N.C.S.	Front	Walter L. Czubay (RCD #206; USCS #997)	Astoria (NYC)	NY
P 147	D.C. Penal	D.C. Penal Institutions	Ccard	D.C. Penal Institutions	Lorton	VA
P 148	Dahl			W.E. Dahl	Hayfield	MN

NO.	PUBLISHER	IMPRINT	SITE	FULL NAME OF PUBLISHER	CITY	STATE
P 149	Dahlem			Richard C. Dahlem	Kenvil	NJ
P 150	Dailey			Frank E. Dailey	Excelsior Spgs.	MO
P 151	Daily News			Los Angeles Daily News	Los Angeles	CA
P 152	Dale	M-D [+ No.]	Front	Charles R. Dale (+ Mitchell Advertising Co)	Lock Haven	PA
P 153	Dannells	Capt. R.A. Dannells [Ccard][+#, Front]	Ccard	Capt. Richard A. Dannells	U.S. Army	
P 154	Davis, D	D. Davis; Davis; DEE	Front	Darrell Davis	Superior	NE
P 155	Davis, JC	J.C. Davis	Front	J.C. Davis	Annville	KY
P 156	Davis, M			Max Davis	U.S. Army	
P 157	Davis, Ral	Ralph E. Davis, etc.	Flap	Ralph E. Davis	Whiteville	NC
P 158	Davis, Ray	D [+ No.]	Front	S/Sgt. Raymond E. Davis	U.S. Army	
P 159	De Montign			Clarence De Montigny	New Bedford	MA
P 160	DeHart			H.B. DeHart	Camden	NJ
P 161	DeLeuze	C.W.D.; CWD	Front	Charles W. DeLeuze	Armed Forces	
P 162	Deming			Fred W. Deming	Hartford	CT
P 163	Denver Dry	Denver Dry Goods Co.	Back	Denver Dry Goods Co.	Denver	CO
P 164	Detroit Ed	The Detroit Edison, etc.	Front	The Detroit Edison Philatelic Soc.	Detroit	MI
P 165	Detroit Fu	Detroit Fuel & S. Co.	Ccard	Detroit Fuel and S. Co.	Detroit	MI
P 166	Detroit Ph	Detroit Philatelic, etc.	Ccard	Detroit Philatelic Society	Detroit	MI
P 167	Detroit St	Detroit Steel Products	Ccard	Detroit Steel Products	Detroit	MI
P 168	Dewitz			Charles E. Dewitz	Unknown	Unk
P 169	Diamond	Diamond Food Mart	Ccard	Diamond Food Mart	Los Angeles	CA
P 170	Dietz			Fred H. Dietz	New York	NY
P 171	Dime			Dime Stores	Many cities	
P 172	Dis Am Vet			Disabled American Veterans	Cincinnati	OH
P 173	Doemick			W.J. Doemick	Brooklyn	NY
P 174	Donaldson	A&K; AK44; D&C; ID; K&D	Front	Iva Donaldson (+ ? Cochran; + Yontz)	Highland Park	MI
P 175	Doughboy	Doughboy Studio, etc.	Ccard	Doughboy Studio	Unknown	Unk
P 176	Dover+Litt			Dover and Littlefield (see Littlefiel)	Alcoa	TN
P 177	Downs	Downs-Smith B&C Co., etc.	Ccard	Downs-Smith B&C Co.	Unknown	Unk
P 178	Drooger			L. Drooger	Armed Forces	
P 179	Dunnavant			Bill Dunnavant	Sidney	OH
P 180	Durkin			L.L. Durkin	Pittsburgh	PA
P 181	Durnbaugh			Gordon A. Durnbaugh	Dayton	OH
P 182	Dusold			Rev. August Dusold	Manitowoc	WI
P 183	Dye	Glenn W. Dye, U.S.N.	Back	Glenn W. Dye	U.S. Navy	
P 184	Earnshaw			Walter L. Earnshaw Co.	Hollywood	CA
P 185	East Texas			East Texas Engraving Co.	Unknown	TX
P 186	Ebach			R.G. Ebach	Saginaw	MI
P 187	Edmunds	Tex Edmunds, etc.	Front	Tex Edmunds (Oklahoma City Stamp Club)	Oklahoma City	OK
P 188	Efengee	Efengee Electric, etc.	Ccard	Efengee Electric SuPly Co.	Unknown	Unk
P 189	Ehde	Martin Ehde, etc.	Ccard	Martin Ehde	Amiret	MN
P 190	Eichenlaub			Al and Louise Eichenlaub	Columbus	OH
P 191	Elgin Café	Elgin Café, etc.	Ccard	Elgin Café	Unknown	Unk
P 192	Elks			Benevolent Protective Order of Elks	Dubuque	IA
P 193	Ellis			H.M. Ellis	New York	NY
P 194	Erwin			Wayne Erwin	Kelso	WA
P 195	Ever Ready	H.G. [w/, w/o Acampa]	Front	Ever Ready Press (artist: Acampa)	New York	NY
P 196	Fabian			Gustave H. Fabian	Hempstead	NY
P 197	Fagenson			Albert Fagenson	East Tawas	MI
P 198	Farnsworth	Marvin C. Farnsworth	Front	Farnsworth, Marvin C.	Newark	NY
P 199	Farnum	HF	Front	House of Farnum	Cleveland	OH
P 200	Fergus			W. Lee Fergus	Glen Ellyn	IL
P 201	Fertig	Al Fertig		Al Fertig	Los Angeles	CA
P 202	Fetzer			Louis F. Fetzer	New York	NY
P 203	Fidelity	F.S.	Front	Fidelity Stamp Co.	Washington	DC
P 204	Field			Alexander Field	New Rochelle	NY
P 205	First Day	Firstday Covers	Flap	Firstday Covers	Teaneck	NJ
P 206	First Nat	First National Bank, etc.	Ccard	First National Bank of Dallas	Dallas	TX

NO.	PUBLISHER	IMPRINT	SITE	FULL NAME OF PUBLISHER	CITY	STATE
P 207	Fleetwood	Fleetwood	Front	Fleetwood Covers (artists: KnaP & Staehle)	Pleasantville	NY
P 208	Flesch			Andrew Flesch	Armed Forces	
P 209	Florists	Florists Telegraph, etc.	Ccard	Florists Telegraph Delivery Association	Unknown	Unk
P 210	Fluegel	Fluegel Cover	Front	Herman Fluegel (Fluegel Covers)	Washington	DC
P 211	Fog	Victory Fog Nozzle Co.	Ccard	Victory Fog Nozzle Company	Los Angeles	NY
P 212	Fort Hamil	Fort Hamilton, etc.	Front	Fort Hamilton Philatelic Society	Hamilton	OH
P 213	Fort Morg	Fort Morgan Herald, etc.	Ccard	Fort Morgan Herald	Unknown	Unk
P 214	Fost+Carp	Foster & Carpenter	Front	Foster & Carpenter	Jamaica Plains	MA
P 215	Foster			William T. Foster	Jamaica Plains	MA
P 216	Fountaine			Bill Fountaine	Columbus	OH
P 217	Francis			Thomas J. Francis	Unknown	Unk
P 218	Franke			H.C. Franke	Philadelphia	PA
P 219	French	HEF	Front	H. Edgar French	Newcastle	IN
P 220	Frye			John R. Frye (see Wayne)	Wayne	MI
P 221	Fuesler			Mrs. C. Fuesler	Dayton	OH
P 222	Fumbarger	William Fumbarger, etc.	Ccard	William Fumbarger	Royal Centre	IN
P 223	Gabel	William P. Gabel, etc.	Back	William P. Gabel	Cleveland	OH
P 224	Gahn			A.O. Gahn	Armed Forces	
P 225	Gantz			M.A. Gantz	Troy	OH
P 226	Garfield			Garfield-Perry Stamp Club	Cleveland	OH
P 227	Garfinkel	MHG; Bison Philatel. etc.	Front	Marvin H. Garfinkel	Buffalo	NY
P 228	Garland	JLG [+ No.]	Front	John L. Garland	Ironwood	MI
P 229	Garrison			Arthur T. Garrison	Bridgeton	NJ
P 230	Gatens			H. J. Gatens	Unknown	Unk
P 231	Gawne			Dorothy Gawne	Amherst	OH
P 232	Gawne	Dorothy Gawne	Ccard	Dorothy Gawne	Amherst	OH
P 233	Gen Coin	General Coin Service etc.	Ccard	General Coin Service	Unknown	Unk
P 234	Gielarow			William J. Gielarowski	Lewiston	ME
P 235	Gilbert	Gilbert & Bennett etc.	Ccard	Gilbert & Bennett Mfg. Co.	Georgetown	CT
P 236	Gillespie			(?First name) Gillespie	Unknown	Unk
P 237	Glase	Paul E. Glase	Front	Paul E. Glase	Reading	PA
P 238	Glenn-Corn	Glennard-Corn etc.	Ccard	Glennard-Corn	Unknown	Unk
P 239	Goede			Sgt. Arthur W. Goede	U.S. Army	
P 240	Goldstein	Paul F. Goldstein	Ccard	Paul F. Goldstein (sometime artist: KnaP)	Brooklyn	NY
P 241	Goodfellow	Goodfellow Field, etc.	Front	49th School Squadron, Goodfellow Field	San Angelo	TX
P 242	Graf	Don Graf, R.C.D. #194	Back	Don Graf	Unknown	Unk
P 243	Grandy	WMG	Front	Winfred M. Grandy	New Haven	CT
P 244	Granite			Granite State Federation	Keene	NH
P 245	Graves	Sgt. Lee C. Graves	Ccard	Sgt. Lee C. Graves	USMC	
P 246	Greenlee	Greenlee	Front	(? first name) Greenlee	Unknown	Unk
P 247	Griffith	J. Neal Griffith, etc.	Back	J. Neal Griffith	Clearfield	PA
P 248	Grimsland	Grimsland	Front	Henry Grimsland	Chicago	IL
P 249	Grover	Forest City, etc.	Back	Don Grover (Forest City Patriotic Envels.)	Ithaca	NY
P 250	Gustafson	CEG	Front	C. Edwin Gustafson	Ironwood	MI
P 251	Hadley	GFH; G.F. Hadley	Front	Grace F. Hadley	Peter-borough	NH
P 252	Hale	Nathan Hale Cachets	Back	Nathan Hale Cachets	Willimantic	CT
P 253	Hall			M.D. Hall	Unknown	Unk
P 254	Hamilton	G.H.H.; Cleveland; Zunks	Front	Gordon H. Hamilton (see Cleveland; Zunks)	Pittsburgh	PA
P 255	Hampshire	The Hampshire Press	Back	The Hampshire Press, Inc.	Cambridge	MA
P 256	Hannay	Infantry Replacement etc.	Front	Col. William V. Hannay	U.S. Army	
P 257	Hans	G.H. Hans	Ccard	G.H. Hans	Unknown	Unk
P 258	Harmer	FAH; F.A.H. [+No.]	Front	Fred A. Harmer	Zanesville	OH
P 259	Harmer	FAH [+ No.]	Ccard	Fred A. Harmer	Zanesville	OH
P 260	Harri	Sgt. George J. Harrington	Ccard	Sgt. George J. Harrington	Air Force	
P 261	Harrington			Ted Harrington	Milwaukee	WI
P 262	Hartman	Hartman Beverage Co.	Ccard	Hartman Beverage Co.	Unknown	Unk
P 263	Harvey	Harvey	Front	Paul Harvey	Kokomo	IN
P 264	Hayes	F.G. Hayes	Front	F.G. Hayes	Unknown	Unk

NO.	PUBLISHER	IMPRINT	SITE	FULL NAME OF PUBLISHER	CITY	STATE
P 265	Haynes	Robert Haynes, etc.	Ccard	Robert Haynes	Toledo	OH
P 266	Heckman			W.B. Heckman	Evanston	IL
P 267	Herschaft	M.C. Herschaft	Front	M.C. Herschaft	Unknown	Unk
P 268	Herst	Herman Herst, Jr.	Ccard	Herman Herst, Jr. (printer: Wesley Smith)	New York	NY
P 269	Hill	H.C. Hill [+ year]	Front	Harry C. Hill	Flint	MI
P 270	Hillerich	J.L.H. [+No.]; JLH [+No.]	Front	Joe Lee Hillerich	Louisville	KY
P 271	Hines	Wm. F. Hines	Front	William F. Hines	Unknown	Unk
P 272	Hinrichs	EA Hinrichs, etc.	Ccard	EA Hinrichs & Co.	Unknown	Unk
P 273	Hise			Walter A. Hise	Baltimore	MD
P 274	Hoerr	Hoerr Feed Store	Ccard	Hoerr Feed Store	Peoria	IL
P 275	Hoerth	Carl C. Hoerth, etc.	Ccard	Carl C. Hoerth	Cheviot	OH
P 276	Holmes	H.C. Holmes, etc.	Back	H.C. Holmes	Uniontown	PA
P 277	Holton	Mrs. Clarence W. Holton	Flap	Mrs. Clarence W. Holton	Los Angeles	CA
P 278	Holtz	Benjamin Holtz, etc.	Ccard	Benjamin Holtz	Wabasha	MN
P 279	Homestead	Homestead Press	Front	Homestead Press (Hallock Card)	Hostelic	NY
P 280	Honolulu	Honolulu Advertiser	Front	The Honolulu Advertiser Stamp Club	Honolulu	HI
P 281	Horner			Anthony J. Horner	New Ulm	MN
P 282	Horowitz			Edward S. Horowitz	Cincinnati	OH
P 283	Host			Cpl. Glenn E. Host	U.S. Army	Unk
P 284	Howe	Howe's Histories; ""Howe""	Front	F.E. Howe	Jacksonville	FL
P 285	Hunt	CPH; C.P.H.	Front	C. Paul Hunt	Huntington	WV
P 286	Huss	Goff; Diana; Huss, etc.	Fr;B	Matthew J. Huss	Evanston	IL
P 287	Hutnick	S.E. Hutnick, M.D.	Back	S.E. Hutnick, M.D. (RCD #70)	West Phila.	PA
P 288	Hyde	A.A. Hyde, etc.	Ccard	Rev. A.A. Hyde	Bonham	TX
P 289	ILG Electr	ILG Electric Ventilating	Ccard	ILG Electric Ventilating Co.	Unknown	Unk
P 290	Ill Bell	Illinois Bell Telephone	Ccard	Illinois Bell Telephone Company	Chicago	IL
P 291	Intercity	Intercity Stamp Company	Front	Intercity Stamp Company	Port Washington	NY
P 292	Internat	Sponsored by I.C.G.	Front	International Cover Guild	Unknown	Unk
P 293	Ioor			Harry Ioor (and Travilla Ioor)	Indianapolis	IN
P 294	Isham	Don R Isham RM 3/C	Ccard	Don R. Isham	U.S. Navy	
P 295	ITE Circui			ITE Circuit Breaker Co.	Unknown	Unk
P 296	Jackson, C	Chester P. Jackson	Back	Chester P. Jackson	Unknown	Unk
P 297	Jackson, G			Gladys Jackson	New York	NY
P 298	James			Lillian James	Venice	CA
P 299	Jancowski			Frank B. Jancowski (Pulaski Philat. Club)	Detroit	MI
P 300	Jarrett	Jarrett [w/, w/o No.]	Front	William R. Jarrett	Sharpsville	IN
P 301	Jensen	Fred E. Jensen, etc.	Ccard	Fred E. Jensen	Los Angeles	CA
P 302	Jessop	Ernest Jessop, etc.	Ccard	Ernest Jessop	Oakland Beach	RI
P 303	Jewish Vet	Dept. of Michigan J.W.V.	Front	Dept. of Michigan Jewish War Veterans	Detroit	MI
P 304	Johns Cov	JCP	Front	Johnson Cover Press	Unknown	Unk
P 305	Johnson, C	Mrs. C.W. Johnson, etc.	Back	Mrs. C.W. Johnson	Springfield	MA
P 306	Johnson, D			Dave Johnson	Toms River	NJ
P 307	Jordan	Jordan; Smartcraft	Front	Edward R. Jordan (see Smartcraft)	Elmhurst (NYC)	NY
P 308	Kelsey	Kelsey Company, The	Ccard	The Kelsey Company	Meriden	CT
P 309	Kennedy			H. Kennedy	Philadelphia	PA
P 310	Kent-Moore			Kent-Moore Organization	Unknown	Unk
P 311	Ketteman			Mrs. Fred Ketteman	Buffalo	NY
P 312	Kidd	J.B. Kidd, etc.	Ccard	J.B. Kidd	Jeannette	PA
P 313	Kiech			William W. Kiech	Riverside	CA
P 314	Kimball	W.W. Kimball Co.	Ccard	W.W. Kimball Co.	Unknown	Unk
P 315	King's	King's Stamp Club, etc.	Front	King's Stamp Club (artist: L.W. Staehle)	Syracuse	NY
P 316	Kirchhofer			M.P.L. Kirchhofer	Massillon	OH
P 317	Kirchner	Mrs. George Kirchner	Back	Mrs. George Kirchner	Elgin	KS
P 318	Klaas	Everett Klaas, etc.	Flap	Everett Klaas	Bellaire	OH
P 319	Klaus			W.E. Klaus	Forest Park	IL
P 320	Klaus Dept	Klaus Department Store	Ccard	Klaus Department Store	Chicago	IL
P 321	Klondike	Karl Klondike, etc.	Ccard	PFC Karl Klondike	U.S. Army	
P 322	Klotzbach			H.E. Klotzbach	Buffalo	NY

NO.	PUBLISHER	IMPRINT	SITE	FULL NAME OF PUBLISHER	CITY	STATE
P 323	Knapp	D. or D.W. Knapp	Front	Dorothy W. Knapp (see Fleetwood)	Rhinebeck	NY
P 324	Knight	Knight Brothers, etc.	Ccard	Knight Brothers	Unknown	Unk
P 325	Knoll	AK; Knoll [+ year]	Front	Arthur F. Knoll	Hamilton	OH
P 326	Kosko	Kosko; Michael Kosko etc.	Fr;B	Michael Kosko, Jr.	Cleveland	OH
P 327	Kotab			William J. Kotab	Cleveland	OH
P 328	Krakora			Mary Krakora	Cleveland	OH
P 329	LA Examine	Los Angeles Examiner	Front	Los Angeles Examiner	Los Angeles	CA
P 330	LA Oil			Los Angeles Oil and Grease Co.	Los Angeles	CA
P 331	Langford	Frederick Langford	Ccard	Frederick Langford	Pasadena	CA
P 332	Larocque			Mrs. Bobs Larocque-Demers	Berlin	NH
P 333	Lawrence	JNL [+ No.]; JN Lawrence	Front	James N. Lawrence	U.S. Navy	
P 334	Layne	Cover by Layne	Front	Maurice G. Layne	Detroit	MI
P 335	Leach	Mrs. Frances Leach	Flap	Mrs. France Leach	Los Angeles	CA
P 336	Lee	Arthur W. Lee	Ccard	Arthur W. Lee	Lakewood	OH
P 337	LeGallez			Abram LeGallez	Slingerlands	NY
P 338	Lehman	Lehman Bros., etc.	Ccard	Lehman Bros.	Unknown	Unk
P 339	Lemponen			Carl T. Lemponen	Conneaut	OH
P 340	Lennon			J.J. Lennon	Armed Forces	
P 341	Leonard	C.C.L.[+No.]; Leonard	Front	C.C. Leonard	Louisville	KY
P 342	Leonhard			W.R. Leonhard	Lawrence	MA
P 343	Levering	L.C.L. [+ No.]	Front	L.C. Levering	Chicago	IL
P 344	Limoges	L [+ No.]	Front	Mrs. Robert Limoges	Louisville	KY
P 345	Lind	Franz Lind	Back	Franz Lind (artist: Carl H. Lind)	West N.Y.	NJ
P 346	Lindhardt	H.J. Lindhardt	Back	H.J. Lindhardt (USCS Member #125)	Unknown	Unk
P 347	Linn			George W. Linn	Columbus	OH
P 348	Linprint	Linprint Patriotic etc.	UR	Linprint, Inc. (George W. Linn)	Columbus	OH
P 349	Linto	William S. Linto, etc.	Back	William S. Linto	Portland	OR
P 350	LiPert			W. LiPert	Detroit	MI
P 351	Littlefiel	Frank Littlefield	Front	Frank Littlefield (see Dover+Litt)	Alcoa	TN
P 352	Local 50	United Brotherhood	Ccard	Brotherhood of Carpenters and Joiners	Knoxville	TN
P 353	Lohr	Joseph J. Lohr, etc.	Ccard	Joseph J. Lohr	New York	NY
P 354	Long			August L. Long	Wanamie	PA
P 355	Louisville	L.S.S.	Front	Louisville Stamp Society	Louisville	KY
P 356	Lowe	JLL [+ No.]	Front	James L. Lowe	Chattanooga	TN
P 357	Lowell	LCC [w/,w/o No.]; Lowell	Front	Lowell Collectors' Club	Lowell	MA
P 358	Lowry	Aristocrats; Coakley	Front	Day Lowry	Richmond	VA
P 359	Luhta			Mary Luhta	Los Angeles	CA
P 360	Lupkin			Irma F. Lupkin	New Haven	IN
P 361	Lupton	Walt Lupton; see Fullname	Front	Walt Lupton (East Coast Lefty or E.C.L.)	Pico	CA
P 362	Mache	Mache	Front	C. Lee Wolf	Mansfield	OH
P 363	Mack			Frank L. Mack	Armed Forces	
P 364	MacMillan			Earl T. MacMillan	Bloomington	IN
P 365	Makomb	Makomb Steel Products Co.	Front	Makomb Steel Products Co.	Macomb	IL
P 366	Malaney	(? first name) Malaney	Front	(? first name) Malaney	U.S. Navy	
P 367	Manoukian			Cpl. Leon Manoukian	U.SAAF	
P 368	Martin	Dr. Charles W. Martin	Flap	Charles W. Martin	Canyon	TX
P 369	Maryland			Maryland Philatelic Society	Unknown	MD
P 370	Masten			Mrs. G.L. Masten	Traverse City	MI
P 371	Master's			Master's Assoc., Puget Sound Navy Yard	Bremerton	WA
P 372	Maul	H.R. Maul, etc.; H. Maul.	Fl;Cc	H.R. Maul	Columbus	OH
P 373	Mayfield			H.M. Mayfield	Chattanooga	TN
P 374	Mayne			John A. Mayne	St. Louis	MO
P 375	Mayo			Sheldon S. Mayo	Waltham	MA
P 376	McBarrar	G.P. McBarrar SM3/C etc.	Ccard	G.P. McBarrar SM3/C	U.S. Navy	
P 377	McCabe			George E. McCabe	Troy	PA
P 378	McCluney	Carl L. McCluney, etc.	Flap	Carl L. McCluney (Holt Cover Service)	Fort Worth	TX
P 379	McClung	C.M. McClung & Co., etc.	Ccard	C.M. McClung & Co.	Unknown	Unk
P 380	McColm			William T. McColm	Huntington	WV

NO.	PUBLISHER	IMPRINT	SITE	FULL NAME OF PUBLISHER	CITY	STATE
P 381	McElroy	S.A. McElroy, etc.	Ccard	S.A. McElroy	Fairmont	WV
P 382	McFarland	C,E,F, or G[+No.]; Fuller	Front	Lester McFarland	Louisville	KY
P 383	McGovern	JEM [w/, w/o No.]	Front	Mrs. Joe McGovern	Louisville	KY
P 384	McKelvey	M. Blair McKelvey	Front	M. Blair Mckelvey	Detroit	MI
P 385	McLaughlin	Cpl. F.L. McLaughlin	Ccard	Cpl. F.L. McLaughlin	U.S. Army	
P 386	Mechanical	Mechanical Products etc.	Flap	Mechanical Products	Unknown	Unk
P 387	Mello+Stan	Mello and Stannard	Back	E.J. Mello and L.W. Stannard	Unknown	Unk
P 388	Meryle			(? first name) Meryle	Unknown	Unk
P 389	Meylan	GJM	Front	Gus J. Meylan	Cleveland	OH
P 390	Mich Bell	Michigan Bell, etc.	Ccard	Michigan Bell Telephone Co.	Unknown	MI
P 391	Mid States			Mid States Press	Unknown	Unk
P 392	Miller	Jimmy Miller, etc.	Ccard	Jimmy Miller and his Saddle Mates	Rutland	VT
P 393	Millinery	Millinery Research	Ccard	Millinery Research, Millinery Industry	New York	NY
P 394	Miner, Willman	Miner, Willman L.	Flap	Willman L. Miner	Owosso	MI
P 395	Minkus	J.M.; Jacques Minkus etc.	Fr;B	Jacques Minkus	New York	NY
P 396	Misjonarz			Nasz Misjonarz	Techny	IL
P 397	Mission	Mission Stamp Club, etc.	Cc, B	Mission Stamp Club	Shelby	OH
P 398	Mitchell	Myrtle Mitchell (typed)		Myrtle Mitchell	Winamac	IN
P 399	Mono Svc	Mono Service Co.	Front	Mono Service Co.	Newark	NJ
P 400	Monty	Monty	Front	Unknown (artist: Monty)	Unknown	Unk
P 401	Morri, EW			E.W. Morrison	Mahomet	IL
P 402	Morri, PC			Paul C. Morrison	East Lansing	MI
P 403	Morris			Elliston P. Morris	Feasterville	PA
P 404	Morse			Frank Morse	Roxbury	MA
P 405	Mott+Wood			Mott and Woodhouse Garage	Unknown	Unk
P 406	Mountain	Mountain States Telephone	Ccard	Mountain States Telephone & Telegraph Co.	Unknown	Unk
P 407	Mueller, B	Benny W. Mueller, etc.	Ccard	Benny W. Mueller	N.Tonawan-da	NY
P 408	Mueller, P			Paul E. Mueller	Chicago	IL
P 409	Muridge	M. Fay Muridge	Front	M. Fay Muridge	Unknown	Unk
P 410	Murrman	GL	Front	Mrs. George Murrman	Iroquois	NY
P 411	Mutual	Mutual Covers	Front	Mutual Cover Club (see Ang)	Louisville	KY
P 412	Muzzy	EJM	Front	E.J. Muzzy	Jamestown	NY
P 413	Muzzy+Nich	M+No.+N	UR	E.J. Muzzy and C. Malcolm Nichols	Jamestown	NY
P 414	Myers	M, MEL; Melba Myers	Fr; B	Melba Myers	Myrtle Point	OR
P 415	Nat Luther	National Lutheran Council	Ccard	National Lutheran Council	Unknown	Unk
P 416	Nat Motor	National Motor Bearing	Cc;Fl	National Motor Bearing Co., Inc.	Redwood	CA
P 417	Nat Soc J			National Society of Junior Collectors	Chattanooga	TN
P 418	Nat Soc St	NSSC; National Soc. etc.	Fr;Fl	National Society of Stamp Collectors	Chattanooga	TN
P 419	Navy Dept.	Navy Department, etc.	Ccard	Navy Dept.	U.S. Navy	
P 420	Navy ship			Navy ship on VE Day or VJ Day	U.S. Navy	
P 421	Navy Yard	Navy Department Navy Yard	Ccard	Navy Yard, Pearl Harbor, Commandant's Office	Pearl Harbor	HI
P 422	Neal	D.N.; Neal	Front	Don W. Neal	Kokomo	IN
P 423	Neal+Harv	N&H; Neal and Harvey	Front	Don W. Neal and Paul Harvey	Kokomo	IN
P 424	Nelson, KE	K.E.N. [w/, w/o No.]	Front	Knute E. Nelson	Jamestown	NY
P 425	Nelson, L			Lawrence Nelson	Sheridan	NY
P 426	New Engl P			New England Postal Employees Assoc.	Keene	NH
P 427	New Mexico	New Mexico School etc.	Ccard	New Mexico School SuPly Co.	Albuquerque	NM
P 428	Newton FN		Front	F.N. Newton, Jr.	Sharon	PA
P 429	Newton RD	Robert D. Newton etc.	Back	Robert D. Newton	Genesco	NY
P 430	Nichols	Nichols, Nick; MN [+No.]	Fr;UR	G. Malcolm Nichols	Jamestown	NY
P 431	Nicholson	T.G. Nicholson	Back	T.G. Nicholson	Portsmouth	VA
P 432	Nielsen	Nielsen, N.F.	Flap	N.F. Nielsen	Equinunk	PA
P 433	Nixon	Scott Nixon, S.F.C. Bldg.	Front	Scott Nixon	Augusta	GA
P 434	Norona			Delf Norona	Moundsville	WV
P 435	Northern O	Northern Ohio Telephone	Ccard	Northern Ohio Telephone Co.	Bellevue	OH
P 436	Northwest	N.W. Good Roads Assoc.	Ccard	Northwest Good Roads Association	Unknown	Unk
P 437	Norton			David M. Norton	Armed Forces	
P 438	NY Tel Co	New York Telephone etc.	Ccard	New York Telephone Company	New York	NY

NO.	PUBLISHER	IMPRINT	SITE	FULL NAME OF PUBLISHER	CITY	STATE
P 439	Ohio Bell	The Ohio Bell Telephone	Ccard	The Ohio Bell Telephone Co.	Columbus	OH
P 440	Ohio Fuel	The Ohio Fuel Gas Co.	Ccard	The Ohio Fuel Gas Company	Columbus	OH
P 441	Ohio State	Ohio State Safety Conf.	Ccard	Ohio State Safety Conf.	Unknown	OH
P 442	Oka	E. Toshiharu Oka, etc.	Ccard	E. Toshiharu Oka	Heart Mountain	WY
P 443	Okla Stamp	Oklahoma City Stamp Club	Front	The Oklahoma City Stamp Club (see Edmunds)	Oklahoma City	OK
P 444	Oldsmobile			Oldsmobile Division	Detroit	MI
P 445	Olson	K.F. Olson	Front	K.F. Olson	Milwaukee	WI
P 446	One A Cov			One A Covers	Schenectady	NY
P 447	Oregon Hob			Oregon Hobby Club	Salem	OR
P 448	Oregon St			Oregon Stamp Society	Portland	OR
P 449	Orlando	R. Orlando	Ccard	R. Orlando	Armed Forces	
P 450	Orr			William S. Orr	Batavia	NY
P 451	Osborn	Glen	Front	Glen Osborn	Pensacola	FL
P 452	Osborne	Allan Osborne	Front	Allan Osborne	Medway	MA
P 453	Pacif G&E	Pacific G & E, etc.	Ccard	Pacific G & E	Unknown	Unk
P 454	Pacific	Pacific Stamp, etc.	Ccard	Pacific Stamp and Hobby Club (Walter Hirsh)	Los Angeles	CA
P 455	Panama	Panama City			Panama City	FL
P 456	Parker			Cpl. Harry C. Parker	USAAF	
P 457	Parkinson	R.L. Parkinson	Front	R.L. Parkinson	Unknown	Unk
P 458	Parrott	Matt Parrott, etc.	Ccard	Matt Parrott & Sons	Unknown	Unk
P 662	Pavlis			K. Pavlis	New York	NY
P 459	Payne, AE			A.E. Payne	Cleveland	OH
P 460	Payne, ER	Payne, Edwin R.	Ccard	Edwin R. Payne	Salem	OR
P 461	Peer	Evans; Harry Keys	Front	W.D. Peer (artists: Evans, Harry Keys)	Canal Winchester	OH
P 462	Penn-Harr	Penn-Harris, etc.	Ccard	Penn-Harris	Unknown	Unk
P 463	PentArts	PentArts	Front	See Collectors Surplus	Kansas City	MO
P 464	Peoples			Peoples Outfitting Co.	Unknown	Unk
P 465	Peters	Peters [w/, w/o No.]	Front	Raymond Peters	Dubuque	IA
P 466	Petrasek			Edward Petrasek	Pittsburgh	PA
P 467	Pflanz	Charles H. Pflanz, etc.	Ccard	Charles H. Pflanz	Norwich	NY
P 468	Phila Elec	Philadelphia Electric Co.	Ccard	Philadelphia Electric Company	Philadelphia	PA
P 469	Phila Quar			Philadelphia Quartermaster Depot	Philadelphia	PA
P 470	Phill, CR	CRP; CR Phillips	Front	Charles R. Phillips	Cambridge City	IN
P 471	Phill, M			Mrs. Malcolm Phillips	Des Moines	IA
P 472	Phill+Cox	P and C	Front	Charles R. Phillips and Delma Cox	Cambridge City	IN
P 473	Pictorial	Pictorial Envelope Co.	Front	Pictorial Envelope Co.	Greenwood	MS
P 474	Pilgrim	Pilgrim Cachets, etc.	Front	Pilgrim Cachets (John Alden)	Bergenfield	NJ
P 475	Pisarof			Peter Pisarof	So. St. Paul	MN
P 476	Pittsburgh	Pittsburgh-Standard	Ccard	Pittsburgh-Standard Envelope Co.	Pittsburgh	PA
P 477	Polish			Polish Club (W. Kalanowski)	Unknown	Unk
P 478	Polonus			Polonus Philatelic Society	Chicago	IL
P 479	Pontiac	Pontiac Motor Division	Ccard	Pontiac Motor Division, General Motors	Pontiac	MI
P 480	PoPenger			Walter T. PoPenger	Akron	OH
P 481	Porto-Serv	Porto-Server		Porto-Server (Tarson Co.)	Chicago	IL
P 482	Post Off			United States Post Office Dept.	Washington	DC
P 483	Postmaster	Albert Goldman	Front	Albert Goldsman, Postmaster, N.Y., N.Y.	New York	NY
P 484	Powell			Bert Powell	Chicago	IL
P 485	Powers	Powers Press, Ames, Iowa	Front	Powers Press	Ames	IA
P 486	Premier	Premier Press	Back	Premier Press	Indianapolis	IN
P 487	Price, EK	Earl K. Price, etc.	Ccard	Earl K. Price	Harrisburg	PA
P 488	Price, R	RP [+ No.]	Front	Robert Price	Connersville	IN
P 489	Propeller		Ccard	Propeller Club	Unknown	Unk
P 490	Puls	EEP [w/, w/o No.]	Front	Edwin E. Puls	Birmingham	MI
P 491	Punkis			Walter Punkis	Unknown	Unk
P 492	Quigley	Quig	Front	H.L. Quigley	Seattle	WA
P 493	Radford			Edward P. Radford	St. Petersburg	FL
P 494	Rameco			Rameco Stamp Co.	Middleburgh	NY
P 495	Rankin			H.E. Rankin	Memphis	TN

NO.	PUBLISHER	IMPRINT	SITE	FULL NAME OF PUBLISHER	CITY	STATE
P 496	Rathkamp			Rathkamp Memorial Society	Asbury Park	NJ
P 497	Rayl			W.F. Rayl	Clarksburg	WV
P 498	Reuss	Reuss	Front	Oswald Reuss	Northamp-ton	MA
P 499	Reynolds	A.J.R.	Front	Allen Jesse Reynolds	Connersville	IN
P 500	Richard	Nora J. Richard, etc.	Ccard	Nora J. Richard	Sayre	PA
P 501	Richards	M.R.		Mrs. M. Richards	Sacramento	CA
P 502	Richardson	Richardson		George Richardson	Washington	DC
P 503	Rinker	Rinker	Front	Kenneth N. Rinker	Sorento	IL
P 504	Rio Grande	Rio Grande Steel etc.	Ccard	Rio Grande Steel Products Co.	Albuqueque	NM
P 505	Risinger			Paul V. Risinger	Stow	OH
P 506	Robbins			Robert Lash Robbins (Postamp Pub. Co.)	Unknown	Unk
P 507	Roberts	A.M. Roberts, etc.	Front	Alfred M. Roberts	Hamburg	NY
P 508	Robertson	Mrs. Lloyd Robertson etc.	Ccard	Mrs. Lloyd J. Robertson	Phillipsburg	KS
P 509	Rohaly	M.R. [+ No.]	Front	Sgt. Michael Rohaly	U.S. Army	
P 510	Rollins			F.E. Rollins	Somerville	MA
P 511	Rosenberg			Charles Rosenberg	Tacoma	WA
P 512	Ross	L.L.R. [+ No.]	Front	Leo L. Ross	Nashville	TN
P 513	Roth	I.M. Roth [+ No.]	Front	PFC Irving Roth	U.S. Army	Unk
P 514	Rothert	Chuck Rothert	Ccard	Chuck Rothert	Santa Barbara	CA
P 515	Roudebush	Chas. H. Roudebush etc.	Back	Charles H. Roudebush	Norwood	OH
P 516	Rowe	C.R. [w/, w/o No.]	Front	Catherine Rowe	Boston	MA
P 517	Rowell			A.R. Rowell	Oakland	CA
P 518	Runge	Runge [w/, w/o No.]	Front	Thornton R. Runge	Cleveland	OH
P 519	Rush, H			Horace Rush	Washington	DC
P 520	Rush, JM	J.M. Rush	Front	John Max Rush	Asheville	NC
P 521	Russell			W.J. Russell	Roosevelt	NY
P 522	Ryscovers	R.Y.S.; Ryscovers [+No.]	Front	Ryscovers (R.Y. Spaulding)	Louisville	KY
P 523	Sadworth	GVS; G.V. Sadworth	Front	George V. Sadworth	Woodhaven	NY
P 524	Saginaw			Saginaw Steering Gear Division	Saginaw	MI
P 525	Salem Vic	Salem Victory Corps, etc.	Ccard	Salem Victory Corps	Salem	MO
P 526	Sampson	BRS	Front	Barbara R. Sampson	Unknown	Unk
P 527	Sanders	Sanders; M. Sanders	Front	Michael Sanders	New York	NY
P 528	Sayama	Cuevas, Sayama; Sayama	Fr;B	Etsuo Sayama	Honolulu	HI
P 529	Schaefer	A.E.S.; A.E. Schaefer	Front	A.E. Schaefer	Saginaw	MI
P 530	Schink			Cpl. Robert K. Schink	USAAF	
P 531	Schirmer			Sgt. Melvin C. Schirmer	U.S. Army	
P 532	Schlichte	Joann Schlichte, etc.	Ccard	Joann Schlichte	Connersville	IN
P 533	Schnecken	M.G. Schneckenberger	Front	M.G. Schneckenberger	East Aurora	NY
P 534	Schultze	Geo. J. Schultze	Flap	Schultze, George J.	Philadelphia	PA
P 535	Schulze			Oscar M. Schulze	Canton	OH
P 536	Schust	MAS	Front	Max A. Schusterman	New York	NY
P 537	Scott+Conn			A.Q. Scott and E.J. Connors	Unknown	Unk
P 538	Sears			Sears Roebuck & Company	Chicago	IL
P 539	Sedgwick	WHS	Front	W.H. Sedgwick	Louisville	KY
P 540	Shaffer, A	ES; Cpl. A.E. Shaffer	Fr;Fl	Cpl. Albert E. Shaffer	U.SAAF	
P 541	Shaffer, E			Evelyn H. Shaffer	San Antonio	TX
P 542	Shane			(? first name) Shane	Unknown	Unk
P 543	Sharon	R.E.S.	Front	Rubie E. Sharon	Hermosa Beach	CA
P 544	Shaw, AD			A.D. Shaw	Unknown	Unk
P 545	Shaw, CF	S [+ No.]	Front	Clifford F. Shaw	Louisville	KY
P 546	Shaw, MM			Marian M. Shaw	Ironwood	MI
P 547	Shaw, TC			Thornton C. Shaw	Sandusky	OH
P 548	Shenton			Seth F. Shenton, Jr.	Indianola	IA
P 549	Sheridan			Corp. L.R. Sheridan	Albuquerque	NM
P 550	Sievert			Louis K. Sievert	Detroit	MI
P 551	Simionescu			Arthur F. Simionescu	Hackensack	NJ
P 552	Sklare			Norman Sklare	Chicago	IL
P 553	Smartcraft	Smartcraft	Front	Smartcraft (see Jordan)	Elmhurst	NY

NO.	PUBLISHER	IMPRINT	SITE	FULL NAME OF PUBLISHER	CITY	STATE
P 554	Smith, AD	ADS [+ No.]	Front	Arthur D. Smith	Iowa City	IA
P 555	Smith, DH	Dorman H. Smith, etc.	Front	Dorman H. Smith (N.E.A. Service, Inc.)	Unknown	Unk
P 556	Smith, LH	Lannie H. Smith, etc.	Back	Lannie H. Smith	Houston	TX
P 557	Smith, RA			R.A. Smith	Shreveport	LA
P 558	Smith, W	Wesley Smith, etc.	Back	Wesley Smith	Kirksville	MO
P 559	Soc Philat			Society of Philatelic Americans	Chicago	IL
P 560	Sosland	Sosland Envelope Co., K.C., Mo.	Back	Sosland Envelope Co.	Kansas City	MO
P 561	Southwest	Southwestern, etc.	Ccard	Southwestern Freight Line	Unknown	Unk
P 562	Southworth			R. Lee Southworth	Fredericks-burg	VA
P 563	Spalding			R.Y. Spalding	Louisville	KY
P 564	Spauld, E			Mrs. Elizabeth Spaulding	Augusta	GA
P 565	Spauld, R	R.Y.S.; Ryscovers [+No.]	Front	R.Y. Spaulding (Ryscovers)	Louisville	KY
P 566	Speede	SS-1- [+ letter]	Front	Speede Service	Carbondale	IL
P 567	Sprague	D.C. Sprague, Jr.	Flap	D.C. Sprague, Jr.	Hollywood	CA
P 568	Squibb			John F. Squibb	Zanesville	OH
P 569	Staehle	L.W. Staehle; LW. St.	Front	Ludwig W. Staehle (see Fleetwood, Fluegel)	New York	NY
P 570	Stamp Rev			Stamp Review	St. Joseph	MO
P 571	Stanard	John D. Stanard, etc.	Front	John D. Stanard	Detroit	MI
P 572	Stawuszew	WS	Front	Cpl. Walter Stawuszewski	U.S. Army	
P 573	Stead			Theodore H. Stead	New London	CT
P 574	Steeg	Adolph Steeg	Ccard	Adolph Steeg	Buffalo	NY
P 575	Stefun	A.J. Stefun	Ccard	A.J. Stefun	Lewisburg	PA
P 576	Steinhardt	A.J.S.	Front	A.J. Steinhardt	Pittsburgh	PA
P 577	Steinway	Theo. E. Steinway	Front	Theodore E. Steinway	New York	NY
P 578	Stendel	H.H. Stendel, etc.	Back	H.H. Stendel (Pictorial Envelope Co.)	Greenwood	MS
P 579	Stephens			(? first name) Stephens	Valhalla	NY
P 580	Stith	G.S.	Front	PFC Glenn Stith	U.S. Army	
P 581	Stoll	Stoll; K. Stoll	Front	Kirby M. Stoll	Louisville	KY
P 582	Stoner	Pvt. Roy E. Stoner	Ccard	Stoner, Pvt. Roy E.	Armed Forces	
P 583	Sturgill	Sturgill	Front	Cairo Sturgill	Unknown	Unk
P 583A	Sunner	Sunner		William Sunner	Brooklyn	NY
P 584	Sun Valley		Ccard	Sun Valley	Unknown	Unk
P 585	Swartz			Mrs. R.H. Swartz	Houston	TX
P 586	Swave+Mill	S.& M.	Front	Horace S. Swavely and Paul J. Miller	Pottstown	PA
P 587	Sweet			John F. Sweet	Waltham	MA
P 588	Symbols			Symbols of Peace Society	Chicago	IL
P 589	Talburt	Talburt	Front	(? first name) Talburt	Unknown	Unk
P 590	Tar-Heel			Tar-Heel Stamp Service	Charlotte	NC
P 591	Taylor			Edwin S. Taylor	Armed Forces	
P 592	Teaneck	Teaneck Stamp Club	Ccard	Teaneck Stamp Club	Teaneck	NJ
P 593	Teich	Curt Teich & Co., Inc.	Back	Curt Teich & Co., Inc.	Chicah	IL
P 594	Teixeira	Capt. Frank L. Teixeira	Ccard	Capt. Frank L. Teixeira	U.S. Army	
P 595	Temple	W.A.T.; WAT	Front	William A. Temple	Des Moines	IA
P 596	Thomason			W.B. Thomason	Portsmouth	VA
P 597	Thorpe	H.R. Thorpe, etc.	Front	H.R. Thorpe	Westfield	MA
P 598	Thr+Bu+Tha	TB&T; T.B.T. [+ No.]	Front	W.R. Threlkel, Philip Burdick, W.R. Tharp	Louisville	KY
P 599	Threl+Thar	T&T [w/, w/o No.]	Front	W.R. Threlkel and W.R. Tharp	Louisville	KY
P 600	Thurman	Emil A. Thurman	Front	Emil A. Thurman	Unknown	Unk
P 601	Tidewater	Tidewater Oil Co., etc.	Ccard	Tidewater Oil Company	Unknown	Unk
P 602	Tijerina			Fernando M. Tijerina	Laredo	TX
P 603	Trail			Trail Blazers	Council Bluffs	IA
P 604	Trans-Miss			Trans-MississiPi Philatelic Society	Unknown	Unk
P 605	Trapani	Cpl. Victor L. Trapani	Ccard	Cpl. Victor L. Trapani	U.S. Army	
P 606	Trent	Trent Printing Company	Ccard	Trent Printing Company	Knoxville	TN
P 607	Turley			Leonard J. Turley	Louisville	KY
P 608	Turner			C.H. Turner	Ponca City	OK
P 609	U.S. Army			U.S. Army Postal Service	U.S. Army	
P 610	U.S. Treas	Treasury Department, etc.	Ccard	United States Treasury Department	Washington	DC

NO.	PUBLISHER	IMPRINT	SITE	FULL NAME OF PUBLISHER	CITY	STATE
P 611	Uher			John Uher	Glassport	PA
P 612	Umbarger			William F. Umbarger	Royal Center	IN
P 613	Union Pac	Union Pacific Railroad	Front	Union Pacific Railroad	Unknown	Unk
P 614	Univ Car	Universal Carloading etc.	Ccard	Universal Carloading Co.	Unknown	Unk
P 615	Univ Engin	Universal Engineering Co.	Ccard	Universal Engineering Co.	Franken-muth	MI
P 616	USMC	Navy Department, etc.	Ccard	Navy Dept., Hqs. U.S. Marine Corps	USMC	
P 617	USO	USO United Service, etc.	Flap	United Service Organizations		
P 618	V Center	V Center, etc.	Ccard	V Center	Waukegan	IL
P 619	Valley	Valley Camp Coal Co., The	Ccard	The Valley Camp Coal Co.	Wheeling	WV
P 620	Van Alsbur			J.H. Van Alsburg	Washington	DC
P 621	Vermond	Andre Vermond, etc.	Ccard	Andre Vermond	Dayton	OH
P 622	VFW	Veterans of Foreign Wars	Front	VFW of the U.S., Dept. of California	Unknown	CA
P 623	Vogel	JE.DoubleR.Y Vogel, etc.	Ccard	Jerry Vogel Music Co., Inc.	New York	NY
P 624	Vollhardt			William N. Vollhardt	Monaca	PA
P 625	Von Los	L- or S- [+ No.]	Front	J.C. Von Losburg	Brooklyn	NY
P 626	WAC			Women's Army Corps	WAC	
P 627	Wallace			Charles A. Wallace	Unknown	Unk
P 628	War Cover			War Cover Associates	Unknown	Unk
P 629	War Dept			United States War Department	Washington	DC
P 630	War Prod 1	War Production Board	Ccard	WPB Bureau of Industrial Conservation	Washington	DC
P 631	War Prod 2		Front	War Production Board	Detroit	MI
P 632	Warner+Swa			Warner & Swasey	Unknown	Unk
P 633	Wash Cover			Washington Cover Club (Art: M. Fay Muridge)	Seattle	WA
P 634	Wash Serv			Washington Service (D.H. Davenport)	Washington	DC
P 635	Wash Stamp			Washington Stamp Exchange (see Artcraft)	Newark	NJ
P 636	Wash Star	Washington Star etc.	Ccard	Washington Evening and Sunday Star	Washington	DC
P 637	Wayne			Wayne Post #11, American Legion (see Frye)	Wayne	MI
P 638	Webb			Mrs. F. Webb	Waterbury	CT
P 639	Weigand			Mae Weigand	Brooklyn	NY
P 640	Wentz	Paul P. Wentz	Front	Paul P. Wentz	Beverly Hills	CA
P 641	Werve			R.P. Werve	Saginaw	MI
P 642	Western			Western UnionTelegraphCo.		
P 643	Weston			M.C. Weston	Brockton	MA
P 644	White, B			Berenice White	Oklahoma City	OK
P 645	White, TM	Trudy White	Front	Trudy M. White	Conimicut	RI
P 646	Wichita			Wichita Stamp Club	Wichita	KS
P 647	Wiley			Capt. Theodore R. Wiley	Wilmington	NC
P 648	Williams	Oliver J. Williams	Ccard	Oliver J. Williams	San Francisco	CA
P 649	Wittenberg	Wittenberg College	Ccard	Wittenberg College	Springfield	OH
P 650	Wol-Detroi			Wolf-Detroit Envelope Company	Detroit	MI
P 651	Wolf, CL	Mache	Front	C. Lee Wolf (see Mache)	Mansfield	OH
P 652	Wolf, ID			I.D. Wolf	Philadelphia	PA
P 653	Wolf, RL			Richard Lee Wolf	Barberton	OH
P 654	Woodall	Woodall Industries	Ccard	Woodall Industries	Unknown	Unk
P 655	Woodbury			Bruce E. Woodbury	Muskegon	MI
P 656	Worl	G.D.W.	Front	Gene D. Worl	Hagerstown	MD
P 657	Wright	Wright	Front	Fred P. Wright	Oswego	NY
P 658	YMCA	YMCA	Ccard	Young Men's Christian Association	Norfolk	VA
P 659	Yontz	Y	Front	Donald A. Yontz	Freeville	NY
P 660	Yudkin	Ly + No.; YL	Front	Yudkin, Sam	Unknown	Unk
P 661	Zunks	Original Order of Zunks	Front	The Original Order of Zunks (see Hamilton)	Cleveland	OH

9

Publisher Imprints Catalogue

THE PUBLISHER Imprints Catalogue tabulates all imprints (names, initials, or symbols) known to me that were placed on wartime patriotic envelopes to identify their publishers. Column headings of the catalogue include Number, Imprint, Illustration, Publisher, and Full Name of Publisher. Properties of this catalogue are:

NUMBER

The number of recognized patriotic envelope publishers has grown over the decades, and with it the number and recognition of complexity of the imprints used by them as identifying marks or legends. The Publisher Imprints Catalogue lists 460 imprints used by the 661 cachet makers (some used none, others used more than one).

Numbers are assigned sequentially to the alphabetically arranged imprints, and imprints are alphabetized by first letter in imprint initials or by first letter of publisher's last name and "Imp" is prefixed to the number. Thus imprint "A" used by publisher "Avy" (full name: Samuel Avy, Jr.) is tabulated as Imp 1, while imprint "Zunks, Original Order of" used by publisher "Zunks" (full name: Gordon H. Hamilton [Cleveland Cover Club]) is tabulated as Imp 460.

IMPRINT and ILLUSTRATION

Because some patriotic envelope publishers used more than one imprint to identify their work, I have assigned each variant its own number according to its alphabetical placement. Thus imprints "A&K" (Imp 2) and "AK 44" (Imp 15) were both used by Iva Donaldson in concert with Donald A. Yontz and Frederick C. Cochran. In addition, imprint "D & C" (Imp 106) was used by Donaldson and Cochran working together.

There are other examples of different numbers for different imprints by the same cachet maker: Imprints "B- [+ No. or letter]" (Imp 41) and "Bee logo" (Imp 50) were both used by Elmer A. Brenn; and imprints "Buxton, Don" (Imp 70), "DB" (Imp 112), and "DEB" (Imp 114) were all used by Donald Buxton.

These are all examples—and there are more in the Imprints Catalogue—of different imprints, same publisher.

The publishers of most patriotic covers encountered by readers will be readily identified by using the Cachet Catalogue. But how to find the publisher of a newly discovered *unlisted* cover? If it contains a publisher imprint, it will reveal its maker through reference to the Publishers Imprints Catalogue.

More than 70 different publisher imprints are illustrated in Figures 1-3 on pages 421-423.

PUBLISHER and
FULL NAME OF PUBLISHER

Names (up to 10 characters and spaces) and full names of publishers are the same as those appearing in the Publishers Catalogue.

PUBLISHER IMPRINTS CATALOGUE

NO.	IMPRINT	ILLLUSTRATION	PUBLISHER	FULL NAME OF PUBLISHER
Imp 1	A		Avy	Samuel Avy, Jr.
Imp 2	A&K [w/, w/o No.]		Donaldson	Iva Donaldson (+ Cochran; + Yontz)
Imp 3	A.E.S.		Schaefer	Albert E. Schaefer (not to be confused with Cpl.. A.E. Shaffer)
Imp 4	A.J.R.		Reynolds	Allen Jesse Reynolds
Imp 5	A.J.S.		Steinhardt	A.J. Steinhardt
Imp 6	AA. [+ No.]		Altenbernd	Adolf Altenbernd
Imp 7	Abbott Laboratories		Abbott	Abbott Laboratories
Imp 8	Abel	Figure 1A	Abel	George H. Abel
Imp 9	AC Spark Plug Division		AC Spark	AC Spark Plug Division
Imp 10	Acme Fast Freight, etc.		Acme Fast	Acme Fast Freight
Imp 11	Adler, Gladys [handstamp]	Figure 1B	Adler	Gladys Adler
Imp 12	ADS [+ No.]	Figure 3M	Smith, AD	Arthur D. Smith
Imp 13	AES		Shaffer, A	Cpl. Albert E. Shaffer
Imp 14	AK		Knoll	Arthur F. Knoll
Imp 15	AK '43 or '44	Figure 2J	Knoll	Arthur F. Knoll
Imp 16	Alden, John		Alden	John Alden (see Pilgrim)
Imp 17	AMC		AMC—Bower	AMC—Bowers Envelope & Lithograph Co.
Imp 18	AMC—Bowers		AMC—Bower	AMC—Bowers Envelope & Lithograph Co.
Imp 19	American Art Service etc.	Figure 1C	Amer Art	American Art Service
Imp 20	American Cancer Society		Amer Canc	American Cancer Society
Imp 21	American Legion Salvage		Amer Legio	American Legion Salvage Committee
Imp 22	American Naval etc.	Figure 1D	Amer Naval	American Naval Cancellation Society
Imp 23	American Patriotic Press		Amer Pat	American Patriotic Press (Harry E. Curtiss)
Imp 24	American Patriotic Press	Figure 1E	Curtiss, H	Harry E. Curtiss (see Amer Pat)
Imp 25	Anderson, C. Stephen		Ander, CS	C. Stephen Anderson
Imp 26	Anderson, Elmer		Ander, EA	Elmer A. Anderson (Pontiac Press)
Imp 27	Andrews Ptg. Co.		Andrews	Andrews Printing Co.
Imp 28	Ang [+ No.]		Ang	Clinton E. Ang (Mutual Covers)
Imp 29	Anti-Pacifist etc.		Anti-Pacif	The Anti-Pacifist Propaganda Committee
Imp 30	Aristocrats		Lowry	Day Lowry
Imp 31	Arizona, State of etc.		Arizona	State of Arizona Dept. of Vocational Educ.
Imp 32	Artcraft	Figure 1F	Artcraft	Washington Stamp Exchange
Imp 33	Artists for Victory	Figure 1G	Artists	Artists for Victory
Imp 34	Arundell		Crosby	Walter G. Crosby
Imp 35	Atwell		Atwell	(? first name) Atwell
Imp 36	Auge		Auge	Sgt. Kenneth G. Auge
Imp 37	Aunt Jenny's Garden Club		Aunt Jenny	Aunt Jenny's Garden Club
Imp 38	Avy, S. Jr.		Avy	Samuel Avy, Jr.
Imp 39	AWC		Cliff	Athol W. Cliff (artist: C.S. Anderson)
Imp 40	Aylward, Rita, Mrs.		Aylward	Mrs. Rita Aylward
Imp 41	B- [+ No. or letter]	Figure 1J	Brenn	Elmer A. Brenn
Imp 42	Bailey, Harry		Bailey	Harry Bailey
Imp 43	Barnes, A.L.		Barnes	A.L. Barnes
Imp 44	Bartley, Deane C.		Bartley	Dean C. Bartley (Washington Cover Club)
Imp 45	Bartz, Ray		Bartz	Ray Bartz
Imp 46	Barwicki, P.F.C. Joseph		Barwicki	PFC (or Cpl) Joseph Barwicki
Imp 47	Bates, Warner		Bates	Warner Bates
Imp 48	Battles, D. Blake		Battles	D. Blake Battles
Imp 49	Bean, L.D.		Bean	Louis D. Bean

NO.	IMPRINT	ILLLUSTRATION	PUBLISHER	FULL NAME OF PUBLISHER
Imp 50	Bee logo	Figure 1K	Brenn	Elmer A. Brenn
Imp 51	Belles-lettres, etc.		Belles-let	Belles-lettres (A.F. Grymes/Thos. Kirksey)
Imp 52	Bellows Co., Senacon		Bellows	The Bellows Co., Senacon Division
Imp 53	Bendix, F.		Bendix	F. Bendix
Imp 54	Benevolent Protective etc		BPOE	Benevolent Protective Order of Elks
Imp 55	Bible Meditation League		Bible Med	The Bible Meditation League
Imp 56	Bible School Park		Bible	Bible School Park
Imp 57	Bison Philatelic, etc.		Garfinkel	Marvin H. Garfinkel
Imp 58	Blumenschine, Sgt. Arthur		Blumen	Sgt. Arthur E. Blumenschine
Imp 59	Bohemian Benedictine etc.		Bohemian	Bohemian Benedictine Order (Benabbey Guild)
Imp 60	Boll, Sgt.Ken		Boll	Sgt. Ken Boll
Imp 61	Boone	Figure 1H	Boone	Richard P. Boone
Imp 62	Borkowski, Leonard	Figure 1I	Borkowski	Leonard Borkowski
Imp 63	Boston Edison Co., etc.		Boston Ed	Boston Edison Company
Imp 64	BRS		Sampson	Barbara R. Sampson
Imp 65	Buchwald, R		Buchwald	R Buchwald
Imp 66	Buckalew, Charles H.	Figure 1L	Buckalew	Charles H. Buckalew
Imp 67	Burdick		Burdick	Philip O. Burdick (Liberty Covers)
Imp 68	Burpee, W. Atlee Co.		Burpee	W. Atlee Burpee Co.
Imp 69	Burris, Gene A.		Burris	Burris, Cpl. Gene A.
Imp 70	Buxton, Don		Buxton, D	Donald Buxton
Imp 71	C [+ No.]		McFarland	Lester McFarland
Imp 72	C [in diamond-shaped box]		Clendennen	William Clendennen
Imp 73	C.C.L. [+ No.]		Leonard	C.C. Leonard
Imp 74	C.H.B.		Buckalew	Charles H. Buckalew
Imp 75	C.P.H.		Hunt	C. Paul Hunt
Imp 76	C.R. [w/, w/o No.]		Rowe	Catherine Rowe
Imp 77	C.W.D.		DeLeuze	Charles W. DeLeuze
Imp 78	CachetCraft	Figure 1M	Cachet Cra	Cachet Craft Cover Svc (Frederick B. Fitts)
Imp 79	Cal-Craft		Cal-Craft	Cal-Craft
Imp 80	C-AMC		Chester	A.M. Chester
Imp 81	Card		Card	Hallock Card (see Homestead Press)
Imp 82	Carpenter [+ city, state]	Figure 1N	Carpenter	N. LeRoy Carpenter
Imp 83	Catholic Order Foresters		Catholic	Catholic Order Foresters
Imp 84	CEB		Bell	Clarence E. Bell
Imp 85	CEG		Gustafson	C. Edwin Gustafson
Imp 86	Chester, A.M.		Chester	A.M. Chester (see AMC—Bower)
Imp 87	Christensen, A.A.		Christens	Sgt. Arthur A. Christensen
Imp 88	Clarke & Wood		Clarke+Woo	(? first name) Clarke + (? first name) Wood
Imp 89	Clendennen, Wm.	Figure 1O	Clendennen	William Clendennen
Imp 90	Cleveland	Figure 1P	Hamilton	Gordon H. Hamilton
Imp 91	Cleveland Cover Club		Cleveland	Cleveland Cover Club (Gordon H. Hamilton)
Imp 92	Clifford, J.W.		Clifford	J.W. Clifford
Imp 93	Coakley		Lowry	Day Lowry
Imp 94	Coleman & Co.		Coleman	Coleman & Co.
Imp 95	Commercial Products		Commercial	Commercial Products Company
Imp 96	Cornell, Lee H [or H.]		Cornell	Lee H. Cornell (artist: Jean Craig)
Imp 97	Cox & Price		Cox+Price	Delma Cox and Robert Price
Imp 98	Cox, Delma		Cox	Delma Cox
Imp 99	Coz-Art Covers		Cozart	Russell Cozart
Imp 100	CPH		Hunt	C. Paul Hunt
Imp 101	Crockett, Gib		Crockett	Gib Crockett
Imp 102	CRP		Phill, CR	Phillips, Charles R.
Imp 103	Cuevas		Sayama	Etsuo Sayama

NO.	IMPRINT	ILLLUSTRATION	PUBLISHER	FULL NAME OF PUBLISHER
Imp 104	CWD		DeLeuze	Charles W. DeLeuze
Imp 105	Czubay	Figure 1R	Czubay	Walter L. Czubay (RCD #206; USCS #997)
Imp 106	D & C		Donaldson	Iva Donaldson (+ Frederick J. Cochran)
Imp 107	D [+ No.]		Davis, Ray	S/Sgt. Raymond E. Davis
Imp 108	D.N.		Neal	Don W. Neal
Imp 109	Davis		Davis, D	Darrell Davis
Imp 110	Davis, D.		Davis, D	Darrell Davis
Imp 111	Davis, Ralph E.		Davis, Ral	Ralph E. Davis
Imp 112	DB		Buxton, D	Donald Buxton
Imp 113	DCC		Conner	Dicken C. Conner (printer: Wilford Brown)
Imp 114	DEB		Buxton, D	Donald Buxton
Imp 115	DEE	Figure 1U	Davis, D	Darrell Davis
Imp 116	Denver Dry Goods Co.		Denver	Denver Dry Goods Co.
Imp 117	Detroit Edison, etc.		Detroit Ed	The Detroit Edison Philatelic Society
Imp 118	Detroit Fuel & S. Co.		Detroit Fu	Detroit Fuel and S. Co.
Imp 119	Detroit Steel Products		Detroit St	Detroit Steel Products
Imp 120	Diana	Figure 2C	Huss	Matthew J. Huss
Imp 121	Don R Isham RM/3C		Isham	Don R. Isham
Imp 122	Doughboy Studio		Doughboy	Doughboy Studio
Imp 123	Downs-Smith B&C Co.		Downs	Downs-Smith B&C Co.
Imp 124	Dye, Glenn W., U.S.N.		Dye	Glenn W. Dye
Imp 125	E [+ No.]		McFarland	Lester McFarland
Imp 126	E.C. [+ No.]		Carter	Earl L. Carter
Imp 127	E.C.L.		Lupton	Walt Lupton
Imp 128	East Coast Lefty	Figure 2Q	Lupton	Walt Lupton
Imp 129	Edmunds, Tex		Edmunds	Tex Edmunds (Oklahoma City Stamp Club)
Imp 130	EEP [w/, w/o No.]		Puls	Edwin E. Puls
Imp 131	Efengee Electric		Efengee	Efengee Electric Supply Co.
Imp 132	Ehde, Martin		Ehde	Martin Ehde
Imp 133	EJM		Muzzy	E.J. Muzzy
Imp 134	Elgin Cafe		Elgin Cafe	Elgin Cafe
Imp 135	Empire		Card	Hallock Card (see Homestead Press)
Imp 136	ES		Unknown	Unknown
Imp 137	Evans		Peer	W.D. Peer (artists: Evans, Harry Keys)
Imp 138	F [+ No.]		McFarland	Lester McFarland
Imp 139	F.A.H. [+ No.]		Harmer	Fred A. Harmer
Imp 140	F.J.C. [+ No.]		Cochran	Fred J. Cochran
Imp 141	F.S.		Fidelity	Fidelity Stamp Co.
Imp 142	FAH		Harmer	Fred A. Harmer
Imp 143	FAH [+ No.]		Harmer	Fred A. Harmer
Imp 144	Farnsworth, Marvin C.		Farnsworth	Marvin C. Farnsworth
Imp 145	Fertig, Al		Fertig	Al Fertig
Imp 146	First National Bank		First Nat	First National Bank of Dallas
Imp 147	Firstday Covers	Figure 1V	First Day	Firstday Covers
Imp 148	Fleetwood	Figure 1W	Fleetwood	Fleetwood Covers (artists: Knapp, Staehle)
Imp 149	Florists Telegraph		Florists	Florists Telegrpah Delivery Association
Imp 150	Fluegel Cover	Figure 1X	Fluegel	Herman Fluegel (Fluegel Covers)
Imp 151	Forest City, etc.		Grover	Don Grover (Forest City Patriotic Envels.)
Imp 152	Fort Hamilton		Fort Hamil	Fort Hamilton Philatelic Society
Imp 153	Fort Morgan Herald		Fort Morg	Fort Morgan Herald
Imp 154	Foster & Carpenter		Fost+Carp	Foster & Carpenter
Imp 155	Fuller		McFarland	Lester McFarland
Imp 156	Fumbarger, William		Fumbarger	William Fumbarger
Imp 157	G [+ No.]		McFarland	Lester McFarland

NO.	IMPRINT	ILLLUSTRATION	PUBLISHER	FULL NAME OF PUBLISHER
Imp 158	G.D.W.		Worl	Gene D. Worl
Imp 159	G.F. Hadley [or G.F.H.]	Figure 2A	Hadley	Grace F. Hadley
Imp 160	G.H.A.		Abel	George H. Abel
Imp 161	G.H.H.		Hamilton	Gordon H. Hamilton (see Cleveland; Zunks)
Imp 162	G.O.B.		Boothroyd	Gordon O. Boothroyd
Imp 163	G.S.		Stith	PFC Glenn Stith
Imp 164	Gabel, William P.		Gabel	William P. Gabel
Imp 165	General Coin Service		Gen Coin	General Coin Service
Imp 166	GFH		Hadley	Grace F. Hadley
Imp 167	GHA		Abel	George H. Abel
Imp 168	Gilbert & Bannett		Gilbert	Gilbert & Bennett Mfg. Co.
Imp 169	GJM		Meylan	Gus J. Meylan
Imp 170	GL		Murrman	Mrs. George Murrman
Imp 171	Glase, Paul E.		Glase	Paul E. Glase
Imp 172	Glennard-Corn		Glenn-Corn	Glennard-Corn
Imp 173	Goff	Figure 2D	Huss	Matthew J. Huss
Imp 174	Goldman, Albert		Postmaster	Albert Goldman, Postmaster, N.Y., N.Y.
Imp 175	Goldstein, Paul F.		Goldstein	Paul F. Goldstein
Imp 176	Goodfellow Field		Goodfellow	49th School Squadron, Goodfellow Field
Imp 177	Graf, Don, R.C.D. #194		Graf	Don Graf
Imp 178	Griffith, J. Neal		Griffith	J. Neal Griffith
Imp 179	Grimsland	Figure 1Y	Grimsland	Henry Grimsland
Imp 180	GVS		Sadworth	George V. Sadworth
Imp 181	H.G. [w/, w/o Acampa]		Ever Ready	Ever Ready Press (artist: Acampa)
Imp 182	Hans, G.H.		Hans	G.H. Hans
Imp 183	Harrington, Sgt. George		Harri	Sgt. George J. Harrington
Imp 184	Hartman Beverage Co.		Hartman	Hartman Beverage Co.
Imp 185	Harvey		Harvey	Paul Harvey
Imp 186	Hayes, F.G.		Hayes	F.G. Hayes
Imp 187	Haynes, Robert		Haynes	Robert Haynes
Imp 188	HEF		French	H. Edgar French
Imp 189	Herschaft, M.C.		Herschaft	M.C. Herschaft
Imp 190	Herst, Herman Jr.		Herst	Herman Herst, Jr. (printer: Wesley Smith)
Imp 191	HF		Farnum	House of Farnum
Imp 192	Hill, H.C. [+ year]	Figure 2B	Hill	Harry C. Hill
Imp 193	Hines, W.F.		Hines	William F. Hines
Imp 194	Hinrichs, EA		Hinrichs	EA Hinrichs & Co.
Imp 195	Hoerr Feed Store		Hoerr	Hoerr Feed Store
Imp 196	Hoerth, Carl C.		Hoerth	Carl C. Hoerth
Imp 197	Holmes, H.C.		Holmes	H.C. Holmes
Imp 198	Holton, Mrs. Clarence W.		Holton	Mrs. Clarence W. Holton
Imp 199	Holtz, Benjamin		Holtz	Benjamin Holtz
Imp 200	Homestead		Card	Hallock Card (see Homestead Press)
Imp 201	Homestead Press		Homestead	Homestead Press (Hallock Card)
Imp 202	Honolulu Advertiser		Honolulu	The Honolulu Advertiser Stamp Club
Imp 203	Howe [in quotes]		Howe	F.E. Howe
Imp 204	Howe's Histories		Howe	F.E. Howe
Imp 205	Huss		Huss	Matthew J. Huss
Imp 206	Hutnick, S.E., M.D.		Hutnick	S.E. Hutnick, M.D. (RCD #70)
Imp 207	Hyde, A.A.		Hyde	Rev. A. A. Hyde
Imp 208	I.C.G., sponsored by		Internat	International Cover Guild (Designer: Boone)
Imp 209	ILG Electric Ventilating		ILG Electr	ILG Electric Ventilating Co.
Imp 210	Illinois Bell Telephone		Ill Bell	Illinois Bell Telephone Company
Imp 211	Infantry Replacement etc.		Hannay	Col. William V. Hannay

NO.	IMPRINT	ILLLUSTRATION	PUBLISHER	FULL NAME OF PUBLISHER
Imp 212	Intercity Stamp Company		Intercity	Intercity Stamp Company
Imp 213	J. Robert Bund		Bund	J. Robert Bund (RCD #302)
Imp 214	J.L.H. [+ No.]		Hillerich	Joe Lee Hillerich
Imp 215	J.M.		Minkus	Jacques Minkus
Imp 216	J.W.C.		Clifford	J.W. Clifford
Imp 217	J.W.V., Dept. of Michigan		Jewish Vet	Dept. of Michigan Jewish War Veterans
Imp 218	JAC		Carter	Earl L. Carter
Imp 219	Jackson, C		Jackson, C	Chester P. Jackson
Imp 220	Jarrett [w/, w/o No.]	Figure 2E	Jarrett	William R. Jarrett
Imp 221	JCP		Johns Cov	Johnson Cover Press
Imp 222	JEM [w/, w/o No.]		McGovern	Mrs. Joe McGovern
Imp 223	Jensen, Fred E.		Jensen	Fred E. Jensen
Imp 224	Jessop, Ernest		Jessop	Ernest Jessop
Imp 225	JLG		Garland	John L. Garland
Imp 226	JLL [+ No.]		Lowe	James L. Lowe
Imp 227	JNL [+ No.]	Figure 2M	Lawrence	James N. Lawrence
Imp 228	Johnson, Mrs. C.W.		Johnson, C	Mrs. C.W. Johnson
Imp 229	Jordan	Figure 2F	Jordan	Edward R. Jordan (see Smartcraft)
Imp 230	JRC [+ No.]		Castellano	Jasper R. Castellano
Imp 231	K.E.N. [w/, w/o No.]		Nelson, KE	Knute E. Nelson
Imp 232	Keys, Harry		Peer	W.D. Peer (artists: Evans, Harry Keys)
Imp 233	Kidd, J.B.		Kidd	J.B. Kidd
Imp 234	Kimball, W.W. Co.		Kimball	W.W. Kimball Co.
Imp 235	King's Stamp Club		King's	King's Stamp Club (artist: L.W. Staehle)
Imp 236	Kirchner, Mrs. George		Kirchner	Mrs. George Kirchner
Imp 237	Klaas, Everett	Figure 2G	Klaas	Everett Klaas
Imp 238	Klaus Department Store		Klaus Dept	Klaus Department Store
Imp 239	Klondike, Karl		Klondike	PFC Karl Klondike
Imp 240	Knapp, D. [w/, w/o No.]	Figure 2H	Knapp	Dorothy W. Knapp (see Fleetwood)
Imp 241	Knapp, D.W. [w/, w/o No.]	Figure 2I	Knapp	Dorothy W. Knapp
Imp 242	Knight Brothers		Knight	Knight Brothers
Imp 243	Knoll [+ year]	Figure 2K	Knoll	Arthur F. Knoll
Imp 244	Kosko		Kosko	Michael Kosko, Jr.
Imp 245	Kosko, Michael		Kosko	Michael Kosko, Jr.
Imp 246	L [+ No.]		Limoges	Mrs. Robert Limoges
Imp 247	L- [+ No.]		Von Los	J.C. Von Losberg
Imp 248	L.C.L. [+ No.]	Figure 2M	Levering	L.C. Levering
Imp 249	L.L.R. [+ No.]		Ross	Leo L. Ross
Imp 250	L.S.S.		Louisville	Louisville Stamp Society
Imp 251	Langford, Frederick		Langford	Frederick Langford
Imp 252	Lawrence, JN		Lawrence	James N. Lawrence
Imp 253	Layne, Cover by		Layne	Maurice G. Layne
Imp 254	LCC [w/, w/o No.]	Figure 2O	Lowell	Lowell Collectors' Club
Imp 255	Leach, Mrs. Frances		Leach	Mrs. Frances Leach
Imp 256	Lee, Arthur W.		Lee	Arthur W. Lee
Imp 257	Lehman Bros.		Lehman	Lehman Bros.
Imp 258	Leonard		Leonard	C.C. Leonard
Imp 259	Liberty Covers		Burdick	Philip O. Burdick (Liberty Covers)
Imp 260	Lind, Franz		Lind	Franz Lind (artist: Carl H. Lind)
Imp 261	Lindhardt, H.J.		Lindhardt	H.J. Lindhardt (USCS Member #125)
Imp 262	Linprint Patriotic etc.		Linprint	Linprint, Inc. (George W. Linn)
Imp 263	Linto, William S.	Figure 2N	Linto	William S. Linto
Imp 264	Littlefield, Frank		Littlefiel	Frank Littlefield (see Dover+Litt)
Imp 265	Lohr, Joseph J.		Lohr	Joseph J. Lohr

NO.	IMPRINT	ILLUSTRATION	PUBLISHER	FULL NAME OF PUBLISHER
Imp 266	Los Angeles Examiner		LA Examine	Los Angeles Examiner
Imp 267	Lowell	Figure 2P	Lowell	Lowell Collectors' Club
Imp 268	Lupton, Walt	Figure 2R	Lupton	Walt Lupton (East Coast Lefty or E.C.L.)
Imp 269	LW. St.		Staehle	Ludwig W. Staehle (see Fleetwood, Fluegel)
Imp 270	Ly [+ No.]		Yudkin	Yudkin, Sam
Imp 271	LY 1		Yudkin	Sam Yudkin
Imp 272	M [+ No.]		Myers	Melba Myers
Imp 273	M [+ No.] + N		Muzzy+Nich	E.J. Muzzy and C. Malcolm Nichols
Imp 274	M.R.		Richards	Mrs. M. Richards
Imp 275	M.R. [+ No.]		Rohaly	Sgt. Michael Rohaly
Imp 276	Mache		Mache	C. Lee Wolf
Imp 277	Mache		Wolf, CL	C. Lee Wolf (see Mache)
Imp 278	Makomb Steel Products Co.		Makomb	Makomb Steel Products Co.
Imp 279	Malaney, (? first name)		Malaney	(? first name) Malaney
Imp 280	Martin, Dr. Charles W.		Martin	Charles W. Martin
Imp 281	MAS		Schust	Max A. Schusterman
Imp 282	Maul, H.		Maul	H.R. Maul
Imp 283	Maul, H.R.		Maul	H.R. Maul
Imp 284	McBarrar, SM3/C G.P.		McBarrar	G.P. McBarrar SM3/C
Imp 285	McCluney, Carl L.		McCluney	Carl L. McCluney (Holt Cover Service)
Imp 286	McClung, C.M. and Co.		McClung	C.M. McClung & Co.
Imp 287	McElroy, S.A.		McElroy	S.A. McElroy
Imp 288	McKelvey, M. Blair		McKelvey	M. Blair McKelvey
Imp 289	McLaughlin, Cpl. F.L.		McLaughlin	Cpl. F.L. McLaughlin
Imp 290	M-D [+ No.]		Dale	Charles R. Dale (+ Mitchell Advertising Co)
Imp 291	Mechanical Products		Mechanical	Mechanical Products
Imp 292	MEL [+ No.]		Myers	Melba Myers
Imp 293	Melba Myers		Myers	Melba Myers
Imp 294	Mello and Stannard		Mello+Stan	E.J. Mello and L.W. Stannard
Imp 295	MHG		Garfinkel	Marvin H. Garfinkel
Imp 296	Michigan Bell		Mich Bell	Michigan Bell Telephone Company
Imp 297	Miller, Jimmy		Miller	Jimmy Miller and his Saddle Mates
Imp 298	Millinery Research		Millinery	Millinery Research, Millinery Industry
Imp 299	Minkus, Jacques	Figure 2S	Minkus	Jacques Minkus
Imp 300	Mission Stamp Club		Mission	Mission Stamp Club
Imp 301	Mitchell, Myrtle (typed)		Mitchell	Myrtle Mitchell
Imp 302	MN [+No.]		Nichols	G. Malcolm Nichols
Imp 303	Mono Service Co.		Mono Svc	Mono Service Co.
Imp 304	Monty		Monty	Unknown (artist: Monty)
Imp 305	Mountain States Telephone		Mountain	Mountain States Telephone & Telegraph Co.
Imp 306	Mueller, Benny W.		Mueller, B	Benny W. Mueller
Imp 307	Muridge, M. Fay	Figure 2T	Muridge	M. Fay Muridge
Imp 308	Mutual Covers		Ang	Clinton E. Ang (Mutual Covers)
Imp 309	Mutual Covers		Mutual	Mutual Cover Club (see Ang)
Imp 310	N&H		Neal+Harv	Don W. Neal and Paul Harvey
Imp 311	N.C.S.		Czubay	Walter L. Czubay (RCD #206)
Imp 312	N.W. Good Roads Assoc./		Northwest	Northwest Good Roads Association
Imp 313	Nathan Hale Cachets		Hale	Nathan Hale Cachets
Imp 314	National Lutheran Council		Nat Luther	National Lutheran Council
Imp 315	National Motor Bearing		Nat Motor	National Motor Bearing Co., Inc.
Imp 316	Navy Department Navy Yard		Navy Yard	Navy Yard, Pearl Harbor, Commandant's Off.
Imp 317	Navy Department, etc.		Navy Dept.	Navy Department
Imp 318	Navy Depatment, etc.		USMC	Navy Dept., U.S. Marine Corps
Imp 319	Neal		Neal	Don W. Neal

NO.	IMPRINT	ILLLUSTRATION	PUBLISHER	FULL NAME OF PUBLISHER
Imp 320	Neal and Harvey		Neal+Harv	Don W. Neal and Paul Harvey
Imp 321	New Mexico School etc.		New Mexico	New Mexico School Supply Co.
Imp 322	New York Telephone		NY Tel Co	New York Telephone Company
Imp 323	Newton, Robert D. etc.		Newton RD	Robert D. Newton
Imp 324	Nichols	Figure 2U	Nichols	G. Malcolm Nichols
Imp 325	Nicholson, T.G.		Nicholson	T.G. Nicholson
Imp 326	Nick	Figure 2V	Nichols	G. Malcolm Nichols
Imp 327	Nixon, Scott		Nixon	Scott Nixon
Imp 328	Northern Ohio Telephone		Northern	Northern Ohio Telephone Co.
Imp 329	NSSC		Nat Soc	National Society of Stamp Collectors
Imp 330	Ohio Bell Telephone		Ohio Bell	The Ohio Bell Telephone Co.
Imp 331	Ohio Fuel Gas Co.		Ohio Fuel	The Ohio Fuel Gas Company
Imp 332	Ohio State Safety Conf.		Ohio State	Ohio State Safety Conf.
Imp 333	Oka, E. Toshiharu		Oka	E. Toshiharu Oka
Imp 334	Oklahoma City Stamp Club		Okla Stamp	The Oklahoma City Stamp Club (see Edmunds)
Imp 335	Olson, K.F.		Olson	K.F. Olson
Imp 336	Orlando, R.		Orlando	R. Orlando
Imp 337	Osborn, Glen		Osborn	Glen Osborn
Imp 338	Osborne, Allan		Osborne	Allan Osborne
Imp 339	P and C		Phill+Cox	Charles R. Phillips and Delma Cox
Imp 340	Pacific G & E, etc.		Pacif G&E	Pacific G & E
Imp 341	Pacific Stamp and Hobby		Pacific	Pacific Stamp and Hobby Club (Walter Hirsh)
Imp 342	Panama City		Panama	Panama City
Imp 343	Parkinson, R.L.		Parkinson	R.L. Parkinson
Imp 344	Parrott, Matt & Sons		Parrott	Matt Parrott & Sons
Imp 345	Pavois		Butzen	Albert C. Butzen (Pavois)
Imp 346	Payne, Edwin R.		Payne, E.R.	Edwin R. Payne
Imp 347	PB [+ No.]		Burdick	Philip O. Burdick (Liberty Covers)
Imp 348	Penn-Harris, etc.		Penn-Harr	Penn-Harris
Imp 349	PentArts		Coll Surp	Collectors Surplus (Pent Arts)
Imp 350	PentArts		PentArts	See Collectors Surplus
Imp 351	Peters [w/, w/o No.]		Peters	Raymond Peters
Imp 352	Pflanz, Charles H.		Pflanz	Charles H. Pflanz
Imp 353	Philadelphia Electric Co.		Phila Elec	Philadelphia Electric Company
Imp 354	Phillips, CR		Phill, CR	Phillips, Charles R.
Imp 355	Pictorial Envelope Co.		Pictorial	Pictorial Envelope Co.
Imp 356	Pilgrim Cachets	Figure 2W	Pilgrim	Pilgrim Cachets (John Alden)
Imp 357	Pittsburgh-Standard Envelope Co.		Pittsburgh	Pittsburgh-Standard Envelope Company
Imp 358	Pontiac Motor Division		Pontiac	Pontiac Motor Division, General Motors
Imp 359	Porto-Server	Figures 2X & 2Y	Porto-Serv	Porto-Server (Tarrson Co.)
Imp 360	Powers Press, Ames, Iowa		Powers	Powers Press
Imp 361	Price, Earl K.		Price, EK	Earl K. Price
Imp 362	Quig		Quigley	H.L. Quigley
Imp 363	R.C.	Figure 1Q	Cozart	Russell Cozart
Imp 364	R.C.D. 70		Hutnick	S.E. Hutnick, MD (RCD #70)
Imp 365	R.E.S.		Crosby	William G. Crosby (artist: Ruby E. Sharon)
Imp 366	R.E.S.	Figure 3J	Sharon	Rubie E. Sharon
Imp 367	R.H.C.		Clark	Ralph H. Clark
Imp 368	R.Y.S.		Ryscovers	Ryscovers (R.Y. Spaulding)
Imp 369	Ray in the [K.C.] Star		Citret	Harry Citret
Imp 370	Reuss		Reuss	Oswald Reuss
Imp 371	Richard, Nora J.		Richard	Nora J. Richard
Imp 372	Richardson	Figures 3A, 3B, & 3C	Richardson	George Richardson
Imp 373	Rinker		Rinker	Kenneth N. Rinker

NO.	IMPRINT	ILLLUSTRATION	PUBLISHER	FULL NAME OF PUBLISHER
Imp 374	Rio Grande Steel etc.		Rio Grande	Rio Grande Steel Products Co.
Imp 375	Robbins, Robert Lash	Figure 3D	Robbins	Robert Lash Robbins (Postamp Pub. Co.)
Imp 376	Roberts, A.M.		Roberts	Alfred M. Roberts
Imp 377	Robertson, Mrs. Lloyd		Robertson	Mrs. Lloyd J. Robertson
Imp 378	Roth, I.M. [+ No.]		Roth	PFC Irving M. Roth
Imp 379	Roudebush, Chas. H.		Roudebush	Charles H. Roudebush
Imp 380	RP [+ No.]		Price, R	Robert Price
Imp 381	Runge [w/, w/o No.]	Figure 3E	Runge	Thornton R. Runge
Imp 382	Rush, J.M.		Rush, JM	John Max Rush
Imp 383	Ryscovers [+ No.]		Ryscovers	Ryscovers (R.Y. Spaulding)
Imp 384	S [+ No.]		Shaw, CF	Clifford F. Shaw
Imp 385	S- [+ No.]		Von Los	J.C. Von Losberg
Imp 386	S.& M.		Swave+Mill	Horace S. Swavely and Paul J. Miller
Imp 387	Sadworth, G.V.	Figure 3F	Sadworth	George V. Sadworth
Imp 388	Salem Victory Corps		Salem Vic	Salem Victory Corps
Imp 389	Sanders		Sanders	Michael Sanders
Imp 390	Sanders, M.		Sanders	Michael Sanders
Imp 391	Sayama, Etsuo	Figures 3G & 3H	Sayama	Etsuo Sayama
Imp 392	Schaefer, A.E.		Schaefer	A.E. Schaefer
Imp 393	Schlichte, Joann		Schlichte	Joann Schlichte
Imp 394	Schneckenberger, M.G.		Schnecken	M.G. Scheckenberger
Imp 395	Sgt. H.J. Anderson		Ander, HJ	Sgt. H.J. Anderson
Imp 396	Shaffer, Cpl. A.E.	Figure 3I	Shaffer, A	Cpl. Albert E. Shaffer
Imp 397	Smartcraft	Figure 3K	Jordan	Edward R. Jordan
Imp 398	Smartcraft	Figure 3L	Smartcraft	Smartcraft (see Jordan)
Imp 399	Smith, Dorman H.		Smith, DH	Dorman H. Smith (N.E.A. Service, Inc.)
Imp 400	Smith, Lannie H.	Figures 3N, 3O	Smith, LH	Lannie H. Smith
Imp 401	Smith, Wesley		Smith, W	Wesley Smith
Imp 402	Social Security, etc.		Social Sec	Dept. oif Social Security, St. Paul, MN
Imp 403	Social Security, etc.		Social Sec	Dept. of Social Security, St. Paul, MN
Imp 404	Sosland Envelope Co., K.C., Mo.		Sosland	Sosland Envelope Co.
Imp 405	Southwestern Freight etc.		Southwest	Southwestern Freight Line
Imp 406	Sprague, D.C., Jr.		Sprague	D.C. Sprague, Jr.
Imp 407	SS-1- [+ letter]		Speede	Speede Service
Imp 408	Staehle, L.W.	Figure 3P	Staehle	Ludwig W. Staehle (see Fleetwood, Fluegel)
Imp 409	Stanard, John D.		Stanard	John D. Stanard
Imp 410	Steeg, Adolph		Steeg	Adolph Steeg
Imp 411	Stefun, A.J.		Stefun	A.J. Stefun
Imp 412	Steinway, Theo. E.		Steinway	Theodore E. Steinway
Imp 413	Stendel, H.H.		Stendel	H.H. Stendel (Pictorial Envelope Co.)
Imp 414	Stoll		Stoll	Kirby M. Stoll
Imp 415	Stoll, K.		Stoll	Kirby M. Stoll
Imp 416	Stoner, Pvt. Roy E.		Stoner	Pvt. Roy E. Stoner
Imp 417	Sturgill		Sturgill	Cairo Sturgill
Imp 418	T&T [w/, w/o No.]	Figure 3S	Threl+Thar	W.R. Threlkel and W.R. Tharp
Imp 419	T.B.T. [+ No.]		Thr+Bu+Tha	W.R. Threlkel, Philip Burdick, W.R. Tharp
Imp 420	Talburt		Talburt	(? first name) Talburt
Imp 421	TANS		All Nation	The All Nations Society
Imp 422	TAWM		Amer War M	The American War Mothers
Imp 423	TB&T		Thr+Bu+Tha	W.R. Threlkel, Philip Burdick, W.R. Tharp
Imp 424	TCS		Coll Soc	The Collectors Society
Imp 425	Teaneck Stamp Club		Teaneck	Teaneck Stamp Club
Imp 426	Teich, Curt & Co., Inc.		Teich	Curt Teich & Co. Inc.
Imp 427	Teixeira, Capt. Frank L.	Figure 3Q	Teixeira	Capt. Frank L. Teixeira

NO.	IMPRINT	ILLLUSTRATION	PUBLISHER	FULL NAME OF PUBLISHER
Imp 428	Thorpe, H.R.	Figure 3T	Thorpe	H.R. Thorpe
Imp 429	Thurman, Emil A.		Thurman	Emil A. Thurman
Imp 430	Tidewater Oil Co.		Tidewater	Tidewater Oil Company
Imp 431	Trapani, Cpl. Victor L.		Trapani	Cpl. Victor L. Trapan98
Imp 432	Treasury Department		U.S. Treas	United States Treasdury Department
Imp 433	Trent Printing Company		Trent	Trent Printing Company
Imp 434	Union Pacific Railroad		Union Pac	Union Pacific Railroad
Imp 435	Universal Carloading		Univ Car	Universal Carloading Co.
Imp 436	Universal Engineering Co.		Univ Engin	Universal Engineering Co.
Imp 437	USO United Service		USO	United Service Organizations
Imp 438	V Center		V Center	V Center
Imp 439	Vermond, Andre		Vermond	Andre Vermond
Imp 440	Veterans of Foreign Wars		VFW	VFW of the U.S., Dept. of California
Imp 441	Victory Envelopes, etc.		Advertiser	The Advertisers Press (Capitol Stamp Co.)
Imp 442	Victory Fog Nozzle Co.		Fog	Victory Fog Nozzle Company
Imp 443	Vogel, JE.DoubleR.Y		Vogel	Jerry Vogel Music Co., Inc.
Imp 444	W.A.T.		Temple	William A. Temple
Imp 445	W.G.C.		Crosby	William G. Crosby
Imp 446	Washington Star		Wash Star	Washington Evening and Sunday Star
Imp 447	WAT	Figure 3R	Temple	William A. Temple
Imp 448	Wentz, Paul P.	Figure 3U	Wentz	Paul P. Wentz
Imp 449	White, Trudy M.	Figure 3V	White	Trudy M. White
Imp 450	WHS		Sedgwick	W.H. Sedgwick
Imp 451	Wittenberg College		Wittenberg	Wittenberg College
Imp 452	WMG [or W.M.G.]		Grandy	Winfred M. Grandy
Imp 453	Woodall Industries		Woodall	Woodall Inductries
Imp 454	Wright		Wright	Fred P. Wright
Imp 455	WS		Stawuszew	Cpl. Walter Stawuszewski
Imp 456	Y		Yontz	Donald A. Yontz
Imp 457	YMCA		YMCA	Young Men's Cristian Association
Imp 458	Zoo-Bay	Figure 1T	Czubay	Walter L. Czubay (RCD #206)
Imp 459	Zubay	Figure 1S	Czubay	Watler L. Czubay (RCD # 206)
Imp 460	Zunks, Original Order of	Figure 3W	Zunks	Gordon H. Hamilton (Cleveland Cover Club)

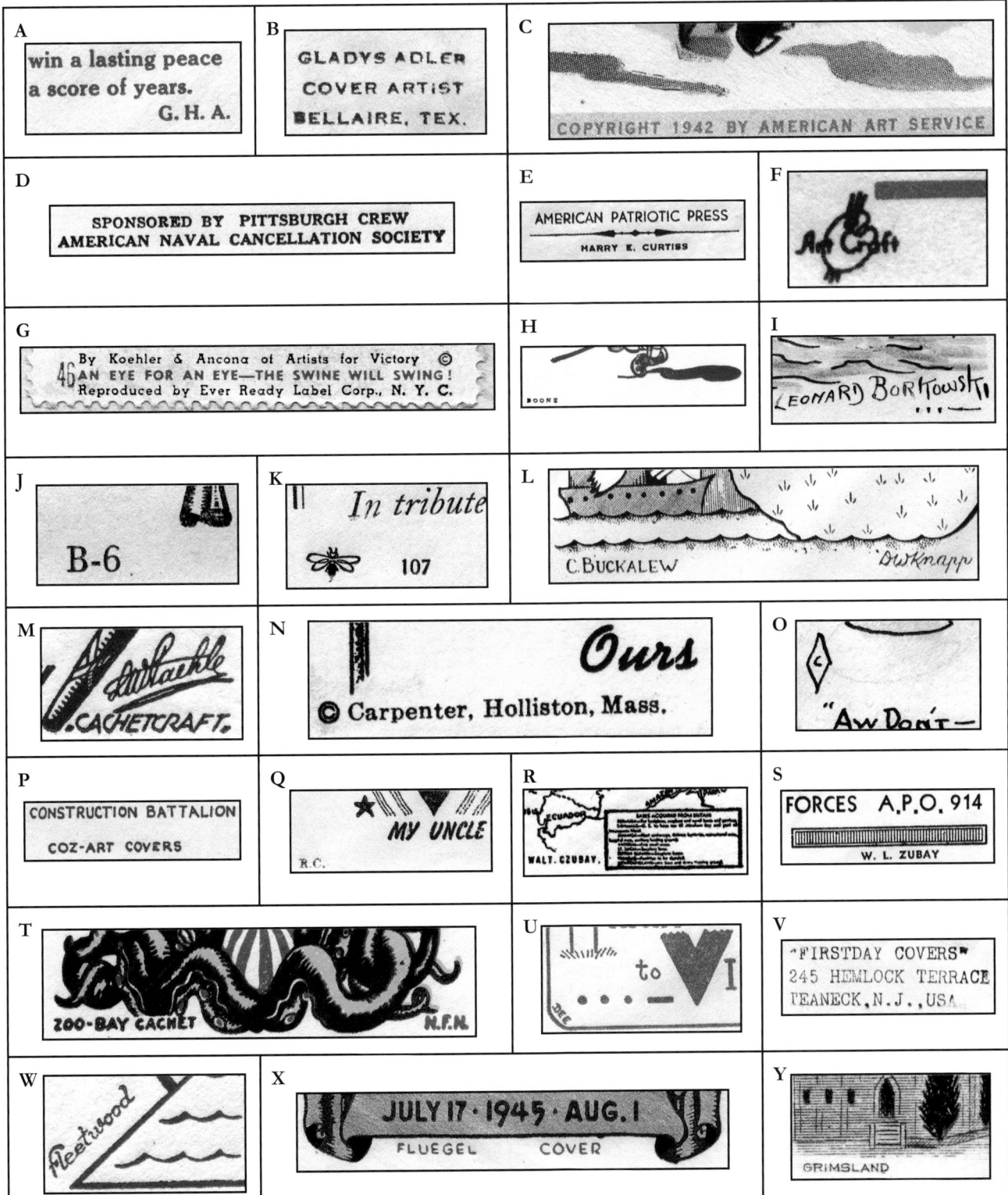

Figure 1. Patriotic envelope publisher imprints, publishers Abel to Grimsland, with numbers assigned to them in Publisher Imprints Catalogue. A, George H. Abel, 8. B, Gladys Adler, 11. C, American Art Service, 19. D, American Naval Cancellation Society, 22. E, American Patriotic Press, 24. F, Artcraft, 32. G, Artists for Victory, 33. H, Richard P. Boone, 61. I, Leonard Borkowski, 62. J & K, Elmer A. Brenn, 41 & 50. L, Charles H. Buckalew, 66. M, CachetCraft, 78. N, N. LeRoy Carpenter, 82. O, William Clendennen, 89. P & Q, Russell Cozart, 99 & 363. R, S, & T, Walter L. Czubay, 105, 459, & 458. U, Darrell Davis, 115. V, Firstday Covers, 147. W, Fleetwood Covers, 148. X, Herman F. Fluegel, 150. Y, Henry Grimsland, 179.

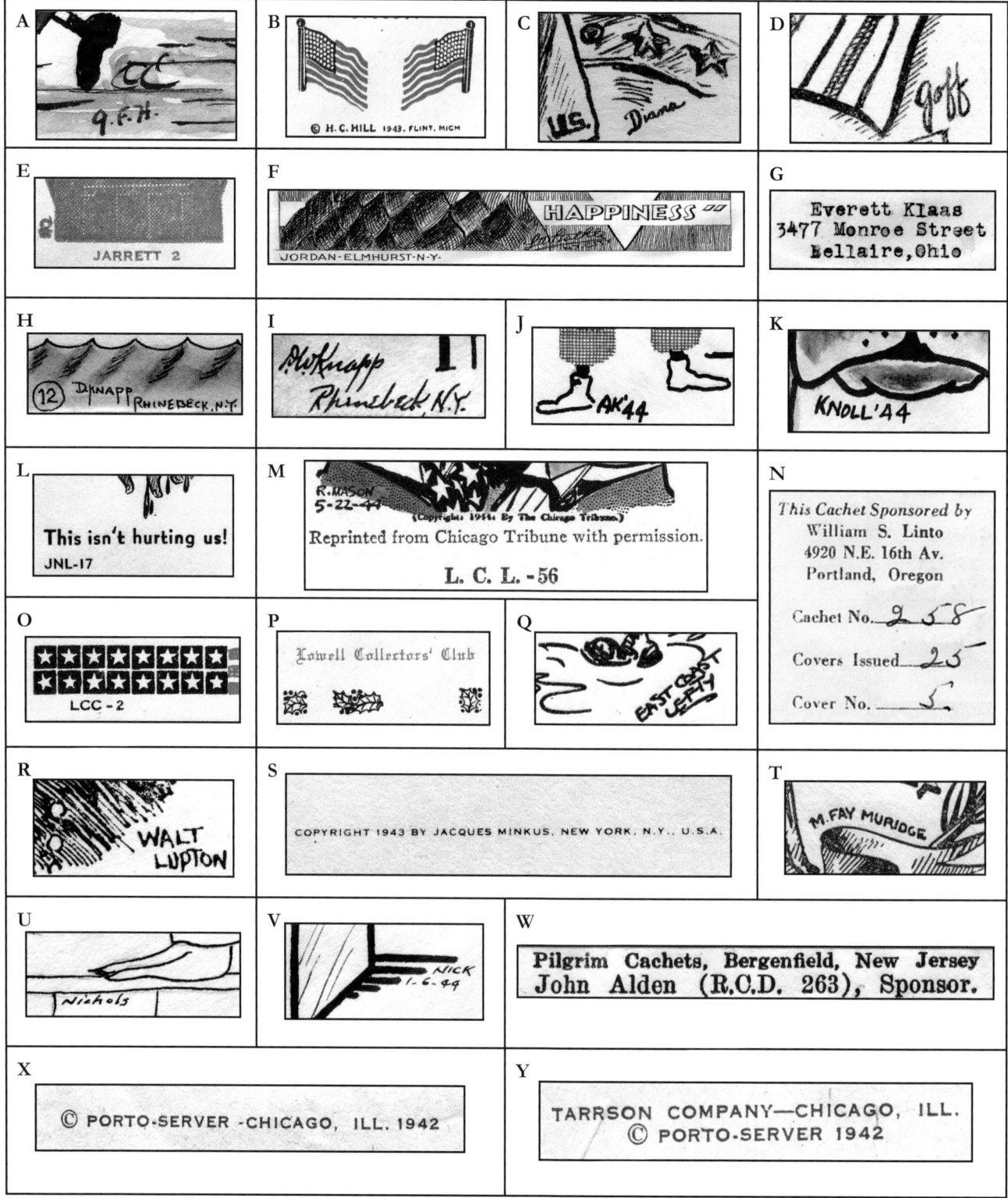

Figure 2. Patriotic envelope publisher imprints, publishers Hadley to Porto-Server, with numbers assigned to them in Publisher Imprints Catalogue. A, Grace F. Hadley, 159. B, Harry C. Hill, 192. C & D, Matthew J. Huss, 120 & 173. E, William R. Jarrett, 220. F, Edward R. Jordan (Smartcraft), 229. G, Everett Klaas, 237. H & I, Dorothy W. Knapp, 240 & 241. J & K, Arthur F. Knoll, 15 & 243. L, James N. Lawrence, 227. M, L.C. Levering, 248. N, William S. Linto, 263. O & P, Lowell Collectors Club, 254 & 267. Q & R, Walt Lupton, 128 & 268. S, Jacques Minkus, 299. T, M. Fay Muridge, 307. U & V, G. Malcolm Nichols, 324 & 326. W, Pilgrim Cachets, 356. X & Y, Porto-Server, 359.

Figure 3. Patriotic envelope publisher imprints, publishers Richardson to Zunks, with numbers assigned to them in Publisher Imprints Catalogue. A, B, & C, George Richardson, 372. D, Robert Lash Robbins, 375. E, Thornton R. Runge, 381. F, George V. Sadworth, 386. G & H, Etsuo Sayama, 391. I, Cpl. A.E. Shaffer, 396. J, Ruby E. Sharon, 366. K & L, Smartcraft, 397 & 398. M, Arthur D. Smith, 12. N & O, Lannie H. Smith, 400. P, Ludwig W. Staehle, 408. Q, Capt. Frank L. Texeira, 427. R, William A. Temple, 447. S, W.R. Threlkel and W.R. Tharp, 418. T, H.R. Thorpe, 428. U, Paul R. Wentz, 448. V, Trudy M. White, 449. W, Original Order of Zunks, 460.

Select Bibliography

Books

Annual Report of the Postmaster General for the Fiscal Year Ending June 30, 1942 (Washington, DC: United States Government Printing Office, 1942).

Annual Report of the Postmaster General for the Fiscal Year Ending June 30, 1943 (Washington, DC: United States Government Printing Office, 1944).

Baur, Brian C. *Franklin D. Roosevelt and the Stamps of the United States 1933-1945* (Sidney, OH: Linn's Stamp News, Amos Press, Inc., 1993).

Berg, Robin. World War II Envelope Art of Cécile Cowdery (Lakeville, MN: USM, Inc., 1992).

Billingham, Mrs. Anthony. *America's First Two Years : The Story of American Volunteers in Britain 1939-1941* (London: John Murray and the Pilot Press, 1942).

Bradley, James, with Ron Powers. *Flags of Our Fathers* (New York: Bantam Books, 2000).

Brett, George. *Philately Printing Methods and Techniques* (State College, PA: Pennsylvania State University, 1985).

Churchill, Winston S. *Their Finest Hour* (Boston: Houghton Mifflin Company, 1949).

Cusick, Allison. *Photo Cachet Catalog—Linprint.* (Stewartsville, NJ: FDC Publishing Co., 1976).

Davis, G.H. *The Transports* (Reston, VA: The Bureau Issues Association, Inc., 1999).

Dictionary of American Naval Fighting Ships, Vol. 4 (Washington, DC: Navy Department Office of the Chief of Naval Operations, Naval History Division, 1969).

Fest, Joachim C. *Hitler* (New York: Harcourt Brace Jovanovich, 1973).

Grant, Robert W. *The Handbook of Civil War Patriotic Envelopes and Postal History* (Hanover, Massachusetts: Robert W. Grant, 1977).

Isaacson, Walter. *Benjamin Franklin: An American Life* (New York: Simon & Schuster, 2003).

Kehr, Ernest A. *The Romance of Stamp Collecting: Notes from the World of Stamps, Stamp Collecting, and Stamp Collectors* (New York, 1957).

Kennedy, David M. *Freedom from Fear: The American People in Depression and War, 1929-1945* (New York: Oxford University Press, 1999).

Kent, David A, Editor in Chief. *Catalog of United States Naval Postmarks* (New Britain, CT: Universal Ship Cancellation Society, Fifth Edition, 1997).

Laurence, Robert. *The George Walcott Collection of Used Civil War Patriotic Covers* (Hanover, Massachusetts: Robert W. Grant, 1975).

Lingeman, Richard R. *Don't You Know There's a War On?: The American Home Front 1941-1945* (New York: G.P. Putnam's Sons, 1970).

Loso, Foster, W., and Heyliger de Windt. *20th Century U.S. Fancy Cancellations* (Wolfeboro, NH: Foster W. Loso and Heyliger de Windt, 1952).

Manchester, William. *American Caesar: Douglas MacArthur 1880-1964* (Boston: Little, Brown and Company, 1978).

Monty, Dr. Richard A. *Specialized Catalogue of Jacques Minkus F.D.C.s and Patriotic Cachets* (Stewartsville, NJ: FDC. Publishing Co., 1977).

Morison, Samuel Eliot. *The Battle of the Atlantic 1939-1943* (Boston: Little, Brown and Company, 1947).

Parks, M. Douglas. *The Cachet Catalogue of Staehle and Knapp* (Ogallala, NE: M. Douglas Parks, 1981).

Phillips, Cabell. *The 1940s: Decade of Triumph and Trouble* (New York: Macmillan Publishing Co., 1975).

Pogue, Forrest C. *George C. Marshall: Ordeal and Hope, 1939-1942* (New York: The Viking Press, 1966).

Prange, Gordon W., Donald M. Goldstein, and Ketherine V. Dillion. *Miracle at Midway* (New York: McGraw-Hill Book Company, 1982).

Rawlins, R.D. *Naval Cover Cachet Makers Catalog* (New Britain, CT: Universal Ship Cancellation Society, 1985).

Sherman, Lawrence, Editor. *United States Post Office in World War II* (Chicago: The Chicago Collectors Club, 2002).

Stroebel, William H. *Walter G. Crosby, Philatelic Cachet Specialist* (Mesa, AZ: Burgus Printing Company, 1992).

United States Holocaust Memorial Museum. *Historical Atlas of the Holocaust* (New York: Macmillan Publishing USA, 1996).

United States Post Office Department. *Postage Stamps of the United States: An Illustrated Description of all United Atates Postage and Special Services Stamps Issued by the Post Office Department from July 1, 1847, to December 31, 1963* (Washington, DC: United States Government Printing Office, 1964).

Weinberg, Gerhard L. *A World at Arms: A Global History of World War II* (Cambridge, U.K.: Cambridge University Press, 1994).

Wood, Kenneth A. *This is Philately* (Albany, OR: Van Dahl Publications, 1982).

Periodicals

"A memorable Christmas present for everyone on your list! Gimbels new patriotic envelopes," *Stamps* 45 (12) :400, Dec 18, 1943.

Bahry, Ted. "Uncommon valor: U.S. Marines and the Iwo Jima stamp," *American Philatelist* 109 (2):135-141, Feb 1995.

Baumann, Fred W. "Win the War stamp issued 50 years ago," *Linn's Stamp News*, Jul 20, 1992, p.10

Brennan, Jan, and John Joseph Brennan. "A chat with Dorothy Wallace Knapp," *First Days* 27 (1):28-36, Jan 1982.

Caba, C. Craig. "The first cachets from Tokyo," *American Philatelist* 110 (5):438-439, 1996.

Cohen, Sidney L. "William S. Linto—WWII patriotic covers," *First Days* 31 (2):156-165, Mar 1, 1986.

Fiset, Louis. "Non-philatelic patriotic covers," *The Prexie Era*, newsletter of the USSS/BIA 1938 Presidential Era Study Group, 319-10, Winter 2005.

"For your patriotic covers as well as every single letter you write! Gimbels new patriotic envelopes," *Linn's Weekly Stamp News*, Nov 11, 1943, p. 7.

"Gimbels famous stamp department patriotic envelopes," *Cover News* 4 (5):4, Dec 1940.

Haag, John J. "King of cachets 1941," *Stamps* 38 (13):447-448, Mar 28, 1942

———. "1943 'King of Cachets,'" *Stamps* 47:14-15, Apr 1, 1944.

Herst, Herman Jr. "Victory, Vermont, fakes," *First Days* 31 (2):180-181, Mar 1, 1986.

Hollister, Paul. "Gimbel's World War II patriotics," *Western Stamp Collector* 39:10, Nov 27, 1965.

Hubartt, Paul. "Paul Hubartt remembers . . . Fluegel cachets," *First Days* 35 (3):473-476, Jun 1, 1990.

Ilma, Viola. "Interview of the month: Jacques Minkus a colossus," *Stamp Show News* 4 (4):12-13, 57-60, Dec 1978.

Klug, Janet. "Hawaii's World War II patriotic covers," *Scott's Stamp Monthly* 17 (5):23, May 1999.

Knapp, Wally. "Dorothy W. Knapp—a fond remembrance," *First Days* 32 (4):408-416, Jun 1, 1987.

Kroos, Arthur G. Jr. "The unknown Weigands, Part I," *First Days* 43 (7):447-451, Sep 1, 1998.

———. "The unknown Weigands, Part II," *First Days* 43 (8): 575-587, Oct 15, 1998.

———. "The unknown Weigands, Part III," *First Days* 43 (9)627-629, Dec 1, 1998.

Lowe, James Lewis. "A boy's adventures into patriotic covers," *Patriotic Patter* 7:1-2, Apr 1996.

Ma, Peter. "Etsuo Sayama: The Hawaiian cachetmaker of patriotic covers," *First Days* 31 (3)348-354, Apr 15, 1986.

Nafziger, Ralph, and Richard Sverid. "William S. Linto—Oregon cachet maker," *First Days* 28 (8):1306-1311, 1983.

Rush, John Max. "Patriotic covers," *Cover News* 6 (1):4, Sep 1942.

———."Patriotic cover collecting," *Cover News* 7 (12):4, Aug 1944.

———. "Patriotic cover parade," *Western Stamp Collector* 19 (21):5, Jan 10, 1945.

Miller, Paul J. "Classes and types of patriotics," *Stamps* 53(11)430, Dec 15, 1945.

Monty, Richard. "From trite to complex—another look," *American Philatelist* 91:633, Aug 1977.

Rawlins, R.D. "Alex Hesse, Hall of Fame selectee," *United States Ship Cancellation Society Log* 64 (8):11, Aug 1997.

Russell, Gene H. "The 'Crosby' Technique," *First Days* 24 (3):84-85, May-Jun 1975.

Sommers, Paul M. "Staehle and Teixeira patriotic varieties," *First Days* 42 (8):584-585, Dec 1, 1997.

———. "Date errors on Teixeira patriotic varieties pose vexing questions," *First Days* 49 (2):23-25, Mar 1, 2004.

———. "Teixeira: After a few bad dates, we need to talk," *First Days* 49 (6):32-33, Sep 1, 2004.

"Stamped with America's approval Gimbels presents with pride a new series of patriotic envelopes emblazoned with 20 prize-winning designs in color," *Stamps* 39 (12):414-415, Jun 20, 1942.

Wright, Pat. "Frank Loper Teixeira, cachetmaker," *First Days* 24 (3):32-33, May-Jun, 1979.

———. "Fluegel's headache series," *First Days* 32 (4):408-416, Jun 1, 1987.

Youngblood, Wayne."Art & envelopes," *American Philatelist* 119 (2):122-126, Feb 2005.

Zubatsky, David S. "J. Neal Griffith: a biography and catalog of his first day and patriotic cachets," *First Days* 48 (3):11-13, Apr 15, 2003.

———. "J. Neal Griffith: a biography and catalog of his first day and patriotic cachets, Part II," *First Days* 48 (4):23-26, Jun 1, 2003.

Index